Mich.
No. 30041

THIS BOOK HAS BEEN SENT TO YOU AT THE SUGGESTION OF

GEORGE OWEN

Please accept it with our compliments

McGRAW-HILL BOOK COMPANY, Inc.

Ex Libris: J. A. NICHOLLS

Boundary Layer Theory

BY

Dr HERMANN SCHLICHTING

Professor at the Engineering University of Braunschweig
Director of the Aerodynamische Versuchsanstalt Göttingen
Head of the Institute for Aerodynamics of
the Deutsche Forschungsanstalt für Luftfahrt, Braunschweig, Germany

Translated by

Dr J. KESTIN

Professor at Brown University in Providence, Rhode Island

Fourth Edition

McGRAW-HILL BOOK COMPANY, INC.
NEW YORK · TORONTO · LONDON
VERLAG G. BRAUN · KARLSRUHE

1960

BOUNDARY LAYER THEORY

 Library of Congress Catalog Card Number 59-15472

55328

First English Edition (Second Edition of the book) published in 1955

Foreword

To the First English Edition

Boundary layer theory is the cornerstone of our knowledge of the flow of air and other fluids of small viscosity under circumstances of interest in many engineering applications. Thus many complex problems in aerodynamics have been clarified by a study of the flow within the boundary layer and its effect on the general flow around the body. Such problems include the variations of minimum drag and maximum lift of airplane wings with Reynolds number, wind tunnel turbulence, and other parameters. Even in those cases where complete mathematical analysis is at present impracticable, the boundary layer concept has been extraordinarily fruitful and useful.

The development of boundary layer theory during its first fifty years is a fascinating illustration of the birth of a new concept, its slow growth for many years in the hands of its creator and his associates, its belated acceptance by others, and the later almost exponential rise in the number of contributors to its further development.

The first decade following the classical paper of Prandtl in 1904 brought forth fewer than 10 papers by Prandtl and his students, a rate of about one paper per year. During the past year over 100 papers were published on various aspects of boundary layer theory and related experiments. The name of H. Schlichting first appears in 1930 with his doctoral thesis on the subject of wake flow. Shortly thereafter Schlichting devoted major effort to the problem of the stability of laminar boundary layer flow.

My own interest in the experimental aspects of boundary layer flow began in the late twenties. With the appearance of Schlichting's papers intensive attempts were made to find the amplified disturbances predicted by the theory. For 10 years the experimental results not only failed to confirm this theory but supported the idea that transition resulted from the presence of turbulence in the free air stream as described in a theory set forth by G. I. Taylor. Then on a well-remembered day in August, 1940, the predicted waves were seen in the flow near a flat plate in a wind tunnel of very low turbulence. The theory of stability described in the papers of Tollmien and Schlichting was soon confirmed quantitatively as well as qualitatively.

German periodicals available in the United States after the war referred to a series of lectures by Schlichting on boundary layer theory which had been published in 1942. This document of 279 pages with 116 figures was not available for some time. An English translation was given limited distribution as NACA Technical Memorandum No. 1217 in 1949. These lectures were completely rewritten to include material previously classified, confidential, or secret from Germany and other countries.

The result was the book of 483 pages and 295 figures published in 1951 in the German language. When this book became known to research workers and educators in the United States, there was an immediate request from several quarters for an English translation, since no comparable book was available in the English language.

The technical content of the present English edition is described in the author's preface. The emphasis is on the fundamental physical ideas rather than on mathematical refinement. Methods of theoretical analysis are set forth along with such experimental data as are pertinent to define the regions of applicability of the theoretical results or to give physical insight into the phenomena.

Aeronautical engineers and research scientists owe a debt of gratitude to Professor Schlichting for this timely review of the present state of boundary layer theory.

Washington D. C., December 13, 1954 Hugh L. Dryden

Author's Preface to the Second English Edition

The first English edition of this book appeared in 1955. It was not a literal translation of the previous German edition. Taking into account the progress achieved in the meantime, I had completely rewritten two chapters and had made many smaller additions in various places throughout the book. The first English edition was very well received, particularly in the English-speaking countries, and there is little doubt that Dr. J. Kestin's success with the translation contributed to it in no small measure.

The first German edition of "Boundary Layer Theory" was reprinted without changes in 1954, but the new edition went out of print in 1957. Consequently, I have decided to publish a thoroughly revised new edition in the German language. This appeared in 1958 as the third edition of the book. Owing to the great volume of new research results obtained in the intervening period of time, the third edition had to be enlarged by some 120 pages and 80 figures. In particular, the chapters on compressible boundary layers (Chap. XV), on thermal boundary layers (Chap. XIV) and transition (Chaps. XVI and XVII) were considerably increased in size.

Since, in addition, the first English edition went out of print in 1958, I have gladly accepted the suggestion advanced by the two Publishers, Messrs. McGraw-Hill in New York and Messrs. G. Braun in Karlsruhe and prepared a new English edition which more nearly reflects the present status in the development of this branch of science.

I owe a great debt of gratitude to Professor J. Kestin who once more undertook the arduous task of preparing the translation. The present second English edition is based, substantially, on the contents of the third German edition of the book which appeared in 1958. While engaged on the work of translation, Dr. J. Kestin made many valuable suggestions for additions, particularly in Chapters XI and XIV, which I accepted gladly. One of my co-workers, Dr. K. Gersten, rewrote several sections on heat transfer in Chapters XIV and XIX, and I wish to record my thanks to him.

I hope that this new English edition will again be found useful by engineers working in industry and in research establishments and by students of mechanical engineering and machine design as well as by physicists and chemists who have to deal with problems of fluid flow.

Braunschweig, May 1960 H. Schlichting

Translator's Preface to the Second English Edition

It is once more my pleasure and privilege to record the immense benefits which I derived from my association with Professor H. Schlichting. A very close touch was maintained with the Author during the preparation of this new edition and, moreover, I was given the opportunity of spending two periods of time with Professor

H. Schlichting at his Institutes in Goettingen and Braunschweig during which I learned many things from him. I wish to thank Messrs. McGraw-Hill and the authorities of AGARD for making these memorable visits possible.

I owe a particular debt of gratitude to Dr. P. D. Richardson, Assistant Professor at Brown University and Mr. W. Pechau, Assistant at the Institute for Fluid Mechanics in Braunschweig who kindly consented to read the proofs and who made many valuable suggestions. Both publishers, Messrs. G. Braun of Karlsruhe and Messrs. McGraw-Hill of New York, spared no trouble in meeting our wishes regarding the production of the book.

Braunschweig, May 1960 J. Kestin

From Author's Preface to First German Edition

Since about the beginning of the current century modern research in the field of fluid dynamics has achieved great successes and has been able to provide a theoretical clarification of observed phenomena which the science of classical hydrodynamics of the preceding century failed to do. Essentially three branches of fluid dynamics have become particularly well developed during the last fifty years; they include boundary layer theory, gas dynamics, and aerofoil theory. The present book is concerned with the branch known as boundary layer theory. This is the oldest branch of modern fluid dynamics; it was founded by L. Prandtl in 1904 when he succeeded in showing how flows involving fluids of very small viscosity; in particular, water and air, the most important ones from the point of view of applications, can be made amenable to mathematical analysis. This was achieved by taking the effects of friction into account only in regions where they are essential, namely in the thin boundary layer which exists in the immediate neighbourhood of a solid body. This concept made it possible to clarify many phenomena which occur in flows and which had previously been incomprehensible. Most important of all, it has become possible to subject problems connected with the occurrence of drag to a theoretical analysis. The science of aeronautical engineering was making rapid progress and was soon able to utilize these theoretical results in practical applications. It did, on the other hand, pose many problems which could be solved with the aid of the new boundary layer theory. Aeronautical engineers have long since made the concept of a boundary layer one of everyday use and it is now unthinkable to do without it. In other fields of machine design in which problems of flow occur, in particular in the design of turbomachinery, the theory of boundary layers made much slower progress, but in modern times these new concepts have come to the fore in such applications as well.

The present book has been written principally for engineers. It is the outcome of a course of lectures which the Author delivered in the Winter Semester of 1941—42 for the scientific workers of the Aeronautical Research Institute in Brunswick. The subject matter has been utilized after the war in many special lectures held at the Engineering University in Brunswick for students of mechanical engineering and physics. Dr. H. Hahnemann prepared a set of lecture notes after the first series of lectures had been given. These were read and amplified by the Author. They were subsequently published in mimeographed form by the Office for Scientific Documentation (Zentrale für wissenschaftliches Berichtswesen) and distributed to a limited circle of interested scientific workers.

Several years after the war the Author decided completely to re-edit this older compilation and to publish it in the form of a book. The time seemed particularly propitious because it appeared ripe for the publication of a comprehensive book, and because the results of the research work carried out during the last ten to twenty years rounded off the whole field.

The book is divided into four main parts. The first part contains two introductory chapters in which the fundamentals of boundary layer theory are expounded without the use of mathematics and then proceeds to prepare the mathematical and physical justification for the theory of laminar boundary layers and includes the theory of thermal boundary layers. The third part is concerned with the phenomenon of transition from laminar to turbulent flow (origin of turbulence), and the fourth part is devoted to turbulent flows. It is now possible to take the view that the theory of laminar boundary layers is complete in its main outline. The physical relations have been completely clarified; the methods of calculation have been largely worked out and have, in many cases, been simplified to such an extent that they should present no difficulties to engineers. In discussing turbulent flows use has been made essentially only of the semi-empirical theories which derive from Prandtl's mixing length. It is true that according to present views these theories possess a number of shortcomings but nothing superior has so far been devised to take their place, nothing, which is useful to the engineer. No account of the statistical theories of turbulence has been included because they have not yet attained any practical significance for engineers.

As intimated in the title the emphasis has been laid on the theoretical treatment of problems. An attempt has been made to bring these considerations into a form which can be easily grasped by engineers. Only a small number of results has been quoted from among the very voluminous experimental material. They have been chosen for their suitability to give a clear, physical insight into the phenomena and to provide direct verification of the theory presented. Some examples have been chosen, namely those associated with turbulent flow, because they constitute the foundation of the semi-empirical theory. An attempt was made to demonstrate that essential progress is not made through an accumulation of extensive experimental results but rather through a small number of fundamental experiments backed by theoretical considerations.

Braunschweig, October 1950 H. Schlichting

From Author's Preface to Third (German) Edition

The first edition of this book which appeared in 1951 met with an unexpectedly good reception and the demand for it abroad, particularly in the U.S.A., was very great. Having received many requests from my professional colleagues, I have resolved to bring out an English translation of my book. This was prepared by Dr. J. Kestin of Brown University and appeared in 1955. The English translation contained numerous additions and modifications at that time, but I found it impossible to revise the whole manuscript thoroughly and in detail in order to bring it completely up to date.

In the present edition I have made an attempt to include all the significant papers which appeared in large numbers during the intervening years. I trust, however, that the revision left the principal aims of the book unaffected and that it still presents the theoretical considerations in a form which is accessible to engineers and that the voluminous experimental material is used principally as a substantiation of and illustration to the analysis. I have retained the original subdivision into Parts and Chapters and endeavoured to encompass all the revisions in the same framework, that is, without introducing any new chapter headings.

It might be useful to enumerate some of the additions: Chapters IX and XIII contain large new sections on exact solutions and the effect of suction; Chapter XV was considerably expanded and in the chapters on transition, particularly in Chapter XVII, I have included numerous examples of the application of the stability theory. The new results on the effect of heat transfer and compressibility on transition have been included. Chapter XXII on turbulent boundary layers has been completely rewritten and is now based on Truckenbrodt's method which leads to convenient quadratures and which has now become widely accepted. In discussing the effect of compressibility on turbulent boundary layers I have confined myself to a few short remarks about flat plates in Chapter XXI. It seems to me that these considerations are still in a fluid state and no definitive treatment can be given. I believe, just as in the previous edition, that I am still justified in not describing the statistical theory of turbulence. This, admittedly, has contributed materially to our better understanding of turbulent flows, but it has not yet acquired any importance for engineers.

The references to individual papers given at the end of each chapter as well as the bibliography at the end of the book have been expanded considerably. The book acquires about 120 new pages and 80 new figures. I trust that in spite of its increased volume, the book still provides a *comprehensive outline* of an important branch of fluid mechanics.

In preparing the manuscript I enjoyed the helpful assistance of several of my professional colleagues, and I wish to put on record my gratitude to them. In particular, I wish to thank Dr. E. Truckenbrodt who helped with the rewriting of Chapter XXII and to Dr. H. Görtler who advised me on the revision of Chapter IX. I also wish to thank my correspondents, too numerous to mention individually by name, who drew my attention to inexactitudes of expression and printing errors. I have made an effort to remove them all.

I would have found it impossible to digest the flood of recent papers without the able assistance which I received from my co-workers, Messrs. K. Gersten, E. Adams and E. G. Feindt. In this connection Mr. N. Scholtz's assistance with the original edition must not be forgotten.

Thanks are due to Messrs. Gersten, Pechaŭ, Riegels and Rotta for their assistance with the reading of the proofs, to my secretary, Miss Behrens, and to my daughter Heike for the careful preparation of the final typescript. Messrs. Braun are to be thanked for their cooperation and for the excellent production of the book.

Braunschweig, March 1958 H. Schlichting

Contents

page

Part C. Transition

Part D. Turbulent boundary layers

Tables

List of most commonly used symbols

In order not to depart too drastically from the conventions normally employed in papers on the subject it was found necessary to use the same symbol to denote several different quantities. Thus, for example, λ denotes the resistance coefficient of pipe flow, both laminar and turbulent, and in the theory of stability of laminar boundary layers it denotes the wavelength of a disturbance. Similarly, k denotes thermal conductivity in the theory of thermal boundary layers, and the height of a protuberance in the discussion of the influence of roughness o turbulent flow.

The following is a list of symbols most commonly used in the book.

I. General symbols

A = wetted area, or frontal area
d, D = diameter
g = acceleration due to gravity
h = channel width
l, L = length
p = pressure
$q = \frac{1}{2}\,\varrho\, V^2$ = dynamic head
r, ϕ, z = cylindrical co-ordinates
R = radius
u = mean velocity (in pipe)
$U(x)$ = velocity in potential flow
u, v, w = velocity components
V = free stream velocity
ϱ = density (mass per unit volume)
ω = angular velocity

II. Viscous flow, turbulence

A_τ = eddy viscosity
b = width of jet or wake
c_D = drag coefficient
c_f = skin friction coefficient
c_f' = local skin friction coefficient
L, H = shape factors of velocity profile
k = height of roughness element (protuberance)
k_S = height of grain for equivalent sand roughness
l = mixing length
R = Reynolds number
T = turbulence intensity (also degree or level of turbulence)
u', v', w' = components of turbulent velocity
$\overline{u'^2}, \overline{v'^2}, \overline{u'v'} \ldots$ = temporal means of turbulent velocities
U = maximum velocity at pipe centre

U_∞ = free stream velocity
$v_* = \sqrt{\tau_0/\varrho}$ = friction velocity
y = distance from wall
δ = boundary layer thickness
δ^* = displacement thickness
ε = apparent (virtual) kinematic viscosity in turbulent flow ("eddy viscosity")
$\eta = yv_*/\nu$ = dimensionless distance from wall
θ = momentum thickness
$\varkappa$ = empirical constant in turbulent flow; $l = \varkappa y$
λ = resistance coefficient of pipe flow
Λ = shape factor of laminar boundary layer velocity profile
μ = absolute viscosity
$\nu = \mu/\varrho$ = kinematic viscosity
τ = shearing stress (force per unit area)
τ_0 = shearing stress at a wall
$\phi = u/v_*$ = dimensionless velocity
ψ = stream function

III. Transition from laminar to turbulent flow

$c = \beta/\alpha = c_r + ic_i$
c_i = amplification (or damping) factor
c_r = wave propagation velocity of disturbance
$\mathsf{R}_{crit} = (U_m\delta^*/\nu)_{crit}$ = critical Reynolds number
u', v' = velocity components of disturbance
$U(y)$ = velocity profile in boundary layer
U_m = velocity in potential flow
$\beta = \beta_r + i\beta_i$
β_i = amplification (or damping) factor
β_r = circular frequency of disturbance
γ = intermittency factor
$\lambda = 2\pi/\alpha$ = wavelength of disturbance
$\phi(y)$ = amplitude of stream function of disturbance

IV. Thermal boundary layers and gasdynamics

$a = k/\varrho g c_p$ = thermal diffusivity
$c = \sqrt{\gamma p/\varrho}$ = velocity of sound
c_p, c_v = specific heats at constant pressure and volume, respectively
$\mathsf{E} = U_\infty^2/gc_p \Delta T$ = Eckert number (see p. 297)
$\mathsf{G} = g\beta l^3 \Delta T/\nu^2$ = Grashof number
k = thermal conductivity
$\mathsf{M} = V/c$ = Mach number
$\mathsf{N} = \alpha l/k$ = Nusselt number
$\mathsf{P} = \nu/a$ = Prandtl number
q = heat flux (quantity of heat per unit area and time)
$\mathsf{R_i} = -\{(g/\varrho)(d\varrho/dy)\}/(dU/dy)_W^2$ = Richardson number
$\mathsf{S} = \mathsf{N}/\mathsf{RP}$ = Stanton number

T = temperature
T_{ad} = adiabatic wall temperature
α = coefficient of heat transfer
β = coefficient of thermal expansion
$\gamma = c_p/c_v$ = isentropic exponent
δ_T = thickness of thermal boundary layer
ΔT = temperature difference
ω = exponent in viscosity-temperature relation

Abbreviations

The following abbreviations have been used throughout the book:

ARC	Aeronautical Research Council (Great Britain).
R & M	Reports and Memoranda
ASME	American Society of Mechanical Engineers (U.S.A.).
AVA	Aerodynamische Versuchsanstalt Göttingen (Germany).
ETH	Eidgenössische Technische Hochschule, Federal Institute of Technology, Zürich (Switzerland).
NACA	National Advisory Committee for Aeronautics (USA).
NASA	National Aeronautics and Space Administration (USA). Rep Report TM Technical Memorandum TN Technical Note
VDI	Verein Deutscher Ingenieure.
ZAMM	Zeitschrift für angewandte Mathematik und Mechanik.
ZAMP	Zeitschrift für angewandte Mathematik und Physik.
ZFM	Zeitschrift für Flugtechnik und Motorluftschiffahrt.
JAS	Journal of Aeronautical Sciences or Journal of Aero/Space Sciences.

BOUNDARY LAYER THEORY

Introduction

Towards the end of the 19th century the science of fluid mechanics began to develop in two directions which had practically no points in common. On the one side there was the science of *theoretical hydrodynamics* which was evolved from Euler's equations of motion for a frictionless, non-viscous fluid and which achieved a high degree of completeness. Since, however, the results of this so-called classical science of hydrodynamics stood in glaring contradiction to experimental results — in particular as regards the very important problem of pressure losses in pipes and channels, as well as with regard to the drag of a body which moves through a mass of fluid — it had little practical importance. For this reason, practical engineers, prompted by the need to solve the important problems arising from the rapid progress in technology, developed their own highly empirical science of *hydraulics*. The science of hydraulics was based on a large number of experimental data and differed greatly in its methods and in its objects from the science of theoretical hydrodynamics.

At the beginning of the present century L. Prandtl distinguished himself by showing how to unify these two divergent branches of fluid dynamics. He achieved a high degree of correlation between theory and experiment and paved the way to the remarkably successful development of fluid mechanics which has taken place over the past fifty years. It had been realized even before Prandtl that the discrepancy between the results of classical hydrodynamics and experiment were, in very many cases, due to the fact that the theory neglected *fluid friction*. Moreover, the complete equations of motion for flows with friction (the Navier-Stokes equations) had been known for a long time. However, owing to the great mathematical difficulties connected with the solution of these equations (with the exception of a small number of particular cases), the way to a theoretical treatment of viscous fluid motion was barred. Furthermore, in the case of the two most important fluids, namely water and air, the viscosity is very small and, consequently, the forces due to viscous friction are, generally speaking, very small compared with the remaining forces (gravity and pressure forces). For this reason it was very difficult to comprehend that the frictional forces omitted from the classical theory influenced the motion of a fluid to so large an extent.

In a paper on "Fluid motion with very small friction", read before the Mathematical Congress in Heidelberg in 1904, L. Prandtl showed how it was possible to analyze viscous flows precisely in cases which had great practical importance. He proved that the flow about a solid body can be divided into two regions: a very thin layer in the neighbourhood of the body *(boundary layer)* where friction plays an essential part, and the remaining region outside this layer, where friction may be neglected. With the aid of this hypothesis Prandtl succeeded in giving a physically penetrating explanation of the importance of viscosity in the assessment of drag and paved the way for the theoretical analysis of viscous flows, achieving at the same time a maximum degree of simplification of the attendant mathematical difficulties. He thus took the first step towards a re-unification of theory and practice. This *boundary layer theory* proved extremely fruitful in that it provided an effective tool for the development of fluid dynamics. Since the beginning of the current century the new theory has been developed at a very fast rate under the additional stimulus obtained from the recently founded science of aerodynamics. In a very short time it became one of the foundation stones of modern fluid dynamics together with the other very important developments — the aerofoil theory and the science of gas dynamics.

The boundary layer theory finds its application in the calculation of the skin friction drag which acts on a body as it is moved through a fluid: for example the drag experienced by a flat plate at zero incidence, the drag of a ship, of an aeroplane wing, aircraft nacelle, or turbine blade. Boundary layer flow has the peculiar property that under certain conditions the flow in the immediate neighbourhood of a solid wall becomes reversed causing the boundary layer to separate from it. This is accompanied by a more or less pronounced formation of eddies in the wake of the body. Thus the pressure distribution is changed and differs markedly from that in a frictionless stream. The deviation in pressure distribution from the ideal is the cause of form drag and its calculation is thus made possible with the aid of boundary layer theory. Boundary layer theory gives an answer to the very important question of what shape must a body be given in order to avoid this detrimental separation. Separation can also occur in the internal flow through a channel and is not confined to external flows past solid bodies. Problems connected with the flow of fluids through the channels formed by the blades of turbomachines (rotary compressors and turbines) can also be treated with the aid of boundary layer theory. Furthermore, phenomena which occur at the point of maximum lift of an aerofoil and which are associated with stalling can be understood only on the basis of boundary layer theory. Finally, problems of heat transfer also belong to the class of problems in boundary layer theory.

At first the boundary layer theory was developed mainly for the case of laminar flow in an incompressible fluid, as in this case the phenomenological hypothesis for shearing stresses already existed in the form of Stokes' law. This topic was subsequently developed in a large number of research papers and reached such a stage of perfection that at present the problem of laminar flow can be considered to have been solved in its main outline. Later the theory was extended to include turbulent, incompressible boundary layers which are more important from the point of view of practical applications. It is true that in the case of turbulent flows O. Reynolds introduced the fundamentally important concept of apparent, or virtual turbulent friction as far back as 1880. However, this concept was in itself insufficient to make the theoretical analysis of turbulent flows possible. Great progress was achieved with the introduction of Prandtl's mixing length theory (1925) which, together with systematic experiments, paved the way for the theoretical treatment of turbulent flows with the aid of boundary layer theory. However, a rational theory of fully developed turbulent flows is still non-existent, and in view of the extreme complexity of such flows it will remain so for a considerable time. One cannot even be certain that science will ever be successful in this task. In modern times the phenomena which occur in the boundary layer of a compressible flow have become the subject of intensive investigations, the impulse having been provided by the rapid increase in the speed of flight of modern aircraft. In addition to a velocity boundary layer such flows develop a thermal boundary layer and its existence plays an important part in the process of heat transfer between the fluid and the solid body past which it flows.

The phenomenon of transition from laminar to turbulent flow which is fundamental for the science of fluid dynamics was first investigated at the end of the 19th century, namely by O. Reynolds. In 1914 L. Prandtl carried out his famous experiments with spheres and succeeded in showing that the flow in the boundary layer can also be either laminar or turbulent and, furthermore, that the problem of separation, and hence the problem of the calculation of drag, is governed by this transition. He initiated his theoretical investigation of transition from laminar to turbulent flow in the year 1921 and after many efforts a measure of success was achieved in recent times when it became possible to derive theoretical results which are in excellent agreement with experiments †.

Modern investigations in the field of fluid dynamics in general, as well as in the field of boundary layer research, are characterized by a very close relation between theory and experiment. The most important steps forwards have, in most cases, been taken as a result of a small number of fundamental experiments backed by theoretical considerations.

A review of the development of boundary layer theory which stresses the mutual cross-fertilization between theory and experiment is contained in an article written by A. Betz ‡.

For about twenty years after its inception the boundary layer theory was being developed mainly in L. Prandtl's Institute in Goettingen. In later years other research workers, particularly those in Great Britain and in the U.S.A., also took an active part in its development. The Second World War greatly stimulated research in the field of fluid dynamics in general, and along with it, research in the field of boundary layer theory made great strides; so much so that at the present time the literature on the subject has become almost intractable, and the number of original contributions has reached one hundred per annum §.

The first survey of this branch of science was given in 1931 by W. Tollmien in two articles in the "Handbuch der Experimentalphysik"*. Shortly afterwards L. Prandtl published a comprehensive presentation in the "Aerodynamic Theory", edited by W. F. Durand. The most recent survey of this field of science was given by A. D. Young in "Modern Developments in Fluid Dynamics — High Speed Flow" edited by L. Howarth.

---

† H. Schlichting, Entstehung der Turbulenz, Handb. d. Physik, vol. VIII/1, pp. 351—450, 1959.

‡ A. Betz, Ziele, Wege und konstruktive Auswertung der Strömungsforschung, Zeitschr. VDI **91**, 253 (1949).

§ H. L. Dryden: Fifty years of boundary-layer theory and experiment. Science, **121**, 375—380, (1955).

* *Cf.* the bibliography on p. 632.

Part A. Fundamental laws of motion for a viscous fluid

CHAPTER I

Outline of fluid motion with friction

a. Real and perfect fluids

Most theoretical investigations in the field of fluid dynamics are based on the concept of a perfect, i. e. frictionless and incompressible, fluid. In the motion of such a perfect fluid, two contacting layers experience no tangential forces (shearing stresses) but act on each other with normal forces (pressures) only. This is equivalent to stating that a perfect fluid offers no internal resistance to a change in shape. The theory describing the motion of a perfect fluid is mathematically very far developed and supplies in many cases a satisfactory description of real motions, such as e. g. the motion of surface waves of the formation of liquid jets. On the other hand the theory of perfect fluids fails completely to account for the drag of a body. In this connexion it leads to the statement that a body which moves uniformly through a fluid which extends to infinity experiences no drag (D'Alembert's paradox).

This unacceptable result of the theory of a perfect fluid can be traced to the fact that the inner layers of a real fluid transmit tangential as well as normal stresses, this being also the case near a solid wall wetted by a fluid. These tangential or friction forces in a real fluid are connected with a property which is called the *viscosity* of the fluid.

Because of the absence of tangential forces, on the boundary between a perfect fluid and a solid wall there exists, in general, a difference in relative tangential velocities, i. e. there is slip. On the other hand, in real fluids the existence of intermolecular attractions causes the fluid to adhere to a solid wall and this gives rise to shearing stresses.

The existence of tangential (shearing) stresses and the *condition of no slip* near solid walls constitute the essential differences between a perfect and a real fluid. Certain fluids which are of great practical importance, such as water and air, have very small coefficients of viscosity. In many instances, the motion of such *fluids of small viscosity* agrees very well with that of a perfect fluid, because in most cases the shearing stresses are very small. For this reason the existence of viscosity is completely neglected in the theory of perfect fluids, mainly because this introduces a far-reaching simplification of the equations of motion, as a result of which an extensive mathematical theory becomes possible. It is, however, important to stress the fact that even in fluids with very small viscosities, unlike in perfect fluids, the condition of no slip near a solid boundary prevails. This condition of no slip introduces in many cases very large discrepancies in the laws of motion of perfect and real fluids. In particular, the very large discrepancy between the value of drag in a real and a perfect fluid has its physical origin in the condition of no slip near a wall.

This book deals with the motion of fluids of small viscosity, because of the great practical importance of the problem. During the course of the study it will become clear how this partly consistent and partly divergent behaviour of perfect and real fluids can be explained.

b. Viscosity

The nature of viscosity can best be visualized with the aid of the following experiment: Consider the motion of a fluid between two very long parallel plates, one of which is at rest, the other moving with a constant velocity parallel to itself, as shown in Fig. 1.1 Let the distance between the plates be h, the pressure being constant

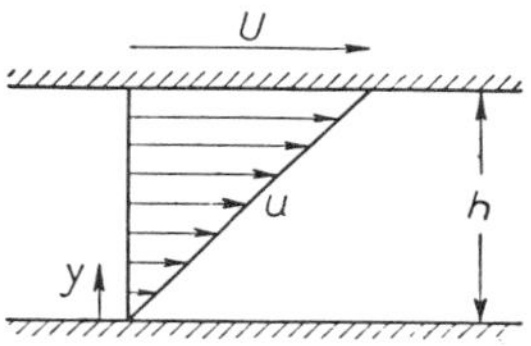

Fig. 1.1. Velocity distribution in a viscous fluid between two parallel flat walls (Couette flow)

throughout the fluid. Experiment teaches that the fluid adheres to both walls, so that its velocity at the lower plate is zero, and that at the upper plate is equal to the velocity of the plate, U. Furthermore, the velocity distribution in the fluid between the plates is linear, so that the fluid velocity is proportional to the distance y from the lower plate, and we have

$$u(y) = \frac{y}{h} U . \tag{1.1}$$

In order to support the motion it is necessary to apply a tangential force to the upper plate, the force being in equilibrium with the frictional forces in the fluid. It is known from experiments that this force (taken per unit area of the plate) is proportional to the velocity U of the upper plate, and inversely proportional to the distance h. The frictional force per unit area, denoted by τ (frictional shearing stress) is, therefore, proportional to U/h, for which in general we may also substitute $\mathrm{d}u/\mathrm{d}y$. The proportionality factor between τ and $\mathrm{d}u/\mathrm{d}y$, which we shall denote by μ, depends on the nature of the fluid. It is small for "thin" fluids, such as water or alcohol, but large in the case of very viscous liquids, such as oil of glycerine. Thus we have obtained the fundamental relation for fluid friction in the form

$$\tau = \mu \frac{\mathrm{d}u}{\mathrm{d}y} . \tag{1.2}$$

The quantity μ is a property of the fluid and depends to a great extent on its temperature. It is a measure of the *viscosity* of the fluid. The law of friction given by eqn. (1.2) is known as *Newton's law of friction*. Eqn. (1.2) can be regarded as the definition of viscosity. It is, however, necessary to stress that the example considered in Fig. 1.1 constitutes a particularly simple case of fluid motion. A generalization of this simple case is contained in Stokes' law of friction (cf. Chap. III). The dimensions of viscosity can be deduced without difficulty from eqn. (1.2)†. The shearing stress is measured in lbf/ft² and the velocity gradient du/dy in $\sec^{-1}$. Hence

$$\mu = \left[\frac{\text{lbf sec}}{\text{ft}^2}\right]$$

where the square brackets are used to denote units. The above is not the only, or even the most widely, employed unit of viscosity. Table 1.1 lists the various units together with their conversion factors.

Table 1.1. Viscosity conversion factors‡

a. Absolute viscosity μ

	kgf sec/m²	kgf hr/m²	g/cm sec
kgf sec/m²	1	277.8×10^{-6}	98.1
kgf hr/m²	3,600	1	0.35316×10^{6}
g/cm sec (poise)	0.010019	2.833×10^{-6}	1
kg/m hr	2.831×10^{-5}	7.8655×10^{-9}	2.788×10^{-3}
lbf sec/ft²	4.882	1.356×10^{-3}	478.96
lbf hr/ft²	1.7578×10^{4}	4.882	1.7244×10^{6}
lb/ft sec	0.1517	42.139×10^{-6}	14.882

	kg/m hr	lbf sec/ft²	lbf hr/ft²	lb/ft sec
kgf sec/m²	3.5316×10^{4}	0.2048	56.89×10^{-6}	6.5919
kgf hr/m²	127.1×10^{6}	737.28	0.2048	2.373×10^{4}
g/cm sec (poise)	360	2.088×10^{-3}	0.58×10^{-6}	0.06721
kg/m hr	1	5.798×10^{-6}	1.6107×10^{-9}	0.1866×10^{-3}
lbf sec/ft²	0.1724×10^{6}	1	277.7×10^{-6}	32.185
lbf hr/ft²	620.8×10^{6}	3,600	1	11.587×10^{4}
lb/ft sec	5.358×10^{3}	0.03107	8.631×10^{-6}	1

b. Kinematic viscosity ν

	m²/sec	m²/hr	cm²/sec	ft²/sec	ft²/hr
m²/sec	1	3,600	1×10^{4}	10.7639	3.875×10^{4}
m²/hr	277.8×10^{-6}	1	2.778	299.9×10^{-4}	10.7639
cm²/sec (stokes)	1×10^{-4}	0.36	1	10.7639×10^{-4}	3.875
ft²/sec	0.092903	334.45	929.03	1	3,600
ft²/hr	25.806×10^{-6}	0.092903	0.25806	277.8×10^{-6}	1

† We shall consistently use in this book the gravitational or engineering system of units; in accordance with international agreement the symbols kgf and lbf will be used to denote the respective units of *force*; the corresponding units of *mass* will be denoted by the abbreviations kg and lb respectively.

‡ From British Standard Code B. S. 1042: 1943, amended March 1946

Eqn. (1.2) is related to Hooke's law for an elastic solid body in which case the shearing stress is proportional to the strain

$$\tau = G\gamma \quad \text{with} \quad \gamma = \frac{\partial \xi}{\partial y} . \tag{1.3}$$

Here G denotes the modulus of torsion, γ the change in angle between two lines which were originally at right angles, and ξ denotes the displacement in the direction of abscissae (Figs. 3.4 and 3.5). Whereas in the case of an elastic solid the shearing stress is proportional to the *magnitude of the strain*, γ, experience teaches that in the case of fluids it is proportional to the *rate of change of strain* $\mathrm{d}\gamma/\mathrm{d}t$. If we put

$$\tau = \mu \frac{\mathrm{d}\gamma}{\mathrm{d}t} = \mu \frac{\mathrm{d}}{\mathrm{d}t}\left(\frac{\partial \xi}{\partial y}\right) = \mu \frac{\partial}{\partial y}\left(\frac{\mathrm{d}\xi}{\mathrm{d}t}\right),$$

we shall obtain, as before,

$$\tau = \mu \frac{\partial u}{\partial y}$$

because $\xi = ut$. We shall revert to this analogy with the equations of the theory of elasticity in Chap. III, when we shall derive the general law of friction, first enunciated by Stokes.

In all fluid motions in which frictional and inertia forces interact it is important to consider the ratio of the viscosity, μ, to the density, ϱ, known as the *kinematic viscosity*, and denoted by ν:

$$\nu = \frac{\mu}{\varrho} . \tag{1.4}$$

Numerical values: In the case of liquids the viscosity, μ, is nearly independent of pressure and decreases at a high rate with increasing temperature. In the case of gases, to a first approximation, the viscosity can be taken to be independent of pressure but it increases with temperature. The kinematic viscosity, ν, for liquids has the same type of temperature dependence as μ, because the density, ϱ, changes only slightly with temperature, However, in the case of gases, for which ϱ decreases considerably with increasing temperature, ν increases rapidly with temperature. Table 1.2 contains some numerical values of ϱ, μ and ν for water and air. (Please turn to page 8.)

Table 1.3 contains some additional useful data.

Table 1.3. Kinematic viscosity

Liquid	Temperature		$\nu \times 10^6$
	°C	°F	[ft²/sec]
Glycerine	20	68	7319
Mercury	0	32	1·35
Mercury	100	212	0·980
Lubricating oil	20	68	4306
Lubricating oil	40	104	1076
Lubricating oil	60	140	323

Table 1.2. Density, viscosity, and kinematic viscosity of water and air in terms of temperature

Temperature		Water			Air at a pressure of 760 mm Hg (14·696 lbf/in²)		
		Density ϱ	Viscosity $\mu \times 10^6$	Kinematic viscosity $\nu \times 10^6$	Density ϱ	Viscosity $\mu \times 10^6$	Kinematic viscosity $\nu \times 10^6$
[° C]	[° F]	[lbf sec²/ft⁴]	[lbf sec/ft²]	[ft²/sec]	[lbf sec²/ft⁴]	[lbf sec/ft²]	[ft²/sec]
—20	—4	—	—	—	0·00270	0·326	122
—10	14	—	—	—	0·00261	0·338	130
0	32	1·939	37·5	19·4	0·00251	0·350	140
10	50	1·939	27·2	14·0	0·00242	0·362	150
20	68	1·935	21·1	10·9	0·00234	0·375	160
40	104	1·924	13·68	7·11	0·00217	0·399	183
60	140	1·907	9·89	5·19	0·00205	0·424	207
80	176	1·886	7·45	3·96	0·00192	0·449	234
100	212	1·861	5·92	3·19	0·00183	0·477	264

Conversion factors: 1 kgf sec²/m⁴ = 0·01903 lbf sec²/ft⁴ (= slug/ft³)
1 lbf sec²/ft⁴ = 32·1719 lb/ft³ (lb = lb mass; lbf = lb force)
1 kgf sec²/m⁴ = 9·80665 kg/m³ (kg = kg mass; kgf = kg force)
1 kg/m³ = 16·02 lb/ft³

c. Compressibility

Compressibility is a measure of the change of volume of a liquid or gas under the action of external forces. In this connexion we can define a *modulus of elasticity*, E, of volume change, by the equation

$$\varDelta p = -E\,\frac{\varDelta V}{V_0}\,. \tag{1.5}$$

Here $\varDelta V/V_0$ denotes the relative change in volume brought about by a pressure increase $\varDelta p$. The compressibility of liquids is very small: e. g. for water $E = 280{,}000$ lbf/in² which means that a pressure increase of 1 atm (14.7 lbf/in²) causes a relative change in volume of about 1/20,000, i. e. 0·005 per cent. Other liquids show similar properties so that their compressibility can be neglected in most cases, and flows of liquids can be regarded as incompressible.

In the case of gases, the modulus of elasticity, E, is equal to the initial pressure p_0, if the changes are isothermal, as can easily be deduced from the perfect gas law†. For air at NTP (atmospheric pressure and ice-point temperature) $E = 14{\cdot}7$ lbf/in², which means that air is about 20,000 times more compressible than water. Similar conditions obtain for other gases.

In order to answer the question of whether it is necessary to take into account the compressibility of gases in problems of fluid flow it is necessary to consider whether

† From the perfect gas law it can be deduced that the change in volume, $\varDelta V$, caused by a change of pressure $\varDelta p$, satisfies the relation $(p_0 + \varDelta p)\,(V_0 + \varDelta V) = p_0\,V_0$. Hence $\varDelta p \approx -p_0\,\varDelta V/V_0$.

the changes in pressure brought about by the motion of the fluid cause large changes in volume. Instead of considering volumes it is also possible to estimate the change in density, ϱ. Owing to the conservation of mass, we can write: $(V_0 + \Delta V)(\varrho_0 + \Delta\varrho) = V_0 \varrho_0$, so that $\Delta\varrho/\varrho_0 = -\Delta V/V_0$, and eqn. (1.5) can be written as

$$\Delta p = E \frac{\Delta\varrho}{\varrho_0} . \tag{1.5a}$$

Consequently the flow of a gas can be considered incompressible when the relative change in density remains very small, $\Delta\varrho/\varrho_0 \ll 1$. As known from Bernoulli's equation $p + \frac{1}{2} \varrho w^2 = \text{const}$ (w = velocity of flow), the change of pressure, Δp, brought about by the flow is of the order of the dynamic head $q = \frac{1}{2} \varrho w^2$, so that eqn. (1.5a) becomes

$$\frac{\Delta\varrho}{\varrho_0} \approx \frac{q}{E} . \tag{1.6}$$

If, therefore, $\Delta\varrho/\varrho_0$ should be small compared with unity then, as seen from eqn. (1.6), we must also have $q/E \ll 1$. It has thus been proved that flows of gases can be treated as incompressible, with a good degree of approximation, if the dynamic head is small compared with the modulus of elasticity.

The same result can be expressed in a different way if the velocity of sound is introduced into the equation. According to Laplace's equation the velocity of sound is $c^2 = E/\varrho_0$. Hence the condition $\Delta\varrho/\varrho_0 \ll 1$ from eqn. (1.6) can also be written

$$\frac{\Delta\varrho}{\varrho_0} \approx \frac{\varrho_0}{2} \frac{w^2}{E} \approx \frac{1}{2} \left(\frac{w}{c}\right)^2 \ll 1 .$$

The ratio of the velocity of flow, w, to the velocity of sound, c, is known as the **Mach** number

$$\mathsf{M} = \frac{w}{c} . \tag{1.7}$$

The preceding argument leads to the conclusion that compressibility can be neglected in the treatment of the flow of gases if

$$\tfrac{1}{2} \mathsf{M}^2 \ll 1 , \quad \text{(approximately incompressible)} \tag{1.8}$$

i. e. if the Mach number is small compared with unity, or, in other words, if the flow velocity is small compared with the velocity of sound. In the case of air, with a velocity of sound of about c = 1100 ft/sec, the change in density is $\Delta\varrho/\varrho_0 = \frac{1}{2} \mathsf{M}^2 = 0.05$ for a flow velocity w = 330 ft/sec. This value can be accepted as the outside limit when a gaseous flow can be considered incompressible.

In what follows we shall often assume the fluid to be incompressible, which will restrict the results to small Mach numbers. However, on several occasions, in particular in Chaps. XIV, XV, XVII and XXI, our results will be extended to include compressible fluids.

d. The Hagen-Poiseuille equations of flow through a pipe

The elementary law of friction for a simple flow with shear described in Section Ib can be applied to the important, and more general, case of flow through a straight pipe of circular cross-section having a constant diameter $D = 2\,R$. The velocity at the wall is zero, because of adhesion, and reaches a maximum on the axis, Fig. 1.2. The velocity remains constant on cylindrical surfaces which are concentric with the axis, and the individual cylindrical laminae slide over each other, the velocity being purely axial everywhere. A motion of this kind is called *laminar*. At a sufficiently large distance from the entrance section the velocity distribution across the section becomes independent of the co-ordinate along the direction of flow.

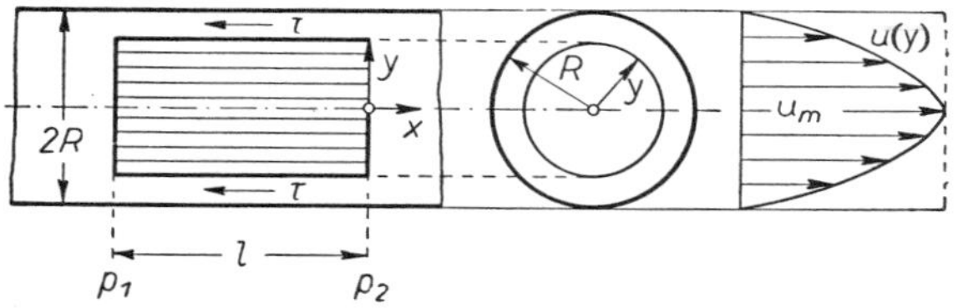

Fig. 1.2. Laminar flow through a pipe

The fluid moves under the influence of the pressure gradient which acts in the direction of the axis, whereas in sections which are perpendicular to it the pressure may be regarded as constant. Owing to friction individual layers act on each other with a shearing stress which is proportional to the velocity gradient $\mathrm{d}u/\mathrm{d}y$. Hence, a fluid particle is accelerated by the pressure gradient and retarded by the frictional shearing stress. No additional forces are present, and in particular inertia forces are absent, because along every stream-line the velocity remains constant. In order to establish the condition of equilibrium we consider a coaxial fluid cylinder of length l and radius y, Fig. 1.2. The condition of equilibrium in the x-direction requires that the pressure force $(p_1 - p_2)\,\pi\,y^2$ acting on the faces of the cylinder be equal to the shear $2\,\pi y l \cdot \tau$ acting on the circumferential area, whence we obtain

$$\tau = \frac{p_1 - p_2}{l}\,\frac{y}{2}\,. \tag{1.9}$$

In accordance with the law of friction, eqn. (1.2), we have in the present case

$$\tau = -\,\mu\,\mathrm{d}u/\mathrm{d}y$$

because u decreases with y, so that eqn. (1.9) leads to

$$\frac{\mathrm{d}u}{\mathrm{d}y} = -\,\frac{p_1 - p_2}{\mu\,l}\,\frac{y}{2}$$

and upon integration we find

$$u(y) = \frac{p_1 - p_2}{\mu\,l}\left(C - \frac{y^2}{4}\right).$$

The constant of integration, C, is obtained from the condition of no slip at the wall. Thus $u = 0$ at $y = R$, so that $C = R^2/4$, and finally

$$u(y) = \frac{p_1 - p_2}{4 \mu l} (R^2 - y^2) . \tag{1.10}$$

The velocity is seen to be distributed parabolically over the radius, Fig. 1.2, and the maximum velocity on the axis becomes

$$u_m = \frac{p_1 - p_2}{4 \mu l} R^2 .$$

The volume Q flowing through a section per unit time can be easily evaluated since the volume of the paraboloid of revolution is equal to $\frac{1}{2} \times$ base area $\times$ height. Hence

$$Q = \frac{\pi}{2} R^2 u_m = \frac{\pi R^4}{8 \mu l} (p_1 - p_2) . \tag{1.11}$$

Eqn. (1.11) states that the volume rate of flow is proportional to the first power of the pressure drop per unit length $(p_1 - p_2)/l$ and to the fourth power of the radius of the pipe. If the mean velocity over the cross-section $\bar{u} = Q/\pi R^2$ is introduced, eqn. (1.11) can be rewritten as

$$p_1 - p_2 = 8 \mu \frac{l}{R^2} \bar{u} . \tag{1.12}$$

Eqn. (1.11) was first deduced by G. Hagen [5] and shortly afterwards by J. Poiseuille [8]. It is known as the Hagen-Poiseuille equation of laminar flow through a pipe.

Eqn. (1.11) can be utilized for the experimental determination of the viscosity, μ. The method consists in the measurement of the rate of flow and of the pressure drop across a fixed portion of a capillary tube of known radius. Thus enough data are provided to determine μ from eqn. (1.11).

The type of flow to which eqns. (1.10) and (1.11) apply exists in reality only for relatively small radii and flow velocities. For larger velocities and radii the character of the motion changes completely: the pressure drop ceases to be proportional to the first power of the mean velocity as indicated by eqn. (1.12), but becomes approximately proportional to the second power of u. The velocity distribution across a section becomes much more uniform and the well-ordered laminar motion is replaced by a flow in which irregular and fluctuating radial and axial velocity components are superimposed on the main motion, so that, consequently, intensive mixing in a radial direction takes place. In such cases Newton's law of friction, eqn. (1.2), ceases to be applicable. This is the case of *turbulent* flow, to be discussed in great detail later in Chap. XX.

e. Principle of similarity; the Reynolds and Mach numbers

The type of fluid motion discussed in the preceding Section was very simple because every fluid particle moved under the influence of frictional and pressure forces only, inertia forces being everywhere equal to zero. In a divergent or convergent channel fluid particles are acted upon by inertia forces in addition to pressure and friction forces.

In the present section we shall endeavour to answer a very fundamental question, namely that concerned with the conditions under which flows of different fluids about two geometrically similar bodies, and with identical initial flow velocities, display geometrically similar stream-lines. Such motions which have geometrically similar stream-lines are called *dynamically similar*, or *similar flows*. For two flows about geometrically similar bodies (e. g. about two spheres) with different fluids, different velocities and different linear dimensions, to be similar, it is evidently necessary that the following condition should be satisfied: at all geometrically similar points the forces acting on a fluid particle must bear a fixed ratio at every instant of time.

We shall now consider the important case when only frictional and inertia forces are present. Elastic forces which may be due to changes in volume will be excluded, i. e. it will be assumed that the fluid is incompressible. Gravitational forces will also be excluded so that, consequently, free surfaces are not admitted, and in the interior of the fluid the force of gravity is assumed to be balanced by buoyancy. Under these assumptions the condition of similarity is satisfied only if at all corresponding points the ratio of inertia and friction forces is the same. In a motion parallel to the x-axis the inertia force per unit volume has the magnitude of $\varrho\, \mathrm{D}u/\mathrm{D}t$, where u denotes the component of velocity in the x-direction and $\mathrm{D}/\mathrm{D}t$ denotes the substantive derivative. In the case of steady flow we can replace it by $\varrho\, \partial u/\partial x \cdot \mathrm{d}x/\mathrm{d}t = \varrho\, u\, \partial u/\partial x$, where $\partial u/\partial x$ denotes the change in velocity with position. Thus the inertia force per unit volume is equal to $\varrho\, u\, \partial u/\partial x$. For the friction force it is easy to deduce an expression from Newton's law of friction, eqn. (1.2). Considering a fluid particle for which the x-direction coincides with the direction of motion, Fig. 1.3, it is found that the resultant of shearing forces is equal to

$$\left(\tau + \frac{\partial \tau}{\partial y}\,\mathrm{d}y\right) \mathrm{d}x\,\mathrm{d}z - \tau\,\mathrm{d}x\,\mathrm{d}z = \frac{\partial \tau}{\partial y}\,\mathrm{d}x\,\mathrm{d}y\,\mathrm{d}z\,.$$

Hence the friction force per unit volume is equal to $\partial\tau/\partial y$, or by eqn. (1.2), to $\mu\, \partial^2 u/\partial y^2$.

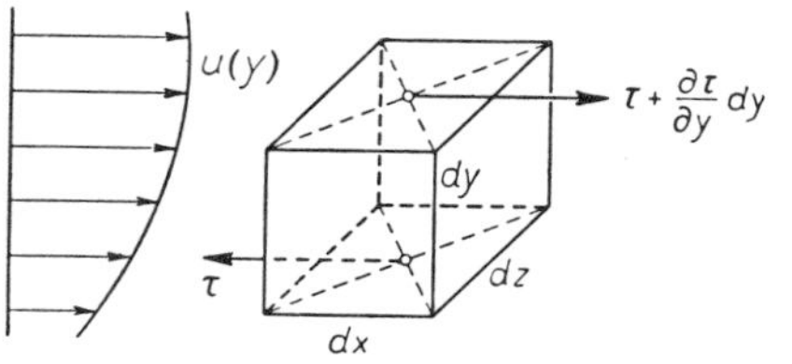

Fig. 1.3. Frictional forces acting on a fluid particle

Consequently, the condition of similarity, i. e. the condition that at all corresponding points the ratio of the inertia to the friction force must be constant, can be written as:

$$\frac{\text{Inertia force}}{\text{Friction force}} = \frac{\varrho\, u\, \partial u/\partial x}{\mu\, \partial^2 u/\partial y^2} = \text{const}\,.$$

It is now necessary to investigate how these forces are changed when the magnitudes which determine the flow are varied. The latter include the density ϱ, the viscosity μ, a representative velocity, e. g. the free stream velocity V, and a characteristic linear dimension of the body, e. g. the diameter d of the sphere.

The velocity u at some point in the velocity field is proportional to the free stream velocity V, the velocity gradient $\partial u/\partial x$ is proportional to V/d, and similarly $\partial^2 u/\partial y^2$ is proportional to V/d^2. Hence the ratio

$$\frac{\text{Inertia force}}{\text{Friction force}} = \frac{\varrho\, u\, \partial u/\partial x}{\mu\, \partial^2 u/\partial y^2} = \frac{\varrho\, V^2/d}{\mu\, V/d^2} = \frac{\varrho\, V d}{\mu}\,.$$

Therefore, the condition of similarity is satisfied if the quantity $\varrho\, V\, d/\mu$ has the same value in both flows. The quantity $\varrho\, V\, d/\mu$, which, with $\mu/\varrho = \nu$, can also be written as $V\, d/\nu$, is a dimensionless number because it is the ratio of the two forces. It is known as the *Reynolds number*, R. Thus two flows are similar when the Reynolds number

$$\mathsf{R} = \frac{\varrho\, V d}{\mu} = \frac{V d}{\nu} \tag{1.13}$$

is equal for both. This principle was first enunciated by Osborne Reynolds [9] in connexion with his investigations into the flow through pipes and is known as Reynolds' principle of similarity.

The fact that the Reynolds number is dimensionless can be at once verified directly by considering the dimensions

$$\varrho\left[\frac{\text{lbf sec}^2}{\text{ft}^4}\right], \quad V\left[\frac{\text{ft}}{\text{sec}}\right], \quad d\,[\text{ft}]\,, \quad \mu\left[\frac{\text{lbf sec}}{\text{ft}^2}\right].$$

Hence

$$\frac{\varrho\, V d}{\mu} = \frac{\text{lbf sec}^2}{\text{ft}^4}\cdot\frac{\text{ft}}{\text{sec}}\cdot \text{ft}\cdot\frac{\text{ft}^2}{\text{lbf sec}} = 1$$

which proves that the Reynolds number is, in fact, dimensionless.

Method of indices: Instead of the consideration of the condition of dynamic similarity, Reynolds' principle can also be deduced by considering dimensions by the method of indices. In this connexion use is made of the observation that all physical laws must be of a form which is independent of the particular system of units employed. In the case under consideration the physical quantities which determine the flow are: the free stream velocity, V, a representative linear dimension of the body, d, as well as the density, ϱ, and the viscosity, μ. We now ask whether there exists a combination of these quantities in the form

$$V^\alpha\, d^\beta\, \varrho^\gamma\, \mu^\delta\,,$$

which would be dimensionless. If F denotes force, L - length and T - time, a dimensionless combination will be obtained if

$$V^\alpha\, d^\beta\, \varrho^\gamma\, \mu^\delta = \mathsf{F}^0\, \mathsf{L}^0\, \mathsf{T}^0\,.$$

Without restricting the generality of the argument it is permissible to assign the value of unity to one of the four indices α, β, γ, δ, because any arbitrary power of a dimensionless quantity is also dimensionless. Assuming $\alpha = 1$, we obtain

$$V\, d^{\beta}\, \varrho^{\gamma}\, \mu^{\delta} = \frac{\mathsf{L}}{\mathsf{T}}\, \mathsf{L}^{\beta} \left(\frac{\mathsf{F}\,\mathsf{T}^2}{\mathsf{L}^4}\right)^{\gamma} \left(\frac{\mathsf{F}\,\mathsf{T}}{\mathsf{L}^2}\right)^{\delta} = \mathsf{F}^0\, \mathsf{L}^0\, \mathsf{T}^0 .$$

Equating the exponents of L, T, and F on both sides of the expression we obtain three equations:

$$\begin{aligned} \mathsf{F}: &\qquad \gamma + \delta = 0 \\ \mathsf{L}: &\qquad 1 + \beta - 4\gamma - 2\delta = 0 \\ \mathsf{T}: &\qquad -1 + 2\gamma + \delta = 0 . \end{aligned}$$

the solution of which is

$$\beta = 1, \qquad \gamma = 1, \qquad \delta = -1 .$$

This shows that there exists a unique dimensionless combination of the four quantities V, d, ϱ and μ, namely the Reynolds number R.

Dimensionless quantities: The reasoning followed in the preceding derivation of the Reynolds number can be extended to include the case of different Reynolds numbers in the consideration of the velocity field and forces (normal and tangential) for flows with geometrically similar boundaries. Let the position of a point in the space around the geometrically similar bodies be indicated by the co-ordinates x, y, z; then the ratios x/d, y/d, z/d are its dimensionless co-ordinates. The velocity components are made dimensionless by referring them to the free stream velocity V, thus u/V, v/V, w/V, and the normal and shearing stresses, p and τ, can be made dimensionless by referring them to the double of the dynamic head, i. e. to $\varrho\, V^2$ thus: $p/\varrho\, V^2$ and $\tau/\varrho\, V^2$. The previously enunciated principle of dynamical similarity can be expressed in an alternative form by asserting that for the two geometrically similar systems with equal Reynolds numbers the dimensionless quantities $u/V, \ldots, p/\varrho V^2$ and $\tau/\varrho V^2$ depend only on the dimensionless co-ordinates x/d, y/d, z/d. If, however, the two systems are geometrically, but not dynamically, similar, i. e. if their Reynolds numbers are different, then the dimensionless quantities under consideration must also depend on the characteristic quantities V, d, ϱ, μ of the two systems. Applying the principle that physical laws must be independent of the system of units, it follows that the dimensionless quantities $u/V, \ldots, p/\varrho V^2, \tau/\varrho V^2$ can only depend on a dimensionless combination of V, d, ϱ, and μ which is unique, being the Reynolds number $\mathsf{R} = V\, d\, \varrho/\mu$. Thus we are led to the conclusion that for the two geometrically similar systems which have different Reynolds numbers and which are being compared, the dimensionless quantities of the field of flow can only be functions of the three dimensionless space co-ordinates x/d, y/d, z/d and of the Reynolds number R.

The preceding dimensional analysis can be utilized to make an important assertion about the total force exerted by a fluid stream on an immersed body. The force acting on the body is the surface integral of all normal and shearing stresses acting on it. If P denotes the component of the resultant force in any given direction, it is possible to write a dimensionless force coefficient of the form $P/d^2\, \varrho\, V^2$, but instead of the area d^2 it is customary to choose a different characteristic area, A, of the immersed body, e. g. the frontal area exposed by the body to the flow direction which is, in the case of a sphere, equal to $\pi d^2/4$. Hence the dimensionless force coefficient becomes $P/A \varrho V^2$. Dimensional analysis leads to the conclusion that for geometrically similar systems this coefficient can depend only on the dimensionless group formed from V, d, ϱ, and μ, i. e. on the Reynolds number. The component of the resultant force parallel to the undisturbed initial velocity is referred to as the drag D, and the component perpendicular to that direction is called lift, L. Hence the dimensionless coefficients for lift and drag become

$$C_L = \frac{L}{\frac{1}{2}\varrho V^2 A} \quad \text{and} \quad C_D = \frac{D}{\frac{1}{2}\varrho V^2 A}, \tag{1.14}$$

if the dynamic head $\frac{1}{2}\varrho V^2$ is selected for reference instead of the quantity ϱV^2. Thus the argument leads to the conclusion that the dimensionless lift and drag coefficients for geometrically similar systems, i. e. for geometrically similar bodies which have the same orientation with respect to the free stream velocity, are functions of one variable only, namely the Reynolds number:

$$C_L = f_1(\mathsf{R})\ ; \qquad C_D = f_2(\mathsf{R})\ . \tag{1.15}$$

It is necessary to stress once more that this important conclusion from Reynolds' principle of similarity is valid only if the assumptions underlying it are satisfied, i. e. if the forces acting in the flow are due to friction and inertia only. In the case of compressible fluids, when elastic forces are important, and for motions with free surfaces, when gravitational forces must be taken into consideration, eqns. (1.15) do not apply. In such cases it is necessary to deduce different similarity principles in which the dimensionless Froude number $\mathsf{F} = V/\sqrt{g\,d}$ (for gravity and inertia) and the dimensionless Mach number $\mathsf{M} = V/c$ (for compressible flows) are included.

The importance of the similarity principle given in eqns. (1.14) and (1.15) is very great as far as the sciences of theoretical and experimental fluid mechanics are concerned. First, the dimensionless coefficients, C_L, C_D, and R are independent of the system of units. Secondly, their use leads to a considerable simplification in the extent of experimental work. In most cases it is impossible to determine the functions $f_1(\mathsf{R})$ and $f_2(\mathsf{R})$ theoretically and experimental methods must be used.

Supposing that it is desired to determine the drag coefficient C_D for a specified shape of body, e. g. a sphere, then without the application of the principle of similarity it would be necessary to carry out drag measurements for four independent variables, V, d, ϱ, and μ, and this would constitute a tremendous programme of work. It follows, however, that the drag coefficient for spheres of different diameters with different stream velocities and different fluids depends solely on one variable, the Reynolds number. Fig. 1.4 represents the drag coefficient of circular cylinders as a function of the Reynolds number and shows the excellent agreement between experiment and Reynolds' principle of similarity. The experimental points for the drag coefficient of circular cylinders of widely differing diameters fall on a *single* curve. The same applies to points obtained for the drag coefficient of spheres plotted against the Reynolds number in Fig. 1.5. The sudden decrease in the value of the drag coefficient which occurs near $\mathsf{R} = 5 \times 10^5$ in the case of circular cylinders and near $\mathsf{R} = 3 \times 10^5$ in the case of spheres will be discussed, in more detail, later.

Fig. 1.6 reproduces photographs of the stream-lines about circular cylinders in oil taken by F. Homann [6]. They give a good idea of the changes in the field of flow associated with various Reynolds numbers. For small Reynolds numbers the wake is laminar, but at increasing Reynolds numbers at first very regular vortex patterns,

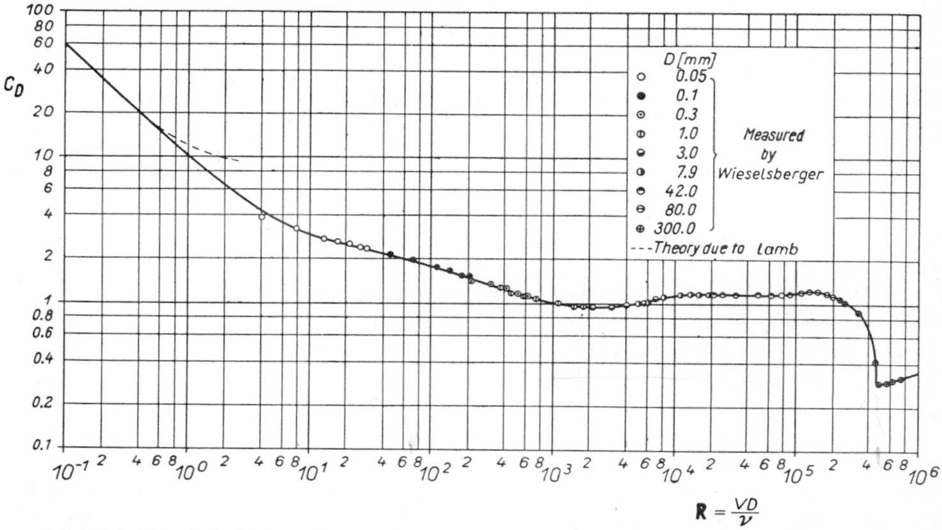

Fig. 1.4. Drag coefficient for circular cylinders as a function of the Reynolds number

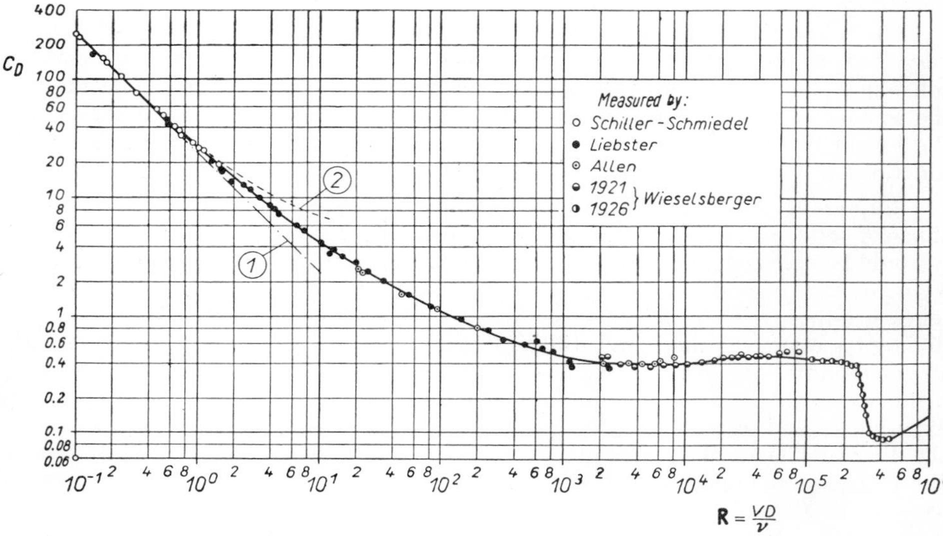

Fig. 1.5. Drag coefficient for spheres as a function of the Reynolds number
Curve (1): Stokes' theory, eqn. (6.10); curve (2): Oseen's theory, eqn. (6.13)

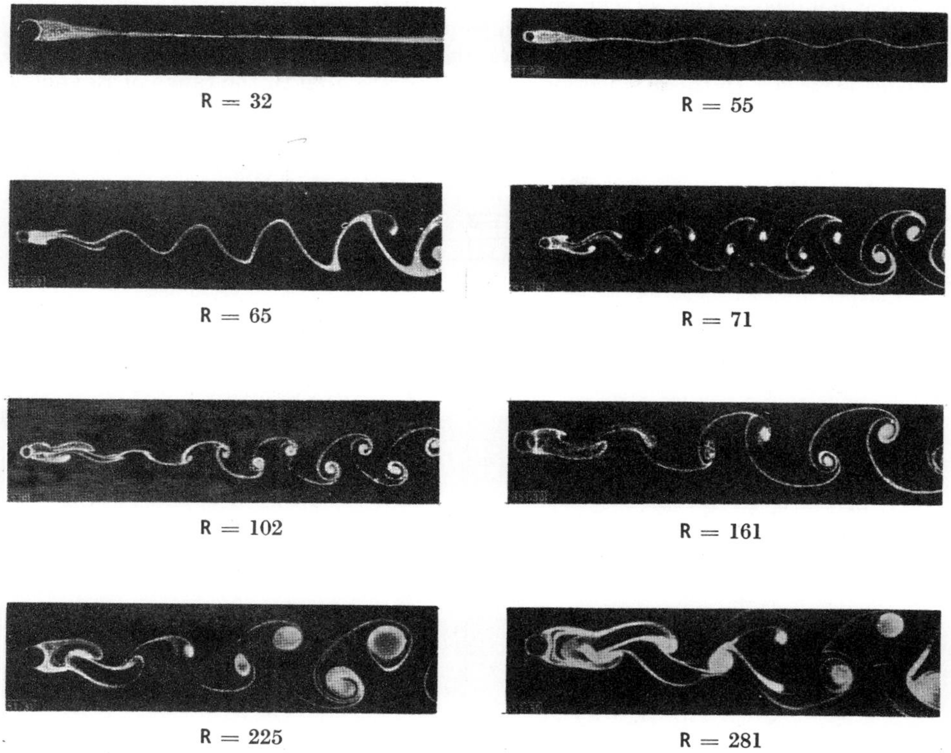

Fig. 1.6. Field of flow of oil about a circular cylinder at varying Reynolds numbers; transition from laminar flow to a vortex street, from Homann [6]

known as Kármán's vortex streets, are formed. At still higher Reynolds numbers, not shown here, the vortex patterns become irregular and turbulent in character.

Influence of compressibility: The preceding argument was conducted under the assumption that the fluid was incompressible, and it was found that the dimensionless dependent quantities were functions of one dimensionless argument, the Reynolds number, only. When the fluid is compressible they depend on an additional dimensionless number, the Mach number $\mathsf{M} = V/c$ which can be regarded, as shown in Sec. I c, as a measure of the compressibility of the flowing medium. In the case of such flows, i. e. when compressibility plays an essential part, the dimensionless coefficients depend on both parameters R and M. Equation (1.15) is then replaced by

$$C_L = f_1(\mathsf{R}, \mathsf{M}) \; ; \qquad C_D = f_2(\mathsf{R}, \mathsf{M}) \tag{1.16}$$

An example of such a relationship is given in Fig. 1.7 which shows a plot of the drag coefficient C_D of spheres in terms of the Reynolds number $\mathsf{R} = VD/\nu$ and the Mach number $\mathsf{M} = V/c$. The curve for $\mathsf{M} = 0{\cdot}3$ is practically coincident with that in Fig. 1.5 for incompressible flow which proves that up to $\mathsf{M} \ll 0{\cdot}3$ the influence of the Mach number is negligible. On the other hand at higher Mach numbers the influence is large. In this connection it is noteworthy that in the range of Reynolds numbers covered by the diagram, its influence recedes more and more as the Mach number is increased.

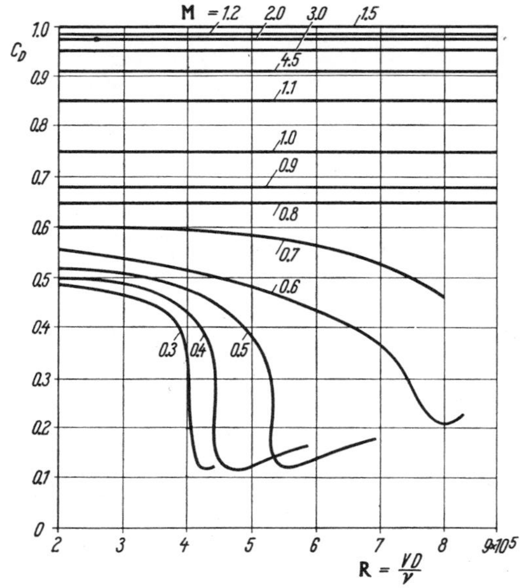

Fig. 1.7. Drag coefficient of spheres in terms of the Reynolds and Mach numbers as measured by A. Naumann [7]

f. Comparison between the theory of perfect fluids and experiment

In the cases of the motion of water and air, which are the most important ones in engineering applications, the Reynolds numbers are very large because of the very low viscosities of these fluids. It would, therefore, appear reasonable to expect very good agreement between experiment and a theory in which the influence of viscosity is neglected altogether, i. e. with the theory of perfect fluids. In any case it seems useful to begin the comparison with experiment by reference to the theory of perfect fluids, if only on account of the large number of existing explicit mathematical solutions.

In fact, for certain classes of problems, such as wave formation and tidal motion, excellent results were obtained with the aid of this theory†. Most problems to be discussed in this book consist in the study of the motion of solid bodies through fluids at rest, or of fluids flowing through pipes and channels. In such cases the use of the theory of perfect fluids is limited because its solutions do not satisfy the con-

† *Cf.* e. g. B. H. Lamb: Hydrodynamics, 6th ed., New York, 1945.

dition of no slip at the solid surface which is always the case with real fluids even at very small viscosities. In a perfect fluid there is slip at a wall, and this circumstance introduces, even for small viscosities, such fundamental differences that it is rather surprising to find in some cases (e. g. in the case of very slender, stream-line bodies) that the two solutions display a good measure of agreement. The greatest discrepancy between the theory of a perfect fluid and experiment exists in the consideration of drag. The perfect fluid theory leads to the conclusion that when an arbitrary solid body moves through an infinitely extended fluid at rest it experiences no force acting in the direction of motion, i. e. that its drag is zero (D'Alembert's paradox). This result is in glaring contradiction to observed fact, as drag is measured on all bodies, even if it can become very small in the case of a stream-line body in steady flow parallel to its axis.

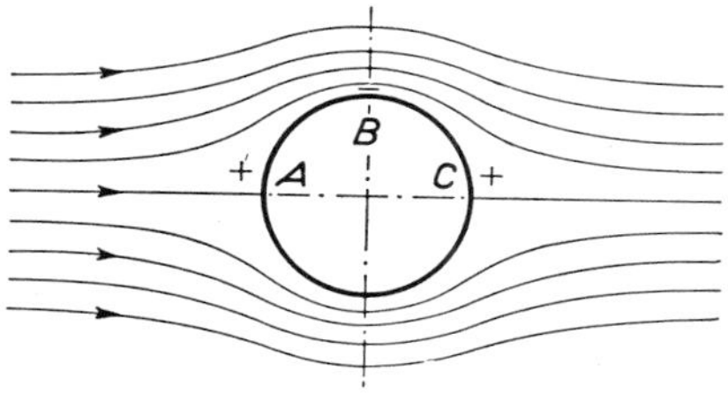

Fig. 1.8. Frictionless flow about a circular cylinder

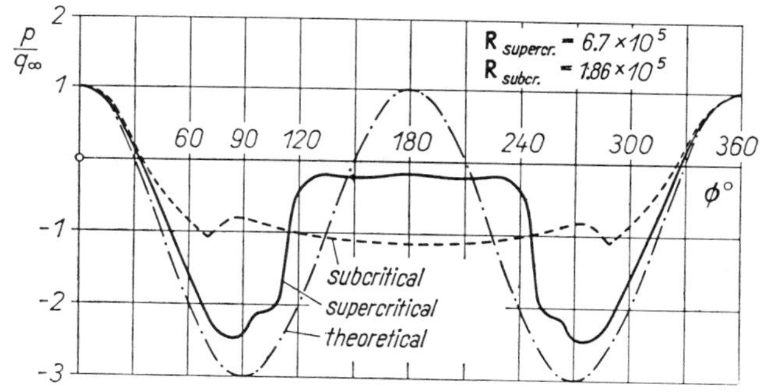

Fig. 1.9. Pressure distribution around a circular cylinder in the subcritical and supercritical range of Reynolds numbers ($q_\infty = \frac{1}{2} \varrho V^2$ = dynamic head of free stream), as measured by O. Flachsbart [3]

By way of illustration we now propose to make some remarks concerning the flow about a circular cylinder. The arrangement of stream-lines for a perfect fluid is given in Fig. 1.8. It follows at once from considerations of symmetry that the resultant force in the direction of motion (drag) is equal to zero. The pressure distribution according to the theory of frictionless motion is given in Fig. 1.9, together with the results of measurements. Measurements indicate that the pressure distribution differs considerably depending on whether the Reynolds number lies in the range of large (subcritical) or small (supercritical) values of the drag coefficient, Fig. 1.4. Experimental and calculated values show a measure of agreement on the front side, but at the rear of the cylinder the discrepancies between experiment and theory are very large, and explain the large drag experienced by a circular cylinder. On the whole, the pressure distribution at high Reynolds numbers deviates less from the theoretical than at low Reynolds numbers. The large variation of pressure distribution with Reynolds number will be discussed in detail in the next chapter. A corresponding pressure distribution curve around a meridian section of a sphere is reproduced in Fig. 1.10. Here, too, measurements show large differences for the two Reynolds numbers, and, again, the smaller Reynolds number lies in the range of large drag coefficients, whereas the larger value lies in the range of small drag coefficients, Fig. 1.5. In this case the measured pressure distribution curve for the large Reynolds number approximates the theoretical curve of frictionless flow very well over the greatest part of the circumference.

Considerably better agreement between the theoretical and measured pressure distribution is obtained for a stream-line body in a flow parallel to its axis [4], Fig. 1.11. Good agreement exists here over almost the whole length of the body, with the exception of a small region near its trailing end. As will be shown later this circumstance is a consequence of the gradual pressure increase in the downstream direction.

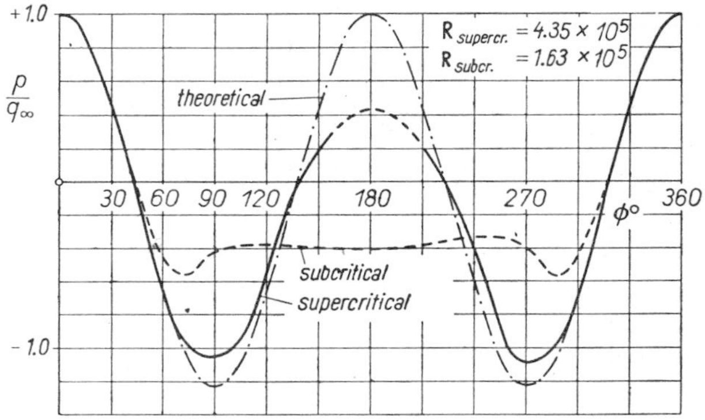

Fig. 1.10. Pressure distribution around a sphere in the subcritical and supercritical range of Reynolds numbers, as measured by O. Flachsbart [2]

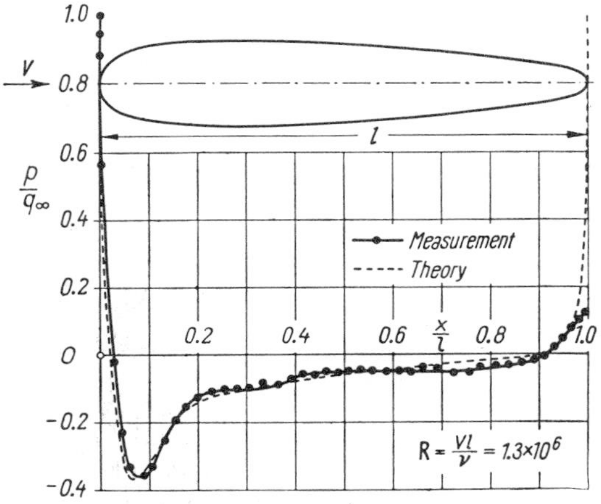

Fig. 1.11. Pressure distribution about a stream-line body of revolution; comparison between theory and measurement, after Fuhrmann [4]

Although, generally speaking, the theory of perfect fluid does not lead to useful results as far as drag calculations are concerned, the lift can be calculated from it very successfully. Fig. 1.12 represents the relation between the lift coefficient and angle of incidence, as measured by A. Betz [1] in the case of a Joukovsky aerofoil of infinite span and provides a comparison with theory. In the range of incidence angles $\alpha = -10°$ to $10°$ the agreement is seen to be good and the small differences can be explained by the influence of friction. The measured and calculated pressure distributions agree very well too, as shown in Fig. 1.13.

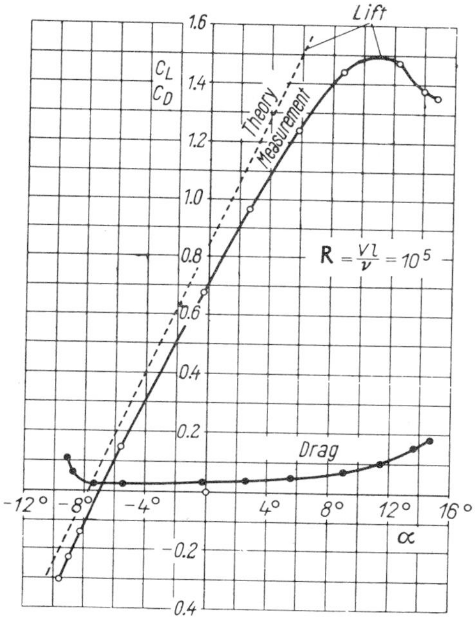

Fig. 1.12. Lift and drag coefficient of a Joukovsky profile in plane flow, as measured by Betz [1]

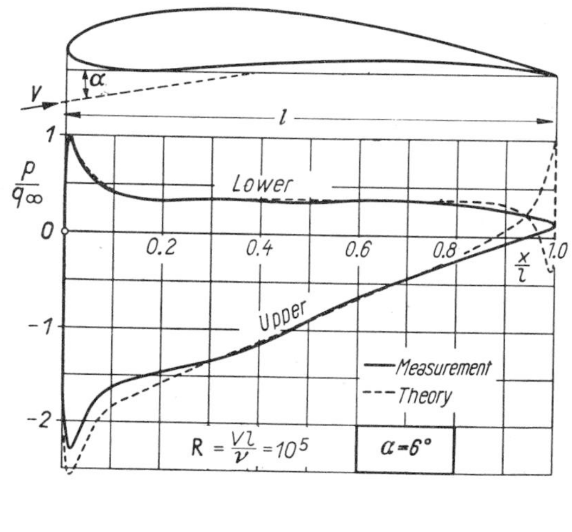

Fig. 1.13. Comparison between the theoretical and measured pressure distribution for a Joukovsky profile at equal lifts, after A. Betz [1]

References

[1] A. Betz, Untersuchung einer Joukowskyschen Tragfläche. ZFM **6**, 173—179 (1915).
[2] O. Flachsbart, Neuere Untersuchungen über den Luftwiderstand von Kugeln. Phys. Z. **28**, 461 (1927).
[3] O. Flachsbart, Winddruck auf Gasbehälter. Reports of the Aerodyn. Versuchsanstalt in Göttingen. IVth series, pp. 134—138 (1932).
[4] G. Fuhrmann, Theoretische und experimentelle Untersuchungen an Ballonmodellen. Diss. Goettingen 1910 — Jahrb. d. Motorluftschiff-Studienges. 1911/12, p. 63.
[5] G. Hagen, Über die Bewegung des Wassers in engen zylindrischen Röhren. Pogg. Ann. **46**, 423 (1839).
[6] F. Homann, Einfluß großer Zähigkeit bei Strömung um Zylinder. Forschg. Ing.-Wes. **7**, 1—10 (1936).
[7] A. Naumann, Luftwiderstand von Kugeln bei hohen Unterschallgeschwindigkeiten. Allgem. Wärmetechnik. **4**, 217—221 (1953).
[8] J. Poiseuille, Récherches expérimentelles sur le mouvement des liquides dans les tubes de très petits diamètres. Comptes Rendus **11**, 961 and 1041 (1840); **12**, 112 (1841); in more detail: Mémoires des Savants Etrangers, **9** (1846).
[9] O. Reynolds, Phil. Trans, Roy, Soc., London, (1883) or Collected-Papers **II**, 51.

CHAPTER II

Outline of boundary layer theory

a. The boundary layer concept

In the case of fluid motions for which the measured pressure distribution nearly agrees with the perfect fluid theory, such as the flow past the stream-line body in Fig. 1.11, or the aerofoil in Fig. 1.13, the influence of viscosity at high Reynolds numbers is confined to a very thin layer in the immediate neighbourhood of the solid wall. If the condition of no slip were not to be satisfied in the case of a real fluid there would be no appreciable difference between the field of flow of the real fluid as compared with that of a perfect fluid. The fact that at the wall the fluid adheres to it means, however, that frictional forces retard the motion of the fluid in a thin layer near the wall. In that thin layer the velocity of the fluid increases from zero at the wall (no slip) to its full value which corresponds to external frictionless flow. The layer under consideration is called the *boundary layer*, and the concept is due to L. Prandtl [13].

Fig. 2.1. Motion along a thin flat plate, from Prandtl-Tietjens
l = length of plate;
Reynolds number $\mathsf{R} = Vl/\nu = 3$

Figure 2.1 reproduces a picture of the motion of water along a thin flat plate in which the stream-lines were made visible by the sprinkling of particles on the surface of the water. The traces left by the particles are proportional to the velocity of flow. It is seen that there is a very thin layer near the wall in which the velocity is considerably smaller than at a larger distance from it. The thickness of this boundary layer increases along the plate in a downstream direction. Fig. 2.2 represents diagrammatically the velocity distribution in such a boundary layer at the plate, with the dimensions across it considerably exaggerated. In front of the leading edge of the plate the velocity distribution is uniform. With increasing distance from the leading edge in the downstream direction the thickness, δ, of the retarded layer increases continuously, as increasing quantities of fluid become affected. Evidently the thickness of the boundary layer decreases with decreasing viscosity.

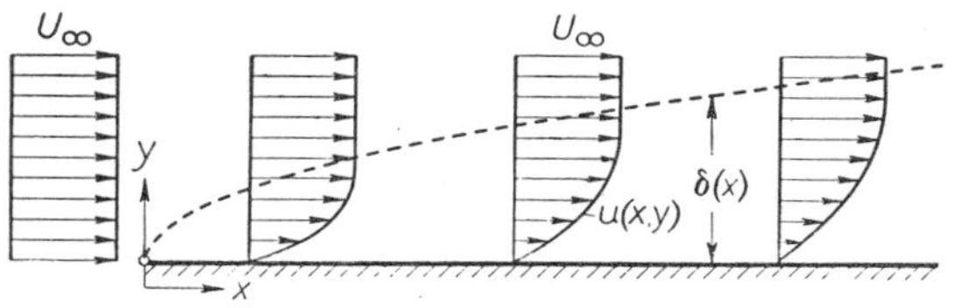

Fig. 2.2. Sketch of boundary layer on a flat plate in parallel flow at zero incidence

On the other hand, even with very small viscosities (large Reynolds numbers) the frictional shearing stresses $\tau = \mu\, \partial u/\partial y$ in the boundary layer are considerable because of the large velocity gradient across the flow, whereas outside the boundary layer they are very small. This physical picture suggests that the field of flow in the case of fluids of small viscosity can be divided, for the purpose of mathematical analysis, into two regions: the thin boundary layer near the wall, in which friction must be taken into account, and the region outside the boundary layer, where the forces due to friction are small and may be neglected, and where, therefore, the perfect fluid theory offers a very good approximation. Such a division of the field of flow, as we shall see in more detail later, brings about a considerable simplification of the mathematical theory of the motion of fluids of low viscosity. In fact, the theoretical study of such motions was only made possible by Prandtl when he introduced this concept.

We now propose to explain the basic concepts of boundary layer theory with the aid of purely physical ideas and without the use of mathematics. The mathematical boundary layer theory which forms the main topic of this book will be discussed in the succeeding chapters.

The decelerated fluid particles in the boundary layer do not, in all cases, remain in the thin layer which adheres to the body along the whole wetted length of the wall. In some cases the boundary layer increases its thickness considerably in the downstream direction and the flow in the boundary layer becomes reversed. This causes the decelerated fluid particles to be forced outwards, which means that the boundary layer is separated from the wall. We then speak of *boundary layer separation*. This phenomenon is always associated with the formation of vortices and with large energy losses in the wake of the body. It occurs primarily near blunt bodies, such as circular cylinders and spheres. Behind such a body there exists a region of strongly decelerated flow (so-called wake), in which the pressure distribution deviates considerably from that in a frictionless fluid, as seen from Figs. 1.9 and 1.10 in the respective cases of a cylinder and sphere. The large drag of such bodies can be explained by the existence of this large deviation in pressure distribution, which is, in turn, a consequence of boundary layer separation.

Estimation of boundary layer thickness: The thickness of a boundary layer which has not separated can be easily estimated in the following way. Whereas friction forces can be neglected with respect to inertia forces outside the boundary layer, owing to low viscosity, they are of a comparable order of magnitude inside it. The inertia force per unit volume is, as explained in Section I e, equal to $\varrho\, u\, \partial u/\partial x$. For a plate of length l the gradient $\partial u/\partial x$ is proportional to U/l, where U denotes the velocity outside the boundary layer. Hence the inertia force is of the order $\varrho\, U^2/l$. On the other hand the friction force per unit volume is equal to $\partial \tau/\partial y$, which, on the assumption of laminar flow, is equal to $\mu\, \partial^2 u/\partial y^2$. The velocity gradient $\partial u/\partial y$ in a direction perpendicular to the wall is of the order U/δ so that the friction force per unit volume is $\partial \tau/\partial y \sim \mu\, U/\delta^2$. From the condition of equality of the friction and inertia forces the following relation is obtained:

$$\mu \frac{U}{\delta^2} \sim \frac{\varrho\, U^2}{l}$$

or solving for the boundary layer thickness δ†:

$$\delta \sim \sqrt{\frac{\mu\, l}{\varrho\, U}} = \sqrt{\frac{\nu\, l}{U}}\,. \tag{2.1}$$

The numerical factor which is, so far, still undetermined will be deduced later (Chap. VII) from the exact solution given by H. Blasius [1], and it will turn out that it is equal to 5, approximately. Hence for *laminar* flow in the boundary layer we have

$$\delta = 5\sqrt{\frac{\nu\, l}{U}}\,. \tag{2.1a}$$

The dimensionless boundary layer thickness, referred to the length of the plate, l, becomes:

$$\frac{\delta}{l} = 5\sqrt{\frac{\nu}{U\, l}} = \frac{5}{\sqrt{\mathsf{R}_l}}\,, \tag{2.2}$$

where R_l denotes the Reynolds number related to the length of the plate, l. It is seen from eqn. (2.1) that the boundary layer thickness is proportional to $\sqrt{\nu}$ and to $\sqrt{l}$. If l is replaced by the variable distance x from the leading edge of the plate, it is seen that δ increases proportionately to $\sqrt{x}$. On the other hand the relative boundary layer thickness δ/l decreases with increasing Reynolds number at $1/\sqrt{\mathsf{R}}$ so that in the limiting case of frictionless flow, with $\mathsf{R} \to \infty$, the boundary layer thickness vanishes.

We are now in a position to estimate the shearing stress τ_0 on the wall, and consequently, the total drag. According to Newton's law of friction (1.2) we have

$$\tau_0 = \mu \left(\frac{\partial u}{\partial y}\right)_0,$$

where subscript o denotes the value at the wall, i. e. for $y = 0$. With the estimate

† A more rigorous definition of boundary layer thickness is given at the end of this section.

$(\partial u/\partial y)_0 \sim U/\delta$ we obtain $\tau_0 \sim \mu\, U/\delta$ and, inserting the value of δ from eqn. (2.1), we have

$$\tau_0 \sim \mu\, U \sqrt{\frac{\varrho\, U}{\mu\, l}} = \sqrt{\frac{\mu\, \varrho\, U^3}{l}}\,. \tag{2.3}$$

Thus the frictional stress near the wall is proportional to the power $U^{3/2}$.

We can now form a dimensionless stress with reference to $\varrho\, U^2$, as explained in Chap. I, and obtain

$$\frac{\tau_0}{\varrho\, U^2} \sim \sqrt{\frac{\mu}{\varrho\, U l}} = \frac{1}{\sqrt{\mathsf{R}_l}} \tag{2.3a}$$

This result agrees with the dimensional analysis in Chap. I, which predicted that the dimensionless shearing stress could depend on the Reynolds number only.

The total drag D on the plate is equal to $bl\tau_0$ where b denotes the width of the plate. Hence, with the aid of eqn. (2.3) we obtain

$$D \sim b \sqrt{\varrho\, \mu\, U^3 l}\,. \tag{2.4}$$

The laminar frictional drag is thus seen to be proportional to $U^{3/2}$ and $l^{1/2}$. Proportionality to $l^{1/2}$ means that doubling the plate length does not double the drag, and this result can be understood by considering that the downstream part of the plate experience a smaller drag than the leading portion because the boundary layer is thicker towards the trailing edge. Finally, we can write down an expression for the dimensionless drag coefficient in accordance with eqn. (1.14) in which the reference area A will be replaced by the wetted area bl. Hence eqn. (2.4) gives that

$$C_D \sim \sqrt{\frac{\mu}{\varrho\, U l}} = \frac{1}{\sqrt{\mathsf{R}_l}}\,.$$

The numerical factor follows from H. Blasius' exact solution, and is 1·328, so that the drag of a plate in parallel laminar flow becomes

$$C_D = \frac{1{\cdot}328}{\sqrt{\mathsf{R}_l}}\,. \tag{2.5}$$

The following numerical example will serve to illustrate the preceding estimation: Laminar flow, stipulated here, is obtained, as is known from experiment, for Reynolds numbers Ul/ν not exceeding about 5×10^5 to 10^6. For larger Reynolds numbers the boundary layer becomes turbulent. We shall now calculate the boundary layer thickness for the flow of air ($\nu = 0{\cdot}144 \times 10^{-3}$ ft²/sec) at the end of a plate of length $l = 3$ ft at a velocity $U = 48$ ft/sec. This gives $\mathsf{R}_l = Ul/\nu = 10^6$ and from eqn. (2.2)

$$\frac{\delta}{l} = \frac{5}{10^3} = 0{\cdot}005; \quad \delta = 0{\cdot}18 \text{ in}\,.$$

The drag coefficient from eqn. (2.5) is $C_D = 0{\cdot}0013$ i. e. exceedingly small when compared with that for a circular cylinder, Fig. 1.4.

Definition of boundary layer thickness: The definition of the boundary layer thickness is to a certain extent arbitrary because transition from the velocity in the boundary to that outside it takes place asymptotically. This is, however, of no practical importance, because the velocity in the boundary layer attains a value which is very close to the external velocity already at a small distance from the wall. It is possible to define the boundary layer thickness as that distance from the wall where the velocity differs by 1 per cent. from the external velocity. With this definition the numerical factor in eqn. (2.2) has the value 5. Instead of the boundary layer thickness, another quantity, the *displacement thickness* δ^*, is sometimes used, Fig. 2.3. It is defined by the equation

$$U\,\delta^* = \int_{y=0}^{\infty} (U - u)\,\mathrm{d}y\,. \tag{2.6}$$

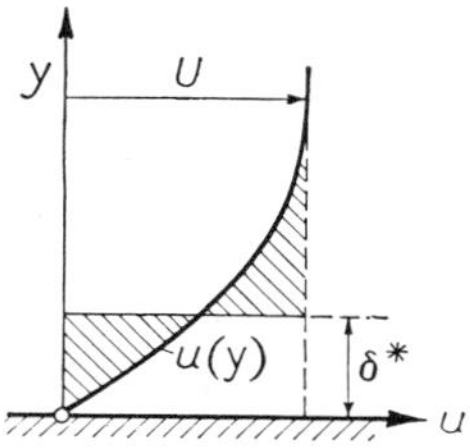

Fig. 2.3. Displacement thickness δ^* in a boundary layer

The displacement thickness indicates the distance by which the external streamlines are shifted owing to the formation of the boundary layer. In the case of a plate in parallel flow and at zero incidence the displacement thickness is about $\frac{1}{3}$ of the boundary layer thickness δ given in eqn. (2.1a).

b. Separation and vortex formation

The boundary layer near a flat plate in parallel flow and at zero incidence is particularly simple, because the static pressure remains constant in the whole field of flow. Since outside the boundary layer the velocity remains constant the same applies to the pressure because in the frictionless flow Bernoulli's equation remains valid. Furthermore, the pressure remains sensibly constant over the width of the boundary layer at a given distance x. Hence the pressure over the width of the boundary layer has the same magnitude as outside the boundary layer at the same distance, and the same applies to cases of arbitrary body shapes when the pressure outside the boundary layer varies along the wall with the length of arc. This fact is expressed by saying that the external pressure is "impressed" on the boundary layer. Hence in the case of the motion past a plate the pressure remains constant throughout the boundary layer.

The phenomenon of boundary layer separation mentioned previously is intimately connected with the pressure distribution in the boundary layer. In the boundary layer on a plate no separation takes place as no back-flow occurs.

In order to explain the very important phenomenon of boundary layer separation let us consider the flow about a blunt body, e. g. about a circular cylinder, as shown

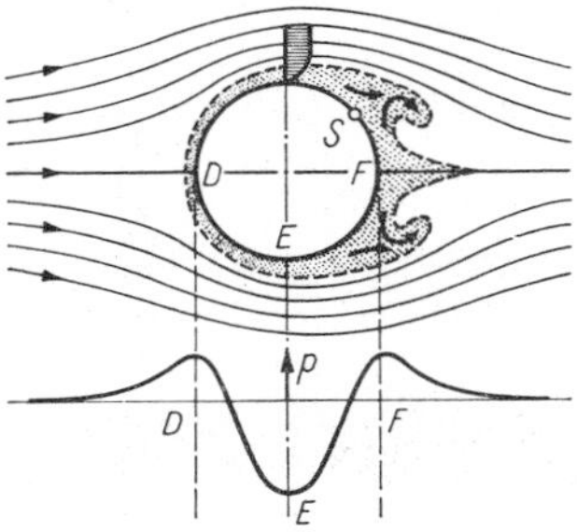

Fig. 2.4. Boundary layer separation and vortex formation on a circular cylinder (diagrammatic)
S = point of separation

in Fig. 2.4. In frictionless flow, the fluid particles are accelerated on the upstream half from D to E, and decelerated on the downstream half from E to F. Hence the pressure decreases from D to E and increases from E to F. When the flow is started up the motion in the first instant is very nearly frictionless, and remains so as long as the boundary layer remains thin. Outside the boundary layer there is a transformation of pressure into kinetic energy along $D\,E$, the reverse taking place along $E\,F$, so that a particle arrives at F with the same velocity as it had at D. A fluid particle which moves in the immediate vicinity of the wall in the

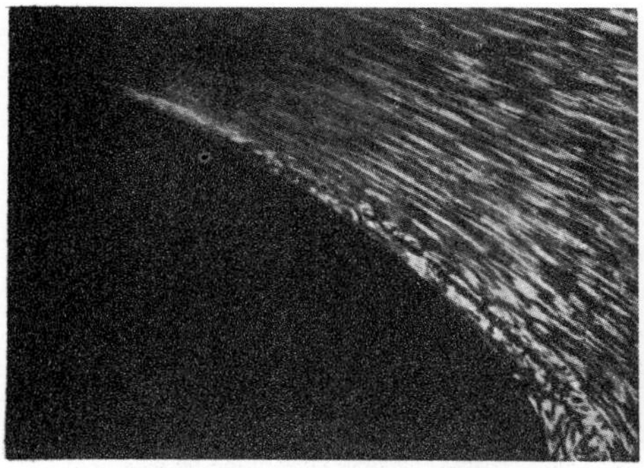

Fig. 2.5a

Fig. 2.5b

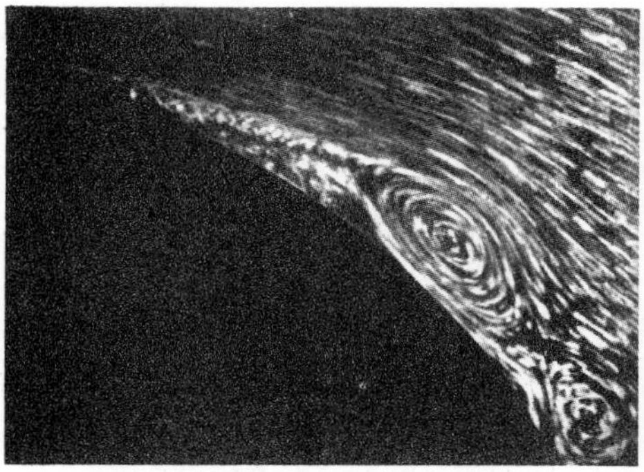

Fig. 2.5c

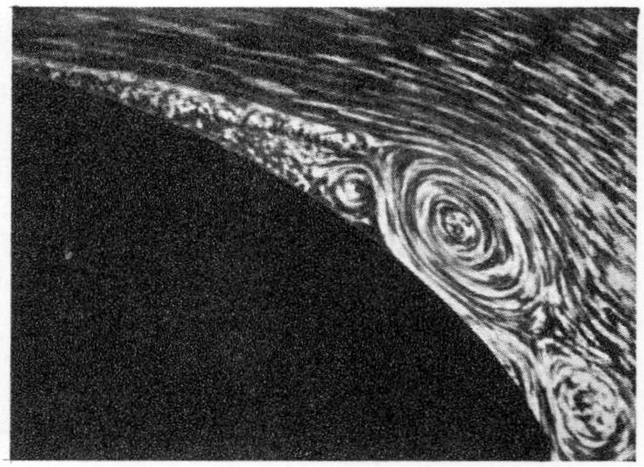

Fig. 2.5d

Fig. 2.5a, b, c, d. Development of boundary layer separation with time, after Prandtl-Tietjens

boundary layer remains under the influence of the same pressure field as that existing outside, because the external pressure is impressed on the boundary layer. Owing to the large friction forces in the thin boundary layer such a particle consumes so much of its kinetic energy on its path from D to E that the remainder is too small to surmount the "pressure hill" from E to F. Such a particle cannot move far into the region of increasing pressure between E and F and its motion is, eventually, arrested. The external pressure causes it then to move in the opposite direction. The photographs reproduced in Fig. 2.5 illustrate the sequence of events when a fluid flow is started near the downstream side of a round body. The pressure increases along the body contour from left to right, the flow having been made visible by sprinkling aluminium dust on the surface of the water. The boundary layer can be easily recognized by reference to the short traces. In Fig. 2.5a, taken shortly after the start of the motion, the reverse motion has just begun. In Fig. 2.5b the reverse motion has penetrated a considerable distance forward and the boundary layer has thickened appreciably. Fig. 2.5c shows how this reverse motion gives rise to a vortex, whose size is increased still further in Fig. 2.5d. The vortex becomes separated shortly afterwards and moves downstream in the fluid. This circumstance changes completely the field of flow in the wake, and the pressure distribution suffers a radical change, as compared with frictionless flow. The final state of motion can be inferred from Fig. 2.6. In the eddying region behind the cylinder there is considerable suction, as seen from the pressure distribution curve in Fig. 1.9. This suction causes a large pressure drag on the body.

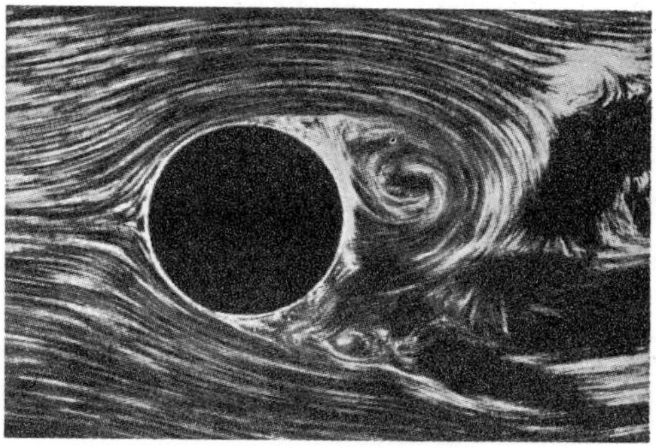

Fig. 2.6. Instantaneous photograph of flow with complete boundary layer separation in the wake of a circular cylinder, after Prandtl-Tietjens

At a larger distance from the body it is possible to discern a regular pattern of vortices which move alternately clockwise and counterclockwise, and which is kown as a Kármán vortex street [9], Fig. 2.7 (see also Fig. 1.6). In Fig. 2.6 a vortex moving in a clockwise direction can be seen to be about to detach itself from the body before joining the pattern. In a further paper, von Kármán [10] proved that such vortices are generally unstable with respect to small disturbances parallel to themselves. The only arrangement which shows neutral equilibrium is that with $h/l = 0{\cdot}281$ (Fig. 2.8). The vortex street moves with a velocity u, which is smaller than the flow velocity U in front of the body. It can be regarded as a highly idealized picture of the motion in the wake of the body. The kinetic energy contained in the velocity field of the vortex street must be continually created, as the body moves through the fluid. On the basis of this representation it is possible to deduce an expression for drag from the perfect fluid theory. Its magnitude per unit length of the cylindrical body is given by

$$D = \varrho\, U^2\, h \left[2{\cdot}83\, \frac{u}{U} - 1{\cdot}12 \left(\frac{u}{U}\right)^2\right].$$

The width h, and the velocity ratio u/U must be known from experiment.

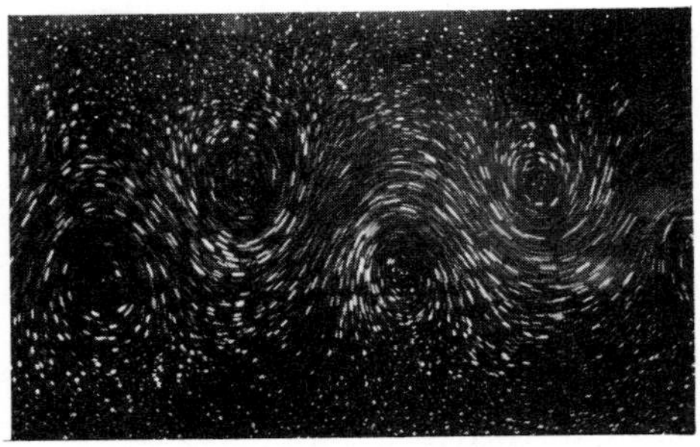

Fig. 2.7. Kármán vortex street, from A. Timme [21]

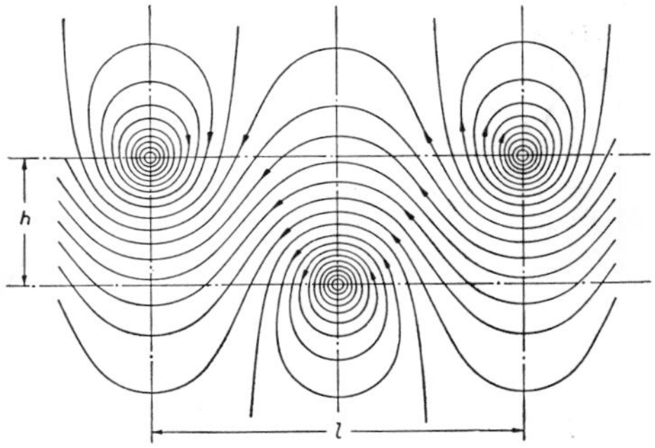

Fig. 2.8. Kármán vortex street (diagrammatic); stream-lines drawn in a system of co-ordinates moving with the vortex street

The frequency with which vortices are shed in a Kármán vortex street behind a circular cylinder was first extensively measured by H. Blenk, D. Fuchs and L. Liebers [2]. A regular Kármán street is observed only in the range of Reynolds numbers $V\,D/\nu$ from about 60 to 5000. At lower Reynolds numbers the wake is laminar and has the form visible in the first two photographs of Fig. 1.6; at higher Reynolds numbers there is complete turbulent mixing. Measurements show that in the regular range given above, the dimensionless frequency,

$$\frac{nD}{V} = \mathsf{S}\,, \qquad \text{(Strouhal number)}$$

also known as the Strouhal number [20], depends uniquely on the Reynolds number. This relationship is shown plotted in Fig. 2.9 which is based on the more recent measurements performed by A. Roshko [16]. The experimental points which were obtained with cylinders of different diameters D and at different velocities V arrange themselves well on a single curve. At the higher Reynolds numbers the Strouhal number remains approximately constant at $\mathsf{S} = 0{\cdot}21$. When the diameters of the cylinders are small and the velocities are moderate, the resulting frequencies lie in the acoustic range. For example, the familiar "aeolian tones" emitted by telegraph wires are the result of these phenomena. At a velocity of $V = 10$ m/sec (30·48 ft/sec) and a wire of 2 mm (0·079 in) in diameter, the frequency becomes $n = 0{\cdot}21\,(10/0{\cdot}002) = 1050\ \text{sec}^{-1}$, and the corresponding Reynolds number $\mathsf{R} \approx 1200$.

Two recent papers by C. C. Lin [11] and U. Domm [4] concern themselves with the theory of the Kármán vortex street.

The boundary layer theory succeeds in this manner, i.e. with the aid of the explanation of the phenomenon of separation, in throwing light on the occurrence of pressure or form drag in addition to viscous drag. The danger of boundary layer separation exists always in regions with an adverse pressure gradient and the

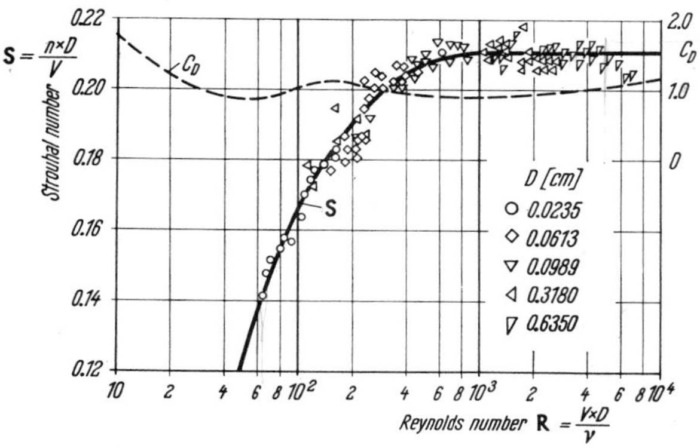

Fig. 2.9. The Strouhal number in terms of the Reynolds number for the flow past a circular cylinder as measured by A. Roshko [16]

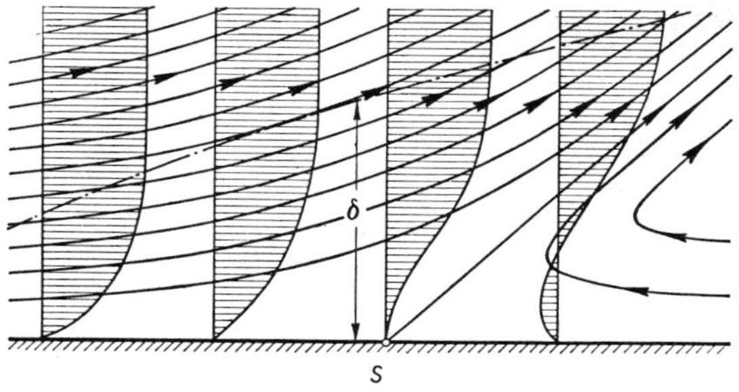

Fig. 2.10. Diagrammatic representation of flow in the boundary layer near a point of separation

S = point of separation

likelihood of its occurrence increases in the case of steep pressure curves, i.e. behind bodies with blunt ends. The preceding argument explains also why the experimental pressure distribution shown in Fig. 1.11 for the case of a slender stream-line body differs so little from that predicted for frictionless flow. The pressure increase in the downstream direction is here so gradual that there is no separation. Consequently, there is no appreciable pressure drag and the total drag consists mainly of viscous drag and is, therefore, small.

The stream-lines in the boundary layer near separation are shown diagrammatically in Fig. 2.10. Owing to the reversal of the flow there is a considerable thickening of the boundary layer, and associated with it, there is a flow of boundary layer material into the outside region. At the point of separation one stream-line intersects the wall at a definite angle, and the point of separation itself is determined by the condition that the velocity gradient normal to the wall vanishes there:

$$\left(\frac{\partial u}{\partial y}\right)_{wall} = 0 \quad \text{(separation)} . \tag{2.7}$$

The precise location of the point of separation can be determined only with the aid of an exact calculation, i. e. by the integration of the boundary layer equations.

Separation, as described for the case of a circular cylinder, can also occur in a highly divergent channel, Fig. 2.11. In front of the throat the pressure decreases in the direction of flow, and the flow adheres completely to the walls, as in a frictionless fluid. However, behind the throat the divergence of the channel is so large that the boundary layer becomes separated from both walls, and vortices are formed. The stream fills now only a small portion of the cross-sectional area of the channel.

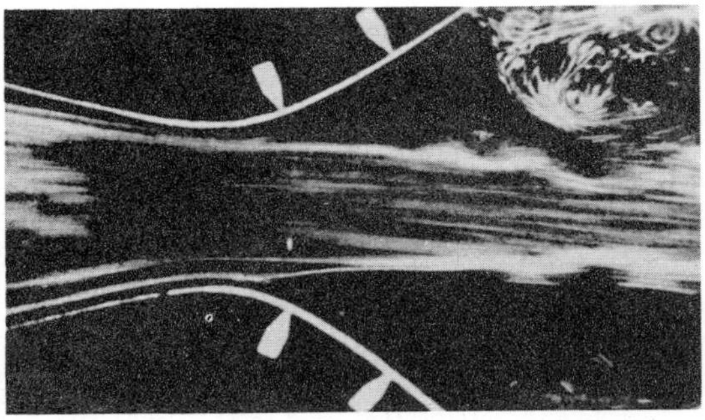

Fig. 2.11. Flow with separation in a highly divergent channel, from Prandtl-Tietjens

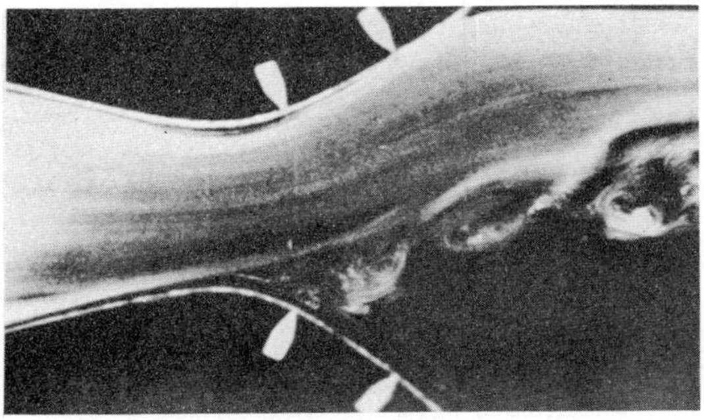

Fig. 2.12. Flow with boundary layer suction on upper wall of highly divergent channel

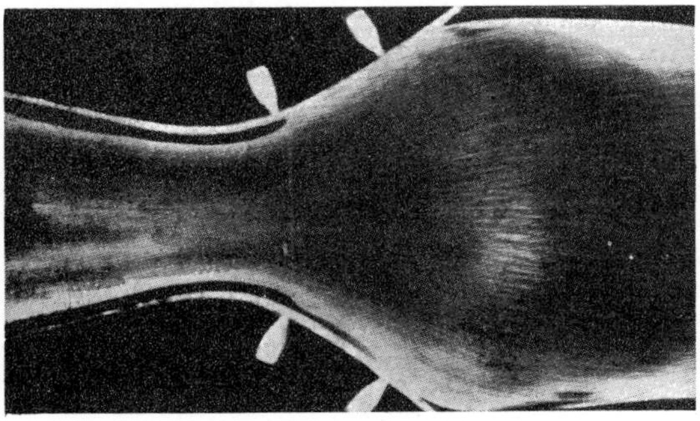

Fig. 2.13. Flow with boundary layer suction on both walls of highly divergent channel

The photographs in Figs. 2.14 and 2.15† prove that the adverse pressure gradient together with friction near the wall determine the process of separation which is independent of such other circumstance as e.g. the curvature of the wall. The first picture shows the motion of a fluid against a wall at right angles to it (plane stagnation flow). Along the stream-line in the plane of symmetry which leads to the stagnation point there is a considerable pressure increase in the direction of flow. No separation, however, occurs, because no wall friction is present. There is no separation near the wall, either, because here the flow in the boundary layer takes place in the direction of decreasing pressure on both sides of the plane of symmetry. If now a thin wall is placed along the plane of symmetry at right angles to the first wall, Fig. 2.15, the new boundary layer will show a pressure increase in the direction of flow.

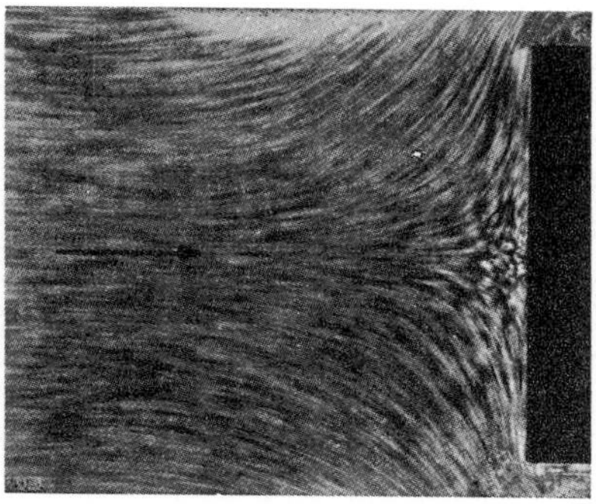

Fig. 2.14. Free stagnation flow without separation, as photographed by Foettinger

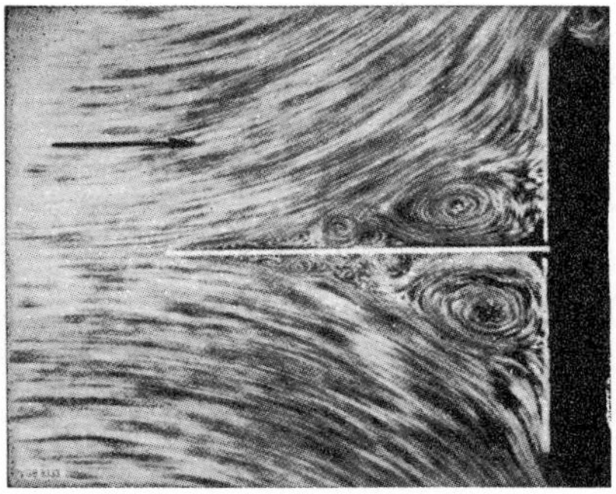

Fig. 2.15. Decelerated stagnation flow with separation, as photographed by Foettinger

Consequently, separation now occurs near the plane wall. The incidence of separation is often rather sensitive to small changes in the shape of the solid body, particularly when the pressure distribution is strongly affected by this change in shape. A very instructive example is given in the pictures of Fig. 2.16 which show photographs of the flow field about a model of a motor vehicle (the Volkswagen delivery van), [12, 18]. When the nose was flat giving it an angular shape (a), the flow past the fairly sharp corners in front caused large suction followed by a large pressure increase along the side walls. This led to complete separation and to the formation of a wide wake behind the body. The drag coefficient of the vehicle with this angular shape had a value of $C_D = 0{\cdot}76$. The large suction near the front end and the separation along the side walls were eliminated when the shape was changed by adding the round nose shown at (b). Simultaneously, the drag coefficient became markedly smaller and had a value of $C_D = 0{\cdot}42$.

Separation is also important for the lifting properties of an aerofoil. At small incidence angles (up to about 10°) the flow does not separate on either side and closely approximates frictionless conditions. The pressure distribution for such a case ("sound" flow, Fig. 2.17a) was given in Fig. 1.13. With increasing incidence there

† Figs. 2.14 and 2.15 have been taken from the paper "Strömungen in Dampfkesselanlagen" by H. Foettinger, Mitteilungen der Vereinigung der Groß-Kesselbesitzer, No. 73, p. 151 (1939).

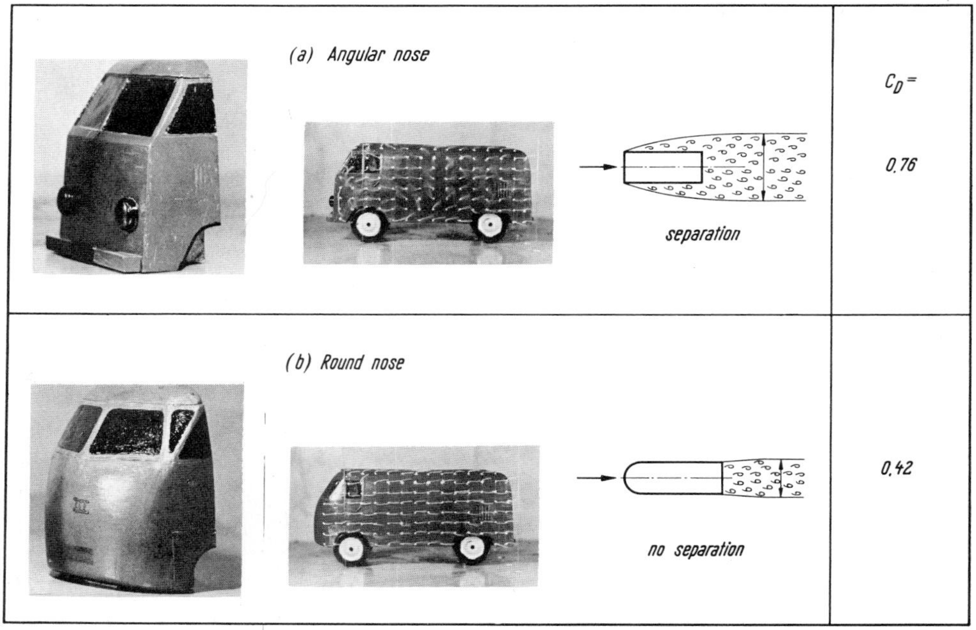

Fig. 2.16. Flow about a model of a motor vehicle (Volkswagen delivery van), after E. Moeller [12]. a) Angular nose with separated flow along the whole of the side wall and large drag coefficient ($C_D = 0{\cdot}76$); b) Round nose with no separation and small drag coefficient ($C_D = 0{\cdot}42$)

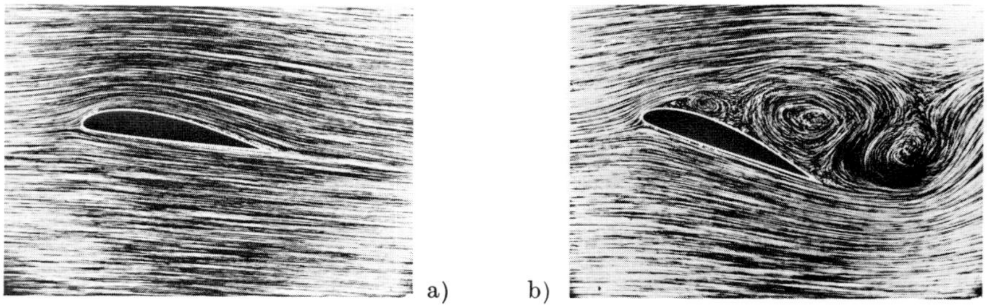

Fig. 2.17 a, b. Flow around an aerofoil, after Prandtl. a) 'sound' flow, b) flow with separation

is danger of separation on the suction side of the aerofoil, because the pressure increase becomes steeper. For a given angle of incidence, which is about 15°, separation finally occurs. The separation point is located fairly closely behind the leading edge. The wake, Fig. 2.17 b, shows a large "dead-water" area. The frictionless, lift-creating flow pattern has become disturbed, and the drag has become very large. The beginning of separation nearly coincides with the occurrence of maximum lift of the aerofoil.

c. Turbulent flow in a pipe and in a boundary layer

Measurements show that the type of motion through a circular pipe which was calculated in Section Id, and in which the velocity distribution was parabolic, exists only at low and moderate Reynolds numbers. The fact that in the laminar motion under discussion fluid laminae slide over each other, and that there are no radial velocity components so that the pressure drop is proportional to the first power of the mean flow velocity, constitutes an essential characteristic of this type of flow. This characteristic of the motion can be made clearly visible by introducing a dye into the stream and by discharging it through a thin tube, Fig. 2.18. At the moderate Reynolds numbers associated with laminar flow the dye is visible in the form of a clearly defined thread extending over the whole length of the pipe, Fig. 2.18a. By increasing the flow velocity it is possible to reach a stage when the fluid particles cease to move along straight lines and the regularity of the motion breaks down. The coloured thread becomes mixed with the fluid, its sharp outline becomes blurred and eventually the whole cross-section becomes coloured, Fig. 2.18b.

a)

b)

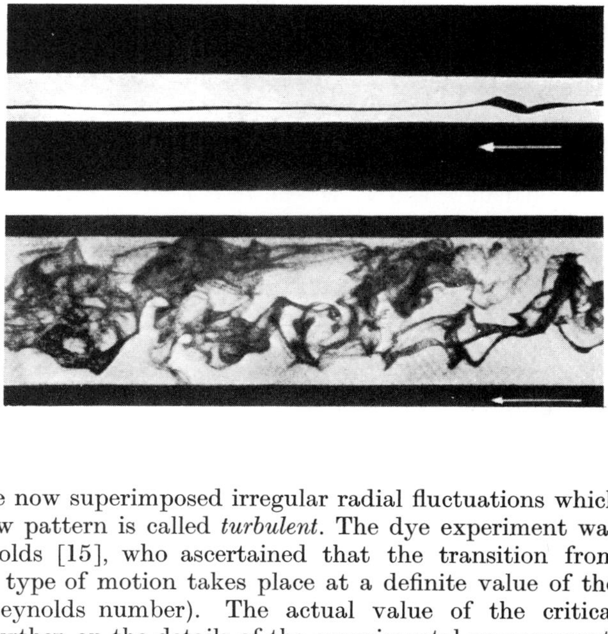

Fig. 2.18. The Reynolds dye experiment. Flow in water made visible by the injection of a dye, after W. Dubs [5]. a) laminar flow, $\mathsf{R} = 1150$; b) turbulent flow, $\mathsf{R} = 2520$

On the axial motion there are now superimposed irregular radial fluctuations which effect the mixing. Such a flow pattern is called *turbulent*. The dye experiment was first carried out by O. Reynolds [15], who ascertained that the transition from the laminar to the turbulent type of motion takes place at a definite value of the Reynolds number (critical Reynolds number). The actual value of the critical Reynolds number depends further on the details of the experimental arrangement, in particular on the amount of disturbance suffered by the fluid before entering the pipe. With an arrangement which is as free from disturbances as possible critical Reynolds numbers $(\bar{u}d/\nu)_{crit}$ exceeding 10^4 can be attained ($\bar{u}$ = denotes the mean velocity averaged over the cross-sectional area). With a sharp-edged entrance the critical Reynolds number becomes approximately

$$\left(\frac{\bar{u}\, d}{\nu}\right)_{crit} = \mathsf{R}_{crit} \approx 2300, \text{ (pipe)}. \tag{2.8}$$

This value can be regarded as the lower limit for the critical Reynolds number below which even strong disturbances do not cause the flow to become turbulent.

In the turbulent region the pressure drop becomes approximately proportional to the square of the mean flow velocity. In this case a considerably larger pressure difference is required in order to pass a fixed quantity of fluid through the pipe, as compared with laminar flow. This follows from the fact that the phenomenon of turbulent mixing dissipates a large quantity of energy which causes the resistance to flow to increase considerably. Furthermore, in the case of turbulent flow the velocity distribution over the cross-sectional area is much more even than in laminar flow. This circumstance is also to be explained by turbulent mixing which causes an exchange of momentum between the layers near the axis of the tube and those near the walls. Most pipe flows which are encountered in engineering appliances occur at such high Reynolds numbers that turbulent motion prevails as a rule. The laws of turbulent motion through pipes will be discussed in detail in Chap. XX.

In a way which is similar to the motion through a pipe, the flow in a boundary layer along a wall also becomes turbulent when the external velocity is sufficiently large. Experimental investigations into the transition from laminar to turbulent flow in the boundary layer were first carried out by L. J. M. Burgers [3] and B. G. van der Hegge Zijnen [8] as well as by M. Hansen [7]. The transition from laminar to turbulent flow in the boundary layer becomes most clearly discernible by a sudden and large increase in the boundary layer thickness and in the shearing stress near the wall. According to eqn. (2.1), with l replaced by the current coordinate x, the dimensionless boundary layer thickness $\delta/\sqrt{\nu\, x/U_\infty}$ becomes constant for laminar flow, and is, as seen from eqn. (2.1a), approximately equal to 5. Fig. 2.19

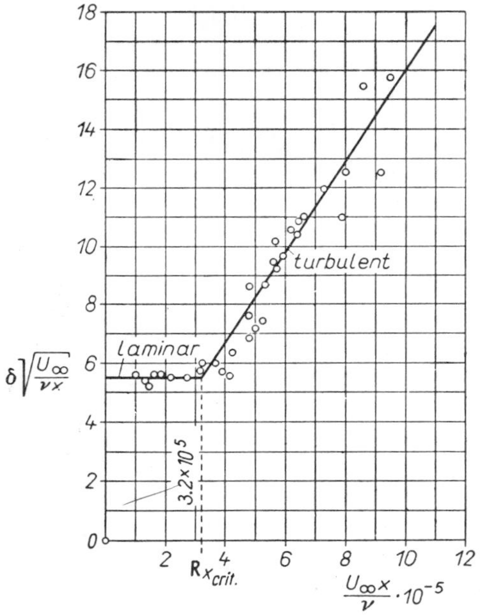

Fig. 2.19. Boundary layer thickness plotted against the Reynolds number based on the current length x along a plate in parallel flow at zero incidence, as measured by Hansen [7]

contains a plot of this dimensionless boundary layer thickness against the Reynolds number $U_\infty x/\nu$. At $\mathsf{R}_x > 3{\cdot}2 \times 10^5$ a very sharp increase is clearly visible, and an identical phenomenon is observed in a plot of wall shearing stress. The sudden increase in these quantities denotes that the flow has changed from laminar to turbulent. The Reynolds number R_x based on the current length x is related to the Reynolds number $\mathsf{R}_\delta = U_\infty \, \delta/\nu$ based on the boundary layer thickness through the equation

$$\mathsf{R}_\delta = 5 \sqrt{\mathsf{R}_x}$$

as seen from eqn. (2.1a). Hence to the critical Reynolds number

$$\mathsf{R}_{x\,crit} = \left(\frac{U_\infty \, x}{\nu}\right)_{crit} = 3{\cdot}2 \times 10^5 \quad \text{(plate)}$$

there corresponds $\mathsf{R}_{\delta\,crit} \approx 2800$. The boundary layer on a plate is laminar near the leading edge and becomes turbulent further downstream. The abscissa x_{crit} of the point of transition can be determined from the known value of $\mathsf{R}_{x\,crit}$. In the case of a plate, as in the previously discussed pipe flow, the numerical value of R_{crit} depends to a marked degree on the amount of disturbance in the external flow, and the value $\mathsf{R}_{x\,crit} = 3{\cdot}2 \times 10^5$ should be regarded as a lower limit. With exceptionally disturbance-free external flow, values of $\mathsf{R}_{x\,crit} = 10^6$ and higher have been attained.

A particularly remarkable phenomenon connected with the transition from laminar to turbulent flow occurs in the case of blunt bodies, such as circular cylinders or spheres. It will be seen from Figs. 1.4 and 1.5 that the drag coefficient of a circular cylinder or a sphere suffers a sudden and considerable decrease near Reynolds numbers VD/ν of about 5×10^5 or 3×10^5 respectively. This fact was first observed on spheres by G. Eiffel [6]. It is a consequence of transition which causes the point of separation to move downstream, because, in the case of a turbulent boundary layer, the accelerating influence of the external flow extends further due to turbulent mixing. Hence the point of separation which lies near the equator for a laminar boundary layer moves over a considerable distance in the downstream direction. In turn, the dead area decreases considerably, and the pressure distribution becomes more like that for frictionless motion, (Fig. 1.10). The decrease in the dead-water region considerably reduces the pressure drag, and that shows itself as a jump in the curve $C_D = f(\mathsf{R})$. L. Prandtl [14] proved the correctness of the preceding reasoning by mounting a thin wire ring at a short distance in front of the equator of a sphere. This causes the boundary layer to become artificially turbulent at a lower Reynolds number and the decrease in the drag coefficient takes place earlier than would otherwise be the case. Figs. 2.20 and 2.21 reproduce photographs of flows which have been made visible by smoke. They represent the subcritical pattern with a large value of the drag coeficient and the supercritical pattern with a small dead-water area and a small value of the drag coefficient. The supercritical pattern was achieved with Prandtl's tripping wire. The preceding experiment shows in a convincing manner that the jump in the drag curve of a circular cylinder and sphere can only be interpreted as a boundary layer phenomenon. Other bodies with a blunt or rounded stern, (e.g. elliptic cylinders) display a type of relationship between drag coefficient and Reynolds number which is substantially similar. With increasing slenderness the jump in the curve becomes progressively less pronounced.

For a stream-line body, such as that shown in Fig. 1.11 there is no jump, because no appreciable separation occurs; the very gradual pressure increase on the back of such bodies can be overcome by the boundary layer without separation. As we shall also see later in greater detail, the pressure distribution in the external flow exerts a decisive influence on the position of the transition point. The boundary

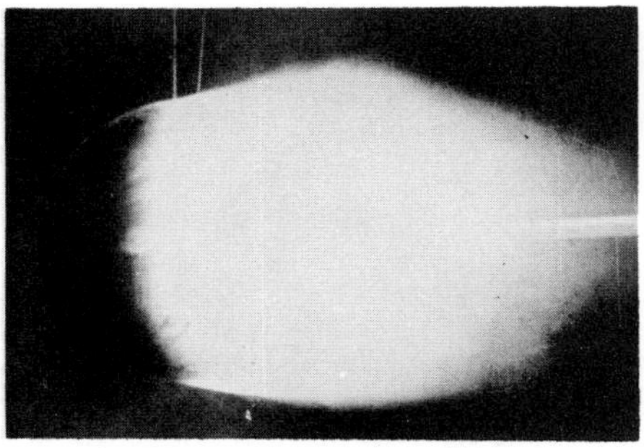

Fig. 2.20. Flow past a sphere at a subcritical Reynolds number; from Wieselsberger [22]

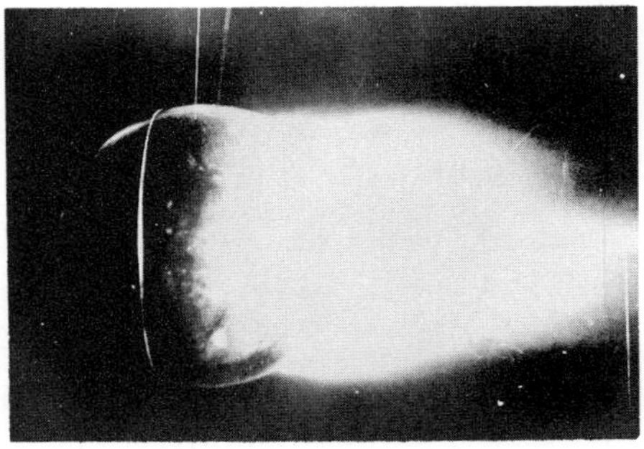

Fig. 2.21. Flow past a sphere at a supercritical Reynolds number; from Wieselsberger [22].) The supercritical flow pattern is achieved by the mounting of a thin wire ring (tripping wire)

layer is laminar in the region of pressure decrease, i. e. roughly from the leading edge to the point of minimum pressure, and becomes turbulent, in most cases, from that point onwards throughout the region of pressure increase. In this connexion it is important to state that separation can only be avoided when the flow in the boundary layer is turbulent. A laminar boundary layer, as we shall see later, can support only a very small pressure rise so that separation would occur even with very slender bodies. In particular, this remark also applies to the flow past an aerofoil with a pressure distribution similar to that in Fig. 1.13. In this case separation is most likely to occur on the suction side. A smooth flow pattern around an aerofoil, conducive to the creation of lift, is possible only with a turbulent boundary layer. Summing up it may be stated that the small drag of slender bodies as well as the lift of aerofoils are made possible through the existence of a turbulent boundary layer.

Boundary layer thickness: Generally speaking, the thickness of a turbulent boundary layer is larger than that of a laminar boundary layer owing to greater energy losses in the former. Near a smooth flat plate at zero incidence the boundary layer increases downstream in proportion to $x^{0 \cdot 8}$ (x = distance from leading edge). It will be shown later in Chap. XXI that the boundary layer thickness variation in turbulent flow is given by the equation

$$\frac{\delta}{l} = 0{\cdot}37 \left(\frac{U_\infty l}{\nu}\right)^{-1/5} = 0{\cdot}37\,(\mathsf{R}_l)^{-1/5}, \tag{2.9}$$

which corresponds to eqn. (2.2) for laminar flow. Table 2.1 gives values for the boundary layer thickness calculated from eqn. (2.9) for several typical cases of air and water flows.

Table 2.1. Thickness of boundary layer, δ, at trailing edge of flat plate at zero incidence in parallel turbulent flow

U_∞ = free stream velocity; l = length of plate; ν = kinematic viscosity

	U_∞ [ft/sec]	l [ft]	$R_l = \frac{U_\infty l}{\nu}$	δ [in]
Air	100	3	$2{\cdot}0 \times 10^6$	0·73
$\nu = 150 \times 10^{-6}$ ft²/sec	200	3	$4{\cdot}0 \times 10^6$	0·64
	200	15	$2{\cdot}0 \times 10^7$	2·30
	500	25	$8{\cdot}3 \times 10^7$	2·90
	750	25	$1{\cdot}25 \times 10^8$	2·68
Water	5	5	$2{\cdot}3 \times 10^6$	1·19
$\nu = 11 \times 10^{-6}$ ft²/sec	10	15	$1{\cdot}35 \times 10^7$	2·52
	25	150	$3{\cdot}4 \times 10^8$	13·1
	50	500	$2{\cdot}3 \times 10^9$	29·8

Methods for the prevention of separation: Separation is mostly an undesirable phenomenon because it entails large energy losses. For this reason methods have been devised for the artificial prevention of separation. The simplest method, from the physical point of view, is to move the wall with the stream in order to reduce the velocity difference between them, and hence to remove the cause of boundary layer formation, but this is very difficult to achieve in engineering practice. However, Prandtl† has shown on a *rotating circular cylinder* that this method is very effective. On the side where the wall and stream move in the same direction separation is completely prevented. Moreover, on the side where the wall and stream move in opposite directions, separation is slight so that on the whole it is possible to obtain a good experimental approximation to perfect flow with circulation and a large lift.

Another very effective method for the prevention of separation is *boundary layer suction.* In this method the decelerated fluid particles in the boundary layer are removed through slits in the wall into the interior of the body. With sufficiently strong suction separation can be prevented. Boundary layer suction was used on a circular cylinder by L. Prandtl in his first fundamental investigation into boundary layer flow. Separation can be almost completely eliminated with suction through a slit at the back of the circular cylinder. Instances of the effect of suction can be seen in Figs. 2.12 and 2.13 on the example of flows through a highly divergent channel. Fig. 2.11 demonstrates that without suction there is strong separation. Fig. 2.12 shows how the flow adheres to the one side on which suction is applied, whereas from Fig. 2.13 it is seen that the flow completely fills the channel cross-section when both suction slits are put into operation. In the latter case the stream-lines assume a pattern which is very similar to that in frictionless

† Prandtl-Tietjens: Hydro- and Aero-dynamics.

flow. In later years suction was successfully used in aeroplane wings to increase the lift. Owing to suction on the upper surface near the trailing edge, the flow adheres to the aerofoil at considerably larger incidence angles than would otherwise be the case, stalling is delayed, and much larger maximum lift values are achieved [19].

After having given a short outline of the fundamental physical principles of fluid motions with very small friction, i. e. of the boundary layer theory, we shall proceed to develop a rational theory of these phenomena from the equations of motion of viscous fluids. The description will be arranged in the following way: We shall begin in Part A by deriving the general Navier-Stokes equations from which, in turn, we shall derive Prandtl's boundary layer equations with the aid of the simplifications which can be introduced as a consequence of the small values of viscosity. This will be followed in Part B by a description of the methods for the integration of these equations for the case of laminar flow. In Part C we shall discuss the problem of the origin of turbulent flow, i. e. we shall discuss the process of transition from laminar to turbulent flow, treating it as a problem in the stability of laminar motion. Finally, Part D will contain the boundary layer theory for completely developed turbulent motions. Whereas the theory of laminar boundary layers can be treated as a deductive sequence based on the Navier-Stokes differential equations for viscous fluids, the same is not, at present, possible for turbulent flow, because the mechanism of turbulent flow is so complex that it cannot be mastered by purely theoretical methods. For this reason a treatise on turbulent flow must draw heavily on experimental results and the subject must be presented in the form of a semi-empirical theory.

References

[1] H. Blasius, Grenzschichten in Flüssigkeiten mit kleiner Reibung. Z. Math. u. Phys. **56**, 1 (1908).

[2] H. Blenk, D. Fuchs and L. Liebers, Über die Messung von Wirbelfrequenzen. Luftfahrtforschung vol. **XII**, p. 38—41 (1935).

[3] J. M. Burgers, Proceedings of the First International Congress for Applied Mechanics. Delft, 113 (1924).

[4] U. Domm, Ein Beitrag zur Stabilitätstheorie der Wirbelstraßen unter Berücksichtigung endlicher und zeitlich anwachsender Wirbelkerndurchmesser. Ing. Arch. **22**, 400—410, (1954).

[5] W. Dubs, Über den Einfluß laminarer und turbulenter Strömung auf das Röntgenbild von Wasser und Nitrobenzol. Ein röntgenographischer Beitrag zum Turbulenzproblem. Helv. phys. Acta **12**, 169—228 (1939).

[6] G. Eiffel, Sur la résistance des sphères dans l'air en mouvement. Comptes Rendus **155**, 1597 (1912).

[7] M. Hansen, Die Geschwindigkeitsverteilung in der Grenzschicht an der längsangeströmten ebenen Platte. ZAMM **8**, 185—199 (1928); NACA TM 585 (1930).

[8] B. G. van der Hegge Zijnen, Measurements of the velocity distribution in the boundary layer along a plane surface. Thesis Delft 1924.

[9] Th. von Kármán, Nachr. d. Wiss. Ges. Göttingen, Math. Phys. Klasse, 509 (1911) and 547 (1912).

[10] Th. von Kármán and H. Rubach, Über den Mechanismus des Flüssigkeits- und Luftwiderstandes. Phys. Z. **49** (1912).

[11] C. C. Lin, On periodically oscillating wakes in the Oseen approximation. R. von Mises Anniversary volume, "Studies in Mathematics and Mechanics". Academic Press, New York, pp. 170—176, (1950).

[12] E. MÖLLER, Luftwiderstandsmessungen am VW-Lieferwagen. Automobiltechnische Zeitschrift, Jahrg. **53**, No. 6, pp. 1—4 (1951).
[13] L. PRANDTL, Über Flüssigkeitsbewegung bei sehr kleiner Reibung. Proceedings 3rd. Intern. Math. Congr., Heidelberg 1904. Reprinted in "Vier Abhandlungen zur Hydrodynamik und Aerodynamik" Göttingen 1927; NACA TM 452 (1928).
[14] L. PRANDTL, Über den Luftwiderstand von Kugeln. Göttinger Nachr. 177 (1914).
[15] O. REYNOLDS, Phil. Trans. **174**, 935—982 (1883), Scientific Papers **2**, 51.
[16] A. ROSHKO, On the development of turbulent wakes from vortex streets. NACA Rep. 1191 (1954).
[17] H. RUBACH, Über die Entstehung und Fortbewegung des Wirbelpaares bei zylindrischen Körpern. (Thesis Göttingen 1914) VDI-Forschungsheft No. 185 (1916).
[18] H. SCHLICHTING, Aerodynamische Untersuchungen an Kraftfahrzeugen. Report of the Technische Hochschule Braunschweig, 1954, pp. 130—139.
[19] O. SCHRENK, Versuche mit Absaugflügeln. Luftfahrtforschung **XII**, 10—27 (1935).
[20] V. STROUHAL, Über eine besondere Art der Tonerregung. Ann. Phys. und Chemie. New series vol. **5**, p. 216—251 (1878).
[21] A. TIMME, Über die Geschwindigkeitsverteilung in Wirbeln. Ing. Arch. **25**, 205—225 (1957).
[22] C. WIESELSBERGER, Der Luftwiderstand von Kugeln. ZFM. **5**, 140—144 (1914).

CHAPTER III

Derivation of the equations of motion of a compressible viscous fluid

(Navier-Stokes equations)

a. Fundamental equations of motion and continuity applied to fluid flow

We shall now proceed to derive the equations of motion of a compressible viscous fluid. In the general case of three-dimensional motion the velocity field is specified by the velocity vector

$$\boldsymbol{w} = \boldsymbol{i}\, u + \boldsymbol{j}\, v + \boldsymbol{k}\, w$$

where u, v, w are the three orthogonal components, by the pressure p, and by the density ϱ. For the determination of these five quantities there exist five equations: the continuity equation (conservation of mass), the three equations of motion (conservation of momentum) and the thermodynamic equation of state $p = f(\varrho)$†.

The equation of continuity expresses the fact that for a unit volume there is a balance between the masses entering and leaving per unit time, and the change in density. In the case of non-steady flow of a compressible fluid this condition leads to the equation:

$$\frac{\partial \varrho}{\partial t} + \operatorname{div}(\varrho\, \boldsymbol{w}) = 0\,, \tag{3.1}$$

whereas for an incompressible fluid, with $\varrho = \text{const}$, the equation of continuity assumes the simplified form

$$\operatorname{div} \boldsymbol{w} = 0\,. \tag{3.1 a}$$

The equations of motion are derived from Newton's Second Law, which states that the product of mass and acceleration is equal to the sum of external forces acting on the body. In fluid motion it is necessary to consider the following two classes of forces: forces acting throughout the mass of the body (gravitational forces) and forces acting on the boundary (pressure and friction). If $\boldsymbol{F} = \varrho\, \boldsymbol{g}$ denotes the gravitational force per unit volume ($\boldsymbol{g}$ = vector of acceleration due to gravity)

† If the equation of state contains temperature as an additional variable, a further equation is supplied by the principle of the conservation of energy in the form of the First Law of thermodynamics; *cf.* Chap. XIV.

and $\boldsymbol{P}$ denotes the force on the boundary per unit volume, then the equations of motion can be written in the following vector form

$$\varrho \frac{\mathrm{D}\boldsymbol{w}}{\mathrm{D}t} = \boldsymbol{F} + \boldsymbol{P} \tag{3.2}$$

with

$$\boldsymbol{F} = \boldsymbol{i}\,X + \boldsymbol{j}\,Y + \boldsymbol{k}\,Z \qquad \text{body force} \tag{3.3}$$

and

$$\boldsymbol{P} = \boldsymbol{i}\,P_x + \boldsymbol{j}\,P_y + \boldsymbol{k}\,P_z \qquad \text{surface force}\,. \tag{3.4}$$

The symbol $\mathrm{D}\boldsymbol{w}/\mathrm{D}t$ denotes here the substantive acceleration which consists of the local contribution (in non-steady flow) $\partial \boldsymbol{w}/\partial t$, and the convective contribution (due to translation) $\mathrm{d}\boldsymbol{w}/\mathrm{d}t = (\boldsymbol{w}\ \mathrm{grad})\ \boldsymbol{w}$†

$$\frac{\mathrm{D}\boldsymbol{w}}{\mathrm{D}t} = \frac{\partial \boldsymbol{w}}{\partial t} + \frac{\mathrm{d}\boldsymbol{w}}{\mathrm{d}t}\,.$$

The body forces are to be regarded as given external forces, but the surface forces depend on the *state of strain* (velocity field) of the fluid. The system of surface forces determines a *state of stress*, and it is now our task to indicate the relationship between stress and strain, noting that it can only be given empirically. In the case of elastic solid bodies this relation is given by Hooke's law, and for liquids and gases it is given by Stokes' law of friction. The two laws are so intimately related to each other that in deriving either of them the other is obtained at the same time. The only difference between them is that in Hooke's law for elastic bodies the forces which oppose the deformation of a body are proportional to the *magnitude* of the strain, whereas in Stokes' law of friction in fluids, these forces are proportional to the *rate-of-strain*.

We shall begin the investigation by describing in the following section the relation between the stresses and strains insofar as it is common to both solid elastic bodies and fluids. Since this relation is simpler to understand in the case of solid elastic bodies we shall begin with the derivation of Hooke's law. A very simple transposition of terms will then finally furnish a description of the stress system in a fluid in motion (Stokes' law).

b. General stress system in a deformable body

In order to write down expressions for the forces acting on the boundary, let us imagine a small parallelepiped of volume $\mathrm{d}V = \mathrm{d}x \cdot \mathrm{d}y \cdot \mathrm{d}z$ isolated from the body, Fig. 3.1, whose lower left-hand forward vertex coincides with the point x, y, z.

† The symbol $(\boldsymbol{w}$ grad$)\ \boldsymbol{w}$ often used in German books is pseudovectorial. It suggests the Cartesian components in an easy manner, but it is not invariant under transformation. It should be noted that $(\boldsymbol{w}$ grad$)\ \boldsymbol{w}$ must be replaced by

$$(\boldsymbol{w}\ \mathrm{grad})\ \boldsymbol{w} = \mathrm{grad}\ \tfrac{1}{2}\ \boldsymbol{w}^2 - \boldsymbol{w} \times \mathrm{curl}\ \boldsymbol{w}$$

for the equations to become invariant. Here $\boldsymbol{w}^2 = \boldsymbol{w} \cdot \boldsymbol{w}$.

On the two faces of area $\mathrm{d}y \cdot \mathrm{d}z$ which are perpendicular to the x-axis there act two resultant stresses (vectors = surface force per unit area):

$$\boldsymbol{p}_x \quad \text{and} \quad \boldsymbol{p}_x + \frac{\partial \boldsymbol{p}_x}{\partial x}\,\mathrm{d}x \text{ respectively}. \tag{3.5}$$

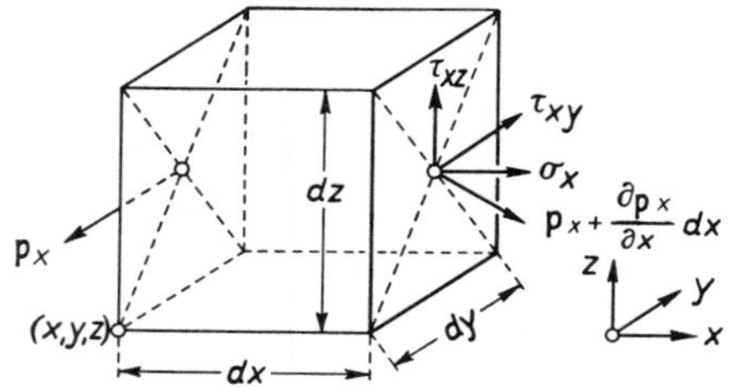

Fig. 3.1 Derivation of the expressions for the stress tensor of an inhomogeneous stress system

(Subscript x denotes that the stress vector acts on a elementary plane which is perpendicular to the x-direction.) Similar terms are obtained for the faces $\mathrm{d}x \cdot \mathrm{d}z$ and $\mathrm{d}x \cdot \mathrm{d}y$ which are perpendicular to the y- and z-axes respectively. Hence the three components of the surface force are:

$$\begin{array}{ll} \text{plane} \perp \text{direction } x: & \dfrac{\partial \boldsymbol{p}_x}{\partial x} \cdot \mathrm{d}x \cdot \mathrm{d}y \cdot \mathrm{d}z \\ \quad ,, \quad ,, \quad ,, \quad y: & \dfrac{\partial \boldsymbol{p}_y}{\partial y} \cdot \mathrm{d}x \cdot \mathrm{d}y \cdot \mathrm{d}z \\ \quad ,, \quad ,, \quad ,, \quad z: & \dfrac{\partial \boldsymbol{p}_z}{\partial z} \cdot \mathrm{d}x \cdot \mathrm{d}y \cdot \mathrm{d}z \end{array}$$

and the resultant surface force $\boldsymbol{P}$ per unit volume is, therefore, given by

$$\boldsymbol{P} = \frac{\partial \boldsymbol{p}_x}{\partial x} + \frac{\partial \boldsymbol{p}_y}{\partial y} + \frac{\partial \boldsymbol{p}_z}{\partial z}\,. \tag{3.6}$$

The quantities $\boldsymbol{p}_x$, $\boldsymbol{p}_y$, $\boldsymbol{p}_z$ are vectors which can be resolved into components *perpendicular* to each face, i.e. into normal stresses denoted by σ with a suitable subscript indicating the direction, and into components *parallel* to each face, i.e. into shearing stresses denoted by τ. The symbol for a shearing stress will be provided with two subscripts: the first subscript indicates the axis to which the face is perpendicular, and the second indicates the direction to which the shearing stress is parallel. With this notation we have

$$\left.\begin{aligned} \boldsymbol{p}_x &= \boldsymbol{i}\,\sigma_x + \boldsymbol{j}\,\tau_{xy} + \boldsymbol{k}\,\tau_{xz} \\ \boldsymbol{p}_y &= \boldsymbol{i}\,\tau_{yx} + \boldsymbol{j}\,\sigma_y + \boldsymbol{k}\,\tau_{yz} \\ \boldsymbol{p}_z &= \boldsymbol{i}\,\tau_{zx} + \boldsymbol{j}\,\tau_{zy} + \boldsymbol{k}\,\sigma_z\,. \end{aligned}\right\} \tag{3.7}$$

The stress system is seen to require nine scalar quantities for its description. These nine quantities form a *stress tensor*. The set of nine components of the stress tensor is sometimes called the stress matrix:

$$\Pi = \begin{pmatrix} \sigma_x & \tau_{xy} & \tau_{xz} \\ \tau_{yx} & \sigma_y & \tau_{yz} \\ \tau_{zx} & \tau_{zy} & \sigma_z \end{pmatrix}. \tag{3.8}$$

It is easy to prove that the pairs of shearing stresses with subscripts which differ only in their order are equal. This follows by taking moments about any axis and establishing the condition of equilibrium of the elementary volume. Thus e. g. for the z-axis we obtain

$$\tau_{xy} \cdot \mathrm{d}y\,\mathrm{d}z \cdot \mathrm{d}x = \tau_{yx} \cdot \mathrm{d}x\,\mathrm{d}z \cdot \mathrm{d}y\,.$$

Hence

$$\tau_{xy} = \tau_{yx}; \quad \text{and similarly} \quad \tau_{xz} = \tau_{zx} \quad \text{and} \quad \tau_{yz} = \tau_{zy}\,.$$

The stress matrix (3.8) contains only six different stress components and becomes symmetrical with respect to the principal diagonal:

$$\Pi = \begin{pmatrix} \sigma_x & \tau_{xy} & \tau_{xz} \\ \tau_{xy} & \sigma_y & \tau_{yz} \\ \tau_{xz} & \tau_{yz} & \sigma_z \end{pmatrix}. \tag{3.9}$$

The surface force per unit volume can be calculated from eqns. (3.6), (3.7), and (3.9) and becomes

$$\begin{aligned} \boldsymbol{P} = \boldsymbol{i} & \left(\frac{\partial\sigma_x}{\partial x} + \frac{\partial\tau_{xy}}{\partial y} + \frac{\partial\tau_{xz}}{\partial z}\right) \cdots\cdots \text{comp. } x \\ + \boldsymbol{j} & \left(\frac{\partial\tau_{xy}}{\partial x} + \frac{\partial\sigma_y}{\partial y} + \frac{\partial\tau_{yz}}{\partial z}\right) \cdots\cdots \text{comp. } y \\ + \boldsymbol{k} & \left(\underbrace{\frac{\partial\tau_{xz}}{\partial x}}_{\substack{\text{face} \\ yz}} + \underbrace{\frac{\partial\tau_{yz}}{\partial y}}_{\substack{\text{face} \\ zx}} + \underbrace{\frac{\partial\sigma_z}{\partial z}}_{\substack{\text{face} \\ xy}}\right) \cdots\cdots \text{comp. } z \end{aligned} \tag{3.9a}$$

Introducing the expression (3.9a) into the equation of motion (3.2), and resolving into components we have:

$$\left.\begin{aligned} \varrho \frac{\mathrm{D}u}{\mathrm{D}t} &= X + \left(\frac{\partial\sigma_x}{\partial x} + \frac{\partial\tau_{xy}}{\partial y} + \frac{\partial\tau_{xz}}{\partial z}\right) \\ \varrho \frac{\mathrm{D}v}{\mathrm{D}t} &= Y + \left(\frac{\partial\tau_{xy}}{\partial x} + \frac{\partial\sigma_y}{\partial y} + \frac{\partial\tau_{yz}}{\partial z}\right) \\ \varrho \frac{\mathrm{D}w}{\mathrm{D}t} &= Z + \left(\frac{\partial\tau_{xz}}{\partial x} + \frac{\partial\tau_{yz}}{\partial y} + \frac{\partial\sigma_z}{\partial z}\right). \end{aligned}\right\} \tag{3.10}$$

If the fluid is *frictionless* all shearing stresses vanish; only the normal stresses remain in the equation, and they are, moreover, equal. Their negative is defined as the pressure at the point x, y, z in the fluid:

$$\begin{aligned} \tau_{xy} &= \tau_{xz} = \tau_{yz} = 0 \\ \sigma_x &= \sigma_y = \sigma_z = -p. \end{aligned}$$

The fluid pressure is seen to be equal to the arithmetical mean of the normal stresses taken with a negative sign. It is convenient to introduce the arithmetical mean of the three normal stresses as a useful numerical quantity in the case of a *viscous fluid* also. It is called the pressure in the fluid and it has the property of being invariant with respect to transformations of the system of co-ordinates, as it is an invariant of the stress tensor, being defined as

$$\tfrac{1}{3}(\sigma_x + \sigma_y + \sigma_z) = \bar{\sigma} = -p. \tag{3.11}$$

The system of the three equations (3.10) contains the six stresses σ_x, σ_y, σ_z, τ_{xy}, τ_{xz}, τ_{yz}. The next task is to determine the relation between them and the strains so as to enable us to introduce the velocity components u, v, w into eqn. (3.10). Before giving this relation in Secs. IIId and IIIe we shall investigate the system of strains in greater detail.

c. General strain system

The strain system of any continuum, whether an elastic solid, a liquid or a gas, can be described in two alternative ways. The first method is to describe the deformation of a given volume by three elongations ε_x, ε_y, ε_z and by three angular

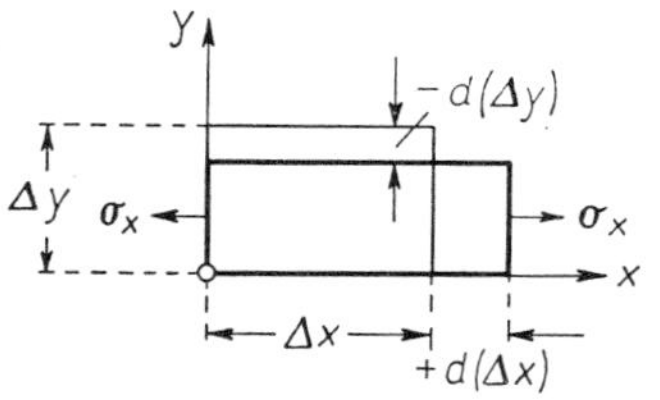

Fig. 3.2. Expansion in the direction of the x-axis and contraction in the direction of the y-axis caused by a normal stress σ_x

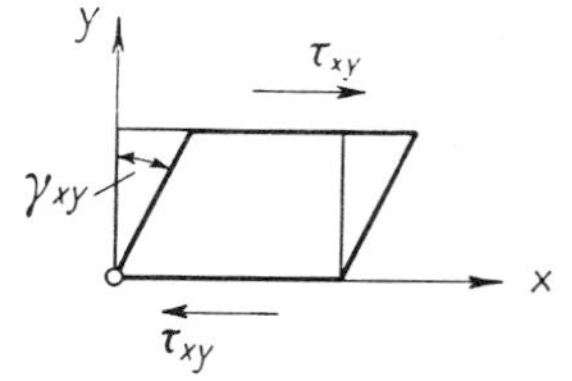

Fig. 3.3. Angular displacement caused by a shearing stress τ_{xy}

displacements γ_{xy}, γ_{zy}, γ_{xz}, i. e. by *six strains* in all. The quantities ε_x, ε_y, ε_z denote relative changes in length (elongations) of an elementary volume in the three co-ordinate directions caused by the normal stresses. Thus e.g. $\varepsilon_x = \mathrm{d}(\Delta x)/\Delta x$, where Δx is the original length of the element, and $\mathrm{d}(\Delta x)$ denotes the change in length, Fig. 3.2. The angular displacements γ are given by the changes in the angles (originally right angles) formed by the axes of co-ordinates, and caused by the shearing stresses. Thus e.g. γ_{xy} denotes the change in the angle between the x- and y-axes, Fig. 3.3. The relative change in volume (volume dilatation) is then

$$\frac{d(\Delta V)}{\Delta V} = e = \varepsilon_x + \varepsilon_y + \varepsilon_z \,. \tag{3.12}$$

The second method of describing a state of strain consists in the use of the displacement vector

$$\boldsymbol{s} = \boldsymbol{i}\,\xi + \boldsymbol{j}\,\eta + \boldsymbol{k}\,\zeta \tag{3.13}$$

of a point. If the co-ordinates of a point before deformation are x, y, z, then after deformation they become $x + \xi$, $y + \eta$, $z + \zeta$. The state of strain is fully determined, if for every point of the continuum the components of the displacement vector are given:

$$\xi = \xi(x,y,z); \quad \eta = \eta(x,y,z); \quad \zeta = \zeta(x,y,z)\,.$$

The six strain parameters ε_x, ε_y, ε_z, γ_{xy}, γ_{yz}, γ_{zx}, can, obviously, be expressed in terms of the three displacement parameters ξ, η, ζ. Since this relationship will be required in the following section, we shall derive it here. From Fig. 3.4 and 3.5 we deduce without difficulty:

$$\left.\begin{aligned} &\varepsilon_x = \frac{\partial \xi}{\partial x}\,; \quad \varepsilon_y = \frac{\partial \eta}{\partial y}\,, \quad \varepsilon_z = \frac{\partial \zeta}{\partial z} \\ &\gamma_{xy} = \frac{\partial \xi}{\partial y} + \frac{\partial \eta}{\partial x}\,, \quad \gamma_{yz} = \frac{\partial \eta}{\partial z} + \frac{\partial \zeta}{\partial y}\,, \quad \gamma_{zx} = \frac{\partial \zeta}{\partial x} + \frac{\partial \xi}{\partial z}\,, \\ &e = \operatorname{div} \boldsymbol{s}\,. \end{aligned}\right\} \tag{3.14}$$

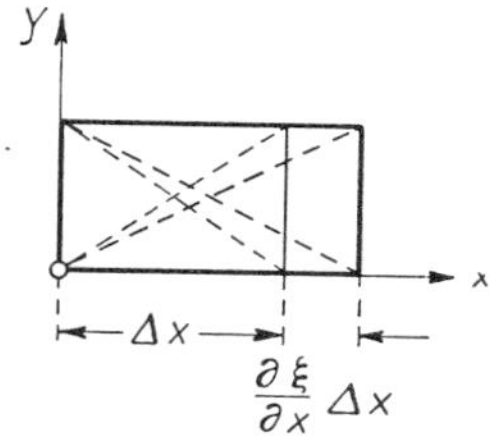

Fig. 3.4. Pure expansion due to displacement $\xi(x)$

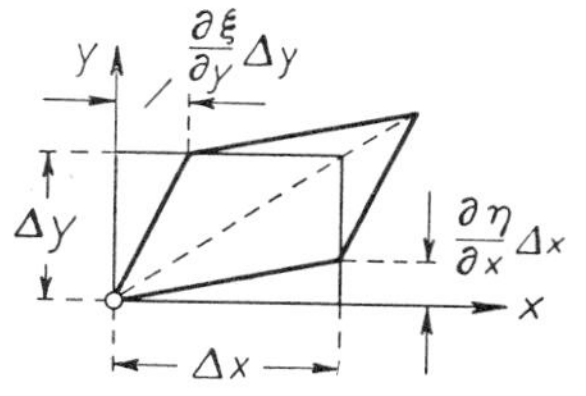

Fig. 3.5. Angular deformation due to displacements $\xi(y)$ and $\eta(x)$

d. Relation between stress system and strain system for solid bodies (Hooke's law)

The relationship between the stress system and the strain system for the case of elastic solid bodies is given by Hooke's law which states that stresses are proportional to strains. The relation between shearing stresses, τ, and angular displacements, γ, has the simpler form, and from Fig. 3.3 we can deduce:

$$\tau_{xy} = G\,\gamma_{xy}; \quad \tau_{yz} = G\,\gamma_{yz}; \quad \tau_{zx} = G\,\gamma_{zx}\,. \tag{3.15}$$

where G denotes the modulus of elasticity in torsion (shear modulus) measured in lbf/ft^2.

The relationship between the elongations, ε, and the normal stresses, σ, for the general case with three normal stresses is slightly more complicated in form than eqn. (3.15). The reason for it lies in the fact that a normal stress σ_x in the x-direction, Fig. 3.2, causes an elongation in the x-direction whose magnitude is $\varepsilon_x = \sigma_x/E$, with E denoting the modulus of elasticity, as well as contractions at right angles to it. These are proportional to the elongation, ε_x, and for the contraction in the y-direction we can write $\varepsilon_y = -\varepsilon_x/m = -\sigma_x/m\,E$, where $1/m$ is known as Poisson's ratio and has the value 3/10, approximately, for solid elastic bodies. The total strain in the x-direction, taking into account the contractions due to σ_y and σ_z, becomes

$$\varepsilon_x = \frac{\sigma_x}{E} - \frac{1}{m}\left(\frac{\sigma_y}{E} + \frac{\sigma_z}{E}\right).$$

Thus the relation between the strains, ε, and the normal stresses, σ, becomes:

$$\left.\begin{aligned} E\,\varepsilon_x &= \sigma_x - \frac{1}{m}(\sigma_y + \sigma_z) \\ E\,\varepsilon_y &= \sigma_y - \frac{1}{m}(\sigma_z + \sigma_x) \\ E\,\varepsilon_z &= \sigma_z - \frac{1}{m}(\sigma_x + \sigma_y). \end{aligned}\right\} \tag{3.16}$$

The volume dilatation, or dilatation for short, $e = \varepsilon_x + \varepsilon_y + \varepsilon_z$ is, consequently, given by

$$e = \frac{1}{E}\,\frac{m-2}{m}\,(\sigma_x + \sigma_y + \sigma_z). \tag{3.17}$$

and becomes equal to zero for $m = 2$. The modulus of elasticity, E, the shear modulus, G, and the inverse of Poisson's ratio, m, are connected through the equation

$$G = \frac{m\,E}{2(m+1)}. \tag{3.18}$$

So far we have related the six strain parameters $\varepsilon_x, \ldots, \gamma_{zx}$ and the three displacement parameters ξ, η, ζ in eqn. (3.14) on the one hand and the strain parameters and the six stresses $\sigma_x, \ldots, \tau_{zx}$ on the other. In order to complete the task outlined at the end of Sec. III b it now remains to express the six stress parameters $\sigma_x, \ldots, \tau_{zx}$ in terms of the three displacement parameters ξ, η, ζ. To achieve this it is necessary to eliminate the six strains $\varepsilon_x, \ldots, \gamma_{zx}$, from the twelve equations (3.14), (3.15) and (3.16).

The elimination of the angular displacements, γ, can be achieved at once upon comparing eqns. (3.15) with the second row of (3.14); this gives the last line in eqn. (3.20) below.

The elimination of the ε requires some calculation. From (3.16) and (3.12), with the aid of (3.18), we obtain

$$\sigma_x + \sigma_y + \sigma_z = \frac{m\,E}{m-2}\,e = 2\,G\,\frac{m+1}{m-2}\,e. \tag{3.19}$$

Thus the first eqn. (3.16) becomes

$$E\,\varepsilon_x = \frac{m+1}{m}\,\sigma_x - \frac{E\,e}{m-2}$$

or

$$\sigma_x = \frac{m\,E}{m+1}\left(\varepsilon_x + \frac{e}{m-2}\right) = 2\,G\left(\varepsilon_x + \frac{e}{m-2}\right).$$

Finally it is desirable to introduce the arithmetic mean, $\bar{\sigma}$, of the normal stresses from eqn. (3.11). The last equation is then

$$\sigma_x = 2\,G\,\varepsilon_x + \bar{\sigma} + 2\,G\,\frac{e}{m-2} - \frac{1}{3}\left(\sigma_x + \sigma_y + \sigma_z\right),$$

and upon replacing the last term with the aid of eqn. (3.19) we have

$$\sigma_x = \bar{\sigma} + 2\,G\,\varepsilon_x - \frac{2}{3}\,G\,e$$

and two corresponding equations for σ_y and σ_z. If we now replace $\varepsilon_x, \ldots$ by the displacements from (3.14), we obtain equations in which the six stresses are expressed in terms of the three displacement components:

$$\left.\begin{aligned}
\sigma_x &= \bar{\sigma} + 2\,G\,\frac{\partial \xi}{\partial x} - \frac{2}{3}\,G\,\mathrm{div}\,\boldsymbol{s}\\
\sigma_y &= \bar{\sigma} + 2\,G\,\frac{\partial \eta}{\partial y} - \frac{2}{3}\,G\,\mathrm{div}\,\boldsymbol{s}\\
\sigma_z &= \bar{\sigma} + 2\,G\,\frac{\partial \zeta}{\partial z} - \frac{2}{3}\,G\,\mathrm{div}\,\boldsymbol{s}\\
\tau_{xy} = G\left(\frac{\partial \xi}{\partial y} + \frac{\partial \eta}{\partial x}\right);\quad
\tau_{yz} &= G\left(\frac{\partial \eta}{\partial z} + \frac{\partial \zeta}{\partial y}\right);\quad
\tau_{zx} = G\left(\frac{\partial \zeta}{\partial x} + \frac{\partial \xi}{\partial z}\right).
\end{aligned}\right\} \tag{3.20}$$

Eqns. (3.20) can be written down in a more lucid form if matrix notation is used. We then obtain for the stress matrix from eqn. (3.9)

$$\begin{pmatrix} \sigma_x & \tau_{xy} & \tau_{xz} \\ \tau_{xy} & \sigma_y & \tau_{yz} \\ \tau_{xz} & \tau_{yz} & \sigma_z \end{pmatrix} = \tag{3.21}$$

$$= \begin{pmatrix} \bar{\sigma} & 0 & 0 \\ 0 & \bar{\sigma} & 0 \\ 0 & 0 & \bar{\sigma} \end{pmatrix} + G \begin{pmatrix} \frac{\partial \xi}{\partial x} & \frac{\partial \xi}{\partial y} & \frac{\partial \xi}{\partial z} \\ \frac{\partial \eta}{\partial x} & \frac{\partial \eta}{\partial y} & \frac{\partial \eta}{\partial z} \\ \frac{\partial \zeta}{\partial x} & \frac{\partial \zeta}{\partial y} & \frac{\partial \zeta}{\partial z} \end{pmatrix} + G \begin{pmatrix} \frac{\partial \xi}{\partial x} & \frac{\partial \eta}{\partial x} & \frac{\partial \zeta}{\partial x} \\ \frac{\partial \xi}{\partial y} & \frac{\partial \eta}{\partial y} & \frac{\partial \zeta}{\partial y} \\ \frac{\partial \xi}{\partial z} & \frac{\partial \eta}{\partial z} & \frac{\partial \zeta}{\partial z} \end{pmatrix} - \frac{2}{3}\,G \begin{pmatrix} \mathrm{div}\,\boldsymbol{s} & 0 & 0 \\ 0 & \mathrm{div}\,\boldsymbol{s} & 0 \\ 0 & 0 & \mathrm{div}\,\boldsymbol{s} \end{pmatrix}$$

This is the general form of Hooke's law for an elastic solid body. It contains the assumption that stresses are proportional to the *magnitude* of the respective displacements.

e. Relation between stress and strain system for liquids and gases (Stokes' law of friction)

In the case of the flow of liquids and gases *Stokes' law of friction* can be derived at once from eqn. (3.21). The only difference consists in making the stresses proportional to the *rate of change of strain* with time (*rate-of-strain* for short). In this manner the stress tensor of a fluid in motion is obtained by replacing the displacement $\boldsymbol{s} = \boldsymbol{i}\,\xi + \boldsymbol{j}\,\eta + \boldsymbol{k}\,\zeta$ in eqn. (3.21) by its time-derivative

$$\frac{\mathrm{d}\boldsymbol{s}}{\mathrm{d}t} = \boldsymbol{w} = \boldsymbol{i}\,u + \boldsymbol{j}\,v + \boldsymbol{k}\,w\,,$$

which is identical with the flow velocity vector. The shear modulus G (lbf/ft^2) should simultaneously be replaced by the viscosity μ (lbf sec/ft^2) and the arithmetic mean of the normal stresses $\bar{\sigma}$ is replaced by the fluid pressure $-\,p$, in accordance with eqn. (3.11). Hence Stokes' hypothesis, written in the form of a stress matrix, becomes

$$\begin{pmatrix} \sigma_x & \tau_{xy} & \tau_{xz} \\ \tau_{xy} & \sigma_y & \tau_{yz} \\ \tau_{xz} & \tau_{yz} & \sigma_z \end{pmatrix} = \tag{3.22}$$

$$= \begin{pmatrix} -p & 0 & 0 \\ 0 & -p & 0 \\ 0 & 0 & -p \end{pmatrix} + \mu \begin{pmatrix} \frac{\partial u}{\partial x} & \frac{\partial u}{\partial y} & \frac{\partial u}{\partial z} \\ \frac{\partial v}{\partial x} & \frac{\partial v}{\partial y} & \frac{\partial v}{\partial z} \\ \frac{\partial w}{\partial x} & \frac{\partial w}{\partial y} & \frac{\partial w}{\partial z} \end{pmatrix} + \mu \begin{pmatrix} \frac{\partial u}{\partial x} & \frac{\partial v}{\partial x} & \frac{\partial w}{\partial x} \\ \frac{\partial u}{\partial y} & \frac{\partial v}{\partial y} & \frac{\partial w}{\partial y} \\ \frac{\partial u}{\partial z} & \frac{\partial v}{\partial z} & \frac{\partial w}{\partial z} \end{pmatrix} - \frac{2}{3}\mu \begin{pmatrix} \operatorname{div}\boldsymbol{w} & 0 & 0 \\ 0 & \operatorname{div}\boldsymbol{w} & 0 \\ 0 & 0 & \operatorname{div}\boldsymbol{w} \end{pmatrix}$$

which is analogous to eqn. (3.21). Finally it is convenient to subtract the pressure from the normal stresses, by putting

$$\sigma_x = -p + \sigma_x'\,; \quad \sigma_y = -p + \sigma_y'; \quad \sigma_z = -p + \sigma_z'\,, \tag{3.23}$$

so that the frictional terms of the stress components can be written as:

$$\left.\begin{aligned} \sigma_x' &= \mu\left(2\,\frac{\partial u}{\partial x} - \frac{2}{3}\operatorname{div}\boldsymbol{w}\right); \quad & \tau_{xy} &= \mu\left(\frac{\partial u}{\partial y} + \frac{\partial v}{\partial x}\right) \\ \sigma_y' &= \mu\left(2\,\frac{\partial v}{\partial y} - \frac{2}{3}\operatorname{div}\boldsymbol{w}\right); \quad & \tau_{yz} &= \mu\left(\frac{\partial v}{\partial z} + \frac{\partial w}{\partial y}\right) \\ \sigma_z' &= \mu\left(2\,\frac{\partial w}{\partial z} - \frac{2}{3}\operatorname{div}\boldsymbol{w}\right); \quad & \tau_{xz} &= \mu\left(\frac{\partial w}{\partial x} + \frac{\partial u}{\partial z}\right). \end{aligned}\right\} \tag{3.24}$$

In the case of an incompressible viscous fluid the last term in eqn. (3.22) can be dropped, because in this case div $\boldsymbol{w} = 0$, and for an incompressible non-viscous fluid eqn. (3.22) simplifies to $\sigma_x = \sigma_y = \sigma_z = -p$, $\tau_{xy} = \tau_{yz} = \tau_{xz} = 0$, as expected. Furthermore, the last result is also valid in the case of a non-viscous, but compressible, fluid.

f. The Navier-Stokes equations

With the aid of eqns. (3.23) the non-viscous pressure terms can be separated in the equation of motion (3.10) so that they become

$$\left.\begin{aligned}
\varrho \frac{Du}{Dt} &= X - \frac{\partial p}{\partial x} + \left(\frac{\partial \sigma_x'}{\partial x} + \frac{\partial \tau_{xy}}{\partial y} + \frac{\partial \tau_{xz}}{\partial z}\right) \\
\varrho \frac{Dv}{Dt} &= Y - \frac{\partial p}{\partial y} + \left(\frac{\partial \tau_{xy}}{\partial x} + \frac{\partial \sigma_y'}{\partial y} + \frac{\partial \tau_{yz}}{\partial z}\right) \\
\varrho \frac{Dw}{Dt} &= Z - \frac{\partial p}{\partial z} + \left(\frac{\partial \tau_{xz}}{\partial x} + \frac{\partial \tau_{yz}}{\partial y} + \frac{\partial \sigma_z'}{\partial z}\right).
\end{aligned}\right\} \tag{3.25}$$

Introducing Stokes' hypothesis from eqn. (3.24) we obtain the resultant surface force in terms of the velocity components, e.g. for the x-direction we obtain with the aid of eqn. (3.9a):

$$P_x = \frac{\partial \sigma_x}{\partial x} + \frac{\partial \tau_{xy}}{\partial y} + \frac{\partial \tau_{xz}}{\partial z} = -\frac{\partial p}{\partial x} + \frac{\partial \sigma_x'}{\partial x} + \frac{\partial \tau_{xy}}{\partial y} + \frac{\partial \tau_{xz}}{\partial z}$$

$$P_x = -\frac{\partial p}{\partial x} + \frac{\partial}{\partial x}\left[2\,\mu \frac{\partial u}{\partial x} - \frac{2}{3}\,\mu \operatorname{div} \boldsymbol{w}\right] + \frac{\partial}{\partial y}\left[\mu\left(\frac{\partial u}{\partial y} + \frac{\partial v}{\partial x}\right)\right] + \frac{\partial}{\partial z}\left[\mu\left(\frac{\partial w}{\partial x} + \frac{\partial u}{\partial z}\right)\right]$$

and corresponding expressions for the y- and z-components. In the general case of a compressible flow, the viscosity μ must be regarded as dependent on the space co-ordinates, because μ varies considerably with temperature (Table 1.2), and the changes in velocity and pressure together with the heat due to friction bring about considerable temperature variations. The temperature dependence of viscosity $\mu(T)$ must be obtained from experiments (*cf.* Chap. XV).

If these expressions are introduced into the fundamental equations (3.10), we obtain

$$\varrho \frac{Du}{Dt} = X - \frac{\partial p}{\partial x} + \frac{\partial}{\partial x}\left[\mu\left(2\frac{\partial u}{\partial x} - \frac{2}{3}\operatorname{div} \boldsymbol{w}\right)\right] + \frac{\partial}{\partial y}\left[\mu\left(\frac{\partial u}{\partial y} + \frac{\partial v}{\partial x}\right)\right] + \frac{\partial}{\partial z}\left[\mu\left(\frac{\partial w}{\partial x} + \frac{\partial u}{\partial z}\right)\right]$$

$$\varrho \frac{Dv}{Dt} = Y - \frac{\partial p}{\partial y} + \frac{\partial}{\partial y}\left[\mu\left(2\frac{\partial v}{\partial y} - \frac{2}{3}\operatorname{div} \boldsymbol{w}\right)\right] + \frac{\partial}{\partial z}\left[\mu\left(\frac{\partial v}{\partial z} + \frac{\partial w}{\partial y}\right)\right] + \frac{\partial}{\partial x}\left[\mu\left(\frac{\partial u}{\partial y} + \frac{\partial v}{\partial x}\right)\right]$$

$$\varrho \frac{Dw}{Dt} = Z - \frac{\partial p}{\partial z} + \frac{\partial}{\partial z}\left[\mu\left(2\frac{\partial w}{\partial z} - \frac{2}{3}\operatorname{div} \boldsymbol{w}\right)\right] + \frac{\partial}{\partial x}\left[\mu\left(\frac{\partial w}{\partial x} + \frac{\partial u}{\partial z}\right)\right] + \frac{\partial u}{\partial y}\left[\mu\left(\frac{\partial v}{\partial z} + \frac{\partial w}{\partial y}\right)\right]$$

(3.26a, b, c)

These very well known differential equations form the basis of the whole science of fluid mechanics. They are usually referred to as the Navier-Stokes equations. It is necessary to include here the equation of continuity which, as seen from eqn. (3.1), assumes the following form for compressible flow:

$$\frac{\partial \varrho}{\partial t} + \frac{\partial (\varrho u)}{\partial x} + \frac{\partial (\varrho v)}{\partial y} + \frac{\partial (\varrho w)}{\partial z} = 0 . \tag{3.27}$$

The above equations do not give a complete description of the motion of a compressible fluid because changes in pressure and density effect temperature variations and principles of *thermodynamics* must, therefore, enter into the considerations. From thermodynamics we obtain, in the first place, the characteristic equation (equation of state) which combines pressure, density and temperature, and which for a perfect gas has the form

$$p - \varrho g R T = 0 , \tag{3.28}$$

with R denoting the gas constant and T denoting the absolute temperature. Secondly, if the process is not isothermal, it is further necessary to make use of the energy equation which draws up a balance between heat and mechanical energy (First Law of thermodynamics), and which furnishes a differential equation for the temperature distribution. The energy equation will be discussed in greater detail in Chap. XIV. The final equation of the system is given by the empirical viscosity law $\mu(T)$. In all, if the forces X, Y, Z are considered given, there are seven equations for the seven variables u, v, w, p, ϱ, T, μ.

For isothermal processes these reduce to five equations (3.26a, b, c), (3.27) and (3.28) for the five unknowns u, v, w, p, ϱ.

Incompressible flow: The above system of equations becomes further simplified in the case of incompressible fluids (ϱ = const) even if the temperature is not constant. First, as already shown in eqn. (3.1a), we have div $\boldsymbol{w} = 0$. Secondly, since temperature variations are, generally speaking, small in this case, the viscosity may be taken to be constant. The equation of state as well as the energy equation become superfluous as far as the calculation of the field of flow is concerned. The field of flow can now be considered independently from the equations of thermodynamics. The equation of motion (3.26a, b, c) and (3.27) can be simplified and, if the acceleration terms are written out fully, they assume the following form:

$$\left.\begin{aligned}
\varrho\left(\frac{\partial u}{\partial t} + u\frac{\partial u}{\partial x} + v\frac{\partial u}{\partial y} + w\frac{\partial u}{\partial z}\right) &= X - \frac{\partial p}{\partial x} + \mu\left(\frac{\partial^2 u}{\partial x^2} + \frac{\partial^2 u}{\partial y^2} + \frac{\partial^2 u}{\partial z^2}\right)\\
\varrho\left(\frac{\partial v}{\partial t} + u\frac{\partial v}{\partial x} + v\frac{\partial v}{\partial y} + w\frac{\partial v}{\partial z}\right) &= Y - \frac{\partial p}{\partial y} + \mu\left(\frac{\partial^2 v}{\partial x^2} + \frac{\partial^2 v}{\partial y^2} + \frac{\partial^2 v}{\partial z^2}\right)\\
\varrho\left(\frac{\partial w}{\partial t} + u\frac{\partial w}{\partial x} + v\frac{\partial w}{\partial y} + w\frac{\partial w}{\partial z}\right) &= Z - \frac{\partial p}{\partial z} + \mu\left(\frac{\partial^2 w}{\partial x^2} + \frac{\partial^2 w}{\partial y^2} + \frac{\partial^2 w}{\partial z^2}\right)
\end{aligned}\right\} \tag{3.29a, b, c}$$

$$\frac{\partial u}{\partial x} + \frac{\partial v}{\partial y} + \frac{\partial w}{\partial z} = 0 . \tag{3.30}$$

With known body forces there are four equations for the four unknowns u, v, w, p.

If vector notation is used the simplified Navier-Stokes equations for incompressible flow, eqns. (3.29a, b, c), can be shortened to

$$\varrho \frac{\mathrm{D}\boldsymbol{w}}{\mathrm{D}t} = \boldsymbol{F} - \operatorname{grad} p + \mu \nabla^2 \boldsymbol{w}\,, \tag{3.31}$$

where the symbol ∇^2 denotes the Laplace operator, $\nabla^2 = \partial^2/\partial x^2 + \partial^2/\partial y^2 + \partial^2/\partial z^2$. The above Navier-Stokes equations differ from Euler's equations of motion by the viscous terms $\mu \nabla^2 \boldsymbol{w}$.

The solutions of the above equations become fully determined physically when the *boundary* and *initial conditions* are specified. In the case of viscous fluids the condition of no slip on solid boundaries must be satisfied, i.e. on a wall both the normal and tangential component of the velocity must vanish:

$$v_n = 0\,, \qquad v_t = 0 \quad \text{on solid walls}\,. \tag{3.32}$$

The equations under discussion were first derived by M. Navier [2] in 1827 and by S. D. Poisson [3] in 1831, on the basis of an argument which involved the consideration of intermolecular forces. Later the same equations were derived without the use of any such hypotheses by B. de Saint Venant [5] in 1843 and by G. G. Stokes [4] in 1845. Their derivations were based on the same assumption as made here, namely that the normal and shearing stresses are linear functions of the rate of deformation, in conformity with the older law of friction, due to Newton.

Since Stokes' hypothesis is evidently completely arbitrary, it is not *a priori* certain that the Navier-Stokes equations give a true description of the motion of a fluid. It is, therefore, necessary to verify them, and that can only be achieved by experiment. In this connexion it should, in any case, be noted that the enormous mathematical difficulties encountered when solving the Navier-Stokes equations have so far prevented us from obtaining a single solution in which the convective terms interact in a general way with the friction terms. However, known solutions, such as laminar flow through a circular pipe, as well as boundary layer flows, to be discussed later, agree so well with experiment that the general validity of the Navier-Stokes equations can hardly be doubted.

Cylindrical co-ordinates: We shall now transform the Navier-Stokes equations to cylindrical co-ordinates for future reference. If r, ϕ, z denote the radial, azimuthal, and axial co-ordinates, respectively, of a three-dimensional system of co-ordinates, and v_r, v_ϕ, v_z denote the velocity components in the respective directions, then the transformation of variables [1] for the case of incompressible fluid flow, eqns. (3.30) and (3.31), leads to the following system of equations:

$$\varrho\left(\frac{\partial v_r}{\partial t} + v_r \frac{\partial v_r}{\partial r} + \frac{v_\phi}{r}\frac{\partial v_r}{\partial \phi} - \frac{v_\phi{}^2}{r} + v_z \frac{\partial v_r}{\partial z}\right) =$$

$$= F_r - \frac{\partial p}{\partial r} + \mu\left(\frac{\partial^2 v_r}{\partial r^2} + \frac{1}{r}\frac{\partial v_r}{\partial r} - \frac{v_r}{r^2} + \frac{1}{r^2}\frac{\partial^2 v_r}{\partial \phi^2} - \frac{2}{r^2}\frac{\partial v_\phi}{\partial \phi} + \frac{\partial^2 v_r}{\partial z^2}\right) \tag{3.33a}$$

$$\varrho\left(\frac{\partial v_\phi}{\partial t} + v_r \frac{\partial v_\phi}{\partial r} + \frac{v_\phi}{r}\frac{\partial v_\phi}{\partial \phi} + \frac{v_r\, v_\phi}{r} + v_z \frac{\partial v_\phi}{\partial z}\right) =$$

$$= F_\phi - \frac{1}{r}\frac{\partial p}{\partial \phi} + \mu\left(\frac{\partial^2 v_\phi}{\partial r^2} + \frac{1}{r}\frac{\partial v_\phi}{\partial r} - \frac{v_\phi}{r^2} + \frac{1}{r^2}\frac{\partial^2 v_\phi}{\partial \phi^2} + \frac{2}{r^2}\frac{\partial v_r}{\partial \phi} + \frac{\partial^2 v_\phi}{\partial z^2}\right) \tag{3.33 b}$$

$$\varrho\left(\frac{\partial v_z}{\partial t} + v_r \frac{\partial v_z}{\partial r} + \frac{v_\phi}{r}\frac{\partial v_z}{\partial \varphi} + v_z \frac{\partial v_z}{\partial z}\right) =$$

$$= F_z - \frac{\partial p}{\partial z} + \mu\left(\frac{\partial^2 v_z}{\partial r^2} + \frac{1}{r}\frac{\partial v_z}{\partial r} + \frac{1}{r^2}\frac{\partial^2 v_z}{\partial \phi^2} + \frac{\partial^2 v_z}{\partial z^2}\right) \tag{3.33 c}$$

$$\frac{\partial v_r}{\partial r} + \frac{v_r}{r} + \frac{1}{r}\frac{\partial v_\phi}{\partial \phi} + \frac{\partial v_z}{\partial z} = 0\,. \tag{3.33 d}$$

The stress components assume the form

$$\left.\begin{aligned}
\sigma_r &= -p + 2\mu \frac{\partial v_r}{\partial r} &;\quad \tau_{r\phi} &= \mu\left[r\frac{\partial}{\partial r}\left(\frac{v_\phi}{r}\right) + \frac{1}{r}\frac{\partial v_r}{\partial \phi}\right]\\
\sigma_\phi &= -p + 2\mu\left(\frac{1}{r}\frac{\partial v_\phi}{\partial \phi} + \frac{v_r}{r}\right) &;\quad \tau_{\phi z} &= \mu\left(\frac{\partial v_\phi}{\partial z} + \frac{1}{r}\frac{\partial v_z}{\partial \phi}\right)\\
\sigma_z &= -p + 2\mu \frac{\partial v_z}{\partial z} &;\quad \tau_{rz} &= \mu\left(\frac{\partial v_r}{\partial z} + \frac{\partial v_z}{\partial r}\right).
\end{aligned}\right\} \tag{3.34}$$

References

[1] L. Hopf, Zähe Flüssigkeiten. Contribution to Handbuch der Physik, vol. **VII**, edited by H. Geiger and K. Scheel, Berlin 1927.

[2] M. Navier, Mémoire sur les Lois du Mouvements des Fluides. Mem. de l'Acad. d. Sci. **6**, 389 (1827).

[3] S. D. Poisson, Mémoire sur les Equations générales de l'Equilibre et du Mouvement des Corps solides Elastique et des Fluides. J. de l'Ecole polytechn. **13**, 1 (1831).

[4] G. G. Stokes, On the Theories of the Internal Friction of Fluids in Motion. Trans. of the Cambr. Phil. Soc. **8** (1845).

[5] B. de St. Venant, Comptes Rendus **17**, 1240 (1843).

CHAPTER IV

General properties of the Navier-Stokes equations

Before passing on to the integration of the Navier-Stokes equations in the following chapters, it now seems pertinent to discuss some of their general properties. In doing so we shall restrict ourselves to incompressible viscous fluids.

a. Derivation of Reynolds' principle of similarity from the Navier-Stokes equations

Until the present day no general methods have become available for the integration of the Navier-Stokes equations. Furthermore, solutions which are valid for all values of viscosity are known only for some particular cases, e.g. for Poiseuille flow through a circular pipe, or for Couette flow between two parallel walls, one of which is at rest, the other moving along its own plane with a constant velocity (see Fig. 1.1). For this reason the problem of calculating the motion of a viscous fluid was attacked by first tackling limiting cases, that is, by solving problems for very large viscosities, on the one hand, and for very small viscosities on the other, because in this manner the mathematical problem is considerably simplified. However, the case of moderate viscosities cannot be interpolated between these two extremes.

Even the limiting cases of very large and very small viscosities present great mathematical difficulties so that research into viscous fluid motion proceeded to a large extent by experiment. In this connexion the Navier-Stokes equations furnish very useful hints which point to a considerable reduction in the quantity of experimental work required. It is often possible to carry out experiments on *models*, which means that in the experimental arrangement a geometrically similar model of the actual body, but reduced in scale, is investigated in a wind tunnel, or other suitable arrangement. This always raises the question of the *dynamic similarity* of fluid motions which is, evidently, intimately connected with the question of how far results obtained with models can be utilized for the prediction of the behaviour of the full-scale body.

As already explained in Chap. I, two fluid motions are dynamically similar if, with geometrically similar boundaries, the velocity fields are geometrically similar, i.e. if they have geometrically similar stream-lines.

This question was answered in Chap. I for the case in which only inertia and viscous forces take part in the process. It was found there that for the two motions the Reynolds numbers must be equal (Reynolds' principle of similarity). This conclusion was drawn by estimating the forces in the stream; we now propose to deduce it again directly from the Navier-Stokes equations.

The Navier-Stokes equations express the condition of equilibrium, namely that for each particle there is equilibrium between body forces (weight), surface forces and inertia forces. The surface forces consist of pressure forces (normal forces) and friction forces (shear forces). Body forces are important only in cases when there is a free surface or when the density distribution is inhomogeneous. In the case of a homogeneous fluid in the absence of a free surface there is equilibrium between the weight of each particle and its hydrostatic buoyancy force, in the same way as at rest. Hence in the motion of a homogeneous fluid, in the absence of a free surface, body forces can be cancelled if pressure is taken to mean the difference between that in motion and at rest. In the following argument we shall restrict our attention to cases for which this assumption is true because they are the most important ones in applications. Thus the Navier-Stokes equations will now contain only forces due to pressure, viscosity, and inertia.

Under these assumptions and conventions the Navier-Stokes equations for an incompressible fluid, restricted to steady flow and in vector form, simplify to

$$\varrho\,(\boldsymbol{w}\,\mathrm{grad})\,\boldsymbol{w} = -\,\mathrm{grad}\,p + \mu\,\nabla^2\boldsymbol{w}\,. \tag{4.1}$$ †

This differential equation must be independent of the choice of the units for the various physical quantities, such as velocity, pressure, etc., which appear in it.

We now consider flows about two geometrically similar bodies of different linear dimensions in streams of different velocities, e. g. flows past two spheres, in which the densities and viscosities may also be different. We shall investigate the condition for dynamic similarity with the aid of the Navier-Stokes equations. Evidently, dynamic similarity will prevail if with a suitable choice of the units of length, time and force, the Navier-Stokes eqn. (4.1) is so transformed that it becomes identical for the two flows with geometrically similar boundaries. Now, it is possible to free oneself from the fortuitously selected units if dimensionless quantities are introduced into eqn. (4.1). This is achieved by selecting certain suitable characteristic magnitudes in the flow as our units and by referring all others to them. Thus e. g. the free stream velocity and the diameter of the sphere can be selected as the respective units of velocity and length.

Let V, l, and p_1 denote these characteristic reference magnitudes. If we now introduce into the Navier-Stokes eqn. (4.1) the dimensionless ratios

$$\text{velocity}\qquad \boldsymbol{W} = \frac{\boldsymbol{w}}{V}$$

$$\text{lengths}\qquad X = \frac{x}{l}\,,\quad Y = \frac{y}{l}\,,\quad Z = \frac{z}{l}$$

$$\text{pressure}\qquad P = \frac{p}{p_1}\,,$$

we obtain

$$\varrho\,\frac{V^2}{l}\,(\boldsymbol{W}\,\mathrm{grad})\,\boldsymbol{W} = -\,\frac{p_1}{l}\,\mathrm{grad}\,P + \frac{\mu V}{l^2}\,\nabla^2\boldsymbol{W}$$

† See footnote on p. 43.

or, dividing by $\varrho V^2/l$:

$$(\boldsymbol{W} \operatorname{grad}) \boldsymbol{W} = -\frac{p_1}{\varrho V^2} \operatorname{grad} P + \frac{\mu}{\varrho V l} \nabla^2 \boldsymbol{W}. \qquad (4.2)\dagger$$

The fluid motions under consideration can become similar only if the solutions expressed in terms of the respective dimensionless variables are identical. This requires that for both motions the respective dimensionless Navier-Stokes equations differ only by a factor common to all terms. The quantity $p_1/\varrho V^2$ represents the ratio of pressure to the double of the dynamic head and is unimportant for the dynamic similarity of the two motions because in incompressible flow a change in pressure causes no change in volume. The second factor $\varrho V l/\mu$ is, however, very important and must assume the same value for both motions if they are to be dynamically similar. Hence dynamic similarity is assured if for the two motions

$$\frac{\varrho_1 V_1 l_1}{\mu_1} = \frac{\varrho_2 V_2 l_2}{\mu_2}.$$

This principle was discovered by Osborne Reynolds when he investigated fluid motion through pipes and is, therefore, known as the *Reynolds principle of similarity.* The dimensionless ratio

$$\frac{\varrho V l}{\mu} = \frac{V l}{\nu} = \mathsf{R} \qquad (4.3)$$

is called the Reynolds number. Here the ratio of the dynamic viscosity μ, to the density ϱ, denoted by $\nu = \mu/\varrho$, is the kinematic viscosity of the fluid, introduced earlier. Summing up we can state that flows about geometrically similar bodies are dynamically similar when the Reynolds numbers for the flows are equal.

Thus Reynolds' similarity principle has been deduced once more, this time from the Navier-Stokes equations, having been previously derived first from an estimation of forces and secondly from dimensional analysis.

b. Frictionless flows as "solutions" of the Navier-Stokes equations

It may be worth noting, parenthetically, that the solutions for incompressible *frictionless* flows may also be regarded as exact solutions of the Navier-Stokes equations, because in such cases the frictional terms vanish identically. In the case of incompressible, frictionless flows the velocity vector can be represented as the gradient of a potential:

$$\boldsymbol{w} = \operatorname{grad} \Phi,$$

where the potential Φ satisfies the Laplace equation

$$\nabla^2 \Phi = 0.$$

We then also have grad $(\nabla^2 \Phi) = \nabla^2$ (grad $\Phi) = 0$, that is, $\nabla^2 \boldsymbol{w} = 0$.

Thus the frictional terms in eqn. (4.1) vanish identically for potential flows, but generally speaking both boundary conditions (3.32) for the velocity cannot then be satisfied simultaneously. If the normal component must assume prescribed values along a boundary, then, in potential

† See footnote on p. 43.

flow, the tangential component is thereby determined so that the no slip condition cannot be satisfied at the same time. For this reason one cannot regard potential flows as physically meaningful solutions of the Navier-Stokes equations, because they do not satisfy the prescribed boundary conditions. There exists, however, an important exception to the preceding statement which occurs when the solid wall is in motion and when this condition does not apply. The simplest particular case is that of flow past a rotating cylinder when the potential solution does constitute a meaningful solution to the Navier-Stokes equations, as explained in greater detail on p. 71. The reader may refer to two papers, one by G. Hamel [2] and one by J. Ackeret [1], for further details.

The succeeding sections will be restricted to the consideration of plane (two-dimensional) flows because for such cases only is it possible to indicate some general properties of the Navier-Stokes equations, and, on the other hand, plane flows constitute by far the largest class of problems of practical importance.

c. The Navier-Stokes equations interpreted as vorticity transport equations

In the case of two-dimensional non-steady flow in the x,y-plane the velocity vector becomes

$$\boldsymbol{w} = \boldsymbol{i}\, u(x,y,t) + \boldsymbol{j}\, v(x,y,t)$$

and the system of equations (3.29) and (3.30) transforms into

$$\left.\begin{aligned} \frac{\partial u}{\partial t} + u\frac{\partial u}{\partial x} + v\frac{\partial u}{\partial y} &= \frac{1}{\varrho}X - \frac{1}{\varrho}\frac{\partial p}{\partial x} + \nu\left(\frac{\partial^2 u}{\partial x^2} + \frac{\partial^2 u}{\partial y^2}\right) \\ \frac{\partial v}{\partial t} + u\frac{\partial v}{\partial x} + v\frac{\partial v}{\partial y} &= \frac{1}{\varrho}Y - \frac{1}{\varrho}\frac{\partial p}{\partial y} + \nu\left(\frac{\partial^2 v}{\partial x^2} + \frac{\partial^2 v}{\partial y^2}\right) \\ \frac{\partial u}{\partial x} + \frac{\partial v}{\partial y} &= 0\,, \end{aligned}\right\} \qquad \textbf{(4.4 a, b, c)}$$

which furnishes three equations for u, v, and p.

We now introduce the vector of vorticity, curl $\boldsymbol{w}$, which reduces to the one component about the z-axis for two-dimensional flow:

$$\frac{1}{2}\,\text{curl}\,\boldsymbol{w} = \omega_z = \omega = \frac{1}{2}\left(\frac{\partial v}{\partial x} - \frac{\partial u}{\partial y}\right). \qquad (4.5)$$

Frictionless motions are irrotational so that curl $\boldsymbol{w} = 0$ in such cases. Eliminating pressure from eqns. (4.4a, b) we obtain

$$\frac{\partial \omega}{\partial t} + u\frac{\partial \omega}{\partial x} + v\frac{\partial \omega}{\partial y} = \nu\left(\frac{\partial^2 \omega}{\partial x^2} + \frac{\partial^2 \omega}{\partial y^2}\right) \qquad (4.6)$$

or, in shorthand form

$$\frac{\mathrm{D}\omega}{\mathrm{D}t} = \nu\,\nabla^2\omega\,. \qquad (4.7)$$

This equation is referred to as the *vorticity transport*, or *transfer*, *equation*. It states that the substantive variation of vorticity, which consists of the local and convective terms, is equal to the rate of dissipation of vorticity through friction. Eqn. (4.6), together with the equation of continuity (4.4c), form a system of two equations for the two velocity components u and v.

Finally, it is possible to transform these two equations with two unknowns into one equation with one unknown by introducing the stream function $\psi(x, y)$. Putting

$$u = \frac{\partial \psi}{\partial y} \; ; \; v = -\frac{\partial \psi}{\partial x} \, , \tag{4.8}$$

we see that the continuity equation is satisfied automatically. In addition the vorticity from eqn. (4.5) becomes

$$\omega = -\tfrac{1}{2} \nabla^2 \psi \, , \tag{4.9}$$

and the vorticity transport equation (4.6) becomes

$$\frac{\partial \nabla^2 \psi}{\partial t} + \frac{\partial \psi}{\partial y} \frac{\partial \nabla^2 \psi}{\partial x} - \frac{\partial \psi}{\partial x} \frac{\partial \nabla^2 \psi}{\partial y} = \nu \nabla^4 \psi \, . \tag{4.10}$$

In this form the vorticity transport equation contains only one unknown, ψ. The left-hand side of eqn. (4.10) contains, as was the case with the Navier-Stokes equations, the inertia terms, whereas the right-hand side contains the frictional terms. It is a fourth-order partial differential equation in the stream function ψ. Its solution in general terms is, again, very difficult, owing to its being non-linear.

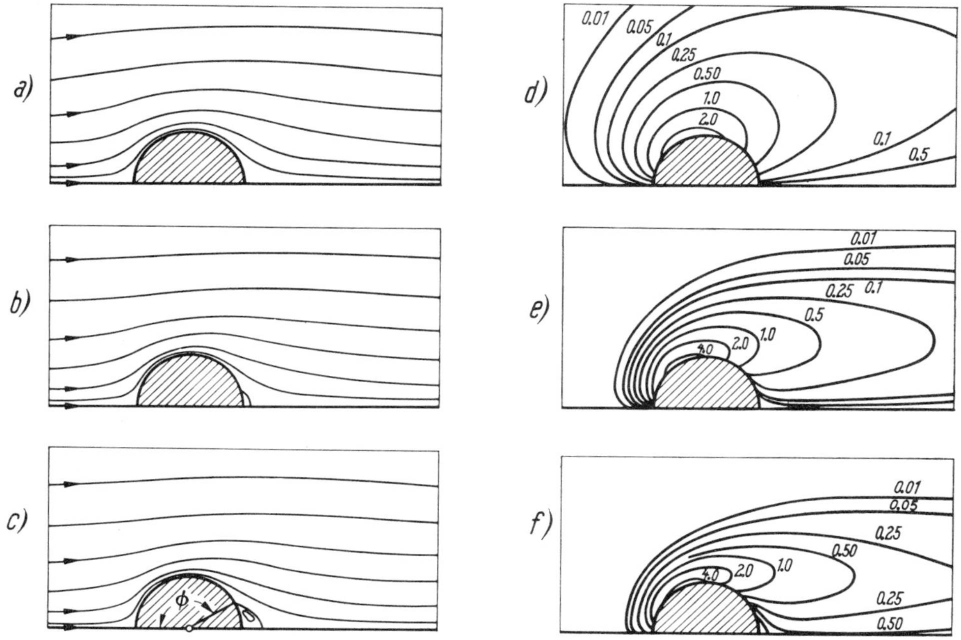

Fig. 4.1 Patterns of motion in a viscous flow past a sphere at different Reynolds numbers $\mathsf{R} = VD/\nu$ derived from the vorticity transport equation (4.10) by V. G. Jenson [3].

a, b, c, Patterns of stream-lines; d, e, f, Distribution of vorticity $\omega D/V = \text{const.}$

a, d	$\mathsf{R} = 5$,	$C_D = 8{\cdot}0$,	no separation
b, e	$\mathsf{R} = 20$,	$C_D = 2{\cdot}9$,	separation at $\phi = 171°$
c, f	$\mathsf{R} = 40$,	$C_D = 1{\cdot}9$,	separation at $\phi = 148°$

V. G. Jenson [3] found a solution to the vorticity transport equation (4.10) for the case of a sphere. The resulting patterns of stream-lines for different Reynolds numbers are seen plotted in Fig. 4.1 which also contains diagrams of the distribution of vorticity in the flow field. The smallest Reynolds number included, $\mathsf{R} = 5$ in Figs. 4.1a and 4.1d, corresponds to the case when the viscous forces by far outweigh the inertia forces and the resulting flow can be described as creeping motion, Sec. IVd and Chapter VI. In this case the whole flow field is rotational and the patterns of stream-lines forward and aft are nearly identical. As the Reynolds number is increased the sphere develops on its rear a separated region with back-flow and the intensity of vorticity is progressively more concentrated near the downstream portion of the sphere, whereas in the forward portion the flow becomes nearly irrotational. The flow patterns under consideration, which have been deduced from the Navier-Stokes equation, allow us to recognize the characteristic changes which take place in the stream as the Reynolds number is made to increase, even if at the highest Reynolds number reached, $\mathsf{R} = 40$ in Figs. 4.1c and 4.1f, the boundary-layer pattern has not yet had a chance to develop fully.

d. The limiting case of very large viscosity (very small Reynolds number)

In very slow motions or in motions with very large viscosity the viscous forces are considerably greater than the inertia forces because the latter are of the order of the velocity squared, whereas the former are linear with velocity. To a first approximation it is possible to neglect the inertia terms with respect to the viscous terms so that from eqn. (4.10) we obtain

$$\nabla^4 \psi = 0 \, . \tag{4.11}$$

This is, now, a linear equation which is considerably more amenable to mathematical treatment than the complete equation (4.10). Flows described by eqn. (4.11) proceed with very small velocities and are sometimes called *creeping motions*. The omission of the inertia terms is permissible from the mathematical point of view because the order of the equation is not thereby reduced, so that with the simplified differential equation (4.11) it is possible to satisfy as many boundary conditions as with the full equation (4.10).

Creeping motions can also be regarded as solutions of the Navier-Stokes equations in the *limiting case of very small Reynolds numbers* ($\mathsf{R} \to 0$), because the Reynolds number represents the ratio of inertia to friction forces.

Solutions of eqn. (4.11) for the creeping motion of a viscous fluid were found by G. G. Stokes in the case of a sphere and by H. Lamb in the case of a circular cylinder. Stokes' solution can be applied to the falling of particles of mist in air, or to the motion of small spheres in a very viscous oil, when the velocities are so small that inertia forces can be neglected with good accuracy. Furthermore, the *hydrodynamic theory of lubrication*, i. e. the theory of the motion of lubricating oil in the very narrow channel between the journal and bearing uses this simplified equation of motion as its starting point. In the latter case it will be observed that if the velocities are not very small, the very small clearance heights and the relatively large viscosity of the oil, ensure that the viscous forces are much larger than the inertia forces. However, apart from the theory of lubrication, the field of application of the theory of creeping motion is fairly insignificant.

From the point of view of practical applications the second extreme case, namely that of very small viscous forces in eqn. (4.10) compared with the inertia forces, is of far greater importance. Since the two most important fluids, namely water and air, have very small viscosities, the case under consideration occurs, generally speaking, already at moderately high velocities. This is the *limiting case of very large Reynolds numbers* ($\mathsf{R} \to \infty$). In this case the process of mathematical simplification of the differential eqn. (4.10) requires a considerable amount of care. It is not permissible simply to omit the viscous terms, i. e. the right-hand side of eqn. (4.10). This would reduce the order of the equation from four to two, and the solution of the simplified equation could not be made to satisfy the full boundary conditions of the original equation. The problem which was outlined in the preceding sentences belongs essentially to the realm of *boundary layer theory*. We now propose to discuss briefly the general statements which can be made about the solutions of the Navier-Stokes equations for the special case of small viscous forces as compared with the inertia forces, that is in the limiting case of very large Reynolds numbers.

e. The limiting case of very small viscous forces (very large Reynolds numbers)

The following analogy may serve to illustrate the character of the solutions of the Navier-Stokes equations for the limiting case of very small viscosity, i. e. of very small friction terms, as compared with the inertia terms. The temperature distribution $\theta\ (x, y)$ about a hot body in a fluid stream is described by the following differential equation, Chap. XIV:

$$\varrho\, g\, c \left(\frac{\partial \theta}{\partial t} + u\,\frac{\partial \theta}{\partial x} + v\,\frac{\partial \theta}{\partial y}\right) = k \left(\frac{\partial^2 \theta}{\partial x^2} + \frac{\partial^2 \theta}{\partial y^2}\right) . \tag{4.12}$$

Here g denotes the gravitational acceleration, ϱ, c, and k denote the density, specific heat, and conductivity of the fluid respectively; θ is the difference between the local temperature and that at a very large distance from the body, where the temperature, T, is constant and equal to T_∞, i. e. $\theta = T - T_\infty$. The velocity field $u(x, y)$ and $v\ (x, y)$ in eqn. (4.12) is assumed to be known. The temperature distribution on the boundaries of the body defined by $T_0 \gtrless T_\infty$ is prescribed and in the simplest case it is constant with respect to space and time but, generally speaking, it varies with both. From the physical point of view eqn. (4.12) represents the heat balance for an elementary volume. The left-hand side represents the quantity of heat exchanged by convection, whereas the right-hand side is the quantity of heat exchanged by conduction. The frictional heat generated in the fluid is neglected. If $T_0 > T_\infty$ the problem is that of determining the temperature field around a hot body which is cooled. By inspection it is seen that eqn. (4.12) is of the same form as eqn. (4.6) for the vorticity ω. In fact they become identical if the vorticity is replaced by the temperature difference and the kinematic viscosity ν by the ratio $k/\varrho\, g\, c$ known as the thermal diffusivity. The boundary condition $\theta = 0$ at a large distance from the body corresponds to the condition $\omega = 0$ for the undisturbed parallel stream also at a large distance from the body. Hence we may expect that the solutions of the two equations, i. e. the distribution of vorticity and that of temperature around the body will be similar in character.

Now, the temperature distribution around the body may be perceived intuitively, to a certain extent. In the limiting case of zero velocity (fluid at rest) the influence of the heated body will extend uniformly on all sides. With very small velocities the fluid around the body will still be affected by it in all directions. With increasing velocity of flow, however, it is clearly seen that the region affected by the higher temperature of the body shrinks more and more into a narrow zone in the immediate vicinity of the body and into a tail of heated fluid behind it, Fig. 4.2.

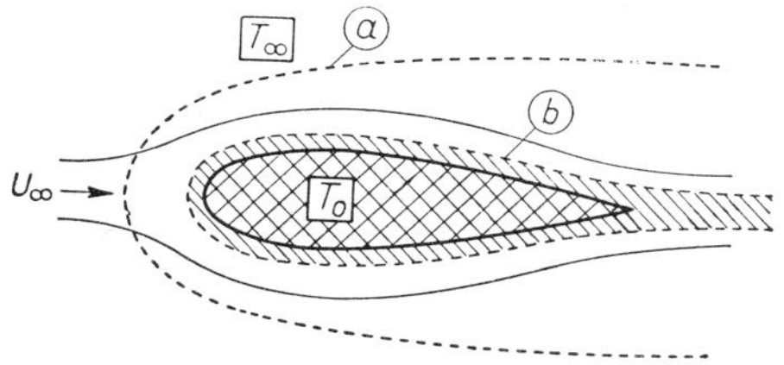

Fig. 4.2. Analogy between temperature and vorticity distribution in the neighbourhood of a body placed in a stream of fluid

a), b) Limits of region of increased temperature
a) for small velocities
b) for large velocities of flow

The solution of eqn. (4.6) must, as mentioned, be of a character similar to that for vorticity. At small velocities (viscous forces large compared with inertia forces) there is vorticity in the whole region of flow around the body. On the other hand for large velocities (viscous forces small compared with inertia forces) we may expect a field of flow in which vorticity is confined to a small layer along the surface of the body and in a wake behind the body, whereas the rest of the field of flow remains, practically speaking, free from vorticity (see Fig. 4.1). It is, therefore, to be expected that in the limiting case of very small viscous forces, i. e. at large Reynolds numbers, the solutions of the Navier-Stokes equations are so constituted as to permit a subdivision of the field of flow into an external region which is free from vorticity and a thin layer near the body together with a wake behind it. In the first region the flow may be expected to satisfy the equations of frictionless flow, the potential flow theory being used for its evaluation, whereas in the second region vorticity is inherent, and, therefore, the Navier-Stokes equations must be used for its evaluation. Viscous forces are important, i. e. of the same order of magnitude as inertia forces, only in the second region known as the *boundary layer*. This concept of a boundary layer was introduced into the science of fluid mechanics by L. Prandtl at the beginning of the present century: it has proved to be very fruitful. The subdivision of the field of flow into the frictionless external flow and the essentially viscous boundary layer flow permitted the reduction of the mathematical difficulties inherent in the Navier-Stokes equations to such an extent that it became possible to integrate them for a large number of cases. The description of these methods of integration forms the subject of the boundary layer theory presented in the succeeding chapters.

From a numerical analysis of the available solutions of the Navier-Stokes equations it is also possible to show directly that in the limiting case of very large

Reynolds numbers there exists a thin boundary layer in which the influence of viscosity is concentrated. We shall revert to this topic in Chap. V.

The previously discussed limiting case in which viscous forces heavily outweigh inertia forces (*creeping motion*, i. e. very small Reynolds number) results in a considerable mathematical simplification of the Navier-Stokes equations. By omitting the inertia terms their order is not reduced, but they become linear. The second limiting case, when inertia forces outweigh viscous forces (*boundary layer*, i. e. very large Reynolds number) presents greater mathematical difficulties than creeping motion. For, if we simply substitute $\nu = 0$ in the Navier-Stokes equations (3.29), or in the stream function equation (4.10), we thereby suppress the derivatives of the highest order and with the simpler equation of lower order it is impossible to satisfy simultaneously all boundary conditions of the complete differential equations. This means, evidently, that the solutions of the simplified differential equations have no physical meaning.

It is now possible to conclude that a solution for the limiting case of very large Reynolds number can have physical meaning, when it is obtained from the Navier-Stokes equations by passing to the limit $\nu \to 0$ in the integral solution, but not in the differential equation itself.

f. Mathematical illustration of the process of going to the limit $R \to \infty$

Since the preceding argument constitutes one of the fundamental principles of boundary layer theory it may be worth while to illustrate the basic ideas involved by quoting a mathematical example which was first given by L. Prandtl†.

Let us consider the damped vibration of a point-mass described by the differential equation

$$m \frac{d^2x}{dt^2} + k \frac{dx}{dt} + c\,x = 0\,. \tag{4.13}$$

Here m denotes the vibrating mass, c the spring constant, k the damping factor, x the length co-ordinate measured from the position of equilibrium and t-time. The following initial conditions may be prescribed:

$$t = 0: \quad x = 0\,; \quad \frac{dx}{dt} = 1\,. \tag{4.14}$$

In analogy with the Navier-Stokes equations with very small viscosity, ν, we consider the case of very small mass, m, because for $m = 0$ the term of highest order vanishes in eqn. (4.13). If we simply substitute $m = 0$ in the differential equation, we are led to the first order differential equation

$$k \frac{dx}{dt} + c\,x = 0\,. \tag{4.15}$$

Putting $x = A\,e^{\lambda t}$ we have to evaluate λ from $k\,\lambda + c = 0$ so that $\lambda = -c/k$, and hence the solution

$$x = A\,e^{-(c/k)\cdot t}. \tag{4.16}$$

The first initial condition $x = 0$ at $t = 0$ cannot be satisfied with the aid of this solution, but the second condition, namely $dx/dt = 1$ for $t = 0$, can be satisfied.

† L. Prandtl: Anschauliche und nützliche Mathematik. Lectures delivered at Goettingen University in the Winter Semester of 1931/32.

If we solve the complete differential equation (4.13) with the same assumption for x, we obtain the quadratic

$$m\,\lambda^2 + k\,\lambda + c = 0$$

and hence,

$$\lambda_{1,2} = \frac{1}{2\,m}\left(-k \pm \sqrt{k^2 - 4\,c\,m}\right).$$

Since we shall suppose that m tends to zero, the roots can be expanded into a series. Retaining the first two terms only we have

$$\lambda_{1,2} = \frac{1}{2\,m}\left[-k \pm k\left(1 - \frac{2\,c\,m}{k^2}\right)\right]$$

and further,

$$\lambda_1 = -\frac{c}{k}\;;\quad \lambda_2 = -\frac{k}{m} + \frac{c}{k} \approx -\frac{k}{m}\,.$$

The second term in λ_2 can be neglected, because m is very small. Thus λ_1 corresponds to the solution of the simplified equation of the first order (4.15), whereas λ_2 is the "lost" solution. The general solution of eqn. (4.13) is obtained as a sum of the two particular solutions:

$$x = A_1\,e^{\lambda_1 t} + A_2\,e^{\lambda_2 t} = A_1\,e^{-(c/k)\,t} + A_2\,e^{-(k/m)\,t}\,.$$

Since for $t = 0$ we must have $x = 0$, we obtain $A_2 = -A_1$ and

$$x = A_1\left(e^{-(c/k)\,t} - e^{-(k/m)\,t}\right). \tag{4.17}$$

In order to determine A_1 we make use of the second initial condition $t = 0$, $\mathrm{d}x/\mathrm{d}t = 1$. The first term of the complete solution is identical with the solution (4.16) of the simplified first-order differential equation, which could not be made to satisfy the first initial condition (4.14). This has now been rendered possible owing to the appearance of the second term.

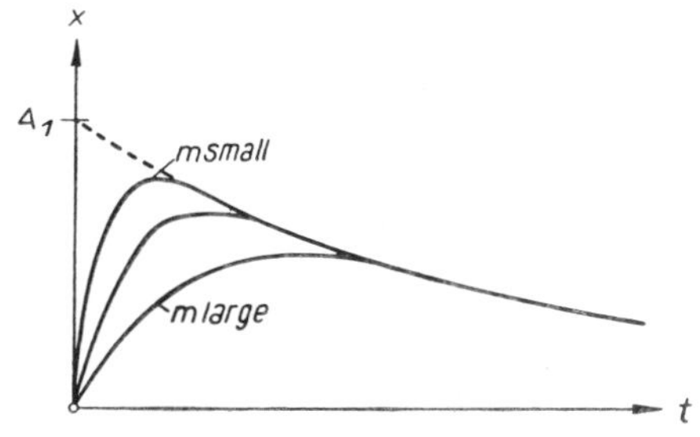

Fig. 4.3. Solutions of the vibration equation (4.13) for small m and large m. For small m the solution is of the 'boundary layer' type

Fig. 4.3 gives a graphical representation of the solution of eqn. (4.17). The first term starts with A_1 at $t = 0$ and decreases slowly with increasing t (broken line). We shall refer to it as to the slowly varying solution. Taken on its own, it can satisfy only one of the two prescribed initial conditions. The second term is important only for small values of t, owing to the smallness of m. It varies rapidly and for large values of t it becomes small very quickly. The second term enables the whole solution (full line) to satisfy also the second initial condition. We shall refer to the second term as the quickly varying solution

If we, now, compare this example with the Navier-Stokes equations, we conclude that the solution of frictionless potential flow corresponds to the slowly varying solution. It can also satisfy only one boundary condition, namely the vanishing of the normal velocity at a wall. The quickly varying solution finds its analogue in an additional, boundary layer solution which is determined by the viscosity, and which differs from zero only in the very narrow boundary layer near the wall. It is to be noted that the second boundary condition (no slip at the wall) can only be satisfied if this boundary layer solution is added, thus making the whole solution physically real.

This simple example exhibits the same mathematical features as those discussed in the preceding chapter. It is, namely, not permissible simply to omit the viscous terms in the Navier-Stokes equations when performing the process of going over to the limit for very small viscosity (very large Reynolds number). This can only be done in the integral solution itself.

We shall demonstrate later in greater detail that it is not necessary to retain the full Navier-Stokes equations for the process of finding the limit for $\mathsf{R} \to \infty$. For the sake of mathematical simplification it will prove possible to omit certain terms in it, particularly certain small viscous terms. It is, however, important to note that not all viscous terms can be neglected, as this would depress the order of the Navier-Stokes equations.

References

[1] J. Ackeret, Über exakte Lösungen der Stokes-Navier Gleichungen inkompressibler Flüssigkeiten bei veränderten Grenzbedingungen. ZAMP **3**, 259—271 (1952).
[2] G. Hamel, Über die Potentialströmung zäher Flüssigkeiten. ZAMM **21**, 129—139 (1941).
[3] V. G. Jenson, Viscous flow round a sphere at low Reynolds numbers (< 40). Proc. Roy. Soc. London, A **249**, 346—366 (1959).

CHAPTER V

Exact solutions of the Navier-Stokes equations

In general the problem of finding exact solutions of the Navier-Stokes equations presents insurmountable mathematical difficulties. This is, primarily, a consequence of their being non-linear, so that the application of the principle of superposition, which serves so well in the case of frictionless potential motions, is excluded. Nevertheless, it is possible to find exact solutions in certain particular cases, mostly when the quadratic convective terms vanish in a natural way. In this chapter we shall devote our attention to the discussion of several exact solutions. Incidentally, it will be shown that in the case of small viscosity many of the exact solutions have a *boundary layer structure* which means that the influence of viscosity is confined to a thin layer near the wall.

a. Parallel flow

Parallel flows constitute a particularly simple class of motions. A flow is called parallel if only one velocity component is different from zero, all fluid particles moving in one direction. For example: if the components v and w are zero everywhere, it follows at once from the equation of continuity that $\partial u/\partial x \equiv 0$, which means that the component u cannot depend on x. Thus for parallel steady flow we have

$$u = u(y,z,t); \quad v \equiv 0; \quad w \equiv 0 \,. \tag{5.1}$$

Further, it follows also immediately from the Navier-Stokes equations (3.29) for the y- and z-directions† that $\partial p/\partial y = 0$, and $\partial p/\partial z = 0$, so that the pressure depends only on x. In addition, in the equation for the x-direction all convective terms vanish. Hence

$$\varrho \frac{\partial u}{\partial t} = -\frac{\mathrm{d}p}{\mathrm{d}x} + \mu\left(\frac{\partial^2 u}{\partial y^2} + \frac{\partial^2 u}{\partial z^2}\right), \tag{5.2}$$

which is a linear differential equation for $u(y, z, t)$.

1. Two-dimensional flow through a straight channel and Couette flow. A very simple solution of eqn. (5.2) is obtained for the case of steady flow in a channel

† In the following argument the term pressure denotes the difference between the total pressure and the hydrostatic pressure (pressure at rest). This causes the body forces to cancel, as they are in equilibrium with the hydrostatic pressure.

with two parallel flat walls, Fig. 5.1. Let the distance between the walls be denoted by $2b$, so that eqn. (5.2) can be written

$$\frac{dp}{dx} = \mu \frac{d^2u}{dy^2} \tag{5.3}$$

with the boundary condition: $u = 0$ for $y = \pm b$. Since $\partial p/\partial y = 0$ the pressure gradient in the direction of flow is constant, as seen from eqn. (5.3). Thus $dp/dx =$ const and the solution is

$$u = -\frac{1}{2\mu}\frac{dp}{dx}(b^2 - y^2)\,. \tag{5.4}$$

The resulting velocity profile, Fig. 5.1, is parabolic.

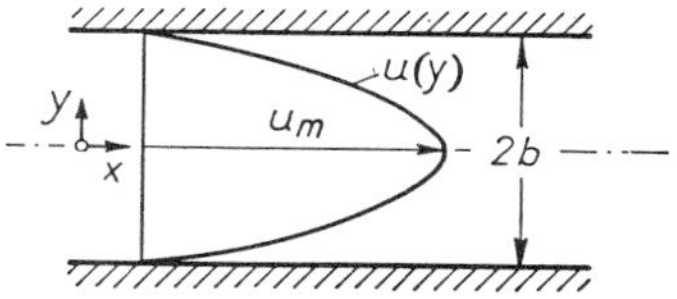

Fig. 5.1. Two-dimensional parallel flow with parabolic velocity distribution

Another simple solution of eqn. (5.3) is obtained for the so-called Couette flow between two parallel flat walls, one of which is at rest, the other moving in its own plane with a velocity U, Fig. 5.2. With the boundary conditions

$$y = 0: \quad u = 0\,; \qquad y = h: \quad u = U$$

we obtain the solution

$$u = \frac{y}{h}U - \frac{h^2}{2\mu}\frac{dp}{dx}\frac{y}{h}\left(1 - \frac{y}{h}\right), \tag{5.5}$$

which is shown in Fig. 5.2. In particular for a vanishing pressure gradient we have

$$u = \frac{y}{h}U\,. \tag{5.5a}$$

This particular case is known as simple Couette flow, or simple shear flow. The general case of Couette flow is a superposition of this simple case over the flow between two flat walls. The shape of the velocity profile is determined by the dimensionless pressure gradient

$$P = \frac{h^2}{2\mu U}\left(-\frac{dp}{dx}\right).$$

For $P > 0$, i. e. for a pressure decreasing in the direction of motion, the velocity is positive over the whole width of the channel. For negative values of P the velocity over a portion of the channel width can become negative, that is *back-flow* may occur near the wall which is at rest, and it is seen from Fig. 5.2 that this happens when $P < -1$. In this case the dragging action of the faster layers exerted on fluid particles in the neighbourhood of the wall is insufficient to overcome the influence of the adverse pressure gradient. This type of Couette flow with a pressure gradient has some importance in the hydrodynamic theory of lubrication. The flow in the narrow clearance between journal and bearing is, by and large, identical with Couette flow with a pressure gradient (*cf.* Sec. VIc).

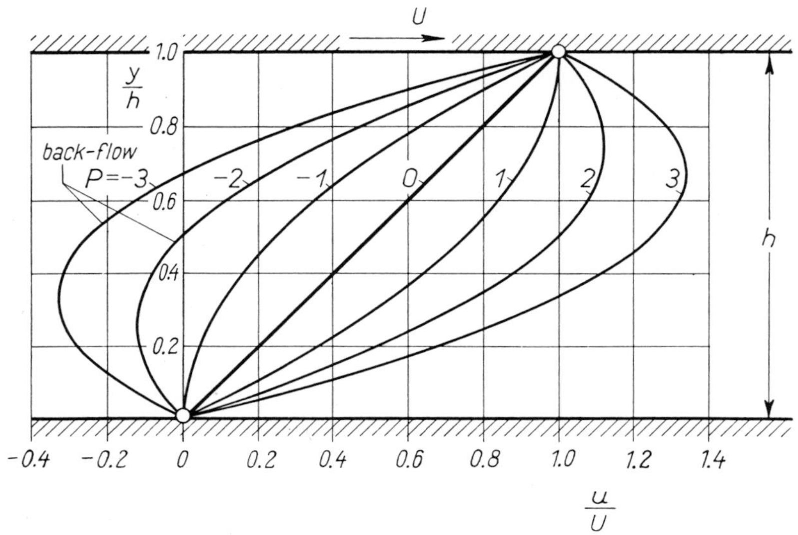

Fig. 5.2. Couette flow between two parallel flat walls
$P > 0$, pressure decrease in direction of wall motion; $P < 0$, pressure increase; $P = 0$, zero pressure gradient

2. The Hagen-Poiseuille theory of flow through a pipe. The flow through a straight tube of circular cross-section is the case with rotational symmetry which corresponds to the preceding case of two-dimensional flow through a channel. Let the x-axis be selected along the axis of the pipe, Fig. 1.2, and let y denote the radial co-ordinate measured from the axis outwards. The velocity components in the tangential and radial directions are zero; the velocity component parallel to the axis, denoted by u, depends on y alone, and the pressure is constant in every cross-section. Of the three Navier-Stokes equations in cylindrical co-ordinates, eqns. (3.33), only the one for the axial direction remains, and it simplifies to

$$\mu \left(\frac{\mathrm{d}^2 u}{\mathrm{d}y^2} + \frac{1}{y} \frac{\mathrm{d}u}{\mathrm{d}y} \right) = \frac{\mathrm{d}p}{\mathrm{d}x} , \tag{5.6}$$

the boundary condition being $u = 0$ for $y = R$. The solution of eqn. (5.6) gives the velocity distribution

$$u\,(y) = - \frac{1}{4\,\mu} \frac{\mathrm{d}p}{\mathrm{d}x} \, (R^2 - y^2) , \tag{5.7}$$

where $-\mathrm{d}p/\mathrm{d}x = (p_1 - p_2)/l =$ const is the pressure gradient, to be regarded as given. Solution (5.7), which was obtained here as an exact solution of the Navier-

Stokes equations, agrees with the solution in eqn. (1.10) which was obtained in an elementary way. The velocity over the cross-section is distributed in the form of a paraboloid of revolution. The maximum velocity on the axis is

$$u_m = \frac{R^2}{4\,\mu}\left(-\frac{\mathrm{d}p}{\mathrm{d}x}\right).$$

The mean velocity $\bar{u} = \frac{1}{2}\,u_m$, that is

$$\bar{u} = \frac{R^2}{8\,\mu}\left(-\frac{\mathrm{d}p}{\mathrm{d}x}\right), \tag{5.8}$$

and the volume rate of flow becomes

$$Q = \pi\,R^2\,\bar{u} = \frac{\pi\,R^4}{8\,\mu}\left(-\frac{\mathrm{d}p}{\mathrm{d}x}\right). \tag{5.9}$$

The laminar flow described by the above solution occurs in practice only as long as the Reynolds number $\mathsf{R} = u\,d/\nu$ (d = pipe diameter) has a value which is less than the so-called critical Reynolds number, in spite of the fact that the above formulae constitute an exact solution of the Navier-Stokes equations for arbitrary values of $\mathrm{d}p/\mathrm{d}x$, R, and μ, or hence, of u, R, and μ. According to experiments

$$\left(\frac{\bar{u}\,d}{\nu}\right)_{crit} = \mathsf{R}_{crit} = 2300$$

approximately. For $\mathsf{R} > \mathsf{R}_{crit}$ the flow pattern is entirely different and becomes *turbulent*. We shall discuss this type of flow in greater detail in Chap. XX.

The relation between the pressure gradient and the mean velocity of flow is normally represented in engineering applications by introducing a *resistance coefficient of pipe flow*, λ. This coefficient is defined by setting the pressure gradient proportional to the dynamic head, i. e. to the square of the mean velocity of flow, according to the equation†

$$-\frac{\mathrm{d}p}{\mathrm{d}x} = \frac{\lambda}{d}\,\frac{\varrho}{2}\,\bar{u}^2. \tag{5.10}$$

Introducing the expression for $\mathrm{d}p/\mathrm{d}x$ from eqn. (5.9) we obtain

$$\lambda = \frac{2\,d}{\varrho\,\bar{u}^2}\,\frac{8\,\mu\,\bar{u}}{R^2} = \frac{32\,\mu}{\varrho\,\bar{u}R}$$

that is

$$\lambda = \frac{64}{\mathsf{R}}, \tag{5.11}$$

with

$$\mathsf{R} = \frac{\varrho\,\bar{u}\,d}{\nu}. \tag{5.12}$$

Here R denotes the Reynolds number calculated for the pipe diameter and mean velocity of flow. The laminar equation for pressure loss in pipes, eqn. (5.11), is

† This quadratic law which assumes $\mathrm{d}p/\mathrm{d}x \sim u^2$ fits turbulent flow very well. It is retained for laminar flow, although in that range $\mathrm{d}p/\mathrm{d}x \sim u$. Thus for laminar flow λ ceases to be a constant.

in excellent agreement with experimental results for the laminar range, as seen from Fig. 5.3 which reproduces experimental points measured by G. Hagen [9]. From this it is possible to infer that the Hagen-Poiseuille parabolic velocity distribution represents a solution of the Navier-Stokes equations which is in agreement with experimental results [24]. It is also possible to indicate an exact solution of the Navier-Stokes equations for the case of a pipe with a circular annular cross-section [22]. The problem of laminar and turbulent flow through pipes with excentric annular cross-sections was discussed theoretically in ref. [34] which also contains experimental results.

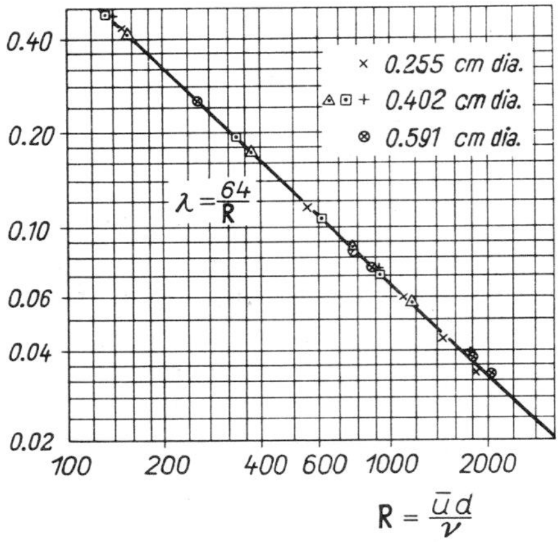

Fig. 5.3. Laminar flow through pipe; resistance coefficient, λ, plotted against Reynolds number (measured by Hagen), from Prandtl-Tietjens

3. The flow between two concentric rotating cylinders. A further example which leads to a simple exact solution of the Navier-Stokes equations is afforded by the flow between two concentric rotating cylinders, both of which move at different but steady rotational speeds. We shall denote the inner and outer radii by r_1, and r_2 respectively, and similarly, the two angular velocities by ω_1, and ω_2. The Navier-Stokes equations (3.33) for plane polar co-ordinates reduce to

$$\varrho \frac{u^2}{r} = \frac{dp}{dr} ; \tag{5.13}$$

and

$$\frac{d^2u}{dr^2} + \frac{d}{dr}\left(\frac{u}{r}\right) = 0 \tag{5.14}$$

with u denoting the circumferential velocity. The boundary conditions are $u = r_1 \omega_1$ for $r = r_1$ and $u = r_2 \omega_2$ for $r = r_2$. The solution of (5.14) which satisfies these requirements is

$$u(r) = \frac{1}{r_2^2 - r_1^2}\left[r(\omega_2 r_2^2 - \omega_1 r_1^2) - \frac{r_1^2 r_2^2}{r}(\omega_2 - \omega_1)\right] . \tag{5.15}$$

Equation (5.13) determines the radial pressure distribution resulting from the motion.

The case when the inner cylinder is at rest, while the outer cylinder rotates, has some practical significance. In this instance the torque transmitted by the outer cylinder to the fluid becomes

$$M_2 = 4\,\pi\,\mu\,h\,\frac{r_1{}^2\,r_2{}^2}{r_2{}^2 - r_1{}^2}\,\omega_2\,, \tag{5.16}$$

where h is the height of the cylinder. The moment M_1 with which the fluid acts on the inner cylinder has the same magnitude. The arrangement under consideration has been used occasionally for the determination of viscosity. The angular velocity of the external cylinder and the moment acting on the inner cylinder are measured, so that the viscosity can be evaluated with the aid of eqn. (5.16).

In the particular case of a single cylinder rotating in an infinite fluid ($r_2 \to \infty$, $\omega_2 = 0$) eqn. (5.15) gives $u = r_1{}^2\,\omega_1/r$, and the torque transmitted by the fluid to the cylinder becomes $M_1 = 4\,\pi\,\mu\,h\,r_1{}^2\,\omega_1$. The velocity distribution in the fluid is the same as that around a line vortex of strength $\Gamma_1 = 2\,\pi\,r_1{}^2\,\omega_1$ in frictionless flow, or

$$u = \frac{\Gamma}{2\,\pi\,r}\,.$$

It is seen, therefore, that the case of frictionless flow in the neighbourhood of a vortex line constitutes a solution of the Navier-Stokes equations (*cf.* Sec. IVb). In this connexion it may be instructive to mention an example of an exact *non-steady* solution of the Navier-Stokes equations, namely that which describes the process of decay of a vortex through the action of viscosity. The distribution of the tangential velocity component u with respect to the radial distance r and time t is given by

$$u(r,t) = \frac{\Gamma_0}{2\,\pi\,r}\,\{1 - \exp\,(- r^2/4\,\nu\,t)\}\,,$$

as derived by C. W. Oseen [23] and G. Hamel [10]. This velocity distribution is represented graphically in Fig. 5.4. Here Γ_0 denotes the circulation of the vortex filament at time $t = 0$, i. e. at the moment when viscosity is assumed to begin its action. An experimental investigation of this process was undertaken by A. Timme [36].

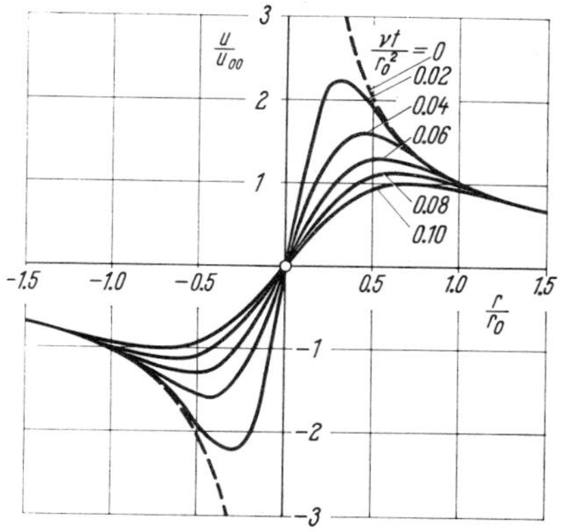

Fig. 5.4. Velocity distribution at varying times in the neighbourhood of a vortex filament caused by the action of viscosity
Γ_0 = circulation of the vortex filament at time $t = 0$ when viscosity begins to act; $u_{00} = \Gamma_0/2\,\pi\,r_0$

4. The suddenly accelerated plane wall; Stokes' first problem. We now proceed to calculate some *non-steady* parallel flows. Since the convective acceleration terms vanish identically, the friction forces interact with the local acceleration. The simplest flows of this class occur when motion is started impulsively from rest. We shall begin with the case of the flow near a flat plate which is suddenly accelerated from rest and moves in its own plane with a constant velocity U_0. This is one of the problems which were solved by G. Stokes in his celebrated memoir on pendulums [32a]†. Selecting the x-axis along the wall in the direction of U_0, we obtain the simplified Navier-Stokes equation

$$\frac{\partial u}{\partial t} = \nu \frac{\partial^2 u}{\partial y^2} . \tag{5.17}$$

The pressure in the whole space is constant, and the boundary conditions are:

$$\left.\begin{array}{lll} t \leq 0: & u = 0 & \text{for all } y; \\ t > 0: & u = U_0 & \text{for } y = 0; \quad u = 0 \quad \text{for } y = \infty . \end{array}\right\} \tag{5.18}$$

The differential equation (5.17) is identical with the equation of heat conduction which describes the propagation of heat in the space $y > 0$, when at time $t = 0$ the wall $y = 0$ is suddenly heated to a temperature which exceeds that in the surroundings. The partial differential equation (5.17) can be reduced to an ordinary differential equation by the substitution

$$\eta = \frac{y}{2\sqrt{\nu t}} . \tag{5.19}$$

If we, further, assume

$$u = U_0 f(\eta) , \tag{5.20}$$

we obtain the following ordinary differential equation for $f(\eta)$:

$$f'' + 2\eta f' = 0 \tag{5.21}$$

with the boundary conditions $f = 1$ at $\eta = 0$ and $f = 0$ at $\eta = \infty$. The solution is

$$u = U_0 \operatorname{erfc} \eta , \tag{5.22}$$

where

$$\operatorname{erfc} \eta = \frac{2}{\sqrt{\pi}} \int_\eta^\infty \exp(-\eta^2)\, d\eta = 1 - \operatorname{erf} \eta = 1 - \frac{2}{\sqrt{\pi}} \int_0^\eta \exp(-\eta^2)\, d\eta ;$$

the *complementary error function*, erfc η, has been tabulated ‡. The velocity distribution is represented in Fig. 5.5, and it may be noted that the velocity profiles for varying times are 'similar', i. e. they can be reduced to the same curve by changing the

† Some authors refer to this problem as the 'Rayleigh problem'; there is no justification for it, as it can be found fully discussed and solved in ref. [32a].

‡ See e. g. Sheppard, "The Probability Integral", British Assoc. Adv. Sci.: Math. Tables vol. vii (1939) and Works Project Administration "Tables of the Probability Function", New York, 1941.

scale along the axis of ordinates. The complementary error function which appears in eqn. (5.22) has a value of about 0·01 at $\eta = 2{\cdot}0$. Taking into account the definition of the thickness of the boundary layer, δ, we obtain

$$\delta = 2\,\eta_\delta \sqrt{\nu t} \approx 4 \sqrt{\nu t}\,. \tag{5.23}$$

It is seen to be proportional to the square root of the product of kinematic viscosity and time.

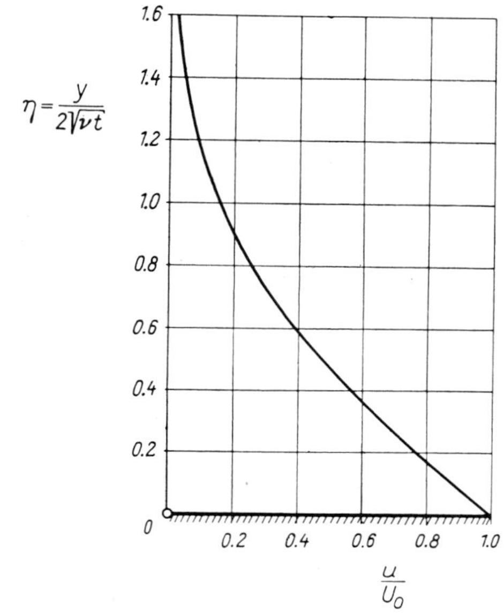

Fig. 5.5. Velocity distribution above a suddenly accelerated wall

5. Flow formation in Couette motion. The substitution (5.19) which leads to eqn. (5.21) does not, in general, lead to a solution of the so-called heat conduction equation (5.17) if more complicated boundary conditions are imposed. Since eqn. (5.17) is linear, solutions for it can be obtained by the use of the Laplace transformation and by more direct methods developed in connexion with the study of the conduction of heat in solids [5a]. Many results obtained, e. g. for the temperature variation in an infinite or semi-infinite solid, can be directly transposed and used for the solution of problems in viscous flow. Thus the preceding problem in which the formation of the boundary layer near a suddenly accelerated wall has been investigated can also be solved for the case when the wall moves in a direction parallel to another flat wall at rest and at a distance h from it. This is the problem of flow formation in Couette motion, i. e. the problem of how the velocity profile varies with time tending asymptotically to the linear distribution shown in Fig. 1.1. The differential equation is the same as before, eqn. (5.17), but with modified boundary conditions which now are:

$$t \leq 0;\; u = 0 \;\text{ for all } y, \text{ if } 0 \leq y \leq h;$$

$$t > 0:\; u = U_0 \text{ for } y = 0;\; u = 0 \text{ for } y = h\,.$$

The solution of eqn. (5.17) which satisfies the boundary and initial conditions can be obtained in the form of a series of complementary error functions

$$\frac{u}{U_0} = \sum_{n=0}^{\infty} \operatorname{erfc}\,[2n\,\eta_1 + \eta] - \sum_{n=0}^{\infty} \operatorname{erfc}\,[2(n+1)\,\eta_1 - \eta] \tag{5.24}$$
$$= \operatorname{erfc}\,\eta - \operatorname{erfc}\,(2\,\eta_1 - \eta) + \operatorname{erfc}\,(2\,\eta_1 + \eta) - \operatorname{erfc}\,(4\eta_1 - \eta) + \operatorname{erfc}\,(4\,\eta_1 + \eta) - \ldots + \ldots$$

where $\eta_1 = h/2\sqrt{\nu t}$ denotes the dimensionless distance between the two walls. The solution is represented in Fig. 5.6. The early profiles are still approximately similar and remain so, as long as the boundary layer has not spread to the stationary wall. The succeeding velocity profiles are no longer "similar" and tend asymptotically to the linear distribution of the steady state.

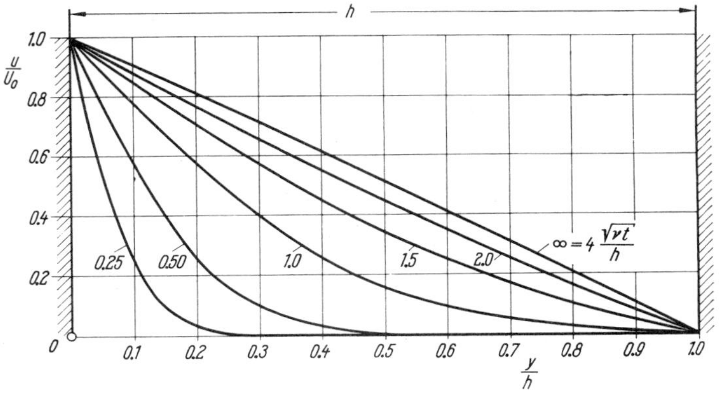

Fig. 5.6. Flow formation in Couette motion

6. Flow in a pipe, starting from rest. The acceleration of a fluid in a pipe is closely related to the preceding examples. Suppose that the fluid in an infinitely long pipe of circular cross-section is at rest for $t < 0$. At the instant $t = 0$ a pressure gradient dp/dx, which is constant in time, begins to act along it. The fluid will begin to move under the influence of viscous and inertia forces, and the velocity profile will approach asymptotically the parabolic distribution in Hagen-Poiseuille flow. The solution of this problem which leads to a differential equation involving Bessel functions was given by F. Szymanski [33]. The velocity profile is drawn in Fig. 5.7 for various instants. It is noteworthy that in the early stages the velocity near the axis is approximately constant over the radius and that viscosity makes itself felt in a narrow layer near the wall. The influence of viscosity reaches the pipe centre only in the later stages of motion, and the velocity profile tends asymptotically to the parabolic distribution for steady flow. The corresponding solution for an annular circular cross-section was given by W. Mueller [22].

The analogous case when the pressure gradient is removed instantly was solved by W. Gerbers [8a].

The acceleration of a fluid over the whole length of pipe discussed here must be carefully distinguished from the acceleration of a fluid in the inlet portions of a pipe in steady flow. The rectangular velocity profile which exists in the entrance section is gradually transformed as

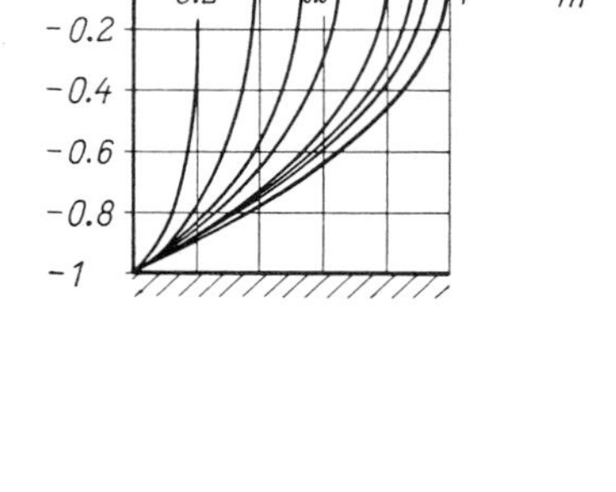

Fig. 5.7. Velocity profile in a circular pipe during acceleration, as given by F. Szymanski [33]; $\tau = \nu t/R^2$

the fluid progresses through the pipe with x increasing, and tends, under the influence of viscosity, to assume the Hagen-Poiseuille parabolic distribution. Since here $\partial u/\partial x \neq 0$ the flow is not one-dimensional, and the velocity depends on x, as well as on the radius. This problem was discussed by H. Schlichting [30], who gave the solution for two-dimensional flow through a straight channel, and by L. Schiller [29], B. Punnis [26] and Langhaar [18a] for axially symmetrical flow (circular pipe); see also Chaps. IX and XII.

7. The flow near an oscillating flat plate; Stokes' second problem. In this Section we propose to discuss the flow about an infinite flat wall which executes linear harmonic oscillations parallel to itself and which was first treated by G. Stokes [32a] and later by Lord Rayleigh [26a]. Let x denote the co-ordinate parallel to the direction of motion and y the co-ordinate perpendicular to the wall. Owing to the condition of no slip at the wall, the fluid velocity at it must be equal to that of the wall. Supposing that this motion is given by

$$y = 0: \qquad u(0,t) = U_0 \cos nt \; . \tag{5.25}$$

we find that the fluid velocity $u(y, t)$ is the solution of eqn. (5.17), together with the boundary condition (5.25), which, as already mentioned, is known from the theory of heat conduction. For the case under consideration

$$u(y,t) = U_0 \, e^{-ky} \cos(nt - ky) \; . \tag{5.26}$$

It is easy to verify that eqn. (5.26) is the required solution if

$$k = \sqrt{\frac{n}{2\,\nu}} \; .$$

Putting $\eta = ky = y\sqrt{n/2\,\nu}$ we have

$$u(y,t) = U_0 \, e^{-\eta} \cos(nt - \eta) \; . \tag{5.26a}$$

The velocity profile $u(y, t)$ thus has the form of a damped harmonic oscillation, the amplitude of which is $U_0\, e^{-y\sqrt{n/2\nu}}$, in which a fluid layer at a distance y has a phase lag $y\sqrt{n/2\,\nu}$ with respect to the motion of the wall. Fig. 5.8 represents this motion for several instants of time. Two fluid layers, a distance $2\,\pi/k = 2\,\pi\sqrt{2\,\nu/n}$ apart, oscillate in phase. This distance can be regarded as a kind of wave length of the motion: it is sometimes called the *depth of penetration* of the viscous wave. The layer which is carried by the wall has a thickness of the order $\delta \sim \sqrt{\nu/n}$ and decreases for decreasing kinematic viscosity and increasing frequency†.

The preceding solution does not take into account any initial conditions in the fluid and represents, therefore, the so-called *steady-state solution.* Under normal conditions the plate would begin to oscillate when the fluid is at rest and we would have the additional initial conditions:

$$t < 0: u = 0 \text{ for all } y \, .$$

† The solution in eqn. (5.26a) represents also the temperature distribution in the earth which is caused by the periodic fluctuation of the temperature on the surface, say, from day to day or over the seasons in a year.

The solution which satisfies the previous boundary conditions as well as the present initial conditions is known from the study of heat conduction [22]. Assuming that at $y = 0$ $u = U_0 \sin nt$ so that at $t = 0$ we have $u = 0$ at $y = 0$ we obtain

$$u(y, t) = U_0 \, e^{-\eta} \sin(nt - \eta) - \frac{2 \nu U_0}{\pi} \int_0^\infty \frac{n}{n^2 + \nu^2 \xi^4} \, e^{-\nu \xi^2 t} \, \xi \cos \xi y \, d\xi \qquad (5.26\text{b})$$

where ξ is the variable of integration. The solution is seen to consist of a steady-state term, similar to eqn. (5.26a), and a transient which dies out as $t \to \infty$.

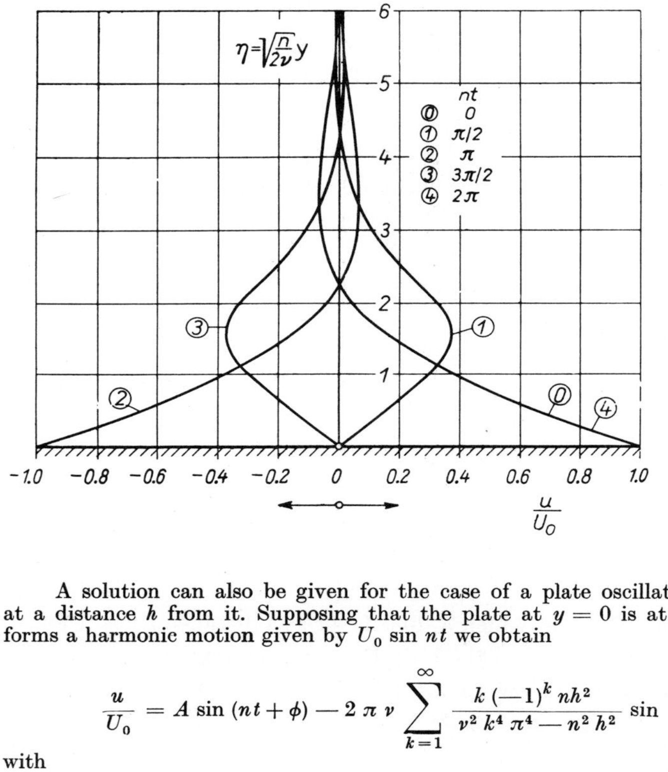

Fig. 5.8. Velocity distribution in the neighbourhood of an oscillating wall

A solution can also be given for the case of a plate oscillating parallel to another plate at a distance h from it. Supposing that the plate at $y = 0$ is at rest and that at $y = h$ performs a harmonic motion given by $U_0 \sin nt$ we obtain

$$\frac{u}{U_0} = A \sin(nt + \phi) - 2 \pi \nu \sum_{k=1}^{\infty} \frac{k(-1)^k nh^2}{\nu^2 k^4 \pi^4 - n^2 h^2} \sin \frac{k \pi y}{h} \, e^{-\nu^2 k^2 \pi^2 t/h^2} \qquad (5.26\text{c})$$

with

$$A = \left[\frac{\cosh 2 (n/2\nu)^{1/2} y - \cos 2 (n/2\nu)^{1/2} y}{\cosh 2 (n/2\nu)^{1/2} h - \cos 2 (n/2\nu)^{1/2} h} \right]^{1/2} \qquad (5.26\text{d})$$

and

$$\phi = \arg \left[\frac{\sinh (n/2\nu)^{1/2} (1 + i)}{\sinh (n/2\nu)^{1/2} (1 - i)} \right]. \qquad (5.26\text{e})$$

The solution consists again of a steady-state term and a transient which dies out with increasing time.

Bodies of various shapes, performing torsional oscillations under the influence of an elastic restoring couple exerted by a suspension wire, have been often used to measure the viscosity of fluids. The viscosity of the fluid is deduced from the period, $T = 2\pi/n$, and from the logarithmic decrement, λ, of the resulting damped oscillation. In this connexion the following schemes have been used: a disk oscillating in a large container, a disk oscillating between two fixed plates, a pile of disks oscillating in a container, a hollow sphere filled with the fluid oscillating in a medium of very low viscosity and a cylindrical container filled with the fluid and oscillating in a medium of very low viscosity. In problems of this kind, as distinct from the oscillating plate considered earlier, the motion of the solid boundary is not prescibed, but is determined by the forces acting on the body. Consequently the solution involves the partial differential equation describing the motion of the fluid, such as e. g. (5.17). When the oscillating body is axially symmetrical, the equation has the form

$$\frac{\partial \Omega}{\partial t} = \nu \left(\frac{\partial^2 \Omega}{\partial r^2} + \frac{3}{r} \frac{\partial \Omega}{\partial r} + \frac{\partial^2 \Omega}{\partial z^2} \right)$$

where $\Omega(r, \phi, z, t)$ denotes the angular velocity at a point in the fluid. The motion of the oscillating body satisfies further the ordinary differential equation

$$I\ddot{\alpha} + I\, n_0^2\, \alpha = M_f$$

where α is the angular amplitude, I is the moment of inertia of the body, n_0 is the natural circular frequency of the body and suspension in a vacuum, and M_f is the moment due to viscous forces. The latter, in turn, depends on the velocity gradient of the solution to the equation of motion of the fluid.

A comprehensive analysis of problems of this kind is contained in two papers by J. Kestin and L. N. Persen [17, 18], who have shown that the motion consists of a damped harmonic oscillation about a shifting zero position, the motion of the latter being given by a decaying function. For sufficiently large but not very large values of time t, only the damped harmonic oscillation need be taken into account. In all cases the principal solution is given in the form

$$\alpha = A_1\, e^{\sigma_1 t} + A_2\, e^{\sigma_2 t}, \tag{5.26f}$$

where A_1 und A_2 are constants and σ_1, σ_2 are two complex conjugate roots (with negative real parts) of a transcendental equation of the type

$$\sigma^2 + 1 + \sigma^{3/2}\, D(\varrho, m_k) = 0. \tag{5.26g}$$

The function $D(\varrho, m_k)$ depends on the geometrical arrangement and contains one or several *similarity parameters* m_k. These, in turn depend on the viscosity, μ, and on the density, ϱ, of the fluid.

The solution is seen sketched in Fig. 5.9. Fig. 5.9a represents the exponentially decaying part of the solution. As already mentioned previously, the motion can be interpreted physically as a shift in the zero-position; for example, when an infinite disk oscillates in an infinite expanse of fluid, the zero-shift is described by the equation

$$F(t) = -\frac{m}{\pi} \int_0^\infty \frac{\xi^{1/2} \exp(-\xi\, n_0\, t) d\xi}{(\xi^2 + 1)^2 + m^2\, \xi^3} \tag{5.26h}$$

where ξ is the integration variable, and

$$m = \frac{\pi\, R^4\, \varrho \sqrt{\nu / n_0}}{I}$$

is the characteristic parameter for a disk of radius R wetted on both sides. The principal solution given in eqn. (5.26f) represents a damped harmonic oscillation and is shown plotted in Fig. 5.9b, whereas the resulting motion is shown in Fig. 5.9c. The motion can be arbitrarily divided into three intervals. In the first interval the part represented by eqn. (5.26h) predominates and the motion is not isochronous. In the second interval the transient has decayed so much that the motion becomes practically isochronous and quasi-harmonic. The third interval is reached only after a very long period of time and is of little practical importance. The body oscillates with a very small amplitude, all to one side of the position of rest, namely that opposite to the initial amplitude. The ordinates of interval 3 have been increased by a factor of 10 in Fig. 5.9 in order to make it clearer.

It is interesting to note that the period of oscillation $T = 2\,\pi/n$ always exceeds the natural period $T_0 = 2\,\pi/n_0$ owing to an apparent increase in the moment of inertia I. This 'induced moment of inertia' effect is due to the state of motion created in the fluid, i. e. to the transfer of kinetic energy from the oscillating body to the fluid, and the increase in the period ($T > T_0$) is much larger than that caused by damping alone.

Problems of this kind have occupied the attention of many research workers, among them J. C. Maxwell [19a], O. E. Meyer [20], P. Mariens and A. van Paemel [19], R. P. Kanwal [14], G. F. Carrier [5] and G. F. Newell and his co-workers [22a].

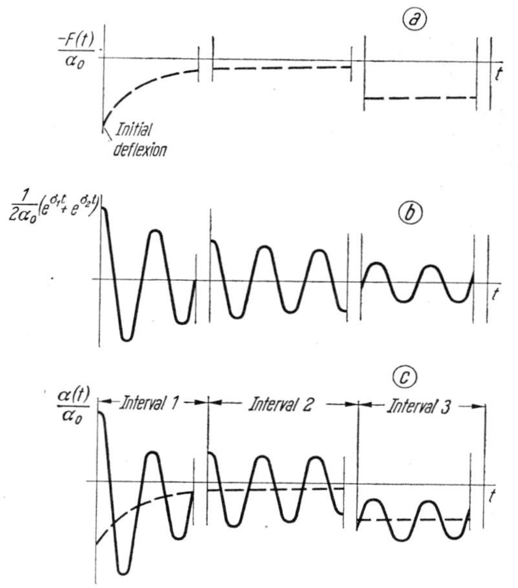

Fig. 5.9. Motion of an oscillating system after J. Kestin and L. N. Persen [17]. a) Zero-shift; b) Damped harmonic oscillation; c) Resultant motion (Note: ordinates in interval 3 increased by a factor of 10)

b. Other exact solutions

The preceding examples on one-dimensional flows were very simple, because the convective acceleration which renders the equations non-linear vanished identically everywhere. We shall now proceed to examine some exact solutions in which these terms are retained, so that non-linear equations will have to be considered. We shall, however, restrict ourselves to steady flows.

8. Stagnation in plane flow (Hiemenz flow). The first simple example of this type of flow, represented in Fig. 5.10, is that leading to a stagnation point in plane, i. e. two-dimensional flow. The velocity distribution in frictionless potential flow in the neighbourhood of the stagnation point at $x = y = 0$ is given by

$$U = a\,x\,; \qquad V = -\,a\,y\,,$$

where a denotes a constant. This is an example of a plane potential flow which arrives from the y-axis and impinges on a flat wall placed at $y = 0$, divides into two streams on the wall and leaves in both directions. The viscous flow must adhere to the wall, whereas the potential flow slides along it. In potential flow the pressure is given by Bernoulli's equation. If p_0 denotes the stagnation pressure, and p is the pressure at an arbitrary point, we have in potential flow

$$p_0 - p = \tfrac{1}{2}\,\varrho(U^2 + V^2) = \tfrac{1}{2}\,\varrho\, a^2\,(x^2 + y^2)\,.$$

For viscous flow, we now make the assumptions

$$u = x\, f'(y)\,; \qquad v = -f(y) \tag{5.27}$$

and

$$p_0 - p = \tfrac{1}{2}\,\varrho a^2\,[x^2 + F(y)]\,. \tag{5.28}$$

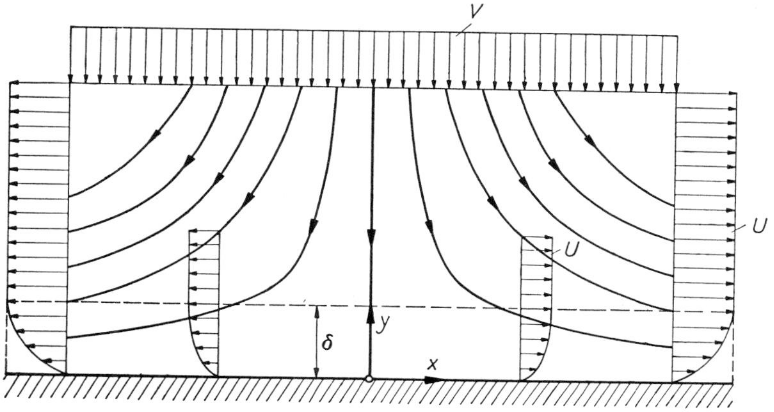

Fig. 5.10
Stagnation in plane flow

In this way the equation of continuity (4.4c) is satisfied identically, and the two Navier-Stokes equations of plane flow (4.4a, b) are sufficient to determine the functions $f(y)$ and $F(y)$. Substituting eqns. (5.27) and (5.28) into eqn. (4.4a, b) we obtain two ordinary differential equations for f and F:

$$f'^2 - f\,f'' = a^2 + \nu\, f''' \tag{5.29}$$

and

$$f\,f' = \tfrac{1}{2}\,a^2\,F' - \nu\, f''\,. \tag{5.30}$$

The boundary conditions for f and F are obtained from $u = v = 0$ at the wall, where $y = 0$, and $p = p_0$ at the stagnation point, as well as from $u = U = a\,x$ at a large distance from the wall. Thus

$$y = 0:\quad f = 0;\quad f' = 0;\quad F = 0;\qquad y = \infty:\quad f' = a\,.$$

Eqns. (5.29) and (5.30) are the two differential equations for the functions $f(y)$ and $F(y)$ which determine the velocity and pressure distribution. Since $F(y)$ does not appear in the first equation, it is possible to begin by determining $f(y)$ and then to proceed to find $F(y)$ from the second equation. The non-linear differential equation (5.29) cannot be solved in closed terms. In order to solve it numerically it is convenient to remove the constants a^2 and ν by putting

$$\eta = \alpha\, y; \qquad f(y) = A\, \phi(\eta).$$

Thus

$$\alpha^2 A^2 (\phi'^2 - \phi\, \phi'') = a^2 + \nu\, A\, \alpha^3\, \phi'''.$$

where the prime now denotes differentiation with respect to η. The coefficients of the equation become all identically equal to unity if we put

$$\alpha^2 A^2 = a^2; \qquad \nu\, A\, \alpha^3 = a^2 .$$

or

$$A = \sqrt{\nu a}\,; \qquad \alpha = \sqrt{\frac{a}{\nu}}.$$

so that

$$\eta = \sqrt{\frac{a}{\nu}}\, y; \qquad f(y) = \sqrt{a\nu}\, \phi(\eta)\,. \tag{5.31}$$

The differential equation for $\phi(\eta)$ now has the simple form

$$\phi''' + \phi\, \phi'' - \phi'^2 + 1 = 0 \tag{5.32}$$

with the boundary conditions

$$\eta = 0: \quad \phi = 0\,, \quad \phi' = 0; \qquad \eta = \infty: \quad \phi' = 1\,.$$

The velocity component parallel to the wall becomes

$$\frac{u}{U} = \frac{1}{a}\, f'(y) = \phi'(\eta)\,.$$

The solution of the differential equation (5.32) was first given in a thesis by K. Hiemenz [11] and later improved by L. Howarth [13]. It is shown in Fig. 5.11 (see also Table 5.1). The curve $\phi'(\eta)$ begins to increase linearly at $\eta = 0$ and tends asymptotically to unity. At approximately $\eta = 2{\cdot}4$ we have $\phi' = 0{\cdot}99$, i. e. the final value is reached there with an accuracy of 1 per cent. If we consider the corresponding distance from the wall, denoted by $y = \delta$, as the boundary layer, we have

$$\delta = \eta_\delta \sqrt{\frac{\nu}{a}} = 2{\cdot}4 \sqrt{\frac{\nu}{a}}\,. \tag{5.33}$$

Hence again, as before, the layer which is influenced by viscosity is small at low kinematic viscosities and proportional to $\sqrt{\nu}$. The pressure gradient $\partial p/\partial y$ becomes proportional to $\varrho\, a \sqrt{\nu\, a}$ and is also very small for small kinematic viscosities.

It is, further, worth noting that the dimensionless velocity distribution u/U and the boundary layer thickness from eqn. (5.33) are independent of x, i. e. they do not vary along the wall.

The type of flow under consideration does not occur near a plane wall only, but also in two-dimensional flow past any cylindrical body, provided that it has a blunt nose near the stagnation point. In such cases the solution is valid for a small neighbourhood of the stagnation point, if the portion of the curved surface can be replaced by its tangent plane near the stagnation point.

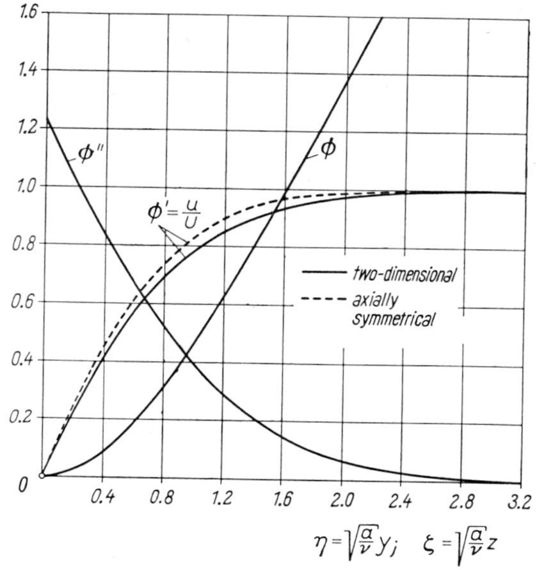

Fig. 5.11. Velocity distribution of plane and rotationally symmetrical flow at a stagnation point

9. Stagnation in three-dimensional flow. In a similar way it is possible to obtain an exact solution of the Navier-Stokes equations for the three-dimensional case of flow with stagnation, i. e. for the axisymmetrical case. A fluid stream impinges on a wall at right angles to it and flows away radially in all directions. Such a case occurs in the neighbourhood of a stagnation point of a body of revolution in a flow parallel to its axis.

To solve the problem we shall use cylindrical co-ordinates r, ϕ, z, and we shall assume that the wall is at $z = 0$, the stagnation point is at the origin and that the flow is in the direction of the negative z-axis. We shall denote the radial and axial components in frictionless flow by U and W respectively, whereas those in viscous flow will be denoted by $u = u(r,z)$, and $w = w(r,z)$. In accordance with eqn. (3.33) the Navier-Stokes equation for rotational symmetry can be written as

$$\left.\begin{aligned} u\frac{\partial u}{\partial r} + w\frac{\partial u}{\partial z} &= -\frac{1}{\varrho}\frac{\partial p}{\partial r} + \nu\left(\frac{\partial^2 u}{\partial r^2} + \frac{1}{r}\frac{\partial u}{\partial r} - \frac{u}{r^2} + \frac{\partial^2 u}{\partial z^2}\right)\\ u\frac{\partial w}{\partial r} + w\frac{\partial w}{\partial z} &= -\frac{1}{\varrho}\frac{\partial p}{\partial z} + \nu\left(\frac{\partial^2 w}{\partial r^2} + \frac{1}{r}\frac{\partial w}{\partial r} + \frac{\partial^2 w}{\partial z^2}\right)\\ \frac{\partial u}{\partial r} + \frac{u}{r} &+ \frac{\partial w}{\partial z} = 0 \end{aligned}\right\} \quad (5.34)$$

because $v_\phi \equiv 0$ and $\partial/\partial \phi = 0$, and we have put $v_r = u$ and $v_z = w$. The boundary conditions are

$$z = 0: \quad u = 0, \quad w = 0; \qquad z = \infty: \quad u = U. \tag{5.34a}$$

Table 5.1. Functions occurring in the solution of plane and axially symmetrical flow with stagnation point. Plane case from L. Howarth [13] and H. Goertler [8]; axially symmetrical case from N. Froessling [7]

plane				axially symmetrical			
$\eta = \sqrt{\frac{a}{\nu}}\, y$	ϕ	$\frac{d\phi}{d\eta} = \frac{u}{U}$	$\frac{d^2\phi}{d\eta^2}$	$\sqrt{2}\cdot\zeta = \sqrt{\frac{2a}{\nu}}\, z$	ϕ	$\frac{d\phi}{d\zeta} = \frac{u}{U}$	$\frac{d^2\phi}{d\zeta^2}$
0	0	0	1·2326	0	0	0	1·3120
0·2	0·0233	0·2266	1·0345	0·2	0·0127	0·1755	1·1705
0·4	0·0881	0·4145	0·8463	0·4	0·0487	0·3311	1·0298
0·6	0·1867	0·5663	0·6752	0·6	0·1054	0·4669	0·8910
0·8	0·3124	0·6859	0·5251	0·8	0·1799	0·5833	0·7563
1·0	0·4592	0·7779	0·3980	1·0	0·2695	0·6811	0·6283
1·2	0·6220	0·8467	0·2938	1·2	0·3717	0·7614	0·5097
1·4	0·7967	0·8968	0·2110	1·4	0·4841	0·8258	0·4031
1·6	0·9798	0·9323	0·1474	1·6	0·6046	0·8761	0·3100
1·8	1·1689	0·9568	0·1000	1·8	0·7313	0·9142	0·2315
2·0	1·3620	0·9732	0·0658	2·0	0·8627	0·9422	0·1676
2·2	1·5578	0·9839	0·0420	2·2	0·9974	0·9622	0·1175
2·4	1·7553	0·9905	0·0260	2·4	1·1346	0·9760	0·0798
2·6	1·9538	0·9946	0·0156	2·6	1·2733	0·9853	0·0523
2·8	2·1530	0·9970	0·0090	2·8	1·4131	0·9912	0·0331
3·0	2·3526	0·9984	0·0051	3·0	1·5536	0·9949	0·0202
3·2	2·5523	0·9992	0·0028	3·2	1·6944	0·9972	0·0120
3·4	2·7522	0·9996	0·0014	3·4	1·8356	0·9985	0·0068
3·6	2·9521	0·9998	0·0007	3·6	1·9769	0·9992	0·0037
3·8	3·1521	0·9999	0·0004	3·8	2·1182	0·9996	0·0020
4·0	3·3521	1·0000	0·0002	4·0	2·2596	0·9998	0·0010
4·2	3·5521	1·0000	0·0001	4·2	2·4010	0·9999	0·0006
4·4	3·7521	1·0000	0·0000	4·4	2·5423	0·9999	0·0003
4·6	3·9521	1·0000	0·0000	4·6	2·6837	1·0000	0·0001

For the frictionless case we can write

$$U = a\, r\,; \qquad W = -\, 2\, a\, z\,. \tag{5.35}$$

where a is a constant. It is seen at once that such a solution satisfies the equation of continuity. Denoting once more the stagnation pressure by p_0 we find the pressure in ideal flow:

$$p_0 - p = \tfrac{1}{2}\,\varrho\,(U^2 + W^2) = \tfrac{1}{2}\,\varrho\, a^2\,(r^2 + 4\, z^2)\,.$$

In the case of viscous flow we assume the following form of the solutions for the velocity and pressure distributions

$$u = r\, f'(z); \qquad w = -\,2\, f(z) \tag{5.36}$$

$$p_0 - p = \tfrac{1}{2}\,\varrho\, a^2\,[r^2 + F(z)]. \tag{5.37}$$

It can be easily verified that a solution of the form (5.36) satisfies the equation of continuity identically, whereas the equations of motion lead to the following two equations for $f(z)$ and $F(z)$:

$$f'^2 - 2\,f\,f'' = a^2 + \nu\, f''' \tag{5.38}$$

$$2\,f\,f' = a^2\,F' - \nu\, f''. \tag{5.39}$$

The boundary conditions for $f(z)$ and $F(z)$ follow from eqn. (5.34a), and are

$$z = 0: \quad f = f' = 0, \quad F = 0; \qquad z = \infty: \quad f' = a.$$

As before, the first of the two equations for f and F can be freed of the constants a^2 and ν by a similarity transformation, which is identical with that in the plane case, thus

$$\zeta = \sqrt{\frac{a}{\nu}}\, z; \qquad f(z) = \sqrt{a\,\nu}\;\phi(\zeta).$$

The differential equation for $\phi(\zeta)$ simplifies to

$$\phi''' + 2\,\phi\,\phi'' - \phi'^2 + 1 = 0 \tag{5.40}$$

with the boundary conditions

$$\zeta = 0: \quad \phi = \phi' = 0; \qquad \zeta = \infty: \quad \phi' = 1.$$

The solution of eqn. (5.40) was first given by F. Homann [12] in the form of a power series. The plot of $\phi' = u/U$ is given in Fig. 5.11 together with the plane case, and the values for ϕ' given in Table 5.1 have been taken from a paper by N. Froessling [7].

10. Flow near a rotating disk. A further example of an exact solution of the Navier-Stokes equations is furnished by the flow around a flat disk which rotates about an axis perpendicular to its plane with a uniform angular velocity ω in a fluid otherwise at rest. The layer near the disk is carried by it through friction and is thrown outwards owing to the action of centrifugal forces. This is compensated by particles which flow in an axial direction towards the disk to be in turn carried and ejected centrifugally. Thus the case is seen to be one of fully three-dimensional flow, i. e. there exist velocity components in the radial direction, r, the circumferential direction, ϕ, and the axial direction, z, which we shall denote respectively by u, v, and w. An axonometric representation of this flow field is shown in Fig. 5.12. At first the calculation will be performed for the case of an infinite rotating plane. It will then be easy to extend the result to include a disk of finite diameter $D = 2\,R$, on condition that the edge effect is neglected.

Taking into account rotational symmetry as well as the notation for the problem we can write down the Navier-Stokes equations (3.33) as:

$$
\left.\begin{aligned}
u\frac{\partial u}{\partial r}-\frac{v^2}{r}+w\frac{\partial u}{\partial z} &= -\frac{1}{\varrho}\frac{\partial p}{\partial r}+\nu\left\{\frac{\partial^2 u}{\partial r^2}+\frac{\partial}{\partial r}\left(\frac{u}{r}\right)+\frac{\partial^2 u}{\partial z^2}\right\}\\
u\frac{\partial v}{\partial r}+\frac{uv}{r}+w\frac{\partial v}{\partial z} &= \nu\left\{\frac{\partial^2 v}{\partial r^2}+\frac{\partial}{\partial r}\left(\frac{v}{r}\right)+\frac{\partial^2 v}{\partial z^2}\right\}\\
u\frac{\partial w}{\partial r}+w\frac{\partial w}{\partial z} &= -\frac{1}{\varrho}\frac{\partial p}{\partial z}+\nu\left\{\frac{\partial^2 w}{\partial r^2}+\frac{1}{r}\frac{\partial w}{\partial r}+\frac{\partial^2 w}{\partial z^2}\right\}\\
\frac{\partial u}{\partial r}+\frac{u}{r}+\frac{\partial w}{\partial z} &= 0\,.
\end{aligned}\right\}\qquad (5.41)
$$

The no slip condition at the wall gives the following boundary conditions:

$$
\left.\begin{aligned}
z=0:&\quad u=0\,,\quad v=r\,\omega\,,\quad w=0\,,\\
z=\infty:&\quad u=0\,,\quad v=0\,.
\end{aligned}\right\}\qquad (5.42)
$$

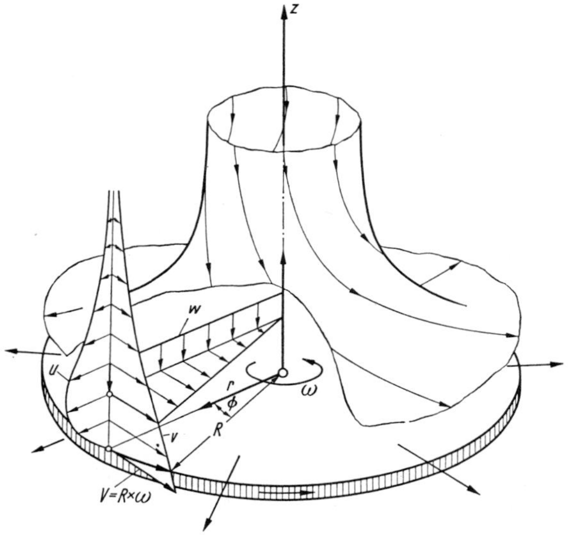

Fig. 5.12. Flow in the neighbourhood of a disk rotating in a fluid at rest

Velocity components: u-radial, v-circumferential, w-axial. A layer of fluid is carried by the disk owing to the action of viscous forces. The centrifugal forces in the thin layer give rise to secondary flow which is directed radially outwards

We shall begin by estimating the thickness, δ, of the layer of fluid 'carried' by the disk [25]. It is clear that the thickness of the layer of fluid which rotates with the disk owing to friction decreases with the viscosity and this view is confirmed when compared with the results of the preceding examples. The centrifugal force per unit volume which acts on a fluid particle in the rotating layer at a distance r from the axis is equal to $\varrho\, r\, \omega^2$. Hence for a volume of area $\mathrm{d}r \cdot \mathrm{d}s$ and height, δ, the centrifugal force becomes: $\varrho\, r\, \omega^2\, \delta\, \mathrm{d}r\, \mathrm{d}s$. The same element of fluid is acted upon by a shearing stress τ_w, pointing in the direction in which the fluid is slipping, and forming an angle, say θ, with the circumferential velocity. The radial component of the shearing stress must now be equal to the centrifugal force, and hence

$$\tau_w \sin\theta \, dr \, ds = \varrho \, r \, \omega^2 \, \delta \, dr \, ds$$

or

$$\tau_w \sin\theta = \varrho \, r \, \omega^2 \, \delta \, .$$

On the other hand the circumferential component of the shearing stress must be proportional to the velocity gradient of the circumferential velocity at the wall. This condition gives

$$\tau_w \cos\theta \sim \mu \, r \, \omega / \delta \, .$$

Eliminating τ_w from these two equations we obtain

$$\delta^2 \sim \frac{\nu}{\omega} \tan\theta \, .$$

If it is assumed that the direction of slip in the flow near the wall is independent of the radius, the thickness of the layer carried by the disk becomes

$$\delta \sim \sqrt{\frac{\nu}{\omega}} \, ,$$

which is identical with the result obtained in the case of the oscillating wall on p. 75. Further, we can write for the shearing stress at the wall

$$\tau_w \sim \varrho \, r \, \omega^2 \, \delta \sim \varrho \, r \, \omega \sqrt{\nu \, \omega} \, .$$

The torque, which is equal to the product of shearing stress at the wall, area and arm becomes

$$M \sim \tau_w R^3 \sim \varrho \, R^4 \, \omega \sqrt{\nu \, \omega} \, , \tag{5.43}$$

R denoting the radius of the disk.

In order to integrate the system of equations (5.41) it is convenient to introduce a dimensionless distance from the wall, $\zeta \sim z/\delta$, thus putting

$$\zeta = z \sqrt{\frac{\omega}{\nu}} \, . \tag{5.44}$$

Further, the following assumptions are made for the velocity components and pressure

$$u = r \, \omega \, F(\zeta); \qquad v = r \, \omega \, G(\zeta); \qquad w = \sqrt{\nu \, \omega} \, H(\zeta) \tag{5.45}$$
$$p = p\,(z) = \varrho \, \nu \, \omega \, P(\zeta) \, .$$

Inserting these equations into eqns. (5.41) we obtain a system of four simultaneous ordinary differential equations for the functions F, G, H, and P:

$$\left.\begin{aligned} 2\,F + H' &= 0 \\ F^2 + F' H - G^2 - F'' &= 0 \\ 2\,F\,G + H\,G' - G'' &= 0 \\ P' + H\,H' - H'' &= 0 \, . \end{aligned}\right\} \tag{5.46}$$

The boundary conditions can be calculated from eqn. (5.42) and are:

$$\zeta = 0 : \quad F = 0 , \quad G = 1 , \quad H = 0 , \quad P = 0$$
$$\zeta = \infty : \quad F = 0 , \quad G = 0 .$$

The first solution of the system of eqns. (5.46) by an approximate method was given by Th. von Kármán [15]; later W. G. Cochran [6] calculated more accurate values by a method of numerical integration†. They are given in Table 5.2 and plotted in Fig. 5.13.

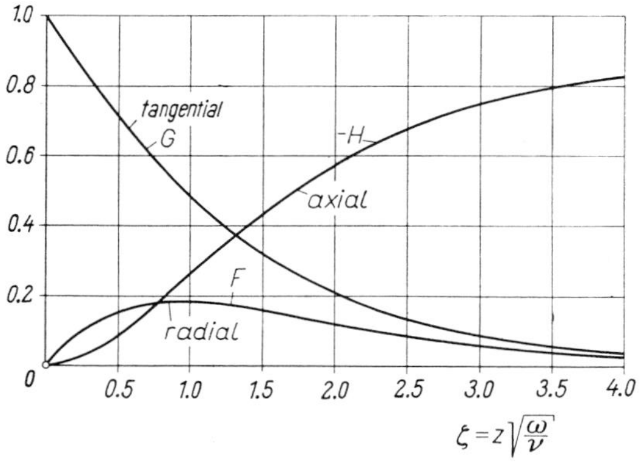

Fig. 5.13. Velocity distribution near a disk rotating in a fluid at rest

In the case under discussion, just as in the example involving a stagnation point, the velocity field is the first to be evaluated from the equation of continuity and the equations of motion parallel to the wall. The pressure distribution is found subsequently from the equation of motion perpendicular to the wall.

It is seen from Fig. 5.13 that the distance from the wall over which the peripheral velocity is reduced to half the disk velocity is $\delta_{0\cdot5} \approx \sqrt{\nu/\omega}$. It is to be noted from the solution that when $\delta \approx \sqrt{\nu/\omega}$ is small, the velocity components u and v have appreciable values only in a thin layer of thickness $\sqrt{\nu/\omega}$. The velocity component w, normal to the disk is, at any rate, small and of the order $\sqrt{\nu\,\omega}$. The inclination of the relative stream-lines near the wall with respect to the circumferential direction, if the wall is imagined at rest and the fluid is taken to rotate at a large distance from the wall, becomes

$$\tan \phi_0 = -\left(\frac{\partial u/\partial z}{\partial v/\partial z}\right)_{z=0} = -\frac{F'(0)}{G'(0)} = \frac{0{\cdot}510}{0{\cdot}616} = 0{\cdot}838 ,$$

or

$$\phi_0 = 39{\cdot}6^\circ .$$

Although the calculation is, strictly speaking, applicable to an infinite disk only, we may utilize the same results for a finite disk, provided that its radius R is large

† This solution was obtained in the form of a power series near $\zeta = 0$ and an asymptotic series for large values of ζ which were then joined together for moderate values of ζ.

compared with the thickness δ of the layer carried with the disk. We shall now evaluate the turning moment of such a disk. The contribution of an annular disk element of width $\mathrm{d}r$ on radius r is $\mathrm{d}M = -2\pi r\,\mathrm{d}r\,r\,\tau_{z\phi}$, and hence the moment for a disk wetted on one side becomes

$$M = -2\pi \int_0^R r^2 \tau_{z\phi}\,\mathrm{d}r\,.$$

Table 5.2. The functions for the velocity and pressure distribution in the neighbourhood of a disk rotating in a fluid at rest; calculated by W. G. Cochran [6]; see eqns. (5.45)

$\zeta = z\sqrt{\frac{\omega}{\nu}}$	F	G	$-H$	P	F'	$-G'$
0	0	1·0	0	0	0·510	0·616
0·1	0·046	0·939	0·005	0·092	0·416	0·611
0·2	0·084	0·878	0·018	0·167	0·334	0·599
0·3	0·114	0·819	0·038	0·228	0·262	0·580
0·4	0·136	0·762	0·063	0·275	0·200	0·558
0·5	0·154	0·708	0·092	0·312	0·147	0·532
0·6	0·166	0·656	0·124	0·340	0·102	0·505
0·7	0·174	0·607	0·158	0·361	0·063	0·476
0·8	0·179	0·561	0·193	0·377	0·032	0·448
0·9	0·181	0·517	0·230	0·388	0·006	0·419
1·0	0·180	0·468	0·266	0·395	—0·016	0·391
1·1	0·177	0·439	0·301	0·400	—0·033	0·364
1·2	0·173	0·404	0·336	0·403	—0·046	0·338
1·3	0·168	0·371	0·371	0·405	—0·057	0·313
1·4	0·162	0·341	0·404	0·406	—0·064	0·290
1·5	0·156	0·313	0·435	0·406	—0·070	0·268
1·6	0·148	0·288	0·466	0·405	—0·073	0·247
1·7	0·141	0·264	0·495	0·404	—0·075	0·228
1·8	0·133	0·242	0·522	0·403	—0·076	0·210
1·9	0·126	0·222	0·548	0·402	—0·075	0·193
2·0	0·118	0·203	0·572	0·401	—0·074	0·177
2·1	0·111	0·186	0·596	0·399	—0·072	0·163
2·2	0·104	0·171	0·617	0·398	—0·070	0·150
2·3	0·097	0·156	0·637	0·397	—0·067	0·137
2·4	0·091	0·143	0·656	0·396	—0·065	0·126
2·5	0·084	0·131	0·674	0·395	—0·061	0·116
2·6	0·078	0·120	0·690	0·395	—0·058	0·106
2·8	0·068	0·101	0·721	0·395	—0·052	0·089
3·0	0·058	0·083	0·746	0·395	—0·046	0·075
3·2	0·050	0·071	0·768	0·395	—0·040	0·063
3·4	0·042	0·059	0·786	0·394	—0·035	0·053
3·6	0·036	0·050	0·802	0·394	—0·030	0·044
3·8	0·031	0·042	0·815	0·393	—0·025	0·037
4·0	0·026	0·035	0·826	0·393	—0·022	0·031
4·2	0·022	0·029	0·836	0·393	—0·019	0·026
4·4	0·018	0·024	0·844	0·393	—0·016	0·022
∞	0	0	0·886	0·393	0	0

Here $\tau_{z\phi} = \mu(\partial v/\partial z)_0$ denotes the circumferential component of the shearing stress. From eqn. (5.45) we obtain

$$\tau_{z\phi} = \varrho\, r\, \nu^{1/2}\, \omega^{3/2}\, G'(0)\,.$$

Hence the moment for a disk wetted on both sides becomes

$$2\,M = -\pi\,\varrho\,R^4(\nu\omega^3)^{1/2}\,G'(0) = 0{\cdot}616\,\pi\,\varrho\,R^4(\nu\omega^3)^{1/2}\,. \tag{5.47}$$

It is customary to introduce the following dimensionless moment coefficient,

$$C_M = \frac{2\,M}{\frac{1}{2}\,\varrho\,\omega^2\,R^5}\,. \tag{5.48}$$

This gives

$$C_M = -\frac{2\pi G'(0)\,\nu^{1/2}}{R\,\omega^{1/2}}$$

or, defining a Reynolds number based on the radius and tip velocity,

$$\mathsf{R} = \frac{R^2\,\omega}{\nu}\,,$$

and introducing the numerical value $-2\pi\,G'(0) = 3{\cdot}87$, we obtain finally

$$\boxed{C_M = \frac{3{\cdot}87}{\mathsf{R}^{1/2}}}\,. \tag{5.49}$$

Fig. 5.14 shows a plot of this equation, curve (1), and compares it with measurements [35]. For Reynolds numbers up to about $\mathsf{R} = 3 \times 10^5$ there is excellent agreement between theory and experiment. At higher Reynolds numbers the flow becomes turbulent, and the respective case is considered in Chap. XXI.

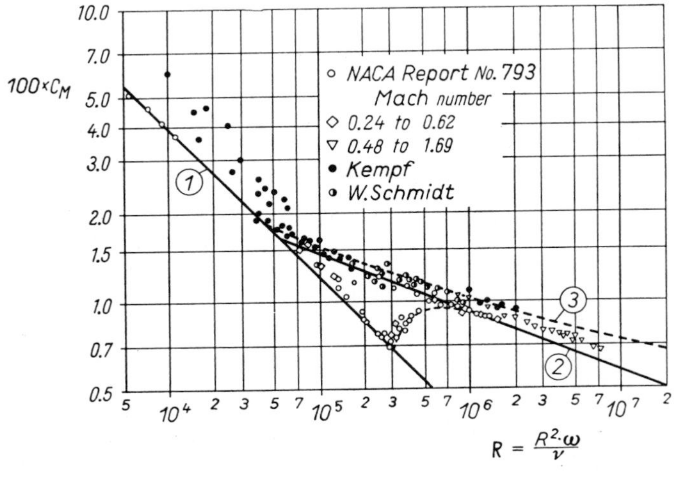

Fig. 5.14. Turning moment on a rotating disk; curve (1) from eqn. (5.49), *laminar*; curves (2) and (3) from eqns. (21.25) and (21.28), *turbulent*

Curves (2) and (3) in Fig. 5.14 are obtained from the turbulent flow theory. Older measurements, carried out by G. Kempf [16] and W. Schmidt [31], show tolerable agreement with theoretical results. Prior to these solutions, D. Riabouchinsky [27], [28] established empirical formulae for the turning moment of rotating disks which were based on very careful measurements. These formulae showed very good agreement with the theoretical equations discovered subsequently.

The quantity of liquid which is pumped outwards as a result of the centrifuging action on the one side of a disk of radius R is

$$Q = 2\pi\, R \int_{z=0}^{\infty} u\, \mathrm{d}z\,.$$

Calculation shows that

$$Q = 0{\cdot}886\, \pi\, R^2 \sqrt{\nu\, \omega} = 0{\cdot}886\, \pi\, R^3\, \omega\, \mathsf{R}^{-1/2}\,. \tag{5.50}$$

The quantity of fluid flowing towards the disk in the axial direction is of equal magnitude. It is, further, worthy of note that the pressure difference over the layer carried by the disk is of the order $\varrho\, \nu\, \omega$ i. e. very small for small viscosities. The pressure distribution depends only on the distance from the wall and there is no radial pressure gradient.

When the radius of the disk, R, is not very large compared with the boundary layer thickness, δ, it is necessary to take into account the fact that the velocity components u, v, w, eqns. (5.45), are also functions of the radius r and cease to be simply proportional to it, as implied. This causes the transverse gradient $(\partial v/\partial z)_0$ to increase faster with r than allowed for in the preceding calculation. In fact, the gradient becomes infinite at the edge itself, but its integral in the turning moment remains finite. A further remark on this "edge effect" will be given in Chap. XXI.

The problem of a rotating disk in a housing is discussed in Chap. XXI.

It is particularly noteworthy that the solution for the rotating disk as well as the solutions obtained for the flow with stagnation are, in the first place, exact solutions of the Navier-Stokes equations and, in the second, that they are of a *boundary layer type*, in the sense discussed in the preceding chapter. In the limiting case of very small viscosity these solutions show that the influence of viscosity extends over a very small layer in the neighbourhood of the solid wall, whereas in the whole of the remaining region the flow is, practically speaking, identical with the corresponding ideal (potential) case. These examples show further that the boundary layer has a thickness of the order $\sqrt{\nu}$. The one-dimensional examples of flow discussed previously display the same boundary layer character. In this connexion the reader may wish to consult a paper by G. K. Batchelor [3] which discusses the solution of the Navier-Stokes equations for the case of two co-axial, rotating disks placed at a certain distance apart, as well as a paper by K. Stewartson [32]. Interesting experimental results are described in the papers by K. G. Picha and E. R. G. Eckert [23a], W. E. Welsh Jr. and J. P. Hartnett [37].

11. Flow in convergent and divergent channels. A further class of exact solutions of the Navier-Stokes equations can be obtained in the following way: Let it be assumed that the family of straight lines passing through a point in a plane constitute the streamlines of a flow.

Let the velocity differ from line to line, which means that it is assumed to be a function of the polar angle ϕ. The rays along which the velocity vanishes can then be regarded as the solid walls of a convergent or a divergent channel. The continuity equations can be satisfied by assuming that the velocity along every ray is inversely proportional to the distance from the origin. Hence the radial velocity u has the form $u \sim F(\phi)/r$, or, if F is to be dimensionless,

$$u = \frac{v}{r} F(\phi) .$$

The peripheral velocity vanishes everywhere. Introducing this form into the Navier-Stokes equations written in polar co-ordinates, eqn. (3.33), and eliminating pressure from the equations in the r and ϕ directions, we obtain the following ordinary differential equation for $F(\phi)$:

$$2FF' + 4\,F' + F''' = 0 .$$

Integrating once, we are led to the equation

$$F^2 + 4\,F + F'' + K = 0 . \tag{5.51}$$

The constant K denotes the radial pressure gradient at the walls, $K = -(1/\varrho)\,(\partial p/\partial r)\,(r^3/\nu^2)$, where we have $F = 0$ for $\phi = 0$ and $\phi = \alpha$. The solution of eqn. (5.51) was given by G. B. Jeffery [13a] and independently G. Hamel [10]. The function F can be expressed explicitly as an elliptic function of ϕ.

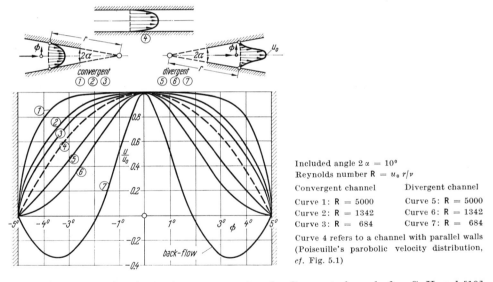

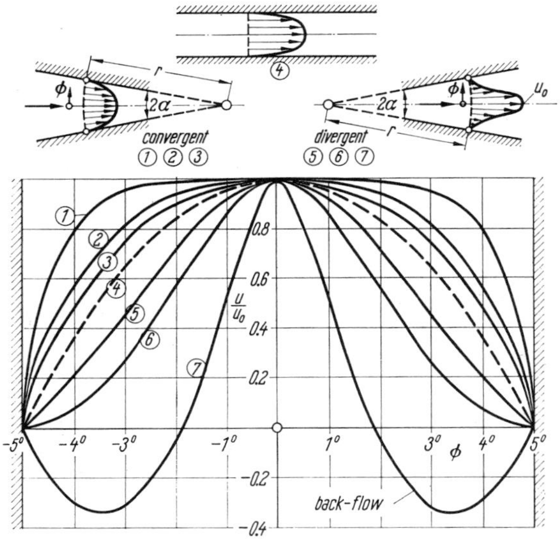

Included angle $2\alpha = 10°$
Reynolds number $R = u_0\,r/\nu$

Convergent channel	Divergent channel
Curve 1: R = 5000	Curve 5: R = 5000
Curve 2: R = 1342	Curve 6: R = 1342
Curve 3: R = 684	Curve 7: R = 684

Curve 4 refers to a channel with parallel walls (Poiseuille's parobolic velocity distribution, *cf.* Fig. 5.1)

Fig. 5.15. Velocity distribution in a convergent and a divergent channel after G. Hamel [10] and K. Millsaps and K. Pohlhausen [21]

We shall now briefly sketch the character of the solution refraining from discussing the details of the derivation. The graph in Fig. 5.15 shows a family of velocity profiles for a convergent and a divergent channel for different Reynolds numbers plotted on the basis of the numerical calculations performed by K. Millsaps and K. Pohlhausen [21]. The velocity distribution for the convergent and for the divergent channel differ markedly from each other. In the latter case, they also differ markedly for different Reynolds numbers. In a *convergent* channel the velocity distribution for the highest Reynolds number ($\mathsf{R} = 5000$) remains nearly constant over a large centre-portion and decreases steeply to zero near the walls; thus it exhibits in this case a marked "boundary-layer character".

In a *divergent* channel the shape of the velocity profiles is markedly affected by the Reynolds number and by the angle of divergence. It is seen from Fig. 5.15 that the velocity is positive over the whole cross-section when the Reynolds number is large, curves (5) and (6). At the lowest Reynolds numbers, however, curve (7), it becomes negative near the walls which denotes back-flow. It can be deduced from additional examples of Hamel's solution that with larger angles of divergence back-flow occurs earlier, i. e. at lower Reynolds numbers. Back-flow constitutes the early phase of the development of separation. In a real flow, in most cases, separation does not occur symmetrically on both walls, the flow separating on the one side and adhering to the wall on the other.

In the paper referred to above, G. Hamel has set himself the problem of calculating all three-dimensional flows whose stream-lines are identical with those of a potential flow. The solution consisted of stream-lines in the shape of logarithmic spirals. The case of radial flow considered here, and the case of potential vortex-flow, discussed in Sec. V. 3 constitute particular examples of this general solution.

The preceding example of an exact solution exhibits once more the *boundary-layer character* of the flow. In particular, in the case of a convergent channel, the existence of a thin layer near the wall is confirmed together with the fact that the influence of viscosity is concentrated in it. Further, the calculation confirms that the boundary layer thickness increases as $\sqrt{\nu}$ here too. The divergent case exhibits an additional phenomenon, that of back-flow, and, resulting from it, separation. This is an essential property of all boundary-layer flows and we shall discuss it later in greater detail on the basis of the equations of boundary-layer flow. Its existence is fully confirmed by experiment.

The cases of two-dimensional and axi-symmetrical flow through channels with small angles of divergence have been investigated earlier by H. Blasius [4] from first principles, i. e. with the aid of the Navier-Stokes equations. In this connexion it was shown that laminar flow can support only a very small pressure increase without the incidence of separation. The condition for the avoidance of back-flow at the wall in a divergent tube of radius $R(x)$ was found to be $\mathrm{d}R/\mathrm{d}x \leq 12/\mathsf{R}$. (condition for separation), where $\mathsf{R} = \bar{u}\, d/\nu$ denotes the Reynolds number referred to the mean velocity of flow through the channel and to its diameter. In more modern times M. Abramowitz [1] extended these calculations for divergent channels, and discovered that the point of separation moves downstream from the channel entrance as the Reynolds number is increased and as the angle of divergence is decreased.

A solution for the flow through a convergent channel which is based on the boundary layer equations and which is not, therefore, an exact solution of the Navier-Stokes equations was obtained by K. Pohlhausen and will be discussed in Sec. IXb.

This example concludes the discussion of exact solution of the Navier-Stokes equations and the next topic will deal with approximate solutions. In the previous description an exact solution meant a solution of the Navier-Stokes equations in which all its terms were taken into account, provided that they did not vanish identically for the problem. In the following chapter we shall concern ourselves with approximate solutions of the Navier-Stokes equations, that is, with solutions which are obtained when small terms are neglected in the differential equations themselves. As already mentioned in Chap. IV, the two limiting cases of very large and very small viscosity are of particular importance. In very slow, or so-called creeping motion, viscous forces are very large compared with inertia forces, and in boundary layer motion they are very small. Whereas in the first case it is permissible to omit the inertia terms completely, no such simplification is possible in boundary layer theory, because if the viscous terms are simply disregarded the physically essential condition of no slip at the solid boundary cannot be met.

References

[1] M. ABRAMOWITZ, On backflow of a viscous fluid in a diverging channel. Jour. Math. Phys. **28**, p. 1—21 (1949).
[2] A. G. AZPEITIA and G. F. NEWELL, Slow oscillations of a thin finite disk in an infinite fluid. Brown University Report AF 891/8, 1957.
[3] G. K. BATCHELOR, Note on a class of solutions of the Navier-Stokes equations representing steady non rotationally symmetric flow. Quart. Mech. Appl. Math. Vol. **IV**, pp. 29—41, (1951).
[4] H. BLASIUS, Laminare Strömung in Kanälen wechselnder Breite. Z. Math. u. Physik **58**, 225 (1910).
[5] G. F. CARRIER, Integral equation boundary layer problem. "Fifty years of boundary layer research." Braunschweig 1955, pp. 13—20.
[5a] H. S. CARSLAW and J. C. JAEGER, Conduction of heat in solids, Clarendon Press, Oxford 1947.
[6] W. G. COCHRAN, The flow due to a rotating disk. Proc. Cambridge Phil. Soc. **30**, 365 (1934).
[7] N. FRÖSSLING, Verdunstung, Wärmeübertragung und Geschwindigkeitsverteilung bei zweidimensionaler und rotationssymmetrischer laminarer Grenzschichtströmung. Lunds. Univ. Arsskr. N. F. Avd. 2, **35**, No. 4 (1940).
[8] H. GÖRTLER, Zahlentafeln universeller Funktionen zur neuen Reihe für die Berechnung laminarer Grenzschichten. Report No. 34 of the Deutsche Versuchsanstalt für Luftfahrt, 1957.
[8a] W. GERBERS, Zur instationären, laminaren Strömung einer inkompressiblen zähen Flüssigkeit in kreiszylindrischen Rohren. Zeitschr. angew. Physik **3**, 267—271 (1951).
[9] G. HAGEN, Über die Bewegung des Wassers in engen zylindrischen Röhren. Pogg. Ann. **46**, 423 (1839).
[10] G. HAMEL, Spiralförmige Bewegung zäher Flüssigkeiten. Jahresber. d. Dt. Mathematiker-Vereinigung **34** (1916); see also W. TOLLMIEN, Handbuch der Experimental-Physik **IV**, Part **1**, 257.
[11] K. HIEMENZ, Die Grenzschicht an einem in den gleichförmigen Flüssigkeitsstrom eingetauchten geraden Kreiszylinder. (Thesis Göttingen 1911). Dingl. Polytech. J. **326**, 321 (1911).
[12] F. HOMANN, Der Einfluß großer Zähigkeit bei der Strömung um den Zylinder und um die Kugel. ZAMM **16**, 153—164 (1936); and Forschg. Ing.-Wes. **7**, 1—10 (1936).
[13] L. HOWARTH, On the calculation of the steady flow in the boundary layer near the surface of a cylinder in a stream. ARC R & M 1632 (1935).
[13a] G. B. JEFFERY, Steady motions of a viscous fluid. Phil. Mag. **29**, 455 (1915).
[14] R. P. KANWAL, Rotatory and longitudinal oscillations of axi-symmetric bodies in a viscous fluid. Quart. J. Mech. and Appl. Math. (Oxford) **8**, 146 (1955).
[15] TH. VON KÁRMÁN, Laminare und turbulente Reibung. ZAMM **1**, 233—252 (1921); NACA T M. 1092 (1946).
[16] G. KEMPF, Über Reibungswiderstand rotierender Scheiben. Vorträge auf dem Gebiet der Hydro- und Aerodynamik, Innsbruck Congr., 1922; Berlin, 168, 1924.
[17] J. KESTIN and L. N. PERSEN, Slow oscillations of bodies of revolution in a viscous fluid. Proc. 9th Intern. Congress App. Mech., Brussels 1957, vol. 3 p. 326.
[18] J. KESTIN and H. E. WANG, Corrections for the oscillating-disk viscometer. J. Appl. Mech. **24**, 197 (1957).
[18a] H. L. L. LANGHAAR, Steady flow in the transition length of a straight tube. Jour. Appl. Mech. **9**, A 55 (1942).
[19] P. MARIENS und O. VAN PAEMEL, Theory and experimental verification of the oscillating-disk method for viscosity measurements in fluids. Appl. Sci. Res. **5**, 411 (1956).
[19a] MAXWELL, J. C.: On the viscosity or internal friction of air and other gases. Phil. Trans. Roy. Soc. London **156**, 249 (1866).
[20] O. E. MEYER, Über die Bestimmung der inneren Reibung nach Coulomb's Verfahren. Ann. d. Phys. (Wiedemann) **32**, 642 (1887).
[21] K. MILLSAPS and K. POHLHAUSEN, Thermal distribution in Jeffery-Hamel flows between nonparallel plane walls. Jour. Aero. Sci. Vol. **20**, p. 187—196 (1953).
[22] W. MÜLLER, Zum Problem der Anlaufströmung einer Flüssigkeit im geraden Rohr mit Kreisring- und Kreisquerschnitt. ZAMM **16**, 227 (1936).
[22a] G. F. NEWELL and others, Theory of oscillation type viscometers, Parts I—V. ZAMP, **8**, 433 (1957), **8**, 450 (1957), **9**, 97 (1958), **10**, 15 (1959), **10**, 159 (1959).

[23] C. W. Oseen, Ark. f. Math. Astron. och. Fys. **7** (1911); Hydromechanik p. 82, Leipzig 1927.
[23a] K. G. Picha and E. R. G. Eckert, Study of the air flow between coaxial disks rotating with arbitrary velocities in an open or enclosed space. Proc. 3rd. US Nat'l. Congr. Appl. Mech. 1959, p. 791.
[24] J. Poiseuille, Récherches experimentelles sur le mouvement des liquides dans les tubes de très petits diamètres. Comptes Rendus **11**, 961 and 1041 (1840); **12**, 112 (1841); in more detail: Mémoires des Savants Etrangers **9**, (1846).
[25] L. Prandtl, Führer durch die Strömungslehre. 3. ed, 342, 1949. Engl. transl. Blackie and Son, London, 1952.
[26] B. Punnis, Zur Berechnung der laminaren Einlaufströmung im Rohr. Diss. Göttingen 1947.
[26a] Lord Rayleigh, On the motion of solid bodies through viscous liquid, Phil. Mag. **21**, 697 (1911); also Sci. Papers, **VI**, 29.
[27] D. Riabouchinsky, Bull. de l'Institut Aerodyn. de Koutchino, **5**, p. 5—34 Moscow (1914); See also Jour. Roy. Aero. Soc. **39**, p. 340—348 and pp. 377—379 (1935).
[28] D. Riabouchinsky, Sur la résistance de frottement des disques tournant dans un fluide et les équations integrales appliquées à ce problème. C. R. **233**, pp. 899—901 (1951).
[29] L. Schiller, Untersuchungen über laminare und turbulente Strömung. VDI-Forschungsheft 248 (1922).
[30] H. Schlichting, Laminare Kanaleinlaufströmung. ZAMM **14**, 368—373 (1934).
[31] W. Schmidt, Ein einfaches Meßverfahren für Drehmomente. Z. VDI. **65**, 441—444 (1921).
[32] K. Stewartson, On the flow between two rotating coaxial disks. Proc. Cambr. Phil. Soc. **49**, 333—341 (1953).
[32a] G. G. Stokes, On the effect of the internal friction of fluids on the motion of pendulums. Cambr. Phil. Trans. **IX**, 8 (1851); Math. and Phys. Papers, **III**, 1, Cambridge 1901.
[33] F. Szymanski, Quelques solutions exactes des équations de l'hydrodynamique de fluide visqueux dans le cas d'un tube cylindrique. J. de math. pures et appliquées, Series 9, **11**, 67 (1932); see also Intern. Congr. Appl. Mech. Stockholm **I**, 249 (1930).
[34] L. N. Tao and W. F. Donovan, Through-flow in concentric and excentric annuli of fine clearance with and without relative motion of the boundaries. Trans. Amer. Soc. Mech. Eng. **77**, p. 1291—1301 (1955).
[35] Th. Theodorsen and A. Regier, Experiments on drag of revolving discs, cylinders, and streamline rods at high speeds. NACA Report 793 (1944).
[36] A. Timme, Über die Geschwindigkeitsverteilung in Wirbeln. Ing. Arch. **25**, 205—225 (1957).
[37] W. E. Welsh Jr. and J. P. Hartnett, Velocity measurements in the boundary layer and in the main flow between two coaxial disks rotating with equal velocities in air. Proc. 3rd. US Nat'l. Congress Appl. Mech. 1959, p. 847.

CHAPTER VI

Very slow motion

a. The differential equations for the case of very slow motion

In this chapter we propose to discuss some approximate solutions of the Navier-Stokes equations which are valid in the limiting case when the viscous forces are considerably greater than the inertia forces. Since the inertia forces are proportional to the square of the velocity whereas the viscous forces are only proportional to its first power, it is easy to appreciate that a flow for which viscous forces are dominant is obtained when the velocity is very small, or, speaking more generally, when the Reynolds number is very small. When the inertia terms are simply omitted from the equations of motion the resulting solutions are valid approximately for $\mathsf{R} \ll 1$. This fact can also be deduced from the dimensionless form of the Navier-Stokes equations, eqns. (4.2), where the inertia terms are seen to be multiplied by a factor $\mathsf{R} = \varrho\, V\, l/\mu$ compared with the viscous terms. In this connexion we may remark that in each particular case it is necessary to examine in detail the quantities with which this Reynolds number is to be formed. However, apart from some special cases, motions at very low Reynolds numbers, sometimes also called *creeping motions*, do not occur too often in practical applications†.

It is seen from eqns. (3.31) that when the inertia terms are neglected the incompressible Navier-Stokes equations assume the form

$$\text{grad}\, p = \mu\; \nabla^2 \boldsymbol{w}\,, \tag{6.1}$$

$$\text{div}\; \boldsymbol{w} = 0\,, \tag{6.2}$$

or, in extended form

$$\left.\begin{aligned} \frac{\partial p}{\partial x} &= \mu \left(\frac{\partial^2 u}{\partial x^2} + \frac{\partial^2 u}{\partial y^2} + \frac{\partial^2 u}{\partial z^2}\right) \\ \frac{\partial p}{\partial y} &= \mu \left(\frac{\partial^2 v}{\partial x^2} + \frac{\partial^2 v}{\partial y^2} + \frac{\partial^2 v}{\partial z^2}\right) \\ \frac{\partial p}{\partial z} &= \mu \left(\frac{\partial^2 w}{\partial x^2} + \frac{\partial^2 w}{\partial y^2} + \frac{\partial^2 w}{\partial z^2}\right) \end{aligned}\right\} \tag{6.3}$$

$$\frac{\partial u}{\partial x} + \frac{\partial v}{\partial y} + \frac{\partial w}{\partial z} = 0\,. \tag{6.4}$$

---

† In the case of a sphere falling in air ($\nu = 160 \times 10^{-6}$ ft²/sec) we obtain e. g. $\mathsf{R} = V\, d/\nu = 1$, when the diameter $d = 0{\cdot}04$ in ($= 0{\cdot}00333$ ft) and the velocity $V = 0{\cdot}048$ ft/sec.

This system of equations must be supplemented with the same boundary conditions as the full Navier-Stokes equations, namely those expressing the absence of slip in the fluid at the walls, i. e. the vanishing of the normal and tangential components of velocity:

$$v_n = 0\,, \quad v_t = 0 \qquad \text{at walls}\,. \tag{6.5}$$

An important characteristic of creeping motion can be obtained at once from eqn. (6.1), when the divergence of both sides is formed and when it is noticed that the operations div and ∇^2 on the right-hand side may be performed in the reverse order. Thus, with eqn. (6.2) we have

$$\operatorname{div}\operatorname{grad}\, p = \nabla^2 p = 0\,. \tag{6.6}$$

The pressure field in creeping motion satisfies the potential equation and the pressure $p(x,y,z)$ is a potential function.

The equations for *two-dimensional* creeping motion become particularly simple in form with the introduction of the stream function ψ defined by $u = \partial\psi/\partial y$ and $v = -\,\partial\psi/\partial x$. As explained in Chap. IV, and as seen from eqns. (6.3), when pressure is eliminated from the first two equations, the stream function must satisfy the equation

$$\nabla^4 \psi = 0\,.$$

The stream function of plane creeping motion is thus a bipotential (biharmonic) function.

In the remaining sections of this chapter we propose to discuss three examples of creeping motion: 1. Parallel flow past a sphere; 2. The hydrodynamic theory of lubrication; 3. The Hele-Shaw flow.

b. Parallel flow past a sphere

The oldest known solution for a creeping motion was given by G. G. Stokes who investigated the case of parallel flow past a sphere [13]. We shall now describe the result of his calculations without going into the mathematical details of the theory. We shall base our description on that given by L. Prandtl [10]. The solution of eqns. (6.3) and (6.4) for the case of a sphere of radius R, the centre of which coincides with the origin, and which is placed in a parallel stream of uniform velocity U_∞, Fig. 6.1, along the x-axis can be represented by the following equations for the pressure and velocity components:

$$\left.\begin{aligned}
u &= U_\infty\left[\frac{3}{4}\,\frac{Rx^2}{r^3}\left(\frac{R^2}{r^2}-1\right)-\frac{1}{4}\,\frac{R}{r}\left(3+\frac{R^2}{r^2}\right)+1\right]\\
v &= U_\infty\,\frac{3}{4}\,\frac{Rxy}{r^3}\left(\frac{R^2}{r^2}-1\right)\\
w &= U_\infty\,\frac{3}{4}\,\frac{Rxz}{r^3}\left(\frac{R^2}{r^2}-1\right)\\
p-p_\infty &= -\frac{3}{2}\,\frac{\mu\, U_\infty\, Rx}{r^3}
\end{aligned}\right\} \tag{6.7}$$

where $r^2 = x^2 + y^2 + z^2$ has been introduced for the sake of brevity. It is easy to verify that these expressions satisfy eqns. (6.3) and (6.4) and that the velocity vanishes at all points on the surface of the sphere. The pressure on the surface becomes

$$p - p_\infty = -\frac{3}{2}\,\mu\,\frac{x}{R^2}\,U_\infty\,. \tag{6.7a}$$

The maximum and minimum of pressure occurs at points, P_1 and P_2 respectively, their values being

$$p_{1,2} - p_\infty = \pm\,\frac{3}{2}\,\frac{\mu\,U_\infty}{R}\,. \tag{6.7b}$$

The pressure distribution along a meridian of the sphere as well as along the axis of abscissae, x, is shown in Fig. 6.1. The shearing stress distribution over the sphere can also be calculated from the above formulae. It is found that the shearing stress has its largest value at point A where $\tau = \frac{3}{2}\,\mu\,U_\infty/R$ and is equal to the pressure rise at P_1 or pressure decrease at P_2. Integrating the pressure distribution and the shearing stress over the surface of the sphere we obtain the total drag

$$D = 6\pi\,\mu\,R\,U_\infty\,. \tag{6.8}$$

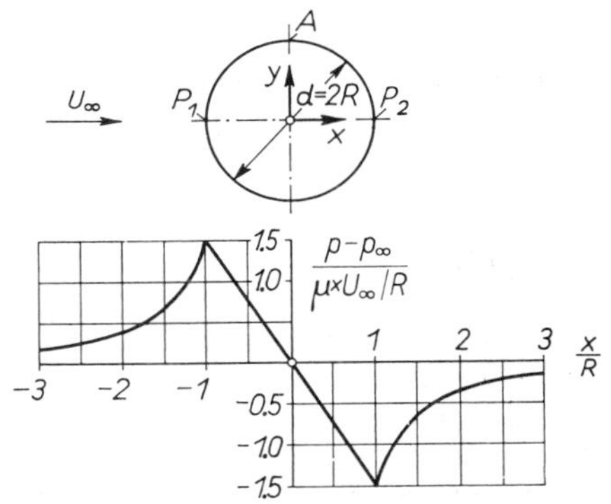

Fig. 6.1. Pressure distribution around a sphere in parallel uniform flow

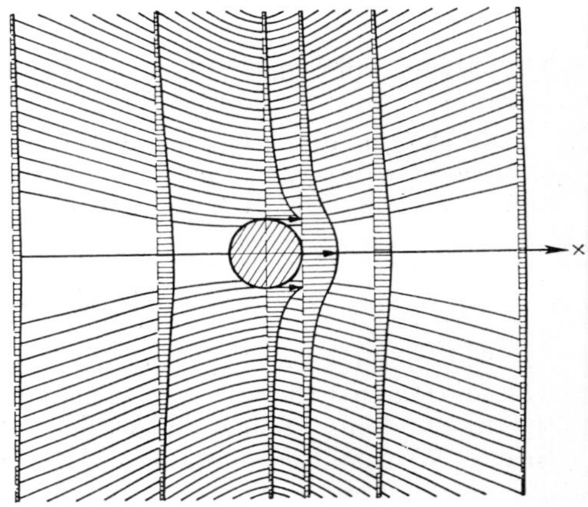

Fig. 6.2. Stream-lines and velocity distribution in Stokes' solution for a sphere in parallel flow

This is the very well known *Stokes equation* for the drag of a sphere. It can be shown that one third of the drag is due to the pressure distribution and that the remaining two thirds are due to the existence of shear. It is further remarkable that the drag is proportional to the first power of velocity. If a drag coefficient is formed by referring the drag to the dynamic head $\frac{1}{2}\,\varrho\,U_\infty^2$ and the frontal area, as is done in the case of higher Reynolds numbers, or if we put

$$D = C_D\,\pi\,R^2\,(\tfrac{1}{2}\,\varrho\,U_\infty^2)\,, \tag{6.9}$$

then
$$C_D = \frac{24}{\mathsf{R}} \; ; \quad \mathsf{R} = \frac{U_\infty d}{\nu} \, . \tag{6.10}$$

A comparison between Stokes' equation and experiment was given in Fig. 1.5 from which it is seen that it applies only to cases when $\mathsf{R} < 1$. The pattern of stream-lines in front of and behind the sphere must be the same, as by reversing the direction of free flow, i. e. by changing the sign of velocity components in eqns. (6.3) and (6.4) the system is transformed into itself. The stream-lines in viscous flow past a sphere are shown in Fig. 6.2. They were drawn as they would appear to an observer in front of whom the sphere is dragged with a constant velocity U_∞. The sketch contains also velocity profiles at several cross-sections. It is seen that the sphere drags with it a very wide layer of fluid which extends over about one diameter on both sides. At very high Reynolds numbers this boundary layer becomes very thin.

Oseen's improvement: An improvement of Stokes' solution was given by C. W. Oseen [9], who took the inertia terms in the Navier-Stokes equations partly into account. He assumed that the velocity components can be represented as the sum of a constant and a perturbation term. Thus

$$u = U_\infty + u' \; ; \qquad v = v' \; ; \qquad w = w' \, , \tag{6.11}$$

where u', v' and w' are the perturbation terms, and as such, small with respect to the free stream velocity U_∞. It is to be noted, however, that this is not true in the immediate neighbourhood of the sphere. With the assumption (6.11) the inertia terms in the Navier-Stokes eqns. (3.29) are decomposed in two groups, e. g.:

$$U_\infty \frac{\partial u'}{\partial x}, \quad U_\infty \frac{\partial v'}{\partial x}, \ldots \quad \text{and} \quad u' \frac{\partial u'}{\partial x}, \quad u' \frac{\partial v'}{\partial x}, \ldots$$

The second group is neglected as it is small of the second order compared with the first group. Thus we obtain the following equations of motion from the Navier-Stokes equations:

$$\left.\begin{aligned}
\varrho\, U_\infty \frac{\partial u'}{\partial x} + \frac{\partial p}{\partial x} &= \mu\, \nabla^2 u' \\
\varrho\, U_\infty \frac{\partial v'}{\partial x} + \frac{\partial p}{\partial y} &= \mu\, \nabla^2 v' \\
\varrho\, U_\infty \frac{\partial w'}{\partial x} + \frac{\partial p}{\partial z} &= \mu\, \nabla^2 w' \\
\frac{\partial u'}{\partial x} + \frac{\partial v'}{\partial y} + \frac{\partial w'}{\partial z} &= 0 \, .
\end{aligned}\right\} \tag{6.12}$$

The boundary conditions are the same as for the Navier-Stokes equations, but the Oseen equations are linear as was the case with the Stokes equations.

The pattern of stream-lines is now no longer the same in front of and behind the sphere. This can be recognized if reference is made to eqns. (6.12), because if we change the sign of the velocities and of the pressure, the equations do not transform into themselves, whereas the Stokes equations (6.3) did. The stream-lines of the Oseen equations are plotted in Fig. 6.3, and the observer is again assumed to be at rest with respect to the flow at a large distance from the sphere; it is imagined that the sphere is dragged with a constant velocity U_∞. The flow in front of the sphere is very similar to that given by Stokes, but behind the sphere the stream-lines are closer together which means that the velocity is larger than in the former case. Furthermore, behind the sphere some particles follow its motion as is, in fact, observed experimentally at large Reynolds numbers.

The improved expression for the drag coefficient now becomes

$$C_D = \frac{24}{\mathsf{R}}\left(1 + \frac{3}{16}\,\mathsf{R}\right); \qquad \mathsf{R} = \frac{U_\infty d}{\nu}. \tag{6.13}$$

Experimental results show, Fig. 1.5, curve (2), that Oseen's equation is applicable up to $\mathsf{R} = 5$ approximately.

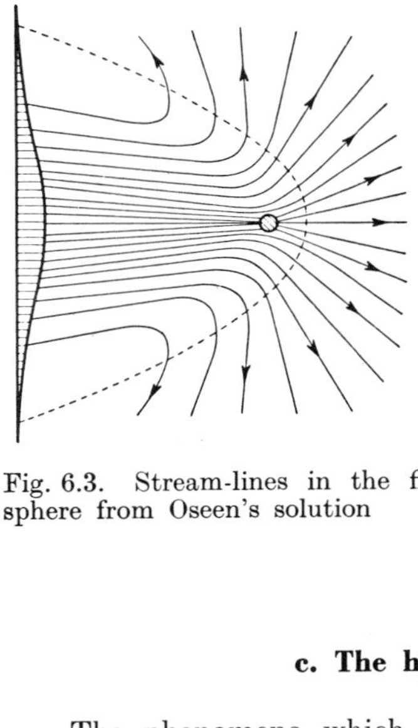

Fig. 6.3. Stream-lines in the flow past a sphere from Oseen's solution

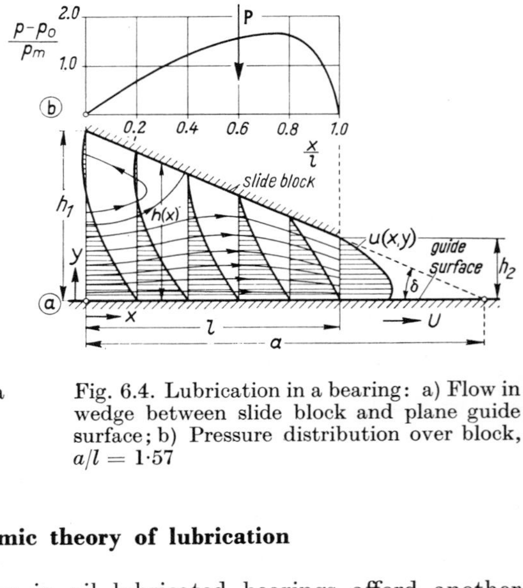

Fig. 6.4. Lubrication in a bearing: a) Flow in wedge between slide block and plane guide surface; b) Pressure distribution over block, $a/l = 1{\cdot}57$

c. The hydrodynamic theory of lubrication

The phenomena which take place in oil lubricated bearings afford another example of flow in which viscous forces are predominant. From the practical point of view these phenomena are very important. At high velocities the clearance between two machine elements which are in relative motion (e. g. journal and bearing) is filled by an oil stream in which extremely large pressure differences may be created. As a consequence the revolving journal is lifted somewhat by the oil film and metallic contact between the moving parts is prevented. The essential features of this type of motion can be understood on the example of a slide block or slipper moving on a plane guide surface, Fig. 6.4, it being important that they are inclined at a small angle δ to each other. We shall assume that the sliding surfaces are very large in a transverse direction with respect to the motion so that the problem is one in two dimensions†. In order to obtain a steady-state problem let us assume that the block is at rest and that the plane guide is forced to move with a constant velocity U with respect to it. The x-axis is assumed in the direction of motion, and the y-axis is at right angles to the plane of the guide. The height $h(x)$ of the wedge between the block and the guide is assumed to be very small compared with the length l of the block.

This motion is a more general example of that considered in Section V. 1, i. e. of the motion between two parallel flat walls with a pressure gradient. The essential difference consists in the that fact here the two walls are inclined at an angle to each other. For this reason the convective acceleration $u\,\partial u/\partial x$ is evidently different from zero. An estimation of the viscous and inertia forces shows immediately that, in spite of that, in all cases of practical importance the viscous forces are predominant. The largest viscous term in the equation of motion for the x-direction is equal to $\mu \partial^2 u/\partial y^2$. Hence we can make the following estimate:

$$\frac{\text{Inertia force}}{\text{Viscous force}} = \frac{\varrho\, u\, \partial u/\partial x}{\mu\, \partial^2 u/\partial y^2} = \frac{\varrho\, U^2/l}{\mu\, U/h^2} = \frac{\varrho\, Ul}{\mu} \cdot \left(\frac{h}{l}\right)^2 .$$

The inertia forces can be neglected with respect to the viscous forces if the reduced Reynolds number

$$\mathsf{R}^* = \frac{Ul}{\nu}\left(\frac{h}{l}\right)^2 \ll 1 . \qquad (6.14)$$

or, by way of numerical example:

$$U = 40 \text{ ft/sec}; \qquad l = 4 \text{ in} = 0{\cdot}333 \text{ ft}$$

$$\nu = 4 \times 10^{-4} \text{ ft}^2/\text{sec}; \; h = 0{\cdot}008 \text{ in} .$$

This leads to a value of the Reynolds number referred to the length of the block of $U\,l/\nu = 25{,}000$, whereas the reduced Reynolds number $\mathsf{R}^* = 0{\cdot}1$.

The differential equations of creeping motion, eqns. (6.3), can be further simplified for the case under consideration. The equation for the y-direction can be omitted altogether because the component v is very small with respect to u. Further, in the equation for the x-direction $\partial^2 u/\partial x^2$ can be neglected with respect to $\partial^2 u/\partial y^2$, because the former is smaller than the latter by a factor of the order $(h/l)^2$. The pressure distribution must satisfy the condition that $p = p_0$ at both ends of the slipper. Compared with the case of flow between parallel sliding walls, the pressure gradient in the direction of motion, $\partial p/\partial x$, is no longer constant, but the very small pressure gradient in the y-direction can be neglected. With these simplifications the differential equations (6.3) reduce to

$$\frac{\mathrm{d}p}{\mathrm{d}x} = \mu \frac{\partial^2 u}{\partial y^2} , \qquad (6.15)$$

† The two-dimensional theory was first formulated by O. Reynolds, *cf.* Phil. Trans. Roy. Soc. (1886), Pt. I, see also Ostwalds Klassiker No. 218, p. 39.

and the equation of continuity in differential form can be replaced by the condition that the volume of flow in every section must be constant:

$$Q = \int_0^{h(x)} u \,\mathrm{d}y = \text{const} . \tag{6.16}$$

The boundary conditions are:

$$\begin{aligned} y = 0: \quad u = U; \qquad x = 0: \quad p = p_0 \\ y = h: \quad u = 0 ; \qquad x = l : \quad p = p_0 . \end{aligned} \tag{6.17}$$

The solution of eqn. (6.15) which satisfies the boundary conditions (6.17) is similar to eqn. (5.5), namely

$$u = U\left(1 - \frac{y}{h}\right) - \frac{h^2 p'}{2\mu}\frac{y}{h}\left(1 - \frac{y}{h}\right) . \tag{6.18}$$

where $p' = \mathrm{d}p/\mathrm{d}x$ denotes the pressure gradient, which must be determined in such a way as to satisfy the continuity equation (6.16), and the boundary conditions for pressure. Inserting (6.18) into (6.16) we first obtain

$$Q = \frac{Uh}{2} - \frac{h^3 p'}{12\mu}$$

or, solving for p':

$$p' = 12\mu\left(\frac{U}{2h^2} - \frac{Q}{h^3}\right) . \tag{6.19}$$

Hence by integration

$$p(x) = p_0 + 6\mu U \int_0^x \frac{\mathrm{d}x}{h^2} - 12\mu Q \int_0^x \frac{\mathrm{d}x}{h^3} . \tag{6.20}$$

Inserting the condition $p = p_0$ at $x = l$ we obtain the value

$$Q = \tfrac{1}{2} U \int_0^l \frac{\mathrm{d}x}{h^2} \Big/ \int_0^l \frac{\mathrm{d}x}{h^3} . \tag{6.21}$$

Thus the mass flow is known when the shape of the wedge is given as the function $h(x)$. Eqn. (6.19) gives the pressure gradient, and eqn. (6.20) gives the pressure distribution over the slipper.

The quantities

$$b_1(x) = \int_0^x \mathrm{d}x/h^2 \quad \text{and} \quad b_2(x) = \int_0^x \mathrm{d}x/h^3 \tag{6.22}$$

which appear in eqn. (6.20) depend only on the geometrical shape of the gap between the slider and the plane. Their ratio

$$c(x) = b_1(x)/b_2(x) \tag{6.23}$$

which has the dimension of a length plays an important part in the theory of lubrication; its value for the whole channel

$$H = c(l) = \left(\int_0^l \mathrm{d}x/h^2\right)/\left(\int_0^l \mathrm{d}x/h^3\right) \tag{6.24}$$

is sometimes called the *characteristic thickness*. With its aid, the equation of continuity (6.21) can be contracted to

$$Q = \tfrac{1}{2}\, U\, H \tag{6.25}$$

from which its physical interpretation is evident. The pressure can now be written

$$p(x) = p_0 + 6\,\mu\, U\, b_1(x) - 12\,\mu\, Q\, b_2(x) \tag{6.26}$$

and the pressure gradient becomes

$$p' = \frac{6\,\mu\, U}{h^2}\left(1 - \frac{H}{h}\right) \tag{6.27}$$

which shows that the pressure has a maximum or a minimum at a place where the channel thickness is equal to its characteristic value, $h = H$.

Often it is desirable to maintain a positive excess of pressure $p - p_0$, and the preceding equation can be used to derive the condition for it. Assuming that $p - p_0 = 0$ at $x = 0$ and that the thickness H is placed at $x = x_H$, we must have

$$\left.\begin{aligned} &h(x) > H \text{ for } 0 < x < x_H, \text{ implying } p' > 0\\ &h(x) < H \text{ for } x_H < x < l\,, \text{ implying } p' < 0\,. \end{aligned}\right\} \tag{6.28}$$

These conditions lead to a wedge-like shape which is convergent in the direction of flow and which admits local both positive and negative gradient $\mathrm{d}h/\mathrm{d}x$. Since H depends on the shape of the whole channel, the direction of the pressure gradient at a section cannot be determined from $\mathrm{d}h/\mathrm{d}x$ at the section alone unlike in potential flow.

In the case of a wedge with flat faces for which $h(x) = \delta(a - x)$, where a and δ are constants, see Fig. 6.4, we obtain finally

$$Q = U\delta\,\frac{a\,(a - l)}{2\,a - l}$$

and for the pressure distribution

$$p(x) = p_0 + 6\,\mu U \frac{x\,(l - x)}{h^2\,(2\,a - l)}\,. \tag{6.29}$$

The relations become somewhat simpler if the shape of the channel is described by the gap widths h_1 and h_2 at inlet and exit, respectively, see Fig. 6.4. The characteristic width now becomes equal to the harmonic mean

$$H = \frac{2\,h_1\,h_2}{h_1 + h_2}\,, \tag{6.30}$$

and the condition for positive pressure excess, eqn. (6.28) now requires that the channel should be convergent. In this notation, the pressure distribution is given by

$$p(x) = p_0 + 6\,\mu\, U \frac{l}{h_1^2 - h_2^2} \cdot \frac{(h_1 - h)(h - h_2)}{h^2}\,, \tag{6.31}$$

and the resultant of the pressure forces can be computed by integration, when we obtain

$$P = \int_0^l p\,\mathrm{d}x = \frac{6\,\mu\, U\, l^2}{(k-1)^2 h_2^2}\left[\ln k - \frac{2(k-1)}{k+1}\right], \tag{6.32}$$

with $k = h_1/h_2$. The resultant of the shearing stresses can be calculated in a similar manner:

$$F = -\int_0^l \mu\left(\frac{\mathrm{d}u}{\mathrm{d}y}\right)_0 \mathrm{d}x = \frac{\mu\, U\, l}{(k-1)\, h_2}\left[4 \ln k - \frac{6(k-1)}{k+1}\right]. \tag{6.33}$$

It is interesting to note [6] that the resultant pressure force possesses a maximum for $k = 2{\cdot}2$ approximately, when its value is

$$P_{\max} \approx 0{\cdot}16 \frac{\mu\, U\, l^2}{h_2^2}$$

and when

$$F = F_1 \approx 0{\cdot}75 \frac{\mu\, U\, l}{h_2}\,.$$

The coefficient of friction P/F is proportional to h_2/l and can be made very small.

The co-ordinates of the centre of pressure, x_c, can be shown to be equal to

$$x_c = \tfrac{1}{2}\, l \left[\frac{2\,k}{k-1} - \frac{k^2 - 1 - 2\,k \ln k}{(k^2-1)\ln k - 2\,(k-1)^2}\right]. \tag{6.34}$$

For small angles of inclination between block and slide ($k \approx 1$), the pressure distribution from eqn. (6.29) is nearly parabolic, the characteristic thickness and centre of pressure being very nearly at $x = \frac{1}{2}\, l$. Putting $h_m = h(\frac{1}{2} l)$ we can find that the pressure difference becomes

$$p_m = \mu\, U \frac{l^2}{(2\,a - l)\, h_m^2}\,. \tag{6.35}$$

If we compare this result with that for creeping motion past a sphere in eqn. (6.7b), we notice that in the case of the slipper the pressure difference is greater by a factor $(l/h_m)^2$. Since l/h_m is of the order of 500 to 1000 ($l = 4$ in, $h_m = 0{\cdot}004$ to $0{\cdot}008$ in), the prevailing pressures are seen to assume very large values†. The occurrence of such high pressures in slow viscous motion is a peculiar property of the type of flow

† Numerical example: $U = 30$ ft/sec; $\mu = 8 \times 10^{-4}$ lbf sec/ft²; $l = 4$ in $= 0{\cdot}333$ ft; $a = 2\,l = 8$ in $= 0{\cdot}667$ ft; $h_m = 0{\cdot}008$ in $= 0{\cdot}000667$ ft. Hence $\mu\, U/(2\,a - l) = 0{\cdot}024$ lbf/ft²; $p_m = 0{\cdot}024 \times 500^2/144 = 41{\cdot}7$ lbf/in².

encountered in lubrication. At the same time it is recognized that the angle formed between the two solid surfaces is an essential feature of the flow.

The pressure and velocity distribution, and the shape of stream-lines for the case of a plane slipper are given in Fig. 6.4. It will be noticed that back-flow occurs in the region of pressure rise near the wall at rest, just as was the case with the channel in Fig. 5.2, when the pressure increased in the direction of wall motion. W. Froessel [1] calculated the pressure distribution and thrust supported by a slipper of finite width as well as by a spherical slipper and confirmed these calculations by experiment.

In many cases when the width of the slipper is finite, the assumption that the flow is one-dimensional made earlier is insufficient, and the existence of a component w in the z-direction must be taken into account; here z is perpendicular to the plane of the sketch in Fig. 6.4. The equation preceding eqn. (6.19) must now be supplemented by

$$Q_z = \int_0^h w \, \mathrm{d}y = \tfrac{1}{2} \, \mathrm{h} \, W - \frac{h^3}{12\,\mu} \cdot \frac{\partial p}{\partial z} \tag{6.36}$$

and the equation of continuity becomes

$$\frac{\partial}{\partial x} \int_0^h u \, \mathrm{d}y + \frac{\partial}{\partial z} \int_0^h w \, \mathrm{d}y = 0 \tag{6.37}$$

or

$$\frac{\partial}{\partial x}\left(h^3 \frac{\partial p}{\partial x}\right) + \frac{\partial}{\partial z}\left(h^3 \frac{\partial p}{\partial y}\right) = 6\,\mu \left[\frac{\partial}{\partial x}(h\,U) + \frac{\partial}{\partial z}(h\,W)\right], \tag{6.38}$$

which is known as *Reynolds' equation of lubrication*. Here W denotes the component of the velocity of the boundary in the z-direction at a given x.

In the case of a journal and bearing there must be eccentricity between them in order to create a wedge of variable height which is essential if a thrust is to be created. The relevant theory, based on the preceding principles, as well as on exact two-dimensional theory, was developed in great detail by A. Sommerfeld [12], L. Guembel [2] and G. Vogelpohl [15, 16]. It has also been extended to include the case of bearings with finite width [1, 7, 15], when it was found that the decrease in thrust supported by such a bearing is very considerable due to the sidewise decrease in the pressure. Most theoretical calculations have been conducted under the assumption of constant viscosity. In reality heat is evolved through friction and the temperature of the lubricating oil is increased. Since the viscosity of oil decreases rapidly with increasing temperature (Table 1.2), the thrust also decreases greatly. In more recent times F. Nahme [8, 15] extended the hydrodynamic theory of lubrication to include the effect of the variation of viscosity with temperature (*cf.* Chap. XIV).

With large velocities and high temperatures (low viscosity), the reduced Reynolds number R^* from eqn. (6.14) can assume values near or exceeding unity. This means that inertia forces become comparable with viscous forces and the validity of the theory may be questioned. It is possible to improve the theory, and to extend it to higher Reynolds numbers, by a step-by-step procedure. The neglected inertia terms can be calculated from the first approximation and introduced as external forces so that a second approximation is obtained. This procedure corresponds to Oseen's improved solution for the flow past a sphere. Such calculations have been performed by W. Kahlert [5], who found that the inertia corrections in the case of a plane slipper or circular bearing do not exceed 10 per cent. of the solution under consideration for values of up to $\mathsf{R}^* = 5$ approx. A comparison between theoretical and experimental results is contained in a recent book by G. Vogelpohl [15], and in an earlier paper [17].

G. I. Taylor and P. G. Saffman [14] have demonstrated, contrary to what is commonly thought, that the effects of compressibility may become very important at these very low Reynolds numbers in spite of the fact that the Mach number may be very low too. Attention to this possibility was first drawn by J. Harrison [3] in connexion with air-lubricated bearings.

d. The Hele-Shaw flow

Another remarkable solution of the three-dimensional equations of creeping motion, eqns. (6.3) and (6.4), can be obtained for the case of flow between two parallel flat walls separated by a small distance $2h$. If a cylindrical body of arbitrary cross-section is inserted between the two plates at right angles so that it completely fills the space between them, the resulting pattern of stream-lines is identical with that in potential flow about the same shape. H. S. Hele-Shaw [4] used this method to obtain experimental patterns of stream-lines in potential flow about arbitrary bodies. It is easy to prove that the solution for creeping motion from eqns. (6.3) and (6.4) possesses the stream-lines as the corresponding potential flow.

We select a system of co-ordinates with its origin in the centre between the two plates, and make the x, y-plane parallel to the plates, the z-axis being perpendicular to them. The body is assumed to be placed in a stream of velocity U_∞ parallel to the x-axis. At a large distance from the body the velocity distribution is parabolic, as in the motion in a rectangular channel which was considered in Section V.1. Hence

$$x = \infty: \qquad u = U_\infty \left(1 - \frac{z^2}{h^2}\right), \qquad v = 0, \qquad w = 0 .$$

A solution of eqns. (6.3) and (6.4) can be written as:

$$\left.\begin{aligned} u = u_0(x, y)\left(1 - \frac{z^2}{h^2}\right); \qquad v = v_0(x, y)\left(1 - \frac{z^2}{h^2}\right); \qquad w \equiv 0 \\ p = -\frac{2\,\mu}{h^2}\int_{x_0}^{x} u_0(x, y)\,\mathrm{d}x = -\frac{2\,\mu}{h^2}\int_{y_0}^{y} v_0(x, y)\,\mathrm{d}y\,, \end{aligned}\right\} \qquad (6.39)$$

where $u_0(x, y)$, $v_0(x, y)$ and $p_0(x, y)$ denote the velocity and pressure distribution of the two-dimensional potential flow past the given body. Thus u_0, v_0 and p_0 satisfy the equations

$$\left.\begin{aligned} u_0 \frac{\partial u_0}{\partial x} + v_0 \frac{\partial u_0}{\partial y} &= -\frac{1}{\varrho}\frac{\partial p_0}{\partial x} \\ u_0 \frac{\partial v_0}{\partial x} + v_0 \frac{\partial v_0}{\partial y} &= -\frac{1}{\varrho}\frac{\partial p_0}{\partial y} \\ \frac{\partial u_0}{\partial x} + \frac{\partial v_0}{\partial y} &= 0\,. \end{aligned}\right\} \qquad (6.40\,\mathrm{a, b, c})$$

First we notice at once from the solution (6.39) that the equation of continuity and the equation of motion in the z-direction are satisfied. The fact that the equations of motion in the x- and y-directions are also satisfied follows from the potential character of u_0 and v_0. The functions u_0 and v_0 satisfy the condition of irrotationality

$$\partial u_0/\partial y - \partial v_0/\partial x = 0\,,$$

so that the potential equations $\nabla^2 u_0 = 0$ and $\nabla^2 v_0 = 0$, where $\nabla^2 = \partial^2/\partial x^2 + \partial^2/\partial y^2$, are satisfied.

The first two equations (6.3) reduce to $\partial p/\partial x = \mu\, \partial^2 u/\partial z^2$ and $\partial p/\partial y = \mu\, \partial^2 v/\partial z^2$; they are, however, satisfied, as seen from (6.39). Thus eqns. (6.39) represent a solution of the equations for creeping motion. On the other hand the flow represented by eqns. (6.39) has the same stream-lines as potential flow about the body, and the stream-lines for all parallel layers $z =$ const are congruent. The condition of no slip at the plates $z = \pm h$ is seen to be satisfied by eqn. (6.39), but the condition of no slip at the surface of the body is not satisfied.

The ratio of inertia to viscous forces in Hele-Shaw motion, just as in the case of the motion of lubricating oil, is given by the reduced Reynolds number

$$\mathsf{R}^* = \frac{U_\infty L}{\nu}\left(\frac{h}{L}\right)^2 \ll 1\,,$$

where L denotes a characteristic linear dimension of the body in the x, y-plane. If R^* exceeds unity the inertia terms become considerable and the motion deviates from the simple solution (6.39).

The solution given by eqn. (6.39) can be improved in the same manner as Stokes' solution for a sphere or the solution for very slow flow. The inertia terms are calculated from the first approximation and introducted into the equations as external forces, and an improved solution results. This was carried out by F. Riegels [11] for the case of Hele-Shaw flow past a circular cylinder.

For $\mathsf{R}^* > 1$ the stream-lines in the various layers parallel to the walls cease to be congruent. The slow particles near the two plates are deflected more by the presence of the body than the faster particles near the centre. This causes the stream-lines to appear somewhat blurred and the phenomenon is more pronounced at the rear of the body than in front of it, Fig. 6.5.

Solutions in the case of creeping motion are inherently restricted to very small Reynolds numbers. In principle it is possible to extend the field of application to larger Reynolds numbers by successive approximation, as mentioned previously. However, in all cases the calculations become so complicated that it is not practicable to carry out more than one step in the approximation. For this reason it is not possible to reach the region of moderate Reynolds numbers from this direction. To all intents and purposes the region of moderate Reynolds numbers in which the inertia and viscous forces are of comparable magnitude throughout the field of flow has not been investigated by mathematical means at all.

It is, therefore, the more useful to have the possibility of integrating the Navier-Stokes equation for the other limiting case of very large Reynolds numbers. Thus we are led to the boundary layer theory which will form the subject of the succeeding chapters.

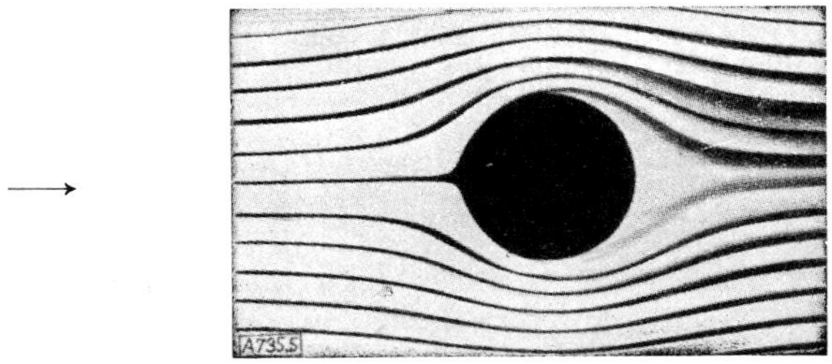

Fig. 6.5. Hele-Shaw flow past circular cylinder at $R^* = 4$, after Riegels [11]

References

[1] W. Frössel, Reibungswiderstand und Tragkraft eines Gleitschuhes endlicher Breite. Forschg. Ing.-Wes. **13**, 65 (1942).
[2] L. Gümbel and E. Everling, Reibung und Schmierung im Maschinenbau, Berlin 1925.
[3] W. J. Harrison, The hydrodynamical theory of lubrication with special reference to air as a lubricant, Trans. Cambridge Phil. Soc., **22**, 39 (1913).
[4] H. S. Hele-Shaw, Investigation of the nature of surface resistance of water and of stream motion under certain experimental conditions. Trans. Inst. Nav. Arch. XI, 25 (1898), see also Nature **58**, 34 (1898) and Proc. Roy. Inst. **16**, 49 (1899).
[5] W. Kahlert, Der Einfluß der Trägheitskräfte bei der hydrodynamischen Schmiermitteltheorie, Ing.-Arch. **16**, 321 (1948).
[6] B. H. Lamb, Hydrodynamics 6th. ed., Cambridge 1947, pp. 583, 584.
[7] A. G. Michell, Z. Math. u. Physik **52**, 123 (1905), see also Ostwalds Klassiker No. 218.
[8] F. Nahme, Beiträge zur hydrodynamischen Theorie der Lagerreibung, Ing.-Arch. II, 191 (1940).
[9] C. W. Oseen, Über die Stokessche Formel und über die verwandte Aufgabe in der Hydrodynamik. Arkiv for mathematik, astronomi och fysik **6**, No. 29 (1910).
[10] L. Prandtl, The mechanics of viscous fluids; in W. F. Durand, Aerodynamic theory III (1935).
[11] F. Riegels, Zur Kritik des Hele-Shaw Versuches, ZAMM **18**, 95 (1938).
[12] A. Sommerfeld, Zur hydrodynamischen Theorie der Schmiermittelreibung, Z. Math. u. Physik, **50**, 97 (1904) also Ostwald's Klassiker No. 218 p. 108 and Zur Theorie der Schmiermittelreibung, Z. Techn. Phys. **2**, 58 (1921), also Ostwald's Klassiker No. 218, p. 181.
[13] G. G. Stokes, On the effect of the internal friction of fluids on the motion of pendulums, Cambr. Phil. Trans. IX (1851), also Math. and Phys. Papers, Cambridge 1901, III, 55.
[14] G. I. Taylor and P. G. Saffman, Effects of compressibility at low Reynolds number, Jour. Aero. Sci. **24**, 553 (1957).
[15] G. Vogelpohl, Betriebssichere Gleitlager, Springer, Berlin 1958.
[16] G. Vogelpohl, Beiträge zur Kenntnis der Gleitlagerreibung, VDI-Forschungsheft 386 (1937).
[17] G. Vogelpohl, Ähnlichkeitsbeziehungen der Gleitlagerreibung und untere Reibungsgrenze, Z. VDI., **91**, 379 (1949).

Part B. Laminar boundary layers

CHAPTER VII

Boundary layer equations for two-dimensional flow; boundary layer on a plate

a. Derivation of boundary layer equations for flow along a flat plate

We now proceed to examine the second limiting case, namely that of very small viscosity or very large Reynolds number. An important contribution to the science of fluid motion was made by L. Prandtl [13] in 1904 when he clarified the essential influence of viscosity in flows at high Reynolds numbers and showed how the Navier-Stokes equations could be simplified to yield approximate solutions for this case. We shall explain these simplifications with the aid of an argument which preserves the physical picture of the phenomenon, and it will be recalled that in the bulk of the fluid inertia forces predominate, the influence of viscous forces being vanishingly small.

For the sake of simplicity we shall consider two-dimensional flow of a fluid with very small viscosity about a cylindrical body of slender cross-section, Fig. 7.1. With the exception of the immediate neighbourhood of the surface, the velocities are of the order of the free-stream velocity V, and the pattern of stream-lines and the velocity distribution deviate only slightly from those in frictionless (potential) flow. However, detailed investigations reveal that, unlike in potential flow, the fluid does not slide over the wall, but adheres to it. The transition from zero velocity at the wall to the full magnitude at some distance from it takes place in a very thin layer, the so-called boundary layer. In this manner there are two regions to consider, even if the division between them is not very sharp:

1. A very thin layer in the immediate neighbourhood of the body in which the velocity gradient, normal to the wall, $\partial u/\partial y$, is very large (*boundary layer*). In this region the very small viscosity μ of the fluid exerts an essential influence insofar as the shearing stress $\tau = \mu(\partial u/\partial y)$ may assume large values.
2. In the remaining region no such large velocity gradients occur and the influence of viscosity is unimportant. In this region the flow is frictionless and potential.

In general it is possible to state that the thickness of the boundary layer decreases with viscosity, or, more generally, that it decreases as the Reynolds number increases. It was seen from several exact solutions of the Navier-Stokes equations presented in Chap. V that the boundary layer thickness in proportional to the square root of kinematic viscosity:

$$\delta \sim \sqrt{\nu}\,.$$

When making the simplifications to be introduced into the Navier-Stokes equations it is assumed that this thickness is very small compared with a still unspecified linear dimension, L, of the body:

$$\delta \ll L\,.$$

In this way the solutions obtained from the boundary layer equations are asymptotic and apply to very large Reynolds numbers.

We shall now proceed to discuss the simplification of the Navier-Stokes equations, and in order to achieve it, we shall make an estimate of the order of magnitude of each term. In the two-dimensional problem shown in Fig. 7.1 we shall begin by assuming the wall to be flat and coinciding with the x-direction, the y-axis being

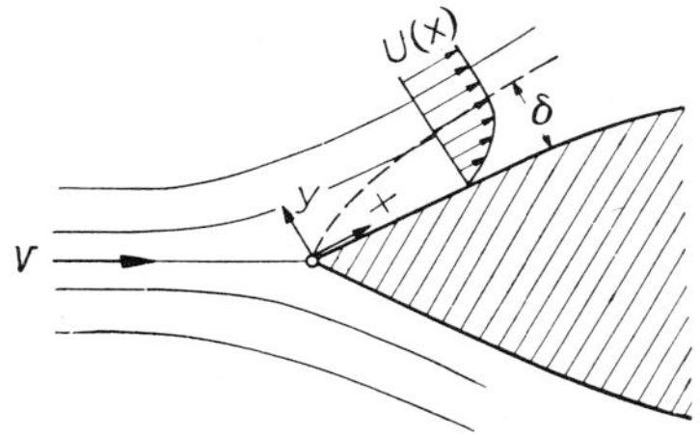

Fig. 7.1. Boundary layer flow along a wall

perpendicular to it. We now rewrite the Navier-Stokes equations in dimensionless form by referring all velocities to the free-stream velocity, V, and by referring all linear dimensions to a characteristic length, L, of the body, which is so selected as to ensure that the dimensionless derivative $\partial u/\partial x$ does not exceed unity in the region under consideration. The pressure is made dimensionless with ϱV^2, and time is referred to L/V. Further, the expression

$$\mathsf{R} = \frac{V L \varrho}{\mu} = \frac{V L}{\nu}$$

denotes the Reynolds number which is assumed very large. Under these assumptions, and retaining the same symbols for the dimensionless quantities as for their dimensional counterparts, we have from the Navier-Stokes equations for plane flow, eqns. (3.29) or (4.4):

direction x:
$$\frac{\partial u}{\partial t} + u\frac{\partial u}{\partial x} + v\frac{\partial u}{\partial y} = -\frac{\partial p}{\partial x} + \frac{1}{\mathsf{R}}\left(\frac{\partial^2 u}{\partial x^2} + \frac{\partial^2 u}{\partial y^2}\right) \qquad (7.1)$$

$$1 \qquad 1 \quad 1 \qquad \delta\,\frac{1}{\delta} \qquad\qquad\qquad \delta^2 \quad 1 \qquad \frac{1}{\delta^2}$$

direction y:
$$\frac{\partial v}{\partial t} + u\frac{\partial v}{\partial x} + v\frac{\partial v}{\partial y} = -\frac{\partial p}{\partial y} + \frac{1}{\mathsf{R}}\left(\frac{\partial^2 v}{\partial x^2} + \frac{\partial^2 v}{\partial y^2}\right) \tag{7.2}$$

$$\delta \qquad 1\ \delta \qquad \delta\ 1 \qquad\qquad \delta^2 \quad \delta \qquad \frac{1}{\delta}$$

continuity:
$$\frac{\partial u}{\partial x} + \frac{\partial v}{\partial y} = 0\,. \tag{7.3}$$

$$1 \qquad 1$$

The boundary conditions are: absence of slip between the fluid and the wall, i. e. $u = v = 0$ for $y = 0$, and $u = U$ for $y \to \infty$.

With the assumptions made previously the dimensionless boundary layer thickness δ/L, for which we shall retain the symbol δ, is very small with respect to unity, ($\delta \ll 1$).

We shall now estimate the order of magnitude of each term in order to be able to drop small terms and thus to achieve the desired simplification of the equations. Since $\partial u/\partial x$ is of the order 1, we see from the equation of continuity that equally $\partial v/\partial y$ is of the order 1, and hence, since at the wall $v = 0$, that in the boundary layer v is of the order δ. Thus $\partial v/\partial x$ and $\partial^2 v/\partial x^2$ are also of the order δ. Further $\partial^2 u/\partial x^2$ is of the order 1. (The orders of magnitude are shown in eqns. (7.1) to (7.3) under the individual terms).

We shall, further, assume that the non-steady acceleration $\partial u/\partial t$ is of the same order as the convective term $u\,\partial u/\partial x$ which means that very sudden accelerations, such as occur in very large pressure waves, are excluded. In accordance with our previous argument some of the viscous terms must be of the same order of magnitude as the inertia terms, at least in the immediate neighbourhood of the wall, and in spite of the smallness of the factor $1/\mathsf{R}$. Hence some of the second derivatives of velocity must become very large near the wall. In accordance with what was said before this can only apply to $\partial^2 u/\partial y^2$ and $\partial^2 v/\partial y^2$. Since the component of velocity parallel to the wall increases from zero at the wall to the value 1 in the free-stream across the layer of thickness δ, we have

$$\frac{\partial u}{\partial y} \sim \frac{1}{\delta} \quad \text{and} \quad \frac{\partial^2 u}{\partial y^2} \sim \frac{1}{\delta^2}\,,$$

whereas $\partial v/\partial y \sim \delta/\delta \sim 1$ and $\partial^2 v/\partial y^2 \sim 1/\delta$. If these values are inserted into eqns. (7.1) and (7.2), it follows from the first equation of motion that the viscous forces in the boundary layer can become of the same order of magnitude as the inertia forces only if the Reynolds number is of the order $1/\delta^2$:

$$\frac{1}{\mathsf{R}} = \delta^2\,. \tag{7.4}$$

The first equation can now be simplified by neglecting $\partial^2 u/\partial x^2$ with respect to $\partial^2 u/\partial y^2$. The third equation, that of continuity, remains unaltered. From the second equation we may infer that $\partial p/\partial y$ is of the order δ. The pressure increase across the boundary layer which would be obtained by integrating the second equation, is of the order δ^2, i. e. very small. Thus the pressure in a direction normal to the boundary layer is practically constant; it may be assumed equal to that at the outer edge of the boundary layer when its value is determined by the frictionless flow. The pressure is said to be 'impressed' on the boundary layer by the outer flow. It may, therefore, be regarded as a known function as far as boundary layer flow is concerned, and it depends only on the co-ordinate x, and on time t.

At the outer edge of the boundary layer the parallel component u becomes equal to that in the outer flow, $U(x,t)$. Since there is no large velocity gradient here, the viscous terms in eqn. (7.1) vanish for large values of R, and consequently, for the outer flow we obtain

$$\frac{\partial U}{\partial t} + U\frac{\partial U}{\partial x} = -\frac{1}{\varrho}\frac{\partial p}{\partial x}, \tag{7.5}$$

where again the symbols denote dimensional quantities.

In the case of steady flow the equation is simplified still further in that the pressure depends only on x. We shall emphasize this circumstance by writing the derivative as $\mathrm{d}p/\mathrm{d}x$, so that

$$p + \tfrac{1}{2}\varrho U^2 = \text{const}. \tag{7.6}$$

The boundary conditions for the external flow are nearly the same as for frictionless flow. The boundary layer thickness is very small and the transverse velocity component v is very small at the edge of the boundary layer ($v/V \sim \delta/L$). Thus potential non-viscous flow about the body under consideration in which the perpendicular velocity component is vanishingly small near the wall offers a very good approximation to the actual external flow. The pressure gradient in the x-direction in the boundary layer can be obtained by simply applying the Bernoulli equation (7.5) to the streamline at the wall in the known potential flow.

Summing up, we are now in a position to write down the simplified Navier-Stokes equations, known as *Prandtl's boundary layer equations*. We return again to dimensional quantities, and obtain:

$$\frac{\partial u}{\partial t} + u\frac{\partial u}{\partial x} + v\frac{\partial u}{\partial y} = -\frac{1}{\varrho}\frac{\partial p}{\partial x} + \nu\frac{\partial^2 u}{\partial y^2} \tag{7.7}$$

$$\frac{\partial u}{\partial x} + \frac{\partial v}{\partial y} = 0 \tag{7.8}$$

with the boundary conditions

$$y = 0: \quad u = v = 0; \qquad y = \infty: \quad u = U(x,t). \tag{7.9}$$

The potential flow $U(x,t)$ is to be considered known; it determines the pressure distribution with the aid of eqn. (7.5). In addition, a suitable boundary layer flow must be prescribed over the whole x, y region under consideration for the instant $t=0$.

In the case of *steady flow* the above system of equations simplifies to

$$u\frac{\partial u}{\partial x} + v\frac{\partial u}{\partial y} = -\frac{1}{\varrho}\frac{\mathrm{d}p}{\mathrm{d}x} + \nu\frac{\partial^2 u}{\partial y^2} \tag{7.10}$$

$$\frac{\partial u}{\partial x} + \frac{\partial v}{\partial y} = 0 \tag{7.11}$$

with the boundary conditions

$$y = 0: \quad u = 0\,, \quad v = 0\,; \qquad y = \infty: \quad u = U(x)\,. \tag{7.12}$$

It is necessary to prescribe, in addition, a velocity profile at the initial section, $x = x_0$, say, by indicating the function $u(x_0, y)$. The problem is thus seen to reduce itself to the calculation of the further change of a given velocity profile with a given potential motion.

The mathematical simplification achieved on the preceding pages is considerable: it is true that, as distinct from the case of creeping motion, the non-linear character of the Navier-Stokes equation has been preserved, but of the three original equations for u, v, and p of the two-dimensional flow problem, one, the equation of motion normal to the wall, has been dropped completely. Thus the number of unknowns has been reduced by one. There remains a system of two simultaneous equations for the two unknowns u and v. The pressure ceased to be an unknown function and can now be evaluated from the potential flow solution for the body with the aid of the Bernoulli equation. Further, one viscous term in the remaining equation of motion has also been dropped.

Finally, we shall note that the estimation of the boundary layer thickness in eqn. (7.4) showed that

$$\frac{\delta}{L} \sim \frac{1}{\sqrt{\mathsf{R}}} = \sqrt{\frac{\nu}{VL}}\,. \tag{7.13}$$

The fact that $\delta \sim \sqrt{\nu}$, inferred from the exact solutions of the Navier-Stokes equations, is thereby confirmed. The numerical coefficient, still missing in eqn. (7.13), will turn out to be equal to 5 for the case of a flat plate at zero incidence, when L will mean the distance from its leading edge.

b. Boundary layer equations for curved walls

The preceding argument was conducted under the assumption of a flat wall, but it can be easily extended to the case of a curved wall. In the case of two-dimensional flow along a curved wall we shall introduce a curvilinear orthogonal system of co-ordinates, whose x-axis will be

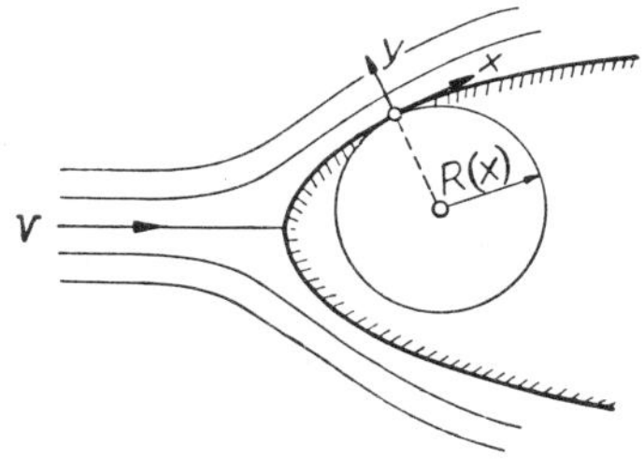

Fig. 7.2. Boundary layer flow along a curved wall

in the direction of the wall, the y-axis being perpendicular to it, Fig. 7.2. The curvilinear net will, thus, consist of curves parallel to the wall and of straight lines perpendicular to them. The corresponding velocity components will be denoted by u and v, and the radius of curvature at a point x will be denoted by $R(x)$, being positive when the wall is convex outwards, and negative when it is concave outwards. W. Tollmien [16] derived expressions for the complete Navier-Stokes equations in such a system of co-ordinates. They are:

$$\frac{\partial u}{\partial t} + \frac{R}{R+y} u \frac{\partial u}{\partial x} + v \frac{\partial u}{\partial y} + \frac{v\, u}{R+y} = - \frac{R}{R+y} \frac{1}{\varrho} \frac{\partial p}{\partial x} + \nu \left\{ \frac{R^2}{(R+y)^2} \frac{\partial^2 u}{\partial x^2} + \frac{\partial^2 u}{\partial y^2} + \right.$$
$$\left. + \frac{1}{R+y} \frac{\partial u}{\partial y} - \frac{u}{(R+y)^2} + \frac{2\,R}{(R+y)^2} \frac{\partial v}{\partial x} - \frac{R}{(R+y)^3} \frac{\mathrm{d}R}{\mathrm{d}x} v + \frac{R\, y}{(R+y)^3} \frac{\mathrm{d}R}{\mathrm{d}x} \frac{\partial u}{\partial x} \right\} \tag{7.14}$$

$$\frac{\partial v}{\partial t} + \frac{R}{R+y} u \frac{\partial v}{\partial x} + v \frac{\partial v}{\partial y} - \frac{u^2}{R+y} = - \frac{1}{\varrho} \frac{\partial p}{\partial y} + \nu \left\{ \frac{\partial^2 v}{\partial y^2} - \frac{2\,R}{(R+y)^2} \frac{\partial u}{\partial x} + \frac{1}{R+y} \frac{\partial v}{\partial y} + \right.$$
$$\left. + \frac{R^2}{(R+y)^2} \frac{\partial^2 v}{\partial x^2} - \frac{v}{(R+y)^2} + \frac{R}{(R+y)^3} \frac{\mathrm{d}R}{\mathrm{d}x} u + \frac{R\, y}{(R+y)^3} \frac{\mathrm{d}R}{\mathrm{d}x} \frac{\partial v}{\partial x} \right\} \tag{7.15}$$

$$\frac{R}{R+y} \frac{\partial u}{\partial x} + \frac{\partial v}{\partial y} + \frac{v}{R+y} = 0\,. \tag{7.16}$$

If the relative orders of magnitude of the individual terms are estimated in the same manner as in the preceding section, the following results will be obtained: On the assumption that the boundary layer thickness is small compared with the radius of curvature of the wall, and for the case when no large variations in curvature occur, so that $\mathrm{d}R/\mathrm{d}x \sim 1$, the first equation of motion and the equation of continuity simplify to the same form as for a flat wall. From the second equation of motion we would obtain $(1/\varrho) \cdot (\partial p/\partial y) = u^2/R$. Thus the pressure gradient in the perpendicular direction is now of the order 1, compared with δ in the previous case. The pressure difference between wall and outer edge of the boundary layer is now of the order δ, so that in the case of a curved wall the pressure p in the boundary layer can still be assumed constant.

We conclude, therefore, that in general the boundary layer equations (7.10) to (7.12) may be applied to the case of a curved wall as well, provided that there are no large variations in curvature, such as would occur near sharp edges.

The derivation of the boundary layer equations given earlier was constantly related to the physical representation in which the existence of a thin viscous layer is assumed but, at the same time, an effort was made to deduce Prandtl's boundary layer equations from the Navier-Stokes equations in a purely mathematical way, without having to make any additional assumptions of a physical nature [15].

c. Some physical properties of boundary layers

It is already possible to draw some important conclusions from the preceding deliberations, i. e. without first discussing the question of the methods of integration. The first important question to answer is to determine the circumstances under which some of the retarded fluid in the boundary layer can be transported into the main stream or, in other words, to find when *separation* of the flow from the wall may occur. When a region with an adverse pressure gradient exists along the wall, the retarded fluid particles cannot, in general, penetrate too far into the region of increased pressure owing to their small kinetic energy. Thus the boundary layer is deflected sideways from the wall, separates from it, and moves into the main stream, Fig. 7.3. In general the fluid particles behind the point of separation follow the pressure gradient and move in a direction opposite to the external stream.

The point of separation is defined as the limit between forward and reverse flow in the layer in the immediate neighbourhood of the wall, or

$$\text{point of separation:} \left(\frac{\partial u}{\partial y}\right)_{y=0} = 0 . \qquad (7.17)\dagger$$

In order to answer the question of whether and where separation occurs, it is necessary, in general, first to integrate the boundary layer equations. Generally speaking the boundary layer equations are only valid as far as the point of separation. A short distance downstream from the point of separation the boundary layer becomes so thick that the assumptions which were made in the derivation of the boundary layer equations no longer apply. In the case of bodies with blunt sterns the separated boundary layer displaces the potential flow from the body by an appreciable distance and the pressure distribution impressed on the boundary layer must be determined by experiment, because the external flow depends on the phenomena connected with separation.

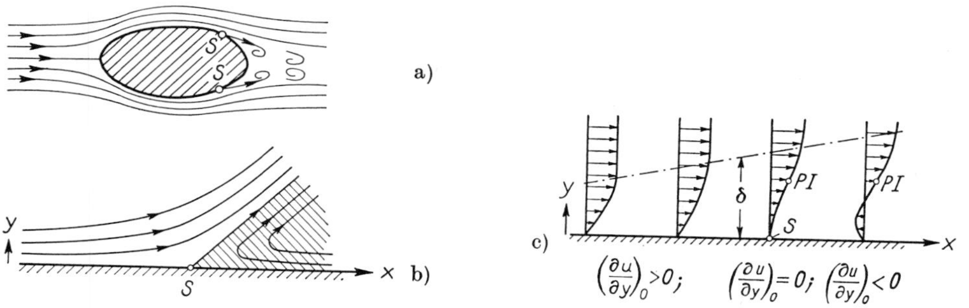

Fig. 7.3. Separation of the boundary layer. a) Flow past a body with separation (S = point of separation). b) Shape of stream-lines near point of separation. c) Velocity distribution near the point of separation (PI = point of inflexion)

The fact that separation in steady flow occurs only in decelerated flow ($\mathrm{d}p/\mathrm{d}x > 0$) can be easily inferred from a consideration of the relation between the pressure gradient $\mathrm{d}p/\mathrm{d}x$ and the velocity distribution $u(y)$ with the aid of the boundary layer equations. From eqn. (7.10) with the boundary conditions $u = v = 0$ we have at $y = 0$

$$\mu \left(\frac{\partial^2 u}{\partial y^2}\right)_{y=0} = \frac{\mathrm{d}p}{\mathrm{d}x} \qquad (7.18)$$

and, further, after differentiation with respect to y:

$$\left(\frac{\partial^3 u}{\partial y^3}\right)_{y=0} = 0 . \qquad (7.19)$$

† The velocity profile at the point of separation is seen to have a zero tangent at the wall. The velocity profiles downstream from the point of separation will show regions of reversed flow near the wall, Fig. 7.3c.

In the immediate neighbourhood of the wall the curvature of the velocity profile depends only on the pressure gradient, and the curvature of the velocity profile at the wall changes its sign with the pressure gradient. For flow with decreasing pressure (accelerated flow, $\mathrm{d}p/\mathrm{d}x < 0$) we have from eqn. (7.18) that $(\partial^2 u/\partial y^2)_{wall} < 0$ and, therefore, $\partial^2 u/\partial y^2 < 0$ over the whole width of the boundary layer, Fig. 7.4. In the region of pressure increase (decelerated flow, $\mathrm{d}p/\mathrm{d}x > 0$) we find $(\partial^2 u/\partial y^2) > 0$. Since, however, in any case $\partial^2 u/\partial y^2 < 0$ at a large distance from the wall, there must exist a point for which $\partial^2 u/\partial y^2 = 0$. This is a point of inflexion† of the velocity profile in the boundary layer, Fig. 7.5.

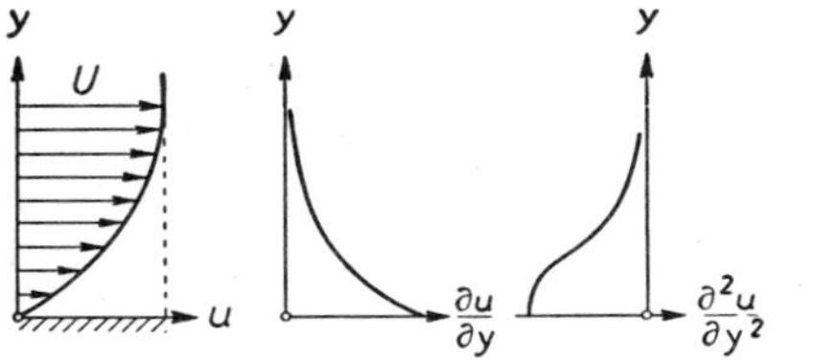

Fig. 7.4. Velocity distribution in a boundary layer with pressure decrease

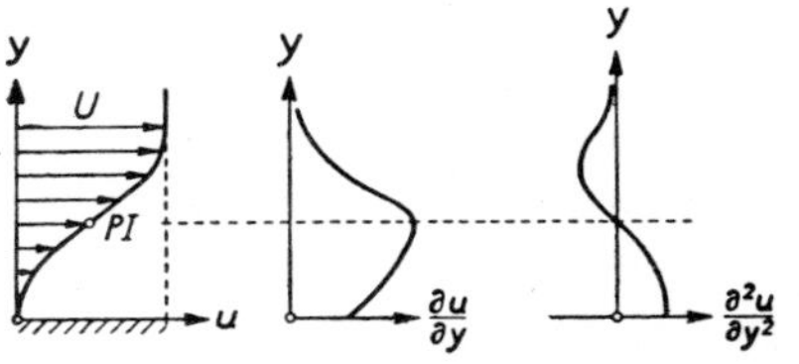

Fig. 7.5. Velocity distribution in a boundary layer with pressure increase; PI = point of inflexion

It follows that in the region of retarded potential flow the velocity profile in the boundary layer always displays a point of inflexion. Since the velocity profile at the point of separation and with a zero tangent must have a point of inflexion, it follows that separation can only occur when the potential flow is retarded.

d. A remark on the integration of the boundary layer equations

In order to integrate the boundary layer equations, whether in the non-steady case, eqns. (7.7) and (7.8), or in the steady case, eqns. (7.10) and (7.11), it is often convenient to introduce a stream function $\psi(x, y, t)$ defined by

$$u = \frac{\partial \psi}{\partial y}\,; \qquad v = -\frac{\partial \psi}{\partial x}\,, \tag{7.20}$$

so that the equation of continuity is thereby satisfied. Introducing this assumption into eqn. (7.7) we have

$$\frac{\partial^2 \psi}{\partial y\,\partial t} + \frac{\partial \psi}{\partial y}\frac{\partial^2 \psi}{\partial x\,\partial y} - \frac{\partial \psi}{\partial x}\frac{\partial^2 \psi}{\partial y^2} = -\frac{1}{\varrho}\frac{\partial p}{\partial x} + \nu\frac{\partial^3 \psi}{\partial y^3}\,, \tag{7.21}$$

which is a partial differential equation of the third order. The boundary conditions require the absence of slip at the wall, or $\partial\psi/\partial y = \partial\psi/\partial x = 0$ at the wall. Further the initial condition at $t = 0$ prescribes the velocity distribution $u = \partial\psi/\partial y$ over the whole region. If this equation for the stream function is compared with the complete Navier-Stokes equations (4.10), it is seen that the boundary layer assumptions have reduced the order of the equation from four to three.

† The existence of a point of inflexion in the velocity profile in the boundary layer is important for its stability (transition from laminar to turbulent flow), see Chap. XVI.

e. Skin friction

When the boundary layer equations are integrated, the velocity distribution can be deduced and the position of the point of separation can be determined. This, in turn, permits us to calculate the viscous drag (skin friction) around the surface by a simple process of integrating the shearing stress at the wall over the surface of the body. The shearing stress at the wall is

$$\tau_0 = \mu \left(\frac{\partial u}{\partial y}\right)_{y=0} .$$

The viscous drag for the case of two-dimensional flow becomes

$$D_f = b \int_{s=0}^{l} \tau_0 \cos \phi \, \mathrm{d}s , \tag{7.22}$$

where b denotes the height of the cylindrical body; ϕ is the angle between the tangent to the surface and the free stream velocity U_∞, and s is the co-ordinate measured along the surface, Fig. 7.6. The process of integration is to be performed

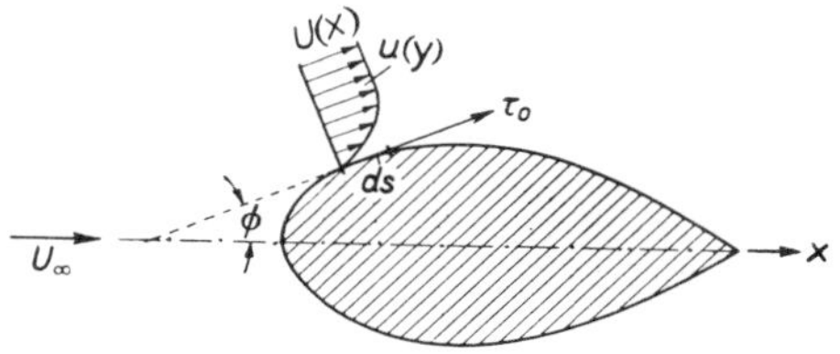

Fig. 7.6. Illustrating the calculation of skin friction

over the whole surface, from the stagnation point at the leading edge to the trailing edge, assuming that there is no separation. Since $\cos \phi \, \mathrm{d}s = \mathrm{d}x$, where x is measured parallel to the free stream velocity, we can also write

$$D_f = b \, \mu \int_{x=0}^{l} \left(\frac{\partial u}{\partial y}\right)_{y=0} \mathrm{d}x , \tag{7.22a}$$

and the integration, as before, is to be extended over the whole wetted surface from the leading to the trailing edge. In order to calculate the skin friction it is necessary to know the velocity gradient at the wall, which can be achieved only through the integration of the differential equations of the boundary layer. If separation occurs before the trailing edge, eqn. (7.22a) is valid only as far as the point of separation. Furthermore, if the laminar boundary layer transforms into a turbulent one, eqn. (7.22a) applies only as far as the point of transition. Behind the point of transition there is turbulent friction, to be discussed in Chap. XXII.

If separation exists, the pressure distribution differs considerably from that in the ideal case of frictionless, potential flow and pressure, or form drag, results. Thus the boundary layer theory explains the fact that, in addition to skin friction, there is also form drag, but its magnitude cannot be calculated with the aid of the boundary layer theory in a simple manner. A rough estimate will, however, be given in Chap. XXIV.

f. The boundary layer along a plate

In the succeeding chapter we shall deduce a number of general properties of the differential equations of the boundary layer. However, before doing that it seems opportune to consider now a specific example and so to gain greater familiarity with the equations. The simplest example of the application of the boundary layer equations is afforded by the flow along a very thin flat plate. Historically this was the first example illustrating the application of Prandtl's boundary layer theory;

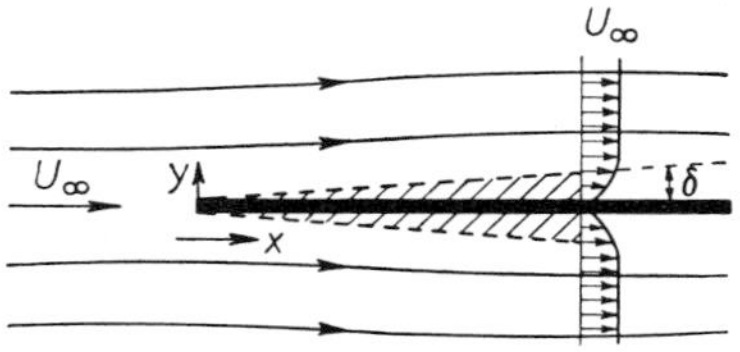

Fig. 7.7. The boundary layer along a flat plate at zero incidence

it was discussed by H. Blasius [2] in his doctor's thesis at Goettingen. Let the leading edge of the plate be at $x = 0$, the plate being parallel to the x-axis and infinitely long downstream, Fig. 7.7. We shall consider steady flow with a free stream velocity, U_∞, which is parallel to the x-axis. The velocity of potential flow is constant in this case, and, therefore, $\mathrm{d}p/\mathrm{d}x \equiv 0$. The boundary layer equations (7.10) to (7.12) become

$$u\frac{\partial u}{\partial x} + v\frac{\partial u}{\partial y} = \nu\frac{\partial^2 u}{\partial y^2}\,, \qquad \frac{\partial u}{\partial x} + \frac{\partial v}{\partial y} = 0\,, \tag{7.23}$$

$$y = 0: \quad u = v = 0\;; \qquad y = \infty: \quad u = U_\infty\,. \tag{7.24}$$

Since the system under consideration has no preferred length it is reasonable to suppose that the velocity profiles at varying distances from the leading edge are similar to each other, which means that the velocity curves $u(y)$ for varying distances x can be made identical by selecting suitable scale factors for u and y†. The scale factors for u and y appear quite naturally as the free stream velocity, U_∞, and the boundary layer thickness, $\delta(x)$, respectively. It will be noted that the latter increases with the current distance x. Hence the principle of similarity of velocity profiles in the boundary layer can be written as $u/U_\infty = \phi(y/\delta)$, where the function ϕ must be the same at all distances x from the leading edge.

We can now estimate the thickness of the boundary layer. From the exact solutions of the Navier-Stokes equations considered previously (Chap. V) it was found, e. g. in the case of a suddenly accelerated plate, that $\delta \sim \sqrt{\nu t}$, where t denoted the time from the start of the motion. In relation to the problem under consideration we may substitute for t the time which a fluid particle consumes while travelling from the leading edge to the point x. For a particle outside the boundary

† The problem of *affinity* or *similarity* of velocity profiles will be considered from a more general point of view in Chap. VIII. The more exact theory shows that the region immediately behind the leading edge must be excluded; see p. 123.

layer this is $t = x/U_\infty$, so that we may put $\delta \sim \sqrt{\nu x/U_\infty}$. We now introduce the new dimensionless co-ordinate $\eta = y/\delta$ so that

$$\eta = y\sqrt{\frac{U_\infty}{\nu x}}. \tag{7.25}$$

The equation of continuity, as already discussed in Sec. VIId, can be integrated by introducing a stream function $\psi(x, y)$. We put

$$\psi = \sqrt{\nu x U_\infty}\, f(\eta), \tag{7.26}$$

where $f(\eta)$ denotes the dimensionless stream function. Thus the velocity components become:

$$u = \frac{\partial \psi}{\partial y} = \frac{\partial \psi}{\partial \eta}\frac{\partial \eta}{\partial y} = U_\infty f'(\eta), \tag{7.27}$$

the prime denoting differentiation with respect to η. Similarly, the transverse velocity component is

$$v = -\frac{\partial \psi}{\partial x} = \frac{1}{2}\sqrt{\frac{\nu U_\infty}{x}}\,(\eta f' - f). \tag{7.28}$$

Writing down the further terms of eqn. (7.23), and inserting, we have

$$-\frac{U_\infty^2}{2x}\eta f' f'' + \frac{U_\infty^2}{2x}(\eta f' - f) f'' = \nu \frac{U_\infty^2}{x\nu} f'''.$$

After simplification, the following ordinary differential equation is obtained:

$$f f'' + 2 f''' = 0. \tag{7.29}$$

As seen from eqns. (7.24), as well as (7.27) and (7.28), the boundary conditions are:

$$\eta = 0: \quad f = 0, \quad f' = 0; \qquad \eta = \infty: \quad f' = 1. \tag{7.30}$$

In this example both partial differential equations (7.23) have been transformed into an ordinary differential equation for the stream function by the substitution (7.25). The resulting differential equation is non-linear and of the third order. The three boundary conditions (7.30) are, therefore, sufficient to determine the solution completely.

The evaluation of the solution of the differential equation (7.29) is not very simple, but we shall describe the method in detail as it is characteristic of the solution of similar problems. The description will be based on an article written by L. Prandtl [14].

The general solution of eqn. (7.29) cannot be given in closed form. It is, therefore, necessary to solve it by purely numerical methods or by a series expansion. H. Blasius obtained the solution in the form of a power series expansion about $\eta = 0$ and an asymptotic expansion for $\eta = \infty$, the two solutions being joined at a suitable point. The power series near $\eta = 0$ is assumed to be of the form

$$f(\eta) = A_0 + A_1\eta + \frac{A_2}{2!}\eta^2 + \frac{A_3}{3!}\eta^3 + \dots$$

$$f'(\eta) = A_1 + A_2\eta + \frac{A_3}{2!}\eta^2 + \frac{A_4}{3!}\eta^3 + \dots.$$

Because of the boundary condition at $\eta = 0$ from eqn. (7.30) we find

$$A_0 = 0\,; \qquad A_1 = 0\,.$$

Substituting this assumption into the differential equation (7.29), we obtain

$$2\,A_3 + \eta\,2\,A_4 + \frac{\eta^2}{2\,!}(A_2^2 + 2\,A_5) + \frac{\eta^3}{3\,!}(4\,A_2\,A_3 + 2\,A_6) + \ldots = 0\,.$$

For the assumed series for f to be a solution of the differential equation all coefficients of the various powers of η must vanish identically. Hence, we have at once†

$$A_3 = 0\,; \qquad A_4 = 0$$

and, further

$$A_5 = -\frac{1}{2}A_2^2\,; \qquad A_6 = 0\,; \qquad A_7 = 0$$

$$A_8 = -\frac{11}{2}A_2\,A_5 = +\frac{11}{4}A_2^3\,, \ldots .$$

Thus only the coefficients A_2, A_5, A_8 ... differ from zero. The coefficient A_2 remains, for the time being, undetermined, because the third boundary condition at $\eta = \infty$ still remains to be satisfied. It is, therefore, reasonable to assume for $f(\eta)$ a series which progresses in powers of η^3. With $A_2 = \alpha$, we put

$$f = \sum_{n=0}^{\infty}\left(-\frac{1}{2}\right)^n \frac{\alpha^{n+1}\,C_n}{(3\,n+2)\,!}\,\eta^{3n+2}\,. \tag{7.31}$$

The first coefficients have been calculated by H. Blasius, and are

$$C_0 = 1\,; \quad C_1 = 1\,; \quad C_2 = 11$$
$$C_3 = 375\,; \quad C_4 = 27{,}897\,; \quad C_5 = 3{,}817{,}137\,.$$

The power series for $f(\eta)$ will now have to be joined to the asymptotic solution for large η, so that the next task is to determine the latter. The *asymptotic expansion* for large values of η is assumed of the form

$$f = f_1 + f_2 + \ldots ,$$

where, for very large values of η, the higher approximation must be small compared with the lower ones, that is e. g. $f_2 \ll f_1$. The first asymptotic approximation which corresponds to potential flow is

$$f_1 = \eta - \beta\,,$$

where β is a constant to be determined later. For this solution we have $f_1'' = 0$, so that when the term $f\,f''$ in eqn. (7.29) is replaced by $f_1\,f_2''$, we obtain the following differential equation for the second approximation

$$(\eta - \beta)\,f_2'' + 2\,f_2''' = 0$$

with the solution

$$\ln f_2'' = \frac{1}{2}\beta\,\eta - \frac{1}{4}\eta^2 + C\,.$$

If we assume the constant of integration to be of the form $C = -\frac{1}{4}\beta^2 + \ln\gamma$, where γ is a new constant of integration, we have

$$f_2'' = \gamma \exp\{-\tfrac{1}{4}(\eta - \beta)^2\}$$

† This follows also from eqns. (7.18) and (7.19), as in the present case $dp/dx = 0$.

and, upon integration,

$$f'_2 = \gamma \int\limits_{\eta=\infty}^{\eta} \exp\{-\tfrac{1}{4}(\eta-\beta)^2\} \tag{7.32}$$

Here $f_2'(\infty) = 0$. Since, further, $f_1'(\infty) = 1$, the solution $f' = f_1' + f_2'$ satisfies the third boundary condition $f'(\infty) = 1$, which was not the case with the power series (7.31). Repeated integration of (7.32) gives the second approximation of the asymptotic solution

$$f = \eta - \beta + \gamma \int\limits_{\infty}^{\eta} \mathrm{d}\eta \int\limits_{\infty}^{\eta} \exp\{-\tfrac{1}{4}(\eta-\beta)^2\}\,\mathrm{d}\eta\,. \tag{7.33}$$

This asymptotic solution still contains two constants of integration β and γ, as it should, because of the three boundary conditions only one has been satisfied. It is possible to improve the solution still further by the same method, assuming $f = f_1 + f_2 + f_3$. The differential equation for f_3 was solved by H. Blasius, but we shall refrain from discussing it here.

The two solutions, the power series about $\eta = 0$ from eqn. (7.31), and the asymptotic solution from eqn. (7.33) now have to be joined so as to represent the same function $f(\eta)$. The power series which satisfies two boundary conditions contains one free constant, α, and the asymptotic solution which satisfies one boundary condition contains two free constants β and γ. The three free constants are determined by making f, f', and f'' equal for the two solutions at a suitable point $\eta = \eta_1$, where both solutions are still usable. Thus three equations for α, β and γ are obtained. The higher derivatives of f from the power series and the asymptotic solution are then seen to be equal in pairs on their own accord. The numerical calculation performed by H. Blasius led to the following numerical values: $\alpha = 0{\cdot}332$; $\beta = 1{\cdot}73$; $\gamma = 0{\cdot}231$. C. Toepfer [17] obtained the solution of the differential equation under consideration by the use of the method due to Runge and Kutta. Further solutions for the velocity profile were obtained by L. Bairstow [1] and S. Goldstein [6], who employed a method which differed somewhat from that due to Blasius.

In more recent times L. Howarth [9] solved the Blasius equation (7.29) with a high degree of accuracy; the values of f, f' and f'' given in Table 7.1 have been taken from his paper.

The variation of the longitudinal component $u/U_\infty = f'(\eta)$ is seen plotted in Fig. 7.8. Comparing it with the profile near a stagnation point, Fig. 5.11, we see that the velocity profile on a flat plate possesses a very small curvature at the wall and turns rather abruptly further from it in order to reach the asymptotic value. At the wall itself the curve has a point of inflexion, since for $y = 0 : \partial^2 u/\partial y^2 = 0$.

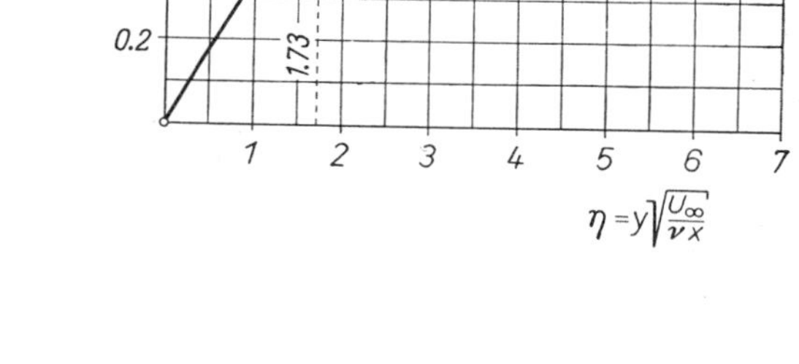

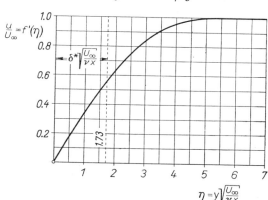

Fig. 7.8. Velocity distribution in the boundary layer along a flat plate after Blasius [2]

The transverse component of the velocity in the boundary layer, given by eqn. (7.28), is represented in Fig. 7.9. It is worth noting here that at the outer edge of the boundary layer, i. e. for $\eta \to \infty$ this component differs from zero; we have

$$v_\infty = 0{\cdot}865\, U_\infty \sqrt{\frac{\nu}{x\, U_\infty}}\,.$$

This means that at the outer edge there is a flow outwards which is due to the fact that the increasing boundary layer thickness causes the fluid to be displaced from the wall as it flows along it. There is no boundary layer separation in the present case, as the pressure gradient is equal to zero.

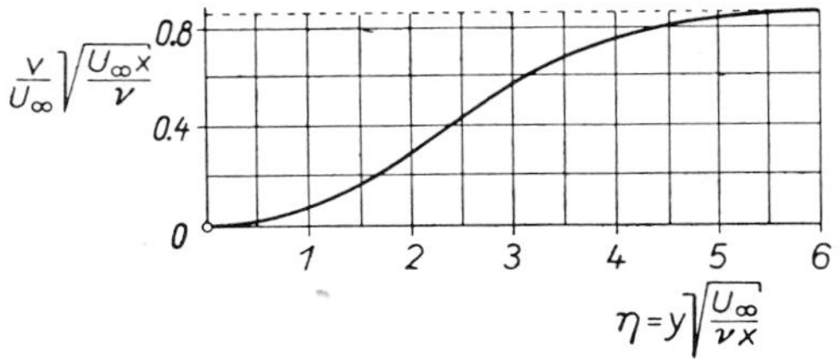

Fig. 7.9. The transverse velocity component in the boundary layer along a flat plate

Skin friction: The skin friction can be easily determined from the preceding data. From eqn. (7.22) we obtain for one side of the plate

$$D = b \int_{x=0}^{l} \tau_0\, \mathrm{d}x\,, \tag{7.34}$$

where b is the width and l is the length of the plate. Now the local shearing stress at the wall is given by

$$\tau_0(x) = \mu \left(\frac{\partial u}{\partial y}\right)_{y=0} = \mu\, U_\infty \sqrt{\frac{U_\infty}{\nu x}}\, f''(0) = \alpha\, \mu\, U_\infty \sqrt{\frac{U_\infty}{\nu x}}\,, \tag{7.35}$$

with $f''(0) = \alpha = 0{\cdot}332$ from Table 7.1. Hence the dimensionless shearing stress becomes:

$$\frac{\tau_0\,(x)}{\varrho\, U_\infty^{\,2}} = 0{\cdot}332 \sqrt{\frac{\nu}{U_\infty\, x}} = \frac{0{\cdot}332}{\sqrt{\mathsf{R}_x}}\,. \tag{7.35a}$$

Consequently, from eqn. (7.34), the skin friction of one side becomes

$$D = \alpha\, \mu\, b\, U_\infty \sqrt{\frac{U_\infty}{\nu}} \int_{x=0}^{l} \frac{\mathrm{d}x}{\sqrt{x}} = 2\, \alpha\, b\, U_\infty \sqrt{\mu\, \varrho\, l\, U_\infty}\,,$$

and for the plate wetted on both sides:

$$2\, D = 4 \alpha\, b\, U_\infty \sqrt{\mu\, \varrho\, l\, U_\infty} = 1{\cdot}328\, b \sqrt{U_\infty^{\,3}\, \mu\, \varrho\, l}\,. \tag{7.36}$$

Table 7.1. The function $f(\eta)$ for the boundary layer along a flat plate at zero incidence, after L. Howarth [9]

$\eta = y\sqrt{\frac{U_\infty}{\nu x}}$	f	$f' = \frac{u}{U_\infty}$	f''
0	0	0	0·33206
0·2	0·00664	0·06641	0·33199
0·4	0·02656	0·13277	0·33147
0·6	0·05974	0·19894	0·33008
0·8	0·10611	0·26471	0·32739
1·0	0·16557	0·32979	0·32301
1·2	0·23795	0·39378	0·31659
1·4	0·32298	0·45627	0·30787
1·6	0·42032	0·51676	0·29667
1·8	0·52952	0·57477	0·28293
2·0	0·65003	0·62977	0·26675
2·2	0·78120	0·68132	0·24835
2·4	0·92230	0·72899	0·22809
2·6	1·07252	0·77246	0·20646
2·8	1·23099	0·81152	0·18401
3·0	1·39682	0·84605	0·16136
3·2	1·56911	0·87609	0·13913
3·4	1·74696	0·90177	0·11788
3·6	1·92954	0·92333	0·09809
3·8	2·11605	0·94112	0·08013
4·0	2·30576	0·95552	0·06424
4·2	2·49806	0·96696	0·05052
4·4	2·69238	0·97587	0·03897
4·6	2·88826	0·98269	0·02948
4·8	3·08534	0·98779	0·02187
5·0	3·28329	0·99155	0·01591
5·2	3·48189	0·99425	0·01134
5·4	3·68094	0·99616	0·00793
5·6	3·88031	0·99748	0·00543
5·8	4·07990	0·99838	0·00365
6·0	4·27964	0·99898	0·00240
6·2	4·47948	0·99937	0·00155
6·4	4·67938	0·99961	0·00098
6·6	4·87931	0·99977	0·00061
6·8	5·07928	0·99987	0·00037
7·0	5·27926	0·99992	0·00022
7·2	5·47925	0·99996	0·00013
7·4	5·67924	0·99998	0·00007
7·6	5·87924	0·99999	0·00004
7·8	6·07923	1·00000	0·00002
8·0	6·27923	1·00000	0·00001
8·2	6·47923	1·00000	0·00001
8·4	6·67923	1·00000	0·00000
8·6	6·87923	1·00000	0·00000
8·8	7·07923	1·00000	0·00000

It is remarkable that the skin friction is proportional to the power $\frac{3}{2}$ of velocity, whereas in creeping motion there was proportionality to the first power of velocity. Further, the drag increases with the square root of the length of the plate. This can be interpreted as showing that the downstream portions of the plate contribute proportionately less to the total drag than the portions near the leading edge, because they lie in the region where the boundary layer is thicker and, consequently, the shearing stress at the wall is smaller. Introducing, as usual, a dimensionless drag coefficient by the definition

$$c_f = \frac{2\,D}{\frac{1}{2}\,\varrho\,A\,U_\infty{}^2}\,,$$

where $A = 2\,b\,l$ denotes the wetted surface area, we obtain from eqn. (7.36) the formula:

$$\boxed{c_f = \frac{1{\cdot}328}{\sqrt{\mathsf{R}_l}}} \tag{7.37}$$

Here $\mathsf{R}_l = U_\infty\,l/\nu$ denotes the Reynolds number formed with the length of the plate and the free stream velocity. This law of friction on a plate, first deduced by H. Blasius, is valid only in the region of laminar flow, i. e. for $\mathsf{R}_l = U_\infty\,l/\nu < 5 \times 10^5$ to 10^6. It is represented in Fig. 21.2 as curve (1). In the region of turbulent motion, $\mathsf{R}_l > 10^6$, the drag becomes considerably greater than that given in eqn. (7.37).

Boundary layer thickness: It is impossible to indicate a boundary layer thickness in an unambiguous way, because the influence of viscosity in the boundary layer decreases asymptotically outwards. The parallel component u tends asymptotically to the value U_∞ of the potential flow (the function $f'(\eta)$ tends asymptotically to 1). If it is desired to define the boundary layer thickness as that distance for which $u = 0{\cdot}99\,U_\infty$, then, as seen from Table 7.1, $\eta \approx 5{\cdot}0$. Hence the boundary layer thickness, as defined here, becomes

$$\delta \approx 5{\cdot}0\sqrt{\frac{\nu\,x}{U_\infty}}\,. \tag{7.38}$$

A physically meaningful measure for the boundary layer thickness is the *displacement thickness* δ^*, which was already introduced in eqn. (2.6), Fig. 2.3. The displacement thickness is that distance by which the external potential field of flow is displaced outwards as a consequence of the decrease in velocity in the boundary layer. The decrease in volume flow due to the influence of friction is $\int_{y=0}^{\infty}(U_\infty - u)\,\mathrm{d}y$, so that for δ^* we have the definition

$$U_\infty\,\delta^* = \int_{y=0}^{\infty}(U_\infty - u)\,\mathrm{d}y$$

or

$$\delta^* = \int_{y=0}^{\infty}\left(1 - \frac{u}{U_\infty}\right)\mathrm{d}y\,. \tag{7.39}$$

With u/U_∞ from eqn. (7.27) we obtain

$$\delta^* = \sqrt{\frac{\nu x}{U_\infty}} \int_{\eta=0}^{\infty} [1 - f'(\eta)]\, d\eta = \sqrt{\frac{\nu x}{U_\infty}} [\eta_1 - f(\eta_1)],$$

where η_1 denotes a point outside the boundary layer. Using the value $f(\eta)$ from the asymptotic solution (7.33) we obtain $\eta_1 - f(\eta_1) = \beta = 1{\cdot}72$ and hence

$$\delta^* = 1{\cdot}72 \sqrt{\frac{\nu x}{U_\infty}}. \tag{7.40}$$

The distance $y = \delta^*$ is shown in Fig. 7.8. This is the distance by which the streamlines of the external potential flow are displaced owing to the effect of friction near the wall. The boundary layer thickness, δ, given in eqn. (7.38), over which the potential velocity is attained to within 1 per cent. is, in round figures, three times larger than the displacement thickness.

We may at this point evaluate the *momentum thickness* θ which will be used later. The loss of momentum in the boundary layer, as compared with potential flow, is given by $\varrho \int_0^\infty u(U_\infty - u)\, dy$, so that a new thickness can be defined by

$$\varrho\, U_\infty^2\, \theta = \varrho \int_{y=0}^{\infty} u\, (U_\infty - u)\, dy$$

or

$$\theta = \int_{y=0}^{\infty} \frac{u}{U_\infty} \left(1 - \frac{u}{U_\infty}\right) dy. \tag{7.41}$$

Numerical evaluation for the plate at zero incidence gives:

$$\theta = \sqrt{\frac{\nu x}{U_\infty}} \int_{\eta=0}^{\infty} f'\,(1 - f')\, d\eta$$

$$\theta = 0{\cdot}664 \sqrt{\frac{\nu x}{U_\infty}}. \tag{7.42}$$

It is necessary to remark here that near the leading edge of the plate the boundary layer theory ceases to apply, since there the assumption $|\partial^2 u/\partial x^2| \ll |\partial^2 u/\partial y^2|$ is not satisfied. The boundary layer theory applies only from a definite value of the Reynolds number $\mathsf{R} = U_\infty\, x/\nu$ onwards. The relationship near the leading edge can only be found from the full Navier-Stokes equations because it involves a singularity at the leading edge itself. An attempt to carry out such a calculation was made by G. F. Carrier and C. C. Lin [4].

The expression for the coefficient of skin friction given in eqn. (7.37) can be regarded as the first term of a series expansion in powers of $1/\sqrt{\mathsf{R}}$. It is remarkable that the next term in the expansion, and hence an extension of the validity of eqn. (7.37) to lower length Reynolds numbers R, can be obtained without any additional integrations. I. Imai pointed out [9a] that this can be achieved by considering the balance of momentum of the fluid contained in a large circle of radius x and centered at the edge of the plate. Thus it is only necessary to know the behaviour of the flow on that circle, i. e. the Blasius solution. Further, by this method it is possible to avoid the difficulties caused by the singularity at the origin when a direct integration is performed and when the term $1/\mathsf{R}^{3/2}$ is reached in the equation for the skin friction. In this manner I. Imai obtained the expression

$$c_f = \frac{1{\cdot}328}{\sqrt{\mathsf{R}_l}} + \frac{2{\cdot}326}{\mathsf{R}_l}\,. \tag{7.37a}$$

The original note [9a] contains further terms in the series and an improved approximation for the local skin friction, τ_0. The correction in eqn. (7.37a) amounts to 2 per cent. at $\mathsf{R}_l = 10^4$ decreasing to 0·2 per cent. at $\mathsf{R}_l = 10^6$.

Experimental investigations: Measurements to test the theory given on the preceding pages were carried out first by J. M. Burgers [3] and B. G. van der Hegge Zijnen [8], and subsequently by M. Hansen [7]. Particularly careful and comprehensive measurements were reported later by J. Nikuradse [12]. It was found that the formation of the boundary layer is greatly influenced by the shape of the leading edge as well as by the very small pressure gradient which may exist in the external flow. J. Nikuradse introduced careful corrections for these possible effects, when he carried out his measurements on a plate in a stream of air. The velocity distribution in the laminar boundary layer has been plotted from Nikuradse's measurements in Fig. 7.10 for several distances from the leading edge. The similarity of the velocity profiles at various distances x from the leading edge predicted by the theory is confirmed by these measurements. The shape of the velocity profile agrees equally well with that calculated with the aid of the theory.

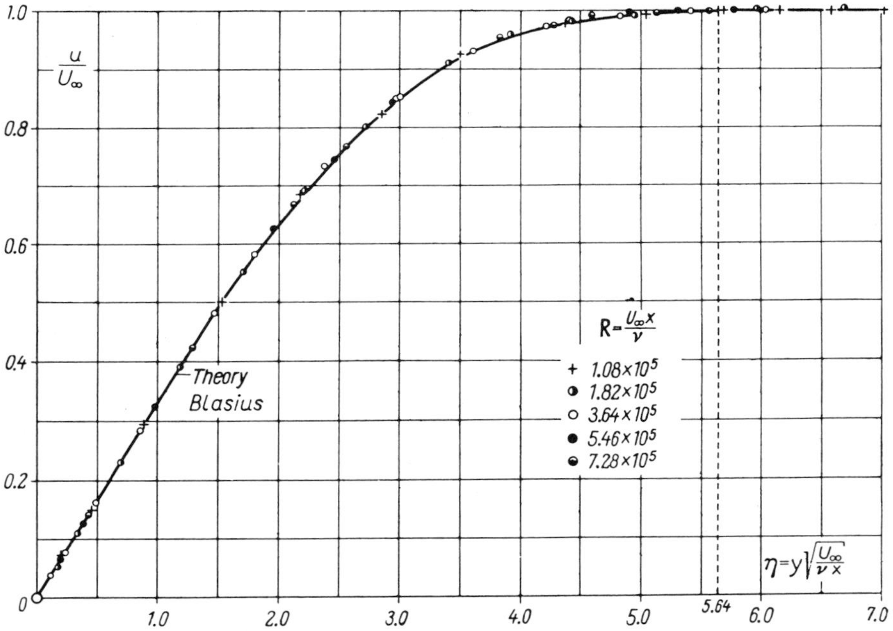

Fig. 7.10. Velocity distribution in the laminar boundary layer on a flat plate at zero incidence, as measured by Nikuradse [12]

The relation between the dimensionless boundary layer thickness $\delta \sqrt{U_\infty/\nu\, x}$ and the Reynolds number formed with the current length, x, was already plotted in Fig. 2.19. This dimensionless thickness remains constant as long as the boundary layer is laminar, and its numerical value is nearly that given in eqn. (7.38). At large Reynolds numbers $U_\infty\, x/\nu$ the boundary layer ceases to be laminar and transition to turbulent motion takes place. This fact can be recognized in Fig. 2.19 by noticing the marked increase in the thickness of the boundary layer as the distance from the leading edge is increased. According to the measurements performed by B. G. van der Hegge Zijnen and M. Hansen transition from laminar to turbulent flow takes place at $U_\infty\, x/\nu = 300{,}000$. This corresponds to a value of the Reynolds number referred to the displacement thickness, $U_\infty\, \delta^*/\nu = 950$. More recent measurements, to be discussed in Chap. XVI, have demonstrated that the value of this 'critical' Reynolds number can become considerably larger in an air stream which is made very free from disturbance. In this way it is possible to reach values of up to about $U_\infty\, x/\nu = 3 \times 10^6$.

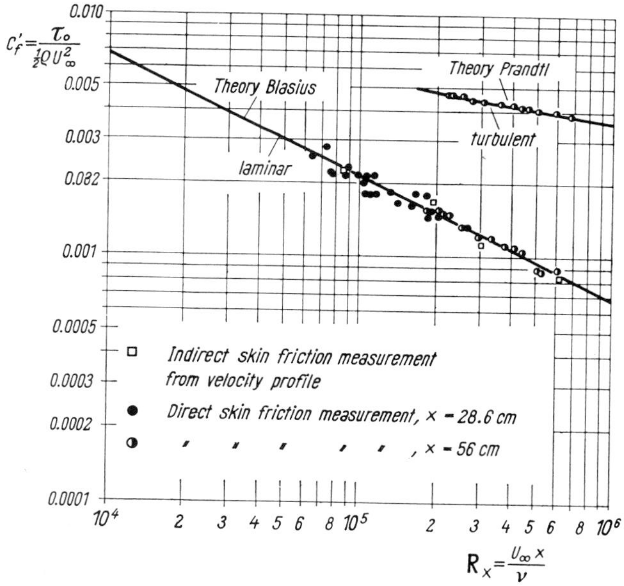

Fig. 7.11. Local coefficient of skin friction on a flat plate at zero incidence in incompressible flow, determined from direct measurement of shearing stress by Liepmann and Dhawan

Theory: laminar from eqn. (7.35 a); turbulent from eqn. (21.12)

The laminar law of friction on a flat plate was also subjected to careful experimental verification. The local shearing stress at the wall can be determined indirectly from the slope of the velocity profile at the wall together with eqn. (7.35). In recent times H. W. Liepmann and S. Dhawan [5, 10] measured the shearing stress directly from the force acting on a small portion of the plate which was arranged so that it could move slightly with respect to the main plate. The results of their very careful measurements are seen reproduced in Fig. 7.11, which shows a plot of the local coefficient of skin friction $c'_f = \tau_0/\frac{1}{2}\varrho U^2_\infty$, against the Reynolds number $\mathsf{R}_x = U_\infty\, x/\nu$. In the range of $\mathsf{R}_x = 2 \times 10^5$ to 6×10^5 both laminar and turbulent flows are possible. It can be seen that direct and indirect measurements are in excellent agreement with each other. Measurements in the laminar range give a striking confirmation of Blasius' eqn. (7.35a) from which $c_f' = 0{\cdot}664/\sqrt{\mathsf{R}_x}$. In the turbulent range there is also good agreement with Prandtl's theoretical formula which will be deduced in Chap. XXI, eqn. (21.12).

g. The role of free-stream turbulence

The preceding derivations, as well as those in Chaps. VIII—XIII, are, of course, valid only for laminar boundary layers; the much more difficult problem of calculating turbulent boundary layers will be discussed later in the book. A laminar boundary layer can be associated with a laminar as well as a turbulent external stream and the possible difference between these two cases merits further consideration, particularly because external streams encountered in practice are almost exclusively turbulent.

It was already pointed out in Chap. I and it will be shown in greater detail in Chaps. XVI and XVIII that the essential characteristic of a turbulent stream consists in the presence of random fluctuations in it. Even when the flow is *quasi-steady* i. e. even if it is steady on the average, the velocity at any point in the flow field performs random oscillations in time, the oscillation affecting both its magnitude and direction in space. When calculating a laminar boundary layer in the presence of a quasi-steady turbulent free stream it is usual to assume that the boundary condition (7.12) at $y = \infty$ involves the time average $\overline{U}(x) = \frac{1}{t}\int\limits_0^t U(x,t)\,\mathrm{d}t$ of the fluctuating potential velocity $U(x, t)$ which is time-dependent. With this assumption it is then possible to make use of the steady-state equations (7.10) and (7.11).

In connexion with their investigation of the effect of turbulence on the transfer of heat, J. Kestin and P. F. Maeder [9b] drew attention to the fact that the preceding assumption need not necessarily lead to a satisfactory solution. Since the boundary condition is time-dependent it is, strictly speaking, necessary to make use of the time-dependent equations (7.7) and (7.8) and to perform the time-averaging process in the solution itself. If the boundary layer equations were linear, the two solutions would be identical, but since they are not, differences must be expected. In other words, the external oscillation will induce oscillations in the laminar boundary layer and these oscillations are likely to be performed about a mean velocity profile which differs from that obtained with the aid of eqns. (7.10) and (7.11) together with the averaged boundary conditions (7.12). The averaging process, like the process of passing to the limit of zero viscosity, should, therefore, in principle, be performed in the final integral solution, and not in the boundary conditions of the differential equation, because the point at which this is done affects the final answer.

So far, the full implications of this remark have not been investigated in detail owing to evident mathematical difficulties. Solutions for very simple cases involving the presence of ordered, but not random oscillations in the free stream have been obtained. They will be discussed in Chap. XI. From the good agreement between measurement and calculation shown in Figs. 7.10 and 7.11 it would appear, at least in the case of a flat plate, that the influence of free-stream turbulence is small. On the other hand, as will be shown in more detail in Chap. XI, and as was shown in the case of heat transfer by J. Kestin, P. F. Maeder and H. E. Wang [9c], larger effects must be expected in cases when there exists in the turbulent free stream an appreciable pressure gradient.

References

[1] L. Bairstow, Skin friction. Jour. Roy. Aero. Soc. **19**, 3 (1925).
[2] H. Blasius, Grenzschichten in Flüssigkeiten mit kleiner Reibung. Z. Math. u. Phys. **56**, 1 (1908). Engl. transl. in NACA Tech. Memo No. 1256.
[3] J. M. Burgers, Proc. of the first Intern. Congr. for Applied Mechanics, Delft 1924.
[4] G. F. Carrier and C. C. Lin, On the nature of the boundary layer near the leading edge of a flat plate. Quarterly of Applied Math. **VI**, 63 (1948).
[5] S. Dhawan, Direct measurements of skin friction. NACA Rep. 1121 (1953).

[6] S. Goldstein, Proc. Cambr. Phil. Soc. **26**, 19 (1936); see also: Modern Developments in Fluid Dynamics, Vol. **I**, p. 135, Oxford (1938).
[7] M. Hansen, Die Geschwindigkeitsverteilung in der Grenzschicht an einer eingetauchten Platte. ZAMM **8**, 185 (1928); NACA Tech. Memo. 585 (1930).
[8] B. G. van der Hegge Zijnen, Measurements of the velocity distribution in the boundary layer along a plane surface. Thesis, Delft 1924.
[9] L. Howarth, On the solution of the laminar boundary layer equations. Proc. Roy. Soc., London, A **164**, 547 (1938).
[9a] I. Imai, Second approximation to the laminar boundary layer flow over a flat plate. J. Aero. Sci. **24**, 155 (1957).
[9b] J. Kestin and P. F. Maeder, Influence of turbulence on transfer of heat from cylinders. NACA TN 4018, 1957.
[9c] J. Kestin, P. F. Maeder and H. E. Wang, On boundary layers associated with oscillating streams, to be published.
[10] H. W. Liepmann and S. Dhawan, Direct measurements of local skin friction in low-speed and high-speed flow. Proc. First US Nat. Congr. Appl. Mech. p. 869, 1951.
[11] J. S. Murphy, Some effects of surface curvature on laminar boundary layer flow. Journ. Aero. Sci. **20**, p. 338—344 (1953).
[12] J. Nikuradse, Laminare Reibungsschichten an der längsangeströmten Platte. Monograph, Zentrale f. wiss. Berichtswesen, Berlin 1942.
[13] L. Prandtl, Über Flüssigkeitsbewegung bei sehr kleiner Reibung. Proceedings of the Third Intern. Math. Kongr. Heidelberg 1904. Reprinted in "Vier Abhdl. zur Hydro- u. Aerodynamik", Göttingen 1927; NACA Tech. Memo. 452 (1928).
[14] L. Prandtl, The mechanics of viscous fluids. In W. F. Durand, Aerodynamic Theory **III**, 85 pp.
[15] H. Schmidt and K. Schroeder, Laminare Grenzschichten. Ein kritischer Literaturbericht. Luftfahrtforschung **19**, 65—97 (1942).
[16] W. Tollmien, Grenzschichttheorie. Handb. d. Exper.-Physik **IV**, Part I, 248 (1931).
[17] C. Töpfer, Bemerkungen zu dem Aufsatz von H. Blasius, "Grenzschichten in Flüssigkeiten mit kleiner Reibung". Z. Math. u. Phys. **60**, 397 (1912).
[18] H. Weyl, Concerning the differential equations of some boundary layer problems. Proc. Nat. Acad. Sci., Washington **27**, 578 (1941).
[19] H. Weyl, On the differential equations of the simplest boundary layer problems. Ann. Math. **43**, 381 (1942).

CHAPTER VIII

General properties of the boundary layer equations

Before passing to the calculation of further examples of boundary layer flow in the next chapter, we propose first to discuss some general properties of the boundary layer equations. In doing so we shall confine our attention to steady, two-dimensional and incompressible boundary layers.

Although the boundary layer equations have been simplified to a great extent, as compared with the Navier-Stokes equations, they are still so difficult from the mathematical point of view that not very many general statements about them can be made. To begin with, it is important to notice that the Navier-Stokes equations are of the elliptic type with respect to the co-ordinates, whereas Prandtl's boundary layer equations are parabolic. It is a consequence of the simplifying assumptions in boundary layer theory that the pressure can be assumed constant in a direction at right angles to the boundary layer, whereas along the wall the pressure can be regarded as being "impressed" by the external flow so that it becomes a given function. The resulting omission of the equation of motion perpendicular to the direction of flow can be interpreted physically by stating that a fluid particle in the boundary layer has zero mass, and suffers no frictional drag as far as its motion in the transverse direction is concerned. It is, therefore, clear that with such fundamental changes introduced into the equations of motion we must anticipate that their solutions will exhibit certain mathematical singularities, and that agreement between observed and calculated phenomena cannot always be expected.

a. Dependence of the characteristics of a boundary layer on the Reynolds number

The assumptions which were made in the derivation of the boundary layer equations are satisfied with an increasing degree of accuracy as the Reynolds number increases. Thus boundary layer theory can be regarded as a process of *asymptotic integration* of the Navier-Stokes equations at very large Reynolds numbers. This statement leads us now to a discussion of the relationship between the Reynolds number and the characteristics of a boundary layer on our individual body under consideration. It will be recalled that in the derivation of the boundary layer equations dimensionless quantities were used; all velocities were referred to the free stream velocity U_∞, all lengths having been reduced with the aid of a characteristic length of the body, L. Denoting all dimensionless magnitudes by a prime, thus $u/U_\infty = u', \ldots, x/L = x', \ldots,$ we obtain the following equations for the steady, two-dimensional case:

$$u'\frac{\partial u'}{\partial x'} + v'\frac{\partial u'}{\partial y'} = U'\frac{dU'}{dx'} + \frac{1}{\mathsf{R}}\frac{\partial^2 u'}{\partial y'^2}, \tag{8.1}$$

$$\frac{\partial u'}{\partial x'} + \frac{\partial v'}{\partial y'} = 0, \tag{8.2}$$

$$y' = 0: \quad u' = v' = 0; \quad y' = \infty: \quad u' = U'(x').$$

Here R denotes the Reynolds number formed with the aid of the reference quantities

$$\mathsf{R} = \frac{U_\infty L}{\nu}.$$

It is seen from eqns. (8.1) and (8.2) that the boundary layer solution depends on one parameter, the Reynolds number R, if the shape of the body, and, hence, the potential motion $U'(x')$ are given. By the use of a further transformation it is possible to eliminate the Reynolds number also from eqns. (8.1) and (8.2). If we put

$$v'' = v'\sqrt{\mathsf{R}} = \frac{v}{U_\infty}\sqrt{\frac{U_\infty L}{\nu}} \tag{8.3}$$

and

$$y'' = y'\sqrt{\mathsf{R}} = \frac{y}{L}\sqrt{\frac{U_\infty L}{\nu}}, \tag{8.4}$$

eqns. (8.1) and (8.2) transform into:

$$u'\frac{\partial u'}{\partial x'} + v''\frac{\partial u'}{\partial y''} = U'\frac{dU'}{dx'} + \frac{\partial^2 u'}{\partial y''^2}, \tag{8.5}$$

$$\frac{\partial u'}{\partial x'} + \frac{\partial v''}{\partial y''} = 0 \tag{8.6}$$

with the boundary conditions: $u' = 0$ and $v'' = 0$ at $y'' = 0$ and $u' = U'$ at $y'' = \infty$. These equations do not now contain the Reynolds number, so that the solutions of this system, i. e. the functions $u'(x', y'')$ and $v''(x', y'')$ are also independent of the Reynolds number. A variation in the Reynolds number causes an affine transformation of the boundary layer, during which the ordinate and the velocity in the transverse direction are multiplied by $\mathsf{R}^{-1/2}$. In other words, for a given body the dimensionless velocity components u/U_∞ and $(v/U_\infty)\cdot(U_\infty L/\nu)^{1/2}$ are functions of the dimensionless co-ordinates x/L and $(y/L)\cdot(U_\infty L/\nu)^{1/2}$; the functions, moreover, do not depend on the Reynolds number any longer.

The practical importance of this *principle of similarity with respect to Reynolds number* consists in the fact that for a given body shape it suffices to find the solution to the boundary layer problem only once in terms of the above dimensionless variables. Such a solution is valid for any Reynolds number, provided that the boundary layer is laminar. In particular, it follows further that the position of the point of separation is independent of the Reynolds number. The angle which is formed between the stream-line through the point of separation and the body, Fig. 7.3, simply decreases in the ratio $1/\mathsf{R}^{1/2}$ as the Reynolds number increases.

Moreover, the fact that separation does take place is preserved when the process of passing to the limit $\mathsf{R} \to \infty$ is carried out. Thus, in the case of body shapes which exhibit separation, the boundary layer theory presents a totally different picture of the flow pattern than the frictionless potential theory, even in the limit of $\mathsf{R} \to \infty$. This argument confirms the conclusion which was already emphatically stressed in Chap. IV, namely that the process of passing to the limit of frictionless flow must not be performed in the differential equations themselves; it may only be undertaken in the integral solution, if physically meaningful results are to be obtained.

b. 'Similar' solutions of the boundary layer equations

A second, and very important, question arising out of the solution of boundary layer equations, is the investigation of the conditions under which two solutions are 'similar'. We shall define here 'similar' solutions as those for which the component u of the velocity has the property that two velocity profiles $u(x, y)$ located at different co-ordinates x differ only by a scale factor in u and y. Therefore, in the case of such 'similar' solutions the velocity profiles $u(x, y)$ at all values of x can be made congruent if they are plotted in co-ordinates which have been made dimensionless with reference to the scale factors. Such velocity profiles will also sometimes be called *affine*. The local potential velocity $U(x)$ at section x is an obvious scale factor for u, because the dimensionless $u(x)$ varies with y from zero to unity at all sections. The scale factor for y denoted by $g(x)$, must be made proportional to the local boundary layer thickness. The requirement of 'similarity' is seen to reduce itself to the requirement that for two arbitrary sections x_1, and x_2 the components $u(x, y)$ must satisfy the following equation

$$\frac{u\,\{x_1, [y/g(x_1)]\}}{U(x_1)} = \frac{u\,\{x_2, [y/g(x_2)]\}}{U(x_2)}. \tag{8.7}$$

The boundary layer along a flat plate at zero incidence considered in the preceding chapter possessed this property of 'similarity'. The free-stream velocity U_∞ was the scale factor for u, and the scale factor for y was equal to the quantity $g = \sqrt{\nu\, x / U_\infty}$ which was proportional to the boundary layer thickness. All velocity profiles became identical in a plot of u/U_∞ against $y/g = y\sqrt{U_\infty/\nu\, x} = \eta$, Fig. 7.8. Similarly, the cases of two- and three-dimensional stagnation flow afforded examples of solutions which proved to be 'similar' in the present sense.

The quest for 'similar' solutions is particularly important with respect to the mathematical character of the solution. In cases when 'similar' solutions exist it is possible, as we shall see in more detail later, to reduce the system of partial differential equations to one involving ordinary differential equations, which, evidently, constitutes a considerable mathematical simplification of the problem. The boundary layer along a flat plate can serve as an example in this respect also. It will be recalled that with the *similarity transformation* $\eta = y\sqrt{U_\infty/\nu\, x}$, eqn. (7.25), we obtained an ordinary differential equation, eqn. (7.29), for the stream function (η), instead of the original partial differential equations.

We shall now concern ourselves with the question of types of potential flows for which such 'similar' solutions exist. This problem was discussed in great detail first by S. Goldstein [4], and later by W. Mangler [11]. The point of departure is to consider the boundary layer equations for plane steady flow, eqns. (7.10) and (7.11), which can be written as

$$\begin{aligned} u\frac{\partial u}{\partial x} + v\frac{\partial u}{\partial y} &= U\frac{\mathrm{d}U}{\mathrm{d}x} + \nu\frac{\partial^2 u}{\partial y^2} \\ \frac{\partial u}{\partial x} + \frac{\partial v}{\partial y} &= 0\,. \end{aligned} \tag{8.8}$$

The boundary conditions being $u = v = 0$ for $y = 0$, and $u = U$ for $y = \infty$. The equation of continuity is integrated by the introduction of the stream function $\psi(x, y)$ with

$$u = \frac{\partial \psi}{\partial y}\,, \qquad v = -\frac{\partial \psi}{\partial x}\,.$$

Thus the first equation of motion becomes

$$\frac{\partial \psi}{\partial y}\frac{\partial^2 \psi}{\partial x\,\partial y} - \frac{\partial \psi}{\partial x}\frac{\partial^2 \psi}{\partial y^2} = U\frac{\mathrm{d}U}{\mathrm{d}x} + \nu\frac{\partial^3 \psi}{\partial y^3} \tag{8.9}$$

with the boundary conditions $\partial\psi/\partial x = 0$ and $\partial\psi/\partial y = 0$ for $y = 0$, and $\partial\psi/\partial y = U$ for $y = \infty$. In order to discuss the question of 'similarity', dimensionless quantities are introduced, as was done in Section VIII a. All lengths are reduced with the aid of a suitable reference length, L, and all velocities are made dimensionless with reference to a suitable velocity, U_∞. As a result the Reynolds number

$$\mathsf{R} = \frac{U_\infty L}{\nu}$$

appears in the equation. Simultaneously the y-co-ordinate is referred to the dimensionless scale factor $g(x)$, so that we put

$$\xi = \frac{x}{L}\,, \qquad \eta = \frac{y\sqrt{\mathsf{R}}}{L\,g(x)}\,. \tag{8.10}$$

The factor $\sqrt{\mathsf{R}}$ for the ordinate already appeared in eqn. (8.4). The stream function is made dimensionless by the substitution

$$f(\xi,\eta) = \frac{\psi(x, y)\sqrt{\mathsf{R}}}{L\,U(x)\,g(x)}\,. \tag{8.11}$$

Consequently, the velocity components become

$$\left.\begin{aligned} u &= \frac{\partial \psi}{\partial y} = U\frac{\partial f}{\partial \eta} = U f'\,, \\ -\sqrt{\mathsf{R}}\;v = \sqrt{\mathsf{R}}\,\frac{\partial \psi}{\partial x} &= L f\frac{\mathrm{d}}{\mathrm{d}x}(U g) + U g\left(\frac{\partial f}{\partial \xi} - L\frac{g'}{g}\eta f'\right), \end{aligned}\right\} \tag{8.12}$$

where the prime in f' denotes differentiation with respect to η, and with respect to x in g'. It is now seen directly from eqn. (8.12) that the velocity profiles $u(x, y)$ are similar in the previously defined sense, when the stream function f depends only on the one variable η, eqn. (8.10), so that the dependence of f on ξ is cancelled. In this case, moreover, the partial differential equation for the stream function, eqn. (8.9), must reduce itself to an ordinary differential equation for $f(\eta)$. If we now proceed to investigate the conditions under which this reduction of eqn. (8.9) takes place, we shall obtain the condition which must be satisfied by the potential flow $U(x)$ for such 'similar' solutions to exist.

If we introduce now the dimensionless variables from (8.10) and (8.11) into eqn. (8.9), we obtain the following differential equation for $f(\xi, \eta)$:

$$f''' + \alpha f f'' + \beta (1 - f'^2) = \frac{U}{U_\infty} g^2 \left(f' \frac{\partial f'}{\partial \xi} - f'' \frac{\partial f}{\partial \xi} \right). \tag{8.13}$$

where α and β are contractions for the following functions of x:

$$\alpha = \frac{Lg}{U_\infty} \frac{\mathrm{d}}{\mathrm{d}x} (Ug) \; ; \qquad \beta = \frac{L}{U_\infty} g^2 U' , \tag{8.14}$$

and where $U' = \mathrm{d}U/\mathrm{d}x$. The boundary conditions for eqn. (8.13) are $f = 0$ and $f' = 0$ for $\eta = 0$ and $f' = 1$ for $\eta = \infty$.

'Similar' solutions exist only when f and f' do not depend on ξ, i. e. when the right-hand side of eqn. (8.13) vanishes. Simultaneously the coefficients α and β on the left-hand side of eqn. (8.13) must be independent of x, i. e. they must be constant. This latter condition, combined with eqn. (8.14), furnishes two equations for the potential velocity $U(x)$ and the scale factor $g(x)$ for the ordinate, so that they can be evaluated. Hence, if similar solutions of boundary layer flow are to exist, the stream function $f(\eta)$ must satisfy the following ordinary differential equation:

$$f''' + \alpha f f'' + \beta (1 - f'^2) = 0 \tag{8.15}$$

with the boundary conditions

$$\eta = 0 : \; f = 0 , \; f' = 0 ; \qquad \eta = \infty : \; f' = 1 . \tag{8.16}$$

This equation was first given by V. M. Falkner and S. W. Skan [2], and its solutions were later studied in detail by D. R. Hartree [7]. We shall revert to this point in the succeeding chapter.

It remains now to determine from eqn. (8.14) the conditions for $U(x)$ and $g(x)$. From (8.14) we obtain, first

$$2\alpha - \beta = \frac{L}{U_\infty} \frac{\mathrm{d}}{\mathrm{d}x} (g^2 U)$$

and hence, if $2\alpha - \beta \neq 0$,

$$\frac{U}{U_\infty} g^2 = (2\alpha - \beta) \frac{x}{L} . \tag{8.17}$$

Further from (8.14) we have

$$\alpha - \beta = \frac{L}{U_\infty} g g' U$$

and hence
$$(\alpha-\beta)\frac{U'}{U}=\frac{L}{U_\infty}\,g^2\,U'\,\frac{g'}{g}=\beta\,\frac{g'}{g}$$

so that upon integration

$$\left(\frac{U}{U_\infty}\right)^{(\alpha-\beta)}=K\,g^{\beta}\,, \tag{8.18}$$

where K is a constant. The elimination of g from eqns. (8.17) and (8.18) yields the velocity distribution of the potential flow

$$\frac{U}{U_\infty}=K^{\frac{2}{2\alpha-\beta}}\left[(2\alpha-\beta)\,\frac{x}{L}\right]^{\frac{\beta}{2\alpha-\beta}} \tag{8.19}$$

and

$$g=\sqrt{(2\alpha-\beta)\,\frac{x}{L}\left(\frac{U}{U_\infty}\right)^{-\frac{1}{2}}} \tag{8.20}$$

It will be recalled that the case $2\alpha-\beta=0$ has been excluded.

As seen from eqn. (8.14) the result is independent of any common factor of α and β, as it can be included in g. Therefore as long as $\alpha \neq 0$ it is permissible to put $\alpha = +1$ without loss of generality. It is, furthermore, convenient to introduce a new constant m to replace β by putting

$$m=\frac{\beta}{2-\beta} \tag{8.21}$$

as in this way the physical meaning of the solution will become clearer. Hence

$$\beta=\frac{2m}{m+1}\,.$$

so that, with $\alpha = 1$, the velocity distribution of the potential flow and the scale factor g for the ordinate become

$$\frac{U}{U_\infty}=K^{(1+m)}\left(\frac{2}{1+m}\,\frac{x}{L}\right)^{m} \tag{8.22}$$

$$g=\sqrt{\frac{2}{m+1}\,\frac{x}{L}\,\frac{U_\infty}{U}}\,, \tag{8.23}$$

and the transformation equation (8.10) for the ordinate is

$$\eta=y\sqrt{\frac{m+1}{2}\,\frac{U}{\nu x}}\,. \tag{8.24}$$

It is thus concluded that similar solutions of the boundary layer equations are obtained when the velocity distribution of the potential flow is proportional to a power of the length of arc, measured along the wall from the stagnation point. Such potential flows occur, in fact, in the neighbourhood of the stagnation point of a wedge whose included angle is equal to $\pi\beta$, as shown in Fig. 8.1. It is easy to verify with the aid of potential theory that we have here

$$U(x) = C\, x^m\,, \tag{8.25}$$

where C is a constant. The relationship between the wedge angle factor β and the exponent m is exactly that given in eqn. (8.21).

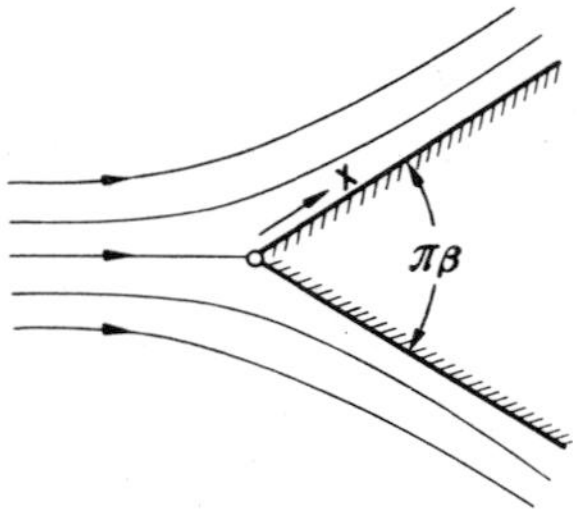

Fig. 8.1. Flow past a wedge. In the neighbourhood of the leading edge the potential velocity distribution is $U(x) = Cx^m$

Particular cases for $\alpha = 1$: (a) For $\beta = 1$ we have $m = 1$, and eqn. (8.22) becomes $U(x) = a\,x$. This is the case of two-dimensional *stagnation flow*, which was considered in Sec. V. 8, and which led to an exact solution of the Navier-Stokes equations. With $\alpha = 1$, and $\beta = 1$, the differential equation (8.15) transforms into eqn. (5.32) which was already considered earlier. The transformation equation for the ordinate, eqn. (8.24), becomes identical with the already familiar equation (5.31), if we put $U/x = a$.

(b) For $\beta = 0$ we have $m = 0$, hence $U(x)$ is constant and equal to U_∞. This is the case of a *flat plate at zero incidence*. It follows from eqn. (8.24) that $\eta = y\sqrt{U_\infty/2\,\nu x}$. This value differs only by a factor $\sqrt{2}$ from that introduced in eqn. (7.25). Correspondingly the differential equation $f''' + ff'' = 0$ which follows from (8.15) differs by a factor 2 in the second term from eqn. (7.29) which was solved earlier. The two equations become identical when transformed to identical definitions of η.

Solution for different values of m will be considered later in Chap. IX.

The case $\alpha = 0$: The case $\alpha = 0$ which has, so far, been left out of account, leads, as is easily inferred from eqn. (8.19), to potential flows $U(x)$ which are proportional to $1/x$ for all values of β. Depending on the sign of U this is the case of a two-dimensional sink or source, and can also be interpreted as flow in a divergent or convergent channel with flat walls. This type of flow will also be considered in greater detail in Chap. IX.

The second case excluded earlier, namely that when $2\alpha - \beta = 0$, leads to 'similar' solutions with $U(x)$ proportional to e^{px}, where p is a positive or negative constant. We shall, however, refrain from discussing this case.

The problem of the existence of similar solutions involving non-steady boundary layers was discussed by H. Schuh [17].

c. Continuation problem; conditions of compatibility at the wall

In the calculation of a boundary layer along a body of given shape it is often required to extend a boundary layer in which the velocity distribution is either known or prescribed as far as a given section x. The problem can be solved, e. g. numerically, see Sec. IX. i, and for this procedure it is necessary to expand the prescribed profile $u(x, y)$ at x into powers of y, with coefficients $a_\nu(x)$ which are functions of x, the expansion being

$$u(x,y) = a_1\, y + \frac{a_2}{2!}\, y^2 + \frac{a_3}{3!}\, y^3 + \dots . \tag{8.26}$$

In this connexion it is important to investigate, whether the coefficients a_1, a_2, ... can have arbitrary values or whether they are in some way related, as well as how they are determined by the external potential flow $U(x)$. It will be shown that only some of the coefficients can be selected freely, whereas the others are connected through certain equations, which may be termed the *conditions of compatibility at the wall.* Several such compatibility conditions have already been introduced in Chap. VII. Equation (7.18) showed that the curvature of the velocity profile $u(y)$ at the wall is determined directly by the pressure gradient of the potential flow; this gives $\mu\, a_2 = \mathrm{d}p/\mathrm{d}x$. Further, eqn. (7.19) shows that the coefficient $a_3 = 0$. These are the conditions of compatibility for a_2 and a_3.

In order to derive the compatibility conditions in a general way we refer to the dimensionless boundary layer equations (8.5) and (8.6), but for the sake of simplicity we shall drop the primes which were used to denote dimensionless quantities. Hence we obtain the equations

$$u\,\frac{\partial u}{\partial x} + v\,\frac{\partial u}{\partial y} + \frac{\mathrm{d}p}{\mathrm{d}x} = \frac{\partial^2 u}{\partial y^2}\,, \tag{8.27a}$$

$$\frac{\partial u}{\partial x} + \frac{\partial v}{\partial y} = 0 \tag{8.27b}$$

together with the boundary conditions: $u = 0$ and $v = 0$ at the wall, $y = 0$, and $u = U$ for $y = \infty$. In these equations x is used for x/L, y for $(y/L)\cdot\sqrt{U_\infty L/\nu}$, u for u/U_∞ and v for $(v/U_\infty)\cdot\sqrt{U_\infty L/\nu}$, and finally, p for $p/\varrho\, U^2_\infty$.

We now introduce the assumption (8.26) into (8.27a), as well as the expression for v, which follows from the continuity equation (8.27b):

$$-v = \frac{a_1'}{2!}\, y^2 + \frac{a_2'}{3!}\, y^3 + \frac{a_3'}{4!}\, y^4 + \dots .$$

Here the prime denotes differentiation with respect to x. Introducing further the abbreviation

$$\frac{\mathrm{d}p}{\mathrm{d}x} = f(x)$$

we obtain the following conditions

$$\left.\begin{aligned}
&a_1 \text{ free};\quad a_2 = f(x);\quad a_3 = 0\\
&a_4 = a_1\, a_1', \quad \text{hence free}\\
&a_5 = 2\, a_1 f';\quad a_6 = 2\, f f'\\
&a_7 = 4\, a_1^2\, a_1'' - a_1\, a_1'^2, \quad \text{hence free}\\
&a_8 = 10\, a_1^2 f'' - 13\, a_1\, a_1' f' + 9\,(a_1\, a_1'' + a_1'^2)\, f\\
&a_9 = 40\, a_1 f f'' - 16\, a_1 f'^2 .
\end{aligned}\right\} \tag{8.28}$$

Consequently, only the coefficients a_1, a_4, a_7, a_{10}, ... are free, and the remaining coefficients are connected with them through the compatibility equations.

L. Prandtl [13] and H. Görtler [5] have shown that the profiles $u(x, y)$ further downstream, which occur in the problem of continuing a boundary layer, must also satisfy these conditions with a reasonable degree of approximation, in order to make the continuation possible. The method of solving the problem of continuing a boundary layer will be explained in detail in Sec. IX. i. When numerical methods are used a gross violation of the conditions of compatibility leads to an erratic sequence of succeeding velocity profiles, as shown by K. Schröder [16]. The compatibility conditions are also important in the approximate methods for the calculation of a two-dimensional laminar boundary layer to be discussed later in Chap. XII.

As a corollary to the behaviour of the boundary layer near the wall it is also possible to make statements about its behaviour at the outer edge where it is joined to the potential flow. These were given by W. Tollmien [18]. In this connexion the papers by F. Riegels [14] and A. Betz [1] may also be consulted.

d. Transformation of the boundary layer equations into the heat conduction equation

R. von Mises [12] published in 1927 a remarkable transformation of the boundary layer equations. This transformation exhibits the mathematical character of the equations even more clearly than the original form. Instead of the Cartesian coordinates x and y, von Mises introduced the stream function ψ, together with the length co-ordinate x as independent variables. Substituting

$$u = \frac{\partial \psi}{\partial y}, \qquad v = -\frac{\partial \psi}{\partial x}$$

into eqns. (7.10) and (7.11), as well as introducing the new co-ordinates $\xi = x$ and $\eta = \psi$ instead of x and y, we obtain

$$\frac{\partial u}{\partial x} = \frac{\partial u}{\partial \xi}\frac{\partial \xi}{\partial x} + \frac{\partial u}{\partial \eta}\frac{\partial \eta}{\partial x} = \frac{\partial u}{\partial \xi} - v\,\frac{\partial u}{\partial \psi},$$

$$\frac{\partial u}{\partial y} = \frac{\partial u}{\partial \xi}\frac{\partial \xi}{\partial y} + \frac{\partial u}{\partial \eta}\frac{\partial \eta}{\partial y} = 0 + u\,\frac{\partial u}{\partial \psi}.$$

Hence, from eqn. (7.10)

$$u\,\frac{\partial u}{\partial \xi} + \frac{1}{\varrho}\frac{\mathrm{d}p}{\mathrm{d}\xi} = \nu\, u\,\frac{\partial}{\partial \psi}\left(u\,\frac{\partial u}{\partial \psi}\right).$$

Introducing, further, the 'total head'

$$g = p + \tfrac{1}{2}\,\varrho\, u^2 \tag{8.29}$$

where the small quantity $\frac{1}{2}\,\varrho\, v^2$ can be neglected, we obtain, reverting to the symbol x for ξ:

$$\frac{\partial g}{\partial x} = \nu\, u\,\frac{\partial^2 g}{\partial \psi^2}. \tag{8.30}$$

We can also put

$$u = \sqrt{\frac{2}{\varrho}\,[g - p(x)]}\,.$$

Equation (8.30) is a differential equation for the total pressure $g(x, \psi)$, and its boundary conditions are:

$$g = p(x) \text{ for } \psi = 0 \quad \text{and} \quad g = p(x) + \frac{1}{2}\varrho U^2 \text{ for } \psi = \infty .$$

In order to represent the flow in the physical plane x, y, it is necessary to transform from ψ to y with the aid of the equation

$$y = \int \frac{d\psi}{u} = \sqrt{\frac{\varrho}{2}} \int_{\psi=0} \frac{d\psi}{\sqrt{g - p(x)}} .$$

Equation (8.30) is related to the heat conduction equation. The differential equation for the one-dimensional case, e. g. for a bar, is given by

$$\frac{\partial T}{\partial t} = a \frac{\partial^2 T}{\partial x^2} , \tag{8.31}$$

where T denotes the temperature, t denotes the time, and a is the thermal diffusivity, see Chap. XIV. However, the transformed boundary layer equation, unlike eqn. (8.31), is non-linear, because the thermal diffusivity is replaced by νu, which depends on the independent variable x, as well as on the dependent variable g.

At the wall, $\psi = 0$, $u = 0$, $g = p$ eqn. (8.30) exhibits an unpleasant singularity. The left-hand side becomes $\partial g/\partial x = dp/dx \neq 0$. On the right-hand side we have $u = 0$, and, therefore, $\partial^2 g/\partial \psi^2 = \infty$. This circumstance is disturbing when numerical methods are used, and is intimately connected with the singular behaviour of the velocity profile near the wall as determined by the compatibility conditions, discussed in the preceding section. A detailed discussion of eqn. (8.30) was given by L. Prandtl [13], who had deduced the transformation a long time before the paper by R. von Mises appeared, without, however, publishing it†.

H. J. Luckert [9] applied eqn. (8.30) to the example of the boundary layer on a flat plate in order to test its practicability. L. Rosenhead and H. Simpson [15] gave a critical discussion of the preceding publication.

e. The momentum and energy integral equations for the boundary layer

A complete calculation of the boundary layer for a given body with the aid of the differential equations is, in many cases, as will be seen in more detail in the next chapter, so cumbersome and time-consuming that it cannot be carried out in practice. It is, therefore, desirable to possess at least approximate methods of solution, to be applied in cases when an exact solution of the boundary layer equations cannot be obtained with a reasonable amount of work, even if their accuracy is only limited. Such approximate methods can be devised if we do not insist on satisfying the differential equations for every fluid particle. Instead, the boundary layer equation is satisfied in a stratum near the wall and near the region of transition to the external

† See footnote on p. 79 of ref. [13] and the letter of L. Prandtl to ZAMM, 8, 249 (1928).

flow by satisfying the boundary conditions, together with certain compatibility conditions. In the remaining region of fluid in the boundary layer only a mean over the differential equation is satisfied, the mean being taken over the whole thickness of the boundary layer. Such a mean value is obtained from the momentum equation which is, in turn, derived from the equation of motion by integration over the boundary layer thickness. Since this equation will be often used in the approximate methods, to be discussed later, we shall deduce it now, writing it down in its modern form. The equation is known as the *momentum integral equation* of boundary layer theory, or as von Kármán's integral condition [8].

We shall restrict ourselves to the case of steady, two-dimensional, and incompressible flow, i. e. we shall refer to eqns. (7.10) to (7.12). Upon integrating the equation of motion (7.10) with respect to y, from $y = 0$ (wall) to $y = h$, where the layer $y = h$ is everywhere outside the boundary layer, we obtain:

$$\int_{y=0}^{h} \left(u \frac{\partial u}{\partial x} + v \frac{\partial u}{\partial y} - U \frac{\mathrm{d}U}{\mathrm{d}x} \right) \mathrm{d}y = -\frac{\tau_0}{\varrho} . \tag{8.32}$$

The shearing stress at the wall, τ_0, has been substituted for $\mu(\partial u/\partial y)_0$, so that eqn. (8.32) is seen to be valid both for laminar and turbulent flows, on condition that in the latter case u and v denote the time averages of the respective velocity components. The normal velocity component, v, can be replaced by $v = -\int_0^y (\partial u/\partial x)\,\mathrm{d}y$, as seen from the equation of continuity, and, consequently, we have

$$\int_{y=0}^{h} \left(u \frac{\partial u}{\partial x} - \frac{\partial u}{\partial y} \int_0^y \frac{\partial u}{\partial x} \mathrm{d}y - U \frac{\mathrm{d}U}{\mathrm{d}x} \right) \mathrm{d}y = -\frac{\tau_0}{\varrho} .$$

Integrating by parts, we obtain for the second term

$$\int_{y=0}^{h} \left(\frac{\partial u}{\partial y} \int_0^y \frac{\partial u}{\partial x} \mathrm{d}y \right) \mathrm{d}y = U \int_0^h \frac{\partial u}{\partial x} \mathrm{d}y - \int_0^h u \frac{\partial u}{\partial x} \mathrm{d}y ,$$

so that

$$\int_0^h \left(2u \frac{\partial u}{\partial x} - U \frac{\partial u}{\partial x} - U \frac{\mathrm{d}U}{\mathrm{d}x} \right) \mathrm{d}y = -\frac{\tau_0}{\varrho} ,$$

which can be contracted to

$$\int_0^h \frac{\partial}{\partial x} [u(U - u)]\, \mathrm{d}y + \frac{\mathrm{d}U}{\mathrm{d}x} \int_0^h (U - u)\, \mathrm{d}y = \frac{\tau_0}{\varrho} .$$

Since in both integrals the integrand vanishes outside the boundary layer, it is permissible to put $h \to \infty$.

We now introduce the displacement thickness δ^* and the momentum thickness θ, which have already been used in Chap. VII. They are defined by

$$\delta^* U = \int_{y=0}^{\infty} (U - u)\, \mathrm{d}y \qquad \text{(displacement thickness)}, \tag{8.33}$$

and

$$\theta U^2 = \int_{y=0}^{\infty} u(U - u)\, \mathrm{d}y \qquad \text{(momentum thickness)}. \tag{8.34}$$

It will be noted that in the first term of the equation preceding (8.33), differentiation with respect to x, and integration with respect to y, may be interchanged as the upper limit h is independent of x. Hence

$$\boxed{\frac{\tau_0}{\varrho} = \frac{\mathrm{d}}{\mathrm{d}x}(U^2\theta) + \delta^* U \frac{\mathrm{d}U}{\mathrm{d}x}}\,. \tag{8.35}$$

This is the *momentum integral equation for two-dimensional incompressible boundary layers*. As long as no statement is made concerning τ_0, eqn. (8.35) applies to laminar and turbulent boundary layers alike. This modern form of the momentum integral equation was first given by H. Gruschwitz [6]. It finds its application in the approximate theories for laminar and turbulent boundary layers (Chap. XII and Chap. XXII). Its extension to axially symmetrical boundary layers will be discussed in Sec. XIIe (see p. 256).

Using a similar approach, K. Wieghardt [20] deduced in recent times an *energy integral equation* for laminar boundary layers. This equation is obtained by multiplying the equation of motion by u and then integrating from $y = 0$ to $y = h > \delta(x)$. Substituting, again, v from the equation of continuity we obtain

$$\varrho \int_0^h \left[u^2 \frac{\partial u}{\partial x} - u \frac{\partial u}{\partial y} \left(\int_0^y \frac{\partial u}{\partial x}\, \mathrm{d}y \right) - u\, U \frac{\mathrm{d}U}{\mathrm{d}x} \right] \mathrm{d}y = \mu \int_0^h u \frac{\partial^2 u}{\partial y^2}\, \mathrm{d}y\,.$$

The second term can be transformed by integrating by parts:

$$\int_0^h \left[u \frac{\partial u}{\partial y} \left(\int_0^y \frac{\partial u}{\partial x}\, \mathrm{d}y \right) \right] \mathrm{d}y = \frac{1}{2} \int_0^h (U^2 - u^2) \frac{\partial u}{\partial x}\, \mathrm{d}y\,,$$

whereas by combining the first with the third term we have

$$\int_0^h \left[u^2 \frac{\partial u}{\partial x} - u\, U \frac{\mathrm{d}U}{\mathrm{d}x} \right] \mathrm{d}y = \frac{1}{2} \int_0^h u \frac{\mathrm{d}}{\mathrm{d}x} (u^2 - U^2)\, \mathrm{d}y\,.$$

Finally, upon integrating the right-hand side by parts, we obtain

$$\frac{1}{2} \varrho \frac{\mathrm{d}}{\mathrm{d}x} \int_0^{\infty} u(U^2 - u^2)\, \mathrm{d}y = \mu \int_0^{\infty} \left(\frac{\partial u}{\partial y} \right)^2 \mathrm{d}y\,. \tag{8.36}$$

The upper limit of integration could here, too, be replaced by $y = \infty$, because the integrands become equal to zero outside the boundary layer. The quantity $\mu(\partial u/\partial y)^2$ represents the energy, per unit volume and time, which is transformed into heat by friction (dissipation, *cf.* Chap. XIV). The term $\frac{1}{2}\varrho(U^2-u^2)$ on the left-hand side represents the loss in mechanical energy (kinetic and pressure energy) taking place in the boundary layer as compared with the potential flow. Hence the term $\frac{1}{2}\varrho\int_0^\infty u(U^2-u^2)\,\mathrm{d}y$ represents the flux of dissipated energy, and the left-hand side represents the rate of change of the flux of dissipated energy per unit length in the x-direction.

If, in addition to the displacement and momentum thickness from eqns. (8.33) and (8.34) respectively, we introduce the dissipation energy thickness δ^{**} from the definition

$$U^3\,\delta^{**} = \int_0^\infty u(U^2-u^2)\,\mathrm{d}y \qquad \text{(energy thickness)} \tag{8.37}$$

we can rewrite the energy integral equation (8.36) in the following simplified form:

$$\frac{\mathrm{d}}{\mathrm{d}x}(U^3\,\delta^{**}) = 2\,\nu\int_0^\infty\left(\frac{\partial u}{\partial y}\right)^2\mathrm{d}y\,, \tag{8.38}$$

which represents the energy equation for two-dimensional laminar boundary layers in incompressible flow†.

In order to visualize the displacement thickness, the momentum thickness, and the energy dissipation thickness, it is convenient to calculate them for the simple case of linear velocity distribution, as shown in Fig. 8.2. In this case we find:

Displacement thickness $\delta^* = \frac{1}{2}\,\delta$
Momentum thickness $\theta = \frac{1}{6}\,\mathrm{d}$
Energy thickness $\delta^{**} = \frac{1}{4}\,\delta$

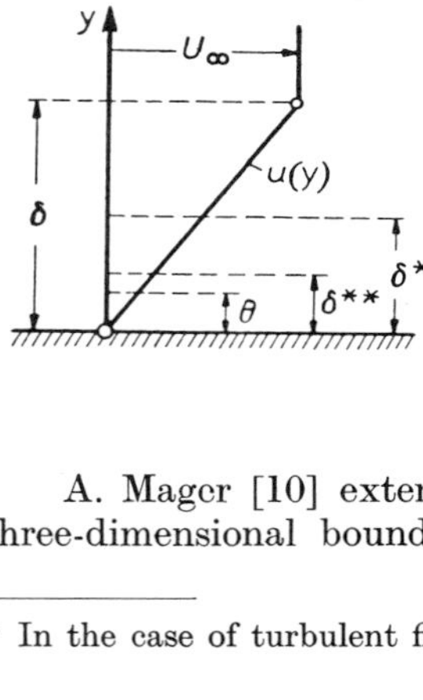

Fig. 8.2. Boundary layer with linear velocity distribution

δ^* = displacement thickness, δ^{**} = energy thickness, θ = momentum thickness

A. Mager [10] extended the above approximate derivation to the case of a three-dimensional boundary layer; see also Sec. XIIe on p. 258.

† In the case of turbulent flows, the momentum energy equation assumes the form

$$\frac{\mathrm{d}}{\mathrm{d}x}(U^3\,\delta^{**}) = 2\int_0^\infty\frac{\tau}{\varrho}\,\frac{\partial u}{\partial y}\,\mathrm{d}y\,.$$

References

[1] A. Betz, Zur Berechnung des Überganges laminarer Grenzschichten in die Außenströmung. "Fifty years of boundary layer research", pp. 63—70, Braunschweig 1955.

[2] V. M. Falkner and S. W. Skan, Some approximate solutions of the boundary layer equations. Phil. Mag. **12**, 865 (1931); ARC R & M 1314 (1930).

[3] Th. Geis, Ähnliche Grenzschichten an Rotationskörpern. "Fifty years of boundary layer research", pp. 294—303, 1955.

[4] S. Goldstein, A note on the boundary layer equations. Proc. Cambr. Phil. Soc. **35**, 388 (1939).

[5] H. Görtler, Weiterentwicklung eines Grenzschichtprofiles bei vorgegebenem Druckverlauf. ZAMM **19**, 129—140 (1939); see also Jour. Roy. Aero. Soc. **45**, 35—50 (1941).

[6] E. Gruschwitz, Die turbulente Reibungsschicht in ebener Strömung bei Druckabfall und Druckanstieg. Ing.-Arch. **2**, 321 (1931).

[7] D. R. Hartree, On an equation occuring in Falkner and Skan's approximate treatment of the equations of the boundary layer. Proc. Cambr. Phil. Soc. **33**, Part II, 223 (1937).

[8] Th. von Kármán, Über laminare und turbulente Reibung. ZAMM **1**, 233 (1912). Engl. transl. in NACA Tech. Memo. 1092.

[9] H. J. Luckert, Über die Integration der Differentialgleichung einer Gleitschicht in zäher Flüssigkeit. Diss. Berlin 1933, reprinted in Schriften d. math. Seminars u. Inst. f. angew. Math. d. Universität Berlin **1**, 245 (1933).

[10] A. Mager, Generalization of boundary layer momentum-integral equations to three-dimensional flows including those of rotating system. NACA Rep. No. 1067 (1952).

[11] W. Mangler, Die „ähnlichen" Lösungen der Prandtlschen Grenzschichtgleichungen. ZAMM **23**, 243 (1943).

[12] R. von Mises, Bemerkungen zur Hydrodynamik. ZAMM **7**, 425—431 (1927).

[13] L. Prandtl, Zur Berechnung der Grenzschichten. ZAMM **18**, 77—82 (1938); see also Jour. Roy. Aero. Soc. **45**, 35—40 (1941) and NACA Tech. Memo. 959 (1940).

[14] F. Riegels and J. Zaat, Zum Übergang von Grenzschichten in die ungestörte Strömung. Nachr. Akad. Wiss. Göttingen, Math. Phys. Klasse, 42—45 (1947).

[15] L. Rosenhead and J. H. Simpson, Note on the velocity distribution in the wake behind a flat plate along a stream. Proc. Cambr. Phil. Soc. **32**, 285 (1936).

[16] K. Schröder, Verwendung der Differenzenrechnung zur Berechnung der laminaren Grenzschicht. Math. Nachrichten **4**, pp. 439—367 (1951).

[17] H. Schuh, Über die „ähnlichen" Lösungen der instationären laminaren Grenzschichtgleichung in inkompressibler Strömung. "Fifty years of boundary layer research" pp. 147—152, Braunschweig 1955.

[18] W. Tollmien, Über das Verhalten einer Strömung längs einer Wand am äußeren Rand ihrer Reibungsschicht. Betz Anniversary volume 218 (1945).

[19] N. Tetervin and C. C. Lin, A general integral form of the boundary layer equation for incompressible flow with an application to the calculation of the separation point of turbulent boundary layers. NACA Tech. Rep. 1046 (1951).

[20] K. Wieghardt, Über einen Energiesatz zur Berechnung laminarer Grenzschichten. Ing.-Arch. **16**, 231 (1948).

CHAPTER IX

Exact solutions of the steady-state boundary layer equations in two-dimensional motion

The present chapter will deal with some exact solutions of the boundary layer equations. A solution will be considered exact when it is a complete solution of the boundary layer equations, irrespective of whether it is obtained analytically, or by numerical methods. On the other hand, Chap. XII will deal with approximate solutions, i. e. with solutions which are obtained from integral relations, such as the momentum and energy integral equations described in the preceding chapter, rather than from differential equations.

There are in existence only comparatively few exact analytical solutions, and we shall discuss them first. Generally speaking, the process of obtaining analytical solutions of the boundary layer equations encounters considerable mathematical difficulties, as already illustrated with the example of a flat plate. The differential equations are non-linear in most cases so that, generally speaking, they can be solved only by power-series expansions or by numerical methods.

In the case of two-dimensional motion, the boundary layer equations and their boundary conditions are given by eqns. (7.10) to (7.12) with (7.6):

$$u \frac{\partial u}{\partial x} + v \frac{\partial u}{\partial y} = U \frac{\mathrm{d}U}{\mathrm{d}x} + \nu \frac{\partial^2 u}{\partial y^2}, \tag{9.1}$$

$$\frac{\partial u}{\partial x} + \frac{\partial v}{\partial y} = 0, \tag{9.2}$$

$$y = 0: \quad u = 0, \quad v = 0; \qquad y = \infty: \quad u = U(x). \tag{9.3}$$

In addition, a velocity profile $u(0, y)$ must be given at an initial section, say, at $x = 0$.

In most cases it is convenient to integrate the equation of continuity by the introduction of a stream function $\psi(x, y)$, so that

$$u = \frac{\partial \psi}{\partial y}; \qquad v = -\frac{\partial \psi}{\partial x}.$$

Consequently the stream function must satisfy the following equation (see also eqn. (7.21)):

$$\frac{\partial \psi}{\partial y} \frac{\partial^2 \psi}{\partial x \, \partial y} - \frac{\partial \psi}{\partial x} \frac{\partial^2 \psi}{\partial y^2} = U \frac{\mathrm{d}U}{\mathrm{d}x} + \nu \frac{\partial^3 \psi}{\partial y^3}, \tag{9.4}$$

with the boundary conditions $\partial\psi/\partial y = 0$ and $\partial\psi/\partial x = 0$ at the wall, $y = 0$, and $\partial\psi/\partial y = U(x)$ at $y = \infty$.

a. Flow past a wedge

The 'similar' solutions discussed in Chap. VIII constitute a particularly simple class of solutions $u(x, y)$ which have the property that the velocity profiles at different distances, x, can be made congruent with suitable scale factors for u and y. The system of partial differential equations (9.1) and (9.2) is now reduced to one ordinary differential equation. It was proved in Chap. VIII that such similar solutions exist when the velocity of the potential flow is proportional to a power of the length co-ordinate measured from the stagnation point, i. e. for

$$U(x) = u_1 \, x^m \, .$$

From eqn. (8.24) it follows that the transformation of the independent variable y, which leads to an ordinary differential equation, is

$$\eta = y \sqrt{\frac{m+1}{2} \frac{U}{\nu x}} = y \sqrt{\frac{m+1}{2} \frac{u_1}{\nu}} \, x^{\frac{m-1}{2}} \, . \tag{9.5}$$

The equation of continuity is integrated by the introduction of a stream function, for which we put

$$\psi(x, y) = \sqrt{\frac{2}{m+1}} \sqrt{\nu u_1} \, x^{\frac{m+1}{2}} f(\eta) \, ,$$

as seen from eqns. (8.11) and (8.23). Thus the velocity components become

$$\left.\begin{aligned} u &= u_1 \, x^m f'(\eta) = U f'(\eta) \, , \\ v &= -\sqrt{\frac{m+1}{2}} \nu u_1 \, x^{m-1} \left\{ f + \frac{m-1}{m+1} \eta f' \right\} . \end{aligned}\right\} \tag{9.6}$$

Introducing these values into the equation of motion (9.1), dividing by $m \, u_1 \, x^{2m-1}$, and putting, as in eqn. (8.21),

$$m = \frac{\beta}{2-\beta} \, ; \qquad \frac{2m}{m+1} = \beta \, , \tag{9.7}$$

we obtain the following differential equation for $f(\eta)$:

$$f''' + f f'' + \beta (1 - f'^2) = 0 \, . \tag{9.8}$$

It will be recalled that it was already given as eqn. (8.15), and that its boundary conditions are

$$\eta = 0: \quad f = 0 \, , \quad f' = 0 \, ; \qquad \eta = \infty: \quad f' = 1 \, .$$

Eqn. (9.8) was first deduced by V. M. Falkner and S. W. Skan, and its solutions were later investigated in detail by D. R. Hartree (see References to Chap. VIII). The solution is represented in Fig. 9.1. In the case of accelerated flow ($m > 0$, $\beta > 0$) the velocity profiles have no point of inflexion, whereas in the case of decelerated flow ($m < 0$, $\beta < 0$) they exhibit a point of inflexion. Separation occurs for

$\beta = -0{\cdot}199$, i. e. for $m = -0{\cdot}091$. This result shows that the laminar boundary layer is able to support only a very small deceleration without separation occuring.

K. Stewartson [41] gave a detailed analysis of the manifold of solutions of eqn. (9.8). According to this analysis, in the range of increasing pressures ($-0.199 < < \beta < 0$) there exists a further solution, that is, in addition to the one discovered by Hartree. The additional solution leads to a velocity profile with back-flow (*cf.* Chap. XII g).

The potential flow given by $U(x) = u_1 x^m$ exists in the neighbourhood of the stagnation point on a wedge, Fig. 8.1, whose included angle β is given by eqn. (9.7). Two-dimensional stagnation flow, as well as the boundary layer on a flat plate at zero incidence, constitute particular cases of the present solutions, the former for $\beta = 1$ and $m = 1$, the latter for $\beta = 0$ and $m = 0$.

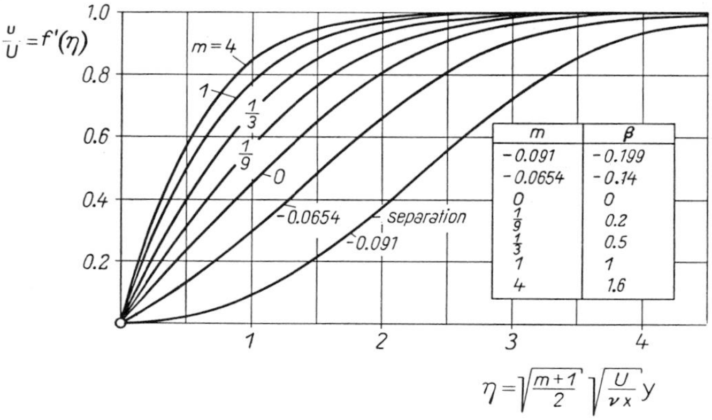

Fig. 9.1. Velocity distribution in the laminar boundary layer in the flow past a wedge given by $U(x) = u_1 x^m$. The exponent m and the wedge angle β (Fig. 8.1) are connected through eqn. (9.7)

The case $\beta = \frac{1}{2}$, $m = \frac{1}{3}$ is worthy of attention. In this case the differential equation for $f(\eta)$ becomes: $f''' + ff'' + \frac{1}{2}(1 - f'^2) = 0$; it transforms into the differential equation of rotationally symmetrical flow with stagnation point, eqn. (5.40), i. e. $\phi''' + 2\,\phi\,\phi'' + 1 - \phi'^2 = 0$ for $\phi(\zeta)$, if we put $\eta = \zeta\sqrt{2}$ and $\mathrm{d}f/\mathrm{d}\eta = \mathrm{d}\phi/\mathrm{d}\zeta$. This means that the calculation of the boundary layer in the rotationally symmetrical case can be reduced to the calculation of two-dimensional flow past a wedge whose included angle is $\pi\,\beta = \pi/2$.

The relationship between the two-dimensional and rotationally symmetrical boundary layers will be further discussed, in a more general form, in Chap. X.

b. Flow in a convergent channel

The case of potential flow given by the equation

$$U(x) = \frac{u_1}{-x} \tag{9.9}$$

is related to flows past a wedge, and also leads to 'similar' solutions. With $u_1 > 0$ it represents two-dimensional motion in a convergent channel with flat walls (sink).

The volume of flow for a full opening angle 2π and for a stratum of unit height is $Q = 2\,\pi\,u_1$ (Fig. 9.2). Introducing the similarity transformation

$$\eta = y\sqrt{\frac{U}{-x\,\nu}} = \frac{y}{x}\sqrt{\frac{u_1}{\nu}} = \frac{y}{x}\sqrt{\frac{Q}{2\pi\,\nu}} \tag{9.10}$$

as well as the stream function

$$\psi(x,y) = -\sqrt{\nu\,u_1}\,f(\eta)$$

we obtain the velocity components

$$u = U\,f'\,; \quad v = -\sqrt{\nu\,u_1}\,\frac{\eta}{x}\,f'\,. \tag{9.11}$$

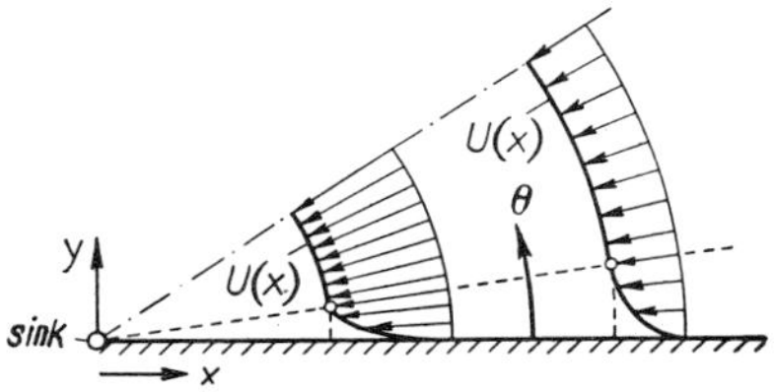

Fig. 9.2. Flow in a convergent channel

Substituting into eqn. (9.1) we obtain the differential equation for the stream function

$$f''' - f'^2 + 1 = 0\,. \tag{9.12}$$

The boundary conditions follow from eqn. (9.3) and are: $f = 0$ and $f' = 0$ at $\eta = 0$, and $f' = 1$ at $\eta = \infty$. This is also a particular case of the class of 'similar' solutions considered in Chap. VIII. Eqn. (9.12) is obtained from the more general differential equation (8.15) for the case of 'similar' boundary layers, if we put $\alpha = 0$ and $\beta = +1$. The example under consideration is one of the rare cases when the solution of the boundary layer differential equations can be obtained analytically in closed form.

First, upon multiplying eqn. (9.12) by f'' and integrating once, we have

$$f''^2 - \tfrac{2}{3}\,(f'-1)^2\,(f'+2) = a\,,$$

where a is a constant of integration. Its value is zero, as $f' = 1$ and $f'' = 0$ for $\eta \to \infty$. Thus

$$\frac{\mathrm{d}f'}{\mathrm{d}\eta} = \sqrt{\frac{2}{3}\,(f'-1)^2\,(f'+2)}$$

or

$$\eta = \sqrt{\frac{3}{2}}\int\limits_0^{f'} \frac{\mathrm{d}f'}{\sqrt{(f'-1)^2\,(f'+2)}}\,,$$

where the additive constant of integration is seen to be equal to zero in view of the boundary condition $f' = 1$ at $\eta = \infty$. The integral can be expressed in closed form as follows:

$$\eta = \sqrt{2}\left\{\tanh^{-1}\frac{\sqrt{2+f'}}{\sqrt{3}} - \tanh^{-1}\sqrt{\frac{2}{3}}\right\},$$

or, solving for $f' = u/U$:

$$f' = \frac{u}{U} = 3\tanh^2\left(\frac{\eta}{\sqrt{2}} + 1{\cdot}146\right) - 2\,. \tag{9.13}$$

Here we have substituted $\tanh^{-1}\sqrt{\frac{2}{3}} = 1{\cdot}146$. Introducing the polar angle $\theta = y/x$, as well as $Q = 2\,\pi\,r\,U$ (r = radial distance from the sink), we can replace η from eqn. (9.10) by

$$\eta = \theta\sqrt{\frac{U\,r}{\nu}} = \frac{y}{x}\sqrt{\frac{U\,r}{\nu}}\,. \tag{9.14}$$

The velocity distribution given by eqn. (9.13) is represented in Fig. 9.3. At $\eta = 3$, approximately, the boundary layer merges with the potential flow. Hence the boundary layer thickness becomes $\delta = 3\,x\sqrt{\nu/U\,r}$; it decreases, as in other examples, as $1/\sqrt{\mathsf{R}}$.

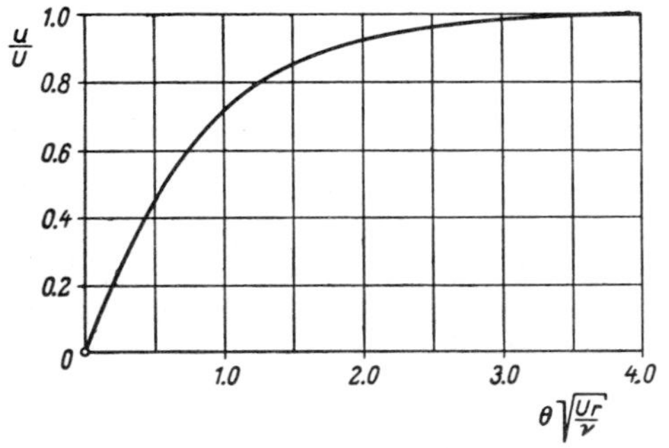

Fig. 9.3. Velocity distribution in the laminar boundary layer of the flow in a convergent channel

The preceding solution was first obtained by K. Pohlhausen [33a]. It will be recalled from Sec. Vb. 11 on p. 90 that the problem of wedge flow discussed here can be solved exactly on the basis of the full Navier-Stokes equations. It can be shown that the exact solutions obtained by G. B. Jeffery and G. Hamel for which numerical calculations were given by K. Millsaps and K. Pohlhausen reduce themselves to the preceding equation (9.13). It should be noted here that the exact solution has been obtained in a polar system of co-ordinates which then involves only one velocity component, the flow being purely radial. The preceding solution was based on the boundary layer approximation and was performed in a Cartesian co-ordinate system, hence there are two non-zero velocity components u and v, eqn. (9.11). S. Goldstein [13a] gave an interesting discussion of this problem.

c. Flow past a cylinder; symmetrical case (the Blasius series)

The class of 'similar' solutions of the boundary layer equations considered so far is comparatively narrow. Apart from the examples of the flat plate, stagnation flow, flow past a wedge, and flow in a convergent channel which have already been described, few additional solutions can be obtained. We shall now consider the general case of the boundary layer on a cylindrical body placed in a stream which is perpendicular to its axis. The method of solution was first given by H. Blasius [3]; it was developed further by K. Hiemenz [25] and L. Howarth [26]. It is necessary to distinguish here two cases depending on whether the cylinder is symmetrical about an axis which is parallel to the stream at a large distance from the body or not. We shall refer to these two cases as to the symmetrical and asymmetrical case respectively.

In either case the velocity of the potential flow is assumed to have the form of a power-series in x, where x denotes the distance from the stagnation point measured along the contour. The velocity profile in the boundary layer is also represented as a similar power-series in x, where the coefficients are assumed to be functions of the co-ordinate y, measured at right angles to the wall (Blasius series). It is important to note in this connexion that L. Howarth succeeded in finding a substitution for the velocity profile which confers universal validity on the y-dependent coefficients. In other words, by a suitable assumption regarding the power series, its coefficients have been made independent of the particulars of the cylindrical body, so that the resulting functions could be evaluated and presented in the form of tables. Thus the calculation of the boundary layer for a given shape becomes very simple if use is made of the tables, provided that the tabulation extends over a sufficiently large number of terms of the series.

The usefulness of Blasius' method is, however, severely restricted by the fact that, precisely in the most important case of very slender body shapes, a large number of terms is required; in fact, their number is so large that it ceases to be practicable to tabulate them all with a reasonable amount of numerical work. This is caused by the circumstance that in the case of slender body sections, e. g. in the case of an ellipse, placed in a stream parallel to its major axis, or in the case of an aerofoil, the potential velocity near the stagnation point in the neighbourhood of the leading edge increases steeply at first and then varies very slowly over a considerable distance downstream. A function of this type cannot be well represented by a power-series with a small number of terms. In spite of this limitation Blasius' method is of great fundamental importance because, in cases when its convergence is insufficient to reach the point of separation, it can be used to calculate analytically and with great accuracy the initial portion of the boundary layer near the stagnation point. The calculation can then be continued with the aid of a suitable numerical method. We shall now describe the principles of the application of Blasius' method to the symmetrical case, and we shall then apply it to the case of a circular cylinder.

Let the potential flow be given by the series

$$U(x) = u_1 x + u_3 x^3 + u_5 x^5 + u_7 x^7 + u_9 x^9 + u_{11} x^{11} + \dots . \tag{9.15}$$

The coefficients u_1, u_3, ... depend only on the shape of the body and are to be considered known. Hence, the pressure term in the boundary layer equation becomes

$$-\frac{1}{\varrho}\frac{\mathrm{d}p}{\mathrm{d}x} = U\frac{\mathrm{d}U}{\mathrm{d}x} = u_1^2 x + 4 u_1 u_3 x^3 + x^5 (6 u_1 u_5 + 3 u_3^2) + \\ + x^7 (8 u_1 u_7 + 8 u_3 u_5) + x^9 (10 u_1 u_9 + 10 u_3 u_7 + 5 u_5^2) + \\ + x^{11} (12 u_1 u_{11} + 12 u_3 u_9 + 12 u_5 u_7) + \dots . \tag{9.16}$$

The continuity equation is integrated by the use of a stream function $\psi(x, y)$. It now remains to make a suitable assumption for the stream function and hence for the velocity components. It appears reasonable to assume a power series for $\psi(x, y)$, in analogy with eqns. (9.15) and (9.16), but with coefficients which are functions of y. If the series for U is terminated with x^k, the pressure term (9.16) ends with the term x^{2k-1}. It follows that if U is approximated by a power-series up to x^k, then the series for ψ must continue as far as the term x^{2k-1}. If, however, the power series for ψ is terminated earlier, and that becomes occasionally necessary in practical calculations, then the result represents the solution of the boundary layer problem with a definite error; its magnitude, evidently, increases as the distance from the stagnation point increases and, in any case, it is necessary to verify the correctness of such an approximate solution.

When making an assumption for the series for ψ it is necessary to arrange the terms in such a way that the functions of the distance from the wall, y, cease to depend on the coefficients $u_1, u_3, u_5, \ldots$ of the potential motion, because only then can they be tabulated once for all.

The distance from the wall is made dimensionless by assuming†

$$\eta = y\sqrt{\frac{u_1}{\nu}}. \tag{9.17}$$

The expression (9.16) makes it plausible to adopt the following form for the stream function:

$$\psi = \sqrt{\frac{\nu}{u_1}}\,\{u_1 x f_1(\eta) + 4 u_3 x^3 f_3(\eta) + 6 u_5 x^5 f_5(\eta) + $$
$$+ 8 u_7 x^7 f_7(\eta) + 10 u_9 x^9 f_9(\eta) + 12 u_{11} x^{11} f_{11}(\eta) + \ldots\}. \tag{9.18}$$

In order to render the functional coefficients $f_1, f_3, \ldots$ independent of the particular properties of the profile, i. e. of $u_1, u_3, \ldots$ it is necessary to split them up as follows:

$$\left.\begin{aligned}
f_5 &= g_5 + \frac{u_3^2}{u_1 u_5} h_5, \\
f_7 &= g_7 + \frac{u_3 u_5}{u_1 u_7} h_7 + \frac{u_3^3}{u_1^2 u_7} k_7, \\
f_9 &= g_9 + \frac{u_3 u_7}{u_1 u_9} h_9 + \frac{u_5^2}{u_1 u_9} k_9 + \frac{u_3^2 u_5}{u_1^2 u_9} j_9 + \frac{u_3^4}{u_1^3 u_9} q_9, \\
f_{11} &= g_{11} + \frac{u_3 u_9}{u_1 u_{11}} h_{11} + \frac{u_5 u_7}{u_1 u_{11}} k_{11} + \frac{u_3^2 u_7}{u_1^2 u_{11}} j_{11} + \\
&\quad + \frac{u_3 u_5^2}{u_1^2 u_{11}} q_{11} + \frac{u_3^3 u_5}{u_1^3 u_{11}} m_{11} + \frac{u_3^5}{u_1^4 u_{11}} n_{11}.
\end{aligned}\right\} \tag{9.19}$$

† This equation is obtained from the Blasius eqn. (7.25) by substituting the first term in (9.15), i. e. $u_1 x$ for U_∞.

Hence, denoting differentiation with respect to η by a dash:

$$u = u_1\, x\, f_1' + 4\, u_3\, x^3\, f_3' + 6\, u_5\, x^5\, f_5' + 8\, u_7\, x^7\, f_7' + \\ + 10\, u_9\, x^9\, f_9' + 12\, u_{11}\, x^{11}\, f'_{11} + \ldots, \tag{9.20}$$

$$v = -\sqrt{\frac{\nu}{u_1}}\, [u_1\, f_1 + 12\, u_3\, x^2\, f_3 + 30\, u_5\, x^4\, f_5 + 56\, u_7\, x^6\, f_7 + \\ + 90\, u_9\, x^8\, f_9 + 132\, u_{11}\, x^{10}\, f_{11} + \ldots]\,. \tag{9.20a}$$

Inserting expressions (9.16). (9.20) and (9.20a) into (9.1), and comparing terms, we obtain a system of simultaneous ordinary differential equations for the functions f_1, f_3, ... the first four of which are:

$$\left.\begin{aligned} f_1'^2 - f_1 f_1'' &= 1 + f_1''' \\ 4 f_1' f_3' - 3 f_1'' f_3 - f_1 f_3'' &= 1 + f_3''' \\ 6 f_1' g_5' - 5 f_1'' g_5 - f_1 g_5'' &= 1 + g_5''' \\ 6 f_1' h_5' - 5 f_1'' h_5 - f_1 h_5'' &= \tfrac{1}{2} + h_5''' - 8 (f_3'^2 - f_3 f_3'')\,. \end{aligned}\right\} \tag{9.21}$$

The boundary conditions for the functions f_1, f_3, ... follow from eqn. (9.3) and are:

$$\left.\begin{aligned} \eta = 0:&\quad f_1 = f_1' = 0; \quad f_3 = f_3' = 0; \quad g_5 = g_5' = 0; \quad h_5 = h_5' = 0\,; \\ \eta = \infty:&\quad f_1' = 1 \quad ; \quad f_3' = \tfrac{1}{4} \quad ; \quad g_5' = \tfrac{1}{6} \quad ; \quad h_5' = 0\,. \end{aligned}\right\} \tag{9.22}$$

These differential equations are all of the third order, and eqn. (9.22) furnishes three boundary conditions for each of them. Only the first equation, that for f_1, is non-linear, being identical with eqn. (5.32) which was obtained in Chap. V for the case of two-dimensional stagnation flow. The remaining differential equations are all linear and their coefficients are determined by the functional coefficients of the preceding terms in the series.

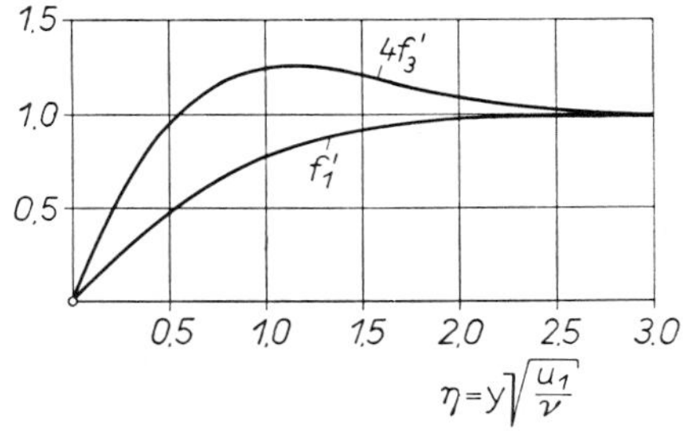

Fig. 9.4. The functions f_1' and f_3' which appear in the Blasius power series, Tables 5.1 and 9.1

The functions f_1 and f_3 have been evaluated by K. Hiemenz [25]; f_1' and f_4' are represented in Fig. 9.4, but f_1' is also included in Fig. 5.11 and Table 5.1 (it was there denoted by ϕ'). L. Howarth [26] improved the tables for f_3, and the functions g_5 and h_5 (Table 9.1) have later been evaluated by N. Froessling [10]. Later still, A. Ulrich [47] considerably extended the scope of these calculations, having evaluated them up to and including the 9th power in x.

Table 9.1. Functional coefficients for the first six terms of the Blasius series, eqn. (9.18), required in the calculation of two-dimensional boundary layers on a cylinder (symmetrical case), after A. N. Tifford [45]

η	f_1'	f_3'	g_5'	h_5'	g_7'	h_7'	k_7'	g_9'	h_9'
0	0	0	0	0	0	0	0	0	0
0·2	0·2266	0·1251	0·1072	0·0141	0·0962	0·0173	0·0016	0·0884	0·0112
0·4	0·4145	0·2129	0·1778	0·0117	0·1563	0·0030	0·0044	0·1413	—0·0079
0·6	0·5663	0·2688	0·2184	—0·0011	0·1879	—0·0286	0·0096	0·1669	—0·0417
0·8	0·6859	0·2997	0·2366	—0·0177	0·1994	—0·0637	0·0174	0·1740	—0·0760
1·0	0·7779	0·3125	0·2399	—0·0331	0·1980	—0·0925	0·0271	0·1700	—0·1019
1·2	0·8467	0·3133	0·2341	—0·0442	0·1896	—0·1102	0·0369	0·1604	—0·1157
1·4	0·8968	0·3070	0·2239	—0·0499	0·1782	—0·1159	0·0452	0·1489	—0·1176
1·6	0·9323	0·2975	0·2123	—0·0504	0·1665	—0·1114	0·0506	0·1375	—0·1101
1·8	0·9568	0·2871	0·2012	—0·0468	0·1558	—0·0997	0·0525	0·1276	—0·0965
2·0	0·9732	0·2775	0·1916	—0·0406	0·1469	—0·0839	0·0510	0·1195	—0·0798
2·2	0·9839	0·2695	0·1839	—0·0332	0·1400	—0·0669	0·0466	0·1132	—0·0628
2·4	0·9905	0·2632	0·1781	—0·0257	0·1349	—0·0507	0·0402	0·1087	—0·0470
2·6	0·9946	0·2586	0·1740	—0·0189	0·1313	—0·0367	0·0330	0·1055	—0·0337
2·8	0·9970	0·2554	0·1712	—0·0133	0·1288	—0·0254	0·0257	0·1033	—0·0231
3·0	0·9984	0·2532	0·1694	—0·0089	0·1273	—0·0168	0·0191	0·1020	—0·0152
3·2	0·9992	0·2519	0·1682	—0·0057	0·1263	—0·0107	0·0135	0·1011	—0·0096
3·4	0·9996	0·2510	0·1675	—0·0035	0·1257	—0·0065	0·0091	0·1006	—0·0058
3·6	0·9998	0·2506	0·1671	—0·0021	0·1254	—0·0038	0·0059	0·1003	—0·0034
3·8	0·9999	0·2503	0·1669	—0·0012	0·1252	—0·0021	0·0036	0·1002	—0·0019
4·0	1·0000	0·2501	0·1668	—0·0006	0·1251	—0·0011	0·0021	0·1001	—0·0010
η	f_1''	f_3''	g_5''	h_5''	g_7''	h_7''	k_7''	g_9''	h_9''
0	1·2326	0·7244	0·6347	0·1192	0·5792	0·1829	0·0076	0·5399	0·1520

In more recent times A. N. Tifford [45] calculated the functions associated with the term x^{11} and improved the accuracy of the existing tables. Table 9.1 contains values of the first derivatives of the functional coefficients required for the terms up to and including x^{11}. These are required for the calculation of the u-component of velocity, as seen from eqns. (9.19) and (9.20). In addition, the table contains values of the second derivative of all functions for $\eta = 0$, because they are required for the evaluation of skin friction and, in particular, of the position of the point of separation (see the Example which follows). This provides a complete set of tables of functional coefficients for six terms of the Blasius series, eqn. (9.18), as it occurs in the calculation of symmetrical cylinders. We now propose to make use of these results in order to calculate the boundary layer on a circular cylinder.

Example: *Circular cylinder.* We shall now apply the preceding method to the case of a circular cylinder. In order to retain uniformity we shall base our

Table 9.1. (continued)

k_9'	j_9'	q_9'	g_{11}'	h_{11}'	k_{11}'	j_{11}'	q_{11}'	m_{11}'	n_{11}'
0	0	0	0	0	0	0	0	0	0
0·0019	0·0125	—0·0062	0·0824	0·0074	—0·0041	0·0165	0·0237	—0·0359	0·0103
—0·0112	0·0288	—0·0124	0·1299	—0·0145	—0·0368	0·0371	0·0514	—0·0721	0·0206
—0·0311	0·0525	—0·0190	0·1511	—0·0489	—0·0799	0·0651	0·0863	—0·1095	0·0307
—0·0501	0·0833	—0·0262	0·1553	—0·0816	—0·1181	0·0992	0·1267	—0·1489	0·0406
—0·0639	0·1171	—0·0341	0·1498	—0·1046	—0·1428	0·1342	0·1666	—0·1895	0·0503
—0·0704	0·1480	—0·0423	0·1397	—0·1152	—0·1520	0·1641	0·1995	—0·2288	0·0595
—0·0703	0·1710	—0·0502	0·1283	—0·1146	—0·1474	0·1841	0·2202	—0·2627	0·0678
—0·0649	0·1829	—0·0567	0·1175	—0·1055	—0·1330	0·1919	0·2266	—0·2874	0·0747
—0·0562	0·1827	—0·0610	0·1083	—0·0911	—0·1131	0·1876	0·2190	—0·2996	0·0796
—0·0460	0·1718	—0·0625	0·1008	—0·0746	—0·0912	0·1731	0·2001	—0·2982	0·0822
—0·0359	0·1528	—0·0610	0·0951	—0·0581	—0·0701	0·1515	0·1737	—0·2834	0·0820
—0·0267	0·1290	—0·0568	0·0910	—0·0432	—0·0516	0·1263	0·1436	—0·2575	0·0790
—0·0190	0·1037	—0·0504	0·0882	—0·0308	—0·0364	0·1003	0·1133	—0·2237	0·0733
—0·0129	0·0795	—0·0426	0·0863	—0·0210	—0·0246	0·0761	0·0854	—0·1858	0·0655
—0·0085	0·0581	—0·0344	0·0851	—0·0138	—0·0160	0·0552	0·0616	—0·1476	0·0563
—0·0053	0·0406	—0·0265	0·0843	—0·0087	—0·0100	0·0383	0·0425	—0·1121	0·0463
—0·0032	0·0271	—0·0195	0·0839	—0·0052	—0·0060	0·0255	0·0281	—0·0814	0·0365
—0·0019	0·0173	—0·0137	0·0836	—0·0030	—0·0035	0·0162	0·0178	—0·0565	0·0275
—0·0010	0·0106	—0·0092	0·0835	—0·0017	—0·0019	0·0099	0·0108	—0·0375	0·0199
—0·0006	0·0062	—0·0059	0·0834	—0·0009	—0·0010	0·0057	0·0063	—0·0238	0·0137

k_9''	j_9''	q_9''	g_{11}''	h_{11}''	k_{11}''	j_{11}''	q_{11}''	m_{11}''	n_{11}''
0·0572	0·0607	—0·0308	0·5100	0·1323	0·0742	0·0806	0·1164	—0·1796	0·0516

calculations on the pressure distribution obtained from potential theory, although in most publications the problem was solved with the aid of an experimentally determined pressure distribution. The ideal velocity distribution in potential irrotational flow past a circular cylinder of radius R and free-stream velocity U_∞ parallel to the x-axis is given by

$$U(x) = 2\,U_\infty \sin\frac{x}{R} = 2\,U_\infty \sin\phi\,. \tag{9.23}$$

The power-series expansion is obtained from eqn. (9.15) by expanding sin (x/R), so that

$$U(x) = 2\,U_\infty\left[\frac{x}{R} - \frac{1}{3!}\left(\frac{x}{R}\right)^3 + \frac{1}{5!}\left(\frac{x}{R}\right)^5 - \frac{1}{7!}\left(\frac{x}{R}\right)^7 + \frac{1}{9!}\left(\frac{x}{R}\right)^9 - \frac{1}{11!}\left(\frac{x}{R}\right)^{11} + \cdots\right]. \tag{9.24}$$

Figure 9.5 shows how the potential velocity distribution from eqn. (9.23) is approximated by the power-series (9.24), when it is successively terminated at x, x^3, x^5, ... It is seen that it is necessary to continue the series (9.24) as far as the power x^7, if it is desired to approximate the sine function closely as far as the downstream stagnation point. In accordance with what was stated earlier, since $k = 9$, it would be necessary to continue the series for u as far as the power $2k - 1 = 17$, i. e. up to x^{17}, if it were desired to take into account all terms up to u^9 in the expansion for U. Since, however, the functional coefficients have only been calculated up to x^{11}, it is necessary to terminate the series for u earlier so that the error committed in this way remains to be estimated separately.

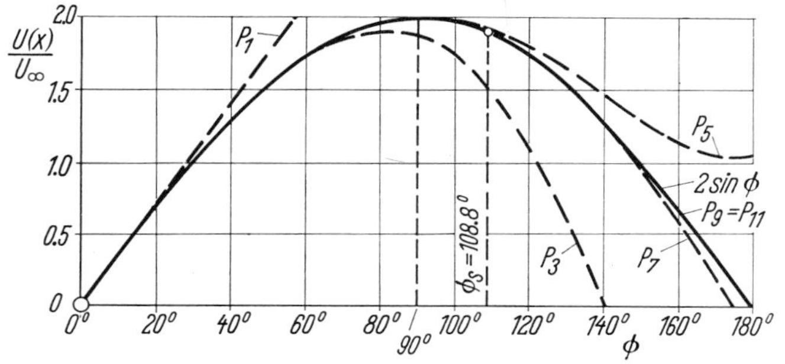

Fig. 9.5. Approximations to the potential velocity distribution past a circular cylinder by power series. P_1, P_3, ... denote power series from eqn. (9.24) terminated successively with x, x^3, ...

Upon comparing eqn. (9.24) with (9.15), we have

$$u_1 = 2\,\frac{U_\infty}{R}\,; \qquad u_3 = -\frac{2}{3!}\,\frac{U_\infty}{R^3}\,; \qquad u_5 = +\frac{2}{5!}\,\frac{U_\infty}{R^5}\,; \quad \ldots \quad \text{and} \quad \eta = \frac{y}{R}\sqrt{\frac{2\,U_\infty R}{\nu}}$$

and, hence, for the velocity distribution

$$\frac{u}{U_\infty} = 2\left\{\frac{x}{R}\,f_1' - \frac{4}{3!}\left(\frac{x}{R}\right)^3 f_3' + \frac{6}{5!}\left(\frac{x}{R}\right)^5 f_5' - \frac{8}{7!}\left(\frac{x}{R}\right)^7 f_7' + \right.$$
$$\left. + \frac{10}{9!}\left(\frac{x}{R}\right)^9 f_9' - \frac{12}{11!}\left(\frac{x}{R}\right)^{11} f_{11}' + \ldots\right\} \tag{9.25}$$

with

$$\left.\begin{aligned} f_5' &= g_5' + \frac{10}{3}\,h_5'\,, \\ f_7' &= g_7' + 7\,h_7' + \frac{70}{3}\,k_7'\,, \\ f_9' &= g_9' + 12\,h_9' + \frac{126}{5}\,k_9' + 84\,j_9' + 280\,q_9'\,, \\ f_{11}' &= g_{11}' + \frac{55}{3}\,h_{11}' + 66\,k_{11}' + 220\,j_{11}' + 462\,q_{11}' + \\ &\quad + 1540\,m_{11}' + \frac{15400}{3}\,n_{11}'\,. \end{aligned}\right\} \tag{9.25a}$$

The velocity profiles for various angles ϕ are seen plotted in Fig. 9.6. The velocity profiles for $\phi > 90°$ have each a point of inflexion. The shearing stress $\tau_0 = \mu\,(\partial u/\partial y)_0$ at the wall, calculated from eqn. (9.25), becomes

$$\frac{\tau_0}{\frac{1}{2}\varrho\, U_\infty^{\,2}}\sqrt{\frac{2\,U_\infty R}{\nu}} = 8\left\{\frac{x}{R}\,f_1''(0) - \frac{4}{3!}\left(\frac{x}{R}\right)^3 f_3''(0) + \frac{6}{5!}\left(\frac{x}{R}\right)^5 f_5''(0) + \right.$$
$$\left. - \frac{8}{7!}\left(\frac{x}{R}\right)^7 f_7''(0) + \frac{10}{9!}\left(\frac{x}{R}\right)^9 f_9''(0) - \frac{12}{11!}\left(\frac{x}{R}\right)^{11} f_{11}''(0) + \dots\right\}. \qquad (9.26)$$

Substituting the coefficients from eqn. (9.25a) and the numerical values from Table 9.1, we obtain

$$\frac{\tau_0}{\frac{1}{2}\varrho\, U_\infty^{\,2}}\sqrt{\frac{U_\infty R}{\nu}} = 6{\cdot}973\,\frac{x}{R} - 2{\cdot}732\left(\frac{x}{R}\right)^3 + 0{\cdot}292\left(\frac{x}{R}\right)^5 - 0{\cdot}0183\left(\frac{x}{R}\right)^7 +$$
$$+ 0{\cdot}000043\left(\frac{x}{R}\right)^9 - 0{\cdot}000115\left(\frac{x}{R}\right)^{11} + \dots\,. \qquad (9.26\,\mathrm{a})$$

The variation of shearing stress over the circumference of the cylinder can be seen plotted in Fig. 9.7.

The position of the point of separation can be found from the condition that the shearing stress must vanish there. This leads to the equation

$$6{\cdot}973 - 2{\cdot}732\,X_S + 0{\cdot}292\,X_S^2 - 0{\cdot}0183\,X_S^3 + 0{\cdot}000\,043\,X_S^4 - 0{\cdot}000\,115\,X_S^5 = 0\,,$$

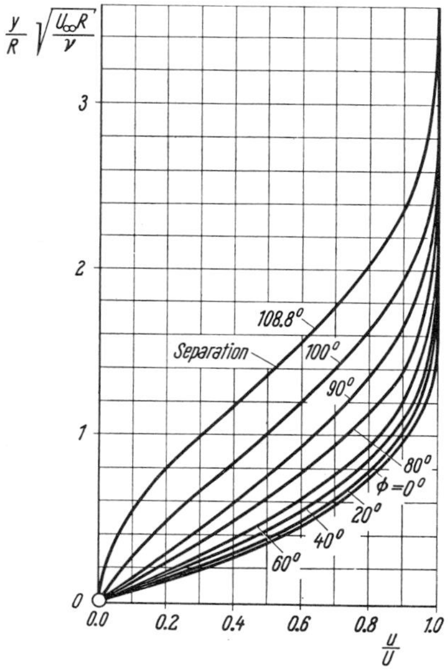

Fig. 9.6. Velocity distribution in the boundary layer on a circular cylinder

ϕ — angle measured from stagnation point

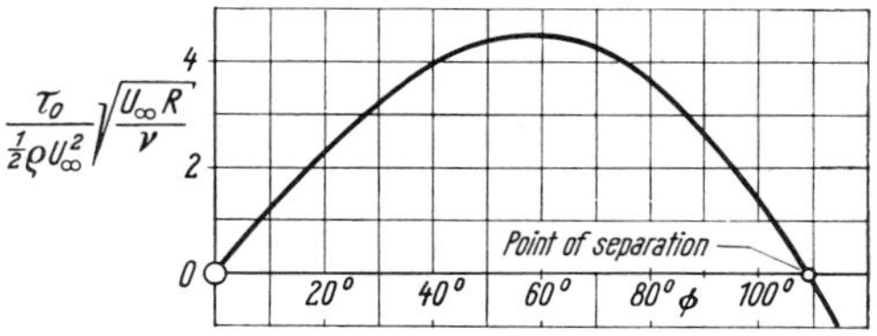

Fig. 9.7. Variation of shearing stress at the wall over the circumference of a circular cylinder for a laminar boundary layer

where $X_S = (x_S/R)^2$. Solving, we find that separation occurs at

$$\phi_S = 108{\cdot}8^\circ .$$

If the power series were terminated at x^9, the point of separation would turn out to be at $\phi_S = 109{\cdot}6^\circ$. It is, therefore, possible to conclude that the Blasius series terminating with x^{11} is, in fact, sufficient to represent the velocity u with a satisfactory degree of accuracy as far as the point of separation.

Alternatively, we can verify this point with reference to the first compatibility condition at the wall, eqn. (7.18). Thus

$$U \frac{\mathrm{d}U}{\mathrm{d}x} = -\nu \left(\frac{\partial^2 u}{\partial y^2}\right)_{y=0} . \tag{9.27}$$

The curvature of the velocity profile at the wall, as calculated from eqn. (9.25), is seen plotted in Fig. 9.8 and compared with the exact value of $U \cdot \mathrm{d}U/\mathrm{d}x$. The agreement is very good for a distance x beyond the point of separation. We may, therefore, conclude that the Blasius series terminating at the term x^{11} satisfies the first compatibility condition on a circular cylinder up to a point which lies beyond the point of separation. It does not, however, necessarily follow that the truncated series represents the velocity profile with sufficient accuracy. H. Goertler [17] verified this point using the experimental pressure distribution obtained by K. Hiemenz. Comparing the results obtained with the aid of a Blasius series with those obtained from an exact numerical solution, he found some deviations in the profiles immediately preceding the point of separation. In this connexion it is necessary to point out that H. Goertler has devised an alternative series for the velocity distribution whose convergence is markedly superior to that of a Blasius series; it will be described in Sec. IXe.

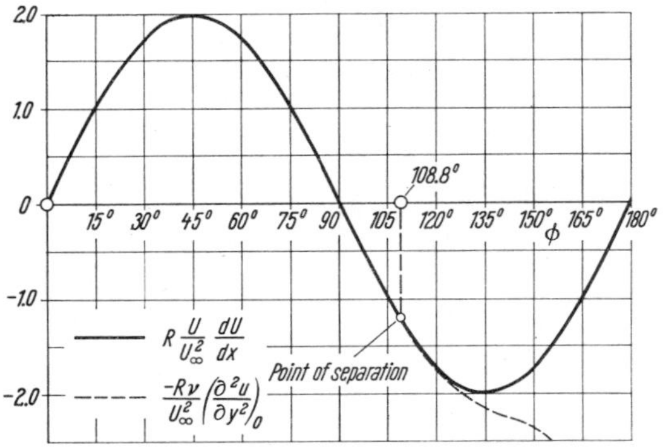

Fig. 9.8. Verification of the first compatibility condition from eqn. (9.27) for the laminar boundary layer on a circular cylinder from Fig. 9.6. The first compatibility condition is satisfied approximately as far as some point beyond separation

In fact, the reader should realize that the preceding scheme of calculation is an intuitive one and that there is no assurance that it leads to a convergent series and so to a genuine approximation to the exact solution of the problem. The latter fact is usually established indirectly, by experiment. M. van Dyke [47a] evaluated the Blasius series for a parabolic cylinder of nose radius R and showed that the resulting series diverges for $x/R > 0{\cdot}62$, where x denotes the usual coordinate measured from the nose along the arc. Even in the series for a circular cylinder, eqn. (9.26a) the coefficients appear to increase after the term $O\{(x/R)^9\}$ showing that the series may become divergent from a certain value of x/R onwards. M. van Dyke showed that the radius of convergence of a Blasius series can be improved by a change of variables which should be properly related to the existing singularities. For example, in the case of the parabolic cylinder the obvious series contains a singularity along the axis at a distance of $\xi = -1/2\ R$ from the vertex, but the radius of convergence can be apparently increased to infinity by expanding in terms of $\xi/(\xi + \frac{1}{2}\ R)$, where ξ is measured along the axis of the parabola.

The essential point in M. van Dyke's argument is to draw attention to the problem of convergence of Blasius series and to make it appear plausible that they almost certainly diverge at a distance of the order of the nose radius.

As already mentioned, in the case of more slender body shapes considerably more terms of the Blasius series are required, if it is desired to obtain the velocity profiles as far as the point of separation. However, the evaluation of further functional coefficients is hindered by considerable difficulties. These are due not only to the fact that for every additional term in the series the number of differential equations to be solved increases, but also, and even more forcibly, the difficulties are due to the need to evaluate the functions for the lower power terms with ever increasing accuracy, if the functions for the higher power terms are to be sufficiently accurate. Thus the chances of carrying out an extension of this method over what has already been achieved are seen to be severely limited. We may mention here, however, that H. Goertler has recently devised a new series expansion for the velocity distribution which is markedly superior as far as its convergence is concerned.

L. Howarth [26] extended the present method to include the asymmetrical case, but the tabulation of the functional coefficients was not carried beyond those corresponding to the power x^2. N. Froessling [10] carried out an extension of this method to the rotationally symmetrical case which will be considered in Chap. X.

Measurements of the pressure distribution around a circular cylinder were reported by K. Hiemenz in his thesis presented to Goettingen University. They were made the basis of his boundary layer calculations. His measurements showed separation at $\phi_S = 81°$, whereas the calculation indicated $\phi_S = 82°$. Later O. Flachsbart published extensive experimental data on the pressure distribution, Fig. 1.9, which point to a large influence of the Reynolds number. For values of the Reynolds number *below the critical* the pressure minimum occurs already near $\phi = 70°$, and the pressure is nearly constant over the whole downstream portion of the cylinder. For Reynolds numbers *above the critical* the pressure minimum shifts to $\phi = 90°$ approximately, in agreement with the potential flow theory and, on the whole, the pressure distribution departs less from that given by the potential theory than in the previous case. Between these values, i. e. near a critical Reynolds number of approx. $U_\infty D/\nu = 3 \times 10^5$ the drag coefficient of the circular cylinder decreases abruptly (Fig. 1.4), and this phenomenon indicates that the boundary layer has become turbulent (see Chap. XVIII).

The laminar boundary layer on a circular cylinder was also investigated by A. Thom [44], at a Reynolds number $U_\infty D/\nu = 28{,}000$ and by A. Fage [6] in the range $U_\infty D/\nu = 1{\cdot}0$ to $3{\cdot}3 \times 10^5$. A paper by L. Schiller and W. Linke [37] contains some considerations concerning pressure drag and skin friction in the region of Reynolds numbers below the critical. In the range of Reynolds numbers from about 60 to about 5000 there exists behind the cylinder a vortex street which shows a regular, periodic structure (Figs. 2.7 and 2.8). The frequency at which vortices are shed in this so-called von Kármán vortex street has been investigated by H. Blenk, D. Fuchs and H. Liebers, and, more recently by A. Roshko (see Chap. II).

d. Boundary layer for the potential flow given by $U(x) = U_0 - ax^n$

A further family of solutions of the boundary layer equations was found by L. Howarth [27] and I. Tani [43]. These solutions relate to the potential flow given by

$$U(x) = U_0 - ax^n \qquad (n = 1, 2, 3 \ldots), \tag{9.28}$$

which, evidently, constitutes a generalized form of the flow along a flat plate (see Sec. VIIf), and becomes identical with it when we put $a = 0$. In the simplest case with $n = 1$, which was discovered by L. Howarth, the flow can be interpreted as that which occurs in a channel which consists of a portion with parallel walls (velocity U_0) followed by either a convergent ($a < 0$) or a divergent ($a > 0$) section†. This is another example of a boundary layer for which the velocity profiles are not similar. L. Howarth introduced the new independent variable

$$\eta = \frac{1}{2}\, y \sqrt{\frac{U_0}{\nu x}}\,, \tag{9.29}$$

which is identical with that used in the flat plate solution at zero incidence. He assumed further

$$x^* = \frac{ax}{U_0}$$

($x^* < 0$ accelerated flow; $x^* > 0$ decelerated flow). It is now possible to stipulate a power series in x^* for the stream function in a manner similar to the case of the cylinder, Sec. IXc, the coefficients being functions of y:

$$\psi(x,y) = \sqrt{U_0\, \nu x}\, \{f_0(\eta) - (8\, x^*)\, f_1(\eta) + (8\, x^*)^2\, f_2(\eta) - + \ldots\}\,. \tag{9.30}$$

Hence the velocity of flow becomes

$$u = \tfrac{1}{2} U_0 \{f_0'(\eta) - (8\, x^*)\, f_1'(\eta) + (8\, x^*)^2\, f_2'(\eta) - + \ldots\}\,. \tag{9.31}$$

Introducing these values into the equations of motion (9.1) and comparing coefficients we obtain a system of ordinary differential equations for the functions $f_0(\eta)$, $f_1(\eta)$, ... The first three of these are:

$$f_0''' + f_0 f_0'' = 0\,,$$
$$f_1''' + f_0 f_1'' - 2 f_0' f_1' + 3 f_0'' f_1 = -1\,,$$
$$f_2''' + f_0 f_2'' - 4 f_0' f_2' + 5 f_0'' f_2 = -\tfrac{1}{8} + 2 f_1'^2 - 3 f_1 f_1''\,,$$

with the boundary conditions

$$\eta = 0: \quad f_0 = f_0' = 0\,; \quad f_1 = f_1' = 0\,; \quad f_2 = f_2' = 0\,;$$
$$\eta = \infty: \quad f_0' = 2\,; \quad f_1' = \tfrac{1}{4}\,; \quad f_2' = 0\,.$$

Only the first equation is non-linear, and it is identical with that for a flat plate at zero incidence‡. All remaining equations are linear and contain only the function f_0 in the homogeneous portion, whereas the non-homogeneous terms are formed with the aid of the remaining functions f_ν. L. Howarth solved the first seven differential equations (up to and including f_6), and calculated tables for them.

The series (9.31) converges well with these values of f_ν in the range $-0{\cdot}1 \le x^* \le +0{\cdot}1$. In the case of decelerated flow ($x^* > 0$) the point of separation is at $x^* = 0{\cdot}12$ approximately, but for the slightly extended range of values the convergence of the series (9.31) is no longer assured. In order to reach the point of separation, L. Howarth used a numerical procedure for the continuation of the solution (see Sec. IXi). Velocity profiles for several values of x^* for both

† When equation (9.28) is written in the form $U(x) = U_0(1 - x/L)$ for $n = 1$, it can also be interpreted as representing the potential flow along a flat wall which starts at $x = 0$ and which abuts on to another infinite wall at right angles to it at $x = L$. It is of the same type as the case of decelerated stagnation flow shown in Fig. 2.15, the stagnation point being at $x = L$.

‡ The independent variable η in the above equations differs from that in Chap. VII by a factor $\frac{1}{2}$.

accelerated and decelerated flow are seen plotted in Fig. 9.9. It should be noted that all profiles in decelerated flow have a point of inflexion. D. R. Hartree [24] repeated these calculations and obtained good agreement with L. Howarth. The case for $a/U_0 = 0{\cdot}125$ was calculated more accurately by D. C. F. Leigh [29] who used an electronic digital computer for the purpose and who paid special attention to the region of separation. The value of the form factor at the point of separation itself was found to be $x^* = 0{\cdot}1198$.

The method employed by L. Howarth was extended by I. Tani [43] to include the cases corresponding to $n \geq 1$ (with $a > 0$). However, I. Tani did not publish any tables of the functional coefficients but confined himself to reporting the final result for $n = 2$, 4 and 8. In his case, too, the poor convergence of the series did not permit him to determine the point of separation with sufficient accuracy and he found himself compelled to use L. Howarth's numerical continuation scheme. The variation of shearing stress at the wall for $a > 0$ and $n = 1$ (L. Howarth) is seen plotted in Fig. 9.10 together with its variation for $n = 2$ and 4 (I. Tani). The break-down of the series expansion near the point of separation is clearly discernible in it.

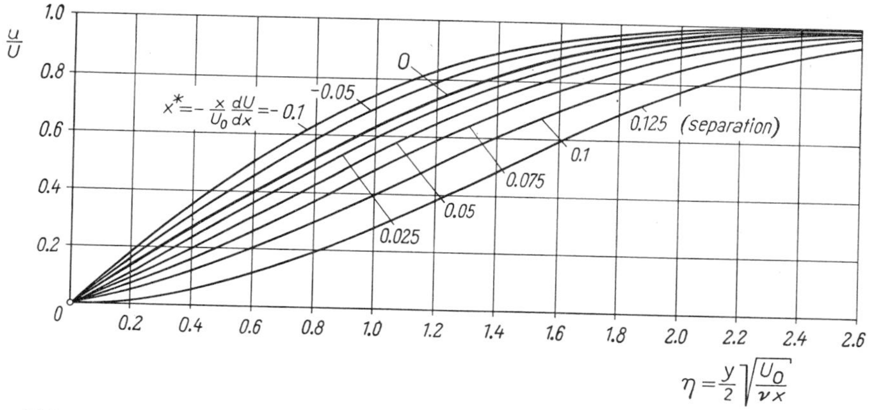

Fig. 9.9. Velocity distribution in the laminar boundary layer for the potential flow given by $U(x) = U_0 - ax$, after Howarth [27]

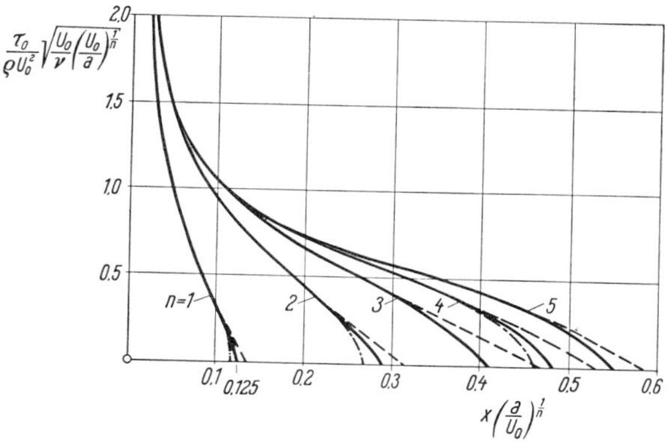

—— Goertler's series and continuation with the aid of the scheme due to Goertler and Witting up to the point of separation

- - - - Result obtained from Goertler's series with 6, 3, 2, 2, 2 terms of the series in the region of slow convergence

—·—· Result of Howarth' calculation ($n = 1$) and of Tani's calculation ($n = 2$, 4); continuation from places where their series with 9 ($n = 1$), 7 ($n = 2$), 6 ($n = 4$) terms fail to provide a sufficient degree of approximation

Fig. 9.10. Shearing stress at the wall for the potential flow given by $U(x) = U_0 - ax^n$ ($a > 0$) for $n = 1, 2, 3, 4$ and 5 after H. Goertler and H. Witting [21]; $n = 1$ calculated by L. Howarth, $n = 2$ and 4 calculated by I. Tani; the Goertler series agrees with these results completely

e. A new series due to H. Goertler

The Blasius series described in Sec. IXc is suitable for the calculation of boundary layers on all cylinders provided that the flow starts with a stagnation point. On the other hand, the series expansions given by L. Howarth and I. Tani and discussed in Sec. IXd are suitable only for the flat plate and for the special case of potential flow given by $U(x) = U_0 - ax^n$. It is natural, therefore, to ask whether it is possible to devise a series which would be suitable for a plate with a prescribed free stream and which would correspond to the Blasius series, that is, one which would make use of universal functional coefficients. Evidently, the same question can be asked in relation to all wedge profiles, i. e. for cases when the boundary layer starts with a family of similar solutions near the stagnation point (*cf.* Sec. IXa). Finally, should it prove possible to derive all these series from one principal series, it would suffice to tabulate the functional coefficient for this one series only. In this manner one would have achieved a complete and exact solution to the problem of integrating the boundary layer equations for two-dimensional flows and for an arbitrary external pressure distribution, that is for all cases of boundary layers along a wall which are of practical importance with the only exception of suction. Moreover, the effective calculation of the boundary layer would have been reduced to a small number of multiplications and additions, due regard being paid to the specific data of a particular problem and use being made of a set of tables of universal functional coefficients.

A generalization of all hitherto known series expansions of this nature was recently attained by H. Goertler [19] who set himself the further goal of improving the convergence of the new series with respect to the old ones, if possible. Success was achieved owing to the introduction of new variables in a manner to ensure that already the first term of the new series satisfies the external compatibility conditions (*cf.* Sec. VIIIc) for all values of x. In this way the first term of the new series alone constitutes a good approximation for a considerable distance downstream and one is justified in hoping that an improved rate of convergence will have been achieved†. This feature is very important for rough calculations. For example, in the case of a circular cylinder the deviation of the first term from the exact solution for a length of 60 per cent. of the distance from stagnation to separation is only 4 per cent. in round figures.

The new variables introduced by H. Goertler [19] are:

$$\xi = \frac{1}{\nu} \int_0^x U(x)\,\mathrm{d}x\,, \tag{9.32}$$

$$\eta = \frac{y\,U(x)}{\sqrt{2\,\nu \int_0^x U(x)\,\mathrm{d}x}}\,. \tag{9.33}$$

Introducing these variables into the boundary layer equations (9.1) and (9.2) together with the boundary conditions (9.3) and assuming a stream function of the form

$$\psi(x, y) = \nu \sqrt{2\,\xi}\, F(\xi, \eta)\,, \tag{9.34}$$

we are led to the following partial differential equation for F:

$$F_{\eta\eta\eta} + F F_{\eta\eta} + \beta(\xi)\,(1 - F_\eta^{\,2}) = 2\,\xi\,(F_\eta F_{\xi\eta} - F_\xi F_{\eta\eta})\,, \tag{9.35}$$

where

$$\beta(x) = 2\,\frac{U'(x)}{\{U(x)\}^2} \int_0^x U(x)\,\mathrm{d}x\,. \tag{9.36}$$

The boundary conditions for $F(\xi, \eta)$ are:

$$\left.\begin{aligned} \eta &= 0: \quad F = 0\,, \quad F_\eta = 0 \\ \eta &= \infty: \quad F_\eta = 1\,. \end{aligned}\right\} \tag{9.37}$$

† Note added in proof. Extensive numerical calculations with the new series show that this hope is not always realized.

The differential equation (9.35) is of a type in which the specific data of a particular problem appear only in the form of the contracted coefficient $\beta(\xi)$ given in eqn. (9.36). For this reason H. Goertler called the function $\beta(\xi)$ the 'principal function'; it can also be given the form

$$\beta(\xi) = \frac{1}{\{\eta_0(x)\}^2} \cdot \frac{\delta^{*2}\, U'(x)}{\nu}$$

where

$$\eta_0(x) = \lim_{\eta\to\infty} \{\eta - F(\xi, \eta)\},$$

and where δ^* denotes the displacement thickness mentioned in Sec. VIIIe. In the simplest special case $\beta(\xi) = \beta_0 = \text{const}$ we recover, obviously, the similar solutions discussed in Sec. IXa, and β_0 then denotes the wedge angle (*cf.* Fig. 8.1).

Now, H. Goertler proceeds to make the very general assumption for the free-stream velocity:

$$U(x) = x^m \{s_0 + s_{1/2}\, x^{(m+1)/2} + s_1\, x^{m+1} + s_{3/2}\, x^{3(m+1)/2} + \ldots\} \qquad (9.38)$$

with $m \neq -1$, $s_0 \neq 0$. The principal function is then obtained in the form

$$\beta(\xi) = \beta_0 + \beta_{1/2}\, \xi + \beta_1\, \xi + \beta_{3/2}\, \xi + \ldots$$

where

$$\beta_0 = \frac{2m}{m+1} \quad \text{or} \quad m = \frac{\beta_0}{2-\beta_0},$$

whereas the succeeding coefficients $\beta_n (n > 0)$ can be calculated from the prescribed free-stream velocity distribution $U(x)$. The stream function is further assumed to be of the form

$$F(\xi, \eta) = F_0(\eta) + F_{1/2}(\eta)\, \xi^{1/2} + F_1(\eta)\, \xi + F_{3/2}(\eta)\, \xi^{3/2} + \ldots . \qquad (9.39)$$

In order to arrive at the universal functional coefficients it is necessary to split up the terms $F_n(\eta)$ according to the following scheme

$$F_{1/2} = \beta_{1/2} f_{1/2}, \qquad F_1 = \beta_{1/2}^{\,2} f_{1/2\,1/2} + \beta_1 f_1 ;$$

$$F_{3/2} = \beta_{1/2}^{\,3} f_{1/2\,1/2\,1/2} + \beta_{1/2} \beta_1 f_{1/2\,1} + \beta_{3/2} f_{3/2} .$$

The functions $f_{1/2}, f_{1/2\,1/2}, f_1$, etc. can now be evaluated once for all. For the two cases $\beta_0 = 0$ and $\beta_1 = 1$, H. Goertler published values of these universal functions of orders 0, 1, 2, 3, 4 and 5 together with their first three derivatives. These suffice, on condition that $s_{1/2} = s_{3/2} = \ldots = 0$. In the case when $\beta = 1$, H. Goertler provided in addition values for the universal functions of orders 0, $\frac{1}{2}$, 1, $\frac{3}{2}$ and 2 without having to impose the preceding limitation. These extensive tables can be found in ref. [20].

In his paper [19], H. Goertler demonstrated that the above scheme is suitable for numerous cases for which hitherto only approximate solutions were known. By way of example, it is worth stating here that in addition to the similar solutions which, as already mentioned, are included as special cases in this new series, the cases treated by L. Howarth and I. Tani and described in Sec. IXd are also included. The diagram in Fig. 9.10 which represents the variation of the dimensionless shearing stress in terms of the current length x displays the agreement between the results obtained from this new series and those due to L. Howarth ($n = 1$) and I. Tani ($n = 2, 4$) in spite of the fact that for the new series there existed only 6, 3 or 2 terms, respectively as against 8 used by L. Howarth and 7 or 6, respectively, used by I. Tani. According to H. Goertler, this new series gives considerably more accurate results for the flat plate at zero incidence than existing methods and achieves it with fewer terms.

f. Flow in the wake of flat plate at zero incidence

The application of the boundary layer equations is not restricted to regions near a solid wall. They can also be applied when a stratum in which the influence of friction is dominating exists in the interior of a fluid. Such a case occurs, among others, when two layers of fluid with different velocities meet, for instance, in the wake behind a body, or when a fluid is discharged through an orifice. We shall consider two examples of this type in the present and in the succeeding sections, and we shall return to them when considering turbulent flow.

As our first example we shall discuss the case of flow in the wake of a flat plate at zero incidence, Fig. 9.11. Behind the trailing edge the two velocity profiles coalesce into one profile in the wake. Its width increases with increasing distance, and its mean velocity decreases. The magnitude of the depression in the velocity curve is directly connected with the drag on the body. On the whole, however, as we shall see later, the velocity profile in the wake, at a large distance from the body, is independent of the shape of the body, except for a scale factor. On the other hand the velocity profile very close to the body is, evidently, determined by the boundary layer on the body, and its shape depends on whether or not the flow has separated.

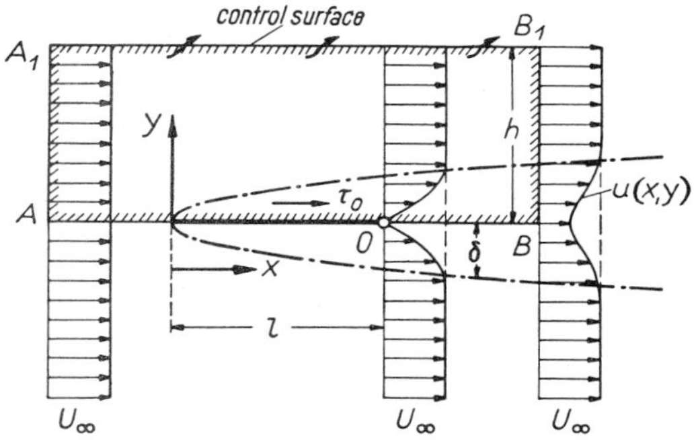

Fig. 9.11. Application of the momentum equation in the calculation of the drag on a flat plate at zero incidence from the velocity profile in the wake

The momentum equation can be used to calculate the drag from the velocity profile in the wake. For this purpose we draw a rectangular control surface AA_1B_1B, as shown in Fig. 9.11. The boundary A_1B_1, parallel to the plate, is placed at such a distance from the body that it lies everywhere in the region of undisturbed velocity, U_∞. Furthermore, the pressure is constant over the whole of the control surface, so that pressure forces do not contribute to the momentum. When calculating the flux of momentum across the control surface it is necessary to remember that, owing to continuity, fluid must leave through the boundary A_1B_1; the quantity of fluid leaving through A_1B_1 is equal to the difference between that entering through A_1A and leaving through B_1B. The boundary AB contributes no term to the momentum in the x-direction because, owing to symmetry, the transverse velocity vanishes along it. The momentum balance is given in tabular form on the next page, and in it the convention is followed that inflowing masses are considered positive, and outgoing masses are taken to be negative. The width of the plate is denoted

Cross-section	Rate of flow	Momentum in direction x
A B	0	0
A A_1	$b \int_0^h U_\infty \, dy$	$\varrho b \int_0^h U_\infty^2 \, dy$
B B_1	$-b \int_0^h u \, dy$	$-\varrho b \int_0^h u^2 \, dy$
A_1 B_1	$-b \int_0^h (U_\infty - u) \, dy$	$-\varrho b \int_0^h U_\infty (U_\infty - u) \, dy$
$\sum$ = Control surface	$\sum$ Rate of flow = 0	$\sum$ Momentum flux = Drag

by b. The total flux of momentum is equal to the drag D on a flat plate wetted on one side. Thus we have

$$D = b \varrho \int_{y=0}^{\infty} u(U_\infty - u) \, dy . \tag{9.40}$$

Integration may be performed from $y = 0$ to $y = \infty$ instead of to $y = h$, because for $y > h$ the integrand in eqn. (9.40) vanishes. Hence the drag on a plate wetted on both sides becomes

$$2 D = b \varrho \int_{-\infty}^{+\infty} u(U_\infty - u) \, dy . \tag{9.41}$$

This equation applies to any symmetrical cylindrical body and not only to a flat plate. It is to be remembered that in the more general case the integral over the profile in the wake must be taken at a sufficiently distant section, and one across which the static pressure has its undisturbed value. Since near a plate there are no pressure differences either in the longitudinal or in the transverse direction, eqn. (9.41) applies to any distance behind the plate. Furthermore, eqn. (9.41) may be applied to any section x of the boundary layer, when it gives the drag on the portion of the plate between the leading edge and that section. The physical meaning of the integral in eqn. (9.40) or (9.41) is that it represents the loss of momentum due to friction. It is identical with the integral in eqn. (8.34) which defined the *momentum thickness* θ, so that eqn. (9.40) can be given the alternative form

$$D = b \varrho U_\infty^2 \theta . \tag{9.42}$$

We shall now proceed to calculate the velocity profile in the wake, in particular, at a large distance x behind the trailing edge of the flat plate. The calculation must be performed in two steps: 1. Through an expansion in the downstream direction from the leading to the trailing edge, i. e. by a calculation which involves the continuation of the Blasius profile on the plate near the trailing edge, and 2. Through an expansion in the upstream direction. The latter is a kind of asymptotic integration for a large distance behind the plate and is valid irrespective of the shape of the body. It will be necessary here to make the assumption that the velocity difference in the wake

$$u_1(x, y) = U_\infty - u(x, y) \tag{9.43}$$

is small compared with U_∞, so that quadratic and higher terms in u_1 may be neglected.

The first calculation was carried out by S. Goldstein [11], who made use of a method of continuing a known solution, to be explained in greater detail in Sec. IXi. The calculation starts with the profile at the trailing edge, calculated with the aid of Blasius' method, and we shall refrain from further discussing it here. The asymptotic expansion in the upstream direction was calculated by W. Tollmien [46]. Since it is typical for problems of flow in the wake, and since we shall make use of it in the more important turbulent case, we propose to devote some time to an account of it.

As the pressure term is equal to zero, the boundary layer equation (9.1) combined with eqn. (9.43) gives

$$U_\infty \frac{\partial u_1}{\partial x} = \nu \frac{\partial^2 u_1}{\partial y^2} \tag{9.44}$$

where the quadratic terms in u_1 and v_1 have been omitted. The boundary conditions are:

$$y = 0: \quad \frac{\partial u_1}{\partial y} = 0 \; ; \quad y = \infty: \quad u_1 = 0 \, .$$

The partial differential equation can, here too, be transformed into an ordinary differential equation by a suitable transformation. Similarly to the assumption (7.25) in Blasius' method for the flat plate we put

$$\eta = y \sqrt{\frac{U_\infty}{\nu x}} \, ,$$

and, in addition, we assume that u_1 is of the form

$$u_1 = U_\infty C \left(\frac{x}{l}\right)^{-\frac{1}{2}} g(\eta) \, , \tag{9.45}$$

where l is the length of the plate, Fig. 9.11.

The power $-\frac{1}{2}$ for x in eqn. (9.45) is justified on the ground that the momentum integral which gives the drag on the plate in eqn. (9.41) must be independent of x. Hence, omitting quadratic terms in u_1, the drag on a plate wetted on both sides, as given in eqn. (9.41), is transformed to

$$2\,D = b\,\varrho\,U_\infty \int\limits_{y=-\infty}^{+\infty} u_1 \, \mathrm{d}y \, .$$

Substituting eqn. (9.45) we obtain

$$2\,D = b\,\varrho\,U_\infty{}^2\,C \sqrt{\frac{\nu\,l}{U_\infty}} \int\limits_{-\infty}^{+\infty} g(\eta)\,\mathrm{d}\eta \, . \tag{9.46}$$

Introducing further, the assumption (9.45) into (9.44), and dividing through by $C\,U_\infty^2 \cdot (x/l)^{-1/2}\,x^{-1}$, we obtain the following differential equation for $g(\eta)$:

$$g'' + \tfrac{1}{2}\,\eta\,g' + \tfrac{1}{2}\,g = 0 \tag{9.47}$$

with the boundary conditions

$$g' = 0 \text{ at } \eta = 0 \quad \text{and} \quad g = 0 \text{ at } \eta = \infty .$$

Integrating once, we have

$$g' + \tfrac{1}{2}\,\eta\,g = 0\,,$$

where the constant of integration vanishes on account of the boundary condition at $\eta = 0$. Repeated integration gives the solution

$$g = \exp\left(-\tfrac{1}{4}\,\eta^2\right) . \tag{9.48}$$

Here the constant of integration appears in the form of a coefficient and can be made equal to unity without loss of generality, as the velocity distribution function u_1 from eqn. (9.45) still contains a free coefficient C. This constant C is determined from the condition that the drag calculated from the loss of momentum, eqn. (9.46), must be equal to that on the plate, eqn. (7.36).

First we notice that

$$\int_{-\infty}^{+\infty} g(\eta)\,\mathrm{d}\eta = \int_{-\infty}^{+\infty} \exp\left(-\tfrac{1}{4}\,\eta^2\right)\mathrm{d}\eta = 2\sqrt{\pi}\,,$$

so that from eqn. (9.46) we have

$$2\,D = 2\sqrt{\pi}\,C\,b\,\varrho\,U_\infty{}^2\sqrt{\frac{\nu\,l}{U_\infty}}\,.$$

On the other hand, from eqn. (7.36) we can write down the skin friction on a plate wetted on both sides in the form:

$$2\,D = 1{\cdot}328\,b\,\varrho U_\infty{}^2\sqrt{\frac{\nu\,l}{U_\infty}}\,.$$

Hence $2\,C\sqrt{\pi} = 1{\cdot}328$ and $C = 0{\cdot}664/\sqrt{\pi}$, and the final solution for the velocity difference in the wake of a flat plate at zero incidence becomes

$$\frac{u_1}{U_\infty} = \frac{0{\cdot}664}{\sqrt{\pi}}\left(\frac{x}{l}\right)^{-1/2}\exp\left\{-\tfrac{1}{4}\,\frac{y^2\,U_\infty}{x\,\nu}\right\}. \tag{9.49}$$

The velocity distribution given by this asymptotic equation is represented in Fig. 9.12. It is remarkable that the velocity distribution is identical with Gauss' error distribution function. As assumed at the beginning, eqn. (9.49) is valid only at great distances from the plate. W. Tollmien verified that it may be used at about $x > 3\,l$. S. Goldstein [12] obtained a second, higher-order approximation for the asymptotic formula.

The calculation of the wake by the method of continuing a known solution, i. e. by proceeding from the trailing edge in a downstream direction was, as already mentioned, carried out by S. Goldstein [11]. Fig. 9.13 contains a plot from which the whole velocity field can be inferred.

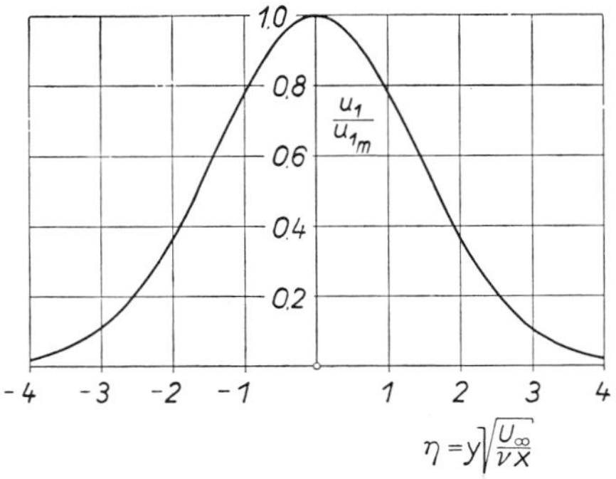

Fig. 9.12. Asymptotic velocity distribution in the laminar wake behind a flat plate from eqn. (9.48)

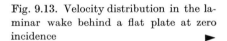

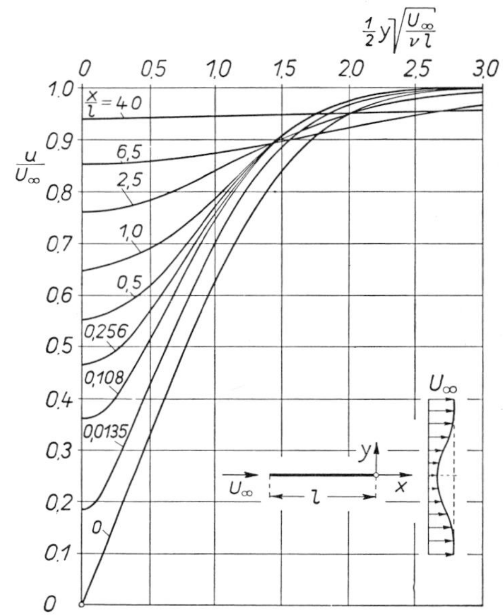

Fig. 9.13. Velocity distribution in the laminar wake behind a flat plate at zero incidence ►

The flow in the wake of a plate as well as in that behind any other body is, in most cases, turbulent. Even in the case of small Reynolds numbers, say $\mathsf{R}_l < 10^6$, when the boundary layer remains laminar as far as the trailing edge, the flow in the wake still becomes turbulent, because the velocity profiles in the wake, all of which possess a point of inflexion, are extremely unstable. In other words, even with comparatively small Reynolds numbers the wake becomes turbulent. Turbulent wakes will be discussed in Chap. XXIII.

g. The two-dimensional jet

The efflux of a jet from an orifice affords a further example of motion in the absence of solid boundaries to which it is possible to apply the boundary layer theory. We propose to discuss the two-dimensional problem so that we shall assume that the jet emerges from a long, narrow slit and mixes with the surrounding fluid. This problem was solved by H. Schlichting [38] and W. Bickley [2]. In practice, in this case as in the previous ones, the flow becomes turbulent. We shall, however, discuss here the laminar case in some detail, since the turbulent jet, which will be considered later, can be analyzed mathematically in an identical way.

The emerging jet carries with it some of the surrounding fluid which was originally at rest because of the friction developed on its periphery. The resulting pattern of stream lines is shown in Fig. 9.14. We shall adopt a system of co-ordinates with its origin in the slit and with its axis of abscissae coinciding with the jet axis. The jet spreads outwards in the downstream direction owing to the influence of friction, whereas its velocity in the centre decreases in the same direction. For the sake of simplicity we shall assume that the slit is infinitely small, but in order to retain a finite volume of flow as well as a finite momentum, it is necessary to assume an infinite fluid velocity in the slit. The pressure gradient $\mathrm{d}p/\mathrm{d}x$ in the x-direction can here, as in the previous example, be neglected, because the constant pressure in the surrounding fluid impresses itself on the jet. Consequently, the total momentum in the x-direction, denoted by J, must remain constant and independent of the distance x from the orifice. Hence

$$J = \varrho \int_{-\infty}^{+\infty} u^2 \, \mathrm{d}y = \text{const} \, . \tag{9.50}$$

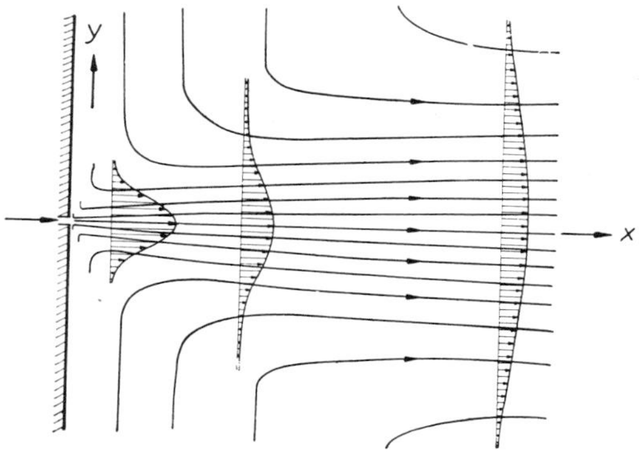

Fig. 9.14. The laminar two-dimensional free jet

It is possible to make a suitable assumption regarding the velocity distribution if it is considered that the velocity profiles $u(x, y)$, just as in the case of a flat plate at zero incidence, are most probably similar, because the problem as a whole possesses no characteristic linear dimension. We shall assume, therefore, that the velocity u is a function of y/b, where b is the width of the jet suitably defined. We shall also assume that b is proportional to x^p. Accordingly we can write the stream function in the form

$$\psi \sim x^p f\left(\frac{y}{b}\right) = x^p f\left(\frac{y}{x^q}\right) .$$

The two unknown exponents p and q will be determined from the following conditions:

1. the flux of momentum in the x-direction is independent of x, according to eqn. (9.50).
2. the acceleration terms and the friction term in eqn. (9.1) are of the same order of magnitude.

This gives two equations for p and q:

$$2p - q = 0 \qquad 2p - 2q - 1 = p - 3q$$

and hence,

$$p = \tfrac{1}{3}\,; \qquad q = \tfrac{2}{3}\,.$$

Consequently the assumptions for the independent variable and for the stream function can be written as

$$\eta = \frac{1}{3\,\nu^{1/2}}\,\frac{y}{x^{2/3}}\,; \qquad \psi = \nu^{1/2}\,x^{1/3}\,f(\eta)\,,$$

if suitable constant factors are included. Therefore, the velocity components are given by the following expressions:

$$\left.\begin{aligned} u &= \frac{1}{3\,x^{1/3}}\,f'(\eta); \\ v &= -\tfrac{1}{3}\,\nu^{1/2}\,x^{-2/3}\,(f - 2\,\eta f')\,. \end{aligned}\right\} \tag{9.51}$$

Introducing these values into the differential equation (9.1), and equating the pressure term to zero, we obtain the following differential equation for the stream function $f(\eta)$:

$$f'^2 + f\,f'' + f''' = 0 \tag{9.52}$$

with the boundary conditions $v = 0$ and $\partial u/\partial y = 0$ at $y = 0$, and $u = 0$ at $y = \infty$. Thus

$$\begin{aligned} \eta &= 0\ :\ f = 0\,,\quad f'' = 0\,; \\ \eta &= \infty:\ f' = 0\,. \end{aligned} \tag{9.53}$$

The solution of eqn. (9.52) is unexpectedly simple. Integrating once we have

$$f\,f' + f'' = 0\,.$$

The constant of integration is zero because of the boundary conditions at $\eta = 0$, and the resulting differential equation of the second order could be integrated immediately if the first term contained the factor 2. This can be achieved by the following transformation:

$$\xi = \alpha\,\eta\,; \qquad f = 2\,\alpha\,F(\xi)\,,$$

where α is a free constant, to be determined later. Thus the above equation transforms into

$$F''' + 2\,F\,F' = 0 \tag{9.54}$$

and the dash now denotes differentiation with respect to ξ. The boundary conditions are

$$\xi = 0\ :\ F = 0\,; \qquad \xi = \infty:\ F' = 0\,. \tag{9.55}$$

and the equation can be integrated once more to give

$$F' + F^2 = 1\,, \tag{9.56}$$

where the constant of integration was made equal to 1. This follows if we put $F'(0) = 1$, which is permissible without loss of generality because of the free constant α in the relation between f and F. Eqn. (9.56) is a differential equation of Riccati's type and can be integrated in closed terms. We obtain

$$\xi = \int_0^F \frac{dF}{1-F^2} = \frac{1}{2} \ln \frac{1+F}{1-F} = \tanh^{-1} F .$$

Inverting this equation we obtain

$$F = \tanh \xi = \frac{1 - \exp(-2\,\xi)}{1 + \exp(-2\,\xi)} . \tag{9.57}$$

Since, further, $dF/d\xi = 1 - \tanh^2 \xi$, the velocity distribution can be deduced from eqn. (9.51), and is

$$u = \tfrac{2}{3}\,\alpha^2\, x^{-1/3}\,(1 - \tanh^2 \xi) . \tag{9.58}$$

The velocity distribution from eqn. (9.58) is seen plotted in Fig. 9.15.

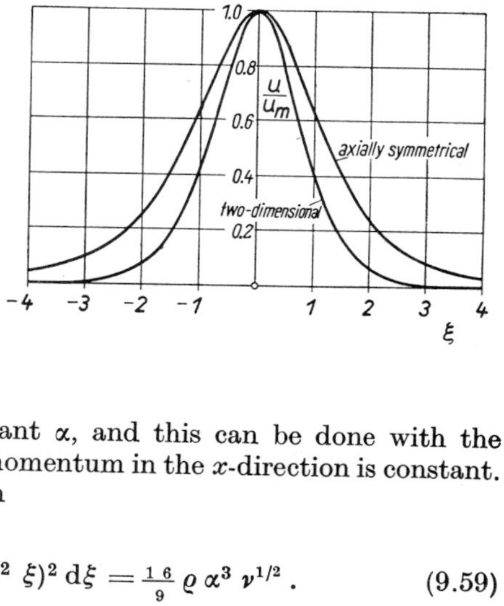

Fig. 9.15. Velocity distribution in a two-dimensional and circular free jet from eqns. (9.58) and (10.19) respectively. For the two-dimensional jet $\xi = 0{\cdot}275\, K^{1/3}\, y/(\nu x)^{2/3}$, and for the circular jet $\xi = 0{\cdot}244\, K'^{1/2}\, y/\nu x$. K and K' denote the kinematic momentum J/ϱ

It now remains to determine the constant α, and this can be done with the aid of condition (9.50), which states that the momentum in the x-direction is constant. Combining eqns. (9.58) and (9.50) we obtain

$$J = \tfrac{8}{3}\,\varrho\,\alpha^3\,\nu^{1/2} \int_0^\infty (1 - \tanh^2 \xi)^2\, d\xi = \tfrac{16}{9}\,\varrho\,\alpha^3\,\nu^{1/2} . \tag{9.59}$$

We shall assume that the flux of momentum, J, for the jet is given. It is proportional to the excess in pressure with which the jet leaves the slit. Introducing the *kinematic momentum* $J/\varrho = K$, we have from eqn. (9.59)

$$\alpha = 0{\cdot}8255 \left(\frac{K}{\nu^{1/2}}\right)^{\frac{1}{3}}$$

and, hence, for the velocity distribution

$$\left.\begin{aligned} u &= 0{\cdot}4543 \left(\frac{K^2}{\nu x}\right)^{\frac{1}{3}} (1 - \tanh^2 \xi)\,, \\ v &= 0{\cdot}5503 \left(\frac{K\nu}{x^2}\right)^{\frac{1}{3}} [2\,\xi\,(1 - \tanh^2 \xi) - \tanh \xi]\,, \\ \xi &= 0{\cdot}2752 \left(\frac{K}{\nu^2}\right)^{\frac{1}{3}} \frac{y}{x^{2/3}}\,. \end{aligned}\right\} \tag{9.60}$$

The transverse velocity at the boundary of the jet is

$$v_\infty = -\,0{\cdot}550 \left(\frac{K\,\nu}{x^2}\right)^{\frac{1}{3}}, \tag{9.61}$$

and the volume rate of discharge per unit height of slit becomes $Q = \varrho \int_{-\infty}^{+\infty} u\,\mathrm{d}y$, or

$$Q = 3{\cdot}3019\,(K\,\nu\,x)^{1/3}\,. \tag{9.62}$$

The volume rate of discharge increases in the downstream direction, because fluid particles are carried away with the jet owing to friction on its boundaries. It also increases with increasing momentum.

The flow in the mixing zone between two parallel streams moving with different velocities and possessing different densities and viscosities is very similar in nature; it was investigated by R. C. Lock [30]. The special case when a wide jet mixes with the surrounding fluid at rest is often referred to as the two-dimensional half-jet. The jet in the immediate neighbourhood of the slit consists of two such half-jets which coalesce into one some distance further downstream.

The corresponding rotationally symmetrical case in which the jet emerges from a small circular orifice will be discussed in Chap. X. The problem of the two-dimensional laminar compressible jet emerging from a narrow slit was solved by S. I. Pai [32] and M. Z. Krzywoblocki [28], and that of the free jet boundary (mixing zone between a jet of finite width and the surrounding air at rest) was considered by D. R. Chapman [4].

Measurements performed by E. N. Andrade [1] for the two-dimensional laminar jet confirm the preceding theoretical argument very well. The jet remains laminar up to $\mathsf{R} = 30$ approximately, where the Reynolds number is referred to the efflux velocity and to the width of the slit. The case of a two-dimensional and that of a circular turbulent jet is discussed in Chap. XXIII. A comprehensive review of all problems involving jets can be found in S. I. Pai's book [33].

h. Flow in the inlet length of a straight channel and a circular pipe

As a further example of two-dimensional flow in the boundary layer, we shall now consider the case of flow in the inlet length of a straight channel with flat parallel walls. At a large distance from the inlet the velocity distribution becomes parabolic over the width of the channel, as indicated in Chap. V. We shall assume that the velocity in the inlet section is uniformly distributed over its width, $2a$, and that its magnitude is U_0. Owing to viscous friction, boundary layers will be formed on both walls, and their width will increase in the downstream direction.

At the beginning, i. e. at small distances from the inlet section, the boundary layers will grow in the same way as they would along a flat plate at zero incidence. The resulting velocity profile will consist of two boundary layer profiles on the two walls joined in the centre by a line of constant velocity. Since the volume of flow must be the same for every section, the decrease in the rate of flow near the walls which is due to friction must be compensated by a corresponding increase near the axis. Thus the boundary layer is formed under the influence of an accelerated external flow, as distinct from the case of the flat plate. At larger distances from the inlet section the two boundary layers gradually merge into each other, and finally the velocity profile is transformed asymptotically into the parabolic distribution of Poiseuille flow.

This process can be analysed mathematically in one of two ways. First, the integration can be performed in the downstream direction so that the boundary layer growth is calculated for an accelerated external stream. Secondly, it is possible to analyse the progressive deviation of the profile from its asymptotic parabolic distribution, i. e. integration can proceed in the upstream direction. Having obtained both solutions, say in the form of series expansions, we can retain a sufficient number of terms in either of them, joining the two solutions at a section where both are still applicable. In this way the flow for the whole inlet length is obtained. The method, which was first used by H. Schlichting [39], will now be outlined in brief.

We assume a system of co-ordinates whose axis of abscissae coincides with that of the channel, Fig. 9.16. For the expansion in the upstream direction we shall measure the ordinate y from the centre-line of the channel, whereas for the expansion in the downstream direction the ordinate y' will be measured from one of the walls. The inlet velocity will be denoted by U_0, and that in the central stream by $U(x)$.

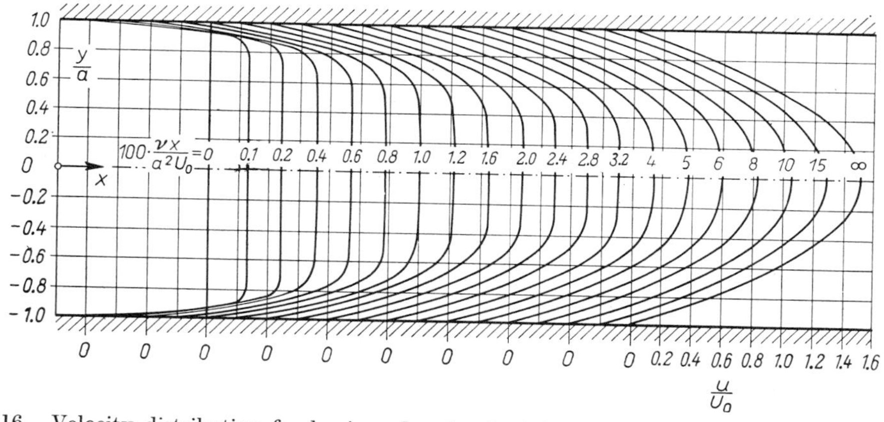

Fig. 9.16. Velocity distribution for laminar flow in the inlet section of a channel

We begin by writing the equation of continuity:

$$\int_{y'=0}^{a} u \, \mathrm{d}y = U_0 \, a \, . \tag{9.63}$$

Introducing the displacement thickness δ^* from eqn. (8.33) we can write

$$\int_{0}^{a} (U - u) \, \mathrm{d}y = U \, \delta^*$$

and with the aid of eqn. (9.63) we can write

$$U(x) = U_0 \frac{a}{a - \delta^*} = U_0 \left[1 + \frac{\delta^*}{a} + \left(\frac{\delta^*}{a}\right)^2 + \dots\right] . \tag{9.64}$$

Near the inlet section the boundary layer develops in the same way as on a flat plate at zero incidence in unaccelerated flow, so that from eqn. (7.40) we have

$$\frac{\delta^*}{a} = 1{\cdot}72 \sqrt{\frac{\nu x}{a^2 U_0}} = 1{\cdot}72\, \varepsilon = K_1\, \varepsilon\,,$$

where

$$\varepsilon = \sqrt{\frac{\nu x}{a^2 U_0}} \tag{9.65}$$

is the characteristic dimensionless inlet length. Eqn. (9.64) can also be written as

$$U(x) = U_0\,[1 + K_1\,\varepsilon + K_2\,\varepsilon^2 + \ldots] \tag{9.66}$$

with $K_1 = 1{\cdot}72$. In this manner the velocity outside the boundary layer has been developed in powers of $\sqrt{x}$. The value of K_1 is known from Blasius' solution for the flat plate, but the remaining coefficients $K_2, K_3, \ldots$ are unknown, as they depend on the boundary layer which has not yet been determined. We now introduce the new variable

$$\eta = \sqrt{\frac{U_0}{\nu x}}\, y'$$

just as was done in the case of the flat plate, and the stream function and the velocity profile in the boundary layer can be expanded into series in ε:

$$\psi(x, y') = U_0\, a\,[\varepsilon f_0(\eta) + \varepsilon^2 f_1(\eta) + \ldots]\,, \tag{9.67}$$

$$u(x, y') = U_0\,[f_0'(\eta) + \varepsilon f_1'(\eta) + \ldots]\,. \tag{9.68}$$

Inserting eqns. (9.66), (9.67) and (9.68) into the equation of motion (9.1) and collecting terms in powers of ε, we obtain differential equations for $f_0, f_1, \ldots$. The differential equation of the first approximation is identical with that obtained by Blasius for the flat plate:

$$f_0\, f_0'' + 2\, f_0''' = 0$$

with the boundary conditions $f_0 = f_0' = 0$ at $\eta = 0$, and $f_0' = 1$ at $\eta = \infty$, the solution of which was already given in Chap. VII. The second approximation is determined by the equation

$$2\, f_1''' + f_0\, f_1'' - f_0'\, f_1' + 2\, f_0''\, f_1 = -\, K_1 \tag{9.69}$$

with the boundary conditions $f_1 = f_1' = 0$ at $\eta = 0$, and $f_1' = K_1$ at $\eta = \infty$. The higher approximations lead to equations of a similar type.

In the series expansion in the upstream direction we assume $u = u_0(y) - u'(x, y)$, where $u_0(y)$ is the parabolic velocity distribution, i. e. $u_0(y) = \frac{3}{2}\, U_0(1 - y^2/a^2)$, and u' is an additional velocity whose higher orders may be neglected in the first approximation. If we put

$$\frac{u'}{U_0} = C_1\, e^{-\lambda_1 \varepsilon^2}\, \psi_1'\left(\frac{y}{a}\right) + C_2\, e^{-\lambda_2 \varepsilon^2}\, \psi_2'\left(\frac{y}{a}\right), \tag{9.70}$$

we obtain the following differential equation for ψ_1

$$\psi_1'''' + 3\,\lambda_1 \left[\frac{1}{2}\left(1 - \frac{y^2}{a^2}\right) \psi_1'' + \psi_1\right] = 0$$

with λ_1 as its eigen-value. The boundary conditions follow from $v = 0$ and $\partial u/\partial y = 0$ at $y = 0$, and are $\psi_1 = \psi_1'' = 0$, and $\psi_1' = 1$ at $y = 0$, since C_1 is still free. In view of the fact that $u = 0$ and $v = 0$ at $y = a$, we must have $\psi_1 = \psi_1'' = 0$ at $y = a$. Numerical calculation yields $\lambda_1 = 18{\cdot}75$ and $C_1 = -\,0{\cdot}3485$ from the joining of the two solutions.

Fig. 9.16 gives an indication of the change in the velocity profile over the inlet length. It is seen that the parabolic profile is formed at about $\nu\, x/a^2\, U_0 = 0{\cdot}16$, so that the actual inlet length is $l_E = 0{\cdot}16a(U_0 a/\nu) = 0{\cdot}04(2a) \cdot \mathsf{R}$ where R denotes the Reynolds number referred to the width of the channel. For example at $\mathsf{R} = 2000$ to 5000 the inlet length extends over 80 to 200 channel widths. Consequently, the flow does not become fully developed at all if the channel is short or if the Reynolds number is comparatively large. The acceleration of the flow near the axis gives rise to an additional pressure drop $\triangle p_{add} = -0{\cdot}601 \times \frac{1}{2}\varrho U_0^2$. Similar remarks apply to the case of flow through a circular pipe, which was solved by B. Punnis [35] Sec. XII e.

An approximate method of calculation for the two-dimensional case which is based on the momentum equation (see Chap. XII), as well as numerous experimental results which reach into the turbulent region, have been reported in two papers by H. Hahnemann and L. Ehret [22] and [23].

The flow in a pipe in whose entrance section there is a certain amount of swirl is somewhat related to the case of flow in the inlet length of a pipe. The swirl decays in the downstream direction and the manner in which it does so has been investigated by L. Talbot [42], and L. Collatz and H. Goertler [5]. On the assumption that the swirl component of velocity is small compared with the axial velocity, the latter being the same as in Hagen-Poiseuille flow, it is found that the swirl component is determined by a linear differential equation of the second order. The first five eigenvalues of this equation have been evaluated. According to Talbot the swirl component dies out almost completely after an inlet length of 40 diameters at a Reynolds number $\mathsf{R} = 10^3$ in good agreement with experimental results.

i. Continuation problem; step-by-step method

The examples which have been considered so far have demonstrated that the analytical calculation of boundary layers is, in most cases, very cumbersome and in many others the amount of work required ceases to be practicable. There is, therefore, an urgent need to devise alternative methods to be applied in cases when analytical methods do not lead to a practicable solution. Under this heading it is necessary to mention first approximate methods which make use of the momentum or energy equation thus replacing the full differential equations. Such methods, to be considered in Chap. XII, lead in most cases to a quick solution, but their accuracy is limited. One alternative method is that of step-by-step integration in which a given profile $u(x_0, y)$ at section x_0 is continued beyond it step-by-step, either analytically or numerically. Since such methods are based on the differential equation of the boundary layer, just as the analytical methods described so far, they may be considered equivalent as far as accuracy is concerned.

In describing the step-by-step method we shall restrict ourselves to the case of steady two-dimensional motion, so that the differential equations are

$$u\frac{\partial u}{\partial x} + v\frac{\partial u}{\partial y} = -\frac{1}{\varrho}\frac{\mathrm{d}p}{\mathrm{d}x} + \nu\frac{\partial^2 u}{\partial y^2} \tag{9.71}$$

$$\frac{\partial u}{\partial x} + \frac{\partial v}{\partial y} = 0\,. \tag{9.72}$$

The aim now is to calculate the development of the boundary layer from a given profile and a given pressure distribution on the basis of eqns. (9.71) and (9.72). Thus the velocity profile $u(x_0, y)$ at an initial section $x = x_0$ is prescribed together with the pressure function

$$\frac{1}{\varrho}\frac{\mathrm{d}p}{\mathrm{d}x} = \nu f(x)\,, \tag{9.73}$$

and we seek to find $u(x, y)$ for $x > x_0$.

The problem under consideration was formulated by L. Prandtl in his first paper on boundary layers, published in 1904, but a method which would operate satisfactorily in practice has not been developed until much later. The reason for it lies in certain singularities exhibited by the boundary layer near the wall.

The analytical solution of this problem was first undertaken by S. Goldstein [11], who investigated various forms of the initial profile. It emerged, however, that the expansions which he obtained did not converge sufficiently rapidly so that, on the whole, the analytical methods did not lead to satisfactory results. In later times numerical step-by-step methods were applied with great success.

The basic idea of the numerical step-by-step method [14, 34] consists in the calculation of the rate of change of velocity in the x-direction, i. e. of $(\partial u/\partial x)$ at (x_0, y) from the given profile $u(x_0, y)$. With this value it is possible to proceed to the next section $x_0 + \Delta x$ by applying the equation

$$u\,(x_0 + \Delta x,\, y) = u\,(x_0,\, y) + \frac{\partial u}{\partial x}(x_0,\, y)\, \Delta x\,. \tag{9.74}$$

The same procedure is then applied to the profile $u(x_0 + \Delta x, y)$, so that $u(x_0 + 2\Delta x, y)$ is obtained, etc. It now remains to be seen, how it is possible to determine $\partial u/\partial x$ at (x_0, y) from $u(x_0, y)$ and the pressure gradient $\mathrm{d}p/\mathrm{d}x$. The left-hand side of eqn. (9.71) can be rewritten with the aid of the equation of continuity, in the form:

$$u\,\frac{\partial u}{\partial x} + v\,\frac{\partial u}{\partial y} = v\,\frac{\partial u}{\partial y} - u\,\frac{\partial v}{\partial y} = -\,u^2\,\frac{\partial}{\partial y}\left(\frac{v}{u}\right),$$

so that eqn. (9.71) becomes

$$-\,u^2\,\frac{\partial}{\partial y}\left(\frac{v}{u}\right) = \nu\,\frac{\partial^2 u}{\partial y^2} - \frac{1}{\varrho}\,\frac{\mathrm{d}p}{\mathrm{d}x} = \nu\left(\frac{\partial^2 u}{\partial y^2} - f(x)\right)$$

or

$$\frac{\partial}{\partial y}\left(\frac{v}{u}\right) = \nu\,\frac{1}{u^2}\left[f(x) - \frac{\partial^2 u}{\partial y^2}\right],$$

and upon integration

$$v = \nu\, u \int_0^y \frac{1}{u^2}\left[f(x) - \frac{\partial^2 u}{\partial y^2}\right] \mathrm{d}y\,.$$

Hence

$$\frac{\partial u}{\partial x} = \nu\,\frac{\partial}{\partial y}\left\{u \int_0^y \frac{1}{u^2}\left[\frac{\partial^2 u}{\partial y^2} - f(x)\right] \mathrm{d}y\right\}$$

since $\partial v/\partial y = -\,\partial u/\partial x$. Finally, carrying out the differentiation indicated, we obtain:

$$\frac{\partial u}{\partial x} = \nu\left\{\frac{\partial u}{\partial y} \int_0^y \frac{1}{u^2}\left[\frac{\partial^2 u}{\partial y^2} - f(x)\right] \mathrm{d}y + \frac{1}{u}\left[\frac{\partial^2 u}{\partial y^2} - f(x)\right]\right\}. \tag{9.75}$$

The right-hand side of this equation contains only derivatives and integrals with respect to y, and can, therefore, be evaluated for the initial section $u(x_0, y)$. Thus we obtain $\partial u/\partial x$ at (x_0, y), and we are in a position to proceed in the x-direction by a distance Δx on condition that $\partial u/\partial x$ remains bounded. It is, however, immediately clear from eqn. (9.75) that the procedure fails if u passes through zero anywhere within the flow; in other words, it is not applicable to velocity profiles with back-flow. Moreover, at the wall itself, i. e. for $y = 0$, the velocity is zero everywhere because of the no slip condition, and the evaluation given by eqn. (9.75) requires particular care. Both terms of eqn. (9.75) assume the indeterminate form 0/0 and must be carefully examined. It is also immediately noticeable that $\partial u/\partial x$ remains regular only if at the wall the expression $\partial^2 u/\partial y^2 - f(x)$ vanishes quadratically. This means that we must have

$$\left(\frac{\partial^2 u}{\partial y^2}\right)_{\substack{x=x_0\\ y=0}} = f(x_0) \quad \text{and} \quad \left(\frac{\partial^3 u}{\partial y^3}\right)_{\substack{x=x_0\\ y=0}} = 0\,.$$

In other words, the method under consideration will function only if the prescribed velocity profile $u(x_0, y)$ satisfies the first two compatibility conditions as given in eqn. (8.28). In this case the indeterminate term 0/0 in eqn. (9.75) becomes

$$\left(\frac{\partial u}{\partial x}\right)_{x=x_0} = \nu\,\frac{\left(\frac{\partial^4 u}{\partial y^4}\right)_{y=0}}{\left(\frac{\partial u}{\partial y}\right)_{y=0}}\,y + (\ldots)\,y^2\,.$$

We see from the preceding argument that the second and third derivatives with respect to y of the initial profile cannot be chosen arbitrarily, as they must be equal to $f(x_0)$ and 0 respectively, and that the fourth derivative with respect to y at $y = 0$ is decisive for the successful continuation of the boundary layer profile. In the next step the initial profile contains $\partial^4 u/\partial y^4$ right away, and a similar argument leads to the conclusion that the fifth and sixth derivatives are not arbitrary and that $\partial^7 u/\partial y^7$ is decisive for further continuation.

Now, if, as in most cases, the initial profile $u(x_0, y)$ is given in tabulated form, or by a graphical plot, the higher derivatives cannot be obtained with the required degree of accuracy without further consideration. It was shown by H. Goertler [14] that it is then convenient to expand the initial velocity profile $u(x_0, y)$, which may be given in tabulated form, into a power series in y at $x = x_0$. Thus

$$u(x, y) = a_1\,y + \frac{a_2}{2!}\,y^2 + \frac{a_3}{3!}\,y^3 + \cdots,$$

where the coefficients are functions of x, and it becomes necessary to determine the values of the coeficients in a manner which would ensure that the conditions of compatibility at the wall, eqn. (8.28), are satisfied. The process of determining these coefficients renders the method very cumbersome.

In a more recent paper H. Goertler [15] presented a variation of this method which simplifies the numerical work considerably. The simplification is of such a nature that the evaluation of one step with 10 to 15 profile points does not require more than one hour's work. From a comparison with L. Howarth's exact numerical data (see Sec. IXd) on boundary layer profiles in retarded flow it appears that good accuracy has been achieved. The above two numerical methods have been further simplified in two papers written by H. Witting [48, 49]. A numerical method based on a scheme of finite differences which is similar to Goertler's was given earlier by K. Schroeder [40]. A. W. Quick and K. Schroeder [36] made use of this method to calculate a range of numerical examples involving boundary layers on wavy walls which showed that the laminar boundary layer is very sensitive to periodic pressure fluctuations. The waviness of the wall decays very fast in the outward direction but the pressure fluctuations exert a powerful influence on the strata near the wall. H. Goertler also performed analytical calculations concerning wavy walls [16, 18] and found good agreement with those due to A. W. Quick and K. Schroeder.

References

[1] E. N. Andrade, The velocity distribution in a liquid-into-liquid jet. The plane jet. Proc. phys. Soc., London, **51**, 784 (1939).
[2] W. Bickley, The plane jet. Phil. Mag. Ser. 7, **23**, 727 (1939).
[3] H. Blasius, Grenzschichten in Flüssigkeiten mit kleiner Reibung. Z. Math. u. Phys. **56**, 1 (1908). Engl. transl. in NACA Tech. Memo. No. 1256.
[4] D. R. Chapman, Laminar mixing of a compressible fluid. NACA Tech. Note 1800 (1949).
[5] L. Collatz and H. Görtler, Rohrströmung mit schwachem Drall. ZAMP **5**, 95—110 (1954); see also Wiss. Zeitschr. Techn. Hochschule Dresden **2**, 347—352 (1952).
[6] A. Fage, The airflow around a circular cylinder in the region where the boundary separates from the surface. Phil. Mag. **7**, 253 (1929).
[7] A. Fage and V. M. Falkner, Further experiments on the flow around a circular cylinder. ARC R & M 1369 (1931).
[8] V. M. Falkner, A further investigation of solution of boundary layer equations. ARC R & M 1884 (1939).
[9] V. M. Falkner, Simplified calculation of the laminar boundary layer. ARC R & M 1895 (1941).
[10] N. Frössling, Verdunstung, Wärmeübergang und Geschwindigkeitsverteilung bei zweidimensionaler und rotationssymmetrischer laminarer Grenzschichtströmung. Lunds. Univ. Arsskr. N. F. Avd. 2, **35**, No. 4 (1940).
[11] S. Goldstein, Concerning some solutions of the boundary layer equations in hydrodynamics. Proc. Cambr. Phil. Soc. **26**, Part I (1930).
[12] S. Goldstein, On the two-dimensional steady flow of a viscous fluid behind a solid body Proc. Roy. Soc. London, A **142**, 545 (1933).
[13] S. Goldstein, On laminar boundary layer flow near a position of separation. Quarterly J. Mech. and Appl. Math. **1**, 43 (1948).
[13a] S. Goldstein ed., Modern developments in fluid dynamics, Clarendon Press, Oxford 1938, v. 1, p. 105.
[14] H. Görtler, Weiterentwicklung eines Grenzschichtprofiles bei gegebenem Druckverlauf. ZAMM **19**, 129 (1939); see also: J. Roy. Aero. Soc. **45**, 35 (1941).
[15] H. Görtler, Ein Differenzenverfahren zur Berechnung laminarer Grenzschichten. Ing.-Arch. **16**, 173—187 (1948).
[16] H. Görtler, Einfluß einer schwachen Wandwelligkeit auf den Verlauf der laminaren Grenzschichten. Parts I und II. ZAMM **25/27**, 233—244 (1947) and **28**, 13—22 (1948).
[17] H. Görtler, Zur Approximation stationärer laminarer Grenzschichtströmungen mit Hilfe der abgebrochenen Blasiusschen Reihe. Arch. d. Math. **1**, No. 3, 235 (1949).
[18] H. Görtler, Reibungswiderstand einer schwach gewellten längsangeströmten Platte. Arch. Math. **1**, pp. 450—453 (1949).
[19] H. Görtler, A new series for the calculation of steady laminar boundary-layer flows. Jour. of Math. and Mechanics **6**, 1 (1957).
[20] H. Görtler, Zahlentafeln universeller Funktionen zur neuen Reihe für die Berechnung laminarer Grenzschichten. Bericht No. 34 of the Deutsche Versuchsanstalt für Luftfahrt, (1957).

[21] H. GÖRTLER and H. WITTING, Zu den Tanischen Grenzschichten. Österr. Ing.-Archiv **XI**, p. 111—122 (1957).
[22] H. HAHNEMANN and L. EHRET, Der Druckverlust der laminaren Strömung in der Anlaufstrecke von geraden, ebenen Spalten. Jahrb. der Deutschen Luftfahrtforschung p. I 21, 1941.
[23] H. HAHNEMANN and L. EHRET, Der Strömungswiderstand in geraden, ebenen Spalten unter Berücksichtigung der Einlaufverluste. Jahrbuch der Deutschen Luftfahrtforschung p. I 186 1942.
[24] D. R. HARTREE, A solution of the laminar boundary layer equation for retarded flow. ARC R & M No. 2426 (1949).
[25] K. HIEMENZ, Die Grenzschicht an einem in den gleichförmigen Flüssigkeitsstrom eingetauchten geraden Kreiszylinder. Thesis Göttingen 1911, Dingl. Polytechn. J. **326**, 32 (1911).
[26] L. HOWARTH, On the calculation of steady flow in the boundary layer near the surface of a cylinder in a stream. ARC R & M 1632 (1935).
[27] L. HOWARTH, On the solution of the laminar boundary layer equations. Proc. Roy. Soc., London, A **164**, 547 (1938).
[28] M. Z. KRZYWOBLOCKI, On steady, laminar two-dimensional jets in compressible viscous gases far behind the slit. Quart. Appl. Math. **7**, 313 (1949).
[29] D. C. F. LEIGH, The laminar boundary-layer equation: A method of solution by means of an automatic computer. Proc. Camb. phil. Soc. **51**, 320—332 (1955).
[30] R. C. LOCK, The velocity distribution in the laminar boundary layer between parallel streams. Quarterly J. Mech. and Appl. Math. **4**, 42 (1951).
[31] R. H. MILLS, A note on some accelerated boundary layer velocity profiles. Jour. Aero. Sci. **5**, 325 (1938).
[32] S. I. PAI, Two-dimensional jet mixing of a compressible fluid. J. Aero. Sci. **16**, 463—469 (1949).
[33] S. I. PAI, Fluid Dynamics of Jets. D. van Nostrand Company, New York 1954.
[33a] K. POHLHAUSEN, Zur näherungsweisen Integration der Differentialgleichung der Grenzschicht, ZAMM **1**, 252 (1921).
[34] L. PRANDTL, Zur Berechnung der Grenzschichten. ZAMM **18**, 77 (1938); see also Jour. Roy. Aero. Soc. **45**, 35 (1941) and NACA Tech. Memo. 959 (1940).
[35] B. PUNNIS, Zur Berechnung der laminaren Einlaufströmung im Rohr. Thesis Göttingen 1947.
[36] A. W. QUICK and K. SCHRÖDER, Verhalten der laminaren Grenzschicht bei periodisch schwankendem Druckverlauf. Math. Nachr. **8**, p. 217—238 (1953).
[37] L. SCHLILER and W. LINKE, Druck- und Reibungswiderstand des Zylinders bei Reynoldsschen Zahlen 5000 bis 40000. ZMF **24**, 193—198 (1933).
[38] H. SCHLICHTING, Laminare Strahlausbreitung. ZAMM **13**, 260 (1933).
[39] H. SCHLICHTING, Laminare Kanaleinlaufströmung. ZAMM **14**, 368 (1934).
[40] K. SCHROEDER, Ein einfaches numerisches Verfahren zur Berechnung der laminaren Grenzschicht. FB 1741 (1943). Later expanded and reprinted in Math. Nachr. **4**, 439 (1951).
[41] K. STEWARTSON, Further solutions of the Falkner-Skan equation. Proc. Camb. phil. Soc. **50**, 454—465 (1954).
[42] L. TALBOT, Laminar swirling pipe flow. Jour. Appl. Mech., Vol. **21**, pp. 1—7 (1954).
[43] I. TANI, On the solution of the laminar boundary layer equations. Jour. Phys. Soc., Japan, **4**, 149—154 (1949). See also "Fifty years of boundary layer research", Braunschweig 1955, pp. 193—200.
[44] A. THOM, The laminar boundary layer of the front part of a cylinder. ARC Report 1176 (1928); see also ARC Report 1194 (1929).
[45] A. N. TIFFORD, Heat transfer and frictional effects in laminar boundary layers. Part 4: Universal Series Solutions. WADC Technical Report, 53—288, Part 4 (August 1954).
[46] W. TOLLMIEN, Grenzschichten, Handb. d. Exper.-Physik **IV**, Pt. I, 267 (1931).
[47] A. ULRICH, Die ebene laminare Reibungsschicht an einem Zylinder. Arch. d. Math. **2**, 33 (1949).
[47a] M. VAN DYKE, On viscous flow near a round leading edge. Proc. 9th Intern. Congress Appl. Mech. Brussels 1957, v. 3, p. 318.
[48] H. WITTING, Über zwei Differenzenverfahren der Grenzschichttheorie. Arch. Math. **4**, p. 247—256 (1953).
[49] H. WITTING, Verbesserung des Differenzenverfahrens von H. Görtler zur Berechnung laminarer Grenzschichten. ZAMP **4**, pp. 376—397 (1953).

CHAPTER X

Axially symmetrical and three-dimensional boundary layers

In the discussion of boundary layers in the preceding chapter we have considered exclusively two-dimensional cases for which the velocity components depended on only two space co-ordinates. At the same time the velocity component in the direction of the third space co-ordinate did not exist. The general three-dimensional case of a boundary layer in which the three velocity components depend on all three co-ordinates has, so far, been hardly elaborated because of the enormous mathematical difficulties associated with the problem. We shall describe the first attempts in this direction at the end of the present chapter.

On the other hand the mathematical difficulties encountered in the study of axially symmetrical boundary layer are considerably smaller and hardly exceed those in the two-dimensional case. Axially symmetrical boundary layers occur e. g. in flows past axially symmetrical bodies; the axially symmetrical jet also belongs under this heading. Two examples, that of the rotating disk and axially symmetrical flow with stagnation, have already been discussed in the chapter on exact solutions of the Navier-Stokes equations.

We shall begin the present chapter with a discussion of some further examples of steady axially symmetrical flows which can be solved with the aid of the differential equations. Non-steady axially symmetrical boundary layers will be considered in Chap. XI, together with non-steady two-dimensional examples, and an approximate method applicable to two-dimensional and axially symmetrical boundary layers will be examined in Chap. XII.

a. Axially symmetrical boundary layers on bodies at rest

1. Rotation near the ground. In Chap. V we have considered the case of flow in the neighbourhood of a disk which rotates in a fluid at rest. The case of motion near a stationary wall, when the fluid at a large distance above it rotates at a constant angular velocity, is closely connected with it. This example was studied by U. T. Boedewadt [7]. One of the essential effects in the example of the disk which rotates in a fluid at rest consists in the fact that in the thin layer near the wall the fluid is thrown outwards owing to the existence of centrifugal forces. The fluid which is forced outwards in a radial direction is replaced by a fluid stream in the axial direction. In the case under consideration, in which the fluid rotates over the wall, there is a similar effect but its sign is reversed: the particles which rotate at a large distance from the wall are in equilibrium under the influence of the centrifugal force which is balanced by a radial pressure gradient. The peripheral velocity of the particles near the wall is reduced, thus decreasing materially the centrifugal force, whereas the radial pressure gradient directed towards the axis remains the same. This set of circumstances causes the particles near the wall to flow radially inwards, and for reasons of continuity that motion must be compensated by an axial flow upwards, as shown in Fig. 10.1. A superimposed field of flow of this nature which occurs in the boundary layer and whose direction deviates from that in the external flow is quite generally referred to as a *secondary flow*.

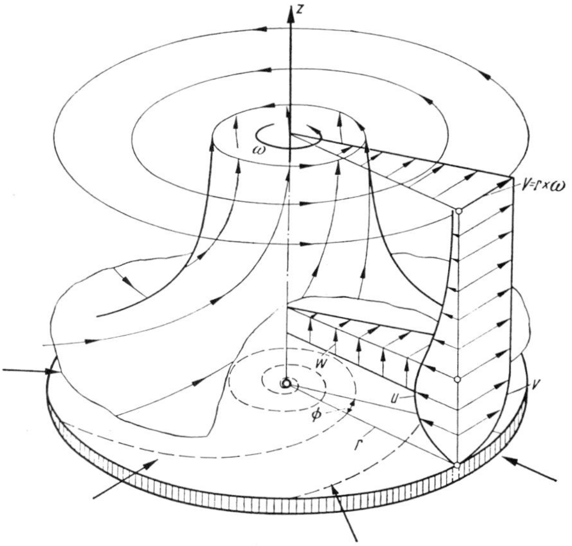

Fig. 10.1. Rotation near the ground

Velocity components: u — radial; v — tangential; w — axial. Owing to friction, the tangential velocity suffers a deceleration in the neighbourhood of the disk at rest. This gives rise to a secondary flow which is directed radially inwards

The secondary flow which accompanies rotation near a solid wall and which has been described in the preceding paragraph can be clearly observed in a teacup: after the rotation has been generated by vigorous stirring and again after the flow has been left to itself for a short while, the radial inward flow field near the bottom will be formed. Its existence can be inferred from the fact that tea leaves form a little heap near the centre at the bottom.

In order to formulate the mathematical problem, we shall assume cylindrical polar co-ordinates r, ϕ, z, the stationary wall being at $z = 0$, see Fig. 10.1. The fluid at a large distance from the wall will be assumed to rotate like a rigid body, with a constant angular velocity ω. We shall denote the velocity component in the radial direction by u, that in the tangential direction by v, the axial component being denoted by w. For reasons of axial symmetry the derivatives with respect to ϕ may be dropped from the Navier-Stokes equations. The solution which we are about to find will be an exact solution of the Navier-Stokes equations, just as was that for the rotating disk, because the terms which are neglected in the boundary layer equations vanish here on their own accord. By eqn. (3.33) we can write down the Navier-Stokes equations as

$$u\frac{\partial u}{\partial r} + w\frac{\partial u}{\partial z} - \frac{v^2}{r} = -\frac{1}{\varrho}\frac{\partial p}{\partial r} + \nu\left\{\frac{\partial^2 u}{\partial r^2} + \frac{\partial}{\partial r}\left(\frac{u}{r}\right) + \frac{\partial^2 u}{\partial z^2}\right\}, \qquad (10.1)$$

$$u\frac{\partial v}{\partial r}+w\frac{\partial v}{\partial z}+\frac{u\,v}{r}=\nu\left\{\frac{\partial^2 v}{\partial r^2}+\frac{\partial}{\partial r}\left(\frac{v}{r}\right)+\frac{\partial^2 v}{\partial z^2}\right\}, \tag{10.2}$$

$$u\frac{\partial w}{\partial r}+w\frac{\partial w}{\partial z}=-\frac{1}{\varrho}\frac{\partial p}{\partial z}+\nu\left\{\frac{\partial^2 w}{\partial r^2}+\frac{1}{r}\frac{\partial w}{\partial r}+\frac{\partial^2 w}{\partial z^2}\right\}, \tag{10.3}$$

$$\frac{\partial u}{\partial r}+\frac{u}{r}+\frac{\partial w}{\partial z}=0\,. \tag{10.4}$$

The boundary conditions are

$$\left.\begin{array}{llll} z=0: & u=0; & v=0; & w=0 \\ z=\infty: & u=0; & v=r\,\omega\,. & \end{array}\right\} \tag{10.5}$$

It is convenient to introduce the dimensionless co-ordinate

$$\zeta=z\sqrt{\frac{\omega}{\nu}} \tag{10.6}$$

in place of z, as in the case of the rotating disk (Sec. V. 10). We assume that the velocity components have the form

$$u=r\,\omega\,F(\zeta)\,;\qquad v=r\,\omega\,G(\zeta)\,;\qquad w=\sqrt{\nu\,\omega}\,H(\zeta)\,. \tag{10.7}$$

The radial pressure gradient can be computed for the frictionless flow at a large distance from the wall from the condition: $(1/\varrho)\cdot(\partial p/\partial r)=V^2/r$, or, with $V=r\,\omega$,

$$\frac{1}{\varrho}\frac{\partial p}{\partial r}=r\,\omega^2\,. \tag{10.8}$$

In the framework of the boundary layer theory it is assumed that the same pressure gradient acts in the viscous layer near the wall. Introducing eqns. (10.7) and (10.8) into eqns. (10.1), (10.2) and (10.4) we obtain a system of ordinary differential equations which is analogous to that in Sec. V. 10:

$$\left.\begin{array}{ll} F^2-G^2+HF'-F''+1 & =0 \\ 2\,G\,F+H\,G'-G'' & =0 \\ 2\,F+H' & =0 \end{array}\right\} \tag{10.9}$$

with the boundary conditions

$$\left.\begin{array}{llll} \zeta=0: & F=0; & G=0; & H=0 \\ \zeta=\infty: & F=0; & G=1\,. & \end{array}\right\} \tag{10.10}$$

The pressure gradient in the z-direction may be assumed equal to zero, as such an assumption is compatible with boundary layer theory. Alternatively, it can be calculated from eqn. (10.3), after the principal solution had been obtained, which then results in an exact solution of the Navier-Stokes equations.

The system of equations (10.9) with the boundary conditions (10.10) was first solved by U. T. Boedewadt [7] in a very laborious way by means of a power series expansion at $\zeta = 0$ and an asymptotic expansion for $\zeta = \infty$. Recently this solution was corrected by A. C. Browning in an unpublished paper. The values of the functions F, G, H according to Browning are given in Table 10.1 and in Fig. 10.2. The horizontal velocity, i. e. the resultant of u and v, is also shown plotted in a polar diagram in Fig. 10.3. The angle between the horizontal velocity component and the peripheral direction depends only on the height, and the vectors in Fig. 10.2 indicate this direction for varying heights. The deviation from the peripheral direction prescribed at a large height is largest near the ground and has a value of 50·6° inwards. The largest deviation of 7·4° outwards occurs for $\zeta = 4{\cdot}63$ so that the largest angular difference, i. e. that between the ground and that at $\zeta = 4{\cdot}63$, is 58°. It is further remarkable that the axial velocity component w does not depend on the distance r from the axis but only on the distance from the ground. The motion at all points is upwards with $w > 0$. As already mentioned, this is caused by the inward flow near the ground, consequent upon the decrease in the centrifugal forces. In any case, as seen from Fig. 10.2, this is compensated by a radial flow outwards at a greater height, but on the whole, the radial flow inwards predominates. The total volume flowing

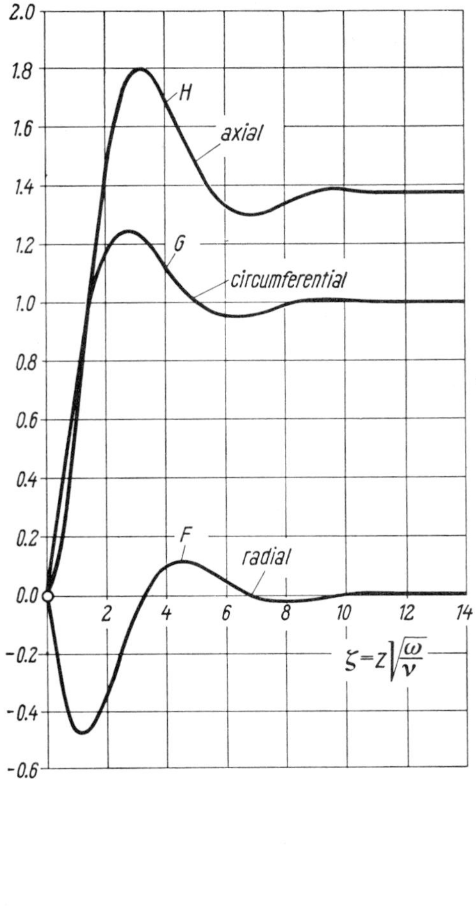

Fig. 10.2. Rotation near a solid wall, after Boedewadt. Velocity distribution in the boundary layer from eqn. (10.7); see also Table 10.1

Fig. 10.3. Rotation near a solid wall, after Boedewadt. Vector representation of the horizontal velocity component

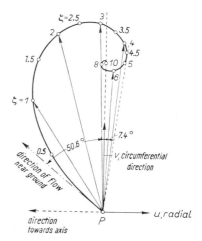

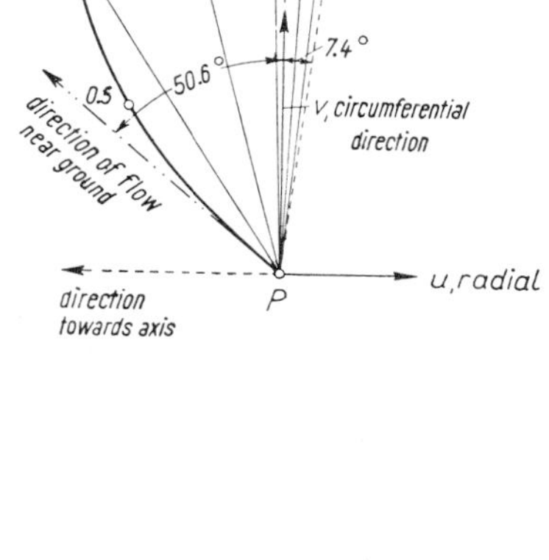

Table 10.1. The functions for the velocity distribution for the case of rotation over a stationary wall, after A. C. Browning†

ζ	F	G	H
0	0	0	0
0·5	−0·343	0·382	0·190
1·0	−0·468	0·731	0·614
1·5	−0·437	1·004	1·076
2·0	−0·318	1·175	1·460
2·5	−0·171	1·246	1·704
3·0	−0·038	1·242	1·800
3·5	+0·056	1·192	1·784
4·0	+0·106	1·123	1·702
4·5	+0·117	1·056	1·590
5·0	+0·103	1·003	1·478
5·5	+0·074	0·969	1·390
6·0	+0·041	0·954	1·332
6·5	+0·013	0·953	1·308
7·0	−0·010	0·959	1·304
7·5	−0·020	0·975	1·320
8·0	−0·023	0·990	1·340
8·5	−0·020	1·000	1·364
9·0	−0·013	1·007	1·382
9·5	−0·006	1·010	1·390
10·0	0·000	1·009	1·390
10·5	+0·003	1·007	1·386
11·0	+0·004	1·005	1·382
11·5	+0·003	1·002	1·380
12·0	+0·001	1·000	1·380
12·5	0·000	1·000	1·380
∞	0·000	1·000	1·380

towards the axis taken over a cylinder of radius R around the z-axis is

$$Q = 2\pi R \int_{z=0}^{\infty} u \, \mathrm{d}z = 2\pi R^2 \sqrt{\omega \nu} \int_0^{\infty} F(\zeta) \, \mathrm{d}\zeta = -\pi R^2 \sqrt{\omega \nu}\, H(\infty)\,.$$

Inserting the numerical value of $H(\infty)$ from Table 10.1 we obtain

$$Q = -1{\cdot}380\, \pi R^2 \sqrt{\omega \nu}\,. \tag{10.11}$$

The volume of flow in the positive z-direction is of equal magnitude. The largest upward motion occurs at $\zeta = 3{\cdot}1$, where $w = 1{\cdot}80 \sqrt{\nu \omega}$. It is also worth noting that the boundary layer extends considerably higher than in the example with the disk rotating in a fluid at rest (Sec. Vb). If the *boundary layer thickness* δ is defined as the height for which the deviation of the peripheral velocity is equal to 2 per cent., we shall obtain $\delta = 8 \sqrt{\nu/\omega}$ as against $\delta = 4 \sqrt{\nu/\omega}$ for the stationary fluid.

† Communicated privately by L. Howarth.

The example of the motion of a vortex source between two parallel walls considered by G. Vogelpohl [62] is related to some extent to the present case. For very small Reynolds numbers the velocity distribution deviates little from the parabolic curve of Poiseuille flow. For large Reynolds numbers the velocity profile approaches rectangular distribution, and a boundary layer is seen to be forming. The corresponding case of turbulent flow was discussed by C. Pfleiderer [46]. In this connexion the paper by E. Becker [5a] may also be consulted.

Similar phenomena can be found in swirling flow through a conical funnel-like channel investigated by K. Garbsch [17]. The potential flow is generated by a sink of strength Q placed at the vertex of the cone and a potential vortex of strength Γ placed along the axis, Fig. 10.4. The solution to the boundary layer equations is obtained by an iterative procedure which is said to lead to a good approximation with a small number of steps only. Two particular cases of such flows have also been investigated with the aid of approximate methods, and they will be mentioned in Chap. XII: A. M. Binnie and D. P. Harris [5] studied pure sink flow ($\Gamma = 0$), and G. I. Taylor [58] and J. C. Cooke [12] studied pure vortex flow ($Q = 0$). In the latter case, as shown in Fig. 10.4, the flow forms a boundary layer on the wall of the conical channel. The flow field in the boundary layer develops a velocity component w in the direction of the cone generators whereas the frictionless core, being a pure swirl, possesses only tangential velocity components v. The secondary flow in the boundary layer transports some fluid towards the vertex. The reader may further wish to study a related paper by H. E. Weber [63].

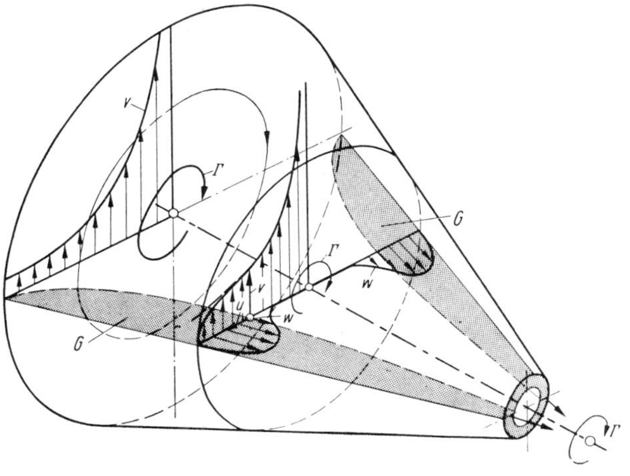

Fig. 10.4. Swirling flow in a convergent conical channel after G. I. Taylor [58]

B = boundary layer on the wall of the conical channel with secondary flow towards the vertex

2. The circular jet. We shall now indicate H. Schlichting's [49] solution for the laminar circular jet which is analogous to the one for a two-dimensional jet given in Sec. IX g. The subject of the investigation is, thus, a jet which leaves a small circular opening and mixes with the surrounding fluid. In most practical cases the circular jet is also turbulent. The turbulent circular jet will be considered in Chap. XXIII, but since it leads to a differential equation which is identical with that for the laminar case we shall discuss the latter in some greater detail.

The pressure can here be regarded constant, as in the two-dimensional case. The system of co-ordinates will be selected with its x-axis in the axis of the jet, the radial distance being denoted by y. The axial and radial velocity components will be denoted by u and v respectively. Owing to the assumption of a constant pressure the flux of momentum in the direction of x is constant once more:

$$J = 2\pi\,\varrho \int_0^\infty u^2\,y\,dy = \text{const.} \tag{10.12}$$

In the adopted system of co-ordinates the equation of motion in the direction of x, under the usual boundary layer simplifications, together with the equation of motion, can be written as

$$u\,\frac{\partial u}{\partial x} + v\,\frac{\partial u}{\partial y} = \nu\,\frac{1}{y}\,\frac{\partial}{\partial y}\left(y\,\frac{\partial u}{\partial y}\right), \tag{10.13}$$

$$\frac{\partial u}{\partial x} + \frac{\partial v}{\partial y} + \frac{v}{y} = 0\,. \tag{10.14}$$

and the boundary conditions are

$$\begin{aligned} y &= 0\ :\quad v = 0\,;\quad \frac{\partial u}{\partial y} = 0 \\ y &= \infty:\quad u = 0\,. \end{aligned} \tag{10.15}$$

As before, the velocity profiles $u(x, y)$ can be assumed similar. The width of the jet will be taken to be proportional to x^n, it being further assumed that

$$\psi \sim x^p\,F(\eta) \qquad \text{with} \qquad \eta = \frac{y}{x^n}\,.$$

In order to determine the exponents p and n we can use the same two conditions as in the two-dimensional case. First the momentum from eqn. (10.12) must be independent of x, and secondly, the inertia and frictional terms in eqn. (10.13) must be of the same order of magnitude. Hence

$$u \sim x^{p-2n}, \quad \frac{\partial u}{\partial x} \sim x^{p-2n-1}, \quad \frac{\partial u}{\partial y} \sim x^{p-3n}, \quad \frac{1}{y}\,\frac{\partial}{\partial y}\left(y\,\frac{\partial u}{\partial y}\right) \sim x^{p-4n}.$$

Thus the following two equations for p and n result:

$$2\,p - 4\,n + 2\,n = 0\,; \qquad 2\,p - 4\,n - 1 = p - 4\,n\,.$$

so that $p = n = 1$. Consequently, we may now put

$$\psi = \nu\,x\,F(\eta) \qquad \text{and} \qquad \eta = \frac{y}{x},$$

from which it follows that the velocity components are

$$u = \frac{\nu}{x}\,\frac{F'}{\eta}\,; \qquad v = \frac{\nu}{x}\left(F' - \frac{F}{\eta}\right). \tag{10.16}$$

Inserting these values into eqn. (10.13), we obtain the following equation for the stream function

$$\frac{FF'}{\eta^2} - \frac{F'^2}{\eta} - \frac{FF''}{\eta} = \frac{\mathrm{d}}{\mathrm{d}\eta}\left(F'' - \frac{F'}{\eta}\right),$$

which can be integrated once to give

$$F F' = F' - \eta F'' . \tag{10.17}$$

The boundary conditions are $u = u_m$ and $v = 0$ for $y = 0$. It follows that $F' = 0$ and $F = 0$ for $\eta = 0$. Since u is an even function of η, F'/η must be even, F' odd and F even. Because of $F(0) = 0$ the constant term in the expansion of F in powers of η must vanish, which determines one constant of integration. The second constant of integration, which will be denoted by γ, can be evaluated as follows: If $F(\eta)$ is a solution of eqn. (10.17), then $F(\gamma\eta) = F(\xi)$ is also a solution. A particular solution of the differential equation

$$F \frac{\mathrm{d}F}{\mathrm{d}\xi} = \frac{\mathrm{d}F}{\mathrm{d}\xi} - \xi \frac{\mathrm{d}^2 F}{\mathrm{d}\xi^2} ,$$

which satisfies the boundary condition $\xi = 0$: $F = 0$, $F' = 0$, is given by

$$F = \frac{\xi^2}{1 + \frac{1}{4}\xi^2} . \tag{10.18}$$

Hence we obtain from eqn. (10.16)

$$u = \frac{\nu}{x}\gamma^2 \frac{1}{\xi}\frac{\mathrm{d}F}{\mathrm{d}\xi} = \frac{\nu}{x}\frac{2\gamma^2}{\left(1 + \frac{1}{4}\xi^2\right)^2} ,$$

$$v = \frac{\nu}{x}\gamma\left(\frac{\mathrm{d}F}{\mathrm{d}\xi} - \frac{F}{\xi}\right) = \frac{\nu}{x}\gamma \frac{\xi - \frac{1}{4}\xi^3}{\left(1 + \frac{1}{4}\xi^2\right)^2} .$$

Here $\xi = \gamma\, y/x$, and the constant of integration γ can now be determined from the given value of momentum.

From eqn. (10.12) we obtain for the momentum of the jet

$$J = 2\pi\varrho \int_0^\infty u^2\, y\, \mathrm{d}y = \frac{16}{3}\pi\varrho\gamma^2\nu^2 .$$

Finally, the above results can be expressed in a form to contain only the kinematic viscosity, ν, and the *kinematic momentum* $K' = J/\varrho$. Thus

$$u = \frac{3}{8\pi}\frac{K'}{\nu x}\frac{1}{\left(1 + \frac{1}{4}\xi^2\right)^2} , \tag{10.19}$$

$$v = \frac{1}{4}\sqrt{\frac{3}{\pi}}\frac{\sqrt{K'}}{x}\frac{\xi - \frac{1}{4}\xi^3}{\left(1 + \frac{1}{4}\xi^2\right)^2} , \tag{10.20}$$

$$\xi = \sqrt{\frac{3}{16\pi}}\frac{\sqrt{K'}}{\nu}\frac{y}{x} . \tag{10.21}$$

Fig. 10.5 represents a stream-line pattern calculated from the preceding equations. The longitudinal velocity u is shown plotted together with that for the two-dimensional jet in Fig. 9.15.

The volume of flow $Q = 2\pi \int_0^\infty u\, y\, dy$ (volume per second), which increases with the distance from the orifice owing to the flow from the surroundings, is represented by the simple equation

$$Q = 8\pi \nu x . \tag{10.22}$$

This equation should be compared with eqn. (9.62) for the two-dimensional jet. It is seen that, unexpectedly, the volume of flow at a given distance from the orifice is independent of the momentum of the jet, i. e. independent of the excess of pressure under which the jet leaves the orifice. A jet which leaves under a large pressure difference (large velocity) remains narrower than one leaving with a smaller pressure difference (small velocity). The latter carries with it comparatively more stationary fluid, namely in a manner to make the volume of flow at a given distance from the orifice equal to that in a faster jet, provided that the kinematic viscosity is the same in both cases.

H. B. Squire [55, 56] was able to find solutions to the boundary layer equations as well as to the complete Navier-Stokes equations and to make a comparison between them for the case of a conical jet which possesses an additional, radial velocity component in its annular orifice. In this latter class of radial jets the velocities are also inversely proportional to the distance from the orifice. The theory can be extended to turbulent flows by replacing the kinematic viscosity with the apparent kinematic viscosity of turbulent flow which in this case remains constant, see Chap. XXIII. The case when a jet impinges at right angles on a wall and is spread along it was solved by M. B. Glauert [19b], who included plane as well as axially symmetrical, and laminar as well as turbulent flows.

The corresponding case of a compressible circular laminar jet was evaluated by M. Z. Krzywoblocki [34] and D. C. Pack [45]. In the subsonic regime, the density on the axis of the jet is larger, and the temperature is smaller than on its boundary. These differences are inversely proportional to the square of the distance from the orifice. According to H. Goertler [21], the case when a weak swirl is superimposed on the jet can also be treated mathematically, and the effect of the swirling motion present in the orifice can be traced in the downstream direction. It turns out that the swirl decreases faster with the distance from the orifice than the jet velocity on the axis.

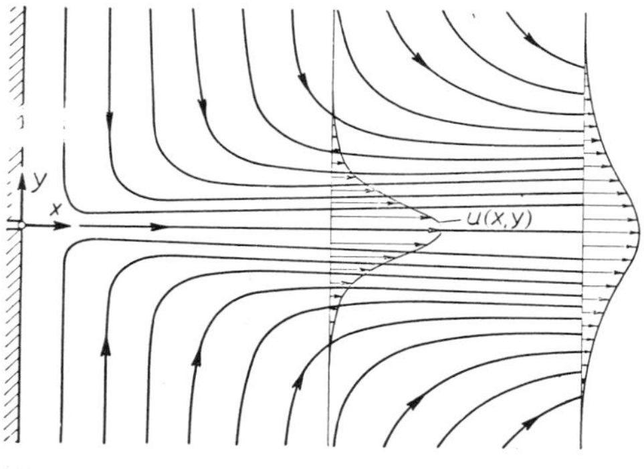

Fig. 10.5. Stream-line pattern for a circular laminar jet

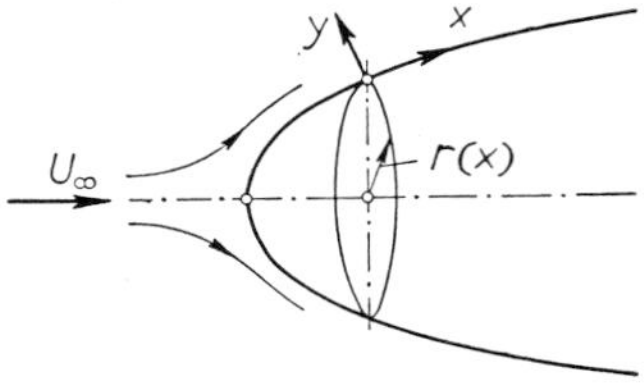

Fig. 10.6. Boundary layer near a body of revolution. System of co-ordinates

3. Boundary layer on a body of revolution. The flow of a viscous fluid past a body of revolution when the stream is parallel to its axis is of great practical importance. The boundary layer equations have been adapted to this case by E. Boltze [8]. Assuming a curvilinear system of co-ordinates (Fig. 10.6), we denote by x the current length measured along a meridian from the stagnation point, y denoting the co-ordinate at right angles to the surface. The contour of the body of revolution will be specified by the radii r (x) of the sections taken at right angles to the axis. We assume that there are no sharp corners so that $\mathrm{d}^2r/\mathrm{d}x^2$ does not assume extremely large values. The velocity components parallel and normal to the wall will be denoted by u and v, respectively, and the potential flow will be given by $U(x)$. According to Boltze the boundary layer equations will then assume the form:

$$\frac{\partial u}{\partial t} + u\frac{\partial u}{\partial x} + v\frac{\partial u}{\partial y} = -\frac{1}{\varrho}\frac{\partial p}{\partial x} + \nu\frac{\partial^2 u}{\partial y^2}, \tag{10.23}$$

$$\frac{\partial(ur)}{\partial x} + \frac{\partial(vr)}{\partial y} = 0 \tag{10.24}$$

with the boundary conditions:

$$y = 0: \quad u = v = 0; \qquad y = \infty: \quad u = U(x, t)\,. \tag{10.25}$$

The equation of motion in the x-direction is seen to remain unchanged compared with two-dimensional flow. An order of magnitude estimate of terms in the equation of motion in the y-direction shows that the pressure gradient normal to the wall $\partial p/\partial y \sim u^2/r \sim 1$. Consequently the pressure difference across the boundary layer is of the order of the boundary layer thickness δ, and it is again possible to assume that the pressure gradient of the potential stream, $\partial p/\partial x$, is impressed on the boundary layer.

In order to integrate eqns. (10.23) to (10.25) for the axially symmetrical case it is once more possible to introduce a stream function $\psi(x, y)$. It is at once apparent that the equation of continuity (10.24) is satisfied identically if we put

$$u = \frac{1}{r}\frac{\partial(\psi r)}{\partial y} = \frac{\partial \psi}{\partial y}, \tag{10.26}$$

$$v = -\frac{1}{r}\frac{\partial(\psi r)}{\partial x} = -\frac{\partial \psi}{\partial x} - \frac{1}{r}\frac{\mathrm{d}r}{\mathrm{d}x}\psi\,. \tag{10.27}$$ †

This transforms eqn. (10.23) into

$$\frac{\partial^2\psi}{\partial t\,\partial y} + \frac{\partial \psi}{\partial y}\frac{\partial^2\psi}{\partial x\,\partial y} - \left(\frac{\partial\psi}{\partial x} + \frac{1}{r}\frac{\mathrm{d}r}{\mathrm{d}x}\psi\right)\frac{\partial^2\psi}{\partial y^2} = -\frac{1}{\varrho}\frac{\partial p}{\partial x} + \nu\frac{\partial^3\psi}{\partial y^3} \tag{10.28}$$

† The equation of continuity can also be satisfied by an alternative stream function $\overline{\psi}$, such that

$$u = \frac{1}{r}\frac{\partial\overline{\psi}}{\partial y}; \qquad v = -\frac{1}{r}\frac{\partial\overline{\psi}}{\partial x}.$$

This form of the stream function was used by E. Boltze when he calculated non-steady axially symmetrical boundary layers, as described in Chap. XI.

with the boundary conditions

$$y = 0: \quad \psi = 0; \frac{\partial \psi}{\partial y} = 0; \qquad y = \infty: \quad \frac{\partial \psi}{\partial y} = U(x,t). \tag{10.29}$$

In addition the velocity field at time $t = 0$ is prescribed.

We shall limit the considerations of this chapter to the case of steady flow, when eqn. (10.28) simplifies to

$$\frac{\partial \psi}{\partial y} \frac{\partial^2 \psi}{\partial x \, \partial y} - \left(\frac{\partial \psi}{\partial x} + \frac{1}{r} \frac{\mathrm{d}r}{\mathrm{d}x} \psi \right) \frac{\partial^2 \psi}{\partial y^2} = U \frac{\mathrm{d}U}{\mathrm{d}x} + \nu \frac{\partial^3 \psi}{\partial y^3} \tag{10.30}$$

with the same boundary conditions as in (10.29).

The boundary layer on a body of revolution can now be determined by the same method as that used in Sec. IX c for the case of a cylinder of arbitrary cross-section. The velocity of the potential flow $U(x)$ is expanded into a power-series in x, and the stream function is assumed to be represented by a similar series in x, with coefficients depending on the wall distance y (Blasius series). It is here also possible to arrange the computation so as to render the coefficient functions of y independent of the parameters of any particular problem. In this manner the functions can be calculated once and applied universally. The method will be briefly explained on the basis of a paper due to N. Froessling [16].

The body contour is assumed given by the series

$$r(x) = r_1 x + r_3 x^3 + r_5 x^5 + \dots, \tag{10.31}$$

the potential flow being defined by the series

$$U(x) = u_1 x + u_3 x^3 + u_5 x^5 + \dots. \tag{10.32}$$

The distance from the wall is represented by a dimensionless co-ordinate

$$\eta = y \sqrt{\frac{2 u_1}{\nu}}, \tag{10.33}$$

and in analogy with eqn. (10.32) the stream function is represented by the Blasius series

$$\psi(x, y) = \sqrt{\frac{\nu}{2 u_1}} \Big\{ u_1 x f_1(\eta) + 2 u_3 x^3 f_3(\eta) + 3 u_5 x^5 f_5(\eta) + + 4 u_7 x^7 f_7(\eta) + \dots \Big\}. \tag{10.34}$$

Denoting differentiation with respect to η by a dash, we have

$$u = u_1 x f_1' + 2 u_3 x^3 f_3' + 3 u_5 x^5 f_5' + 4 u_7 x^7 f_7' + \dots. \tag{10.35}$$

In order to render the functional coefficients $f_1(\eta)$, $f_3(\eta)$, ... independent of the parameters of the particular problem, i. e. of u_1, u_3, ... and r_1, r_3, ..., it is necessary to put further

$$\left.\begin{aligned}
f_3 &= g_3 + \frac{r_3 u_1}{r_1 u_3} h_3 , \\
f_5 &= g_5 + \frac{r_5 u_1}{r_1 u_5} h_5 + \frac{u_3^2}{u_1 u_5} k_5 + \frac{r_3 u_3}{r_1 u_5} j_5 + \frac{r_3^2 u_1}{r_1^2 u_5} q_5 , \\
f_7 &= g_7 + \frac{r_7 u_1}{r_1 u_7} h_7 + \frac{r_3^2 u_3}{r_1^2 u_7} j_7 + \frac{u_3^3}{u_1^2 u_7} k_7 + \frac{r_5 u_3}{r_1 u_7} l_7 + \\
&\quad + \frac{u_3 u_5}{u_1 u_7} p_7 + \frac{r_3^2 u_1}{r_1^3 u_7} q_7 + \frac{r_3 r_5 u_1}{r_1^2 u_7} v_7 + \frac{r_3 u_3^2}{r_1 u_1 u_7} t_7 + \frac{r_5 u_5}{r_1 u_7} z_7 .
\end{aligned}\right\} \tag{10.36}$$

Substituting eqns. (10.31), (10.32) and (10.35) with (10.36) into eqn. (10.30), multiplying by r and comparing terms we obtain a set of differential equations for the functions f_1, g_3, h_3, ... , the first three of which are:

$$\begin{aligned}
f_1''' &= - f_1 f_1'' + \tfrac{1}{2}(f_1'^2 - 1) \\
g_3''' &= - f_1 g_3'' + 2 f_1' g_3' - 2 f_1'' g_3 - 1 \\
h_3''' &= - f_1 h_3'' + 2 f_1' h_3' - 2 f_1'' h_3 - \tfrac{1}{2} f_1 f_1'' .
\end{aligned} \tag{10.37}$$

The boundary conditions are:

$\eta = 0$: all functions together with their first derivatives vanish.

$\eta = \infty$: $f_1' = 1$; $g_3' = \frac{1}{2}$; $g_5' = \frac{1}{3}$; $g_7' = \frac{1}{7}$; all remaining first derivatives vanish.

The first equation of this set is identical with that for three-dimensional stagnation flow which was considered in Chap. V †. The equations for the cubic and quintic terms were solved in N. Froessling's paper mentioned previously, and the relevant numerical values are listed in Table 10.2. The succeeding ten functions of the term x_7 have been evaluated by F. W. Scholkemeyer [52]. The plot of f_1' can be deduced from Fig. 5.11 since $f_1' = \phi'$.

Example: *Sphere.*

We shall now apply the above procedure to the case of a sphere, and we shall treat it in a way similar to the example of a circular cylinder considered in Sec. IX c. We shall again base the calculation on the velocity distribution given by potential theory.

For a sphere of radius R, kept at rest in a free stream of velocity U_∞, the ideal potential velocity distribution is given by

$$U(x) = \frac{3}{2} U_\infty \sin \frac{x}{R} = \frac{3}{2} U_\infty \sin \phi . \tag{10.38}$$

For large, i. e. supercritical Reynolds numbers, the experimentally observed velocity distribution does not differ too much from the ideal, potential flow distribution, as shown in Fig. 1.10. Since in the axially symmetrical case the Blasius series is

† The eqn. for $f_1(\eta)$ transforms into eqn. (5.40) for $\phi(\xi)$, if it is noticed that $\eta = \xi \sqrt{2}$ and $df_1/d\eta = d\phi/d\xi$.

known up to the term x^7, we shall replace sin x/R in eqn. (10.38) by a power series and we shall, likewise, continue it as far as the term x^7. It may be inferred from Fig. 9.5 that sin x/R has been satisfactorily approximated over a considerable distance beyond the velocity maximum. The radius is given by

$$r(x) = R \sin \frac{x}{R} \,. \tag{10.39}$$

Comparing these expressions with the assumptions (10.31) and (10.32), we obtain the following values of the parameters $u_1, u_3, \ldots, r_1, r_3, \ldots$:

$$u_1 = \frac{3}{2}\frac{U_\infty}{R}\,; \quad u_3 = -\frac{1}{4}\frac{U_\infty}{R^3}\,; \quad u_5 = \frac{1}{80}\frac{U_\infty}{R^5}\,; \quad u_7 = -\frac{1}{3360}\frac{U_\infty}{R^7}\,;$$

$$r_1 = 1\,; \quad r_3 = -\frac{1}{6}\frac{1}{R^2}\,; \quad r_5 = \frac{1}{120}\frac{1}{R^4}\,; \quad r_7 = -\frac{1}{5040}\frac{1}{R^6}\,.$$

Hence

$$\eta = \frac{y}{R}\sqrt{\frac{3\,U_\infty R}{\nu}}\,,$$

and the velocity distribution from eqn. (10.35) becomes

$$\frac{u}{U_\infty} = \frac{3}{2}\frac{x}{R} f_1' - \frac{1}{2}\left(\frac{x}{R}\right)^3 \left(g_3' + h_3'\right) + \frac{3}{80}\left(\frac{x}{R}\right)^5 \left[g_5' + h_5' + \frac{10}{3} k_5' + \frac{10}{3} j_5' + \frac{10}{3} q_5'\right] -$$

$$- \frac{1}{840}\left(\frac{x}{R}\right)^7 \left[g_7' + h_7' + \frac{7}{3} k_7' + \frac{7}{3} j_7' + \right.$$

$$\left. + 7\, l_7' + 7\, p_7' + \frac{7}{3} q_7' + \frac{7}{3} t_7' + 7\, v_7' + 7\, z_7'\right]. \tag{10.40}$$

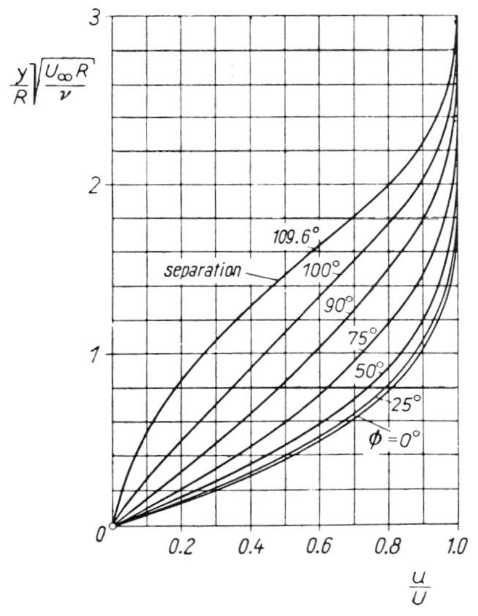

The resulting velocity distribution is represented in Fig. 10.7. The point of separation is given by the equation

$$1 - 0{\cdot}3925\, X_S + 0{\cdot}0421\, X_S^2 - 0{\cdot}00259\, X_S^3 = 0\,,$$

where $X_S = (x_S/R)^2$. Hence $x_S/R = 1{\cdot}913$, and consequently

$$\phi_S = 109{\cdot}6°$$

which is almost the same value as that for the circular cylinder.

Fig. 10.7. Velocity distribution in the boundary layer near a sphere

Table 10.2. The functional coefficients of the Blasius series for the calculation of the boundary layer on a body of revolution; after Froessling [16]

η	f_1'	g_3'	h_3'	g_5'	h_5'	k_5'	j_5'	q_5'	$\eta = 0$
0·0	0·0	0·0	0·0	0·0	0·0	0·0	0·0	0·0	$f_1'' =$ 0·9277
0·2	0·1755	0·1896	0·0090	0·1612	0·0101	0·0255	0·0058	−0·0049	$g_3'' =$ 1·0475
0·4	0·3311	0·3400	0·0176	0·2838	0·0198	0·0324	0·0107	−0·0096	$h_3'' =$ 0·0448
0·6	0·4669	0·4535	0·0254	0·3709	0·0285	0·0241	0·0137	−0·0140	$g_5'' =$ 0·9054
0·8	0·5833	0·5334	0·0316	0·4270	0·0354	0·0051	0·0134	−0·0176	$h_5'' =$ 0·0506
1·0	0·6811	0·5842	0·0358	0·4576	0·0399	−0·0195	0·0096	−0·0204	$k_5'' =$ 0·1768
1·2	0·7614	0·6110	0·0377	0·4683	0·0417	−0·0447	0·0025	−0·0222	$j_5'' =$ 0·0291
1·4	0·8258	0·6193	0·0372	0·4645	0·0409	−0·0665	−0·0064	−0·0229	$q_5'' =$ −0·0244
1·6	0·8761	0·6144	0·0346	0·4515	0·0379	−0·0819	−0·0156	−0·0226	
1·8	0·9142	0·6015	0·0306	0·4335	0·0334	−0·0897	−0·0234	−0·0212	
2·0	0·9422	0·5845	0·0258	0·4139	0·0279	−0·0899	−0·0287	−0·0192	
2·2	0·9622	0·5666	0·0207	0·3952	0·0223	−0·0838	−0·0310	−0·0167	
2·4	0·9760	0·5500	0·0158	0·3787	0·0170	−0·0733	−0·0304	−0·0139	
2·6	0·9853	0·5358	0·0116	0·3652	0·0124	−0·0605	−0·0275	−0·0111	
2·8	0·9912	0·5245	0·0081	0·3549	0·0086	−0·0474	−0·0232	−0·0085	
3·0	0·9949	0·5161	0·0054	0·3473	0·0058	−0·0352	−0·0184	−0·0062	
3·2	0·9972	0·5102	0·0035	0·3420	0·0037	−0·0249	−0·0137	−0·0044	
3·4	0·9985	0·5061	0·0022	0·3385	0·0023	−0·0168	−0·0097	−0·0029	
3·6	0·9992	0·5036	0·0013	0·3363	0·0013	−0·0109	−0·0065	−0·0019	
3·8	0·9996	0·5020	0·0007	0·3350	0·0008	−0·0067	−0·0042	−0·0012	
4·0	0·9998	0·5011	0·0004	0·3342	0·0004	−0·0040	−0·0025	−0·0007	
4·2	0·9999	0·5006	0·0002	0·3338	0·0002	−0·0022	−0·0015	−0·0004	
4·4	0·9999	0·5003	0·0002	0·3336	0·0001	−0·0012	−0·0008	−0·0002	
4·6	1·0000	0·5001	0·0000	0·3334	0·0000	−0·0006	−0·0004	−0·0001	
4·8	1·0000	0·5000		0·3334	0·0000	−0·0003	−0·0002	0·0000	
5·0				0·3334		−0·0001	−0·0001	0·0000	
5·2				0·3334		0·0000	0·0000		
5·4				0·3333					

In connexion with the problem in hand we can repeat our previous remarks concerning the general practicability of applying a Blasius series. The calculation of the functional coefficients beyond the term x^7 involves an unacceptable amount of computation, and, furthermore, the calculation of slender bodies requires considerably more terms which puts a very severe limitation on this method. For further results concerning spheres reference should be made to Sec. XIIe.

4. Relation between axially symmetrical and two-dimensional boundary layers. The boundary layer which exists on a cylindrical body, when it is placed in a stream whose direction is perpendicular to its axis (two-dimensional problem) depends only on the potential flow $U(x)$ around the cylinder. The shape of its cross-section does not enter the calculation explicitly, and influences it only insofar as $U(x)$ depends on it. On the other hand in the axially symmetrical case, e. g. in axial flow past a body of revolution, the boundary layer depends directly on the body because the radius of its cross-section $r(x)$ appears explicitly in the differential equation, apart from influencing the potential velocity distribution $U(x)$. In steady flow the boundary layer equations for two-dimensional flow and for axially symmetrical flow are given by eqns. (7.10), (7.11) and (10.23) and (10.24), respectively. The latter refer to a curvilinear system of co-ordinates with x denoting the current arc length and y denoting the distance from the wall in a direction normal to it. The respective velocity components are denoted by u and v, and the magnitudes with a bar refer to the two-dimensional case. With these symbols, we have for the two-dimensional case:

$$\left.\begin{aligned} \bar{u}\frac{\partial \bar{u}}{\partial \bar{x}} + \bar{v}\frac{\partial \bar{u}}{\partial \bar{y}} &= \bar{U}\frac{\mathrm{d}\bar{U}}{\mathrm{d}\bar{x}} + \nu\frac{\partial^2 \bar{u}}{\partial \bar{y}^2}, \\ \frac{\partial \bar{u}}{\partial \bar{x}} + \frac{\partial \bar{v}}{\partial \bar{y}} &= 0, \end{aligned}\right\} \qquad (10.41)$$

for the axially symmetrical case

$$\left.\begin{aligned} u\frac{\partial u}{\partial x} + v\frac{\partial u}{\partial y} &= U\frac{\mathrm{d}U}{\mathrm{d}x} + \nu\frac{\partial^2 u}{\partial y^2}, \\ \frac{\partial (r\,u)}{\partial x} + \frac{\partial (r\,v)}{\partial y} &= 0. \end{aligned}\right\} \qquad (10.42)$$

Here $r(x)$ denotes the distance of a point on the wall from the axis of symmetry. The first equations of both systems are identical, the difference being only in the appearance of the radius $r(x)$ in the equation of continuity.

It seems thus reasonable to inquire whether it is possible to indicate a transformation which would permit the use of the solutions of the two-dimensional case to derive solutions of the axially symmetrical case. Such a general relationship between two-dimensional and axially symmetrical boundary layers has been discovered by W. Mangler [42]. It reduces the calculation of the laminar boundary layer for an axially symmetrical body to that on a cylindrical body. The given body of revolution is associated with an ideal potential velocity distribution for a cylindrical body, the function being easily calculated from the contour and the potential velocity distribution of the body of revolution. Mangler's transformation is also valid for compressible boundary layers, as well as for thermal boundary layers in laminar flow. We shall, however, consider it here only in relation to incompressible flow.

According to Mangler, the equations which transform the co-ordinates and the velocities of the axially symmetrical problem to those of the equivalent two-dimensional problem are as follows:

$$\left.\begin{aligned} \bar{x} &= \frac{1}{L^2}\int_0^x r^2(x)\,\mathrm{d}x; \qquad \bar{y} = \frac{r(x)}{L}\,y; \\ \bar{u} &= u\,; \qquad \bar{v} = \frac{L}{r}\left(v + \frac{r'}{r}\,y\,u\right); \\ \bar{U} &= U\,, \end{aligned}\right\} \tag{10.43}$$

where L denotes a constant length. Remembering that

$$\frac{\partial f}{\partial x} = \frac{r^2}{L^2}\frac{\partial f}{\partial \bar{x}} + \frac{r'}{r}\,\bar{y}\,\frac{\partial f}{\partial \bar{y}}\,; \qquad \frac{\partial f}{\partial y} = \frac{\partial f}{\partial \bar{y}}\,\frac{r}{L}\,,$$

it is easy to verify that the system of equations (10.42) transforms into eqns. (10.41) by the use of the substitutions (10.43).

The boundary layer on a body of revolution $r(x)$ having the ideal potential velocity distribution $U(x)$ can be evaluated by computing the two-dimensional boundary layer for a velocity distribution $\bar{U}(\bar{x})$, where $U = \bar{U}$ and $\bar{x}$ and x are related by eqn. (10.43). Having calculated the velocity components $\bar{u}$, and $\bar{v}$ for the two-dimensional boundary layer it is possible to determine the components u and v of the axially symmetrical boundary layer with the aid of the transformation equations (10.43).

The method may be better understood with the aid of the following example. We shall consider rotationally symmetrical stagnation flow, for which

$$r(x) = x\,; \qquad U(x) = u_1\,x\,.$$

Hence, from eqn. (10.43), we have

$$\bar{x} = \frac{x^3}{3\,L^2} \quad \text{and consequently} \quad x = \sqrt[3]{3\,L^2\,\bar{x}}\,.$$

The potential flow of the associated two-dimensional flow becomes

$$\bar{U}(x) = u_1\,\sqrt[3]{3\,L^2\,\bar{x}}\,,$$

so that $\bar{U}(\bar{x}) = C\,\bar{x}^{\frac{1}{3}}$, where C denotes a constant. The associated two-dimensional flow belongs to the class of wedge flows discussed in Sec. IXa and is given by $U = C\,x^m$, with $m = \frac{1}{3}$ for the present example. From eqn. (9.7) we find the wedge angle $\beta = 2\,m/(m+1) = \frac{1}{2}$. The associated two-dimensional flow is that past a wedge with an angle $\pi\,\beta = \pi/2$. The fact that axially symmetrical stagnation flow can be reduced to the case of flow past a wedge whose angle is $\pi/2$ was stated in Sec. IXa (p. 144) and is now confirmed.

b. Three-dimensional boundary layers: the boundary layer on a yawed cylinder

Until now we have restricted ourselves almost exclusively to the consideration of two-dimensional and axially symmetrical problems. Problems of two-dimensional and of axially symmetrical flow have this in common that the prescribed potential flow depends only on one space co-ordinate, and the two velocity components in the boundary layer depend on two space co-ordinates each. In the case of a three-dimensional boundary layer the external potential flow depends on two co-ordinates in the wall surface and the flow within the boundary layer possesses all three velocity components which, moreover, depend on all three space co-ordinates in the general case. The flow about a disk rotating in a fluid at rest (Sec. V b), and rotation in the neighbourhood of a fixed wall (Sec. X a) constitute examples of three-dimensional boundary layers, apart from being exact solutions of the Navier-Stokes equations. If the stream-lines of the potential motion are straight lines which either converge or diverge then, essentially, the flow differs from a two-dimensional pattern only in that there is a change in the boundary layer thickness. On the other hand, if the potential motion is curved the pressure gradient across the stream-lines of the potential flow impressing itself upon the boundary layer gives rise to additional influences, such as secondary flow: outside the boundary layer the transverse pressure gradient is balanced with the centrifugal force, but within it the centrifugal forces are decreased because of the decreased velocities and, consequently, the pressure gradient causes mass to flow inwards, i. e. towards the concave side of the potential stream-lines. The rotation of air over a fixed wall affords an example of this behaviour and illustrates the existence of a flow inwards.

A further example of secondary flow is afforded by the motion on the side-wall of the channel formed by turbine or compressor blades or by a deflector. The boundary layer which forms on the wall develops a secondary flow from the pressure side of one blade to the suction side of the next one owing to the curvature of the stream-lines in the external flow field. The secondary flow caused by the side-wall is further affected by the boundary layer on the blades themselves causing the flow pattern through a turbine or compressor stage to become very complex. This presents a very difficult problem to boundary layer theory because the three-dimensional nature of the flow is essential to it. For a long time problems of this kind had been studied by experimental means only [24].

Another important case of a three-dimensional boundary layer is that of an aeroplane wing, the leading edge of which is not perpendicular to the stream, as in the case of swept-back wings and yawed wings. It is known from experience that on the suction side considerable quantities of the fluid move towards the receding end, the phenomenon having a very detrimental effect on the aerodynamic behaviour of the wing.

In two-dimensional motion through a boundary layer, the geometrical shape of the body influences the field of flow only indirectly, i. e. through the velocity distribution of the potential flow which alone enters the calculation. By contrast, three-dimensional boundary layers are affected by both, by the external velocity distribution and by the geometrical shape directly. For example, in the case of a body of revolution the variation of the radius with distance expressed by the function $R(x)$ appears explicitly in the differential equations, see eqn. (10.24).

For the purpose of establishing the boundary layer equations we shall confine ourselves to the simplest case of a plane wall or to a curved wall which is developable into a plane (Fig. 10.8). Let x and z denote the co-ordinates in the wall surface, y denoting (as previously) the co-ordinate which is perpendicular to the wall. The velocity vector of potential flow V will be assumed to have the components $U(x, z)$ and $W(x, z)$, so that in the steady-state case the pressure distribution in the potential stream is given by

$$p + \tfrac{1}{2}\varrho[U^2 + W^2] = \text{const} . \tag{10.44}$$

If we now perform the same estimation, under the assumption of very large Reynolds numbers, relative to the three-dimensional Navier-Stokes equations (3.29), as explained in detail in Sec. VII a in relation to the two-dimensional case, we shall reach the conclusion that in the frictional terms of the equations for the x- and z-directions, respectively, it is possible to neglect the derivatives with respect to the co-ordinates which are parallel to the wall as against the derivative with respect to the co-ordinate at right angles to it. Regarding the equation in the y-direction we again obtain the result that $\partial p/\partial y$ is very small and may be neglected. Thus the pressure is seen to depend on x and z alone, and is impressed on the boundary layer by the potential flow. The estimation further shows that, generally speaking, none of the convective terms may be omitted. The three-dimensional boundary layer equations are, then, as follows:

$$\left.\begin{aligned} u\frac{\partial u}{\partial x}+v\frac{\partial u}{\partial y}+w\frac{\partial u}{\partial z} &= -\frac{1}{\varrho}\frac{\partial p}{\partial x}+\nu\frac{\partial^2 u}{\partial y^2}\\ u\frac{\partial w}{\partial x}+v\frac{\partial w}{\partial y}+w\frac{\partial w}{\partial z} &= -\frac{1}{\varrho}\frac{\partial p}{\partial z}+\nu\frac{\partial^2 w}{\partial y^2}\\ \frac{\partial u}{\partial x}+\frac{\partial v}{\partial y}+\frac{\partial w}{\partial z} &= 0\,. \end{aligned}\right\} \qquad (10.45)$$

with the following boundary conditions:

$$y=0:\quad u=v=w=0\,;\qquad y=\infty:\quad u=U\,;\quad w=W\,. \qquad (10.46)$$

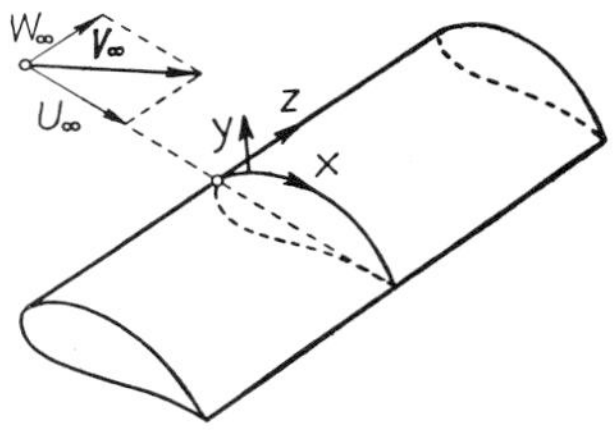

Fig. 10.8. System of co-ordinates for a three-dimensional boundary layer

The pressure gradients $\partial p/\partial x$ and $\partial p/\partial z$ are known from the potential flow in accordance with eqn. (10.44). This is a system of three equations for u, v, and w. For $W=0$ and $w=0$ the system transforms into the familiar system of eqns. (7.10) and (7.11) for two-dimensional boundary layer flow.

Up to the present time no exact solutions of this general system of equations for three-dimensional flow have been found, apart from the examples which we have mentioned previously. Th. Geis [18, 19] investigated the special class of flows which lead to similar solutions. In analogy with wedge flows, the velocity profiles are now similar in the direction of each of the two axes of co-ordinates and this allows us to transform the system (10.45) into a set of ordinary differential equations. L. Prandtl [47] laid down a programme for obtaining approximate solutions with the aid of the momentum theorem, i. e. in a way which is similar to that used in the two-dimensional case, and which will be discussed in greater detail in Chap. XII.

A particular case of three-dimensional boundary layer flow which is considerably more amenable to numerical calculation is that where the potential flow depends on x but not on z, i. e. when

$$U = U(x) ; \qquad W = W(x) . \tag{10.46a}$$

These conditions apply in the case of a yawed cylinder and also, approximately, in the case of a yawed wing at zero lift. The system of equations (10.45) is simplified in that there is no dependence on z. With $W = W_\infty =$ const and taking into account that $-(1/\varrho) \cdot (\partial p/\partial x) = U \cdot (\mathrm{d}U/\mathrm{d}x)$, we obtain

$$\left.\begin{aligned} u \frac{\partial u}{\partial x} + v \frac{\partial u}{\partial y} &= U \frac{\mathrm{d}U}{\mathrm{d}x} + \nu \frac{\partial^2 u}{\partial y^2} \\ u \frac{\partial w}{\partial x} + v \frac{\partial w}{\partial y} &= \nu \frac{\partial^2 w}{\partial y^2} \\ \frac{\partial u}{\partial x} + \frac{\partial v}{\partial y} &= 0 , \end{aligned}\right\} \tag{10.47}$$

with the same boundary conditions as before. In this particular case the system is reducible in the sense that it is possible to calculate u and v from the first and last equation, the solution being identical with that for a two-dimensional case, and subsequently, to complete the calculation of w from the second equation, which is, moreover, linear in w. This renders such cases really simple. Incidentally, it might be noted that the equation for the velocity component w is identical with that for the temperature distribution in a two-dimensional boundary layer, when the Prandtl number is equal to unity (see Chap. XIV).

Specializing the system (10.47) still further for the case when $U(x) = U_\infty =$ const, we obtain the example of the flat plate in yaw but at zero incidence. In this case the pressure term in the first equation vanishes, and the second equation becomes identical with the first when w is replaced by u. Thus the solutions $u(x, y)$ and $w(x, y)$ become proportional, $w(x, y) =$ const $\cdot\, u(x, y)$, or

$$\frac{w}{u} = \frac{W_\infty}{U_\infty} .$$

This means that in the case of a yawed flat plate the resultant of the velocity in the boundary layer which is parallel to the wall is also parallel to the potential flow at all points. The fact that the plate is yawed is seen to have no influence on the formation of the boundary layer (Independence principle).

When the flow in the boundary layer on a yawed flat plate becomes *turbulent*, the right-hand sides of the first two equations (10.47) must be supplemented with the terms due to turbulent Reynolds stresses (Chap. XIX). Then, the two equations can no longer be transformed into each other by the substitution of u for w and vice versa. Consequently, the stream-lines in the boundary layer cease to be parallel to the flow direction in the free-stream, as can be verified by direct experiment [2]. In addition, ref. [2] has established that the displacement thickness of a turbulent boundary layer on a yawed plate grows somewhat faster in the downstream direction than is the case with an unyawed plate. This again demonstrates the inapplicability of the independence principle to turbulent boundary layers.

The calculation of the three-dimensional boundary layer on a yawed cylinder, eqns. (10.47), can be carried out by a method similar to that used in the case of two-dimensional flow about a cylinder whose axis is at right angles to the stream (Sec. IXc), i. e. by assuming a series expansion with respect to the length of arc, x, measured from the stagnation point. For a symmetrical cylinder we may put

$$U(x) = u_1 x + u_3 x^3 + \ldots,$$
$$W(x) = W_\infty = \text{const}.$$

It is further assumed that the velocity components $u(x, y)$ and $v(x, y)$ of this flow (in which the stagnation points lie on a definite line) may also be expressed with the aid of a series in x with coefficients depending on y (Blasius series), the flow pattern being independent of the co-ordinate z measured along the generatrix of the cylinder. Thus putting

$$\eta = y\sqrt{\frac{u_1}{\nu}} \tag{10.48}$$

we obtain

$$u(x,y) = u_1 x f'_1(\eta) + 4 u_3 x^3 f'_3(\eta) + \ldots \tag{10.49}$$

$$v(x,y) = -\sqrt{\frac{\nu}{u_1}}\{u_1 f_1(\eta) + 12 u_3 x^2 f_3(\eta) + \ldots\} \tag{10.50}$$

$$w(x,y) = W_\infty\left\{g_0(\eta) + \frac{u_3}{u_1} x^2 g_2(\eta) + \ldots\right\}. \tag{10.51}$$

The functions f_1, f_3, ... satisfy the differential equations (9.21) and their solutions are given in Tables 9.1 and 5.1, with $f_1(\eta) = \phi(\eta)$. The computation of the component w was first given by W. R. Sears [53]. It was later considerably extended by H. Goertler [20]. The functions g_0, g_2, ... satisfy the differential equations

$$g_0'' + f_1 g_0' = 0, \tag{10.52}$$
$$g_2'' + f_1 g_2' - 2 f_1' g_2 = -12 f_3 g_0', \tag{10.53}$$

whose boundary conditions are

$$\eta = 0: \quad g_0 = 0, \quad g_2 = 0, \ldots$$
$$\eta = \infty: \quad g_0 = 1, \quad g_2 = 0, \ldots.$$

As indicated by L. Prandtl [47] the equation for g_0 can be solved by direct integration, the result being

$$g_0(\eta) = \frac{\int_0^\eta \left\{\exp\left(-\int_0^\eta f_1\,\mathrm{d}\eta\right)\right\}\mathrm{d}\eta}{\int_0^\infty \left\{\exp\left(-\int_0^\eta f_1\,\mathrm{d}\eta\right)\right\}\mathrm{d}\eta}. \tag{10.54}$$

The function $g_0(\eta)$ is seen plotted in Fig. 10.9. Table 10.3 contains values of $g_0(\eta)$ and $g_2(\eta)$.

Table 10.3. The functions $g_0(\eta)$ and $g_2(\eta)$ which occur in problems with stagnation line as calculated from eqns. (10.53) and (10.54), after Goertler [20]

$\eta = y\sqrt{\frac{u_1}{\nu}}$	$g_0(\eta)$	$g_2(\eta)$	$\eta = y\sqrt{\frac{u_1}{\nu}}$	$g_0(\eta)$	$g_2(\eta)$
0	0	0			
0·1	0·0570	0·0521	3·1	0·9913	0·0628
0·2	0·1141	0·1040	3·2	0·9934	0·0503
0·3	0·1709	0·1554	3·3	0·9951	0·0399
0·4	0·2275	0·2056	3·4	0·9964	0·0312
0·5	0·2836	0·2538	3·5	0·9973	0·0243
0·6	0·3389	0·2992	3·6	0·9981	0·0185
0·7	0·3932	0·3408	3·7	0·9986	0·0141
0·8	0·4462	0·3778	3·8	0·9990	0·0107
0·9	0·4975	0·4092	3·9	0·9993	0·0079
1·0	0·5469	0·4345	4·0	0·9995	0·0058
1·1	0·5941	0·4531	4·1	0·9997	0·0042
1·2	0·6388	0·4647	4·2	0·9998	0·0031
1·3	0·6809	0·4692	4·3	0·9998	0·0020
1·4	0·7200	0·4668	4·4	0·9999	0·0016
1·5	0·7562	0·4580	4·5	0·9999	0·0010
1·6	0·7892	0·4431	4·6	1·0000	0·0008
1·7	0·8193	0·4232	4·7	1·0000	0·0005
1·8	0·8462	0·3989	4·8	1·0000	0·0004
1·9	0·8702	0·3714	4·9	1·0000	0·0002
2·0	0·8913	0·3414	5·0	1·0000	0·0002
2·1	0·9098	0·3102	5·1	1·0000	0·0001
2·2	0·9257	0·2784	5·2	1·0000	0·0000
2·3	0·9393	0·2469	5·3	1·0000	0·0000
2·4	0·9509	0·2165	5·4	1·0000	0·0000
2·5	0·9606	0·1876			
2·6	0·9686	0·1607			
2·7	0·9753	0·1362			
2·8	0·9807	0·1141			
2·9	0·9850	0·0945			
3·0	0·9885	0·0774			

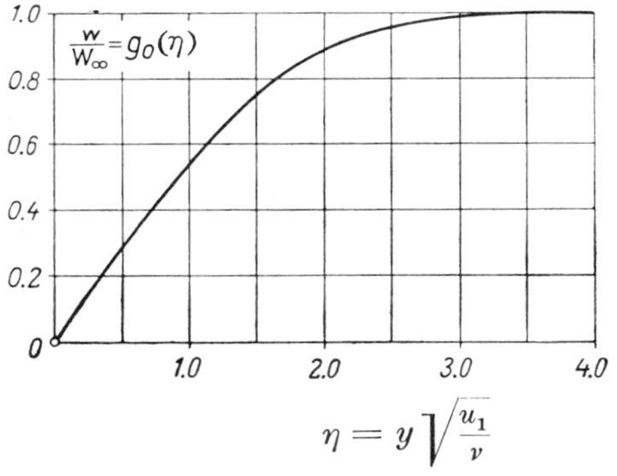

Fig. 10.9. Laminar boundary layer on a yawed cylinder; flow with stagnation line. Velocity distribution for the component parallel to the axis of the cylinder (Table 10.3)

The calculation of the boundary layer on a yawed cylinder which corresponds to the potential velocity distribution given by $U(x) = u_1 x^m$ (*cf.* Chap. IX) was performed by J. C. Cooke and described in two papers [10, 11].

J. M. Wild [65] applied the approximate method to be discussed in Chap. XII to the case under consideration. Fig. 10.10 represents the pattern of stream-lines for a yawed elliptic cylinder of slenderness ratio 6 : 1, placed at an angle of incidence to the stream. The lift coefficient has a value of 0·47. The arrows shown in the sketch indicate the direction of flow of the velocity component parallel to the wall in its immediate neighbourhood, i. e. the value

$$\lim_{x \to 0} (w/u) .$$

The respective stream-line is shown as a broken, line and the potential stream-line is seen plotted for comparison. It is noticeable that the flow direction in the boundary layer is turned by a large angle towards the receding end of the cylinder. This circumstance is very important when flow patterns on yawed wings are observed with the aid of tufts.

The existence of cross-flow which occurs in the boundary layer of a yawed cylinder is important for the aerodynamic properties of swept wings. When yawed or swept-back wings operate at higher lift values the pressure on the suction side near

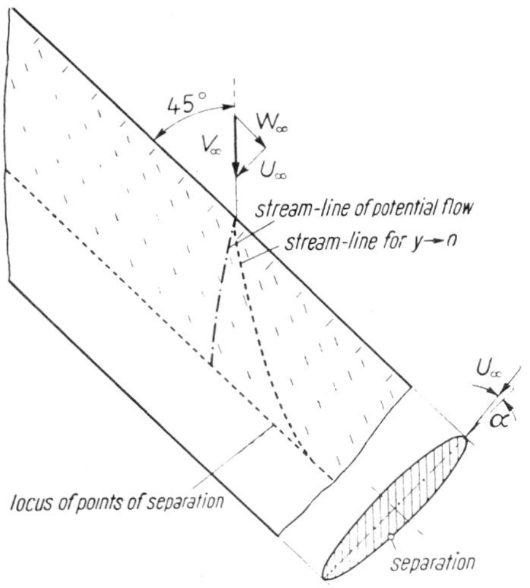

Fig. 10.10. Boundary layer flow about a yawed elliptical cylinder with lift, after J. M. Wild [65]

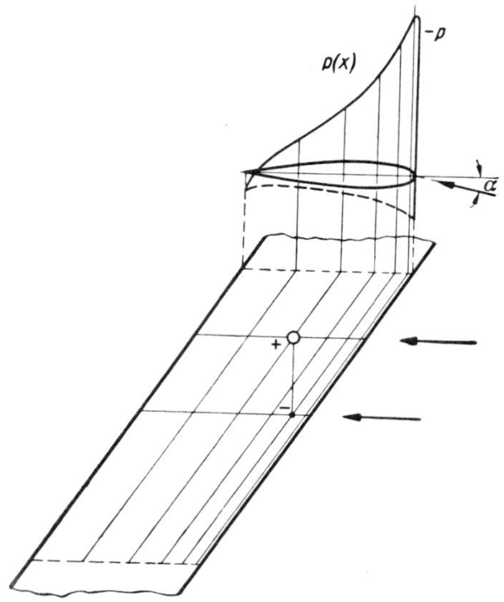

Fig. 10.11. Explanation of origin of cross-flow on a yawed wing at an angle of incidence. Curves of constant pressure (isobars) on the suction side of the wing. Near the leading edge on the upper surface of wing there is a sharp pressure gradient at right angles to main stream and towards receding end causing cross-flow

the leading edge shows a considerable gradient towards the receding tip, the effect being due to the rearward shift of the aerofoil sections of the wing. This phenomenon can be seen from Fig. 10.11 which shows the isobars on the suction side of a yawed wing. The fluid particles which become decelerated in the boundary layer have a tendency to travel in the direction of this gradient, and a cross-flow in the direction of the receding tip results. As demonstrated by measurements performed by R. T. Jones [33] and W. Jacobs [32], the boundary layer on the receding portion thickens, the effect leading to premature separation. In aircraft equipped with swept-back wings separation begins at the receding portion, i. e. near the ailerons, and causes the dreaded one-winged stall to occur. The papers by J. Black [6] and D. Kuechemann [35] contain more details concerning the very complex flow patterns in boundary layers on swept wings.

It is possible to avoid this kind of separation, and hence to prevent one-winged stalling, by equipping the wing with a 'boundary layer fence' which consists of a sheet metal wall placed on the suction side in the forward portion of the wing, thus preventing cross-flow. An aircraft with sweptback wings and a boundary layer fence on each half of the wing is shown in Fig. 10.12. W. Liebe [36] reported on the improvement in wing characteristics which can be attained by these means. A paper by M. J. Queijo, B. M. Jaquet and W. D. Wolhart [48] describes extensive measurements on models provided with 'boundary layer fences'. Recent experimental results obtained by A. Das [13a, 51a] indicate that a 'boundary layer fence' causes a considerable improvement in the flow on its inner side in addition to that on the outer side.

The case with $W = \text{const}$, eqn. (10.46a), is not the only one which has been given attention. H. K. Loos [37] studied the case of flow past a flat plate when the free stream is described by $U = \text{const}$, $W = a_0 + a_1 x$, whereas A. G. Hansen and H. Z. Herzig [25] considered the generalized case with

$$U = \text{const}; \quad W = \sum_n a_n x^n .$$

Fig. 10.12. Jet fighter De Havilland D. H. 110 with swept-back wings and a 'boundary layer fence' at edge of each aileron; from [36]

Since such external flows are not irrotational, the velocity in the boundary layer can become larger than that in the free stream. The excess in velocity is due to the secondary flow in the boundary layer which transfers into it fluid particles from regions of higher energy. It sometimes also happens that the initial velocity profiles in the principal flow direction show regions of back-flow which, nevertheless, do not signify separation; they usually disappear further downstream. This type of behaviour can also be explained as being due to a transfer of energy by the secondary flow. The reader will recognize from the preceding example that the definition of separation is beset with difficulties when three-dimensional boundary layers are being considered. This is due to the fact that the relation between back-flow and shearing stress has ceased to be as simple as in the two-dimensional case [26, 43]. A separation of terms identical with the one encountered in connexion with the free stream described by eqn. (10.46a) can be successfully achieved, according to L. E. Fogarty [15], when considering an infinitely long wing which is made to rotate about a vertical axis (helicopter rotor). It is found that the rotary motion does not affect the downward velocity component and so the incidence of separation remains unaffected. Rotation merely causes the appearance of slight radial velocity components.

A further special case of the general problem described by eqn. (10.45) which is amenable to calculation occurs when the external flow consists of a two-dimensional basic pattern on which there is superimposed a weak disturbance of the kind described by

$$\begin{aligned} U(x,z) &= U_0(x) + U_1(x,z)\,, \qquad U_1 \ll U_0\,,\\ W(x,z) &= \qquad\qquad\; W_1(x,z)\,, \qquad W_1 \ll U_0\,. \end{aligned}$$

The boundary layer flow can then, equally, be separated into a two-dimensional basic pattern with a weak perturbation superimposed on it. The requisite differential equations can, once more, be uncoupled by linearization. Examples of this kind were given by A. Mager [40, 41] and H. S. Tan [57].

Three-dimensional boundary layer flows become even more complicated in cases when the external flow cannot be represented simply by the superposition of two components. The latter case occurs, for example, on a yawed body of revolution. In arrangements of this kind, the direction of velocity components in the boundary layer deviates considerably from that in the free stream at the point; in other words, a strong secondary flow field is generated. An idea of the very complicated three-dimensional flow pattern in such boundary layers is conveyed by the photograph shown in Fig. 10.13b; it was taken by E. A. Eichelbrenner and A. Oudart [66] on the upper side of a yawed ellipsoid of revolution, the flow pattern having been made visible by streaks of dye issuing from drillings on the surface of the body. The photograph shows, in particular, that the pattern of a three-dimensional boundary layer which exists in an adverse pressure gradient is markedly different from that in a two-dimensional boundary layer. The principal difference is this: in the two-dimensional case, the fluid in the boundary layer is generally forced into the external flow if the pressure gradient is sufficiently strong, thus causing separation from the wall, (*cf.* Fig. 7.3b); in the three-dimensional case the fluid particles can escape sideways along the wall. The photograph in Fig. 10.13b clearly exhibits this type of behaviour: the streaks in the neighbourhood of the rear stagnation point, i. e. in the region of a strong adverse pressure gradient (see also Fig. 10.13a), are clearly seen to be deflected sideways, they do, however, remain clinging to the surface. The stream-lines at the surface which are shown in Fig. 10.13c and which have been obtained by calculation show good qualitative agreement with the experimental pattern in Fig. 10.13b. It is, therefore, not at all easy to establish a criterion for separation in a three-dimensional boundary layer, if proper weight is given to this type of behaviour.

It appears to be possible to attempt a theoretical analysis of three-dimensional boundary layers with the aid of a scheme suggested by L. Prandtl [47] who proposed to introduce a curvilinear system of co-ordinates in which the potential- and stream-lines of the free stream would play the part of co-ordinates. This programme was carried out by E. A. Eichelbrenner and A. Oudart [66] when they calculated the laminar case mentioned earlier, and when they made use of the approximate method to be discussed in Chap. XII. It has already been mentioned that good qualitative agreement resulted, as shown in Fig. 10.13c.

In conclusion, attention may be drawn to the calculation of the boundary layer on two mutually perpendicular flat plates at zero incidence performed by G. F. Carrier [9a]. The reader may also wish to consult a paper by K. Gersten [19a] on the same subject.

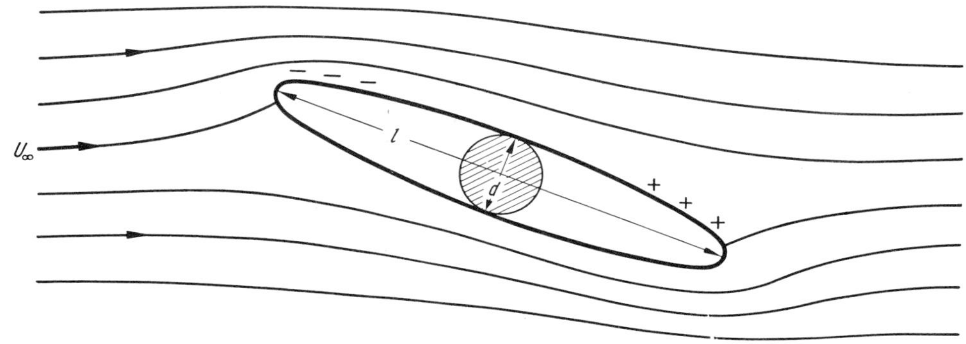

Fig. 10.13a

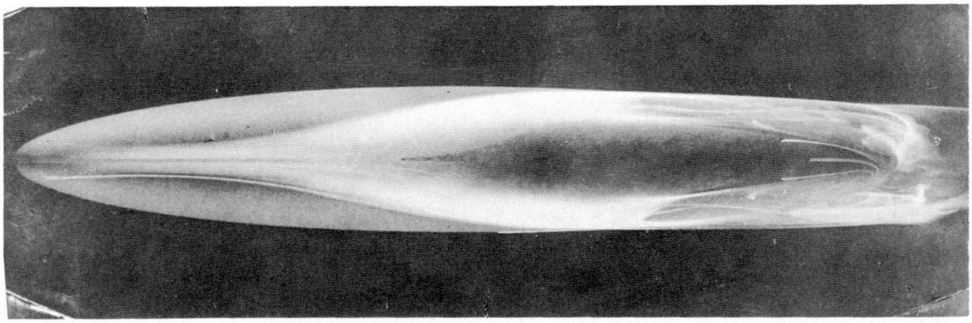

Fig. 10.13b

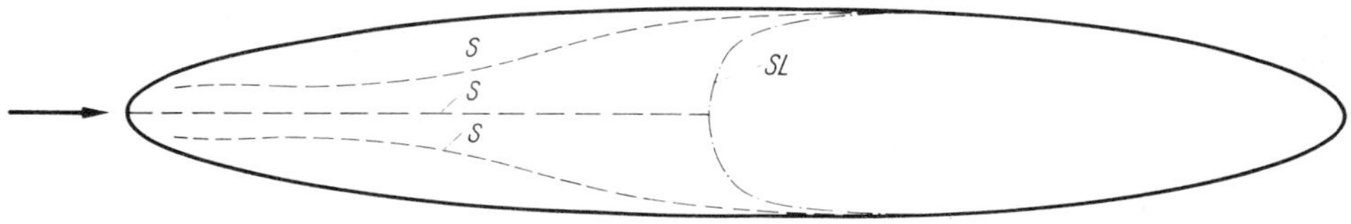

Fig. 10.13c

Figs. 10.13a, b, c. Three-dimensional, laminar boundary layer on upper side of ellipsoid of revolution of aspect ratio $l/d = 6$ and with a $10°$ yaw, after E. A. Eichelbrenner and A. Oudart [66, 66a]

a) Schematic diagram of stream-lines viewed sideways

b) Photograph of the upper side of the ellipsoid of revolution in the water channel of the ONERA in Chatillon sous Bagneux (Paris). Reynolds number $U_\infty l/\nu = 2 \times 10^4$. The flow pattern was made visible by streaks of dye issuing from the surface of the body. The stream-lines in the layers in the neighbourhood of the rear stagnation point show a marked deflexion sideways. This corresponds to separation in a three-dimensional boundary layer

c) Stream-lines at the wall, marked S, obtained by calculation, and theoretical separation line, marked SL; there is satisfactory qualitative agreement with the pattern whose photograph is shown in b)

c. Boundary layers on rotating bodies

The simplest example of a boundary layer on a rotating body is that considered in Sec. Vb. 10, namely the problem of a disk rotating in a fluid at rest. The fluid particles which rotate with the boundary layer are thrown outwards owing to the existence of centrifugal forces ('centrifuging') and are replaced by particles flowing towards the boundary layer in an axial direction. The case of a disk of radius R rotating with an angular velocity ω in an axial stream of velocity U_∞ affords a simple extension of the previous problem. In the latter case the flow is governed by two parameters: the Reynolds number and the rotation parameter, $U_\infty/R\omega$, which is given by the ratio of free-stream to tip velocity. An exact solution to the problem under consideration was given by Miss D.M. Hannah [23]† and A.N. Tifford [59] for the case of laminar flow; H. Schlichting and E. Truckenbrodt [50] provided an approximate solution. E. Truckenbrodt [61] investigated the case of turbulent flow. Fig. 10.14 contains a plot of the torque coefficient, $C_M = M/\frac{1}{2}\,\varrho\,\omega^2\,R^5$, in terms of the Reynolds number and rotation parameter, $U_\infty/R\omega$, obtained from such calculations. Here M denotes the torque on the leading side of the disk only. When the disk rotates we may still assume that separation occurs at the edge of the disk. The 'stagnant' fluid partly rotates with the disk and contributes little to the torque. Any such contribution has been left out of account in C_M in Fig. 10.14. It is seen that the torque increases rapidly with U_∞ at constant angular velocity.

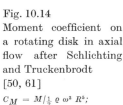

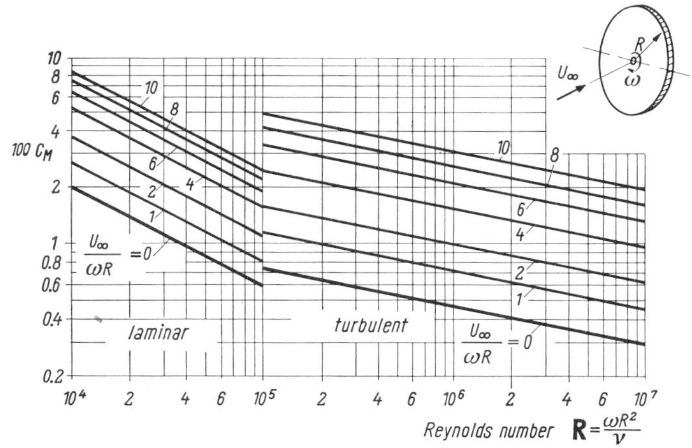

Fig. 10.14
Moment coefficient on a rotating disk in axial flow after Schlichting and Truckenbrodt [50, 61]
$C_M = M/\frac{1}{2}\,\varrho\,\omega^2\,R^5$;
M = torque on leading side of disk

The flow in a circular box provided with a rotating lid shows a marked resemblance to that between two rotating disks mentioned in Chap. V. The case of the flow inside the box was investigated in detail by D. Grohne [22] who discovered two peculiar features in it: first, the flow in the friction-free core in the interior of the box can only be determined by taking into account the influence of the boundary layers which form on the wall, in contrast to normal cases when one naturally assumes that the influence of the flow in a boundary layer results at most in a displacement.

† Actually ref. [23] solves a related problem in which the external field is that due to a source at infinity.

Secondly, the boundary layers are unusual in that they join each other. Similarly, in the arrangement consisting of a rotating channel investigated by H. Ludwieg [38], it is possible to discern two regions of flow when the speed of rotation is sufficiently high, namely a frictionless core and boundary layers which form on the side walls and which give rise to a secondary flow. The theory leads to a large increase of the drag coefficient which is due to rotation and this fact has been confirmed by experiment. Finally, the experimental investigation of the flow between two rotating disks performed by K. G. Picha and E. R. G. Eckert [45a] and by W. E. Welsh Jr. and J. P. Hartnett [63a], mentioned in Sec. Vb. 10, is also noteworthy in that it confirms the existence of a core which rotates like a rigid body in cases when the distance between the two disks is not very large.

Blunt bodies, such as e. g. a sphere or a slender body of revolution, placed in axial streams, show a marked influence of rotation on drag, as evidenced by the measurements performed by C. Wieselsberger [64], and S. Luthander and A. Rydberg [39]. Fig. 10.15 contains a plot of the drag coefficient of a rotating sphere in terms of the Reynolds number. It is seen that the critical Reynolds number, for which the drag coefficient decreases abruptly, depends strongly on the rotation parameter $U_\infty / R\omega$, and the same is true of the position of the point of separa-

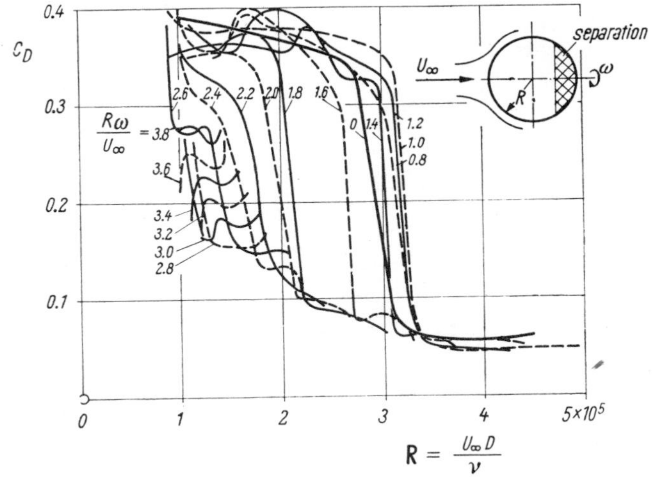

Fig. 10.15. Drag coefficients on a rotating sphere in axial flow, as measured by Luthander and Rydberg [39]

tion. The effect of rotary motion on the position of the line of laminar separation on a sphere is described by the graph in Fig. 10.16; the data for it have been computed by N. E. Hoskin [27]. When the rotation parameter has attained the value $\omega\, R/U_\infty = 5$, the line of separation will have moved by about $10°$ in the upstream direction, as compared with a sphere at rest. The physical reason for this behaviour is connected with the centrifugal forces acting on the fluid particles rotating with the body in its boundary layer. The centrifugal forces have the same effect as an additional pressure gradient directed towards the plane of the equator.

An explanation of the very complex three-dimensional effects in the boundary layer of rotating bodies of revolution in axial flow is contained in two papers by

H. Schlichting [51] and E. Truckenbrodt [60] who used the approximate method of Chap. XII. The papers under consideration contain calculations for both laminar and turbulent boundary layers. In some cases it was possible to calculate the drag in addition to the torque and it was shown that the drag coefficient increases with decreasing $U_\infty/R\omega$. Compare also two papers by C. R. Illingworth [31] and S. T. Chu and A. N. Tifford [13].

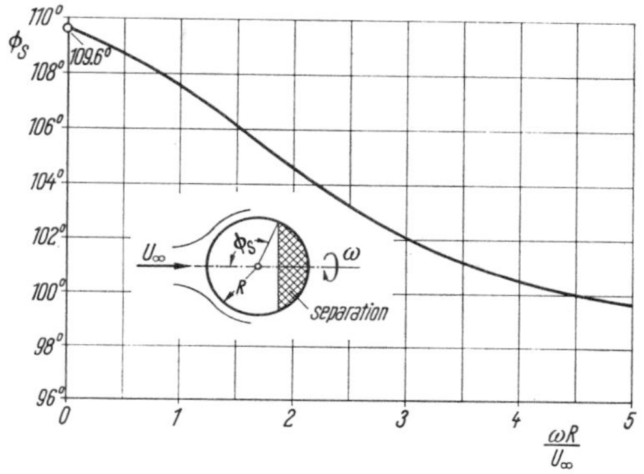

Fig. 10.16. Position of line of laminar separation on sphere rotating in axial stream after N. E. Hoskin [27]

Problems connected with laminar flow about a sphere rotating in a fluid at rest have been discussed by L. Howarth [28] and S. D. Nigam [44]. An extension to the case involving ellipsoids of revolution was provided by B. S. Fadnis [14]. Near the poles, the flow is the same as on a rotating disk and near the equator it is like the one on a rotating cylinder. The accompanying secondary stream causes fluid particles to flow into the boundary layer near the poles, and out of it at the equator. The rate of this secondary flow increases with increasing slenderness, the equatorial area and speed of rotation remaining constant. However, the phenomena in the plane of the equator where the two boundary layers impinge on each other and are thrown outwards can no longer be analyzed with the aid of boundary layer theory.

It has been observed that in axial turbo-machines there may, under certain circumstances, appear an extended zone of dead fluid in the whirl behind the row of stationary blades and near the hub. This phenomenon was described in great detail by K. Bammert and H. Klaeukens [4]. The origin of this dead-water area is connected with the radial increase in pressure in the outward direction which is due to the whirl. Owing to the whirl the axial pressure increase near the hub in the bladeless annulus behind the guides is much greater than at the outer wall. The influence of the boundary layer is here only secondary. Attention may, further, be drawn to an investigation due to K. Bammert and J. Schoen [3] concerning the flow through a rotating hollow shaft. It is observed that a funnel-like free surface is formed at the exit owing to the interaction between centrifugal and viscous forces.

A general review of three-dimensional boundary layers has been given by W. R. Sears [54].

References

[1] E. N. Andrade and H. S. Tsien, Proc. Phys. Soc. London **49**, 381 (1937).

[2] H. Ashkenas and F. R. Riddell, Investigation of the turbulent boundary layer on a yawed flat plate. NACA TN 3383 (1955).

[3] K. Bammert and J. Schoen, Die Strömung von Flüssigkeiten in rotierenden Hohlwellen. Zeitschr. VDI **90**, 81 (1948).

[4] K. Bammert and H. Kläukens, Nabentotwasser hinter Leiträdern von axialen Strömungsmaschinen. Ing. Arch. **17**, 367 (1949); see also K. Bammert, Zeitschr. VDI **92**, 777 (1950).

[5] A. M. Binnie and D. P. Harris, The application of boundary layer theory to swirling liquid flow through a nozzle. Quarterly Jour. Mech. Appl. Math. **3**, 89—106 (1950).

[5a] E. Becker, Beitrag zur Berechnung von Sekundärströmungen. ZAMM Sonderheft, pp. 3—8 (1956), and Mitteilg. aus dem Max-Planck-Inst. f. Strömungsforschung No. 13, 1956.

[6] J. Black, A note on the vortex patterns in the boundary layer flow of a swept-back wing. Jour. Roy. Aero. Soc. **56**, p. 279 (1952).

[7] U. T. Bödewadt, Die Drehströmung über festem Grunde. ZAMM **20**, 241 (1940).

[8] E. Boltze, Grenzschichten an Rotationskörpern. Dissertation Göttingen 1908.

[9] J. M. Burgers, Some considerations on the development of boundary layer in the case of flows having a rotational component. Kon. Akad. van Wetenschappen, Amsterdam, **45**, 1—5, 13—25 (1941).

[9a] G. F. Carrier, The boundary layer in a corner. Q-ly. Appl. Math. **4**, 367—370 (1946).

[10] J. C. Cooke, The boundary layer of a class of infinite yawed cylinders. Proc. Cambr. Phil. Soc. vol. **46**, 645 (1950).

[11] J. C. Cooke, Pohlhausen's method for three-dimensional laminar boundary layer. The Aeronautical Quarterly **III**, Part I, 51 (1951).

[12] J. C. Cooke, On Pohlhausen's method with application to a swirl problem of Taylor. Jour. Aero. Sci. **19**, 486—490 (1952).

[13] S. T. Chu and A. N. Tifford, The compressible laminar boundary layer on a rotating body of revolution. Jcur. Aero. Sci. **21**, 345—346 (1954).

[13a] A. Das, Untersuchungen über den Einfluß von Grenzschichtzäunen auf die aerodynamischen Eigenschaften von Pfeil- und Deltaflügeln, Thesis Braunschweig 1959. See also Zeitschr. f. Flugwiss. **7**, 227—242. (1959).

[14] B. S. Fadnis, Boundary layer on rotating spheroids. ZAMP **V**. 156—163 (1954).

[15] L. E. Fogarty, The laminar boundary layer on a rotating blade. Jour. Aero. Sci. **18**, 247 — 252 (1951).

[16] N. Frössling, Verdunstung, Wärmeübergang und Geschwindigkeitsverteilung bei zweidimensionaler und rotationssymmetrischer laminarer Grenzschichtströmung. Lunds. Univ. Arsskr. N. F. Avd. 2, **35**, No. 4 (1940).

[17] K. Garbsch, Über die Grenzschicht an der Wand eines Trichters mit innerer Wirbel- und Radialströmung. "Fifty years of boundary layer research", Braunschweig 1955, pp. 471—486, see also ZAMM Sonderheft pp. 11—17 (1956).

[18] Th. Geis, Ähnliche Grenzschichten an Rotationskörpern. "Fifty years of boundary layer research", Braunschweig, 1955, 294—303.

[19] Th. Geis, „Ähnliche" dreidimensionale Grenzschichten. Jour. Rat. Mech. Analysis **5**, 643 to 686 (1956).

[19a] K. Gersten, Corner interference effects. Paper presented at AGARD Meeting, Brussels 1959. To be published as AGARD Rep.

[19b] M. B. Glauert, The wall jet. Jour. Fluid Mechanics **1**, 625—643 (1956).

[20] H. Görtler, Die laminare Grenzschicht am schiebenden Zylinder. Arch. Math. **3**, Fasc. 3, p. 216—231 (1952).

[21] H. Görtler, Decay of swirl in an axially symmetrical jet far from the orifice. Revista Math. Hip.-Amer. **IV**, Ser. 14, 143—178 (1954).

[22] D. Grohne, Zur laminaren Strömung in einer kreiszylindrischen Dose mit rotierendem Deckel. ZAMM-Sonderheft der Göttinger Strömungstagung 17—20 (1956).

[23] D. M. Hannah, Forced flow against a rotating disc. ARC R & M 2772 (1952).

[24] A. G. Hansen, H. Z. Herzig and G. R. Costello, A visualization study of secondary flows in cascades. NACA TN 2947 (1953).

[25] A. G. Hansen and H. Z. Herzig, Cross flows in laminar incompressible boundary layers. NACA TN 3651 (1956).

[26] W. D. Hayes, The three-dimensional boundary layer. NAVORD Rep. 1313, NOTS 384 (1951).

[27] N. E. Hoskin, The laminar boundary layer on a rotating sphere. "Fifty years of boundary layer research",Braunschweig, 127—131 (1955).

[28] L. Howarth, Note on the boundary layer on a rotating sphere. Phil. Mag. VII, **42**, 1308—1315 (1951).

[29] L. Howarth, The boundary layer in three-dimensional flow. Part. I, Phil. Mag. VII, **42**, 239—243 (1951).
[30] L. Howarth, The boundary layer in three-dimensional flow. Part II: The flow near a stagnation point. Phil. Mag. VII, **42**, 1433 (1951).
[31] C. R. Illingworth, The laminar boundary layer of a rotating body of revolution. Phil. Mag. **44**, 351, p. 389 (1953).
[32] W. Jacobs, Systematische Sechskomponentenmessungen an Pfeilflügeln. Ing. Arch. 18, 344 (1950).
[33] R. T. Jones, Effects of sweep-back on boundary layer and separation. NACA Rep. No. 884 (1947).
[34] M. Z. Krzywoblocki, On steady, laminar round jets in compressible viscous gases far behind the mouth. Österr. Ing. Arch. **3**, 373 (1949).
[35] D. Küchemann, The effect of viscosity on the type of flow on swept wings. Proc. Symposium Nat. Phys. Lab. (NPL) 1955.
[36] W. Liebe, Der Grenzschichtzaun. Interavia **7**, 4, 215 (1952).
[37] H. K. Loos, A simple laminar boundary layer with secondary flow. Jour. Aero. Sci. **22**, 35 (1955).
[38] H. Ludwieg, Die ausgebildete Kanalströmung in einem rotierenden System. Ing.-Arch. **19**, 296 (1951).
[39] S. Luthander and A. Rydberg, Experimentelle Untersuchungen über den Luftwiderstand bei einer um eine mit der Windrichtung parallelen Achse rotierenden Kugel. Phys. Z. **36**, 552 (1935).
[40] A. Mager, Three-dimensional laminar boundary layer with small cross-flow. Jour. Aero. Sci. **21**, 835—845 (1954).
[41] A. Mager, Thick laminar boundary layer under sudden perturbation. "Fifty years of boundary layer research", Braunschweig, 21—33, 1955.
[42] W. Mangler, Zusammenhang zwischen ebenen und rotationssymmetrischen Grenzschichten in kompressiblen Flüssigkeiten. ZAMM **28**, 97—103 (1948).
[43] F. K. Moore, Three-dimensional laminar boundary layer flow. Jour. Aero. Sci. **20**, 525 — 534 (1953).
[44] S. D. Nigam, Note on the boundary layer on a rotating sphere. ZAMP **5**, 151—155 (1954).
[45] D. C. Pack, Laminar flow in an axially symmetrical jet of compressible fluid, far from the orifice. Proc. Cambr. Phil. Soc. **50**, 98—104 (1954).
[45a] K. G. Picha and E. R. G. Eckert, Study of the air flow between coaxial disks rotating with arbitrary velocities in an open or enclosed space. Proc. 3rd. US Nat'l. Congress Appl. Mech. 1959, p. 791.
[46] C. Pfleiderer, Untersuchungen auf dem Gebiet der Kreiselradmaschinen. VDI-Forschungsheft No. 295 (1927).
[47] L. Prandtl, Über Reibungsschichten bei dreidimensionalen Strömungen. Betz anniversary volume, 59 (1945), or British MAP, Völkenrode REP and Trans. No. 64 (1946); see also Tetervin, NACA Tech. Note 1479 (1947).
[48] M. J. Queijo, B. M. Jaquet and W. D. Wolhart, Wind tunnel investigation at low speed of the effects of chordwise wing fences and horizontal-tail position on the static longitudinal stability characteristics of an airplane model with a 35° swept-back wing. NACA Report No. 1203 (1954).
[49] H. Schlichting, Laminare Strahlausbreitung. ZAMM **13**, 260 (1933).
[50] H. Schlichting and E. Truckenbrodt, Die Strömung an einer angeblasenen rotierenden Scheibe. ZAMM **32**, 97—117 (1952).
[51] H. Schlichting, Die laminare Strömung um einen axial angeströmten rotierenden Drehkörper. Ing. Arch. **21**, 227 (1953).
[51a] H. Schlichting, Einige neuere Ergebnisse über Grenzschichtbeeinflussung, Advances in Aero. Sci. vol. II, Proc. First Intern. Congress in the Aero. Sci., Madrid 1958, Pergamon Press, pp. 563—586 (1959).
[52] F. W. Scholkemeyer, Die laminare Reibungsschicht an rotationssymmetrischen Körpern. Thesis Braunschweig 1943. Abbreviated in Arch. d. Math. **1**, 270—277 (1949).
[53] W. S. Sears, The boundary layer of yawed cylinders. Jour. Aero. Sci. **15**, 1, 49 (1948).
[54] W. R. Sears, Boundary layers in three-dimensional flow. Appl. Mech. Reviews **7**, 281—285 (1954).
[55] H. B. Squire, The round laminar jet. Quarterly Jour. Mech. Appl. Math. **4**, 321—329 47—54, (1951).

[56] H. B. Squire, Radial jets. "Fifty years of boundary layer research", Braunschweig, 47—54, 1955.
[57] H. S. Tan, On laminar boundary layer over a rotating blade. Jour. Aero. Sci. **20**, 780 (1953).
[58] G. I. Taylor, The boundary layer in the converging nozzle of a swirl atomizer. Quarterly Jour. Mech. Appl. Math. **3**, 129—139 (1950).
[59] A. N. Tifford and S. T. Chu, On the flow around a rotating disc in a uniform stream. Jour. Aero. Sci. **19**, 284 (1952).
[60] E. Truckenbrodt, Ein Quadraturverfahren zur Berechnung der Reibungsschicht an axial angeströmten rotierenden Drehkörpern. Ing. Arch. **22**, 21—35 (1954).
[61] E. Truckenbrodt, Die turbulente Strömung an einer angeblasenen rotierenden Scheibe. ZAMM **34**, 150—162 (1954).
[62] G. Vogelpohl, Die Strömung der Wirbelquelle zwischen ebenen Wänden mit Berücksichtigung der Wandreibung. ZAMM **24**, 289 (1944).
[63] H. E. Weber, The boundary layer inside a conical surface due to swirl. Jour. Appl. Mech. **23**, 587—592 (1956).
[63a] W. E. Welsh Jr. and J. P. Hartnett, Velocity measurements in the boundary layer and in the main flow between two coaxial disks rotating with equal velocities in air. Proc. 3rd. US Nat'l. Congress Appl. Mech. 1959, p. 847.
[64] C. Wieselberger, Über den Luftwiderstand bei gleichzeitiger Rotation des Versuchskörpers. Phys. Z. **28**, 84 (1927).
[65] J. M. Wild, The boundary layer of yawed infinite wings. J. Aero. Sci. **16**, 41 (1949).
[66] E. A. Eichelbrenner and A. Oudart, Méthodes de calcul de la couche limite tridimensionelle. Office National d'Etudes et de Récherche Aeronautiques (ONERA). Publication No. 76 (1955).
[66a] E. A. Eichelbrenner, Décollement laminaire en trois dimensions sur un obstacle fini. Office National d'Etudes et de Récherches Aéronautiques (ONERA). Publication No. 89, 1957).

CHAPTER XI

Non-steady boundary layers

a. General remarks on the calculation of non-steady boundary layers

The examples of solutions of the boundary layer equations which have been considered until now referred to steady motion. They are by far the most important cases encountered in practical applications. Nevertheless, in this chapter we propose to consider several examples of motions which depend on time, i. e. of non-steady boundary layers.

The most common examples of non-steady boundary layers occur when the motion is started from rest or when it is periodic. When motion is started from rest both the body and the fluid have zero velocities up to a certain instant of time. The motion begins at that instant and we can consider either that the body is dragged through the fluid at rest, or that the body is at rest and that the external fluid motion varies with time. In this latter case an initially very thin boundary layer is formed near the body and the transition from the velocity of the body to that in the external flow takes place across it. Immediately after the start of the motion the flow in the whole fluid space is irrotational and potential with the exception of a very thin layer near the body. The thickness of the boundary layer increases with time, and it is important to investigate at which instant separation (reverse flow) first occurs as the boundary layer continues to build up. One such example was already considered in Sec. V 4; it was the exact solution of the Navier-Stokes equations for the flow near a wall which is accelerated impulsively from rest and moves in a direction parallel to itself. Also, the start of the flow in a pipe (Sec. V. 6) belongs to the same category.

Further examples of non-steady boundary layers occur when either the body performs a periodic motion in a fluid at rest, or when the body is at rest and the fluid executes a periodic motion. The motion of a fluid near a wall which oscillates in its own plane (Sec. V. 7) affords an example of this type of problem.

The fundamental equations for non-steady boundary layers have already been deduced in Chap. VII. For two-dimensional flows we obtained eqns. (7.7) to (7.9), i. e.

$$\frac{\partial u}{\partial t} + u\,\frac{\partial u}{\partial x} + v\,\frac{\partial u}{\partial y} = -\,\frac{1}{\varrho}\,\frac{\partial p}{\partial x} + \nu\,\frac{\partial^2 u}{\partial y^2} \tag{11.1}$$

$$\frac{\partial u}{\partial x} + \frac{\partial v}{\partial y} = 0\,. \tag{11.2}$$

In the axially symmetrical case eqn. (11.1) remains unchanged provided that x and y are interpreted as the curvilinear co-ordinates parallel and perpendicular to the wall respectively. The equation of continuity, as shown in eqn. (10.24), changes to

$$\frac{\partial (ur)}{\partial x} + \frac{\partial (vr)}{\partial y} = 0\,, \tag{11.3}$$

where $r(x)$ is the radius of the cross-section of the body of revolution. In either case the boundary conditions can be written as

$$y = 0: \quad u = 0\,, \quad v = 0\,; \qquad y = \infty: \quad u = U(x,t)\,.$$

The pressure impressed on the body follows from the non-steady Bernoulli equation (7.5), or

$$-\frac{1}{\varrho}\frac{\partial p}{\partial x} = \frac{\partial U}{\partial t} + U\frac{\partial U}{\partial x}\,, \tag{11.4}$$

where $U(x, t)$ denotes the prescribed non-steady potential motion.

The integration of the non-steady boundary layer equations (11.1) to (11.4) can be carried out in most cases by a process of successive approximations, the method being based on the following physical reasoning: In the first instant, after the motion had started from rest, the boundary layer is very thin and the viscous term $\nu(\partial^2 u/\partial y^2)$ in eqn. (11.1) is very large, whereas the convective terms retain their normal values. The viscous term is then balanced by the non-steady acceleration $\partial u/\partial t$ together with the pressure term in which, at first, the contribution of $\partial U/\partial t$ is of major importance. Selecting a system of co-ordinates which is at rest with respect to the body and assuming that the fluid moves with respect to the body at rest, we can make the assumption that the velocity is composed of two terms

$$u(x,y,t) = u_0(x,y,t) + u_1(x,y,t)\,. \tag{11.5}$$

Under these conditions the first approximation, u_0, satisfies the linear differential equation

$$\frac{\partial u_0}{\partial t} - \nu\frac{\partial^2 u_0}{\partial y^2} = \frac{\partial U}{\partial t} \tag{11.6}$$

with the boundary conditions $y = 0: u_0 = 0\,;\ y = \infty: u_0 = U(x, t)$. The equation for the second approximation, u_1, is obtained with reference to eqn. (11.1) in which the convective terms are calculated from u_0 and in which the convective pressure term can now be taken into account. Hence we have

$$\frac{\partial u_1}{\partial t} - \nu\frac{\partial^2 u_1}{\partial y^2} = U\frac{\partial U}{\partial x} - u_0\frac{\partial u_0}{\partial x} - v_0\frac{\partial u_0}{\partial y} \tag{11.7}$$

with the boundary conditions $u_1 = 0$ at $y = 0$ and $u_1 = 0$ at $y = \infty$. This, too, is a linear equation.

In addition to eqns. (11.6) and (11.7) we have the continuity equation for u_0, v_0 and u_1, v_1. Higher-order approximations u_2, u_3, ... can be obtained in a similar manner. The same method can be applied to the study of periodic boundary layers.

The preceding method is limited in scope in that the iteration on the differential equation itself is difficult to perform for the higher-order terms. The differential equation (11.7) for the second approximation, u_1, is more complicated than that for the first-order term, u_0, eqn. (11.6), and the complexity increases rapidly as higher approximations are considered.

An alternative method has been devised by C. C. Lin [8a] who modelled it on the approach employed for the study of turbulent flows, to be described in Chap. XVIII. It can be used for the solution of problems involving periodic motions in the free stream and relies on forming suitable averages of the quantities under investigation and on a linearization of the equation which describes the oscillatory component of the velocity in the boundary layer. On the other hand, the full equation which describes the *mean* flow is retained.

If the free-stream velocity $U(x, t)$ has an oscillating component, it can be written

$$U(x, t) = \overline{U}(x) + U_1(x, t) \tag{11.8}$$

where the bar denotes an average value with respect to time over one period. Hence the average of the periodic component, $U_1(x, t)$, vanishes. Thus

$$\overline{U_1}(x, t) = 0\,. \tag{11.8a}$$

The velocity components u and v in the boundary layer and the pressure p are also separated into mean and periodic components:

$$\begin{aligned} u(x, y, t) &= \overline{u}(x, y) + u_1(x, y, t) \\ v(x, y, t) &= \overline{v}(x, y) + v_1(x, y, t) \\ p(x, t) &= \overline{p}(x) \quad + p_1(x, t) \end{aligned} \tag{11.9}$$

with

$$\overline{u_1} = \overline{v_1} = \overline{p_1} = 0\,. \tag{11.9a}$$

Substituting from eqn. (11.8) into eqn. (11.4) and taking averages, we obtain

$$\overline{U}\,\frac{\mathrm{d}\overline{U}}{\mathrm{d}x} + \overline{U_1\,\frac{\mathrm{d}U_1}{\mathrm{d}x}} = -\frac{1}{\varrho}\,\frac{\partial\overline{p}}{\partial x}$$

which, substracted from eqn. (11.4) gives

$$\frac{\partial U_1}{\partial t} + \overline{U}_1\,\frac{\partial U_1}{\partial x} + U_1\,\frac{\partial\overline{U}_1}{\partial x} + U_1\,\frac{\partial U_1}{\partial x} - \overline{U_1\,\frac{\partial U_1}{\partial x}} = -\frac{1}{\varrho}\,\frac{\partial p_1}{\partial x}\,.$$

Similarly, eqn. (11.1) will yield

$$\overline{u}\,\frac{\partial\overline{u}}{\partial x} + \overline{v}\,\frac{\partial\overline{u}}{\partial y} = \overline{U}\,\frac{\mathrm{d}\overline{U}}{\mathrm{d}x} + \nu\,\frac{\partial^2\overline{u}}{\partial y^2} + \mathfrak{F}\,, \tag{11.10}$$

where

$$\mathfrak{F} = \overline{U_1\,\frac{\partial U_1}{\partial x}} - \left(\overline{u_1\,\frac{\partial u_1}{\partial x}} + \overline{v_1\,\frac{\partial u_1}{\partial y}}\right) \tag{11.10a}$$

and
$$\underline{\frac{\partial u_1}{\partial t}} + \left(\bar{u}\,\frac{\partial u_1}{\partial x} + \bar{v}\,\frac{\partial u_1}{\partial y}\right) + \left(u_1\,\frac{\partial \bar{u}}{\partial x} + v_1\,\frac{\partial \bar{u}}{\partial y}\right) +$$
$$+ \left(u_1\,\frac{\partial u_1}{\partial x} + v_1\,\frac{\partial u_1}{\partial y}\right) - \left(\overline{u_1\,\frac{\partial u_1}{\partial x} + v_1\,\frac{\partial u_1}{\partial y}}\right) =$$
$$= \underline{\frac{\partial U_1}{\partial t}} + \bar{U}_1\,\frac{\partial U_1}{\partial x} + U_1\,\frac{\partial \bar{U}_1}{\partial x} + U_1\,\frac{\partial U_1}{\partial x} - \overline{U_1\,\frac{\partial U_1}{\partial x}} + \nu\,\underline{\frac{\partial^2 u_1}{\partial y^2}}\,. \tag{11.10b}$$

The essential simplification of the theory consists in retaining only the three underlined terms in eqn. (11.10b), which is thereby linearized and reduces to

$$\frac{\partial u_1}{\partial t} = \frac{\partial U_1}{\partial t} + \nu\,\frac{\partial^2 u_1}{\partial y^2}\,. \tag{11.11}$$

By estimating orders of magnitude it can be shown that the preceding approximation is a valid one if the ratio of the so-called "ac" boundary layer thickness,

$$\delta_0 = \sqrt{2\,\nu/n} \tag{11.12}$$

formed with the frequency n of the oscillation, is small compared with the steady-state boundary layer thickness δ which would exist if $U(x, t)$ were equal to $U(x)$. Hence, for the approximation to be valid we must have

$$2\left(\frac{\delta_0}{\delta}\right)^2 \ll 1 \tag{11.13}$$

which, in practice, restricts the theory to high frequencies. It will be recalled that the quantity δ_0, eqn. (11.12), occured in the solutions to the problems of slow oscillations in fluids at rest which have been considered in Sec. Va. 7.

Equation (11.11) which is linear and related to the so-called heat conduction equation (5.17) describes the oscillating component u_1 of the boundary layer profile and can be solved in terms of the given oscillating component U_1 of the potential flow alone, because the process of linearization has made it independent of the mean motion.

The normal components of the flow can be calculated from the equation of continuity (11.2) which can be split into an average part

$$\frac{\partial \bar{u}}{\partial x} + \frac{\partial \bar{v}}{\partial y} = 0 \tag{11.14}$$

and an oscillating part

$$\frac{\partial u_1}{\partial x} + \frac{\partial v_1}{\partial x} = 0\,. \tag{11.14a}$$

Having solved for the oscillation $u_1(x, y, t)$, $v_1(x, y, t)$ we can return to eqn. (11.10a) and calculate the function $\mathcal{F}$ which appears in eqn. (11.10). The latter now describes the mean motion $\bar{u}(x, y)$.

It should be noted that the equation for the mean flow, eqn. (11.10), has a form which is identical with the steady-state version of the boundary layer equation

(11.1), i. e. when $\partial u/\partial t = 0$ is assumed in it. The only difference consists in the appearance of the additional term $\mathfrak{F}$ which now plays the same part as the term $\overline{U} \cdot \mathrm{d}\overline{U}/\mathrm{d}x$ which originates in the pressure gradient. Both terms represent known functions in the differential equation. The only difference consists in the fact that the mean pressure gradient $\overline{U} \cdot \mathrm{d}\overline{U}/\mathrm{d}x$ is "impressed" on the boundary layer and is independent of the transverse co-ordinate y, whereas the additional term $\mathfrak{F}$ depends on it.

Owing to the existence of oscillatory components, the average flow is different from that which would be obtained if the potential velocity $U(x, t)$ were averaged first and then introduced into eqn. (11.1) with the simplification that $\partial u/\partial t = 0$. The difference consists in the fact that now $\mathfrak{F} \neq 0$, whereas in the other case we would proceed as if we had assumed $\mathfrak{F} = 0$.

It will be stated later in Chaps. XVIII and XIX that the essential characteristic of a steady turbulent stream consists in the fact that on the mean velocity of flow there is superimposed a random three-dimensional, quasi-periodic oscillation. Consequently problems involving turbulent free streams exhibit the same features as those being discussed now; they involve changes in direction as well as in the magnitude of the free-stream velocity U. It was already remarked in Sec. VIIg that it is then customary to neglect the free-stream oscillation and to calculate as if the flow were steady and as if the potential velocity were given by $\overline{U}(x)$ instead of $U(x, t)$. This is equivalent to omitting the additional term $\mathfrak{F}$ in eqn. (11.10) and necessarily leads to an average velocity profile which is different from $\overline{u}(x)$. The preceding remarks show clearly that the order in which the two operations: averaging and solving the equations are performed is not immaterial and affects the final result.

Problems involving oscillations can also be solved by postulating suitable series expansions of the solutions and by making use of the full boundary layer equations, see Sec. XIe, 4, as was done by F. K. Moore [8b, c], F. K. Moore and S. Ostrach [8d] and J. Kestin, P. F. Maeder and H. E. Wang [7a]. These are essentially suitable when the frequency of the oscillation is small, i. e. when the ac. boundary layer thickness is large compared with the boundary layer thickness δ.

H. Schuh [15] and Th. Geis [4] examined that class of solutions of eqns. (11.1) and (11.2) which leads to similar velocity profiles, that is to profiles whose form is given by

$$u(x,y,t) = u_1(x,t) - H(\eta) \quad \text{with} \quad \eta = \frac{y}{N(x,t)}.$$

The class includes, for example, the solutions for the free-stream velocity $U(x, t) = c\, t^n$ which will be discussed in Sec. XIc.

M. J. Lighthill [8] made a general study of the response of a boundary layer to fluctuations of the external flow about a steady mean by the use of the von Kármán-Pohlhausen method. He considered the particular problem of two-dimensional flow about a fixed cylindrical body when fluctuations in the external flow are produced by harmonic fluctuations in the magnitude, but not in the direction of the velocity of the oncoming stream. The solutions given by Lighthill involve an approximation in that they are restricted to terms of the same order as the amplitude of fluctuations and hence, as will be more clearly explained in Sec. XIe. 1 disregard the onset of so-called *secondary* flows; they do however, take into account the existence of pressure gradients.

b. Boundary layer formation after impulsive start of motion

We now propose to analyze the first phases of the motion after it has been started from rest.

The problem can be simplified considerably, as suggested by H. Blasius [2], if it is assumed that the body is accelerated very rapidly, the fluid being at rest, or, in other words, that it is started impulsively. Thus the body assumes its full velocity discontinuously and the velocity remains constant afterwards. In the system of co-ordinates which is, as assumed before, linked with the body, the potential flow is defined by the conditions

$$\left.\begin{aligned} t \leq 0: &\qquad U(x,t) = 0\,, \\ t > 0: &\qquad U(x,t) = U(x)\,, \end{aligned}\right\} \tag{11.15}$$

where $U(x)$ denotes the potential flow about the body in the steady state. In this particular case we have $\partial U/\partial t = 0$, and eqn. (11.6) of the first approximation becomes simply

$$\frac{\partial u_0}{\partial t} - \nu \frac{\partial^2 u_0}{\partial y^2} = 0 \tag{11.6a}$$

with $u_0 = 0$ for $y = 0$, and $u_0 = U(x)$ for $y = \infty$. This equation is identical with that for one-dimensional heat conduction. It was solved in Sec. V.4 for the case of a plate started impulsively in its own plane, while the fluid was at rest at a large distance from it. It was then possible to introduce a new dimensionless variable (*similarity transformation*)†:

$$\eta = \frac{y}{2\sqrt{\nu t}}\,. \tag{11.16}$$

In this manner we obtain the solution in the form

$$u_0(x, y, t) = U(x) \cdot \zeta_0{}'(\eta) = U(x) \operatorname{erf} \eta\,. \tag{11.17}$$

This is the first approximation both for the two-dimensional and for the axi-symmetrical case. Further, if the potential velocity is independent of x, i. e. if $U = U_0 = \text{const}$ (flat plate at zero incidence), eqn. (11.17) constitutes the exact solution of eqn. (11.1), since the convective terms in eqn. (11.7) vanish together with the pressure term so that $u_1 = 0$. In the general case, when the external flow $U(x, t)$ depends on the space co-ordinate, it is necessary to make a distinction between the two-dimensional and the axi-symmetrical cases.

1. Two-dimensional case. We shall begin by considering the two-dimensional case. For this case we assume a power series in time for the stream function stipulating that it has the form

$$\psi(x, y, t) = 2\sqrt{\nu t}\left\{U\,\zeta_0(\eta) + t\,U\,\frac{\mathrm{d}U}{\mathrm{d}x}\,\zeta_1(\eta) + \ldots\right\}. \tag{11.18}$$

† See remark at the beginning of Sec. V a 5, p. 73.

Hence, the velocity components $u = \partial\psi/\partial y$ and $v = -\partial\psi/\partial x$ become:

$$\left.\begin{aligned} u &= U\,\zeta_0' + t\,U\,\frac{\mathrm{d}U}{\mathrm{d}x}\,\zeta_1' + \dots \\ -v &= 2\sqrt{\nu t}\left\{\frac{\mathrm{d}U}{\mathrm{d}x}\,\zeta_0 + t\left[\left(\frac{\mathrm{d}U}{\mathrm{d}x}\right)^2 + U\,\frac{\mathrm{d}^2U}{\mathrm{d}x^2}\right]\zeta_1 + \dots\right\}. \end{aligned}\right\} \tag{11.19}$$

Inserting these expressions into eqn. (11.6) we obtain the differential equation of the first approximation:

$$\zeta_0''' + 2\,\eta\,\zeta_0'' = 0 \tag{11.20}$$

with the boundary conditions $\zeta_0 = \zeta_0' = 0$ at $\eta = 0$ and $\zeta_0' = 1$ at $\eta = \infty$. Eqn. (11.20) is identical with eqn. (5.21) and the solution for ζ_0' is indicated in eqn. (11.17). The function ζ_0' is shown plotted in Fig. 11.1.

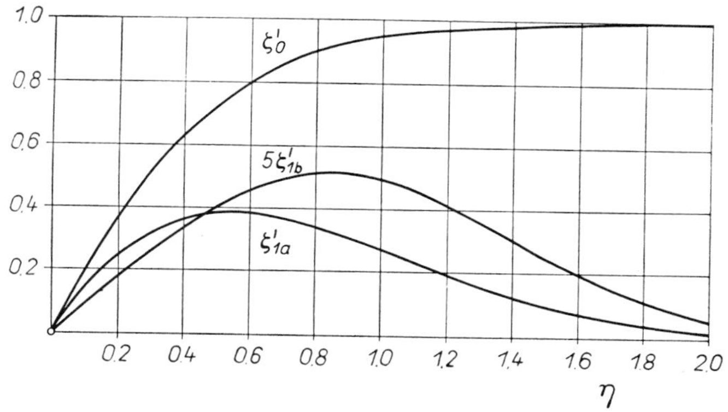

Fig. 11.1. The functions ζ_0' and $\zeta_1' = \zeta_{1a}'$ and ζ_{1b}' for the velocity distribution in the nonsteady boundary layer, eqns. (11.19) and (11.28) for impulsive motion

Combining eqn. (11.7) with (11.18) we obtain the differential equation for the second approximation $\zeta_1(\eta)$ in the form:

$$\zeta_1''' + 2\,\eta\,\zeta_1'' - 4\,\zeta_1' = 4(\zeta_0'^2 - \zeta_0\zeta_0'' - 1)$$

with the boundary conditions $\zeta_1 = \zeta_1' = 0$ at $\eta = 0$ and $\zeta_1' = 0$ at $\eta = \infty$. The solution derived by H. Blasius is:

$$\begin{aligned} \zeta_1' = &-\frac{3}{\sqrt{\pi}}\,\eta\exp(-\eta^2)\,\mathrm{erfc}(\eta) + \frac{1}{2}\,(2\,\eta^2 - 1)\,\mathrm{erfc}^2(\eta) + \frac{2}{\pi}\exp(-2\,\eta^2) + \\ &+ \frac{1}{\sqrt{\pi}}\,\eta\exp(-\eta^2) + 2\,\mathrm{erfc}(\eta) - \frac{4}{3\pi}\exp(-\eta^2) + \\ &+ \left(\frac{3}{\sqrt{\pi}} + \frac{4}{3\pi^{3/2}}\right)\left\{\eta\exp(-\eta^2) - \frac{\sqrt{\pi}}{2}\,(2\,\eta^2 + 1)\,\mathrm{erfc}(\eta)\right\}. \end{aligned} \tag{11.21}$$

The function ζ_1' is shown plotted (as function ζ_{1a}') in Fig. 11.1 and its numerical values are given in Table 11.1. The initial slopes of the two functions, required for the calculation of separation, are given by

$$\zeta_0''(0) = \frac{2}{\sqrt{\pi}}\,; \quad \zeta_1''(0) = \frac{2}{\sqrt{\pi}}\left(1 + \frac{4}{3\pi}\right). \tag{11.22}$$

An exact expression for the next term of the expansion of the stream function in terms of time was obtained by S. Goldstein and L. Rosenhead [5]. E. Boltze [3] previously derived an approximate solution when he considered the axially symmetrical problem (see succeeding section).

The question of the position of the point of separation can be answered with the aid of the second approximation. In this connexion we shall consider the cases of the circular and the elliptic cylinder. The condition for the point of separation is given by $\partial u/\partial y = 0$ for $y = 0$, which leads to the following condition for the time of separation t_s:

$$\zeta_0''(0) + \zeta_1''(0)\, t_s \frac{\mathrm{d}U}{\mathrm{d}x} = 0$$

as seen from eqn. (11.19). With the values (11.22) this becomes

$$1 + \left(1 + \frac{4}{3\pi}\right)\frac{\mathrm{d}U}{\mathrm{d}x}\, t_s = 0\,. \tag{11.23}$$

Equation (11.23) allows us to calculate the instant at which separation begins at a given place. Separation occurs only at points where $\mathrm{d}U/\mathrm{d}x$ is negative. The point of earliest separation occurs at a place where the absolute value of $\mathrm{d}U/\mathrm{d}x$ is largest. It does not follow that this coincides with the downstream stagnation point as will be demonstrated on the example of the elliptic cylinder.

Example: *Circular cylinder*

For the circular cylinder of radius R in a stream of velocity U_∞ we obtain:

$$U(x) = 2\,U_\infty \sin\frac{x}{R} \quad \text{and} \quad \frac{\mathrm{d}U}{\mathrm{d}x} = 2\,\frac{U_\infty}{R}\cos\frac{x}{R}\,,$$

where x denotes the arc measured from the upstream stagnation point. The absolute value of the gradient $\mathrm{d}U/\mathrm{d}x$ has its maximum at the downstream stagnation point, and separation at a time

$$t_s = \frac{R/U_\infty}{2\left(1 + \frac{4}{3\pi}\right)}\,. \tag{11.24}$$

as seen from eqn. (11.23). The distance covered until separation begins is $s_s = t_s\, U_\infty$, so that

$$s_s = \frac{R}{2\left(1 + \frac{4}{3\pi}\right)} = 0{\cdot}351\, R\,.$$

Example: *Elliptic cylinder* [*7*, *20*]

Let the semi-axes of the elliptic cylinder be a and b, and let $k = b/a$ be their ratio, no assumption about their relative magnitude being made, so that $a \gtrless b$. The equation of the ellipse can be written as $x^2/a^2 + y^2/b^2 = 1$. Introducing the angular co-ordinate ϕ, defined by $x/a = \cos\phi$ and $y/b = \sin\phi$, and assuming that the cylinder is started impulsively with a velocity U_∞ in a direction parallel to the axis a, we can write for the velocity distribution along the contour of the ellipse:

$$\frac{U(s)}{U_\infty} = \frac{1+k}{\sqrt{1+k^2\cot^2\phi}}$$

and for the velocity gradient

$$\frac{a}{U_\infty}\frac{\mathrm{d}U}{\mathrm{d}s} = \frac{(1+k)\,k^2\cos\phi}{(\sin^2\phi + k^2\cos^2\phi)^2}\,.$$

It is easy to verify that the maximum value of the velocity gradient coincides with the downstream stagnation point if $k^2 < 4/3$. For $k^2 > 4/3$ the maximum value of the gradient occurs at $\phi = \phi_m$, where

$$\cos^2\phi_m = \frac{1}{3\,(k^2-1)}\,.$$

The maximum values of the gradient become

$$\left.\begin{aligned} k^2 \le \frac{4}{3}:\quad & \frac{b}{U_\infty}\left(\frac{\mathrm{d}U}{\mathrm{d}s}\right)_m = \frac{1+k}{k} \\ k^2 \ge \frac{4}{3}:\quad & \frac{b}{U_\infty}\left(\frac{\mathrm{d}U}{\mathrm{d}s}\right)_m = \frac{3\sqrt{3}}{16}\,\frac{k^3(1+k)}{\sqrt{k^2-1}}\,. \end{aligned}\right\} \qquad (11.25)$$

Inserting the values from (11.25) into eqn. (11.23), we find that the time elapsed until the onset of separation is

$$\left.\begin{aligned} t_s\frac{U_\infty}{a} &= \frac{k^2}{\left(1+\frac{4}{3\pi}\right)(1+k)} && \text{for } k^2 \le \frac{4}{3} \\ t_s\frac{U_\infty}{b} &= \frac{16\sqrt{k^2-1}}{\left(1+\frac{4}{3\pi}\right)3\sqrt{3}\,k^3(1+k)} && \text{for } k^2 \ge \frac{4}{3}\,. \end{aligned}\right\} \qquad (11.26)$$

The distance s traversed by the elliptic cylinder until the onset of separation and given by $s = t_s U_\infty$ is seen plotted in Fig. 11.2 in terms of the ratio of the axes $k = b/a$. The place, where separation occurs first, is given by

$$y_s = 0 \quad \text{for} \quad k^2 \le \frac{4}{3}\,,$$

$$\frac{y_s^2}{b^2} = 1 - \frac{1}{3\,(k^2-1)} \quad \text{for} \quad k^2 \ge \frac{4}{3}\,.$$

For $k = 1$ eqn. (11.26) transforms into eqn. (11.24) for the circular cylinder, Beginning with this value the time t_s for the onset of separation decreases with increasing $k = b/a$, and the position of the point of separation moves from the end of axis a towards the end of axis b. In the limit $b/a \to \infty$, i.e. for a plate at right angles to the direction of motion, we have $t_s = 0$ and $y_s = b$.

Hence the onset of separation is immediate for the case of a flat plate perpendicular to the direction of motion and it takes place at the edge.

The formation of the boundary layer on a rotating cylinder started impulsively was calculated by W. Tollmien [21] by an analogous method in his Goettingen thesis presented in 1924. In this case separation is suppressed on that side of the cylinder where the tangential velocity has the same direction as the velocity of flow.

2. Axially symmetrical problem. The process of boundary layer formation about an axially symmetrical body accelerated impulsively was investigated by E. Boltze [3] in his Goettingen thesis. We consider the boundary layer on a body of revolution whose shape is defined by $r(x)$, Fig. 10.6, and which is set in motion at $t = 0$. The acceleration is impulsive and the cylinder moves in the direction of its axis. The relevant equations are now eqns. (11.1) and (11.3), and the solution can again be represented as a sum of a first approximation, u_0, and a second approximation, u_1, defined by eqns. (11.6) and (11.7) respectively. In view of the changed form of the continuity equation we introduce a different stream function, namely

$$u = \frac{1}{r}\frac{\partial \psi}{\partial y}\,; \qquad v = -\frac{1}{r}\frac{\partial \psi}{\partial x}\,,$$

and we assume it to be of the form

$$\psi(x, y, t) = 2\sqrt{\nu t}\left\{r\,U\,\zeta_0(\eta) + t\left[r\,U\,\frac{\mathrm{d}U}{\mathrm{d}x}\,\zeta_{1a}(\eta) + U^2\,\frac{\mathrm{d}r}{\mathrm{d}x}\,\zeta_{1b}(\eta)\right] + \ldots\right\}. \qquad (11.27)$$

Hence

$$\frac{u}{U} = \zeta_0' + t\left[\frac{\mathrm{d}U}{\mathrm{d}x}\,\zeta_{1a}' + \frac{U}{r}\frac{\mathrm{d}r}{\mathrm{d}x}\,\zeta_{1b}'\right]. \qquad (11.28)$$

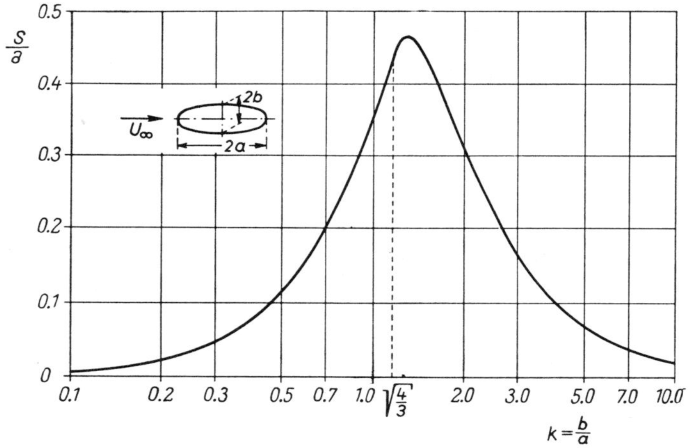

Fig. 11.2. Distance s traversed by elliptic cylinder until the onset of separation in the case of impulsive acceleration from rest

The variable η has the same meaning as in the two-dimensional problem, eqn. (11.16). The differential equation for ζ_0 resulting from eqn. (11.6) is identical with eqn. (11.20) for the two-dimensional problem, as already mentioned. For the second approximation in the expansion in terms of time we now obtain from eqn. (11.7) the following differential equations, defining ζ_{1a} and ζ_{1b}:

$$\left.\begin{aligned} \zeta_{1a}''' + 2\,\eta\,\zeta_{1a}'' - 4\,\zeta_{1a}' &= 4(\zeta_0'^2 - 1 - \zeta_0\,\zeta_0'') \\ \zeta_{1b}''' + 2\,\eta\,\zeta_{1b}'' - 4\,\zeta_{1b}' &= -4\,\zeta_0\,\zeta_0'' \end{aligned}\right\} \qquad (11.29)$$

with the boundary conditions

$$\eta = 0 \ : \quad \zeta_{1a} = \zeta_{1a}' = 0 \ ; \qquad \zeta_{1b} = \zeta_{1b}' = 0 \ ;$$
$$\eta = \infty : \quad \zeta_{1a}' = 0 \ ; \qquad \zeta_{1b}' = 0 \ .$$

The equation for ζ_{1a} is identical with that for ζ_1 of the two-dimensional problem, and the equation for ζ_{1b} was solved numerically by E. Boltze. Numerical values of ζ_{1a} and ζ_{1b} are given in Table 11.1 and the initial slope of ζ_{1b}' is $\zeta_{1b}''(0) = 0{\cdot}169$.

In accordance with eqn. (11.28) the onset of separation is defined by the condition $(\partial u/\partial y)_{y=0} = 0$ which gives

$$\zeta_0''(0) + t_s \left[\frac{\mathrm{d}U}{\mathrm{d}x}\,\zeta_{1a}''(0) + \frac{U}{r}\,\frac{\mathrm{d}r}{\mathrm{d}x}\,\zeta_{1b}''(0)\right] = 0$$

or, with the preceding numerical values for $\zeta_0''(0)$, $\zeta_{1a}''(0) = \zeta_1''(0)$, and $\zeta_{1b}''(0)$

$$1 + t_s \left[\frac{\mathrm{d}U}{\mathrm{d}x}\left(1 + \frac{4}{3\pi}\right) + 0{\cdot}150\,\frac{U}{r}\,\frac{\mathrm{d}r}{\mathrm{d}x}\right] = 0 \ . \tag{11.30}$$

Table 11.1. The functions ζ_{1a}' and ζ_{1b}' for non-steady impulsive motion after E. Boltze [3]

η	ζ_{1a}'	ζ_{1b}'
0	0	0
0·1	0·142	0·017
0·2	0·246	0·034
0·3	0·318	0·051
0·4	0·362	0·066
0·5	0·382	0·080
0·6	0·382	0·091
0·7	0·367	0·099
0·8	0·340	0·103
0·9	0·307	0·102
1·0	0·269	0·099
1·1	0·231	0·092
1·2	0·191	0·083
1·3	0·158	0·072
1·4	0·126	0·061
1·5	0·099	0·050
1·6	0·075	0·040
1·7	0·056	0·031
1·8	0·041	0·023
1·9	0·029	0·016
2·0	0·021	0·011
∞	0	0

E. Boltze calculated two further terms of the expansion for the stream function in eqn. (11.27).

Example: *Sphere*

By way of example E. Boltze computed the process of boundary layer formation on a sphere which is started impulsively from rest. Denoting the radius of the sphere by R and the free-stream velocity by U_∞, we have in this case

$$r = \sin \frac{x}{R}\,; \qquad U(x) = \frac{3}{2}\, U_\infty \sin \frac{x}{R}\,.$$

The beginning of separation now follows from eqn. (11.30), or

$$1 + t_s \frac{3}{2} \frac{U_\infty}{R}\, 1{\cdot}573 \cos \frac{x}{R} = 0\,.$$

Separation sets in at the stagnation point downstream, i. e. at a place where $\cos\,(x/R) = -1$, so that $\frac{3}{2}\, t_s\ U_\infty/R = 1/1{\cdot}573 = 0{\cdot}635$. Taking into account the two further terms of the expansion for the stream function calculated by E. Boltze, we obtain the more accurate value 0·589 for the constant 0·635. Thus the instant of separation for a sphere started impulsively becomes

$$t_s = 0{\cdot}392\, \frac{R}{U_\infty}\,. \tag{11.31}$$

The distance covered in that time is $s_s = U_\infty t_s = 0{\cdot}392\, R$, or, in round figures, 40 per cent. of the radius of the sphere. The point of separation moves from $\phi = \pi$, at first rapidly, and later slowly, towards $\phi \approx 110^\circ$ which is its position in steady flow, and reaches it only after an infinite time. Fig. 11.3 represents the pattern of stream-lines and the velocity distribution for an intermediate instant, which corresponds to a distance of 0·6 R covered by the sphere. This corresponds to a time of 0·6 sec. with a radius of $R = 10$ cm (about 4 in) and a velocity $U_\infty = 10$ cm/sec (about 0·33 ft/sec). The stream-lines are seen plotted in Fig. 11.3 in which the linear scale of the thickness of the boundary layer has been exaggerated for the sake of clarity. For water with $\nu = 0{\cdot}01 \times 10^{-4}$ m²/sec (about $0{\cdot}1 \times 10^{-4}$ ft²/sec) the magnification factor is about 30. The magnitudes of the velocities in the closed vortex are very small and the velocity gradient and the circulation are greatest outside the stream-line $\psi = 0$ at the point of separation.

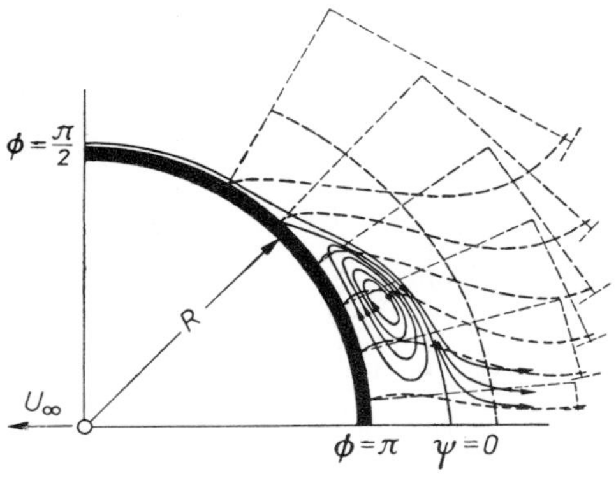

Fig. 11.3. Boundary layer on the downstream side of a sphere accelerated impulsively after the onset of separation; from Boltze [3]. The sphere has traversed a distance of 0·6 R

The idealized process of instantaneous acceleration assumed in the preceding theory is a good approximation to actual cases if the time of acceleration is small compared with the time which elapses before separation sets in.

The process of the formation of a boundary layer on a rotating disk was studied by K. H. Thiriot [18] in his thesis presented to the University of Goettingen. He considered the case of a disk accelerated impulsively in a fluid at rest to a uniform angular velocity, as well as the case of a disk rotating with the fluid and suddenly arrested in its motion. The ultimate state of motion for the first case is the solution for a disk rotating in a fluid at rest given by W. G. Cochran and discussed in Sec. V.10. The final state of motion for the second problem is given by the solution due to U. T. Boedewadt and discussed in Sec. Xa. It concerns the rotation of the fluid body over a fixed plane. A generalization of all these cases has been discussed by K. H. Thiriot [19] in a further paper, when he considered the case of a disk rotating with the fluid body and impulsively accelerated, or decelerated, so that its angular velocity is changed by a small quantity compared with that of the fluid. It is noteworthy that a stationary boundary layer is then formed in the neighbourhood of the rotating disk. The details of the growth of a boundary layer on a disk started impulsively were computed by S. D. Nigam [9].

W. Wuest [24] obtained solutions for three-dimensional non-steady boundary layers on bodies which perform non-steady motions at right angles to the main flow. One example considered was that of a cylinder in steady cross-flow which is made to perform axial periodic oscillations. The case of a wedge which oscillates harmonically in a direction parallel to its leading edge, also considered, contains as special cases those of a flat plate and stagnation flow. The case considered by H. Wundt [25], namely that of a yawed cylinder accelerated impulsively constitutes another example of a three-dimensional, non-steady boundary layer.

c. Boundary layer formation with constant acceleration

The process of boundary layer formation in two-dimensional flow for the case of uniform acceleration of the body has been calculated by H. Blasius. The results are very similar to those for an impulsive start of the motion. The potential velocity of the body is now given in the form

$$\left.\begin{aligned} t \leq 0: \quad & U(x,t) = 0\,, \\ t \geq 0: \quad & U(x,t) = t \cdot w(x)\,. \end{aligned}\right\} \tag{11.32}$$

It is again possible to assume a series in terms of successive approximation, as given by eqn. (11.5). These approximations then satisfy eqns. (11.6) and (11.7). Assuming an expansion of the stream function in terms of time of the form

$$\psi(x,y,t) = 2\sqrt{\nu t}\left\{ t\, w\, \zeta_0(\eta) + t^3\, w\, \frac{\mathrm{d}w}{\mathrm{d}x}\, \zeta_1(\eta) + \dots \right\}$$

and

$$u(x,y,t) = U\left(\zeta_0' + t^2 \frac{\mathrm{d}w}{\mathrm{d}x}\, \zeta_1' + \dots\right), \tag{11.33}$$

it is possible to deduce the following differential equations for $\zeta_0(\eta)$ and $\zeta_1(\eta)$:

$$\left.\begin{aligned} \zeta_0''' + 2\,\eta\,\zeta_0'' - 4\,\zeta_0' &= -4 \\ \zeta_1''' + 2\,\eta\,\zeta_1'' - 12\,\zeta_1' &= -4 + 4(\zeta_0'^2 - \zeta_0\,\zeta_0'') \end{aligned}\right\} \tag{11.34}$$

with the boundary conditions

$$\eta = 0 \quad : \quad \zeta_0 = \zeta_0' = 0\,, \quad \zeta_1 = \zeta_1' = 0\,,$$
$$\eta = \infty : \qquad \zeta_0' = 1\,, \quad \zeta_1' = 0\,.$$

The solution for the function ζ_0' given by H. Blasius is of the form:

$$\zeta_0' = 1 + \frac{2}{\sqrt{\pi}}\,\eta \exp(-\eta^2) - (1 + 2\,\eta^2)\,\mathrm{erfc}\,\eta\,. \tag{11.35}$$

Blasius was also able to give a solution for ζ_1' in closed form. Several numerical values for ζ_0' and ζ_1' are listed in Table 11.2. The initial slopes which are required for the calculation of separation are:

$$\zeta_0''(0) = \frac{4}{\sqrt{\pi}}\,; \qquad \zeta_1''(0) = \frac{31}{15\sqrt{\pi}} - \frac{256}{225\sqrt{\pi^3}} = \frac{4}{\sqrt{\pi}} \times 0{\cdot}427\,.$$

Table 11.2. The functions ζ_0' and ζ_1' for the velocity distribution in the boundary layer, when body is uniformly accelerated

η	ζ_0'	ζ_1'
0	0	0
0·25	0·450	0·137
0·5	0·720	0·150
1·0	0·943	0·020
∞	1·0	0

The beginning of separation in this case is given by eqn. (11.33), and when only the first two terms of the expansion are used we obtain

$$\zeta_0''(0) + t_s^2 \frac{\mathrm{d}w}{\mathrm{d}x}\,\zeta_1''(0) = 0$$

or, with the preceding numerical values of $\zeta_0''(0)$ and $\zeta_1''(0)$:

$$1 + 0{\cdot}427\,t_s^2 \frac{\mathrm{d}w}{\mathrm{d}x} = 0\,,$$

so that

$$t_s^2 \frac{\mathrm{d}w}{\mathrm{d}x} = -\,2{\cdot}34\,.$$

This expression can also be written in the form:

$$1 + 0{\cdot}427\,t_s \frac{\mathrm{d}U}{\mathrm{d}x} = 0\,.$$

Upon comparing with eqn. (11.23), it is seen that for equal values of $\mathrm{d}U/\mathrm{d}x$ separation occurs earlier when the motion is started impulsively than when the acceleration is uniform.

H. Blasius calculated two further terms of the expansion, and with their aid the equation for t_s is obtained in the following modified form:

$$1 + 0{\cdot}427 \frac{\mathrm{d}w}{\mathrm{d}x}\,t_s^2 - 0{\cdot}026\left(\frac{\mathrm{d}w}{\mathrm{d}x}\right)^2 t_s^4 - 0{\cdot}01\,w\,\frac{\mathrm{d}^2w}{\mathrm{d}x^2}\,t_s^4 = 0\,.$$

For the case of a cylinder which is placed symmetrically with respect to the direction of flow the last term vanishes at the downstream stagnation point, and we obtain

$$t_s^2 \frac{\mathrm{d}w}{\mathrm{d}x} = -\,2{\cdot}08\,. \tag{11.36}$$

Example: *Circular cylinder*

For the case of a circular cylinder we have

$$U(x, t) = t\, w(x) = 2\, b\, t \sin \frac{x}{R},$$

where b denotes the constant acceleration. Hence

$$w(x) = 2\, b \sin \frac{x}{R}; \qquad \frac{dw}{dx} = \frac{2\, b}{R} \cos \frac{x}{R}.$$

The point at which separation occurs first coincides, in this case too, with the downstream stagnation point, $\cos(x/R) = -1$. Thus from eqn. (11.36) we obtain

$$t_s^{\,2} = 1{\cdot}04 \frac{R}{b}.$$

The distance covered by the cylinder until separation begins is given by $s = \frac{1}{2}\, b\, t^2_s$, which then becomes $s = 0{\cdot}52\, R$ and is also greater than that for the case of impulsive motion. The argument in Sec. XIb, concerning the point at which separation first occurs, remains valid in the present case. The pattern of stream-lines for the case under consideration is given in Fig. 11.4, which is based on Blasius' work. This pattern corresponds to time $T = t\sqrt{b/R} = 1{\cdot}58$, the distance covered by the cylinder being equal to $1{\cdot}25\, R$. Assuming $R = 10$ cm (about 4 in), $b = 0{\cdot}1$ cm/sec² (about 0·04 in /sec² $= 0{\cdot}0033$ ft/sec²), we obtain $\sqrt{b/R} = 0{\cdot}1$ sec⁻¹, and the time elapsed since the beginning of the motion is $t = 15{\cdot}8$ sec. Fig. 11.4 shows the shape of the resulting boundary layer, the linear scale having been increased in the same way as in Fig. 11.3. For water with $\nu = 0{\cdot}01 \times 10^{-4}$ m²/sec (about $0{\cdot}1 \times 10^{-4}$ ft²/sec) the linear factor is equal to about $\sqrt{10}$.

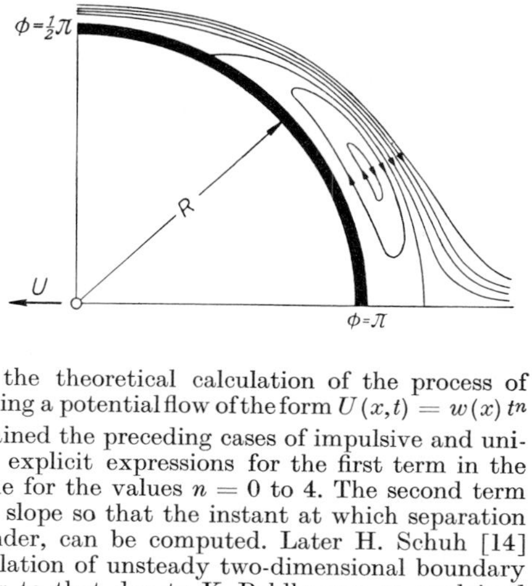

Fig. 11.4. Boundary layer on the downstream side of circular cylinder during start with uniform acceleration after the beginning of separation (Blasius)

Velocity: $U(t) = b \times t$; Pattern at time $T = t\sqrt{b/R} = 1{\cdot}58$; Separation first occurs at $T_s = t_s\sqrt{b/R} = 1{\cdot}02$

In recent times H. Goertler [6] extended the theoretical calculation of the process of boundary layer formation during acceleration assuming a potential flow of the form $U(x,t) = w(x)\, t^n$ with $n = 0, 1, 2, 3, 4$. For $n = 0$ and $n = 1$ he obtained the preceding cases of impulsive and uniform acceleration respectively. H. Goertler gave explicit expressions for the first term in the expansion of the stream function in powers of time for the values $n = 0$ to 4. The second term was evaluated at the wall together with its initial slope so that the instant at which separation begins and the distance covered, e. g. by a cylinder, can be computed. Later H. Schuh [14] achieved a considerable improvement in the calculation of unsteady two-dimensional boundary layers. He used an approximate method, similar to that due to K. Pohlhausen as explained in Chap. XII, and succeeded in calculating boundary layers about bodies of any shape and for any time-dependence of the potential flow velocity.

d. Experimental investigation of the starting process

The process of boundary layer formation can be studied with the aid of the previously discussed analytical methods but it cannot be carried very much beyond

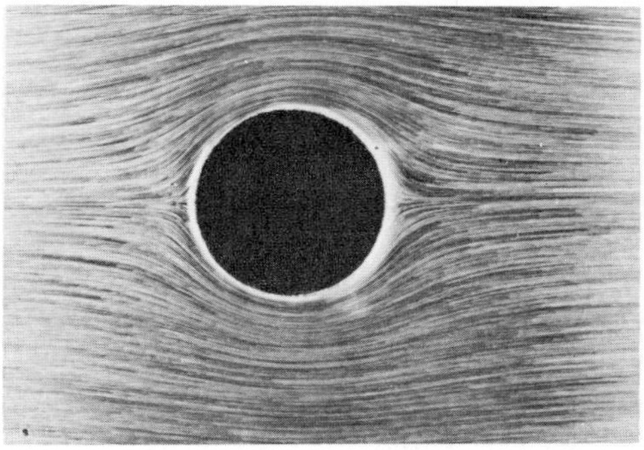

Fig. 11.5a

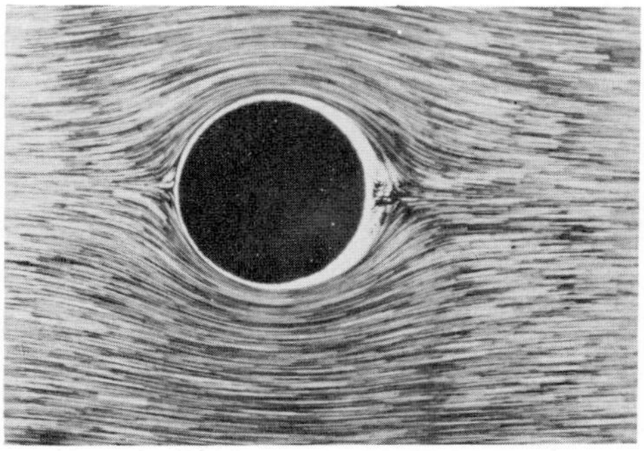

Fig. 11.5b

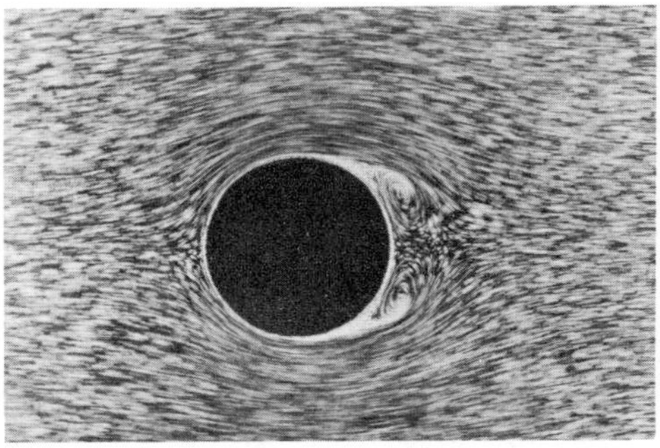

Fig. 11.5c

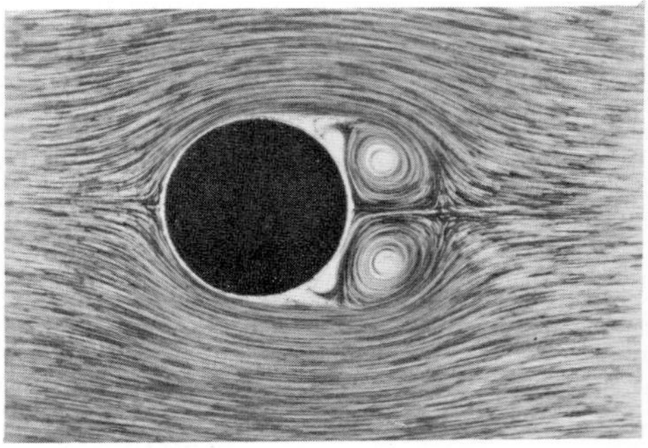

Fig. 11.5d

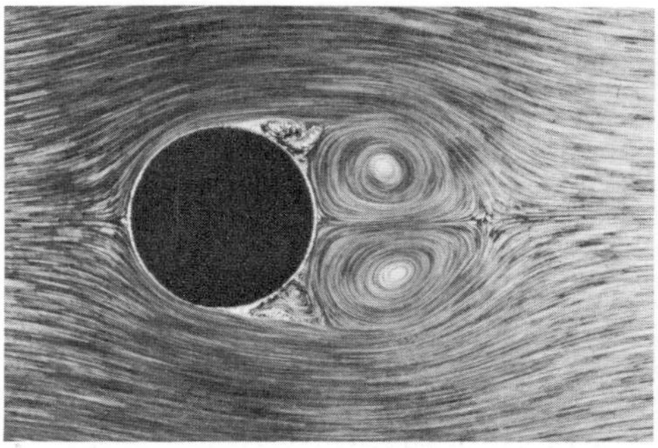

Fig. 11.5e

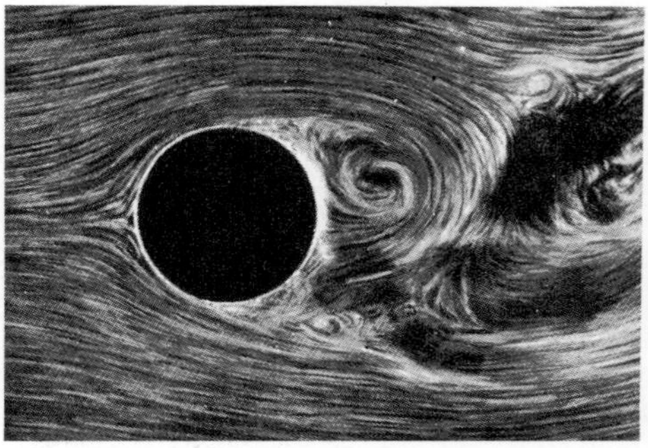

Fig. 11.5f

Fig. 11.5 a to f. Formation of a vortex in flow past a circular cylinder after acceleration from rest (L. Prandtl)

the beginning of separation. The flow pattern outside the boundary layer becomes markedly changed after the onset of separation, particularly on the downstream side of blunt bodies such as a circular cylinder. Consequently, calculations based on the theoretical pressure distribution derived from potential theory give an inaccurate representation of the further course of the process. The photographs in Fig. 11.5 illustrate the development of the flow pattern around a circular cylinder. Figure 11.5a shows that a potential frictionless flow pattern does exist during the first instants after starting. Figure 11.5b represents the moment when separation has just begun at the downstream stagnation point, and in Fig. 11.5c the point of separation has already moved a considerable distance upstream. The stream-line through the point of separation encloses a region where the flow velocities are very small. The vorticity is largest outside this stream-line; it forms a vortex sheet which curls up as the pattern continues to develop and forms two concentrated vortices, Fig. 11.5d. In the free stream behind these vortices it is possible to discern the existence of a stagnation point which coincides with the junction of the two stream-lines through the points of separation. Figure 11.5e shows that the vortices continue to grow. They become unstable with the course of time and are carried away from the body by the external flow, Fig. 11.5f. In the steady-state the motion oscillates and the pressure distribution around the body differs considerably from that stipulated by potential flow theory.

The phenomena under consideration have been investigated in more detail on a circular cylinder by M. Schwabe [16], who measured, in particular, the pressure distribution around the cylinder during the process of acceleration from rest. Pressure distribution curves around the cylinder contour for several phases of the process are given in Fig. 11.6. The distance between the cylinder and the stagnation point in the free stream behind the two vortices is denoted here by d. It is seen that the measured pressure distribution is very close to that in potential flow in the early stages of the process but deviates progressively more from it as time advances. H. Rubach [12] attempted to describe this type of flow about a circular cylinder with the aid of potential theory, assuming the existence of two-symmetrical point-vortices downstream from the body at a position roughly corresponding to that in Fig. 11.5e. It is, however, necessary to remark here that the resemblance to a pattern with two such vortices is only transitory.

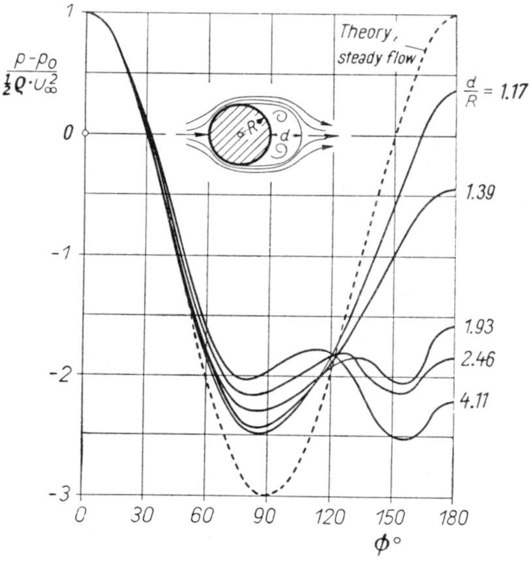

Fig. 11.6. Pressure distribution measured around a circular cylinder during the starting process, after M. Schwabe

In conclusion, it may be worth mentioning that these separation processes occur on a much reduced scale in the case of slender bodies, such as e. g. slender elliptical cylinders, whose longer axes are parallel to the direction of flow, or of aerofoils. Consequently, the experimental pressure distribution around such bodies agrees, in most cases, very closely with that given by potential theory (see also Fig. 1.11).

e. Periodic boundary layer flows

1. Oscillating cylinder in fluid at rest. In order to give an example of a periodic boundary layer flow we now propose to calculate the boundary layer on a body which performs a reciprocating harmonic oscillation of small amplitude in a fluid at rest. This is an extension of the problem of the boundary layer on a flat plate performing harmonic oscillations in its plane which was already discussed in Sec. V.7.

It will be shown in this section that small oscillations of a body in a fluid at rest induce characteristic secondary flows whose nature is such that a *steady* motion is imparted to the whole fluid in spite of the fact that the motion of the body is purely periodic. Effects of this kind occur e. g. when dust patterns are created in a Kundt tube and are of some importance in acoustics.

Suppose that the potential velocity distribution for the cylindrical body which we shall now consider is given by $U_0(x)$. The potential flow in the case of periodic oscillations with a circular frequency n is then given by

$$U(x,t) = U_0(x) \cos(nt) . \tag{11.37}$$

We shall now assume a system of co-ordinates linked with the solid body †. Thus eqns. (11.1) and (11.2) may be applied, the pressure distribution being given by eqn. (11.4). The boundary conditions are $u = 0$ for $y = 0$ and $u = U$ for $y = \infty$.

It is possible to attempt to solve this problem by the method which was used in the case of acceleration from rest, i. e. by calculating successive approximations for the velocity distribution function as defined in eqn. (11.5) and with the aid of eqns. (11.6) and (11.7).

This method appears to be admissible if

$$\left| U \frac{\partial U}{\partial x} \right| \ll \left| \frac{\partial U}{\partial t} \right| .$$

Now $U\,\partial U/\partial x \sim U_m{}^2/d$ where d denotes a linear dimension of the body (e. g. the diameter of the cylinder). On the other hand $\partial U/\partial t \sim U_m \times n$, where U_m denotes the maximum velocity of the body. Thus we have

$$U \frac{\partial U}{\partial x} \Big/ \frac{\partial U}{\partial t} \sim \frac{U_m}{nd} .$$

† In general, such a change in the frame of reference must affect the differential equation, because the equations of motion change, except when the two systems of co-ordinates move with a constant velocity relative to each other. However, when the fluid is incompressible (but not, when it is compressible), frames of reference are completely equivalent if they are in a uniform, even though not constant, translational motion relative to each other (*cf.* M. J. Lighthill [8]).

The maximum velocity U_m is proportional to $n \times s$, where s is the amplitude, so that

$$U \frac{\partial U}{\partial x} \Big/ \frac{\partial U}{\partial t} \sim \frac{s}{d} \ll 1 .$$

The preceding argument shows that the proposed method of solution may be used in cases when the amplitude of oscillation is small compared with the dimensions of the body.

The calculation was performed by H. Schlichting [13] (see also ref. [10]). Since the differential equations (11.6) and (11.7) are linear, it seems convenient to adopt here the complex notation and to write eqn. (11.37) in the form

$$U(x,t) = U_0(x)\, \mathrm{e}^{\mathrm{i}nt},$$

with the convention that only the real parts of the complex quantities in question have physical meaning attached to them. Introducing a dimensionless co-ordinate defined by

$$\eta = y \sqrt{\frac{n}{\nu}}, \tag{11.38}$$

and assuming that the first approximation to the stream function, ψ_0, is of the form

$$\psi_0(x,y,t) = \sqrt{\frac{\nu}{n}}\, U_0(x)\, \zeta_0(\eta)\, \mathrm{e}^{\mathrm{i}nt}$$

and hence

$$u_0(x,y,t) = U_0(x)\, \zeta'_0\, \mathrm{e}^{\mathrm{i}nt}; \qquad v_0(x,y,t) = -\frac{\mathrm{d}U_0}{\mathrm{d}x} \sqrt{\frac{\nu}{n}}\, \zeta_0\, \mathrm{e}^{\mathrm{i}nt}, \tag{11.39}$$

we obtain from eqn. (11.6) the following differential equation for $\zeta_0(\eta)$:

$$\mathrm{i}\, \zeta_0' - \zeta_0''' = \mathrm{i}$$

with the boundary conditions $\zeta_0 = \zeta_0' = 0$ at $\eta = 0$ and $\zeta_0' = 1$ at $\eta = \infty$. The solution is

$$\zeta_0' = 1 - \exp\{-(1-i)\, \eta/\sqrt{2}\}.$$

Reverting to the real notation† we obtain the function

$$u_0(x,y,t) = U_0(x) \left[\cos(nt) - \exp(-\eta/\sqrt{2}) \cos(nt - \eta/\sqrt{2})\right], \tag{11.40}$$

which represents the first approximation to the velocity distribution function. This is the same solution as that for the oscillating flat plate in eqn. (5.26a)‡.

If the second approximation $u_1(x, y, t)$ is now calculated from eqn. (11.7), it is seen that the convective terms on the right-hand side of the equation will contribute terms with $\cos^2 n\, t$. These, in turn, can be reduced to terms with $\cos 2\, n\, t$, $\sin 2\, n\, t$ and steady-state, i. e. time independent terms. Taking into account these circum-

† This is necessary for the correct calculation of the convective terms on the right-hand side in eqn. (11.7)

‡ It should be noted that here, as distinct from Chap. V, the system of co-ordinates is linked with the body; furthermore, the dimensionless co-ordinate η differs from that used in eqn. (5.26a) by a factor $\sqrt{2}$.

stances we can express the stream function of the second approximation in the form

$$\psi_1(x, y, t) = \sqrt{\frac{\nu}{n}}\, U_0(x)\, \frac{\mathrm{d}U_0}{\mathrm{d}x}\, \frac{1}{n}\, \{\, \zeta_{1a}(\eta)\, \mathrm{e}^{2\,int} + \zeta_{1b}(\eta)\, \}$$

and hence

$$u_1\,(x, y, t) = U_0(x)\, \frac{\mathrm{d}U_0}{\mathrm{d}x}\, \frac{1}{n}\, \{\, \zeta_{1a}'\, \mathrm{e}^{2\,int} + \zeta'_{1b}\}\,, \tag{11.41}$$

where ζ_{1a} denotes the periodic and ζ_{1b} the steady-state contribution of the second approximation, respectively. As seen from eqn. (11.7) these two functions satisfy the following differential equations:

$$2\,\mathrm{i}\,\zeta_{1a}' - \zeta_{1a}''' = \tfrac{1}{2}\,(1 - \zeta_0'^2 + \zeta_0\,\zeta_0'')\,,$$

$$-\,\zeta_{1b}''' = \tfrac{1}{2} - \tfrac{1}{2}\,\zeta_0'\,\overline{\zeta_0'} + \tfrac{1}{4}\,(\zeta_0\overline{\zeta_0''} + \overline{\zeta_0}\,\zeta_0'')\,,$$

where the bar over the symbols denotes the respective conjugate complex quantities.

The normal and tangential components of the periodic contribution must vanish at the wall, whereas at a large distance from it only the tangential component vanishes. Putting $\eta' = \eta/\sqrt{2}$ we obtain

$$\zeta_{1a}' = -\frac{\mathrm{i}}{2}\exp\,[-\,(1+\mathrm{i})\,\sqrt{2}\,\eta'] + \frac{\mathrm{i}}{2}\exp\,[-\,(1+\mathrm{i})\,\eta'] - \frac{\mathrm{i}+1}{2}\,\eta'\exp[-\,(1+\mathrm{i})\,\eta']\,.$$

Regarding the steady-state contribution it is found that only the boundary conditions at the wall can be satisfied, and that at a large distance from it it is possible to make the tangential component finite but not zero. Thus

$$\zeta_{1b}' = -\frac{3}{4} + \frac{1}{4}\exp\,(-\,2\,\eta') + 2\sin\eta'\exp\,(-\,\eta') + $$
$$+\,\frac{1}{2}\cos\eta'\exp\,(-\,\eta') - \frac{\eta'}{2}\,(\cos\eta' - \sin\eta')\exp\,(-\,\eta')$$

so that

$$\zeta_{1b}'(\infty) = -\,\tfrac{3}{4}\,.$$

The second approximation is seen to contain a steady-state term which does not vanish at a large distance from the body, i. e. outside the boundary layer. Its magnitude is given by

$$u_1\,(x,\,\infty) = -\,\frac{3}{4\,n}\,U_0\,\frac{\mathrm{d}U_0}{\mathrm{d}x}\,. \tag{11.42}$$

The preceding argument has thus led us to the remarkable result that a potential flow which is periodic with respect to time induces a steady, secondary ('streaming') motion at a large distance from the wall as a result of viscous forces. Its magnitude, given by eqn. (11.42), is independent of the viscosity. The steady-state component of the velocity is such that fluid particles are seen to flow in the direction of decreasing amplitude of that component of the potential velocity which is parallel to the wall.

An example of such a motion, viz. the pattern of streamlines of the steady flow about a circular cylinder which oscillates in a fluid at rest, is shown in Fig. 11.7.

Fig. 11.8 contains a photograph of the flow pattern about a cylinder which performs an oscillatory motion in a tank filled with water. The camera with which the photograph was taken moved with the cylinder and the surface of the water was covered with fine metallic particles which rendered the motion visible. The particles show up as wide bands in the picture owing to the long exposure time and to their reciprocating motion. The fluid particles flow towards the cylinder from above and from below, and move away in both directions parallel to the reciprocating motion of the cylinder. This is in good agreement with the theoretical pattern of stream-lines shown in Fig. 11.7. Similar photographs were also published by E. N. Andrade [1], who induced standing sound waves in a circular cylinder and rendered the resulting secondary flow visible by the addition of smoke.

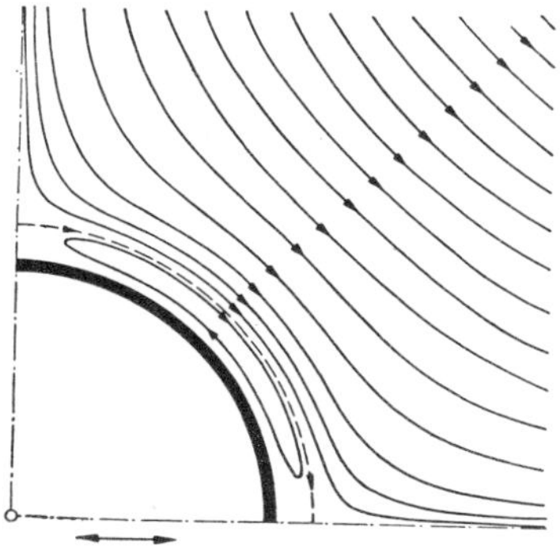

Fig. 11.7. Pattern of stream-lines of the steady secondary motion in the neighbourhood of an oscillating circular cylinder

Fig. 11.8. Secondary flow in the neighbourhood of an oscillating circular cylinder. The camera moves with the cylinder. The metallic particles which serve to render the flow visible show up as wide bands owing to the long exposure time and to their reciprocating motion

It is important to notice here that the first approximation, u_0 in eqn. (11.40), shows that the different layers in the fluid oscillate with different phase shifts compared with the forcing oscillations, and that their amplitudes decrease outwards from the wall. The same features were exhibited by the solutions discussed in Chap. V. The first approximation, u_0, as well as the solutions in Chap. V were obtained from differential equations which did not contain the convective terms

$$u \frac{\partial u}{\partial x}, \quad v \frac{\partial u}{\partial y}, \quad \text{and} \quad U \frac{\partial U}{\partial x}.$$

It can, therefore, be stated that y-dependent phase shifts and amplitudes decaying with distance from the wall are caused exclusively by the action of viscosity. On the other hand, in the second approximation, u_1 in eqn. (11.41), there appears a term which is not periodic and which represents steady streaming superimposed on the oscillatory motion. Hence, it can also be stated that secondary flow has its origin in the convective terms and is due to the interaction between inertia and viscosity. It should be borne in mind that simplifications in which the convective terms have been omitted lead to solutions which are free from streaming and may, therefore, give a misleading representation of the flow. Streaming does, in general, appear only when the solution is carried to at least the second-order approximation.

The present solution provides a good example of the effect of averaging the free stream velocity, as is done in the calculation of laminar boundary layers in the presence of turbulent free streams, and of treating the problem as a steady-state one, mentioned earlier in Secs. VIIg and XIa. Had this been done in the present case, we would obtain from eqn. (11.37) that

$$\bar{U}(x) = 0$$

and this would lead to the trivial quasi-steady solutions

$$u_s = v_s = 0 .$$

On the other hand the time averages of the solutions in eqns. (11.40) and (11.41) will give

$$u = u_0 + u_1 , \quad \bar{u}_0 = 0 , \quad \bar{u}_1 = 0$$

and

$$\bar{u} = \bar{U}_0(x) \frac{\mathrm{d}U_0}{\mathrm{d}x} \frac{1}{n} \bar{\xi}'_{1b} = \left\{ -\tfrac{3}{4} + \tfrac{1}{4} \exp\left(-y\sqrt{\frac{2n}{\nu}}\right) + \right.$$

$$+ 2\sin\left(y\sqrt{\frac{n}{2\nu}}\right)\exp\left(-y\sqrt{\frac{n}{2\nu}}\right) + \tfrac{1}{2}\cos\left(y\sqrt{\frac{n}{2\nu}}\right)\exp\left(-y\sqrt{\frac{n}{2\nu}}\right) -$$

$$\left. -\tfrac{1}{2}\, y\sqrt{\frac{n}{2\nu}}\left[\cos\left(y\sqrt{\frac{n}{2\nu}}\right) - \sin\left(y\sqrt{\frac{n}{2\nu}}\right)\right]\exp\left(-y\sqrt{\frac{n}{2\nu}}\right)\right\} U_0 \frac{\mathrm{d}U_0}{\mathrm{d}x}\frac{1}{n} .$$

Evidently the true average $\bar{u}$ is different from the quasi-steady solution u_s and the same can be said about the equations for the transverse component in v and v_s. The difference is due to the existence of secondary flow which is induced by the oscillation through the action of inertia forces.

The phenomena under consideration offer a simple explanation of Kundt's dust patterns which are used to demonstrate the existence of standing sound waves in a tube. The sound waves in question are longitudinal ones and the maxima of their amplitudes are located at points of maximum amplitude in the standing waves (Fig. 11.9). Thus a secondary flow is induced in the pipe and its velocity near the wall is directed from the point of maximum amplitude to the nodes. At a large distance from the wall the velocity must, evidently, change sign to satisfy the continuity requirement. This induces 'streaming' motion effects, the shifting of the particles of dust, and causes them to form little heaps at the nodes.

It is clear from the preceding description that the quantity of dust used to produce Kundt patterns is of great importance. A large quantity of dust will become agitated and may reach the region of inner flow when vibrations of the tube are excited. Consequently it may not be possible to cause the dust to move away from the points of maximum amplitude. If, however, only a small quantity of it is taken, the influence of the flow near the wall will be stronger and the points of maximum amplitude will soon become free of dust. Problems connected with steady motion which accompany oscillations have been recently treated in greater detail in publications on acoustics, *cf.* [23].

M. J. Lighthill [8] used an approximate method to examine the effect of small periodic oscillations superimposed on a steady flow about a solid body. It turns out that the maxima of the oscillations in the shearing stress at the solid surface anticipate somewhat the maxima of the velocity oscillations; this is due to the fact that the boundary layer responds faster to changes in the pressure gradient than the external flow. The fluctuations in the pressure gradient, naturally, are required to accelerate and to decelerate the oscillating flow. Oscillations in the rate of heat transfer are also treated in the paper, but owing to the nature of the approximation, namely to the fact that only terms of the first order in amplitude are retained, the existence of secondary flow is not revealed by the analysis. In this connexion a paper by M. B. Glauert [4a] may also be consulted.

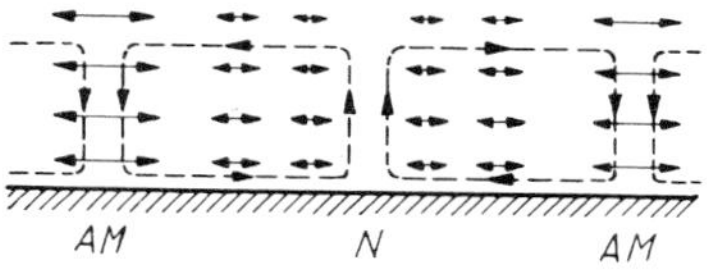

Fig. 11.9. Explanation of the formation of Kundt's dust patterns
AM = amplitude maximum;
N = node of oscillation

2. Oscillating flow through a pipe. The case of the flow of a fluid through a pipe under the influence of a periodic pressure difference affords another example of an oscillating flow in the boundary layer. This type of flow occurs e. g. under the influence of a reciprocating piston, and its theory was given by Th. Sexl [17] and S. Uchida [22]. It will now be assumed that the pipe is very long and circular in cross-section. We shall denote the co-ordinate in the direction of the axis of the pipe by x, denoting the radial distance from it by r. Under the previous assumptions the flow may be taken to be independent of x. When the axial velocity component, u, ceases to depend on x, the other velocity component must vanish together with the convective terms parallel to the tube axis. Thus the Navier-Stokes equation (3.33 c) assumes the form

$$\frac{\partial u}{\partial t} = -\frac{1}{\varrho}\frac{\partial p}{\partial x} + \nu\left(\frac{\partial^2 u}{\partial r^2} + \frac{1}{r}\frac{\partial u}{\partial r}\right), \tag{11.43}$$

which is exact as it implies no additional simplifications. The boundary condition is $u = 0$ for $r = R$ at the wall. We shall assume that the pressure gradient caused by the motion of the piston is harmonic and is given by

$$-\frac{1}{\varrho}\frac{\partial p}{\partial x} = K\cos nt\,, \tag{11.44}$$

where K denotes a constant. It is, again, convenient to use complex notation and to put

$$-\frac{1}{\varrho}\frac{\partial p}{\partial x} = K\,e^{int},$$

attributing physical significance only to the real part.

Assuming that the velocity function has the form $u(r,t) = f(r)\,e^{int}$, and referring to eqn. (11.43), we obtain the following differential equation for the function $f(r)$:

$$f''(r) + \frac{1}{r}f'(r) - \frac{i\,n}{\nu}f(r) = -\frac{K}{\nu}$$

whose solution is given by

$$u(r,t) = -\mathrm{i}\frac{K}{n}\mathrm{e}^{\mathrm{i}nt}\left\{1 - \frac{J_0\left(r\sqrt{\frac{-\mathrm{i}n}{\nu}}\right)}{J_0\left(R\sqrt{\frac{-\mathrm{i}n}{\nu}}\right)}\right\}. \tag{11.45}$$

Here J_0 denotes the Bessel function of the first kind and of zero order. Owing to the linearity of eqn. (11.43), the solutions obtained in eqn. (11.45) can be superimposed for different frequencies. A full discussion of this equation for arbitrary values of n is somewhat tedious owing to the presence of the Bessel function with a complex argument, but the two limiting cases of very large and very small circular frequencies, n, respectively prove to be extremely simple.

Expanding the Bessel function in a series and retaining only the quadratic terms we obtain an expression which is valid for the case of very small values of the dimensionless group $\sqrt{n/\nu}\,R$ (very slow oscillations):

$$u(r,t) = -\mathrm{i}\frac{K}{n}\mathrm{e}^{\mathrm{i}nt}\left\{1 - \frac{1+\frac{\mathrm{i}n}{4\nu}r^2}{1+\frac{\mathrm{i}n}{4\nu}R^2}\right\} \tag{11.46}$$

or, returning to the real notation

$$u(r,t) = \frac{K}{4\nu}\mathrm{e}^{\mathrm{i}nt}(R^2 - r^2) = \frac{K}{4\nu}(R^2 - r^2)\cos(nt).$$

The velocity distribution is seen to be in phase with the exciting pressure distribution, the amplitude being a parabolic function of the radius as was the case in steady flow.

Using the asymptotic expansion of the Bessel function $J_0(z) \to \sqrt{2/\pi z}\,\mathrm{e}^{\mathrm{i}z}\,\mathrm{i}^{-1/2}$ we obtain an expression for very large values of $\sqrt{n/\nu}\,R$:

$$u(r,t) = -\frac{\mathrm{i}K}{n}\mathrm{e}^{\mathrm{i}nt}\left\{1 - \sqrt{\frac{R}{r}}\exp\left[-(1+\mathrm{i})\sqrt{\frac{n}{2\nu}}(R-r)\right]\right\}$$

or, in the real notation

$$u(r,t) = \frac{K}{n}\left\{\sin nt - \sqrt{\frac{R}{r}}\exp\left(-\sqrt{\frac{n}{2\nu}}(R-r)\right)\sin\left[nt - \sqrt{\frac{n}{2\nu}}(R-r)\right]\right\}. \tag{11.47}$$

The second term is quickly damped out as the distance from the wall, $R - r$, increases, provided that $\sqrt{n/\nu}\,R$ is large. Consequently at a large distance from the wall only the first term is important; it is seen to be independent of that distance. This solution has a form typical for boundary layers because at a large distance from the wall the fluid moves as if it were frictionless and, moreover, its phase is shifted by half a period with respect to the exciting force.

The sketch in Fig. 11.10 represents the velocity profile for an intermediate frequency ($\sqrt{n/\nu}\,R = 5$) of oscillation at different instants of one period. When a comparison is made between the velocity profiles and the diagram of the variation of the pressure gradient with time, plotted at the bottom, it emerges that the flow on the axis of the pipe lags behind that in the layers near the wall. It should be noted that in line with our remarks in the preceding section, the present solution is free from secondary flow because the non-linear inertia terms did not appear in the differential equation (11.43). On the other hand, the characteristic phase shifts and amplitude decays can be clearly discerned.

The preceding type of flow was investigated experimentally by E. G. Richardson and E. Tyler [11], who measured the mean with respect to time of the velocity squared, to be denoted by $\overline{u^2}$. In the case of fast oscillation we obtain from eqn. (11.47) the expression

$$\overline{u^2(r)} = \frac{K^2}{2n^2}\left\{1-2\sqrt{\frac{R}{r}}\exp\left[-\sqrt{\frac{n}{2\nu}}(R-r)\right]\cos\left[\sqrt{\frac{n}{2\nu}}(R-r)\right]+ + \frac{R}{r}\exp\left[-2\sqrt{\frac{n}{2\nu}}(R-r)\right]\right\}.$$

If the distance from the wall $y = R - r$ is small compared with the pipe radius R, the ratio R/r can be replaced by unity. Thus, introducing the dimensionless distance from the wall $\eta = (R-r)\sqrt{n/2\nu} = y\sqrt{n/2\nu}$, we have

$$\frac{\overline{u^2(y)}}{K^2/2n^2} = 1 - 2\cos\eta\exp(-\eta) + \exp(-2\eta)\,. \tag{11.48}$$

The variation of this mean is seen plotted against η in Fig. 11.11. The maximum value does not coincide with the axis of the pipe (large distance), but occurs near the wall at $\eta = y\sqrt{n/2\nu} = 2{\cdot}28$. This value agrees very well with measurement (E. G. Richardson's [11] 'annular effect'). In this connexion the reader is also referred to M. Z. Krzywoblocki's calculations for compressible fluids (Chap. X [34]).

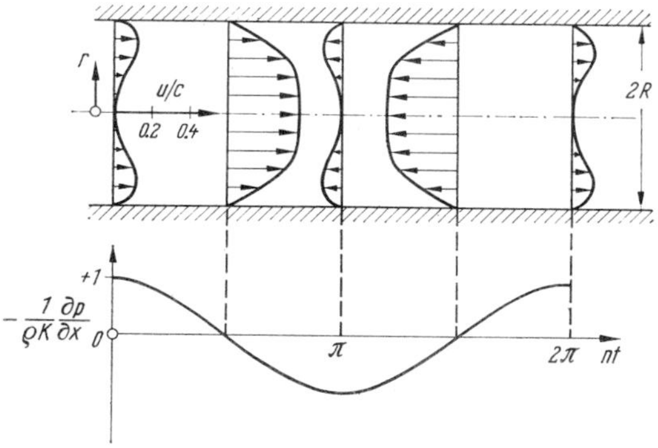

Fig. 11.10. Velocity distribution in oscillating pipe flow at different instants of one period, after S. Uchida [22]

Pressure gradient: $-\frac{\partial p}{\partial x} = \varrho K \cos(nt)$

$k = \sqrt{\frac{n}{\nu}}R$; $c = \frac{K k^2}{8n} = 3{\cdot}125\frac{K}{n}$

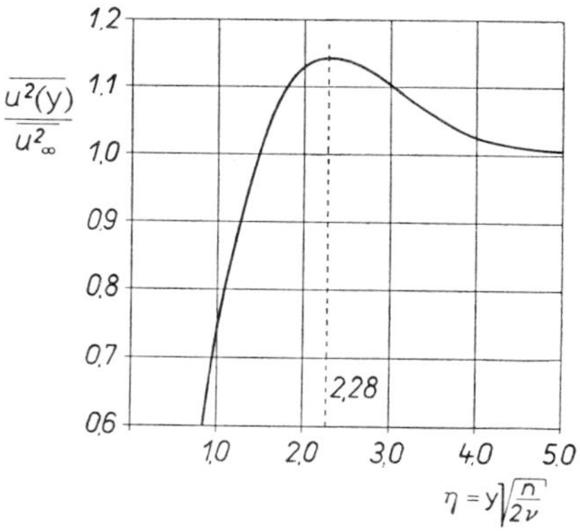

Fig. 11.11. Variation of the mean with respect to time of the velocity squared for periodic pipe flow (E. G. Richardson's [11] 'annular effect')

y = distance from the wall of the pipe; $u^2_\infty = K^2/2n^2$ = mean with respect to time of the velocity squared at large distance from wall

3. C. C. Lin's theory of harmonic oscillations. In the preceding two sections we have considered typical examples of oscillations involving fluids at rest. Problems in which the oscillation is superimposed on a stream are much more important in applications, but also much more difficult to analyse. A certain insight into this type of process can be obtained with the aid of C. C. Lin's theory [8a] described in Sec. XIa.

If the external oscillation is described by the function

$$U_1(x, t) = U_0(x) \sin nt , \tag{11.49}$$

we can find from eqn. (11.11) that the oscillating component of the longitudinal velocity u is given by

$$u_1(x, y, t) = U_0(x) \{ \sin nt - [\exp(-y/\delta)] \cdot [\sin(nt - y/\delta_0)] \} \tag{11.50}$$

in which the y-dependent phase-shift of the different layers is again discernible in the term multiplied by sin $(nt - y/\delta_0)$. It is convenient, once more, to introduce the complex notation, attaching significance only to the *imaginary* part. Then

$$u_1(x, y, t) = U_0(x) \{ \exp\, int \} \cdot \{ 1 - \exp[-(1 + i)\, y/\delta_0] \} , \tag{11.50a}$$

and from the continuity equation (11.14a) we can calculate

$$v_1(x, y, t) = -\left\{ U_0(x)\, \delta_0 \left[\exp\, int\right] \cdot \left[\frac{y}{\delta_0} + \frac{\exp[-(1+i)y/\delta_0] - 1}{1 + i} \right] \right\} . \tag{11.50b}$$

The velocity profile for v_1 also shows the phase shift characteristic of this type of problem. With the aid of the solutions in eqns. (11.50a, b) we can now calculate the additional, virtual pressure gradient $\mathcal{F}$ from eqn. (11.10a). Since the oscillation equation (11.11) is linear, any external oscillation $U_1(x, t)$ can be decomposed in a Fourier series whose terms will have the form (11.49) with a spectrum of frequencies n_k and the resulting virtual pressure gradient can also be computed. In the case of a single harmonic we obtain

$$\mathcal{F} = \tfrac{1}{2} U_0 \frac{dU_0}{dx} F\left(\frac{y}{\delta_0}\right) \tag{11.51}$$

where

$$F\left(\frac{y}{\delta_0}\right) = \exp(-y/\delta_0)\,[(2 + y/\delta_0) \cos(y/\delta_0) - (1 - y/\delta_0) \sin(y/\delta_0) - \exp(-2\, y/\delta_0)] . \tag{11.51a}$$

A diagram of this function is seen plotted in Fig. 11.12. The expression (11.51) shows that deviations between the true mean velocity profile $\overline{u}$ and the quasi-steady velocity profile u_s which would exist if we were to assume $\mathcal{F} = 0$, depend essentially on the amplitude U_0 of the oscillation and on its variation dU_0/dx along the flow. In particular, even a large amplitude of oscillation will produce no change in the velocity profile if it remains constant along the flow, i. e. if $dU_0/dx = 0$. From the diagram in Fig. 11.12 it can be deduced that the largest relative modification of the velocity profile occurs near the wall, because $F(y/\delta_0)$ has the largest value $F = 1$ there. The resulting curvature of the velocity profile at the wall is, therefore, given by

$$\nu \left(\frac{\partial^2 u}{\partial y^2}\right)_{wall} = -\left(\overline{U}\,\frac{d\overline{U}}{dx} + \tfrac{1}{2}\,U_0\,\frac{dU_0}{dx}\right). \tag{11.52}$$

This can be understood physically if it is remembered that the fluid particles nearest to the wall move under relatively small accelerations. Consequently, the additional pressure gradient $\mathcal{F}$ will produce the greatest changes near the wall.

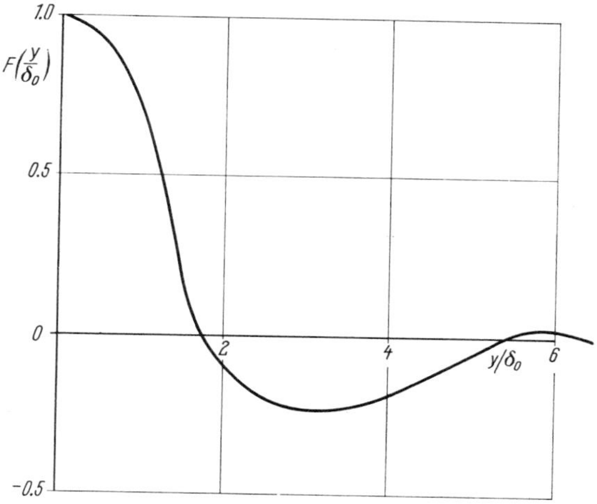

Fig. 11.12. Plot of the function $F(y/\delta_0)$ from eqn. (11.51 a) for a single harmonic component in C. C. Lin's theory [8 a]

If there were a spectrum of harmonics of frequencies kn ($k = 1, 2, \ldots$), i. e. for a free-stream velocity

$$U(x,t) = \overline{U}(x) + \sum_k U_{0k}(x) \sin knt\,, \tag{11.53}$$

we would obtain simply

$$\mathcal{F} = \sum_k \tfrac{1}{2}\,U_{0k}\,\frac{dU_{0k}}{dx}\,F\left(\frac{y}{\delta_{0k}}\right) \tag{11.53 a}$$

with

$$\delta_{0k} = \sqrt{\frac{2\,\nu}{k\,n}}\,. \tag{11.53 b}$$

From what has been said before it is clear that the position of the point of laminar separation is affected by the external oscillations and that the point of separation must oscillate itself. In addition, the rate of dissipation of energy will increase by an amount proportional to

$$\mu\left(\frac{\partial u_1}{\partial y}\right)^2.$$

Finally, the fundamental oscillation induces higher harmonics in the boundary layer oscillation and the latter can be calculated by an iterative procedure described by C. C. Lin [8 a].

4. Progressing wave. As an example of the method of direct series expansion we shall consider the flow in the boundary layer associated with the free-stream velocity given by

$$U(x,t) = U_0\left[1 + \lambda \cos n\left(\frac{x}{U_0} - t\right)\right], \quad \lambda < 1, \tag{11.54}$$

studied by J. Kestin, P. F. Maeder and H. E. Wang [7a]. Eqn. (11.54) represents uniform flow past a flat plate at zero incidence on which there is superimposed a harmonic wave of frequency n and amplitude λU_0 progressing in the x-direction at a velocity U_0.

When the frequency is low, the motion is expected to deviate only little from steady flow, and a series expansion in powers of λ representing a perturbation on the steady-state solution can be postulated. Hence it is assumed that

$$\left.\begin{aligned} u(x,y,t) &= u_0(x,y) + \lambda\, u_1(x,y,t) + \lambda^2 u_2(x,y,t) + \dots \\ v(x,y,t) &= v_0(x,y) + \lambda\, v_1(x,y,t) + \lambda^2 v_2(x,y,t) + \dots . \end{aligned}\right\} \tag{11.55}$$

Substituting these expressions into eqns. (11.1) and (11.2), and equating to zero each coefficient multiplying the ascending powers of λ, we obtain a series of systems of equations, one for each of the successive approximations u_0, v_0; u_1, v_1; etc. The equations for u_0, v_0 are identical with the Blasius equations (7.23), (7.24), and u_0 and v_0 are given by eqns. (7.27) and (7.28) in terms of the Blasius function $f(\eta)$ except for trivial changes in notation.

The equations for the first and higher-order terms are progressively more complicated, and we shall confine ourselves to writing down the equations for u_1, v_1 and u_2, v_2 only. Denoting

$$U_1 = U_0\, \lambda \cos\left[n\left(\frac{x}{U_0} - t\right)\right], \tag{11.56}$$

we have

$$\left.\begin{aligned} &\frac{\partial u_1}{\partial x} + \frac{\partial v_1}{\partial y} = 0 \\ &\frac{\partial u_1}{\partial t} + u_0\frac{\partial u_1}{\partial x} + u_1\frac{\partial u_0}{\partial x} + v_0\frac{\partial u_1}{\partial y} + v_1\frac{\partial u_0}{\partial y} = \frac{\partial U_1}{\partial t} + U_0\frac{\partial U_1}{\partial x} + \nu\left(\frac{\partial^2 u_1}{\partial y^2}\right), \\ &u_1 = v_1 = 0: \quad y = 0; \quad u_1 = U_1: \quad y = \infty, \end{aligned}\right\} \tag{11.56a}$$

and

$$\left.\begin{aligned} &\frac{\partial u_2}{\partial x} + \frac{\partial v_2}{\partial y} = 0 \\ &\frac{\partial u_2}{\partial t} + u_0\frac{\partial u_2}{\partial x} + u_1\frac{\partial u_1}{\partial x} + u_2\frac{\partial u_0}{\partial x} + v_0\frac{\partial u_2}{\partial x} + v_1\frac{\partial u_1}{\partial y} + v_2\frac{\partial u_0}{\partial y} = \\ &\qquad = U_1\frac{\partial U_1}{\partial x} + \nu\left(\frac{\partial^2 u_2}{\partial y^2}\right), \\ &u_2 = v_2 = 0: \quad y = 0; \quad u_2 = 0: \quad y = \infty. \end{aligned}\right\} \tag{11.56b}$$

Next, we seek series expansions in terms of the frequency parameter

$$\beta = \frac{n\,x}{U_0}\,,$$

which puts a restriction on the frequency n, as β must be smaller than unity. Denoting

$$\psi = n\left(\frac{x}{U_0} - t\right)\,,$$

we assume

$$\left.\begin{aligned} u_1 &= U_0 \sum_{\mathrm{I}}^{\infty} \{A_k'(\eta)\,\beta^{k-1}\cos\,\psi + B_k'(\eta)\,\beta^{k-1}\sin\,\psi\} \\ u_2 &= U_0 \sum_{\mathrm{I}}^{\infty} C_k'(\eta)\,\beta^{k-1} + \mathrm{D}_k'(\eta)\,\beta^{k-1}\cos\,2\,\psi + \mathrm{E}_k'(\eta)\,\beta^{k-1}\sin\,2\,\psi\}\,. \end{aligned}\right\} \qquad (11.57)$$

Here, as usual

$$\eta = y\,\sqrt{\frac{U_1}{\nu\,x}}\,,$$

and the form assumed for u_2 makes an allowance for the fact that a secondary-flow term, $C_k'(\eta)\,\beta^{k-1}$ must appear in it. The transverse components v_1 and v_2 can be obtained from the continuity equations by simple integration.

Substituting the forms (11.57) into the respective equations we can derive ordinary differential equations for the functional coefficients A_k, B_k etc. It turns out that

$$A_2 = A_4 = \ldots\ldots = B_1 = B_3 = \ldots\ldots = 0$$

because these coefficients satisfy homogeneous equations with homogeneous boundary conditions. The same symmetry exists with respect to C_k, D_k and E_k.

The ordinary differential equations obtained in this way must be solved numerically. The equations for A_1 and C_1 have been solved with the aid of a digital computer, and the resulting functions are seen plotted in Fig. 11.13. They satisfy the equations

$$\left.\begin{aligned} 2\,A_1''' + f\,A_1'' + f''\,A_1 &= 0 \\ 4\,C_1''' + 2\,f\,C_1'' + 2\,f''\,C_1 + A_1\,A_1'' &= 0 \end{aligned}\right\} \qquad (11.58)$$

with the boundary conditions

$$A_1 = A_1' = C_1 = C_1' = 0: \quad \eta = 0\,; \quad A_1' = 1\,; \quad C_1' = 0: \quad \eta = \infty\,.$$

The time-average skin friction coefficient for a plate wetted on two sides can now be given to order λ^2. It is easy to derive that

$$\overline{C}_f = \frac{n}{2\,\pi}\int_0^{2\,\pi/n} C_f\,\mathrm{d}t = \frac{4\,f''(0)}{\sqrt{\mathsf{R}}}\left\{1 + \lambda^2\,\frac{C_1''(0)}{f''(0)} + \ldots\right\} \qquad (11.59)$$

where the next two terms would be of order $\lambda^2\beta^2$ and λ^4 respectively. The effect of the oscillations is to increase the skin friction coefficient, as compared with its steady-state value, by the terms following unity in the curly bracket of eqn. (11.59). Since

$$f''(0) = 0{\cdot}332 \text{ and } C_1''(0) = 0{\cdot}059\,,$$

we find that

$$\overline{C}_f \approx \frac{1{\cdot}328}{\sqrt{\mathsf{R}}}\,(1 + 0{\cdot}178\,\lambda^2)\,. \tag{11.59a}$$

In their papers mentioned previously, F. K. Moore and S. Ostrach [8b, c, d] used series expansions in terms of the parameters

$$\zeta_{k-1} = \frac{x^k}{U^{k-1}}\cdot\frac{\mathrm{d}^k U}{\mathrm{d}t^k}\,.$$

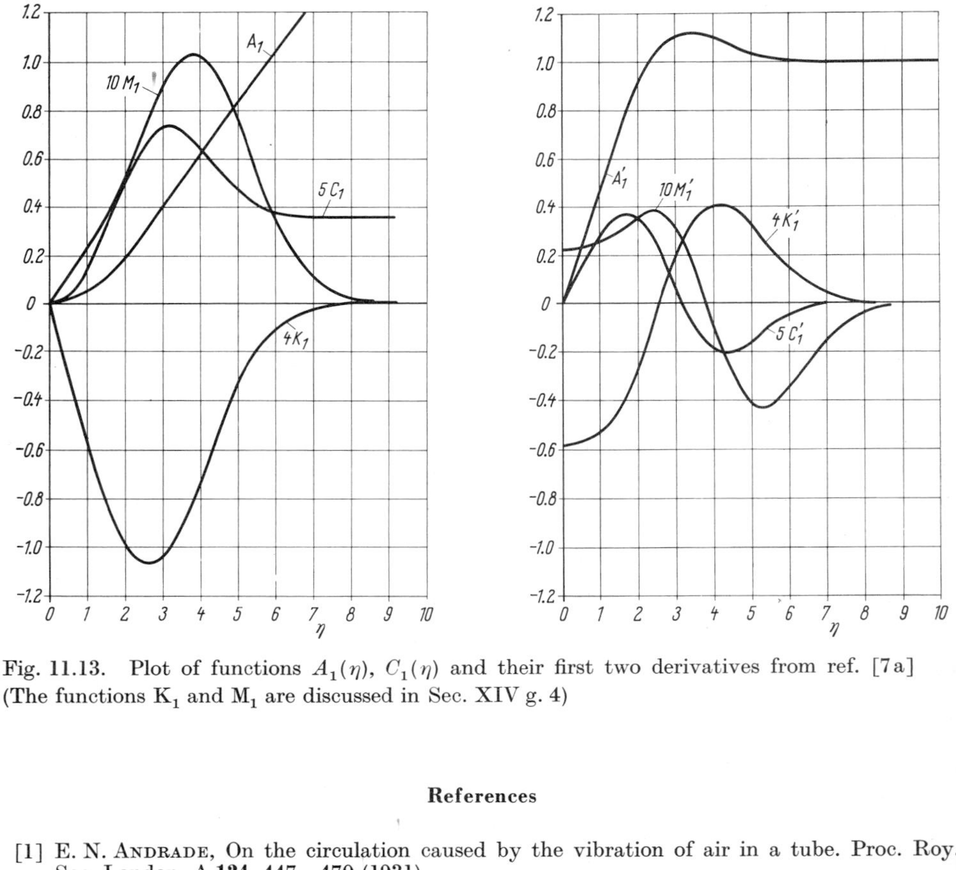

Fig. 11.13. Plot of functions $A_1(\eta)$, $C_1(\eta)$ and their first two derivatives from ref. [7a] (The functions K_1 and M_1 are discussed in Sec. XIV g. 4)

References

[1] E. N. Andrade, On the circulation caused by the vibration of air in a tube. Proc. Roy. Soc. London, A **134**, 447—470 (1931).

[2] H. Blasius, Grenzschichten in Flüssigkeiten mit kleiner Reibung. Z. Math. u. Phys. **56,** 1 (1908).

[3] E. Boltze, Grenzschichten an Rotationskörpern in Flüssigkeiten mit kleiner Reibung. Thesis Göttingen 1908.
[4] Th. Geis, Bemerkung zu den „ähnlichen" instationären laminaren Grenzschichtströmungen. ZAMM **36**, 396—398 (1956).
[4a] M. B. Glauert, The laminar boundary layer on oscillating plates and cylinders. Jour. of Fluid Mech. **1**, 97—110 (1956).
[5] S. Goldstein and L. Rosenhead, Boundary layer growth. Proc. Cambr. Phil. Soc. **32**, 392 (1936).
[6] H. Görtler, Verdrängungswirkung der laminaren Grenzschicht und Druckwiderstand. Ing.-Arch. **14**, 286 (1944).
[7] H. Görtler, Grenzschichtentstehung an Zylindern bei Anfahrt aus der Ruhe. Arch. d. Math. **1**, 138 (1948).
[7a] J. Kestin, P. F. Maeder and H. E. Wang, On boundary layers associated with oscillating streams, to be published.
[8] M. J. Lighthill, The response of laminar skin friction and heat transfer to fluctuations in the stream velocity. Proc. Roy. Soc. A **224**, 1—23 (1954).
[8a] C. C. Lin, Motion in the boundary layer with a rapidly oscillating external flow. Proc. 9th. Intern. Congress Appl. Mech. Brussels 1957, v. 4, p. 155.
[8b] F. K. Moore, Unsteady, laminar boundary-layer flow, NACA TN 2471, 1951.
[8c] S. Ostrach, Compressible laminar layer and heat transfer for unsteady motions of a flat plate. NACA TN 3569, 1955.
[8d] F. K. Moore and S. Ostrach, Average properties of compressible laminar layer on flat plate with unsteady flight velocity. NACA TN 3886, 1956.
[9] S. D. Nigam, Zeitliches Anwachsen der Grenzschicht an einer rotierenden Scheibe bei plötzlichem Beginn der Rotation. Quarterly Amer. Math. 9, 89—91 (1951).
[10] Lord Rayleigh, Phil. Trans. 175 (1883).
[11] E. G. Richardson and E. Tyler, Proc. Phys. Soc. London **42**, 1 (1929).
[12] H. Rubach, Über die Entstehung und Fortbewegung des Wirbelpaares bei zylindrischen Körpern. Thesis Göttingen 1914. VDI-Forschungsheft 185 (1916).
[13] H. Schlichting, Berechnung ebener periodischer Grenzschichtströmungen. Phys. Z. **33**, 327, (1932).
[14] H. Schuh, Calculation of unsteady boundary layers in two-dimensional laminar flow. Zeitschr. Flugw. **I**, 122—131 (1953).
[15] H. Schuh, Über die „ähnlichen" Lösungen der instationären laminaren Grenzschichtgleichungen in inkompressibler Strömung. "Fifty years of boundary layer research", Braunschweig 1955, pp. 147—152.
[16] M. Schwabe, Über Druckermittlung in der instationären ebenen Strömung. Ing.-Arch. **6**, 34 (1935); NACA Tech. Memo. 1039 (1943).
[17] Th. Sexl, Über den von E. G. Richardson entdeckten „Annulareffekt". Z. Phys. **61**, 349 (1930); see also W. Tollmien, Handb. d. Exper.-Phys. **IV**, Pt. 1, 281 (1931).
[18] K. H. Thiriot, Über die laminare Anlaufströmung einer Flüssigkeit über einem rotierenden Boden bei plötzlicher Änderung des Drehungszustandes. ZAMM **20**, 1 (1940).
[19] K. H. Thiriot, Untersuchungen über die Grenzschicht einer Flüssigkeit über einer rotierenden Scheibe bei kleiner Winkelgeschwindigkeitsänderung. ZAMM **22**, 23 (1942).
[20] W. Tollmien, Grenzschichten. Handb. d. Exper.-Physik **IV**, Pt. I, 274 (1931).
[21] W. Tollmien, Die zeitliche Entwicklung der laminaren Grenzschicht am rotierenden Zylinder. Diss. Göttingen 1924; see also Handb. d. Exper.-Physik **IV**, Pt. I, 277 (1931).
[22] S. Uchida, The pulsating viscous flow superposed on the steady laminar motion of incompressible fluid in a circular pipe. ZAMP VII, 403—422 (1956).
[23] P. J. Westervelt, The theory of steady rotational flow generated by a sound field. Jour. Acoust. Soc. Amer. **25**, 60 (1953).
[24] W. Wuest, Grenzschichten an zylindrischen Körpern mit nichtstationärer Querbewegung. ZAMM **32**, 172—178 (1952).
[25] H. Wundt, Wachstum der laminaren Grenzschicht an schräg angeströmten Zylindern bei Anfahrt aus der Ruhe. Ing.-Arch. **23**, 212 (1955).

CHAPTER XII

Approximate methods for the solution of the boundary layer equations

The examples of exact solutions of the boundary layer equations which have been discussed in the preceding chapters have shown that, in most cases, the mathematical difficulties associated with them were very considerable, in spite of the fact that the actual problems under consideration represented very special cases. The general problem involving the flow of a fluid round a body of arbitrary shape, which is particularly important in practical applications, cannot be completely solved with the aid of the analytical methods developed so far. Even the numerical or step-by-step methods require an amount of work which is not acceptable in practice when a large number of examples is to be computed, and if a fast digital computer is not available.

It is, therefore, important to devise approximate methods which would in such cases quickly lead to an answer even if their accuracy were to be inferior to that of the numerical methods. Following Th. von Kármán [12] and K. Pohlhausen [18] it is possible to devise such simplified methods if it is agreed to satisfy the differential equations of boundary layer flow only in the average and over the boundary layer thickness rather than try to satisfy the boundary conditions for every individual fluid particle. Such a mean value function can be obtained from the momentum theorem. This, in turn, is obtained as an integral of the equations of motion over the boundary layer thickness. The momentum theorem which will be made the basis of the approximate method to be discussed in the present chapter has already been deduced in Sec. VIIIe. Before proceeding to apply the method to the general cases of two-dimensional and axially-symmetrical boundary layers with pressure gradients, we shall consider first the essential features of the method as applied to the flat plate at zero incidence. This example is particularly simple in that the pressure gradient vanishes along the whole plate. Moreover, we shall have the opportunity of assessing the power of the approximate method, at least in a particular case, and to compare it with the exact solution which is already known from Chap. VII.

a. Application of the momentum equation to the flow past a flat plate at zero incidence

Applying the momentum equation to the fluid within the control surface shown in Fig. 12.1, we can derive the statement that the flux of momentum through the control surface, considered fixed in space, is equal to the skin friction on the plate $D(x)$ from the leading edge ($x=0$) to the current section at x. The application of the momentum equation to this particular case has already been discussed in Sec. IXf. It was then found, eqn. (9.40), that the drag of a plate wetted on one side is given by

$$D(x) = b\,\varrho \int_{y=0}^{\infty} u(U_\infty - u)\,\mathrm{d}y\,, \tag{12.1}$$

where the integral is to be taken at section x. On the other hand the drag can be expressed as an integral of the shearing stress τ_0 at the wall, taken along the plate

$$D(x) = b \int_0^x \tau_0(x)\,\mathrm{d}x\,. \tag{12.2}$$

Upon comparing eqns. (12.1) and (12.2) we obtain

$$\tau_0(x) = \varrho \frac{\mathrm{d}}{\mathrm{d}x} \int_{y=0}^{\infty} u(U_\infty - u)\,\mathrm{d}y\,. \tag{12.3}$$

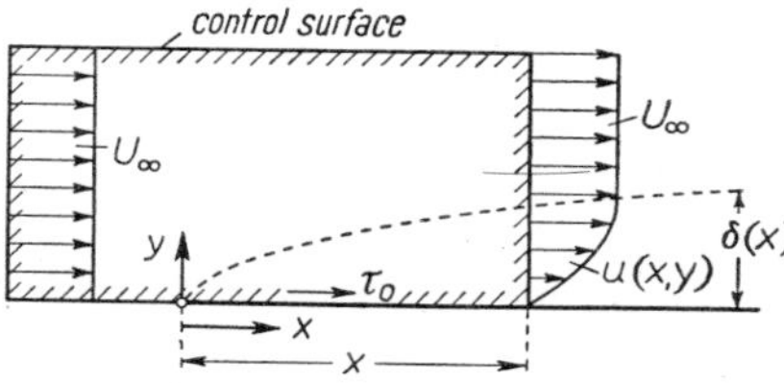

Fig. 12.1. Application of the momentum equation to the flow past a flat plate at zero incidence

This equation can be also deduced in a purely formal way from the boundary layer equation (7.23) by first integrating the equation of motion in the x-direction with respect to y from $y=0$ to $y=\infty$. Equation (12.3) is, finally, obtained without difficulty if the velocity component v is eliminated with the aid of the equation of continuity, and if it is noticed that $\mu(\partial u/\partial y)_{y=0} = \tau_0$.

Introducing the momentum thickness, θ, defined by eqn. (8.34), we have

$$U_\infty{}^2 \frac{\mathrm{d}\theta}{\mathrm{d}x} = \frac{\tau_0}{\varrho}\,. \tag{12.4}$$

The momentum equation in its form (12.4) represents a particular case of the general momentum equation of boundary layer theory as given in eqn. (8.35), being valid for the case of a flat plate at zero incidence. Its physical meaning expresses the fact that the shearing stress at the wall is equal to the loss of momentum in the boundary layer, because in the example under consideration there is no contribution from the pressure gradient.

So far eqn. (12.4) introduced no additional assumptions, as will be the case with the approximate method, but before discussing this matter it might be useful to note a relation between τ_0 and θ, which is obtained from eqn. (12.4) by introducing the exact value for τ_0 from eqn. (7.35a). Putting $\tau_0/\varrho\, U_\infty{}^2 = \alpha \sqrt{\nu/U_\infty x}$ with $\alpha = 0{\cdot}332$, we have

$$\theta = \int_0^x \frac{\tau_0}{\varrho\, U_\infty{}^2}\, dx = 2\,\alpha \sqrt{\frac{\nu\, x}{U_\infty}}$$

and hence

$$\theta = 2\,\frac{\tau_0}{\varrho\, U_\infty{}^2}\, x\,. \tag{12.5}$$

With reference to eqn. (12.3) or (12.4) we can now perform an approximate calculation of the boundary layer along a flat plate at zero incidence. The essence of the approximate method consists in assuming a suitable expression for the velocity distribution $u(y)$ in the boundary layer, taking care that it satisfies the important boundary conditions for $u(y)$, and that it contains, in addition, one free parameter, such as a suitably chosen boundary layer thickness which is finally determined with the aid of the momentum equation (12.3).

In the particular case of a flat plate at zero incidence now being considered it is possible to take advantage of the fact that the velocity profiles are similar. Hence we put

$$\frac{u}{U_\infty} = f\left(\frac{y}{\delta(x)}\right) = f(\eta)\,, \tag{12.6}$$

where $\eta = y/\delta(x)$ is the dimensionless distance from the wall referred to the boundary layer thickness. The similarity of velocity profiles is here accounted for by assuming that $f(\eta)$ is a function of η only, and contains no additional free parameter. The function f must vanish at the wall ($\eta = 0$) and tend to the value 1 for large values of η, in view of the boundary conditions for u. When using the approximate method, it is expedient to place the point at which this transition occurs at a finite distance from the wall, or in other words, to assume a finite boundary layer thickness $\delta(x)$, in spite of the fact that all exact solutions of the boundary layer equations tend asymptotically to the potential flow associated with the particular problem. The boundary layer thickness has no physical significance in this connexion, being only a quantity which it is convenient to use in the computation.

Having assumed the velocity profile in eqn. (12.6), we can now proceed to evaluate the momentum integral (12.3), and we obtain

$$\int_{y=0}^{\infty} u(U_\infty - u)\, dy = U_\infty{}^2\, \delta(x) \int_{\eta=0}^{1} f(1-f)\, d\eta\,. \tag{12.7}$$

The integral in eqn. (12.7) can now be evaluated provided that a specific assumption is made for $f(\eta)$. Putting

$$\alpha_1 = \int_0^1 f(1-f)\, d\eta \tag{12.8}$$

for short, we have

$$\int_{y=0}^{\infty} u(U_\infty - u)\, dy = U_\infty{}^2\, \theta = \alpha_1\, \delta\, U_\infty{}^2$$

or

$$\theta = \alpha_1\, \delta\,. \tag{12.9}$$

The value of the displacement thickness δ^* from eqn. (8.33) will now also be calculated as it will be required later. Putting

$$\alpha_2 = \int_0^1 (1 - f)\, d\eta\,, \tag{12.10}$$

we obtain

$$\delta^* = \alpha_2\, \delta\,. \tag{12.11}$$

Furthermore, the viscous shearing stress at the wall is given by

$$\frac{\tau_0}{\varrho} = \nu \left(\frac{\partial u}{\partial y}\right)_{y=0} = \frac{\nu\, U_\infty}{\delta} \cdot f'(0) = \beta_1 \frac{\nu\, U_\infty}{\delta}\,, \tag{12.12}$$

where

$$\beta_1 = f'(0)\,. \tag{12.13}$$

Introducing these values into the momentum equation (12.4), we obtain $U_\infty^2 \cdot \alpha_1\, d\delta/dx = \beta_1\, \nu\, U_\infty/\delta$, or

$$\delta \frac{d\delta}{dx} = \frac{\beta_1}{\alpha_1} \frac{\nu}{U_\infty}\,.$$

Integration from $\delta = 0$ at $x = 0$ gives the first result of the approximate theory in the form

$$\delta(x) = \sqrt{\frac{2\beta_1}{\alpha_1}} \sqrt{\frac{\nu x}{U_\infty}}\,. \tag{12.14}$$

Hence the shearing stress at the wall from eqn. (12.12) becomes

$$\tau_0(x) = \sqrt{\frac{\alpha_1 \beta_1}{2}}\, \mu\, U_\infty \sqrt{\frac{U_\infty}{\nu\, x}}\,. \tag{12.15}$$

Finally, the total drag on a plate wetted on both sides can be written as $2\,D = 2\,b \int_0^l \tau_0\, dx$, i. e.

$$2\,D = 2\,b \sqrt{2\,\alpha_1 \beta_1} \sqrt{\mu\, \varrho\, l\, U_\infty^3}\,, \tag{12.16}$$

and from eqns. (12.11) and (12.14) we obtain the displacement thickness

$$\delta^* = \alpha_2 \sqrt{\frac{2\beta_1}{\alpha_1}} \sqrt{\frac{\nu\, x}{U_\infty}}\,. \tag{12.17}$$

A comparison of the approximate expressions for the boundary layer thickness, for the shearing stress at the wall, and for drag with the respective formulae of the accurate theory, eqns. (7.40), (7.35) and (7.36), shows that the use of the integral momentum equation leads in all cases to a perfectly correct formulation of the equations. In other words the dependence of these quantities on the current length, x, the free stream velocity, U_∞, and the coefficient of kinematic viscosity, ν, is correctly deduced. Furthermore, the relation between momentum thickness and shearing stress at the wall given by eqn. (12.5) can also be deduced from the approximate calculation, as is easily verified. The still unknown coefficients α_1, α_2 and β_1 can only be calculated if a specific assumption regarding the velocity profile is made, i. e. if the function $f(\eta)$ from eqn. (12.6) is given explicitly.

When writing down an expression for $f(\eta)$, it is necessary to satisfy certain boundary conditions for $u(y)$, i. e. for $f(\eta)$. At least the no slip condition $u = 0$ at $y = 0$ and the condition of continuity when passing from the boundary layer profile to the potential velocity, $u = U$ at $y = \delta$, must be satisfied. Further conditions might include the continuity of the tangent and curvature at the point, where the two solutions are joined. In other words we may seek to satisfy the conditions $\partial u/\partial y = 0$ and $\partial^2 u/\partial y^2 = 0$ at $y = \delta$. In the case of a plate the condition that $\partial^2 u/\partial y^2 = 0$ at $y = 0$ is also of importance and it can be seen from eqn. (7.18) that it is satisfied by the exact solution.

Numerical examples:

We now propose to test the usefulness of the preceding approximate method with the aid of several examples. The quality of the result depends to a great extent on the assumption which is made for the velocity function (12.6). In any case, as already mentioned, the function $f(\eta)$ must vanish at $\eta = 0$ in view of the no slip condition at the wall. Moreover, for large values of η we must have $f(\eta) = 1$. If only a rough approximation is desired, the transition to the value $f(\eta) = 1$ may occur with a discontinuous first derivative. For a better approximation continuity in $\mathrm{d}f/\mathrm{d}\eta$ may be postulated. Independently of the particular assumption for $f(\eta)$ the quantities

$$\delta^* \sqrt{\frac{U_\infty}{\nu x}}, \quad \theta \sqrt{\frac{U_\infty}{\nu x}}, \quad \frac{\tau_0}{\mu U_\infty} \sqrt{\frac{\nu x}{U_\infty}}, \quad c_f \sqrt{\frac{U_\infty l}{\nu}}$$

must be pure numbers. They can be easily calculated from eqns. (12.8) to (12.17).

Table 12.1. Results of the calculation of the boundary layer for a flat plate at zero incidence based on approximate theory

	Velocity distribution $u/U = f(\eta)$	α_1	α_2	β_1	$\delta^* \sqrt{\frac{U_\infty}{\nu x}}$	$\frac{\tau_0}{\mu U_\infty} \sqrt{\frac{\nu x}{U_\infty}}$	$c_f \left(\frac{U_\infty l}{\nu}\right)^{\frac{1}{2}}$	$\frac{\delta^*}{\theta}$
1	$f(\eta) = \eta$	$\frac{1}{6}$	$\frac{1}{2}$	1	1·732	0·289	1·155	3·00
2	$f(\eta) = \frac{3}{2}\eta - \frac{1}{2}\eta^3$	$\frac{39}{280}$	$\frac{3}{8}$	$\frac{3}{2}$	1·740	0·323	1·292	2·70
3	$f(\eta) = 2\eta - 2\eta^3 + \eta^4$	$\frac{37}{315}$	$\frac{3}{10}$	2	1·752	0·343	1·372	2·55
4	$f(\eta) = \sin\left(\frac{\pi}{2}\eta\right)$	$\frac{4-\pi}{2\pi}$	$\frac{\pi-2}{\pi}$	$\frac{\pi}{2}$	1·741	0·327	1·310	2·66
5	exact	—	—	—	1·729	0·332	1·328	2·61

$$\theta \sqrt{\frac{U_\infty}{\nu x}} = \frac{2\tau_0}{\mu U_\infty} \sqrt{\frac{\nu x}{U_\infty}}; \quad c_f \left(\frac{U_\infty l}{\nu}\right)^{\frac{1}{2}} = 2\theta \sqrt{\frac{U_\infty}{\nu x}}$$

Table 12.1 contains results of several calculations with alternative velocity distribution functions. The first two functions are illustrated with the aid of Fig. 12.2. The linear function satisfies only the conditions $f(0) = 0$ and $f(1) = 1$, whereas the cubic function satisfies in addition the conditions $f'(1) = 0$ and $f''(0) = 0$; finally, a fourth degree polynomial can be made to satisfy the additional condition $f''(1) = 0$. The sine function satisfies the same boundary conditions as the polynomial of fourth degree, except for $f''(1) = 0$. The polynomials of third and fourth degree and the sine-function lead to values of shearing stress at the wall which are in error by less than 3 per cent. and may be considered entirely adequate. The values of the displacement thickness δ^* show acceptable agreement with the corresponding exact values.

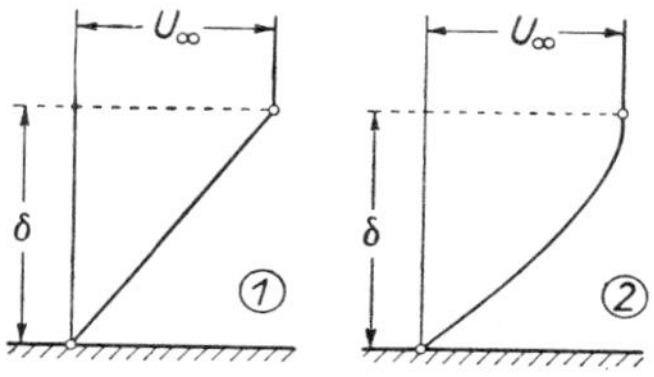

Fig. 12.2. Velocity distribution in the boundary layer on a flat plate at zero incidence

(1) Linear approximation.

(2) Cubic approximation from Table 12.1

It is seen that the approximate method leads to satisfactory results in the case of a flat plate at zero incidence, and the extraordinary simplicity of the calculation is quite remarkable, compared with the complexity of the exact solution.

b. The approximate method due to Th. von Kármán and K. Pohlhausen for two-dimensional flows

We now propose to develop the approximate method of the preceding section so that it can be applied to the general problem of a two-dimensional boundary layer with pressure gradient. The method in its original form was first indicated by K. Pohlhausen [18]. The succeeding description of the method is based on its more modern form as developed by H. Holstein and T. Bohlen [9]. We now choose, as before, a system of co-ordinates in which x denotes the arc measured along the wetted wall and where y denotes the distance from the wall. The basic equation of the momentum theory is obtained by integrating the equation of motion with respect to y from the wall at $y = 0$ to a certain distance $h(x)$ which is assumed to be outside the boundary layer for all values of x. With this notation the momentum equation has the form already given in (8.35), namely

$$U^2 \frac{\mathrm{d}\theta}{\mathrm{d}x} + (2\,\theta + \delta^*)\, U \frac{\mathrm{d}U}{\mathrm{d}x} = \frac{\tau_0}{\varrho}\,. \tag{12.18}$$

This equation gives an ordinary differential equation for the boundary layer thickness, as was the case with the flat plate in the preceding section, provided that a suitable form is assumed for the velocity profile. This allows us to calculate the momentum thickness, the displacement thickness, and the shearing stress at the wall. In choosing a suitable velocity function it is necessary to take into account the same considerations as before, namely those regarding the no slip condition at the wall, as well as the requirements of continuity at the point where this solution is joined to the potential solution. Furthermore, in the presence of a pressure gradient the function must admit the existence of profiles with and without a point of inflexion corresponding to their occurrence in regions of negative and positive pressure gradients. In order to be in a position to calculate the point of separation with the aid of the approximate method the existence of a profile with zero gradient at the wall $(\partial u/\partial y)_{y=0}=0$ must also be possible. On the other hand functions postulating similarity of velocity profiles for various values of x may no longer be prescribed. Following K. Pohlhausen we assume a polynomial of the fourth degree for the velocity function in terms of the dimensionless distance from the wall $\eta = y/\delta(x)$, i. e. we put

$$\frac{u}{U} = f(\eta) = a\,\eta + b\,\eta^2 + c\,\eta^3 + d\,\eta^4 \tag{12.19}$$

in the range $0 \leq \eta \leq 1$, whereas for $\eta \geq 1$ we assume simply $u/U = 1$. We further demand, as before, that the boundary layer should join the potential flow at the finite distance from the wall $y = \delta(x)$.

In order to determine the four free constants a, b, c, d we shall prescribe the following four boundary conditions

$$\left.\begin{aligned} y = 0:\quad & u = 0\,; \qquad \nu\frac{\partial^2 u}{\partial y^2} = \frac{1}{\varrho}\frac{\mathrm{d}p}{\mathrm{d}x} = -U\frac{\mathrm{d}U}{\mathrm{d}x}\,; \\ y = \delta:\quad & u = U\,; \qquad \frac{\partial u}{\partial y} = 0, \quad \frac{\partial^2 u}{\partial y^2} = 0\,. \end{aligned}\right\} \tag{12.20}$$

As seen from eqns. (7.10) to (7.12), they are all satisfied by the exact solution.

These requirements are sufficient to determine the constants a, b, c, d, because the no slip condition at the wall is implicit in eqn. (12.19). The second condition which is satisfied by all exact solutions, as seen from eqn. (7.18), is of particular importance. It determines the curvature of the velocity profile near the wall and makes sure that there is no point of inflexion in the velocity profile in regions of decreasing pressure. Furthermore, regions of increasing pressure contain points of inflexion as required by the exact solution in Chap. VII., Figs. 7.4 and 7.5. Introducing the dimensionless quantity

$$\Lambda = \frac{\delta^2}{\nu}\frac{\mathrm{d}U}{\mathrm{d}x}\,, \tag{12.21}$$

we obtain the following expressions for the coefficients in eqn. (12.19):

$$a = 2 + \frac{\Lambda}{6}\,; \qquad b = -\frac{\Lambda}{2}\,; \qquad c = -2 + \frac{\Lambda}{2}\,; \qquad d = 1 - \frac{\Lambda}{6}\,;$$

and hence for the velocity profile:

$$\frac{u}{U} = F(\eta) + \Lambda\,G(\eta) = (2\,\eta - 2\,\eta^3 + \eta^4) + \frac{1}{6}\Lambda(\eta - 3\,\eta^2 + 3\,\eta^3 - \eta^4)\,. \tag{12.22}$$

where

$$\left.\begin{aligned} F(\eta) &= 2\,\eta - 2\,\eta^3 + \eta^4 = 1 - (1-\eta)^3\,(1+\eta)\,, \\ G(\eta) &= \tfrac{1}{6}\,(\eta - 3\,\eta^2 + 3\,\eta^3 - \eta^4) = \tfrac{1}{6}\,\eta\,(1-\eta)^3\,. \end{aligned}\right\} \tag{12.23}$$

It is easily recognized that the velocity profiles expressed in terms of $\eta = y/\delta(x)$ constitute a one-parameter family of curves, the dimensionless quantity Λ being a shape factor. The dimensionless quantity Λ, which may also be written as

$$\Lambda = \frac{\delta^2}{\nu}\frac{\mathrm{d}U}{\mathrm{d}x} = -\frac{\mathrm{d}p}{\mathrm{d}x}\frac{\delta}{\mu U/\delta},$$

can be interpreted physically as the ratio of pressure forces to viscous forces. In order to obtain a quantity to which real physical significance can be ascribed, it would be necessary to replace δ in the above definition by a linear quantity which itself possesses physical significance, such as the momentum thickness. This will be done later in this section.

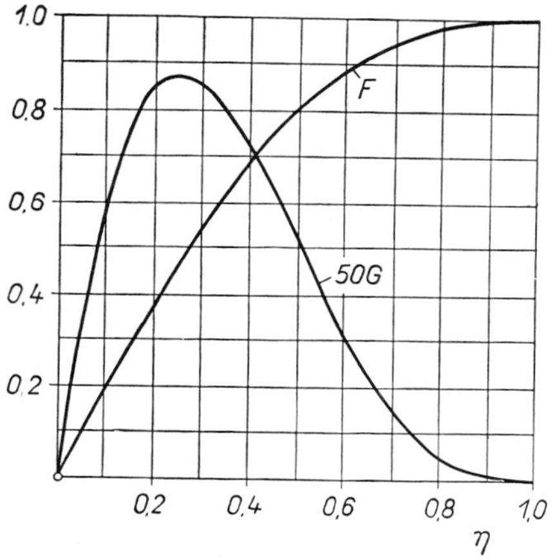

Fig. 12.3. The functions $F(\eta)$ and $G(\eta)$ for the velocity distribution in the boundary layer from eqns. (12.22) and (12.23)

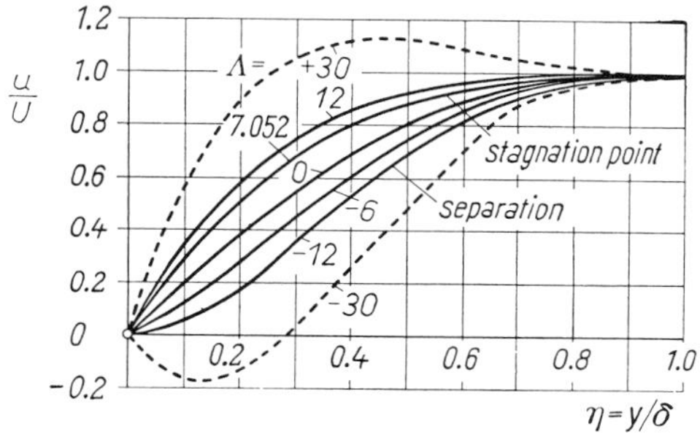

Fig. 12.4. The one-parameter family of velocity profiles from eqn. (12.22)

The two functions $F(\eta)$ and $G(\eta)$ defined by eqn. (12.23), which together compose the velocity distribution function given in eqn. (12.22), are seen plotted in Fig. 12.3. Velocity profiles for various values of Λ are shown in Fig. 12.4. The profile which corresponds to $\Lambda = 0$ is obtained when $\mathrm{d}U/\mathrm{d}x = 0$, i. e. for the boundary layer with no pressure gradient (flat plate at zero incidence), or for a point where the velocity of the potential flow passes through a minimum or a maximum. In this case the velocity profile becomes identical with the fourth degree polynomial used for the flat plate in the preceding section. The profile at separation with $(\partial u/\partial y)_0 = 0$, i. e. with $a = 0$, occurs for $\Lambda = -12$. It will be shown later that the profile at the stagnation point corresponds to $\Lambda = 7{\cdot}052$. For $\Lambda > 12$ values $u/U > 1$ occur in the boundary layer, but this must be excluded in steady flow. Since behind the point of separation the present calculation based, as it is, on the boundary layer concept, loses significance, the shape factor is seen to be restricted to the range $-12 \leq \Lambda \leq +12$.

Before proceeding to calculate the boundary layer thickness $\delta(x)$ from the momentum theorem, it is now convenient to calculate the momentum thickness,

θ, the displacement thickness, δ^*, and the viscous shearing stress at the wall, τ_0, with the aid of the approximate velocity profile in the same way as was done for the flat plate at zero incidence in the preceding section. Thus we obtain from eqns. (8.33) and (8.34), together with eqn. (12.22),

$$\frac{\delta^*}{\delta} = \int_{\eta=0}^{1} [1 - F(\eta) - \Lambda\, G(\eta)]\, d\eta\,,$$

$$\frac{\theta}{\delta} = \int_{\eta=0}^{1} [F(\eta) + \Lambda\, G(\eta)]\,[1 - F(\eta) - \Lambda\, G(\eta)]\, d\eta\,.$$

Computing the definite integrals with the aid of the values of $F(\eta)$ and $G(\eta)$ from eqn. (12.23), we have

$$\frac{\delta^*}{\delta} = \frac{3}{10} - \frac{1}{120}\Lambda\,; \quad \frac{\theta}{\delta} = \left(\frac{37}{315} - \frac{1}{945}\Lambda - \frac{1}{9072}\Lambda^2\right). \tag{12.24}$$

Similarly, the viscous stress at the wall, $\tau_0 = \mu(\partial u/\partial y)_{y=0}$, is given by

$$\frac{\tau_0\,\delta}{\mu U} = 2 + \frac{1}{6}\Lambda\,. \tag{12.25}$$

In order to determine the still unknown shape factor $\Lambda(x)$ and, hence, the function $\delta(x)$ from eqn. (12.21), it is now necessary to refer to the momentum equation (12.18). Multiplying by $\theta/\nu U$ we can represent it in the following dimensionless form:

$$\frac{U\,\theta\theta'}{\nu} + \left(2 + \frac{\delta^*}{\theta}\right)\frac{U'\,\theta^2}{\nu} = \frac{\tau_0\,\theta}{\mu U}\,, \tag{12.26}$$

in which the boundary layer thickness δ does not appear explicitly; this circumstance is not surprising, because it constitutes only a fortuitous quantity associated with the approximate method of calculation and has no particular physical meaning. On the other hand eqn. (12.26) contains the really important physical quantities, viz. the displacement thickness, δ^*, the momentum thickness, θ, and the shearing stress at the wall τ_0. It is, therefore, natural to begin with the calculation of θ from the momentum equation (12.26) and to deduce δ from it with the aid of eqn. (12.24). Following H. Holstein and T. Bohlen [9] it is convenient to introduce for this purpose a second shape factor

$$K = \frac{\theta^2}{\nu}\frac{dU}{dx}\,, \tag{12.27}$$

which is connected with the momentum thickness in the same way as the first shape factor, Λ, was connected with the boundary layer thickness, δ, in eqn. (12.21). In addition we shall put

$$Z = \frac{\theta^2}{\nu}\,, \tag{12.28}$$

so that

$$K = Z\,\frac{dU}{dx}\,. \tag{12.29}$$

It is seen from eqns. (12.21), (12.27) and (12.24) that the shape factors Λ and K satisfy the universal relation

$$K = \left(\frac{37}{315} - \frac{1}{945}\Lambda - \frac{1}{9072}\Lambda^2\right)^2 \Lambda\,. \tag{12.30}$$

Denoting

$$\frac{\delta^*}{\theta} = \frac{\frac{3}{10} - \frac{1}{120}\Lambda}{\frac{37}{315} - \frac{1}{945}\Lambda - \frac{1}{9072}\Lambda^2} = f_1(K)\,, \qquad (12.31)\dagger$$

$$\frac{\tau_0\,\theta}{\mu U} = \left(2 + \frac{1}{6}\Lambda\right)\left(\frac{37}{315} - \frac{1}{945}\Lambda - \frac{1}{9072}\Lambda^2\right) = f_2(K)\,, \tag{12.32}$$

for the sake of brevity, and substituting, K and Z from eqns. (12.27) and (12.28) respectively, together with $f_1(K)$ and $f_2(K)$ from eqns. (12.31) and (12.32), we obtain, further, from the momentum equation (12.25) together with $\theta\,\theta'/\nu = \frac{1}{2}\,\mathrm{d}Z/\mathrm{d}x$, the relation

$$\frac{1}{2}\,U\,\frac{\mathrm{d}Z}{\mathrm{d}x} + [2 + f_1(K)]\,K = f_2(K)\,. \tag{12.33}$$

Finally, we introduce the additional abbreviation

$$2\,f_2(K) - 4\,K - 2\,K\,f_1(K) = F(K) \tag{12.34}$$

or, written out fully,

$$F(K) = 2\left(\frac{37}{315} - \frac{1}{945}\Lambda - \frac{1}{9072}\Lambda^2\right)\left[2 - \frac{116}{315}\Lambda + \left(\frac{2}{945} + \frac{1}{120}\right)\Lambda^2 + \frac{2}{9072}\Lambda^3\right], \tag{12.35}$$

where the relation between Λ and K was given in eqn. (12.30). With all these abbreviations and substitutions the momentum equation (12.33) can now be rewritten in the very condensed form

$$\boxed{\frac{\mathrm{d}Z}{\mathrm{d}x} = \frac{F(K)}{U}\,; \quad K = Z\,U'\,.} \tag{12.36}$$

This is a non-linear differential equation of the first order for $Z = \theta^2/\nu$ as a function of the current length co-ordinate, x. The fact that the form of the function $F(K)$ is very complex does not constitute a real difficulty insofar as the solution of eqn. (12.36) is concerned, because it is a universal function, i. e. one which is independent of the shape of the body and it can, therefore, be calculated once and for all. The functions $K(\Lambda)$ from eqn. (12.30), as well as $f_1(K)$, $f_2(K)$, and $F(K)$ from eqns. (12.31), (12.32), and (12.35), respectively, are given in Table 12.2. The auxiliary function $F(K)$ is represented graphically in Fig. 12.7.

† The quantity $H = \delta^*/\theta$ is also regarded as a shape factor; it is of particular importance for the turbulent boundary layer, *cf.* Chap. XXII. Its value for laminar boundary layers ranges from about 2·3 to 3·5; it assumes values from about 1·3 to 2·2 in the case of turbulent boundary layers. At the point of transition H increases considerably, *cf.* Fig. 16.5.

Solution of eqn. (12.36): Concerning the solution of eqn. (12.36) it is possible to make the following remarks: The calculation should begin at the stagnation point $x = 0$, where $U = 0$ and $\mathrm{d}U/\mathrm{d}x$ is finite and different from zero, unless the body possesses there a sharp cusped edge with zero angle. The initial slope of the integral curve $\mathrm{d}Z/\mathrm{d}x$ would become infinite at the upstream stagnation point were it not for the fact that $F(K)$ vanishes there simultaneously. Thus the function $F(K)$ is seen to have a physically meaningful initial value. The zero of $F(K)$ occurs for values of Λ for which the second bracketed term on the right-hand side of eqn. (12.35) vanishes. Thus

$$F(K) = 0 \text{ for } K = K_0 = 0{\cdot}0770\,, \text{ or for } \Lambda = \Lambda_0 = 7{\cdot}052\,.$$

Hence $\Lambda = 7{\cdot}052$ is the value of the first shape factor at the stagnation point, as already mentioned. In this manner the initial slope of the integral curve at the upstream stagnation point is seen to be of the indefinite form $\frac{0}{0}$ (singular point of eqn. (12.36)), but its value can be easily computed by a simple process of going over to the limit. We obtain

$$Z_0 = \frac{K_0}{U_0'} = \frac{0{\cdot}0770}{U_0'}\,; \quad \left(\frac{\mathrm{d}Z}{\mathrm{d}x}\right)_0 = -\,0{\cdot}0652\,\frac{U_0''}{U_0'^2}\,. \tag{12.36a}$$

Here the subscript o refers to the upstream stagnation point. With these initial values the equation can be conveniently integrated, e. g. by the method of isoclines. Figs. 12.5 and 12.6 illustrate the use of this method as applied to a symmetrical Joukovsky aerofoil at zero incidence. The calculation begins with the values $\Lambda_0 = 7{\cdot}052$ and $K_0 = 0{\cdot}0770$ at the leading edge stagnation point, and becomes completed upon reaching the point of separation with $\Lambda = -\,12$ and $K = -\,0{\cdot}1567$. The velocity function $U(x)$, together with its first derivative $\mathrm{d}U/\mathrm{d}x$†, is given by the potential flow solution. The value of $\mathrm{d}^2U/\mathrm{d}x^2$ is only required at the leading edge, as seen from eqn. (12.36a) for the initial slope of the integral curve.

The procedure used in the computation may be summarized as follows:

1. The potential flow function $U(x)$, together with its derivative $\mathrm{d}U/\mathrm{d}x$, are given in terms of the arc length.
2. Integration of eqn. (12.36) gives $Z(x)$ and the second shape factor $K(x)$ so that the momentum thickness $\theta(x)$ can be calculated from equation (12.27), and the position of the point of separation may be found subsequently.
3. The variation of the first shape factor $\Lambda(x)$ is obtained from eqn. (12.30) and Table 12.2.
4. The displacement thickness, δ^*, and the shearing stress at the wall, τ_0, are found from eqn. (12.31) and (12.32) respectively, together with the values in Table 12.2.
5. The boundary layer thickness $\delta(x)$ follows from eqn. (12.24).
6. Finally, the velocity distribution is found from eqn. (12.22).

† Instead of eqn. (12.36) K. Pohlhausen used in his paper [18] a differential equation for the quantity $z = \delta^2/\nu$ which is analogous to Z. K. Pohlhausen's differential equation containing $\mathrm{d}^2\,U/\mathrm{d}x^2$, in addition to $U(x)$ and $\mathrm{d}U/\mathrm{d}x$. Since the derivatives of $U(x)$ must, in most cases, be obtained by graphical differentiation, the representation due to H. Holstein and T. Bohlen constitutes an essential improvement of the method, as $\mathrm{d}^2\,U/\mathrm{d}x^2$ does not appear in the differential equation at all.

In cases when the potential flow pattern is available the whole calculation can be completed by a skilled computer in about 2 hours.

A. Walz [39] pointed out that eqn. (12.36) can be reduced to a simple quadrature by the introduction of a further approximation without any appreciable loss of

Table 12.2. Auxiliary functions for the approximate calculation of laminar boundary layers after Holstein and Bohlen [9]

Λ	K	$F(K)$	$f_1(K) = \frac{\delta^*}{\theta} = H$	$f_2(K) = \frac{\theta \tau_0}{\mu U}$
15	0·0884	—0·0658	2·279	0·346
14	0·0928	—0·0885	2·262	0·351
13	0·0941	—0·0914	2·253	0·354
12	0·0948	—0·0948	2·250	0·356
11	0·0941	—0·0912	2·253	0·355
10	0·0919	—0·0800	2·260	0·351
9	0·0882	—0·0608	2·273	0·347
8	0·0831	—0·0335	2·289	0·340
7·8	0·0819	—0·0271	2·293	0·338
7·6	0·0807	—0·0203	2·297	0·337
7·4	0·0794	—0·0132	2·301	0·335
7·2	0·0781	—0·0051	2·305	0·333
7·052	0·0770	0	2·308	0·332
7	0·0767	0·0021	2·309	0·331
6·8	0·0752	0·0102	2·314	0·330
6·6	0·0737	0·0186	2·318	0·328
6·4	0·0721	0·0274	2·323	0·326
6·2	0·0706	0·0363	2·328	0·324
6	0·0689	0·0459	2·333	0·321
5	0·0599	0·0979	2·361	0·310
4	0·0497	0·1579	2·392	0·297
3	0·0385	0·2300	2·427	0·283
2	0·0264	0·3004	2·466	0·268
1	0·0135	0·3820	2·508	0·252
0	0	0·4698	2·554	0·235
— 1	—0·0140	0·5633	2·604	0·217
— 2	—0·0284	0·6609	2·647	0·199
— 3	—0·0429	0·7640	2·716	0·179
— 4	—0·0575	0·8698	2·779	0·160
— 5	—0·0720	0·9780	2·847	0·140
— 6	—0·0862	1·0877	2·921	0·120
— 7	—0·0999	1·1981	2·999	0·100
— 8	—0·1130	1·3080	3·085	0·079
— 9	—0·1254	1·4167	3·176	0·059
—10	—0·1369	1·5229	3·276	0·039
—11	—0·1474	1·6257	3·383	0·019
—12	—0·1567	1·7241	3·500	0
—13	—0·1648	1·8169	3·627	—0·019
—14	—0·1715	1·9033	3·765	—0·037
—15	—0·1767	1·9820	3·916	—0·054

accuracy. He found that the function $F(K)$ can be approximated quite closely by the straight line

$$F(K) = a - b\,K\,.$$

With $a = 0{\cdot}470$ and $b = 6$ the approximation is particularly close between the stagnation point and the point of maximum velocity (Fig. 12.7). In this manner eqn. (12.36) reduces to

$$U\,\frac{\mathrm{d}Z}{\mathrm{d}x} = a - b\,K$$

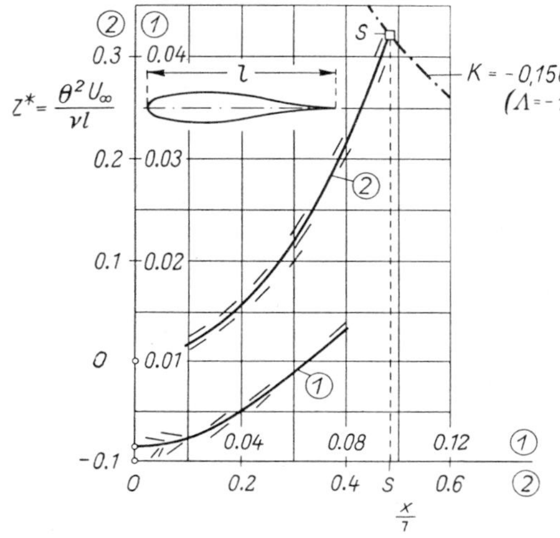

Fig. 12.5. Example of the calculation of the boundary layer by the approximate method due to Pohlhausen and Holstein-Bohlen [9]. Solution of the differential equation (12.36) by the methods of isoclines for the symmetrical Joukovsky aerofoil J 015 at an incidence angle $\alpha = 0$. See also Fig. 12.13

S = point of separation

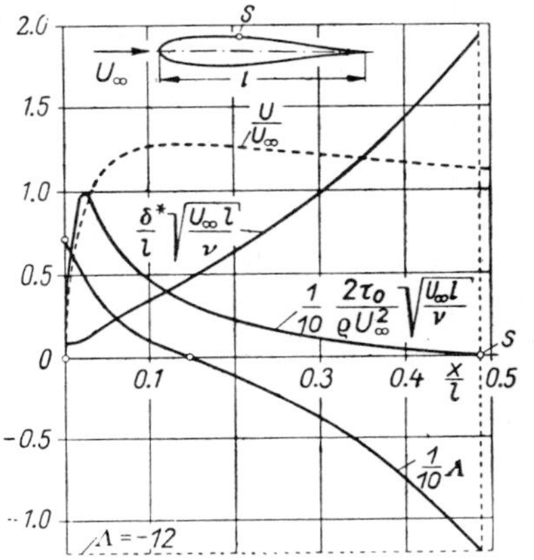

Fig. 12.6

Fig. 12.6. Results of the calculation of the boundary layer for the example in Fig. 12.5

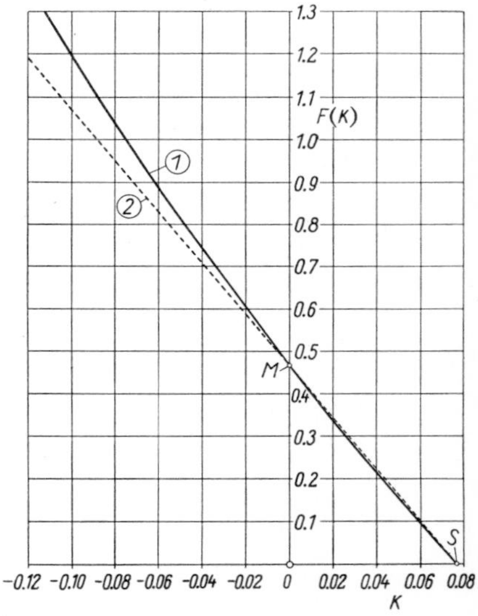

Fig. 12.7. The auxiliary function $F(K)$ for the calculation of laminar boundary layer by the method of Holstein and Bohlen

(1) using eqn. (12.35);
(2) linear approximation $F(K) = 0{\cdot}470 - 6\,K$;
S = stagnation point;
M = velocity maximum

or, substituting the original values for Z and K,

$$\frac{\mathrm{d}}{\mathrm{d}x}\left(\frac{U\,\theta^2}{\nu}\right) = a - (b-1)\,\frac{U\,\theta^2}{\nu}\,\frac{1}{U}\,\frac{\mathrm{d}U}{\mathrm{d}x}\,.$$

This differential equation for $U\,\theta^2/\nu$ can be integrated explicitly to

$$\frac{U\,\theta^2}{\nu} = \frac{a}{U^{b-1}}\int_0^x U^{b-1}\,\mathrm{d}x$$

or, using the numerical values for a and b given earlier:

$$\boxed{\frac{U\,\theta^2}{\nu} = \frac{0{\cdot}470}{U^5}\int_{x=0}^{x} U^5\,\mathrm{d}x\,.} \qquad (12.37)$$

Thus the solution of eqn. (12.36) is seen to reduce to a simple quadrature.

c. Comparison between the approximate and exact solutions

1. Flat plate at zero incidence. It is easy to see from eqn. (12.22) that the Pohlhausen approximation becomes equivalent to Example 3 in Table 12.1 for the case of a flat plate at zero incidence. This case can also be obtained directly from eqn. (12.36), where $U(x) = U_\infty$, $U' \equiv 0$ and hence $K = \Lambda \equiv 0$, so that eqn. (12.36) gives $\mathrm{d}Z/\mathrm{d}x = F(0)/U_\infty = 0{\cdot}4698/U_\infty$. Taking into account that $Z = 0$ at $x = 0$ it follows that $Z = 0{\cdot}4698\; x/U_\infty$, or $\theta = 0{\cdot}686\sqrt{\nu\, x/U_\infty}$ in agreement with Table 12.1. Table 12.1 contains exact and approximate values of the boundary layer parameters for the purpose of comparison. It is seen that agreement is very satisfactory.

2. Two-dimensional stagnation flow. The exact solution of the problem of two-dimensional stagnation flow, for which $U(x) = U' \cdot x$, was given in Sec. V.8. The exact values of displacement thickness, momentum thickness and shearing stress at the wall, calculated with the aid of that theory, are given in Table 12.3.

Table 12.3. Comparison of exact and approximate values of the boundary layer parameters for the case of *two-dimensional stagnation flow*

	$\delta^*\sqrt{\frac{U'}{\nu}}$	$\theta\sqrt{\frac{U'}{\nu}}$	$\frac{\tau_0}{\mu\,U}\sqrt{\frac{\nu}{U'}}$	$\frac{\delta^*}{\theta}$
Approximate method due to K. Pohlhausen	0·641	0·278	1·19	2·31
exact solution	0·648	0·292	1·234	2·21

In the approximate method we have $Z_0 = K_0/U'$ and from eqn. (12.36) it follows that the momentum thickness is given by $\theta\sqrt{U'/\nu} = \sqrt{K_0} = \sqrt{0{\cdot}0770} = 0{\cdot}278$. It is seen from eqn. (12.31) that the displacement thickness is approximated by $\delta^*\sqrt{U'/\nu} = f_1(K_0)\sqrt{K_0} = 0{\cdot}641$ and eqn. (12.32) gives $\tau_0/\mu U \cdot \sqrt{\nu/U'} = f_2(K_0)/\sqrt{K_0} = 0{\cdot}332/0{\cdot}278 = 1{\cdot}19$ for the shearing stress at the wall. The agreement between the approximate and exact values is here also completely satisfactory.

3. Flow past a circular cylinder. A comparison of the result of the approximate calculation for a circular cylinder with the solution due to Hiemenz (Sec. IX c) was given by K. Pohlhausen [18] in his original paper. He used Hiemenz's experimental pressure distribution function for the circular cylinder and compared the results with Hiemenz's solution which takes into account the first three terms of the Blasius series. Hiemenz's solution indicates that separation occurs at an angle $\phi = 82{\cdot}0°$, whereas Pohlhausen's approximate value was $\phi = 81{\cdot}5°$. However, the approximate method leads to values for the boundary layer thickness near the point of separation which are considerably larger than the values obtained by Hiemenz. On the other hand it must be realized that such a comparison is not conclusive, because a Blasius series containing only three terms is in itself inadequate to represent the solution near the point of separation.

δ^* = displacement thickness;
θ = momentum thickness;
τ_0 = shearing stress at the wall

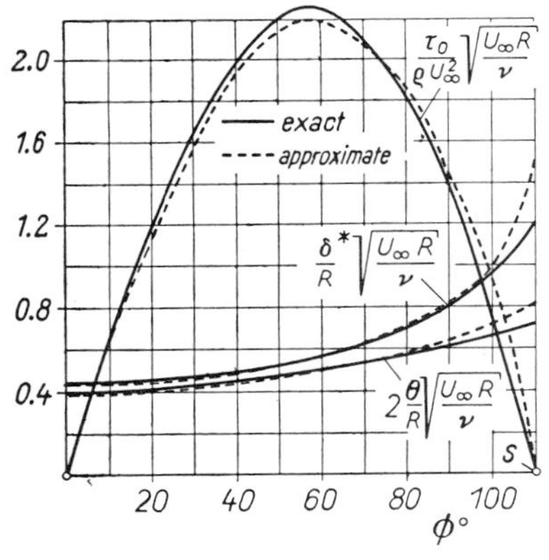

Fig. 12.8. Comparison of Pohlhausen's approximate solution with the exact solution for the case of a circular cylinder

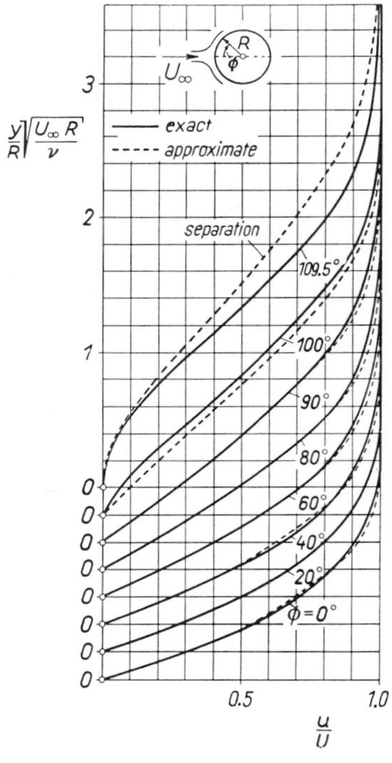

Fig. 12.9. Comparison of Pohlhausen's approximate solution with the exact solution for the case of a circular cylinder; velocity profiles

We now propose to compare the results of the approximate calculation with those obtained with the aid of a Blasius series containing six terms (up to x^{11}), but based on the potential velocity distribution function. As shown in Sec. IX c, this number of terms is sufficiently large to include the point of separation. The position of the point of separation at $\phi = 108{\cdot}8°$ agrees very well with the exact value of $\phi = 109{\cdot}5°$. Fig. 12.8 shows a plot of the boundary layer parameters, displacement thickness, δ^*, momentum thickness, θ, and wall shearing stress, τ_0. The exact and approximate values of the shearing stress at the wall, τ_0, are in almost complete agreement, but near the point of separation the approximate values of θ and δ^* are again higher than the respective exact values, and the deviation increases. A comparison of the velocity distribution curves, shown in Fig. 12.9, leads to the conclusion that in the region of accelerated external flow ($0 < \phi < 90°$) there is almost complete agreement between the exact and approximate solutions, whereas behind the point of minimum pressure and towards the point of separation the discrepancies increase rather rapidly.

H. Goertler [8] made a similar comparison of Pohlhausen's approximation with the exact solution for Howarth's boundary layer associated with the potential flow function $U(x) = U_0 - a\,x$, Sec. IX g, and reached similar conclusions.

No general criterion regarding the admissibility of the approximation has been given so far and it seems that it will be difficult to obtain. Judging by the above and similar calculations as well as by experimental results it appears, however, to be reasonably certain that Pohlhausen's approximate method leads to very satisfactory results in regions of accelerated potential flow. Similarly, it may be stated that in regions of retarded potential flow the approximate solution becomes increasingly less reliable as the point of separation is approached. The position of the point of separation can only be calculated with a certain degree of uncertainty, particularly in cases when the point of separation is situated comparatively far behind the point of minimum pressure†‡.

From the assumption that the velocity profiles constitute a one-parameter family it necessarily follows that the point of separation is determined solely by the value of this parameter. It was, however, shown by I. Tani [32] that the position of the point of separation depends, in addition, on the pressure gradient of the external flow.

---

† For example: G. B. Schubauer [27] measured the position of the point of minimum pressure on an elliptical cylinder of slenderness $a : b = 2{\cdot}96 : 1$ placed in a stream parallel to the major axis. He found that it was located at $x/b = 1{\cdot}3$ and that separation took place at $x/b = 1{\cdot}99$. A calculation based on Pohlhausen's approximation showed very good agreement with measurements for velocity profiles up to the point of minimum pressure but it predicted no separation at all. D. Meksyn [15] developed a method of computation which leads to a value of $x/b = 2{\cdot}02$ for the point of separation in the above example. In his method, the boundary layer equations are transformed into ordinary differential equations which are related to Falkner and Skan's eqn. (9.8).

‡ Here it may be worth mentioning that approximate integration by the method of isoclines in connexion with Pohlhausen's approximation fails in the region of large pressure gradients which occur for $\Lambda > 12$ ($K > 0{\cdot}095$), because the plot of K against Λ turns at this point (Table 12.2) and cannot, therefore, be continued beyond $K = 0{\cdot}095$. Moreover, for $\Lambda > 12$ the velocity profiles become unacceptable as they contain points for which $u/U > 1$ (Fig. 12.4). These difficulties are obviated when eqn. (12.37) is used.

d. Further examples

In this section we propose to summarize some examples illustrating the calculation of boundary layers by the preceding approximate methods which were first given in a paper by H. Schlichting and A. Ulrich [24]. The first set of examples is concerned with elliptical cylinders whose major axes are parallel to the direction of the stream. The ratio of the major to the minor axis of the cylinders ranged over $a/b = 1, 2, 4, 8$ and the potential velocity distribution functions are seen plotted in Figs. 12.10. The value of the velocity maximum is $U_m/U = 1 + b/a$. The characteristic parameters of the boundary layer, namely the displacement thickness, δ^*, the shape factor, Λ, and the shearing stress at the wall, τ_0, are seen plotted in Fig. 12.11. The results for the flat plate at zero incidence have been plotted in the same figure for the purpose of comparison. In the case of a circular cylinder separation occurs

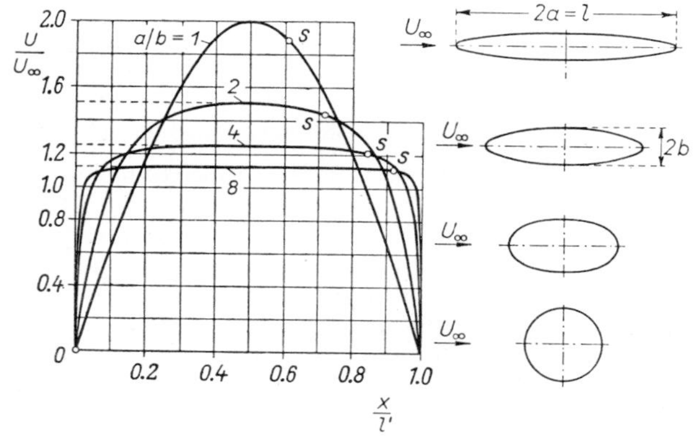

Fig. 12.10. Potential velocity distribution function on elliptical cylinders of slenderness $a/b = 1, 2, 4, 8$, the direction of the stream being parallel to the major axis
S = position of point of separation

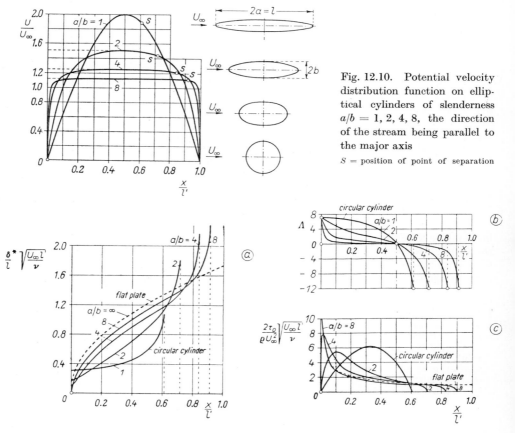

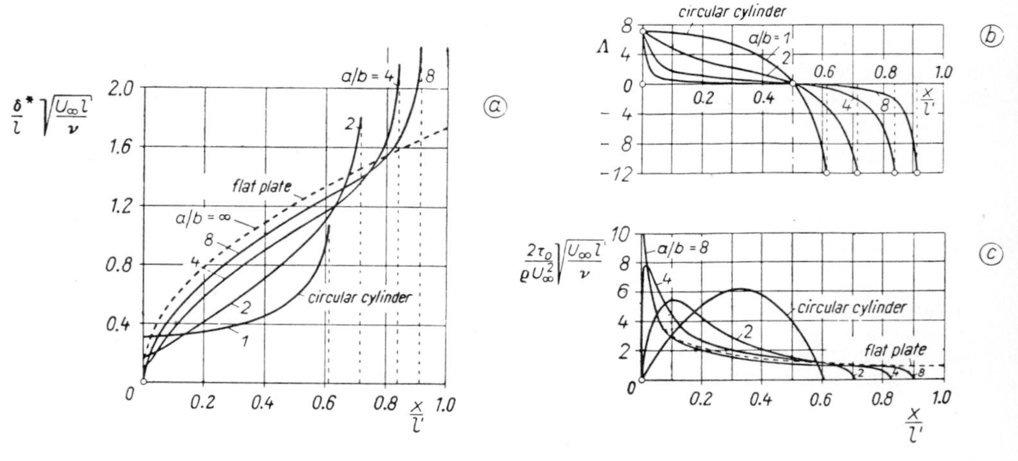

Fig. 12.11. Results of the calculation of boundary layers on elliptical cylinders of slenderness $a/b = 1, 2, 4, 8$, Fig. 12.10. a) Displacement thickness of the boundary layer, b) Shape factor c) Shearing stress at the wall, $2\,l'$ = circumference of the ellipse; $a/b = 1$ circular cylinder; $a/b = \infty$ flat plate

at $x/l' = 0{\cdot}609$, i. e. at $\phi = 109{\cdot}5°$, as already mentioned, ($2\,l'$ = circumference) and moves downstream as the ellipse becomes more slender. The position of the point of separation is marked in the velocity profile plots in Fig. 12.10. The results for an ellipse of $a/b = 8$ differ only very little from those for a flat plate at zero incidence. Fig. 12.12 contains velocity profiles for the boundary layer on an elliptic cylinder with $a/b = 4$. Calculations concerning elliptic cylinders whose minor axes are parallel to the direction of the stream as well as ellipsoids of revolution may be found in a paper by J. Pretsch [22].

A further example is shown in Fig. 12.13 which contains results for a symmetrical Joukovsky aerofoil at zero incidence. The point of minimum pressure is at $x/l' = 0{\cdot}141$, which is very far forward on the aerofoil. The pressure rise at the rear is very gradual so that the point of separation lies very far downstream of the point of minimum pressure, i. e. at $x/l' = 0{\cdot}470$. Since the Joukovsky aerofoil has a cusped trailing edge the potential velocity at the trailing edge is different from zero. For details of additional systematic boundary layer calculations concerning an extensive series of Joukovsky aerofoils with different thickness and camber ratios and at different angles of incidence, reference may be made to a paper by K. Bussmann and A. Ulrich [3].

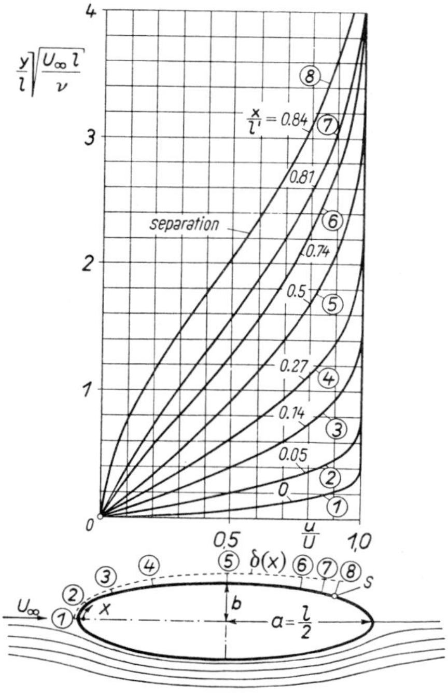

Fig. 12.12. Velocity profiles in the laminar boundary layer on an elliptical cylinder. Ratio of axes $a/b = 4$

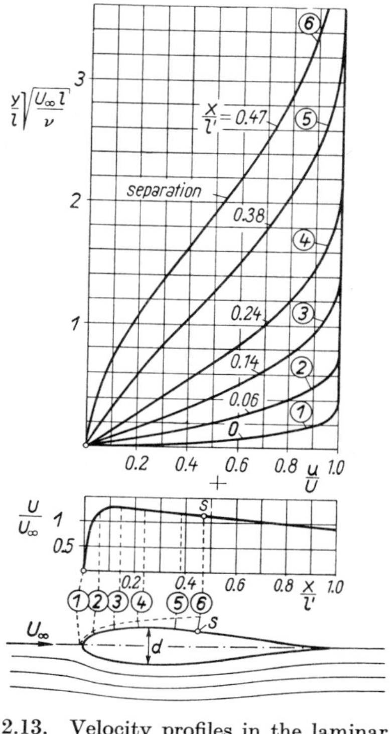

Fig. 12.13. Velocity profiles in the laminar boundary layer and potential velocity function for a Joukovsky aerofoil J 015 of thickness ratio $d/l = 0{\cdot}15$ at an angle of incidence $\alpha = 0$

e. Application of the approximate method to bodies of revolution and three-dimensional boundary layers

An approximate method for the calculation of boundary layers on bodies of revolution in axial flow was first indicated by C. B. Millikan [16]. Since a parabolic velocity distribution was assumed, no point of separation could be obtained. Pohlhausen's approximate method of calculation which was described previously and which is based on a polynomial of 4th degree was extended by S. Tomotika [36, 37] to include a body of revolution.

The following account of the method as applied to bodies of revolution is based on the work of F. W. Scholkemeyer [26], who used the modern version of the momentum equation in a similar way to that employed by H. Holstein and T. Bohlen for the case of two-dimensional flow. The momentum equation for the axially symmetrical case is obtained in the same way as that used in Sec. VIIIe for the two-dimensional case. Starting with eqns. (10.23) and (10.24) we obtain

$$U^2 \frac{d\theta}{dx} + (2\,\theta + \delta^*)\, U \frac{dU}{dx} + U^2 \frac{\theta}{r} \frac{dr}{dx} = \frac{\tau_0}{\varrho}. \tag{12.38}$$

The significance of $r(x)$ may be inferred from Fig. 10.6. Retracing the steps of Sec. XIIb we obtain the following differential equation for the quantity $Z = \theta^2/\nu$:

$$\frac{1}{2} U \frac{dZ}{dx} + [2 + f_1(K)]\, K + \frac{1}{r} \frac{dr}{dx} \frac{U}{U'} K = f_2(K)\,.$$

The quantities $K, f_1(K), f_2(K)$ have the same meaning as in the two-dimensional case, eqns. (12.27) (12.31) and (12.32). Introducing $F(K)$ as before, eqn. (12.34), we have

$$\frac{dZ}{dx} = \frac{1}{U} \left\{ F(K) - 2\,K \frac{1}{r} \frac{dr}{dx} \frac{U}{U'} \right\}; \qquad K = Z\,U'\,. \tag{12.39}$$

The present equation differs from that in the previous case by the second term in the bracket on the right-hand side. The term $1/r \times dr/dx \times U/U'$ is given by the shape of the body and by the corresponding potential flow. Thus the solution can be obtained with the same procedure as in the two-dimensional case. The point of separation is again at $\Lambda = -12$, i.e. at $K = -0{\cdot}1567$, but at the stagnation point the values of the shape factors Λ and K are now different.

If the body of revolution has a blunt nose, we have at $x = 0$, i. e. at the upstream stagnation point,

$$\lim_{x \to 0} \left(\frac{1}{r} \frac{dr}{dx} \frac{U}{U'} \right) = 1\,.$$

With this value the terms in the bracket in eqn. (12.39) reduce to $F(K) - 2\,K$. By following the same argument as in the two-dimensional case it is found that the initial value of K at the stagnation point is determined by the condition $F(K) - 2\,K = 0$, or, explicitly

$$\Lambda_0 = +\,4{\cdot}716\,; \qquad K_0 = 0{\cdot}05708\,.$$

Hence the initial values of the integral curve (12.39) at the stagnation point become

$$\left.\begin{aligned} Z_0 &= \frac{K_0}{U_0'} = \frac{0{\cdot}05708}{U_0'} \\ \left(\frac{dZ}{dx}\right)_0 &= 0\,. \end{aligned}\right\} \tag{12.40}$$

The initial slope is zero for a body of revolution, because for reasons of symmetry we must have $U_0'' = 0$ at the stagnation point. The method of direct integration described in Sec. XIIb can be extended to the case of axially symmetrical bodies, as shown by N. Rott and L. F. Crabtree [23]. Eqn. (12.37) for the momentum thickness is now replaced by

$$\frac{U\,\theta^2}{\nu} = \frac{0{\cdot}470}{r^2\,U^5}\int_0^x r^2\,U^5\,\mathrm{d}x\,. \tag{12.41}$$

The same authors extended the method further to include yawed cylinders.

Some numerical examples have been calculated by F. W. Scholkemeyer [26] in his thesis presented to the Engineering University at Brunswick as well as in the paper by J. Pretsch [22], already quoted. S. Tomotika [37] calculated the boundary layer on a sphere for a range of Reynolds numbers using both potential and measured pressure distributions. A comparison with measurement is given by A. Fage [6], and further results are contained in a paper by W. Moeller [17].

In this connexion it may be worth drawing attention to another axially symmetrical boundary layer problem, namely that associated with laminar flow in the inlet portion of a pipe. Strictly speaking this is not a problem in boundary layer theory but it has been solved with the aid of methods similar to the ones now being considered. The initially rectangular velocity distribution in the entrance section of the pipe ($x = 0$) is gradually transformed into a parabolic, Poiseuille, distribution by the action of viscous forces as sections further downstream are considered. The analogous two-dimensional problem, namely laminar flow in the inlet portion of a rectangular channel, has already been considered in Sec. IXh on the basis of the differential equations of boundary layer flow. The approximate method due to L. Schiller [25] is based on an equation which expresses the condition of equilibrium between momentum, pressure drop and viscous drag in a manner similar to the momentum equation discussed earlier. The velocity profiles in the inlet portion of the pipe are approximated by a constant velocity near the axis of the tube combined with two tangent portions of a parabola near the wall, so that at the wall the velocity becomes equal to zero. At the inlet section the width of the parabolic portions is zero and increases downstream until they coalesce into a single parabola at a definite distance from the entrance. This distance constitutes the theoretical initial length and its magnitude, as calculated by L. Schiller, is given by $x\,\nu/R^2\,\bar{u} = 0{\cdot}115$. Measurements performed by J. Nikuradse Fig. 12.14, show good agreement with Schiller's theory for about a third of the initial length near the entrance (about $x\,\nu/R^2\,u = 0{\cdot}04$). The actual transition to a parabolic velocity profile appears to proceed more slowly than implied in the approximate calculation. An approximate solution to this problem was also given by H. L. Langhaar [12a].

The flow becomes much more complex in axially symmetrical flows in cases when there exists a tangential (whirl) component in addition to the longitudinal component. The field of

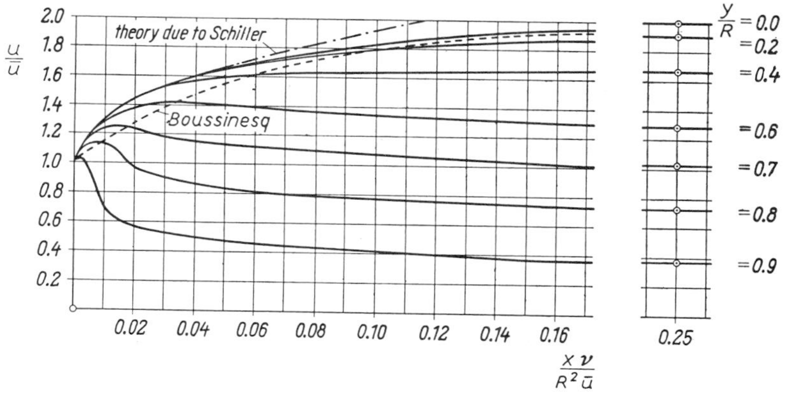

Fig. 12.14. Velocity distribution in the inlet portion of a pipe for the laminar case; measurements performed by Nikuradse and quoted from Prandtl-Tietjens vol. II. Theory due to Schiller [25] and Boussinesq [2]

flow then becomes similar in complexity to the general, three-dimensional case. Examples of such flows were given earlier in Chap. X. Here one might mention the whirling flow in a funnel (Chap. X, [12, 17, 58]) as well as the flow about a rotating body of revolution in an axial stream (Chap. X, [27]). The case of a yawed cylinder (Chap. X, [20]) also belongs to the same class of problems. In the latter case, the momentum equation in the meridional plane (x-direction) must be supplemented with the momentum equation in the transverse plane (y-direction). Choosing the third co-ordinate, z, in the direction normal to the surface, it is found that the two equations under discussion for the case of a body rotating in an axial stream assume the forms given below:

$$U^2 \frac{\mathrm{d}\theta_x}{\mathrm{d}x} + U \frac{\mathrm{d}U}{\mathrm{d}x} (2\,\theta_x + \delta_x^*) + \frac{1}{r}\frac{\mathrm{d}r}{\mathrm{d}x} (U^2\,\theta_x + v_0{}^2\,\theta_y) = \frac{\tau_{x0}}{\varrho}\,, \tag{12.42}$$

$$\frac{v_0}{r^3}\frac{\mathrm{d}}{\mathrm{d}x}(U\,r^3\,\theta_{xy}) = -\frac{\tau_{y0}}{\varrho}\,. \tag{12.43}$$

The following customary abbreviations have been used:

$$\tau_{x0} = \mu \left(\frac{\partial u}{\partial z}\right)_{z=0}; \qquad \tau_{y0} = \mu \left(\frac{\partial v}{\partial z}\right)_{z=0};$$

$$\delta_x^* = \int\limits_{z=0}^{\infty} \left(1 - \frac{u}{U}\right) \mathrm{d}z\,; \qquad \theta_x = \int\limits_{z=0}^{\infty} \frac{u}{U}\left(1 - \frac{u}{U}\right) \mathrm{d}z\,;$$

$$\theta_y = \int\limits_{z=0}^{\infty} \left(\frac{v}{v_0}\right)^2 \mathrm{d}z\,; \qquad \theta_{xy} = \int\limits_{z=0}^{\infty} \frac{u}{U}\,\frac{v}{v_0}\,\mathrm{d}z\,.$$

The tangential velocity distribution $v(x, z)$ is referred to the local tangential velocity at the wall $v_0 = r\,.\,\omega$. The momentum integral equations for the yawed cylinder can be obtained from the above by putting, formally, $r = \text{const}$ and by introducing

$$\theta_{xy} = \int\limits_{z=0}^{\infty} \frac{u}{U}\left(1 - \frac{v}{V_\infty}\right) \mathrm{d}z\,,$$

where V_∞ is the component of the oncoming velocity in the direction of the cylinder generator. W. Dienemann [4] worked out an approximate method for yawed cylinders which was based on the preceding equations. For the case of a rotating body of revolution in axial flow experiments have been done by O. Parr [17 a].

The extension of these approximate methods to the general case of three-dimensional flows is vitiated by very great difficulties, because now the variety of possible velocity distributions has become much larger than was the case with two-dimensional flows, and because exact solutions which could be used to assess the quality of the approximation do not exist, [19,33]. The description of these complex, three-dimensional boundary layer flows can be considerably simplified if the stream-lines and lines of constant potential of the external, irrotational flow are chosen for a curvilinear system of co-ordinates [5, 34]. Nevertheless, an analogue to the two-dimensional procedure due to Pohlhausen proves to be feasible, if it is additionally assumed that the velocities in the boundary layer preserve, essentially, the corresponding directions of the stream-lines in the external flow and that the transverse components constitute only a weak secondary flow which is superimposed on them. The boundary layer equations established by R. Timman [35] as well as E. A. Eichelbrenner and A. Oudart [5] for the case of a slender ellipsoid of revolution at small angle of incidence make use of this idea.

G. Jungclaus [10] gave an extension of Pohlhausen's method to rotating systems and applied it to the case of relative motion in a rotating channel which is important in the theory of centrifugal pumps. The method is capable of making predictions about separation; these predictions show good agreement with experimental results.

f. Other approximate methods

The shortcomings of the approximate method due to Pohlhausen, which, as discussed before, manifest themselves in the region of pressure increase induced Th. von Kármán and C. B. Millikan [11] to develop a different approximate method. At the starting point of this theory use is made of the von Mises transformation (Sec. VIIId) but, on the whole, the details appear to be tedious.

B. Thwaites [38] indicated an approximate method which is very similar to the one described in Sec. XIIb. Instead of making an assumption for the velocity distribution in the boundary layer in the form of a polynomial, he uses the relations between the two shape factors $(\theta/U) \cdot (\partial u/\partial y)_{y=0}$ and $(\theta^2/U) \cdot (\partial^2 u/\partial y^2)_{y=0} = -(\theta^2/\nu)\,(\mathrm{d}U/\mathrm{d}x) = -K$ which correspond to the exact solutions involving the potential flow $U(x) = u_1\, x^m$. The momentum theorem leads to an equation which agrees in form with eqn. (12.36) and which can also be solved by direct integration. The final result does not differ in essence from eqn. (12.37) but the value $K = -0{\cdot}082$ is retained as a criterion for separation. This value gives better agreement with known exact solutions than the value $K = -0{\cdot}1567$ found by K. Pohlhausen.

It seems natural to improve Pohlhausen's method which is based on a polynomial of the 4th degree (P 4-method) by selecting one of a higher order. The additional coefficients can then be used to satisfy additional compatibility conditions at the wall and at the external boundary of the layer. H. Schlichting and A. Ulrich [24] used a polynomial of the 6th degree (P 6-method) for the two-dimensional case and developed the method to a point where it becomes directly useful. The results as far the characteristic parameters and the position of the point of separation are concerned do not differ materially from those of the P 4-method. The main advantage of the P 6-method lies in the circumstance that the higher derivatives of the velocity profile with respect to wall distance are obtained with an increased degree of precision, as compared with the P 4-method. This might become important in investigations into the stability of velocity profiles in the boundary layer (Chaps. XVI and XVII). Further examples of assumptions which work with a single parameter have been considered and compared with exact solutions in a paper by W. Mangler [14]. In this connexion functions other than polynomials have been investigated. Thus, for example, A. Walz [40] made use of the one-parameter family of profiles calculated by D. R. Hartree (see Chap. IXa) and approximated them by polynomials with fractional exponents, whereas A. Betz [1] proposed the use of a simpler series. The approximate method given by A. M. O. Smith [29] compares favourably as regards accuracy and simplicity with those due to A. Walz and B. Thwaites; in it, the external velocity is approximated piecewise by functions of the form $U(x) = u_1 \cdot x^m$ and the solution is made up of the similar solutions (*cf.* Chap. IX) which correspond to that free-stream velocity.

All approximate methods have the common feature that, instead of satisfying the differential equations of boundary layer motion, they only satisfy a mean value taken over the equation of motion, as expressed physically by the momentum theorem. In addition an attempt is made to satisfy some of the compatibility conditions at the wall and at the outer boundary of the layer.

It seems natural to endeavour to produce a fundamental improvement in the above approximate methods in that an attempt is made to satisfy another physically important condition which, just as the momentum equation, is obtained by an averaging process extended over the width of the boundary layer. The energy equation as given in eqn. (8.36) furnishes such a condition. If it is desired to satisfy simultaneously the momentum and the energy equations, in addition to the compatibility conditions at the wall and at the outer edge of the boundary layer, it is necessary to employ a velocity distribution function across the boundary layer which contains two free parameters. The first attempt to use a method of this kind was made by W. G. L. Sutton [30], who restricted himself to the case of a flat plate at zero incidence. K. Wieghardt [42] developed and tested such a method, after a discussion of the possibility of the use of two-parameter profiles in conjunction with the energy equation had been published by M. Mangler [13]. The two free parameters used were the already familiar quantity $K = U' \theta^2/\nu$, and the dimensionless tangent to the velocity profile taken at the wall and given by $(\theta/U) \cdot (\partial u/\partial y)_0$. The velocity profile is represented with the aid of a polynomial of the 11th degree. It is to be expected that the numerical solution of the two simultaneous differential equations for the two free parameters is very much more tedious than was the case with only one free parameter. Consequently a suggestion was made to use the one-parameter method as far as the point of minimum pressure continuing with the two-parameter method from there. By means of calculated examples and comparisons with exact solutions it was shown that this new method gives good results as far as the point of separation.

Wieghardt's method was simplified by A. Walz [40] who reverted to a one-parameter set of velocity profiles by dropping the first compatibility condition at the wall and retaining both the energy and the momentum equations, although it had been thought previously that this compatibility condition at the wall was essential in the problem. Actual calculations seem to substantiate the view that it is more important to satisfy the energy equation than the first compatibility condition at the wall. This view has been confirmed in a paper by I. Tani [31].

N. A. V. Piercy and J. H. Preston [21] indicated a different approximate method for the case of a flat plate at zero incidence in which, having started with a very rough approximation to the velocity profile, successive quadratures are performed. The process of iteration converges very fast towards the exact solution and may be extended to include thermal boundary layers, as demonstrated by H. Schuh [28].

g. Laminar flow against pressure gradient; separation

Flows with adverse pressure gradients (retarded flows) are of great practical importance. In this connexion it is always desired to *avoid separation* from the wall, because this phenomenon is associated with large energy losses. The flow about an aerofoil is a case in point. Owing to the fact that on the suction side the pressure must increase to its free-stream value at the trailing edge, the flow is always likely to separate. The flow in a divergent channel (diffuser) affords another example. The object in using this shape of channel is to convert kinetic energy into pressure energy, and if the angle of divergence is made too large, separation may occur.

It will now be shown with the aid of several examples that a laminar flow can only support very small adverse pressure gradients without separation. Adverse pressure gradients which exist in practical applications would, therefore, almost always lead to separation if the flow were laminar. The circumstance that real flows can support considerable rates of pressure increase in a large number of cases without separation is due to the fact that the flow is mostly *turbulent*. It will be seen later that turbulent flows are capable of overcoming much larger adverse pressure gradients without separation. The best known examples include the cases of flow past circular cylinders and spheres, when separation occurs much further upstream in laminar than in turbulent flow. In practice when adverse pressure gradients exist the flow is almost always turbulent because, in addition, the existence of an adverse pressure gradient favours the transition from laminar to turbulent flow. It is, nevertheless, useful to clarify some of the fundamental relations associated with the prevention of separation on the example of laminar flow, in particular, because laminar flows are much more readily amenable to mathematical treatment than is the case with turbulent flows.

There are several methods of preventing separation. The simplest of them consists in arranging for the adverse pressure gradients to remain below the limit for which separation does occur. A numerical example will serve to make this idea clear. Another possibility consists in controlling the boundary layer, e. g. by suction or by injecting fluid into it, or by addition of an aerofoil at a point, where its presence favourably affects the boundary layer in critical regions. These methods will be discussed more fully in Chap. XIII.

Following L. Prandtl [20] we shall show how it is possible to estimate the permissible magnitude of the adverse pressure gradient for which separation is just prevented. The argument will be based on the Kármán-Pohlhausen approximation discussed in Sec. XIIb. It will be assumed that the boundary layer is acted upon by the pressure distribution determined by the free-stream potential flow up to a point which lies very close to the point of separation, such as point 0 in Fig. 12.15. Starting with this point it will be assumed that the pressure gradient is

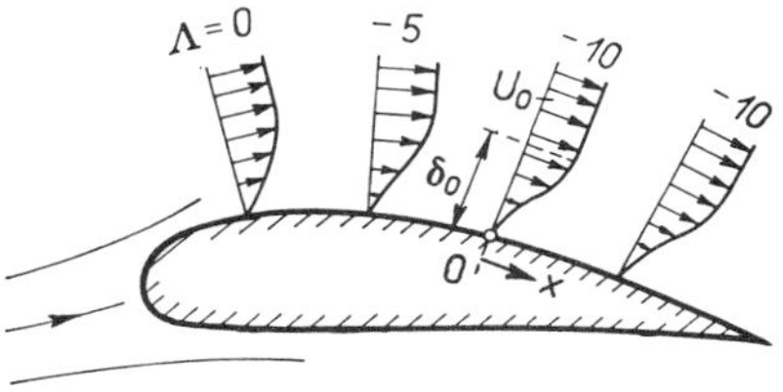

Fig. 12.15. Development of boundary layer in the case when laminar separation is prevented

such that the shape of the velocity profile remains unchanged proceeding downstream, or that, in other words, the shape factor Λ remains constant. Since at separation $\Lambda = -12$ a value of $\Lambda = -10$ will be chosen. As seen from Table 12.2 this leads to a definite value for the second shape factor, namely $K = -0{\cdot}1369$ so that $F(K) = 1{\cdot}523$. Using these values it is seen from eqns. (12.28) and (12.29) that prevention of separation implies the following relationship between the velocity $U(x)$ of potential flow and the momentum thickness $\theta(x)$:

$$\frac{\theta^2}{\nu} = Z = \frac{0{\cdot}1369}{-U'(x)}\,.$$

It follows that $\mathrm{d}Z/\mathrm{d}x = 0{\cdot}1369\; U''/U'^2$, or

$$U\,\frac{\mathrm{d}Z}{\mathrm{d}x} = 0{\cdot}1369\,\frac{UU''}{U'^2} = 0{\cdot}1369\,\sigma\,, \tag{12.44}$$

where

$$\sigma = \frac{U\,U''}{U'^2}\,. \tag{12.45}$$

On the other hand the succeeding velocity profiles are given by the momentum equation (12.36) for $x > 0$, or

$$U\,\frac{\mathrm{d}Z}{\mathrm{d}x} = F(K) = 1{\cdot}523\,, \tag{12.46}$$

where the numerical value for $F(K)$ which corresponds to $\Lambda = -10$ has been inserted. From eqns. (12.44) and (12.46) it follows that the value of the shape factor remains constant at $\Lambda = -10$ if $0{\cdot}1369\,\sigma = 1{\cdot}523$, or if

$$\sigma = \frac{U\,U''}{U'^2} = 11{\cdot}13 \approx 11\,, \tag{12.47}$$

$$\sigma > 11: \text{ no separation;} \qquad \sigma < 11: \text{ separation}\,. \tag{12.47a}$$

The preceding argument shows that the boundary layer can support the adverse pressure gradients if $\sigma > 11$, whereas $\sigma < 11$ implies separation. If σ remains constant at $\sigma = 11$, with $\Lambda = -10$, the boundary layer remains on the verge of separation.

Qualitatively it is at once possible to make the following statement regarding the shape of the potential velocity function $U(x)$ which leads to no separation. In view of eqn. (12.47)

$$U'' > 0$$

is a *necessary condition* for a retarded flow ($U' < 0$) to adhere to the wall. In other words, the magnitude of the negative pressure gradient must decrease in the flow direction, Fig. 12.16.

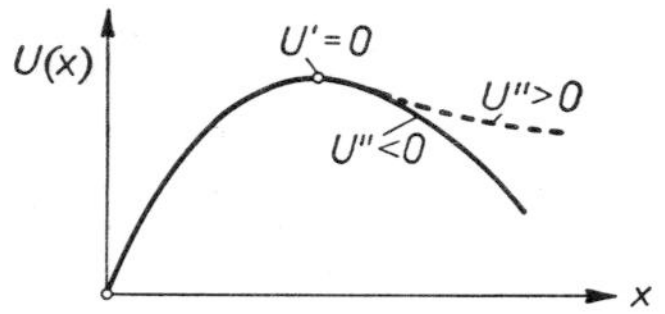

Fig. 12.16. Potential velocity function for a laminar boundary layer with and without separation

Thus separation will always occur if the function $U(x)$ is curved downwards behind its maximum ($U'' < 0$). In the opposite case, when the velocity function curves upwards ($U'' > 0$), separation may be obviated. Even the limiting case of $U'' = 0$ i. e. the case of a velocity which decreases linearly with the length of arc, always leads to separation. This latter remark agrees with the result found in Sec. IX d; it was concerned with the boundary layer associated with a potential flow velocity which decreased linearly, and the solution of the differential equations was quoted from a paper by L. Howarth. The *sufficient condition* for the absence of separation is given by

$$U'' > 11\, U'^2/U\,.$$

We shall now proceed to calculate the potential flow and the variation of boundary layer thickness which are associated with the limiting case of $\sigma = 11$, when the boundary layer remains on the verge of separation. From eqn. (12.47) we have

$$\frac{U''}{U'} = 11 \times \frac{U'}{U}$$

or, upon integrating: $\ln U' = 11 \ln U + \ln(-C_1')$, i. e. $U'/U^{11} = -C_1'$, where C_1' denotes the constant of integration. Repeated integration gives

$$\frac{1}{10}\, U^{-10} = C_1'\, x + C_2\,. \tag{12.48}$$

For $x = 0$ we should have $U(x) = U_0$, so that $C_2 = \frac{1}{10}\, U_0^{-10}$. Putting further $C_1'\, U_0^{10} = C_1$, we obtain from eqn. (12.48)

$$U(x) = \frac{U_0}{(1 + 10\, C_1\, x)^{1/10}}\,. \tag{12.49}$$

Equation (12.49) represents the potential velocity for which separation can just be avoided. The constant C_1 can be determined from the value of the boundary layer thicknes δ_0 at the origin $x = 0$. We have $\Lambda = U'\, \delta^2/\nu = -10$ or $\delta = \sqrt{10\, \nu/(-U')}$. From eqn. (12.49) we obtain

$$U' = -\frac{C_1\, U_0}{(1 + 10\, C_1 x)^{11/10}}$$

and hence

$$\delta = \sqrt{\frac{10\, \nu}{C_1\, U_0}}\, (1 + 10 C_1 x)^{11/20}\,.$$

From $\delta = \delta_0$ at $x = 0$ we have $C_1 = 10\, \nu/U_0\, \delta_0^2$, which gives the final solution for the potential flow and the variation of boundary layer thickness

$$U(x) = U_0 \left(1 + 100 \frac{\nu x}{U_0\, \delta_0^2}\right)^{-0{\cdot}1} \qquad (12.50)\dagger$$

$$\delta(x) = \delta_0 \left(1 + 100 \frac{\nu x}{U_0\, \delta_0^2}\right)^{0{\cdot}55} \qquad (12.51)$$

It is seen that the magnitude of the permissible deceleration (decrease in velocity) is very small, being proportional to $x^{-0{\cdot}1}$. Its value is very nearly realized for the case of constant velocity along the flat plate at zero incidence. In the present case the increase in boundary layer thickness, δ, is proportional to $x^{0{\cdot}55}$; this value also differs but little from the case of a flat plate at zero incidence for which $\delta \sim x^{0{\cdot}5}$.

By way of a further example of retarded flow we shall consider the flow through a divergent channel whose walls are straight. This case is corollary to the case of the boundary layer in a divergent channel treated in Sec. IXb. The flow is seen sketched in Fig. 12.17, where x denotes the radial distance from the source at 0. The wall is assumed to begin at $x = a$ where the entrance velocity of the potential stream is put equal to U_0. The potential flow is given by

$$U(x) = U_0 \frac{a}{x}\,; \qquad U'(x) = -U_0 \frac{a}{x^2}\,; \qquad U''(x) = 2\, U_0 \frac{a}{x^3}\,. \qquad (12.52)$$

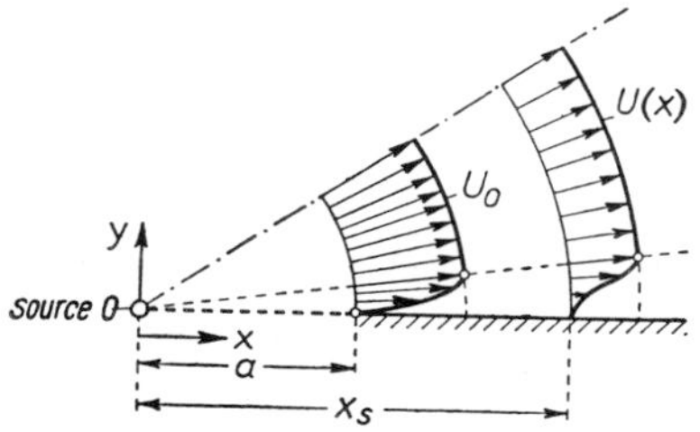

Fig. 12.17. Laminar boundary layer in a divergent channel. Separation occurs at $x_s/a = 1{\cdot}21$ independently of the angle of divergence

Computing the value of the quantity σ from eqn. (12.47), which is decisive for separation, we obtain here $\sigma = 2$. Applying the criterion given in eqn. (12.47a) we conclude that separation occurs in all cases irrespective of the magnitude of the angle of divergence. This example shows very clearly that a laminar stream has only a very limited capacity for supporting an adverse pressure gradient without separation.

According to a calculation performed by K. Pohlhausen the point of separation occurs at $x_s/a = 1{\cdot}213$ and is seen to be independent of the angle of divergence.

† The result from Sec. IXa may be here recalled. By solving the differential equation it was then found that separation occurs in retarded flow when $U(x) = u_1\, x^{-0{\cdot}091}$.

References

[1] A. Betz, Reihendarstellung der Geschwindigkeitsverteilung in laminaren Grenzschichten. Archiv d. Math. **2**, 220 (1950).

[2] J. Boussinesq, Comptes Rendus **113**, 9 and 49 (1891).

[3] K. Bussmann and A. Ulrich, Systematische Untersuchungen über den Einfluß der Profilform auf die Lage des Umschlagpunktes. Preprint for Jahrbuch d. dt. Luftfahrtforschung 1943 in Techn. Berichte **10**, No. 9 (1943); NACA Tech. Memo. 1185 (1947).

[4] W. Dienemann, Berechnung des Wärmeüberganges an laminar umströmten Körpern mit konstanter und ortsveränderlicher Wandtemperatur, ZAMM **33**, 89—109 (1953).

[5] E. A. Eichelbrenner and A. Oudart, Méthode de calcul de la couche limite tridimensionelle. Application à un corps fuselé incliné sur le vent. ONERA Publication No. 76, Chatillon 1955.

[6] A. Fage, Experiments on a sphere at critical Reynolds Numbers. ARC R & M 1766 (1936).

[7] M. B. Glauert and M. J. Lighthill, The axisymmetric boundary layer on a long thin cylinder. Boundary Layer Effects in Aerodynamics. Proc. of a Symposium held at NPL, London 1955.

[8] H. Görtler, Zur Approximation stationärer laminarer Grenzschichtströmungen mit Hilfe der abgebrochenen Blasiusschen Reihe. Arch. d. Math. **1**, 235 (1949).

[9] H. Holstein and T. Bohlen, Ein einfaches Verfahren zur Berechnung laminarer Reibungsschichten, die dem Nährungsansatz von K. Pohlhausen genügen. Lilienthal-Bericht S 10, 5—16 (1940).

[10] G. Jungclaus, Grenzschichtuntersuchungen in rotierenden Kanälen und bei scherenden Strömungen. Report of Max-Planck-Institut f. Strömungsforschung No. 11, Göttingen 1955.

[11] Th. von Kármán and C. B. Millikan, On the theory of laminar boundary layer involving separation. NACA Rep. No. 504 (1934).

[12] Th. von Kármán, Über laminare und turbulente Reibung. ZAMM **1**, 233—252 (1921); NACA Tech. Memo. 1092, (1946).

[12a] H. L. Langhaar, Steady flow in the transition length of a straight tube. Jour. Appl. Mech. **9**, A 55 (1942).

[13] W. Mangler, Ein Verfahren zur Berechnung der laminaren Reibungsschicht. Jb. d. dt. Luftfahrtforschg., **I**, 18 (1941).

[14] W. Mangler, Das Impulsverfahren zur Berechnung der laminaren Reibungsschicht. ZAMM **24**, 251 (1944).

[15] D. Meksyn, Integration of the boundary layer equations. Proc. Roy. Soc. London, A, **237**, 543—559 (1956).

[16] C. B. Millikan, The boundary layer and skin friction for a figure of revolution. Trans. ASME **54**, 29 (1932).

[17] W. Möller, Experimentelle Untersuchungen zur Hydrodynamik der Kugel. Phys. Z. **39**, 57 (1938).

[17a] O. Parr: Die Strömung um einen axial angeströmten rotierenden Drehkörper. Jahrb. Schiffbautechn. Ges. **53** (1959). S. 260—271.

[18] K. Pohlhausen, Zur näherungsweisen Integration der Differentialgleichung der laminaren Reibungsschicht. ZAMM **1**, 252—268 (1921).

[19] L. Prandtl, Über Reibungsschichten bei dreidimensionalen Strömungen. Betz anniversary volume 59, 1945.

[20] L. Prandtl, The mechanics of viscous fluids. In W. F. Durand, Aerodynamic Theory **III**, 112 (1935).

[21] N. A. V. Preston and J. Piercy, A simple solution of the flat plate problem of skin friction and heat transfer. Phil. Mag. (7) **21**, 995 (1936).

[22] J. Pretsch, Die laminare Reibungsschicht an elliptischen Zylindern und Rotationsellipsoiden bei symmetrischer Anströmung. Luftfahrtforschung **18**, 397—402 (1941).

[23] N. Rott and L. F. Crabtree, Simplified laminar boundary layer calculations for bodies of revolution and for yawed wings. Jour. Aero. Sci. **19**, 553 (1952).

[24] H. Schlichting and A. Ulrich, Zur Berechnung des Umschlages laminar-turbulent. Jahrbuch d. dt. Luftfahrtforschung, **I**, 8 (1942); see also Report S 10 of the Lilienthalgesellschaft, 1940.

[25] L. Schiller, Untersuchungen über laminare und turbulente Strömung. Forschungsarb. a. d. Geb. Ing.-Wesen, Heft 248 (1922), ZAMM **2**, 96 (1922), or Phys. Z. **23**, 14, (1922).

[26] F. W. Scholkemeyer, Die laminare Reibungsschicht an rotationssymmetrischen Körpern. Thesis Braunschweig 1943.

[27] G. B. Schubauer, Airflow in a separation laminar boundary layer. NACA Rep. No. 527 (1935).

[28] H. Schuh, Über die Lösung der laminaren Grenzschichtgleichung an der ebenen Platte für Geschwindigkeits- und Temperaturfeld bei veränderlichen Stoffwerten und das Diffusionsfeld bei höheren Konzentrationen. ZAMM **25—27**, 54 (1947) and Oesterr. Ing.-Archiv **2**, 346 (1948); NACA Tech. Memo. 1275.

[29] A. M. O. Smith, Rapid laminar boundary-layer calculations by piecewise application of similar solutions. Jour. Aero. Sci. **23**, 901—912 (1956).

[30] W. G. L. Sutton, An approximate solution of the boundary layer equations for a flat plate. Phil. Mag. **23**, 1146 (1937).

[31] I. Tani, On the approximate solution of the laminar boundary layer equations. Jour. Aero. Sci. **21**, 487—495 (1954).

[32] I. Tani, On the solution of the laminar boundary layer equations. "Fifty years of boundary layer research". Braunschweig 1955, pp. 193—200.

[33] N. Tetervin, Boundary-layer momentum equations for three-dimensional flow. NACA TN 1479 (1947).

[34] R. Timman, The theory of three-dimensional boundary layers. Boundary Layer Effects in Aerodynamics. Proceedings of a Symposium held at NPL, London 1955.

[35] R. Timman and J. A. Zaat, Eine Rechenmethode für dreidimensionale laminare Grenzschichten. "Fifty years of boundary layer research", Braunschweig 1955, pp. 432—445.

[36] S. Tomotika, Laminar boundary layer on the surface of a sphere in a uniform stream. ARC R & M 1678 (1935).

[37] S. Tomotika and I. Imai, On the transition from laminar to turbulent flow in the boundary layer of a sphere. Rep. Aero. Res. Inst. Tokyo Imp. Univ. No. 167 (1938) and S. Tomotika, Proc. Phys. Math. Soc. of Japan **20** (1938).

[38] B. Thwaites, Approximate calculation of the laminar boundary layer. Aero. Quarterly **I**, 245—280 (1949).

[39] A. Walz, Ein neuer Ansatz für das Geschwindigkeitsprofil der laminaren Reibungsschicht. Lilienthal-Bericht 141, 8 (1941).

[40] A. Walz, Anwendung des Energiesatzes von Wieghardt auf einparametrige Geschwindigkeitsprofile in laminaren Grenzschichten. Ing.-Arch. **16**, 243—248 (1948).

[41] E. I. Watson and I. H. Preston, An approximate solution of two flat plate boundary layer problems. ARC R & M 2537 (1951).

[42] K. Wieghardt, Über einen Energiesatz zur Berechnung laminarer Grenzschichten. Ing.-Arch. **16**, 231—242 (1948).

[43] K. Wieghardt, On a simple method for calculating laminar boundary layers. Aero. Quarterly **5**, 25 (1954).

CHAPTER XIII

Boundary layer control

a. Methods of boundary layer control

There are in existence several methods which have been developed for the purpose of artificially controlling the behaviour of the boundary layer. The purpose of these methods is to affect the whole flow in a desired direction by influencing the structure of the boundary layer. As early as in his first paper published in 1904, L. Prandtl described several experiments in which the boundary layer was controlled. He intended to prove the validity of his fundamental ideas by suitably designed experiments and achieved quite remarkable results in this way. Fig. 13.1 shows the flow past a circular cylinder with suction applied on one side of it through a small slit. On the suction side the flow adheres to the cylinder over a considerably larger portion of its surface and separation is avoided; the drag is reduced appreciably, and simultaneously a large cross-force is induced owing to the lack of symmetry in the flow pattern.

Fig. 13.1. Flow past a circular cylinder with suction on one side, after Prandtl

As demonstrated in Chap. XII, a laminar boundary layer can support only very small adverse pressure gradients without the occurence of separation. In the case of turbulent flow the danger of separation is intrinsically reduced, compared with laminar flow, because owing to the turbulent mixing motion there is a continuous flow of momentum from the external flow towards the wall. Nevertheless, even in turbulent flow it is often desirable to prevent separation by adopting suitable *boundary layer control* measures. The problem of boundary layer control has become very important in recent times, in particular in the field of aeronautical engineering; in actual applications it is often necessary to prevent separation in order to reduce drag and to attain high lifts. Several methods of controlling the boundary layer have been developed experimentally, and also on the basis of theoretical considerations [6]. These can be classified as follows:

1. Motion of the solid wall
2. Acceleration of the boundary layer
3. Suction
4. Prevention of transition to turbulent flow by the provision of suitable shapes (laminar profiles).

Methods 1 to 3 will be discussed in the present chapter. Method 4 will be described in Chap. XVII in connexion with the consideration of the theory of transition from laminar to turbulent flow.

1. Motion of the solid wall. The most obvious method of preventing separation is to attempt to prevent the formation of a boundary layer. Since a boundary layer owes its existence to the difference between the velocity of the fluid and that of the solid wall, it is possible to eliminate the formation of a boundary layer by attempting to suppress that difference, i. e. by causing the solid wall to move with the stream. The simplest way of achieving such a result involves the rotation of a circular cylinder. Fig. 13.2 shows the flow pattern which exists about a rotating cylinder placed in a stream at right angles to its axis. On the upper side, where the flow and the cylinder move in the same direction, separation is completely eliminated.

Fig. 13.2. Flow past a rotating cylinder

Furthermore, on the lower side where the direction of fluid motion is opposite to that of the solid wall, separation is developed only incompletely. On the whole the flow pattern which exists in this case approximates very closely the case of frictionless flow past a circular cylinder with circulation. The stream exerts a considerable force on the cylinder at right angles to the mean flow direction, and this is sometimes referred to as the Magnus effect. This effect can be seen, e. g. when a tennis ball is 'sliced' in play. Attempts were also made to utilize the occurrence of lift on rotating cylinders for the propulsion of ships (Flettner's rotor [1]). With the exception of rotating cylinders, the idea of moving the solid wall with the stream can be realized only at the cost of very great practical complications as far as shapes other than cylindrical are concerned, and consequently, this method has not found much practical application. Nevertheless, A. Favre [15b] made a thorough experimental investigation of the influence of a moving boundary on an aerofoil. A portion of the upper surface of the aerofoil was formed into an endless belt which moved over two rollers so that the return motion occurred in the interior of the model. The arrangement proved very effective for the avoidance of separation, and yielded very high maximum lift coefficients ($C_{L\,max} = 3.5$) at high angles of incidence ($\alpha = 55°$). The laminar boundary layer for a flat plate moving in its rear part with the stream has been calculated by E. Truckenbrodt [75].

2. Acceleration of the boundary layer. An alternative method of preventing separation consists in supplying additional energy to the particles of fluid which are being retarded in the boundary layer. This result can be achieved by discharging fluid from the interior of the body with the aid of a special blower (Fig. 13. 3a), or by deriving the required energy directly from the main stream. This latter effect can be produced by connecting the retarded region to a region of higher pressure through a slot in the wing (slotted wing, Fig. 13.3b). In either case additional energy is imparted to the particles of fluid in the boundary layer near the wall.

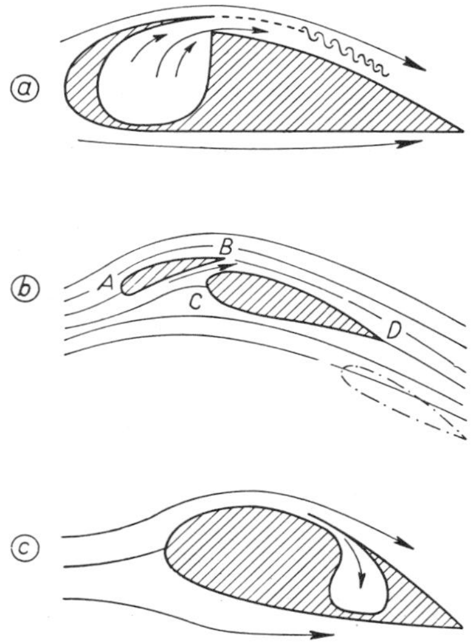

Fig. 13.3. Different arrangements for boundary layer control. a) discharge of fluid, b) slotted wing, c) suction

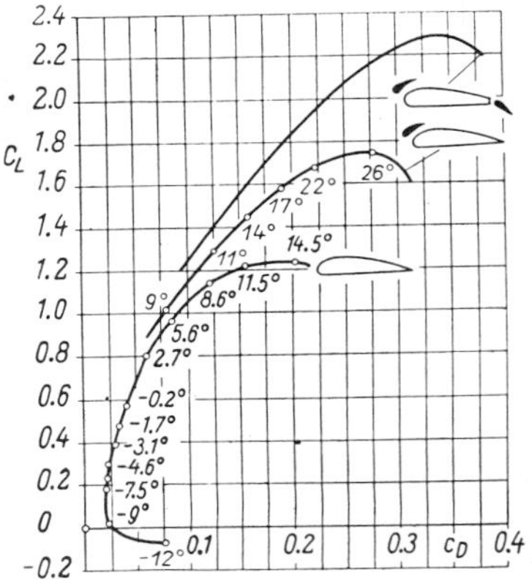

Fig. 13.4. Polar diagram of a wing with forward slot and flap

When fluid is discharged, say in the manner shown in Fig. 13.3a, it is mandatory to pay careful attention to the shape of the slit in order to prevent the jet from dissolving into vortices at a short distance behind the exit section. Recent experiments performed in France [40] have made it very attractive to apply blowing at the trailing edge of an aerofoil in order to increase its maximum lift. Attempts considerably to increase the maximum lift of a flap wing through blowing in the slot have also met with success.

In the case of the slotted wing [5], shown in Fig. 13.3b, the effect is produced as follows: The boundary layer formed on the forward slat A—B is carried into the main stream before separation occurs, and from point C onwards a new boundary layer is formed. Under favourable conditions this new boundary layer will reach the trailing edge D without separation. In this way it is possible to relegate separation to considerably larger angles of incidence, and to achieve much larger lifts. Fig. 13.4 shows a polar diagram (lift coefficient plotted against drag coefficient) for a wing section with and without forward slat and flap. The phenomena in the slot formed by the flap near the trailing edge are, in principle, the same as those at the forward slat. The gain in lift is seen to be very considerable.

The same principle operates when Townsend's ring, or the NACA ring, is applied as a cowling for the engine, because they merely constitute circular slats. G. Fluegel [16] indicated several very effective designs of slats with the aid of which it becomes possible to achieve large changes in the flow direction through channels with very small losses.

3. Suction. The effect of suction consists in the removal of decelerated fluid particles from the boundary layer before they are given a chance to cause separation, Fig. 13.3c. A new boundary layer which is again capable of overcoming a certain adverse pressure gradient is allowed to form in the region behind the slit. With a suitable arrangement of the slits and under favourable conditions separation can be prevented completely. Simultaneously the amount of pressure drag is greatly reduced owing to the absence of separation. The application of suction, which was first tried by L. Prandtl (Fig. 13.1), was later widely used in the design of aircraft wings. By applying suction, considerably greater pressure increases on the upper side of the aerofoil (i. e. lower absolute pressures) are obtained at large angles of incidence, and, consequently, much larger maximum lift values. O. Schrenk [63] investigated a large number of different arrangements of suction slits and their effect on maximum lift.

In more recent times suction was also applied to reduce drag. By the use of suitable arrangements of suction slits it is possible to shift the point of transition in the boundary layer in the downstream direction which causes the drag coefficient to decrease, because laminar drag is substantially smaller than turbulent drag, Fig. 13.9. The effect of the *delay in transition* caused by suction is to reduce the boundary layer thickness which then becomes less prone to turning turbulent [3]. Furthermore, the velocity profiles in a boundary layer with suction, being fuller (Fig. 13.6), have forms which are less likely to induce turbulence compared with those in laminar boundary layers without suction and of equal thickness. Problems connected with the phenomenon of transition and in particular those associated with suction will be discussed more fully in Chap. XVII.

4. Prevention of transition by the provision of suitable shapes. Laminar aerofoils. Transition from laminar to turbulent flow can also be delayed by the use of suitably shaped bodies. The object, as in the case of suction, is to reduce frictional drag by causing the point of transition to move downstream. It has been established that the location of the point of transition in the boundary layer is strongly influenced by the pressure gradient in the external stream. With a decrease in pressure, transition occurs at much higher Reynolds numbers than with pressure increase. A decrease in pressure has a highly stabilizing effect on the boundary layer, and the opposite is true of an increase in pressure along the stream. This circumstance is utilized in modern low-drag aerofoils. The desired result is achieved by displacing the section of maximum thickness far rearwards. In this manner a large portion of the aerofoil remains under the influence of a pressure which decreases downstream and a laminar boundary layer is maintained. We shall revert to this question in Chap. XVII.

The method of boundary layer control by suction, together with the prevention of transition on laminar aerofoils, have the greatest practical importance among all the methods discussed previously. For this reason various mathematical methods for the calculation of the influence of suction on boundary layer flow have been developed, and we now propose to review them briefly.

b. Boundary layer suction

1. Theoretical results

1.1. Fundamental equations. It is simplest to begin the mathematical study of the laminar boundary layer with suction by first considering the case with continuous suction which may be imagined realized with the aid of a porous wall. The usual system of co-ordinates will be adopted, the x-axis being along the wall, and the y-axis being at right angles to it, Fig. 13.5. Suction will be accounted for by prescribing a non-zero normal velocity component $v_0(x)$ at the wall; in the case of

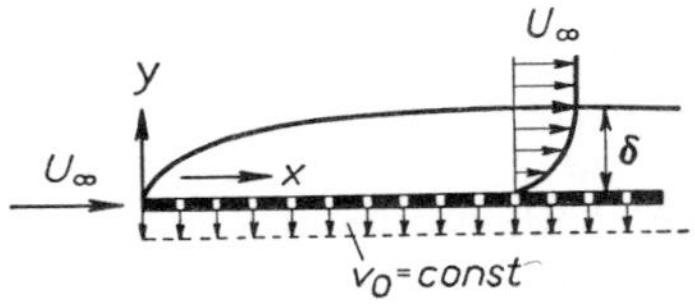

Fig. 13.5. Flat plate with homogeneous suction at zero incidence

suction we shall put $v_0 < 0$, making $v_0 > 0$ for discharge. It will be assumed that the quantity of fluid removed from the stream is so small that only fluid particles in the immediate neighbourhood of the wall are sucked away. This is equivalent to saying that the ratio of suction velocity $v_0(x)$ to free stream velocity U_∞ is very small, say $v_0/U_\infty = 0{\cdot}0001$ to $0{\cdot}01$. The condition of no slip at the wall is retained with suction present, as well as the expression $\tau_0 = \mu(\partial u/\partial y)_0$ for the shearing stress at the wall. The quantity of fluid removed, Q, will be expressed through a dimensionless volume coefficient by putting

$$Q = c_Q \, A \, U_\infty , \tag{13.1}$$

where A denotes the wetted area. For the flat plate $Q = b \int_0^l [-v_0(x)]\, dx$ and $A = b\, l$ so that consequently

$$c_Q = \frac{1}{l\, U_\infty} \int_0^l [-v_0(x)]\, \mathrm{d}x \tag{13.2}$$

and for the case of uniform suction, $v_0 = \text{const}$,

$$c_Q = \frac{-v_0}{U_\infty} . \tag{13.2a}$$

Assuming incompressible two-dimensional flow we have the following differential equations

$$\left.\begin{aligned} \frac{\partial u}{\partial x} + \frac{\partial v}{\partial y} &= 0 \\ u\,\frac{\partial u}{\partial x} + v\,\frac{\partial u}{\partial y} &= -\frac{1}{\varrho}\,\frac{\mathrm{d}p}{\mathrm{d}x} + \nu\,\frac{\partial^2 u}{\partial y^2} \end{aligned}\right\} \qquad (13.3)$$

with the boundary conditions

$$\left.\begin{aligned} y = 0 &: \quad u = 0, \quad v = v_0(x) \\ y = \infty &: \quad u = U(x)\,. \end{aligned}\right\} \qquad (13.4)$$

Evidently, the integration of the above system of equations for the general case of arbitrary body shape, implying an arbitrary velocity function $U(x)$, presents no fewer difficulties than does the case with no suction.

1.2. Exact solutions. The method of using a power-series expansion in terms of the length of arc for the potential velocity described in Sec. IXc can, in principle, be applied in this case as well. Calculations of this kind have been performed by K. Bussmann and A. Ulrich [77] for the case of a circular cylinder. However, the functional coefficients f_1, f_3, f_5, ... from eqn. (9.18) have to be re-calculated for different values of the rate of flow due to suction, and this, obviously, is very tedious. H. Goertler's method, described in Sec. IXe, in which the solution is sought in terms of a suitable series expansion can also be applied to cases when the wall is porous (suction or blowing), [19]. The equation for the velocity distribution in the external flow

$$U(x) = x^m \left\{ s_0 + s_1\, x^{m+1} + s_2\, x^{2(m+1)} + \ldots \right\}$$

must now be supplemented with an equation describing the distribution of this suction velocity in the form

$$v_0(x) = x^{(1/2)(m-1)} \left\{ \sigma_0 + \sigma_1\, x^{m+1} + \sigma_2\, {}^{2(m+1)} + \ldots \right\}.$$

The addition of this new series causes an increase in the number of functions which require tabulation.

In this connection the reader might be referred to a paper by W. Reinboldt [52] which contains a series expansion for the case when the suction velocity changes discontinuously and which is valid in the neighbourhood of the points where jumps occur. Further downstream, where the effect of the discontinuity has decayed, the ordinary step-by-step methods, such as the one discussed in Sec. IXi, regain their validity.

A surprisingly simple solution can be obtained in the case of a *flat plate at zero incidence* with *uniform suction*, Fig. 13.5. The system of differential equations now reduces to

$$\frac{\partial u}{\partial x} + \frac{\partial v}{\partial y} = 0\,; \qquad (13.5\text{a})$$

$$u\,\frac{\partial u}{\partial x} + v\,\frac{\partial u}{\partial y} = \nu\,\frac{\partial^2 u}{\partial y^2} \qquad (13.5\text{b})$$

with the boundary conditions: $u = 0$, $v = v_0 = \text{const} < 0$ for $y = 0$, and $u = U_\infty$ for $y = \infty$. It can be seen at once that this system possesses a particular solution for which the velocity is independent of the current length x [34, 56]. Putting $\partial u/\partial x = 0$ we see from the equation of continuity that $v(x, y) = v_0 = \text{const}$. Hence the equation of motion becomes $v_0\, \partial u/\partial y = \nu\, \partial^2 u/\partial y^2$ with the solution

$$u(y) = U_\infty\,[1 - \exp(v_0 y/\nu)]\,; \quad v(x, y) = v_0 < 0\,. \tag{13.6}$$

It is worth noting that this simple solution is even an exact solution of the complete Navier-Stokes equations.

The displacement thickness and the momentum thickness are

$$\delta^* = \frac{\nu}{-v_0}\,; \qquad \theta = \frac{1}{2}\,\frac{\nu}{-v_0} \qquad (13.7);\ (13.8)$$

and the shearing stress at the wall $\tau_0 = \mu\,(\partial u/\partial y)_0$ becomes simply

$$\tau_0 = \varrho\,(-v_0)\,U_\infty\,, \tag{13.9}$$

and is independent of viscosity. The velocity distribution is seen plotted in Fig. 13.6, curve I. Curve II, drawn for the purpose of comparison, represents the Blasius velocity distribution without suction. It should be noted that the suction profile is fuller. The solution thus discovered can be realized on a flat plate at zero incidence with uniform suction only at some distance from the leading edge, even if suction is applied from the leading edge onwards. The boundary layer, evidently, begins to grow from zero thickness at the leading edge and continues downstream tending asymptotically to the value given in eqn. (13.7). The velocity profile attains the simple form given by eqn. (13.6) only asymptotically, i. e. from the practical point

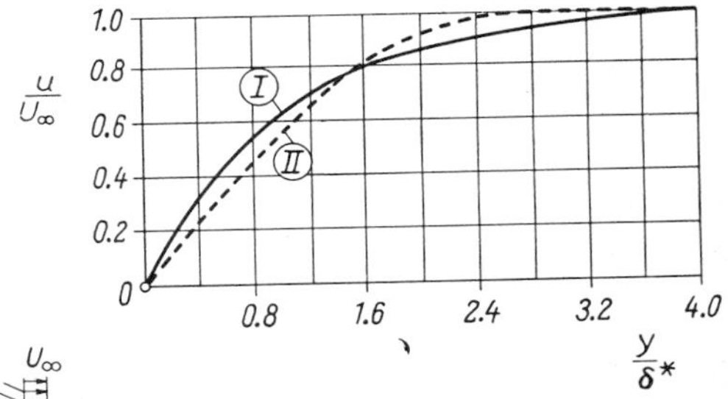

Fig. 13.6. Velocity distribution in the boundary layer on a flat plate at zero incidence
I. uniform suction; 'asymptotic suction profile'
II. no suction; 'Blasius profile'

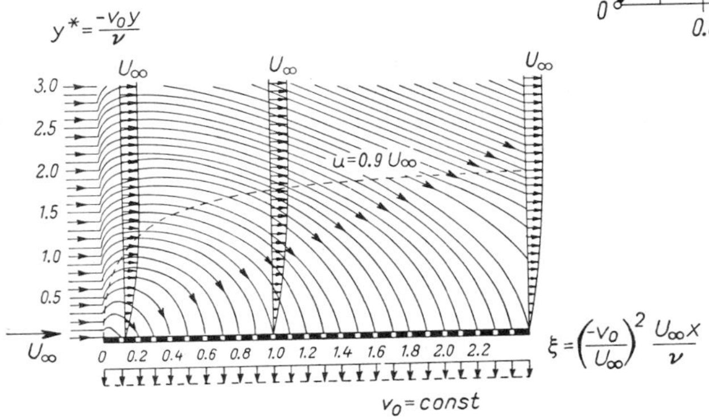

Fig. 13.7. Flat plate with uniform suction; pattern of streamlines

of view after a certain initial length. For these reasons the preceding particular solution may be regarded as the *asymptotic suction profile*. Such an asymptotic velocity profile exists for arbitrary cylindrical bodies (e. g. circular cylinder in an axial stream), as shown by W. Wuest [81].

A more detailed investigation into the flow in the initial length, i. e. before the asymptotic state has been reached, was carried out by R. Iglisch [24], who has shown that the asymptotic state is reached after a length of about

$$\left(\frac{-v_0}{U_\infty}\right)^2 \frac{U_\infty x}{\nu} = 4 \quad \text{or} \quad c_Q \sqrt{\mathsf{R}_x} = 2\,.$$

The velocity profiles in the initial length are not similar among themselves. They are practically identical with those for the case with no suction at short distances from the leading edge (Blasius profiles, Fig. 7.8). The pattern of stream-lines in the initial length is seen drawn in Fig. 13.7, and the velocity profiles are seen plotted in Fig. 13.8. The way in which the boundary layer thickness increases from zero at the leading edge to its asymptotic value given in eqn. (13.7) should be noted. The values in Table 13.1 have been taken from R. Iglisch's paper.

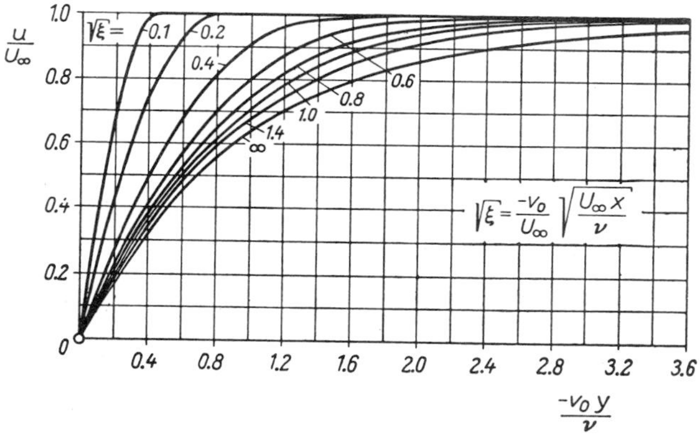

Fig. 13.8. Flat plate with uniform suction; velocity profiles over initial length
The curve $\xi = \infty$ corresponds to the 'asymptotic suction profile' of eqn. (13.6)

Particular interest is attached to the decrease in drag caused by preserving laminar flow with the aid of suction, and, therefore, to the law of friction for the case with suction. This is seen plotted in Fig. 13.9. In the case of very large Reynolds numbers $U_\infty l/\nu$, when the major portion of the plate falls within the region of the asymptotic solution, the drag is given by the simple equation (13.9), whence we can obtain the local drag coefficient

$$c_{f\infty} = \frac{\tau_0}{\frac{1}{2}\varrho U_\infty{}^2} = 2\,\frac{-v_0}{U_\infty} = 2\,c_Q\,. \qquad (13.10)\dagger$$

† This drag is completely independent of viscosity. With $D = \tau_0\, b\, l$ and $Q = (-v_0)\, b\, l$ we find from eqn. (13.9) that

$$D = \varrho\, Q\, U_\infty\,.$$

This is the drag due to sinking, i. e. the drag experienced by a body which is placed in a frictionless stream of velocity U_∞ and which 'swallows' a quantity Q of fluid. The above expression can be deduced very simply by the application of the momentum theorem (*cf.* Prandtl-Tietjens, vol. II).

Table 13.1. Dimensionless boundary layer thickness δ^* and shape factor δ^*/θ for the velocity profiles in the initial length on a flat plate at zero incidence with uniform suction, after R. Iglisch [24]

$$\xi = \left(\frac{-v_0}{U_\infty}\right)^2 \frac{U_\infty x}{\nu}; \qquad \delta^* \text{ — displacement thickness}; \quad \theta \text{ — momentum thickness}$$

ξ	$\frac{-v_0\,\delta^*}{\nu}$	$\frac{\delta^*}{\theta}$
0	0	2·59
0·005	0·114	2·53
0·02	0·211	2·47
0·045	0·303	2·43
0·08	0·381	2·39
0·125	0·450	2·35
0·18	0·511	2·31
0·245	0·566	2·28
0·32	0·614	2·25
0·405	0·658	2·23
0·5	0·695	2·21
0·72	0·761	2·17
0·98	0·812	2·14
1·28	0·853	2·11
2·0	0·911	2·07
2·88	0·948	2·05
5·12	0·983	2·01
8·0	0·996	2·00
∞	1	2

The drag coefficient is larger for small Reynolds numbers, because the shearing stress is greater over the front portion of the plate which falls within the initial region and where the boundary layer is thinner than further downstream. The drag on a plate with a turbulent boundary layer with no suction is shown plotted in Fig. 13.9 for the purpose of comparison. It will be discussed more fully in Chap. XXI.

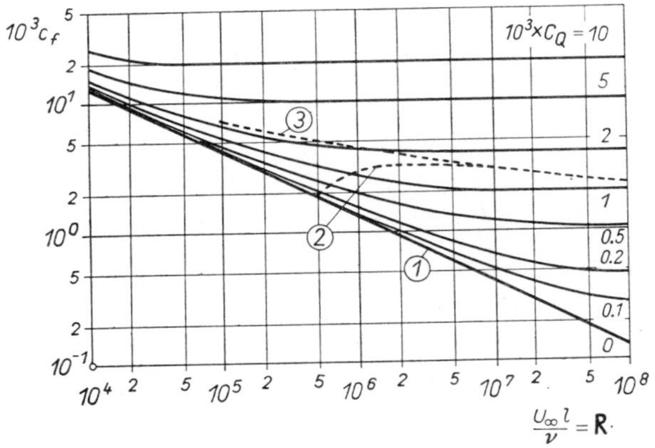

Fig. 13.9. Drag coefficients for the flat plate at zero incidence with uniform suction

$c_Q = (-v_0)/U_\infty$ = volume coefficient of suction

Curves (1), (2) and (3) refer to no suction

(1) laminar

(2) transition from laminar to turbulent

(3) fully turbulent

The saving in drag can be deduced from this diagram, only if the value of the smallest volume coefficient of suction which is capable of ensuring laminar conditions in the boundary layer at large Reynolds numbers, is known. This problem will be investigated in Chap. XVII, together with the phenomenon of transition. It will then be shown that there exists a curve of 'most favourable suction'; it can be seen plotted in Fig. 17.17. It will be noticed that the reduction in drag through suction is very considerable and that the required intensity of suction is very small, as it corresponds to values of the order $c_Q = 10^{-4}$. A solution for the flat plate with uniform suction in a compressible stream was found by H. G. Lew and J. B. Fanucci [29].

J. M. Kay [26] undertook to verify these theoretical results for the flat plate at zero incidence with the aid of experiments. The assumption that uniform suction begins at the leading edge which formed the basis of Iglisch's theoretical calculations was not satisfied in the test plate. The latter, moreover, had a portion near the leading edge completely devoid of suction. Fig. 13.10 shows a comparison between the measured and calculated displacement thickness and momentum thickness respectively. The asymptotic values from eqns. (13.7) and (13.8) are seen to have been confirmed by the measurements. Fig. 13.11 shows a comparison between theory and measurement for various values of ξ; the measurements have been performed by M. R. Head [21]. Again, the agreement is very satisfactory. Measurements performed by P. A. Libby, L. Kaufmann and R. P. Harrington [30] confirm, in addition, the strong stabilizing effect caused by suction (increase in the critical Reynolds number), as will be reported more fully in Sec. XVIIc. The large decrease in the skin friction which results from the preservation of laminar flow when suction is applied, and which is shown in Fig. 13.9, was confirmed by measurements performed by M. Jones and M. R. Head [25], and A. Raspet [46].

Additional *exact solutions* of the boundary layer equations (13.3) and (13.4) are known only for flow patterns which can be associated with similar velocity profiles. The class of similar solutions discussed in Chap. VIII can be extended to include boundary layers with suction and blowing. When the velocity in the external stream can be described by the function $U(x) = u_1 x^m$ and when the suction velocity $v_0(x)$ is proportional to $x^{(1/2)(m-1)}$, we recover from the boundary layer equations the already familiar ordinary differential equation for the stream function $f(\eta)$, first derived by Falkner and Skan, namely

$$f''' + ff'' + \beta(1-f'^2) = 0 \tag{9.8}$$

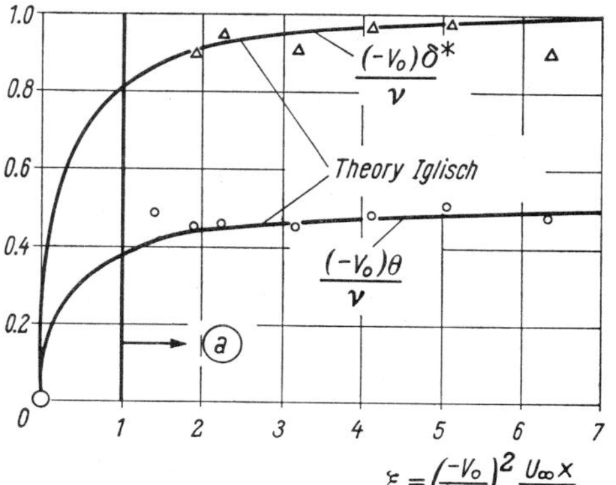

Fig. 13.10. Laminar boundary layer on a flat plate at zero incidence with uniform suction. Displacement thickness δ^* and momentum thickness θ have been measured by J. M. Kay [26]. Theoretical curves after R. Iglisch [24]. Table 13.1

a = section at which suction begins

in which η has been defined in eqn. (9.5). That this is so can be inferred by inspection from eqn. (9.5). In the present case, the stream function $f(\eta)$ has a value which is different from zero at the wall when $\eta = 0$. This value is positive in the case of suction and negative for blowing.

The particular case for $m = 0$ which corresponds to a flat plate with a suction velocity

$$v_0(x) = -\tfrac{1}{2} C \sqrt{\frac{\nu U_\infty}{x}} \qquad \begin{array}{l} C > 0 : \text{suction} \\ C < 0 : \text{blowing} \end{array} \tag{13.11}$$

was investigated by H. Schlichting and K. Bussmann [57, 58]. Extensive tables covering a wide range of values of the parameter C were calculated by H. W. Emmons and D. C. Leigh [15a]. The resulting velocity profiles for several values of the volume coefficient have been plotted in Fig. 13.12. It is worth noting that all velocity profiles for the case of discharge have points of inflexion with $\partial^2 u/\partial y^2 = 0$. This fact is important for the study of transition (Chap. XVI). Similar velocity profiles are also obtained in the case of two-dimensional stagnation flow with a velocity function $U(x) = u_1 x$ with suction, provided that $v_0 = \text{const}$. This case was also investigated in the paper by H. Schlichting and K. Bussmann already quoted.

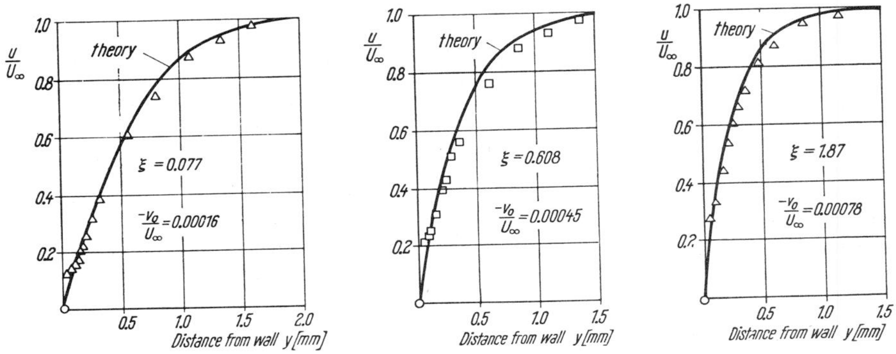

Fig. 13.11. Velocity distribution in the laminar boundary layer on an aerofoil with suction applied through its porous surface. Measurements performed by M. R. Head [21]; comparison with the theory due to R. Iglisch [24]

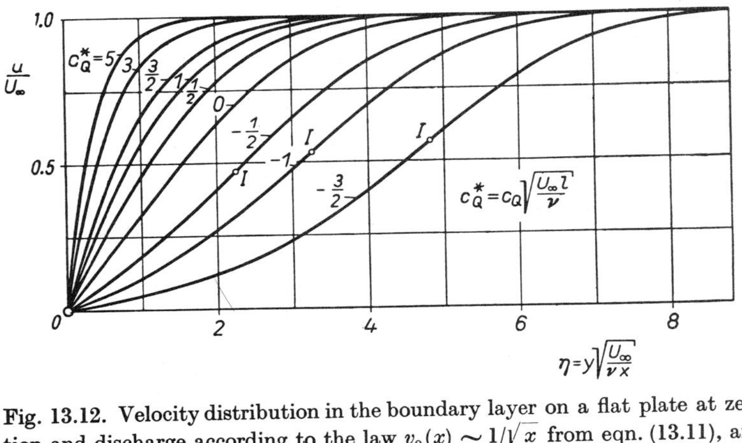

Fig. 13.12. Velocity distribution in the boundary layer on a flat plate at zero incidence with suction and discharge according to the law $v_0(x) \sim 1/\sqrt{x}$ from eqn. (13.11), after K. Bussmann [57] $C = c_Q{}^*$ = reduced volume coefficient of suction. $c_Q{}^* > 0$: suction; $c_Q{}^* < 0$: discharge; I = point of inflexion

The cases corresponding to the values $m = -\frac{1}{9}$ and $m = -\frac{1}{21}$ (pressure increase along flow) of the parameter have been calculated by W. Mangler [33]; that for $m = \frac{1}{9}$ (pressure decrease along flow) was solved by H. Schaefer [54]. E. J. Watson [78] studied the asymptotic behaviour of such similar solutions for large suction velocities. The solutions for the external flow corresponding to $U(x) = u_1 x^m$ form the basis for a series of further investigations aimed at discovering additional exact solutions for laminar boundary layers with suction and blowing:

a) K. D. P. Sinhar [64] studied the case of an infinitely long, yawed cylinder with suction. The velocity distribution along the stream was assumed to be proportional to x^m. The investigation has some bearing on the control of the boundary layer on swept wings.

b) When the temperature of the fluid being blown out is different from that in the external flow, the boundary layer will develop a temperature profile; the resulting thermal boundary layer was calculated in refs. [37] and [82]. The knowledge of the temperature distribution in the boundary layer is of particular importance for the problem of cooling. It turns out that cooling by means of blowing the coolant through a porous wall, so-called transpiration cooling, is much more effective than cooling the wall on the inside. In this connection the papers by B. Brown [8, 9], P. L. Donoughe and J. N. B. Livingood [13] may be consulted.

c) The cooling problem becomes very important at high velocities of flow. G. M. Low [32] found solutions for the case of compressible flow over an isothermal flat plate.

1.3. Approximate solutions. In the general case of an arbitrary body shape and an arbitrary law of suction we must resort to approximate methods based on the momentum equation, and described in Chap. XII. The momentum equation for the case with suction is obtained in exactly the same way as before, except that it is now necessary to take into account the fact that the normal component of the velocity at the wall differs from zero. Performing the same calculation as in Sec. VIIIe, we find that the equation for the normal component of velocity at a distance $y = h$ from the wall now becomes

$$v_h = v_0 - \int_0^h \frac{\partial u}{\partial x}\, dy\,.$$

The calculation is continued in exactly the same way as in Sec. VIIIe, and leads finally to the following momentum equation for the boundary layer with suction

$$U^2 \frac{d\theta}{dx} + (2\,\theta + \delta^*)\, U \frac{dU}{dx} - v_0\, U = \frac{\tau_0}{\varrho}\,. \qquad (13.12)\dagger$$

The additional term $- v_0\, U$, as compared with eqn. (8.35), represents the change in momentum due to suction at the wall.

This equation was used by L. Prandtl [43] to make a simple estimate of the suction velocity which is just sufficient to prevent separation. Assuming that the velocity profiles along the whole length are identical with that at the point of separation, i. e. that for which $\tau_0 = \mu\,(\partial u/\partial y)_0 \doteq 0$, and that, as assumed by Pohlhausen, $\Lambda = -12$, we can deduce from eqn. (12.22) that the velocity is given by

$$u = U \left\{ 6 \left(\frac{y}{\delta}\right)^2 - 8 \left(\frac{y}{\delta}\right)^3 + 3 \left(\frac{y}{\delta}\right)^4 \right\}.$$

† According to K. Wieghardt [79], the energy equation for flow with suction assumes the form

$$\frac{d}{dx}\,(U^3\, \delta^{**}) - v_0\, U^2 = 2 \int_0^\infty \frac{\tau}{\varrho} \frac{\partial u}{\partial y}\, dy.$$

The displacement and momentum thickness follow from eqn. (12.24), and are, respectively

$$\delta^* = \tfrac{2}{5}\,\delta\,; \qquad \theta = \tfrac{4}{35}\,\delta\,,$$

so that

$$\delta^* + 2\,\theta = \tfrac{22}{35}\,\delta\,.$$

Substituting this value into eqn. (13.12) and taking into account that $\mathrm{d}\theta/\mathrm{d}x = 0$, because of the assumption of constant boundary layer thickness, we have

$$v_0 = \frac{22}{35}\,\delta\,\frac{\mathrm{d}U}{\mathrm{d}x}\,. \tag{13.13}$$

Apart from the momentum equation it is necessary to satisfy the equation of motion at the wall as required by the Pohlhausen method. By eqn. (13.3) we then have at $y = 0$:

$$v_0 \left(\frac{\partial u}{\partial y}\right)_0 = U\,\frac{\mathrm{d}U}{\mathrm{d}x} + \nu \left(\frac{\partial^2 u}{\partial y^2}\right)_0. \tag{13.14}$$

In the case under consideration $(\partial u/\partial y)_0 = 0$ and $(\partial^2 u/\partial y^2)_0 = 12\;U/\delta^2$. Hence we obtain from eqn. (13.14) that

$$\delta = \sqrt{\frac{12\,\nu}{(-\,\mathrm{d}U/\mathrm{d}x)}} \tag{13.15}$$

and from eqns. (13.13) and (13.15) that

$$v_0 = -\,2{\cdot}18\,\sqrt{-\,\nu\,\frac{\mathrm{d}U}{\mathrm{d}x}}\,. \tag{13.16}$$

This velocity of suction is seen to be just sufficient to prevent separation all along the wall. Taking as an example the case of flow past a circular cylinder of radius R with $\mathrm{d}U/\mathrm{d}x = -\,2\;U_\infty/R$ at the downstream stagnation point, and applying eqn. (13.16), we obtain that the volume coefficient which must be used to prevent separation is given by

$$c_Q \sqrt{\frac{U_\infty\,R}{\nu}} = 2{\cdot}18\,\sqrt{2} = 3{\cdot}08\,.$$

H. Schlichting [55, 59] indicated an approximate method for the calculation of the boundary layer on a body of arbitrary shape with arbitrary suction $v_0(x)$ applied. The method is similar to the Kármán-Pohlhausen method and is based on the use of the momentum equation. T. B. Torda [72, 73] has made improvements in this method. Papers by L. Trilling [74], B. Thwaites [23, 71], and F. Ringleb [51] contain descriptions of procedures suitable for arbitrary pressure distributions as well as arbitrary distributions of the suction velocity. K. Wieghardt [79] extended these to the case of axially symmetrical bodies and J. T. Stuart [67] solved the case of a rotating disk. E. Truckenbrodt [76] developed an approximate method which is suitable in the two-dimensional as well as in the axially symmetrical case and which excels the other methods in its outstanding simplicity. The whole problem has been reduced here to the solution of an ordinary differential equation of the first order. The equation becomes identical with that given by A. Walz (*cf.* Sec. XIIb) in the limiting case of zero suction i. e. when the wall is impermeable.

The results of calculations for a Joukovsky aerofoil, performed with the aid of this method, are represented graphically in Fig. 13.13. It is seen that the point of separation moves towards the trailing edge as the intensity of suction increases, and that no separation occurs at all from a certain suction intensity onwards.

Corresponding approximate methods for compressible boundary layers with suction and blowing have been developed in refs. [31, 37, 82], with particular attention given to the associated problem in heat transfer which is so important for cooling. Approximate methods, at least for flat plates, are also available for the calculation of turbulent boundary layers with blowing and suction [10, 14, 53]; they all make use of Prandtl's mixing length hypothesis (*cf.* Chap. XIX b).

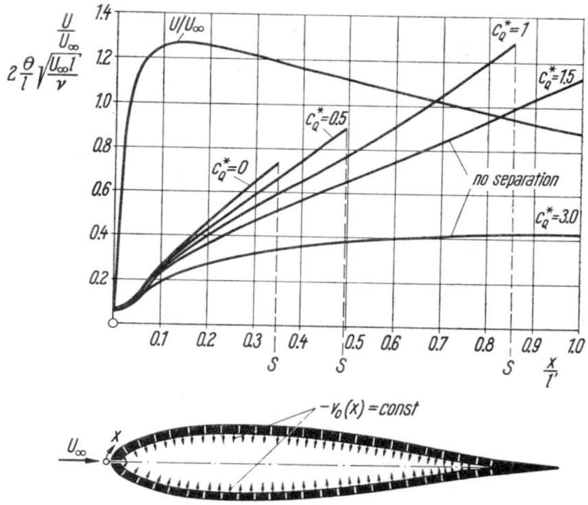

Fig. 13.13. Laminar boundary layer on a symmetrical Joukovsky aerofoil with uniform suction; $v_0(x) = \text{const}$, angle of incidence $\alpha = 0$, as calculated by E. Truckenbrodt [76]

θ = momentum thickness; l' = half perimeter length; $c_{Q^*} = c_Q\sqrt{U_\infty l/\nu}$ = reduced volume coefficient of suction. With increasing suction, i. e. for $c_Q^* > 1{\cdot}12$ no separation occurs at all

2. Experimental results on suction. As early as 1904 L. Prandtl published photographs of flow patterns which demonstrated that suction causes the flow to adhere to the wall even in the case of non-streamlined blunt bodies, such as circular cylinders, in which there would otherwise be strong eddy formation. Figs. 2.12 and 2.13 show the effect of suction on the flow in a divergent channel. Under normal conditions, Fig. 2.11, the flow in a rapidly divergent channel separates violently from the wall, whereas suction applied through two slits on either side causes the flow completely to adhere to it, Fig. 2.13. The first review of available experimental results on suction at the time was given by J. Ackeret [2] in 1926.

When suction is applied to a wing, it is necessary to discern two distinct problems which might arise:

1. It may be desired to increase the maximum lift by delaying separation.
2. It may be desirable to maintain laminar flow and to avoid transition in order to reduce skin friction. We propose to give a short account of the considerations connected with these two problems.

2.1 Increase in lift. Extensive experimental material concerning the increase in the lift coefficient due to suction was collected at the end of the twenties and at the beginning of the thirties in the course of a programme of research instituted at the Aerodynamische Versuchsanstalt in Goettingen under the direction of O. Schrenk. The effect of suction is to preserve the potential flow pattern at higher angles of incidence than would otherwise be the case. O. Schrenk published a comprehensive review of this work in ref. [61]. The scope of these experiments reached such a degree of advancement [62] that at the end of the thirties the Institute in Goettingen was in a position to build two experimental aeroplanes in which suction was applied for the improvement of performance. A detailed description of these experimental aeroplanes was given by J. Stueper [68]. Photographs of the flow field on the wings of one of these experimental aeroplanes are shown in Fig. 13.14. The effect of suction, which was applied in the slit between the wing and the flap, can be inferred clearly from the behaviour of the tufts which are visible in the photographs: Without suction (Fig. 13.14a), the flow is completely separated from the flap; it is brought back completely (Fig. 13.14b) when suction is turned on. A. Gerber [17] investigated systematically certain aspects of suction, such as the best shape of slits, the velocity distribution near the slit, the pressure distribution around it, etc.

More recently, in Great Britain [39] and in the U.S.A. [66], extensive experimental investigations have been carried out into the effect of suction on thin aerofoils. Since at high angles of incidence thin aerofoils develop a sharp negative-pressure peak near the nose on the upperside, it is necessary to apply suction there. In this

a) without suction

b) with suction

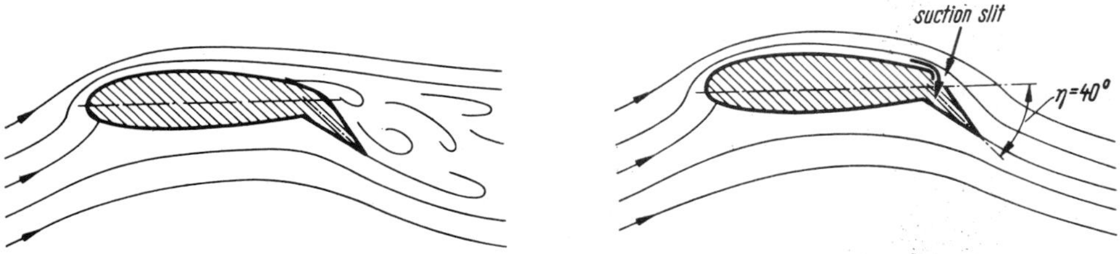

Fig. 13.14. Flow about the wing of the Goettingen experimental aeroplane; the flap is in the down position; the two photographs represent flow without and with suction. a) without suction: the flow is detached from the flap, b) with suction: the flow adheres to the flap

connexion it is important to know whether to apply suction through a porous wall (uniform suction) or through a system of slits. The diagram in Fig. 13.15 shows a comparison between the results of continuous suction and suction applied through slits on a swept-back wing as measured by E. D. Poppleton [41]; see also ref. [22a]. It is clear that the same increase in the lift coefficient can be obtained with a much reduced mass flow when continuous suction is used. The diagram in Fig. 13.16 contains information on the most favourable position of the suction zone at the nose. The measurements carried out on an 8% thick symmetrical aerofoil seem to indicate that continuous suction is most effective when it is confined to the upper-side of the wing and when it extends over a region of $0{\cdot}15\,l$ approximately. The minimum mass flow required to avoid separation depends on the position and the extent of the porous surface and, even more significantly, on the Reynolds number. This, of course, is a very important consideration when results of model experiments are applied to full-scale arrangements. Some data on the dependence of the mass flow on the Reynolds number are shown in Fig. 13.17. They are based on measurements performed by N. Gregory and W. S. Walker [20] on a thin symmetrical aerofoil. The graph shows the minimum volume flow of suction required to avoid

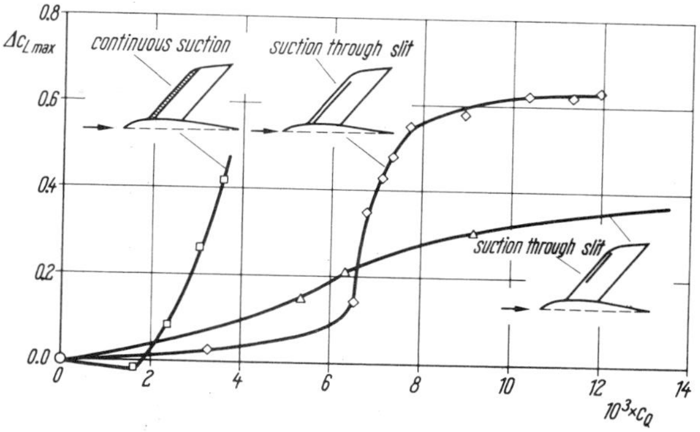

Fig. 13.15. Increase in the maximum lift of a swept-back wing by suction. Comparison between continuous suction and suction applied through slits, as measured by E. D. Poppleton [41]
Reynolds number $\mathsf{R} = 1{\cdot}3 \times 10^6$; relative width of slits $s/l = 0{\cdot}004$

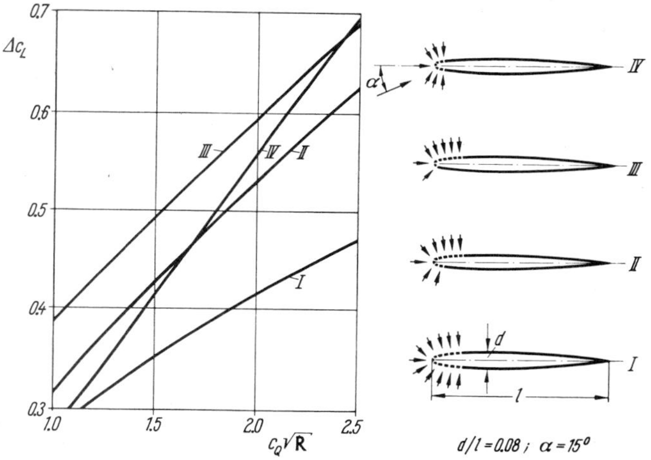

Fig. 13.16. Effect on increase in lift coefficient of changing the position of the porous suction surface for an 8% thick aerofoil at an angle of incidence of $\alpha = 15°$

separation for a fixed angle of incidence of $\alpha = 14°$ plotted in terms of the Reynolds number. Several curves of $c_Q \sqrt{\mathsf{R}}$ = const, which were obtained from the theory of purely laminar flow, have also been plotted for comparison.

2.2. Decrease in drag. An experimental proof of the fact that it is possible to maintain laminar conditions in the boundary layer with the aid of suction was first given by H. Holstein [22], and shortly afterwards by J. Ackeret, M. Ras

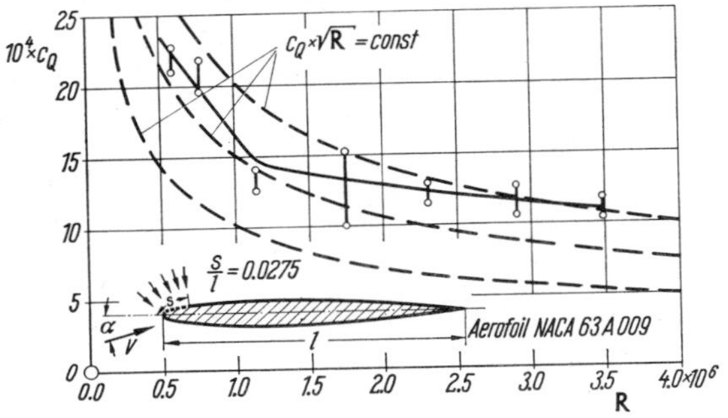

Fig. 13.17. Minimum suction volume required for the prevention of separation as a function of the Reynolds number for an angle of incidence of $\alpha = 14°$, after Gregory and Walker [20]

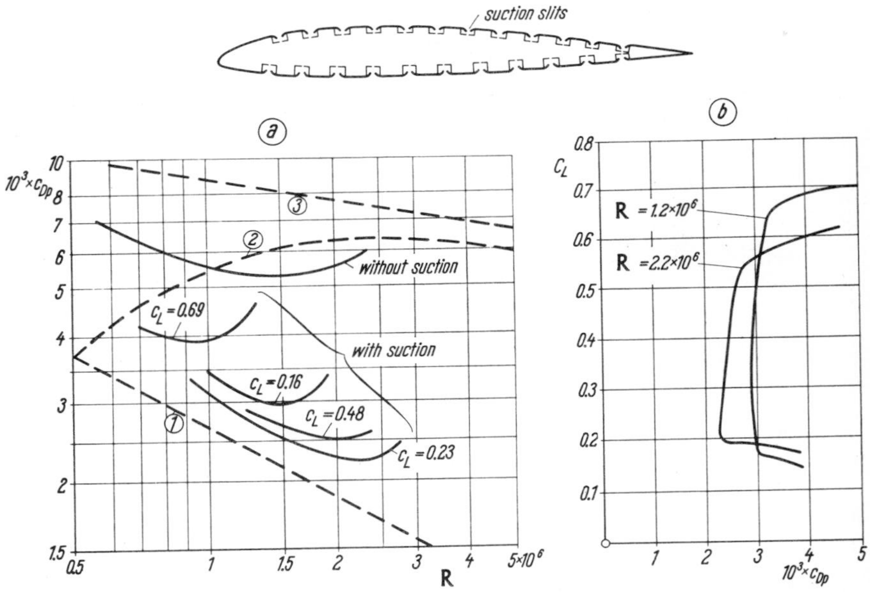

Fig. 13.18. Decrease in the drag of an aerofoil in which transition is delayed by suction through a large number of slits, after W. Penninger [42]. The energy consumption of the pump has been included in the drag coefficient.

a) Optimum values of the drag coefficient in terms of the Reynolds number R.

Curves (1), (2) and (3) without suction; (1) Flat plate, laminar; (2) Flat plate, transitional; (3) Flat plate, fully developed turbulent

b) Polar diagrams for two different Reynolds numbers. The extremely low drag coefficients exist for an increased range of values of the lift coefficient c_L

and W. Pfenninger [3]. W. Pfenninger [42] carried out extensive experiments on the problem of reducing drag by the application of suction through which laminar flow is maintained. Fig. 13.18 reproduces some of his results, obtained with a thin aerofoil which was provided with a large number of suction slits. The graph in Fig. 13.18a shows the optimum values of the skin friction coefficient plotted in terms of the Reynolds number. It is seen that there is a large saving in drag, even if the power consumption of the suction pump is debited against it. The graph shows, further, that, at moderate values of the lift coefficient, even at large Reynolds numbers, the values of the skin friction coefficient are not much higher than those for a flat plate at zero incidence. Moreover, Fig. 13.18b demonstrates that these low values persist over a considerable range of values of the lift coefficient, c_L. Further, the experiments demonstrated that the decrease in the drag effected by maintaining a laminar boundary layer with the aid of suction depends largely on a careful shaping of slits. If this precaution is not taken, the flow may be so much affected by the presence of the slits that transition to turbulent flow occurs readily. Experiments on aerofoils carried out by H. Holstein demonstrated conclusively that a considerable saving in drag can be achieved by suction. In an American paper [7], the possibility of using continuous suction through a porous wall to maintain laminar flow to considerably larger Reynolds number (of the order of $\mathsf{R} = 20 \times 10^6$) was carefully investigated. In this case too, substantial reductions in drag were achieved, allowing for the mechanical work required to maintain it.

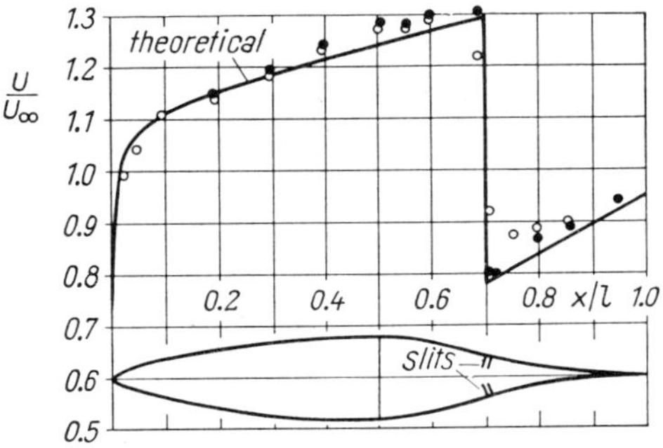

Fig. 13.19. Theoretical and experimental velocity distribution on a symmetrical aerofoil with suction
$c_L = 0$; $\mathsf{R} = 3{\cdot}85 \times 10^6$, after Goldstein [18]
○ = measurement without suction;
● = measurement with suction

When an attempt is made to preserve a laminar boundary layer either by suction, or, as already mentioned, merely by proper shaping, it is very important to have a good knowledge of the potential velocity distribution. In either case it is necessary to arrange for the pressure to decrease over as large a portion of the section as possible. Very extensive experiments on this subject were carried out by S. Goldstein [18] and his collaborators. The calculations led to the determination of the shape of the section of the aerofoil which would produce a prescribed potential velocity distribution and were greatly simplified. In order to obtain aerofoils which maintain a laminar boundary layer as far as the trailing edge it was suggested to use shapes showing a decrease in pressure (an increase in velocity) over the whole length, and only displaying an abrupt pressure increase at one position, as shown in Fig. 13.19. If the slits are arranged at the point of pressure jump, as suggested by Griffith [50], it is possible to secure a laminar boundary layer on thick aerofoils as far as the slit and separation is prevented behind it. B. Regenscheit [47, 48], and B. Thwaites [69] proposed to 'regulate' the lift on very thick aerofoils by varying the intensity of suction and so to obtain a lift which is independent of the angle of incidence. In more recent times there were many proposals to use the air sucked away from the boundary layer for the purpose of increasing the thrust of a jet aircraft [65]. A report prepared by F. Ehlers and A. Walz [15] reviews the numerous investigations into the problem of suction which were carried out in Goettingen during the war.

A comprehensive review of problems concerned with aircraft construction and boundary layer control has been given recently by G. V. Lachmann [27], H. Schlichting [60, 60a] and C. R. Pankhurst [39]. A paper by M. H. Smith [66] contains a comprehensive list of references.

The process of transition from laminar to turbulent flow in the boundary layer with suction will be studied in detail in Sec. XVIIc.

References

[1] J. Ackeret, Das Rotorschiff und seine physikalischen Grundlagen. Vandenhoeck and Rupprecht, Göttingen 1925.

[2] J. Ackeret, Grenzschichtabsaugung. ZVDI **35**, 1153 (1926).

[3] J. Ackeret, M. Ras and W. Pfenninger, Verhinderung des Turbulentwerdens einer Reibungsschicht durch Absaugung. Naturwissenschaften, 622 (1941); see also Helv. phys. Acta **14**, 323 (1941).

[4] S. Attinello, Auftriebserhöhung durch Grenzschichtsteuerung. Interavia **10**, 925—927 (1955).

[5] A. Betz, Die Wirkungsweise von unterteilten Flügelprofilen. Berichte und Abhandlungen d. Wiss. Gesellsch. f. Luftfahrt, No. 6 (1922). NACA Tech. Memo. No. 100 (1922).

[6] A. Betz, Beeinflussung der Reibungsschicht und ihre praktische Verwertung. Schriften d. dt. Akad. d. Luftfahrtforschung, No. 49 (1939).

[7] A. L. Braslow, D. L. Burrows, N. Tetervin and F. Visconti, Experimental and theoretical studies of area suction for the control of the laminar boundary layer. NACA Rep. 1025 (1951).

[8] B. Brown, Exact solutions of the laminar boundary layer equations for a porous plate with variable fluid properties and a pressure gradient in the main stream. Proc. First US Nat'l Congress Appl. Mech. pp. 843—852, 1951.

[9] W. B. Brown and P. L. Donoughe, Tables of exact laminar boundary layer solutions when the wall is porous and fluid properties are variable. NACA TN 2479 (1951).

[10] J. H. Clarke, H. R. Menkes and P. A. Libby, A provisional analysis of turbulent boundary layers with injection. Jour. Aero. Sci. **22**, 255—260 (1955).

[11] R. E. Dannenberg and J. A. Weiberg, Effect of type of porous surface and suction velocity distribution on the characteristics of a 10.5 per cent thick airfoil with area suction. NACA TN 3093 (1953).

[12] A. E. von Doenhoff and L. K. Loftin, Present status of research on boundary-layer control. Jour. Aero. Sci. **16**, 729 (1949).

[13] P. L. Donoughe and J. N. B. Livingood, Exact solutions of laminar boundary layer equations with constant property values for porous wall with variable temperature. NACA Rep. No. 1229 (1955).

[14] W. H. Dorrance and F. J. Dore, The effect of mass transfer on the compressible turbulent boundary layer skin friction and heat transfer. Jour. Aero. Sci. **21**, 404—410 (1954).

[15] F. Ehlers and A. Walz, Über die Verbesserung der Profileigenschaften durch Grenzschichtbeeinflussung. Prof. Betz's anniversary volume, Göttingen pp. 29—35, 1945.

[15a] Emmons, H. W. and D. C. Leigh Tabulation of the Blasius Function with Blowing and Suction. Aero. Research Council, Current Papers, No. 157 (1954).

[15b] A. Favre, Contribution a l'étude expérimentale des mouvements hydrodynamiques a deux dimensions, pp. 1—192. Thèses, Université de Paris, 1938.

[16] G. Flügel, Jahrb. d. Schiffbautechn. Gesellschaft **31**, 87 (1930).

[17] A. Gerber, Untersuchungen über Grenzschichtabsaugung. Rep. of the Aerod. Inst., ETH Zürich, No. 6 (1938).

[18] S. Goldstein, Low-drag and suction airfoils. Jour. Aero. Sci. **15**, 189 (1948).

[19] H. Görtler, On the calculation of steady laminar boundary layer flows with continuous suction. Jour. of Math. and Mech. **6**, No. 2. (1957),

[20] N. Gregory and W. S. Walker, Wind-tunnel tests on the NACA 63 A 009 aerofoil with distributed suction over the nose ARC R & M 2900 (1955).

[21] M. R. Head, The boundary layer with distributed suction. ARC R & M 2783 (1955).

[22] H. Holstein, Messungen zur Laminarhaltung der Grenzschicht an einem Flügel. Lilienthal-Bericht, S **10**, 17—27, 1940.

[22a] C. A. Holzhauser and R. S. Bray, Wind-tunnel and flight investigations of the use of leading-edge area suction for the purpose of increasing the maximum lift coefficient of a 35° swept-wing airplane. NACA Rep. No. 1276 (1956).

[23] D. G. Hurley and B. Thwaites, An experimental investigation of the boundary layer on a porous circular cylinder. ARC R & M 2829 (1955).

[24] R. Iglisch, Exakte Berechnung der laminaren Reibungsschicht an der längsangeströmten ebenen Platte mit homogener Absaugung. Schriften d. dt. Akad. d. Luftfahrtforschung, **8 B**, No. 1 (1944); NACA Tech. Memo. 1205 (1949).

[25] M. Jones and M. R. Head, The reduction of drag by distributed suction. Proc. Third Anglo-American Aeronautical Conference, Brighton, 199—230 (1951).

[26] J. M. Kay, Boundary layer along a flat plate with uniform suction. ARC R & M No. 2628 (1948).

[27] G. V. Lachmann, Boundary layer control. Jour. Roy. Aero. Soc. **59**, 163—198 (1955); see also Aero. Eng. Rev. **13**, 37—51 (1954) and WGL-Jahrbuch pp. 132—144, 1953.

[28] H. G. Lew and R. D. Mathieu, Boundary layer control by porous suction. Dep. Aero. Eng. Pennsylvania State University Rep. No. 3 (1954).

[29] H. G. Lew and J. B. Fanucci, On the laminar compressible boundary layer over a flat plate with suction or injection. Jour. Aero. Sci. **22**, 589—597 (1955).

[30] P. A. Libby, L. Kaufmann and R. P. Harrington, An experimental investigation of the isothermal laminar boundary layer on a porous flat plate. Jour. Aero. Sci. **19**, 127 (1952).

[31] P. A. Libby and A. Pallone, A method for analyzing the heat insulating properties of the laminar compressible boundary layer. Jour. Aero. Sci. **21**, pp. 825—834 (1954).

[32] G. M. Low, The compressible laminar boundary layer with fluid injection. NACA TN 3404 (1955).

[33] W. Mangler, Laminare Grenzschicht mit Absaugen und Ausblasen. Deutsche Luftfahrtforschung UM 3087 (1944).

[34] F. W. Meredith and A. A. Griffith, in "Modern Developments in Fluid Dynamics". Oxford University Press **2**, 534, (1938).

[35] H. S. Mickley, R. C. Ross, A. L. Squyers and W. E. Stewart, Heat, mass, and momentum transfer for flow over a flat plate with blowing or suction. NACA TN 3208 (1954).

[36] F. G. Miles, Sucking away boundary layers, Flight **35** 180 (1939).

[37] M. Morduchow, On heat transfer over a sweat-cooled surface in laminar compressible flow with pressure gradient. Jour. Aero. Sci. **19**, 705—712 (1952).

[38] R. C. Pankhurst, W. G. Raymer and A. N. Devereux, Wind-tunnel tests of the stalling properties of an 8 per cent thick symmetrical section with nose suction through a porous surface. ARC R & M 2666 (1953).

[39] R. C. Pankhurst, Recent British work on methods of boundary layer control. Proc. Symp. at Nat. Phys. Lab. (1955).

[40] Ph. Poisson-Quinton, Recherches théoriques et éxpérimentales sur le controle de circulation par souflage appliqué aux ailes d'avions. ONERA Publication Note Technique No. 37 (1956); see also Jahrbuch der WGL 1956, pp. 29—51 (1957).

[41] E. D. Poppleton, Boundary layer control for high lift by suction at the leading-edge of a 40 degree swept-back wing. ARC R & M 2897 (1955).

[42] W. Pfenninger, Untersuchungen über Reibungsverminderung an Tragflügeln, insbesondere mit Hilfe von Grenzschichtabsaugung. Reports of the Aero. Inst., ETH Zürich, No. 13 (1946); see also Jour. Aero. Sci. **16**, 227 (1949); NACA Tech. Memo. No. 1181 (1947).

[43] L. Prandtl, The mechanics of viscous fluids. In W. F. Durand, "Aerodynamic Theory", III, 1935.
[44] J. H. Preston, The boundary layer flow over a permeable surface through which suction is applied. ARC R & M 2244 (1946).
[45] J. Pretsch, Grenzen der Grenzschichtbeeinflussung. ZAMM **24**, 64 (1944).
[46] A. Raspet, Boundary layer studies on a sailplane. Aero. Eng. Rev. **11**, 6, 52 (1952).
[47] B. Regenscheit, Eine neue Anwendung der Absaugung zur Steigerung des Auftriebes eines Tragflügels. F. B. 1474 (1941).
[48] B. Regenscheit, Versuche über eine neue strömungstechnische Steuerung. UM 3104 (1944).
[49] B. Regenscheit, Absaugung in der Flugtechnik. Jahrbuch WGL 1952, p. 55—63 (1953).
[50] E. J. Richards, W. Walker, and J. Greeming, Tests of a Griffith aerofoil in the 13 × 9 ft tunnel. ARC R & M 2148 (1954).
[51] L. Ringleb, Computation of the laminar boundary layer with suction. Jour. Aero. Sci. **19**, 48 (1952).
[52] W. Rheinboldt, Zur Berechnung stationärer Grenzschichten bei kontinuierlicher Absaugung mit unstetig veränderlicher Absaugegeschwindigkeit. Jour. Rat. Mech. Analysis **5**, 3, 539—596 (1956).
[53] M. W. Rubesin, An analytical estimation of the effect of transpiration cooling on the heat-transfer and skin-friction characteristics of a compressible, turbulent boundary layer. NACA TN 3341 (1954).
[54] H. Schaefer, Laminare Grenzschicht zur Potentialströmung $U = u_1 x^m$ mit Absaugung und Ausblasen. Deutsche Luftfahrtforschung, UM 2043 (1944).
[55] H. Schlichting, Die Grenzschicht an der ebenen Platte mit Absaugung und Ausblasen. Luftfahrtforschung **19**, 293 (1942).
[56] H. Schlichting, Die Grenzschicht mit Absaugung und Ausblasen. Luftfahrtforschung **19**, 179 (1942).
[57] H. Schlichting and K. Bussmann, Exakte Lösungen für die laminare Reibungsschicht mit Absaugung und Ausblasen. Schriften der dt. Akad. d. Luftfahrtforschung **7 B**, No. 2 (1943).
[58] H. Schlichting, Die Beeinflussung der Grenzschicht durch Absaugung und Ausblasen. Jahrb. d. dt. Akad. d. Luftfahrtforschung p. 90 (1943/44).
[59] H. Schlichting, Ein Näherungsverfahren zur Berechnung der laminaren Reibungsschicht mit Absaugung. Ing.-Arch. **16**, 201—220 (1948); NACA Tech. Memo. No. 1216 (1949).
[60] H. Schlichting, Absaugung in der Aerodynamik. Jahrbuch 1956 der WGL, pp. 19—29 (1957); see also L'aspiration de la couche limite en technique aéronautique. Technique et Science Aéronautique No. 4, pp. 149—161 (1956).
[60a] H. Schlichting, Einige neuere Ergebnisse über Grenzschichtbeeinflussung. Advances in Aero. Sci. Vol. II, Proc. First Intern. Congress in the Aero. Sci., Madrid 1958, Pergamon Press, pp. 563—586 (1959).
[61] O. Schrenk, Versuche mit Absaugeflügeln. Luftfahrtforschung **12**, 10—27 (1935).
[62] O. Schrenk, Grenzschichtabsaugung. Luftwissen **7**, 409 (1940).
[63] O. Schrenk, Tragflügel mit Grenzschichtabsaugung. Luftfahrtforschung **2**, 49 (1928); see also ZFM **22**, 259 (1931) and Luftfahrtforschung **12**, 10 (1935), also Luftwissen **7**, 409 (1940); and NACA Tech. Memo. No. 974 (1941).
[64] K. D. P. Sinhar, The laminar boundary layer with distributed suction on an infinite yawed cylinder. ARC Current Paper 214 (1956).
[65] A. M. Smith and H. E. Roberts, The jet airplane utilizing boundary layer air for propulsion. Jour. Aero. Sci. **14**, 97 (1947).
[66] M. H. Smith, Bibliography on boundary layer control. Literature Search No. 6, Library Bulletin. The James Forrestal Research Center. Princeton University (1955).
[67] J. T. Stuart, On the effects of uniform suction on the steady flow due to a rotating disk. Quarterly Journ. Mech. Appl. Math. **7**, 446—457 (1954).
[68] J. Stüper, Flight experiments and tests on two airplanes with suction slots. NACA Tech. Memo. 1232 (1950). Engl. transl. of the ZWB Forschungsbericht No. 1821 (1943).
[69] B. Thwaites, The production of lift independently of incidence. Jour. Roy. Aero. Soc. **52**, 117 (1948).
[70] B. Thwaites, Investigations into the effect of continuous suction on laminar boundary layer flow under adverse pressure gradients. ARC R & M 2514 (1952).
[71] B. Thwaites, On the momentum equation in laminar boundary layer flow. A new method of uniparametric calculation. ARC R & M 2587 (1952).

[72] T. P. Torda, Boundary layer control by continuous surface suction or injection. Jour. Math. Phys. **31**, 3, 206—213 (1952).

[73] T. P. Torda, Boundary layer control by distributed surface suction or injection. Bi-parametric general solution. Jour. Math. Phys. **32**, 4, 312—314 (1954).

[74] L. Trilling, The incompressible boundary layer with pressure gradient and suction. Jour. Aero. Sci. **17**, 335—341 (1950).

[75] E. Truckenbrodt, Die laminare Reibungsschicht an einer teilweise mitbewegten längsangeströmten ebenen Platte. Proc. Braunschwg. Wiss. Ges. **IV**, 181—195 (1952).

[76] E. Truckenbrodt, Ein einfaches Näherungsverfahren zum Berechnen der laminaren Reibungsschicht mit Absaugung. Forschg. Ing. Wes. **22**, 147—157 (1956).

[77] A. Ulrich and K. Bussmann, Die laminare Reibungsschicht am Kreiszylinder mit Absaugung und Ausblasen. Deutsche Luftfahrtforschung UM 2073 (1944).

[78] E. J. Watson, The asymptotic theory of boundary layer flow with suction. ARC R & M 2619 (1952).

[79] K. Wieghardt, Zur Berechnung ebener und drehsymmetrischer Grenzschichten mit kontinuierlicher Absaugung. Ing.-Arch. **22**, 368—377 (1954).

[80] W. Wuest, Entwicklung einer laminaren Grenzschicht hinter einer Absaugestelle. Ing.-Arch. **17**, 199 (1949).

[81] W. Wuest, Asymptotische Absaugegrenzschichten an längsangeströmten zylindrischen Körpern. Ing.-Arch. **23**, 198—208 (1955).

[82] S. W. Yuan, Heat transfer in laminar compressible boundary layer on a porous flat plate with fluid injection. Jour. Aero. Sci. **16**, 741—748 (1949).

CHAPTER XIV

Thermal boundary layers in laminar flow

a. Derivation of the energy equation

The transfer of heat between a solid body and a liquid or gaseous flow is a problem whose consideration involves the science of fluid motion. On the physical motion of the fluid there is superimposed a flow of heat and, generally speaking, the flow field interacts with the temperature field. In order to determine the temperature distribution it is necessary to combine the equations of motion with those of heat conduction. It is intuitively evident that the temperature distribution around a hot body in a fluid stream will often have the same character as the velocity distribution in boundary layer flow. For example, if we imagine a solid body which is placed in a fluid stream and which is heated so that its temperature is maintained above that of the surroundings then it is clear that the temperature of the stream will increase only over a thin layer in the immediate neighbourhood of the body and over a narrow wake behind it, Fig. 4.2. The major part of the transition from the temperature of the hot body to that of the colder surroundings takes place in a thin layer in the neighbourhood of the body which, in analogy with flow phenomena, may be termed the thermal boundary layer. It is evident that flow phenomena and thermal phenomena interact to a high degree.

To begin the investigation of such phenomena, it is necessary to establish the energy balance for a fluid element in motion and to consider it in addition to the equations of motion. For an incompressible fluid the energy balance is determined by the internal energy, the conduction of heat, the convection of heat with the stream and the generation of heat through friction. In a compressible fluid there is an additional term due to the work of expansion (or compression) when the volume is changed. In all cases radiation may also be present, but its contribution is small at moderate temperatures, and we shall neglect it completely. We shall now proceed to establish this energy balance on the basis of the First Law of thermodynamics, considering an elementary volume ΔV of weight

$$\Delta G = \varrho \, g \, \Delta V \, .$$

The quantity of heat $\mathrm{d}Q$ added to the volume externally and through friction serves to increase its internal energy and to perform expansion work:

$$\mathrm{d}Q = \underbrace{\Delta G \cdot c_v \, \mathrm{d}T}_{\substack{\text{internal}\\ \text{energy}}} + \underbrace{p \cdot \mathrm{d}(\Delta V)}_{\substack{\text{expansion}\\ \text{work}}} \qquad [\text{lbf ft}] \, . \tag{14.1}$$

Here c_v [lbf ft/lbf deg] denotes the specific heat at constant volume per unit weight and p is the pressure.

The quantity of heat $\mathrm{d}Q$ consists of two terms: 1. Heat $\mathrm{d}Q_c$ added through conduction, 2. Heat $\mathrm{d}Q_f$ added through friction.

$$\mathrm{d}Q = \mathrm{d}Q_c + \mathrm{d}Q_f \,. \tag{14.2}$$

We shall begin by calculating the *quantity of heat added through conduction:* In accordance with Fourier's equations the heat flux q crossing an area A (= quantity of heat per unit area and time) is proportional to the gradient along the normal to the surface

$$\frac{\mathrm{d}Q_c}{A\mathrm{d}t} = q = -k\,\frac{\partial T}{\partial n}\,. \tag{14.3}$$

where k [lbf/sec deg] is the conductivity, and the direction of the flux is opposite to that of the temperature gradient.

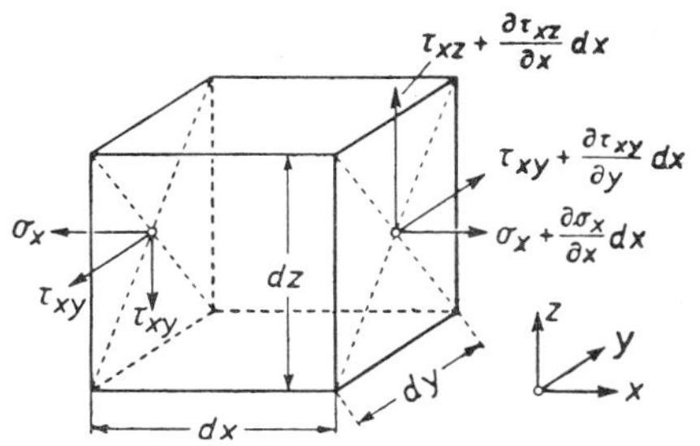

Fig. 14.1. Frictional stresses on a fluid element

With reference to Fig. 14.1 we note that the heat flux per fluid element $\Delta V = \mathrm{d}x \cdot \mathrm{d}y \cdot \mathrm{d}z$ at a section x is $-(k\,\partial T/\partial x)\,(\mathrm{d}y\,\mathrm{d}z)$, whereas at a section $x + \mathrm{d}x$ it is $-[k\,\partial T/\partial x + \partial/\partial x(k\,\partial T/\partial x)\,\mathrm{d}x]\,\mathrm{d}y\,\mathrm{d}z$. Hence the net gain in energy per time $\mathrm{d}t$ due to the flux in the x-direction becomes: $\mathrm{d}Q_{cx} = (\mathrm{d}t\,\mathrm{d}x\,\mathrm{d}y\,\mathrm{d}z)\,[\partial/\partial x\,(k\,\partial T/\partial x)]$. The total quantity of heat introduced by conduction into the element ΔV during time $\mathrm{d}t$ is, thus

$$\mathrm{d}Q_c = \mathrm{d}t\,\Delta V\left\{\frac{\partial}{\partial x}\left(k\,\frac{\partial T}{\partial x}\right) + \frac{\partial}{\partial y}\left(k\,\frac{\partial T}{\partial y}\right) + \frac{\partial}{\partial z}\left(k\,\frac{\partial T}{\partial z}\right)\right\}. \tag{14.4}$$

Next we shall calculate the *heat due to friction.* The total work performed by the normal and shearing stresses of the frictional forces is partly converted into mechanical energy (pressure and kinetic energy), and partly dissipated as heat. We shall now calculate the second term. The total work per unit time of the normal and shearing stresses on the element ΔV and due to friction is

$$\Delta V\left\{\frac{\partial}{\partial x}(\sigma_x\,u + \tau_{xy}\,v + \tau_{xz}\,w) + \frac{\partial}{\partial y}(\tau_{yx}u + \sigma_y v + \tau_{yz}\,w) + \right.$$
$$\left. + \frac{\partial}{\partial z}(\tau_{zx}\,u + \tau_{zy}\,v + \sigma_z w)\right\}. \qquad (14.5)\dagger$$

† With reference to Fig. 14.1 we see that the work per sec. performed by σ_x on the element ΔV is

$$\mathrm{d}y\,\mathrm{d}z\left\{-\sigma_x\,u + \left(\sigma_x + \frac{\partial \sigma_x}{\partial x}\,\mathrm{d}x\right)\left(u + \frac{\partial u}{\partial x}\,\mathrm{d}x\right)\right\} = \Delta V\,\frac{\partial}{\partial x}\,(\sigma_x\,u)\,.$$

In the above equation the symbols σ_x, σ_y, ... τ_{yz} denote the total stresses from eqns. (3.23) and (3.24). The amount of work which is converted into kinetic energy is

$$\Delta V \left\{ u \left(\frac{\partial \sigma_x}{\partial x} + \frac{\partial \tau_{yx}}{\partial y} + \frac{\partial \tau_{zx}}{\partial z} \right) + v \left(\frac{\partial \tau_{xy}}{\partial x} + \frac{\partial \sigma_y}{\partial y} + \frac{\partial \tau_{zy}}{\partial z} \right) + \right.$$

$$\left. + w \left(\frac{\partial \tau_{xz}}{\partial x} + \frac{\partial \tau_{yz}}{\partial y} + \frac{\partial \sigma_z}{\partial z} \right) \right\} = \frac{\mathrm{D}}{\mathrm{D}t} \left[\Delta V \cdot \tfrac{1}{2} \varrho (u^2 + v^2 + w^2) \right]. \qquad (14.6)$$

The expression on the right-hand side of this equation is the substantive rate of change of kinetic energy per unit volume†. In addition to the change in kinetic energy, an amount of work

$$-p \frac{\mathrm{D}}{\mathrm{D}t} \frac{\mathrm{d}(\Delta V)}{\Delta V}$$

is performed on the volume element per unit time. The latter can also be written in the form

$$-p \frac{\mathrm{D}}{\mathrm{D}t} d(\Delta V) = -p \Delta V \left(\frac{\partial u}{\partial x} + \frac{\partial v}{\partial y} + \frac{\partial w}{\partial z} \right). \qquad (14.6\,\mathrm{a})‡$$

We can now subtract from the total energy in eqn. (14.5) the mechanical energy consisting of the change in kinetic energy, eqn. (14.6), and the work of compression given in eqn. (14.6a). The remainder will represent the quantity of mechanical energy transformed into heat through friction. Its value per volume ΔV and time dt is: —

$$\mathrm{d}Q_f = \mathrm{d}t\, \Delta V \left\{ \left(\sigma_x \frac{\partial u}{\partial x} + \tau_{xy} \frac{\partial v}{\partial x} + \tau_{xz} \frac{\partial w}{\partial x} \right) + \right.$$

$$\left. + \left(\tau_{yx} \frac{\partial u}{\partial y} + \sigma_y \frac{\partial v}{\partial y} + \tau_{yz} \frac{\partial w}{\partial y} \right) + \left(\tau_{zx} \frac{\partial u}{\partial z} + \tau_{zy} \frac{\partial v}{\partial z} + \sigma_z \frac{\partial w}{\partial z} \right) \right\} +$$

$$+ \mathrm{d}t\, \Delta V \cdot p \left(\frac{\partial u}{\partial x} + \frac{\partial v}{\partial y} + \frac{\partial w}{\partial z} \right).$$

† The validity of eqn. (14.6) can easily be proved with reference to the equations of motion (3.10). Multiplying the first equation by $u\,\Delta V$, the second by $v\,\Delta V$, and the third by $w\,\Delta V$, and adding together, we find (assuming zero body forces):

$$\varrho \Delta V \left(u \frac{\mathrm{D}u}{\mathrm{D}t} + v \frac{\mathrm{D}v}{\mathrm{D}t} + w \frac{\mathrm{D}w}{\mathrm{D}t} \right) = \Delta V \left\{ u \left(\frac{\partial \sigma_x}{\partial x} + \frac{\partial \tau_{xy}}{\partial y} + \frac{\partial \tau_{xz}}{\partial z} \right) + \right.$$

$$\left. + v \left(\frac{\partial \tau_{xy}}{\partial x} + \frac{\partial \sigma_y}{\partial y} + \frac{\partial \tau_{yz}}{\partial z} \right) + w \left(\frac{\partial \tau_{xz}}{\partial x} + \frac{\partial \tau_{yz}}{\partial y} + \frac{\partial \sigma_z}{\partial z} \right) \right\}.$$

Since the equation of continuity can be written

$$\frac{\mathrm{D}}{\mathrm{D}t} (\varrho\, \Delta V) = 0,$$

eqn. (14.6) follows at once.

‡ This can be seen from

$$-p \frac{\mathrm{D}}{\mathrm{D}t} \mathrm{d}(\Delta V) = -p \Delta V \frac{\mathrm{D}}{\mathrm{D}t} \frac{\mathrm{d}(\Delta V)}{\Delta V} = -p \Delta V \operatorname{div} w.$$

Assuming Stokes' hypothesis, eqn. (3.24), for the normal and shearing stresses, we obtain

$$\mathrm{d}Q_f = \mathrm{d}t \cdot \Delta V \cdot \mu\, \Phi \tag{14.7}$$

where Φ denotes the dissipation function. Hence we have

$$\Phi = 2\left[\left(\frac{\partial u}{\partial x}\right)^2 + \left(\frac{\partial v}{\partial y}\right)^2 + \left(\frac{\partial w}{\partial z}\right)^2\right] + \left(\frac{\partial v}{\partial x} + \frac{\partial u}{\partial y}\right)^2 + \left(\frac{\partial w}{\partial y} + \frac{\partial v}{\partial z}\right)^2 + \\ + \left(\frac{\partial u}{\partial z} + \frac{\partial w}{\partial x}\right)^2 - \frac{2}{3}\left(\frac{\partial u}{\partial x} + \frac{\partial v}{\partial y} + \frac{\partial w}{\partial z}\right)^2. \tag{14.8}$$

Substituting eqns. (14.2), (14.4) and (14.7) into eqn. (14.1) and dividing by $\mathrm{d}t\, \Delta V$, we obtain now

$$\varrho\, g\, c_v \frac{\mathrm{D}T}{\mathrm{D}t} + p \frac{\mathrm{D}}{\mathrm{D}t}\frac{\mathrm{d}(\Delta V)}{\Delta V} = \frac{\partial}{\partial x}\left(k\frac{\partial T}{\partial x}\right) + \frac{\partial}{\partial y}\left(k\frac{\partial T}{\partial y}\right) + \frac{\partial}{\partial z}\left(k\frac{\partial T}{\partial z}\right) + \mu\,\Phi. \tag{14.9}$$

The second term on the left-hand side which represents work of compression can be simplified as follows: The term $\mathrm{d}(\Delta V)/\Delta V$ represents the volume dilatation which is also equal to $\mathrm{d}(\Delta V)/\Delta V = \operatorname{div} \boldsymbol{s}$, where $\boldsymbol{s}$ is the displacement vector. Hence $\mathrm{D}/\mathrm{D}t\ [\mathrm{d}(\Delta V/\Delta V]$ is equal to the divergence of the velocity vector $\boldsymbol{w} = \mathrm{d}\boldsymbol{s}/\mathrm{d}t$, i. e.

$$\frac{\mathrm{D}}{\mathrm{D}t}\frac{\mathrm{d}(\Delta V)}{\Delta V} = \operatorname{div} \boldsymbol{w} = \frac{\partial u}{\partial x} + \frac{\partial v}{\partial y} + \frac{\partial w}{\partial z},$$

and the work of compression per unit volume and time becomes

$$p\frac{\mathrm{D}}{\mathrm{D}t}\frac{\mathrm{d}(\Delta V)}{\Delta V} = p\left(\frac{\partial u}{\partial x} + \frac{\partial v}{\partial y} + \frac{\partial w}{\partial z}\right).$$

For incompressible media this term vanishes, but for compressible fluids it can be further simplified with the aid of the equation of continuity (3.27):

$$\operatorname{div} \boldsymbol{w} = \frac{\partial u}{\partial x} + \frac{\partial v}{\partial y} + \frac{\partial w}{\partial z} = -\frac{1}{\varrho}\left(\frac{\partial \varrho}{\partial t} + u\frac{\partial \varrho}{\partial x} + v\frac{\partial \varrho}{\partial y} + w\frac{\partial \varrho}{\partial z}\right) = -\frac{1}{\varrho}\frac{\mathrm{D}\varrho}{\mathrm{D}t}.$$

Hence

$$p\left(\frac{\partial u}{\partial x} + \frac{\partial v}{\partial y} + \frac{\partial w}{\partial z}\right) = -\frac{p}{\varrho}\frac{\mathrm{D}\varrho}{\mathrm{D}t} = -\frac{p}{\varrho}\frac{\mathrm{D}\varrho}{\mathrm{D}t} - \varrho\frac{\mathrm{D}}{\mathrm{D}t}\left(\frac{p}{\varrho}\right) + \varrho\frac{\mathrm{D}}{\mathrm{D}t}\left(\frac{p}{\varrho}\right).$$

Since

$$-\varrho\frac{\mathrm{D}}{\mathrm{D}t}\left(\frac{p}{\varrho}\right) = -\frac{\mathrm{D}p}{\mathrm{D}t} + \frac{p}{\varrho}\frac{\mathrm{D}\varrho}{\mathrm{D}t}$$

we have

$$p\frac{\mathrm{D}}{\mathrm{D}t}\frac{\mathrm{d}(\Delta V)}{\Delta V} = p\left(\frac{\partial u}{\partial x} + \frac{\partial v}{\partial y} + \frac{\partial w}{\partial z}\right) = -\frac{\mathrm{D}p}{\mathrm{D}t} + \varrho\frac{\mathrm{D}}{\mathrm{D}t}\left(\frac{p}{\varrho}\right). \tag{14.10}$$

Introducing eqn. (14.10) into (14.9), we find

$$\varrho\, g\left\{c_v\frac{\mathrm{D}T}{\mathrm{D}t} + \frac{\mathrm{D}}{\mathrm{D}t}\left(\frac{p}{\varrho g}\right)\right\} = \frac{\mathrm{D}p}{\mathrm{D}t} + \frac{\partial}{\partial x}\left(k\frac{\partial T}{\partial x}\right) + \frac{\partial}{\partial y}\left(k\frac{\partial T}{\partial y}\right) + \frac{\partial}{\partial z}\left(k\frac{\partial T}{\partial z}\right) + \mu\,\Phi.$$

The left-hand side can be further simplified with the aid of the known thermodynamic equation for a perfect gas

$$c_p \, \mathrm{d}T = c_v \, \mathrm{d}T + \mathrm{d}(p/\varrho g) \,. \tag{14.11}$$

Here c_p and c_v denote the specific heats at constant pressure and volume respectively. Hence, finally, the *energy equation* assumes the form

$$\boxed{\varrho g \frac{\mathrm{D}}{\mathrm{D}t}(c_p T) = \frac{\mathrm{D}p}{\mathrm{D}t} + \left\{\frac{\partial}{\partial x}\left(k \frac{\partial T}{\partial x}\right) + \frac{\partial}{\partial y}\left(k \frac{\partial T}{\partial y}\right) + \frac{\partial}{\partial z}\left(k \frac{\partial T}{\partial z}\right)\right\} + \mu \Phi \,.} \tag{14.12}$$

If the properties c_p and k can be assumed independent of temperature, the following simpler form results:

$$\varrho g c_p \frac{\mathrm{D}T}{\mathrm{D}t} = \frac{\mathrm{D}p}{\mathrm{D}t} + k\left(\frac{\partial^2 T}{\partial x^2} + \frac{\partial^2 T}{\partial y^2} + \frac{\partial^2 T}{\partial z^2}\right) + \mu \Phi \,. \tag{14.12 a}$$

For an incompressible fluid the work of compression, $\mathrm{D}p/\mathrm{D}t$, vanishes and $c_p = c_v = c$, so that

$$\varrho g c \frac{\mathrm{D}T}{\mathrm{D}t} = k\left(\frac{\partial^2 T}{\partial x^2} + \frac{\partial^2 T}{\partial y^2} + \frac{\partial^2 T}{\partial z^2}\right) + \mu \Phi \,. \tag{14.12b}$$

b. Temperature increase through adiabatic compression; stagnation temperature

The temperature changes brought about by the dynamic pressure variation in a compressible flow are important for its heat balance. In particular, it appears useful to compare the temperature differences which result from the heat due to friction with those caused by compression. For this reason we shall first evaluate the temperature increase due to compression in a frictionless fluid stream: If the velocity varies along a stream-line the temperature must vary also. In order to simplify the argument it is permissible to assume that the process is adiabatic and reversible because the small value of conductivity and the high rate of change in the thermodynamic properties of state will, in general, prevent any appreciable exchange of heat with the surroundings. In particular we propose to calculate the temperature increase $(\Delta T)_{ad} = T_0 - T_\infty$ which occurs at the stagnation point of a body in a stream and which is due to compression from p_∞ to p_0, Fig. 14.2.

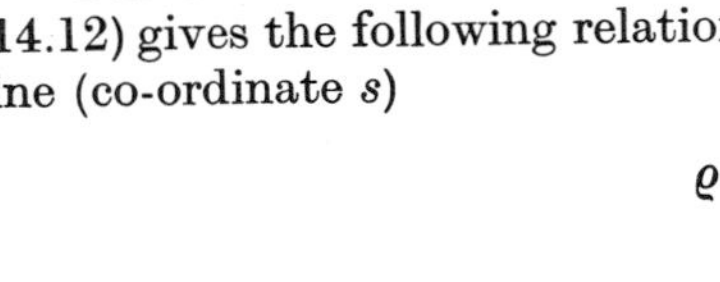

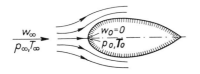

Fig. 14.2. Calculation of the temperature increase at stagnation point due to adiabatic compression $(\Delta T)_{ad} = T_0 - T_\infty$

For the case of zero heat conduction in frictionless flow the energy equation (14.12) gives the following relation between temperature and pressure along a stream-line (co-ordinate s)

$$\varrho g w \frac{\mathrm{d}(c_p T)}{\mathrm{d}s} = w \frac{\mathrm{d}p}{\mathrm{d}s} \,,$$

where $w(s)$ denotes the velocity along a stream-line. Dividing by ϱw and integrating along a stream-line we obtain

$$g\, c_p\, (T - T_\infty) = \int_{p_\infty}^{p} \frac{1}{\varrho} \frac{\mathrm{d}p}{\mathrm{d}s}\, \mathrm{d}s = \int_{p_\infty}^{p} \frac{\mathrm{d}p}{\varrho}\,.$$

From Bernoulli's equation for compressible flow we have

$$\frac{w^2}{2} + \int \frac{\mathrm{d}p}{\varrho} = \text{const}\,, \tag{14.13}$$

so that the temperature increase

$$T - T_\infty = \frac{1}{2\, g\, c_p}\, (w_\infty{}^2 - w^2)\,, \tag{14.13a}$$

and, in particular, the temperature increase at the stagnation point ($w = 0$) due to adiabatic compression becomes

$$T_0 - T_\infty = (\Delta T)_{ad} = \frac{w_\infty{}^2}{2\, g\, c_p}\,. \tag{14.14}$$

Here w_∞ denotes the free-stream velocity (Fig. 14.2). The temperature T_0 assumed by the fluid when the velocity is reduced to zero is known as the *stagnation temperature*, sometimes also referred to as the *total temperature*. The difference $(\Delta T)_{ad} = T_0 - T_\infty$ between the stagnation and the free-stream temperature will here be called the *adiabatic temperature increase*.

Eqn. (14.13a), which is also known as the compressible Bernoulli equation, has been deduced on the assumption that the flow in the stream is reversible i. e. that the entropy remains constant along a streamline. In actual fact eqn. (14.13a) is more

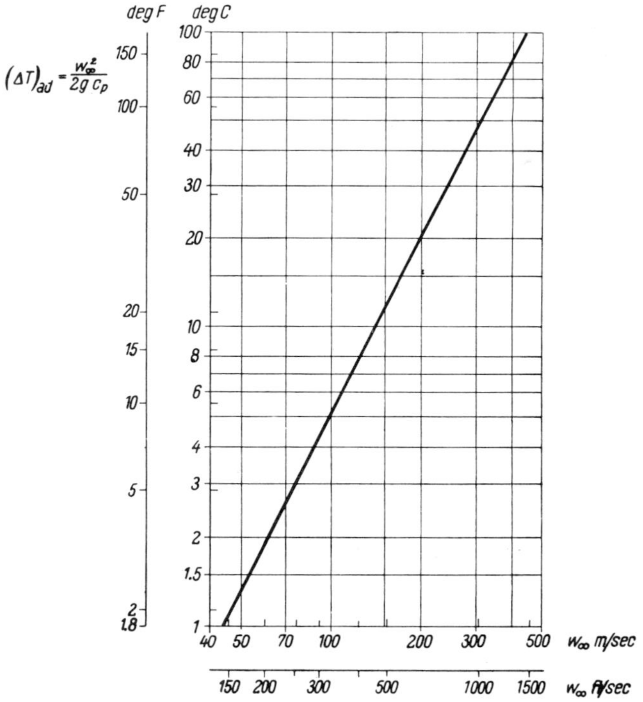

Fig. 14.3. Adiabatic temperature increase at stagnation point for air from eqn. (14.14) ($c_p = 0{\cdot}24$ Btu/lbf deg F)

general than this argument would suggest, as it applies to any one-dimensional stream, such as the flow through a slender nozzle, on condition that there is no external exchange of heat [49′], but irrespective of whether the entropy remains constant or not. The equation can be shown to be approximately true along a streamline in steady three-dimensional flow†. For air with $c_p = 0{\cdot}24$ Btu/lb deg F the adiabatic temperature increase at a velocity of 300 ft/sec has a value of

$$(\Delta T)_{ad} = \frac{300^2}{2 \times 32{\cdot}2 \times 0{\cdot}24 \times 877} = 7{\cdot}5 \text{ deg F}\,.$$

The adiabatic temperature increase calculated for air from eqn. (14.14) is shown plotted in Fig. 14.3. The specific heat, conductivity and other thermal properties for a number of substances are listed in Table 14.1.

Table 14.1. Thermal properties of substances after E. Schmidt [49′]

Substance	Temperature t [deg F]	Specific heat c_p [Btu/lbf degF]	Conductivity k [Btu/ft hr deg F]	Thermal diffusivity $a \times 10^3$ [ft²/hr]	Viscosity $\mu \times 10^6$ [lbf sec/ft²]	Kinematic viscosity $\nu \times 10^3$ [ft²/sec]	Prandtl number P
Water (at 1 atm)	68	0·9986	0·346	5·56	20·58	0·01083	6·88
	100	0·9977	0·360	5·82	14·22	0·007083	4·57
	140	0·9978	0·376	6·14	9·625	0·005145	2·96
	180	1·003	0·387	6·38	7·087	0·004054	2·13
	212	1·006	0·394	6·55	5·776	0·003165	1·71
Mercury	68	0·0333	5·4	194	31·82	0·001238	0·023
Typical aircraft engine oil (at 1 atm)	68	0·439	0·0839	3·43	16,300	9·601	9884
	100	0·457	0·0829	3·30	5,524	2·486	3529
	140	0·479	0·0817	3·15	1,457	0·8826	998
	180	0·501	0·0804	3·01	612·1	0·3950	442
Air (at 1 atm)	—50	0·240	0·0120	530	0·3036	0·106	0·719
	32	0·240	0·0140	746	0·3502	0·146	0·710
	100	0·240	0·0156	947	0·3890	0·187	0·710
	200	0·241	0·0177	1,264	0·4406	0·249	0·710
	400	0·245	0·0213	1,960	0·5279	0·393	0·720
	600	0·251	0·0253	2,785	0·6133	0·559	0·722

c. Theory of similarity in heat transfer

In motions where temperature differences bring about differences in density it is necessary to include buoyancy forces in the equations of motion of a viscous fluid and to treat them as impressed body forces. These buoyancy forces are caused by changes in volume which are associated with the temperature differences. Denoting the coefficient of expansion by β, remembering that for perfect gases $\beta = 1/T$,

† *Cf.* e. g. eqn. (10) on p. 761 of 'Modern Developments in Fluid Dynamics: High Speed Flow' edited by L. Howarth, Clarendon Press, Oxford 1953.

and denoting the temperature difference between a hotter fluid particle and the colder surroundings by $T - T_\infty = \theta$, we can see that the relative change in volume of the hotter particle is $\beta\,\theta$ so that the lift force per unit volume $= \varrho\, \boldsymbol{g}\, \beta\, \theta$, if ϱ denotes the density before heating and $\boldsymbol{g}$ is the vector of gravitational acceleration. The components of the latter will be denoted by g_x, g_y, g_z. Introducing these body forces into the Navier-Stokes equations for steady compressible flow, eqns. (3.26) and (3.27), and assuming that the viscosity is constant, we obtain:

$$\frac{\partial(\varrho u)}{\partial x} + \frac{\partial(\varrho v)}{\partial y} + \frac{\partial(\varrho w)}{\partial z} = 0\,, \tag{14.15}$$

$$\left.\begin{aligned}
\varrho\left(u\frac{\partial u}{\partial x} + v\frac{\partial u}{\partial y} + w\frac{\partial u}{\partial z}\right) &= -\frac{\partial p}{\partial x} + \varrho\, g_x\, \beta\, \theta + \mu\left[\Delta^2 u + \frac{1}{3}\frac{\partial}{\partial x}\operatorname{div}\boldsymbol{w}\right]\\
\varrho\left(u\frac{\partial v}{\partial x} + v\frac{\partial v}{\partial y} + w\frac{\partial v}{\partial z}\right) &= -\frac{\partial p}{\partial y} + \varrho\, g_y\, \beta\, \theta + \mu\left[\Delta^2 v + \frac{1}{3}\frac{\partial}{\partial y}\operatorname{div}\boldsymbol{w}\right]\\
\varrho\left(u\frac{\partial w}{\partial x} + v\frac{\partial w}{\partial y} + w\frac{\partial w}{\partial z}\right) &= -\frac{\partial p}{\partial z} + \varrho\, g_z\, \beta\, \theta + \mu\left[\Delta^2 w + \frac{1}{3}\frac{\partial}{\partial z}\operatorname{div}\boldsymbol{w}\right].
\end{aligned}\right\} \tag{14.16}$$

In addition it is necessary to consider the energy equation (14.12a), also under the assumption of constant properties:

$$\varrho\, g\, c_p\left(u\frac{\partial T}{\partial x} + v\frac{\partial T}{\partial y} + w\frac{\partial T}{\partial z}\right) = k\left(\frac{\partial^2 T}{\partial x^2} + \frac{\partial^2 T}{\partial y^2} + \frac{\partial^2 T}{\partial z^2}\right) + \\ + u\frac{\partial p}{\partial x} + v\frac{\partial p}{\partial y} + w\frac{\partial p}{\partial z} + \mu\,\Phi\,. \tag{14.17}$$

Here the dissipation function, Φ, is given by eqn. (14.8). For perfect gases the equation of state can be written as

$$\frac{p}{\varrho} = g\, R\, T\,. \tag{14.18}$$

In the general case of a compressible medium, eqns. (14.15) to (14.18) form a system of six simultaneous equations for the six variables: u, v, w, p, ϱ, T†. For incompressible media (liquids) the last equation as well as the terms $u\,\partial p/\partial x$ etc. which represent compression work vanish. In this case there are five equations for u, v, w, p, T.

Before proceeding to indicate solutions of the above equations, which we shall discuss in the succeeding sections, we propose, first, to examine them from the point of view of the *principle of similarity* [49′]. In this way we shall discover the dimensionless groups on which the solutions must depend. We begin by introducing dimensionless quantities into eqns. (14.16) and (14.17) in the same manner as in Sec. IVa, when Reynolds' similarity principle was deduced from the Navier-Stokes equations. All lengths will be referred to a representative length l, the velocities will be made dimensionless with reference to the free-stream velocity U_∞, and the pressure will be referred to $\varrho\, U_\infty^2$. The temperature in the energy equation will be made dimension-

† Since the viscosity was assumed constant the above system is valid only for moderate changes in temperature. In the case of large temperature differences (over 50° C or 90° F) μ must be taken to vary with temperature. In this case the equation of motion retains the form (3.26). The six equations under consideration must be supplemented by the empirical viscosity law $\mu(T)$, eqn. (15.1), and, in all, we have a system of seven simultaneous equations for the seven functions $u, v, w, p, \varrho, T, \mu$.

less with reference to the temperature difference $(\Delta T)_0 = T_w - T_\infty$ between the wall and the fluid at a large distance from the body; thus $T^* = T/(\Delta T)_0$. Denoting all dimensionless quantities by a star we obtain from eqns. (14.16) and (14.17) for the two-dimensional case:

$$u^* \frac{\partial u^*}{\partial x^*} + v^* \frac{\partial u^*}{\partial y^*} = -\frac{\partial p^*}{\partial x^*} + \frac{g\,\beta\,\theta\,l}{U_\infty{}^2} + \frac{\nu}{U_\infty l}\left(\frac{\partial^2 u^*}{\partial x^{*2}} + \frac{\partial^2 u^*}{\partial y^{*2}}\right), \qquad (14.19)$$

$$u^* \frac{\partial T^*}{\partial x^*} + v^* \frac{\partial T^*}{\partial y^*} = \frac{k}{\varrho\, g\, c_p\, U_\infty l}\left(\frac{\partial^2 T^*}{\partial x^{*2}} + \frac{\partial^2 T^*}{\partial y^{*2}}\right) + $$
$$+ \frac{U_\infty{}^2}{g\, c_p\,(\Delta T)_0}\left(u^* \frac{\partial p^*}{\partial x^*} + \dots\right) + \frac{\mu\, U_\infty}{\varrho\, g\, c_p\, l\,(\Delta T)_0}\,\Phi^*, \qquad (14.20)$$

i. e. the equation of motion in the x-direction and the energy equation for the two-dimensional case .The dimensionless dissipation function is here given by

$$\Phi^* = 2\left[\left(\frac{\partial u^*}{\partial x^*}\right)^2 + \dots\right] + \dots .$$

It is recognized that the solutions of eqns. (14.19) and (14.20) depend on the following five dimensionless groups:

$$\mathsf{R} = \frac{U_\infty l}{\nu}\,; \quad \frac{g\,\beta\,\theta\,l}{U_\infty{}^2}\,; \quad \frac{k}{\varrho\, g\, c_p\, U_\infty l}\,; \quad \frac{U_\infty{}^2}{g\, c_p\,(\Delta T)_0}\,; \quad \frac{\mu\, U_\infty}{\varrho\, g\, c_p\, l\,(\Delta T)_0}\,.$$

The *first* group is the already familiar Reynolds number. The fourth and fifth groups differ only by the factor R, so that, in all, there are only *four independent dimensionless quantities*. The *second* group can be represented as

$$\frac{g\,\beta\,\theta\,l}{U_\infty{}^2} = \frac{g\,\beta\,\theta\,l^3}{\nu^2}\;\frac{\nu^2}{U_\infty{}^2\, l^2} = \mathsf{G}\,\frac{1}{\mathsf{R}^2}\,.$$

This gives the Grashof number

$$\mathsf{G} = \frac{g\,\beta\,\theta\,l^3}{\nu^2}\,. \qquad (14.21)$$

The *third* quantity can be written as

$$\frac{k}{\varrho\, g\, c_p\, U_\infty l} = \frac{a}{U_\infty l} = \frac{a}{\nu}\;\frac{\nu}{U_\infty l} = \frac{1}{\mathsf{P}}\;\frac{1}{\mathsf{R}}\,,$$

where

$$a = \frac{k}{\varrho\, g\, c_p} \qquad (14.22)$$

is the *thermal diffusivity* [ft²/sec] and

$$\mathsf{P} = \frac{\nu}{a} = \frac{\mu\, g\, c_p}{k} \qquad (14.23)$$

is the dimensionless Prandtl number. It will be noted that it depends only on the properties of the medium. For air $\mathsf{P} = 0{\cdot}7$ approx. and for water at 60 °F $\mathsf{P} = 7$ approx., whereas for oils it is of the order of 1000† owing to their large viscosity

---

† In heat transfer theory the Péclet number

$$\mathsf{P}_e = \frac{U_\infty l}{a}\,,$$

is sometimes used. It is related to the Prandtl number by the relation $\mathsf{P}_e = \mathsf{P}\,\mathsf{R}$.

(see also Table 14.1). The *fourth* dimensionless quantity leads directly to the temperature increase through adiabatic compression as calculated in eqn. (14.14). We have

$$\mathsf{E} = \frac{U_\infty{}^2}{g\, c_p (\Delta T)_0} = 2\, \frac{(\Delta T)_{ad}}{(\Delta T)_0} \quad \text{(Eckert number)}\,, \tag{14.24}$$ †

where E is known as the dimensionless Eckert number. The quantity $\mathsf{E} = U_\infty{}^2/g\, c_p \cdot (\Delta T)_0$ can be retained in incompressible flow also, but the interpretation with reference to adiabatic compression ceases to be valid. It is now possible to conclude that frictional heat and heat due to compression are important for the calculation of the temperature field when the free-stream velocity U_∞ is so large that the adiabatic temperature increase is of the same order of magnitude as the prescribed temperature difference between the body and the stream.

If this prescribed temperature difference is of the same order of magnitude as the absolute temperature of the free stream, which is, for example, the case with a rocket at very high altitude, the Eckert number becomes equivalent to the Mach number, as seen from the following calculation: from the equation of state of a perfect gas

$$\frac{p_\infty}{\varrho_\infty} = g\, R\, T_\infty = g\, T_\infty\, (c_p - c_v) = g\, c_p\, T_\infty\, \frac{\gamma - 1}{\gamma}\,,$$

with $c_p/c_v = \gamma$. Hence the velocity of sound

$$c_\infty{}^2 = \gamma\, p_\infty/\varrho_\infty = g\, T_\infty\, c_p\, (\gamma - 1)\,.$$

Now if $(\Delta T)_0 = T_\infty$

$$\mathsf{E} = \frac{U_\infty{}^2}{g\, c_p\, (\Delta T)_0} = \frac{U_\infty{}^2}{g\, c_p\, T_\infty} = (\gamma - 1)\, \frac{U_\infty{}^2}{c_\infty{}^2} = (\gamma - 1)\, \mathsf{M}^2\,,$$

so that

$$\mathsf{E} = (\gamma - 1)\, \mathsf{M}^2\,, \tag{14.25}$$

where $\mathsf{M} = U_\infty/c_\infty$ is the Mach number. The work of compression and that due to friction become important when the free-stream velocity is comparable with that of sound.

The preceding dimensional analysis leads to the conclusion that the solutions of the above system of equations for the velocity and temperature fields depend on the following four dimensionless groups:

$$\left.\begin{aligned} &\text{Reynolds number} && \mathsf{R} = \frac{U_\infty\, l}{\nu} \\ &\text{Prandtl number} && \mathsf{P} = \frac{\nu}{a} = \frac{\mu\, g\, c_p}{k} \\ &\text{Grashof number} && \mathsf{G} = \frac{g\, \beta\, (\Delta T)_0\, l^3}{\nu^2} \\ &\text{Eckert number} && \mathsf{E} = \frac{U_\infty{}^2}{g\, c_p\, (\Delta T)_0}\,. \end{aligned}\right\} \tag{14.26}$$

† The ratio of the two temperature differences has, so far, not received a separate name. Following a suggestion by Professor E. Schmidt it is proposed to call it after Professor E. R. G. Eckert, and to give it the name of the Eckert number, E.

If $(\Delta T)_0 \approx T_\infty$ the Eckert number is determined by the Mach number in accordance with eqn. (14.25).

In most applications we do not require to know all the details of the temperature and velocity field, but we wish, in the first place, to know the quantity of heat exchanged between the body and the stream. This quantity can be expressed with the aid of a coefficient of heat transfer, α, which is defined either as a local quantity or as a mean quantity over the surface of the body under consideration.

The coefficient of heat transfer is referred to the difference between the temperature of the wall and that of the fluid, the latter being taken at a large distance from the wall. If $q(x)$ denotes the quantity of heat exchanged per unit area and time (= heat flux) at a point x, then according to *Newton's law of cooling* it is assumed that

$$q(x) = \alpha(x) \cdot (T_w - T_\infty) = \alpha(x)\,(\Delta T)_0 . \tag{14.27}$$

The coefficient of heat transfer has the dimension [lbf/sec ft deg] in the gravitational system of units used in this book. At the boundary between a solid body and a fluid the transfer of heat is due solely to conduction. In accordance with Fourier's law the absolute value of the heat flux is (eqn. (14.3)),

$$q(x) = -k\left(\frac{\partial T}{\partial n}\right)_{n=0} . \tag{14.28}$$

Comparing eqns. (14.27) and (14.28) and introducing dimensionless quantities we obtain a local dimensionless coefficient of heat transfer which is known as the Nusselt number N [39].

$$\mathsf{N}(x) = -\frac{\alpha(x)\,l}{k} = -\left(\frac{\partial T^*}{\partial n^*}\right)_{n=0} = -\frac{l}{(\Delta T)_0}\left(\frac{\partial T}{\partial n}\right)_{n=0} .$$

Thus the heat flux becomes

$$q = \frac{k}{l}\,\mathsf{N}\,(T_w - T_\infty) = \frac{k}{l}\,\mathsf{N}\,(\Delta T)_0 . \tag{14.29}$$

In accordance with the preceding argument it is to be expected that the velocity field and the temperature field as well as the local dimensionless coefficient of heat transfer must depend on the dimensionless groups considered previously. Thus

$$\left.\begin{aligned} \frac{w}{U_\infty} &= f_1\,(s^*;\ \mathsf{R, P, G, E}) \\ \frac{T}{T_\infty} &= f_2\,(s^*;\ \mathsf{R, P, G, E}) \\ \mathsf{N} &= f_3\,(s^*;\ \mathsf{R, P, G, E}) . \end{aligned}\right\} \tag{14.30}$$

The symbol s^* denotes here the three dimensionless space co-ordinates. If a mean value of the coefficient of heat transfer is formed by integrating over the whole surface, the space co-ordinate will cease to appear and

$$\mathsf{N}_m = f(\mathsf{R, P, G, E}) \tag{14.30a}$$

for geometrically similar surfaces.

When special solutions are considered then, in most cases, one or more of the dimensionless groups will disappear as the problem will only seldom be of this most general nature. As seen from eqn. (14.26) the temperature field and, hence, the coefficient of heat transfer depend on the Eckert number only when the temperature differences are large (50 to 100 ° C or 100 to 200 ° F) and when, simultaneously, the velocities are very large and of the order of the velocity of sound. With moderate velocities the temperature and velocity fields depend on the Eckert number when temperature differences are small (several degrees). Further, even with moderate velocities, the buoyancy forces in eqn. (14.19) caused by temperature differences are small compared with the inertia and friction forces. In such cases the problem ceases to depend on the Grashof number. Such flows are called *forced flows*. Hence, for *forced convection*

$$\mathsf{N}_m = f(\mathsf{R}, \mathsf{P}) \quad \text{(forced convection)}\,.$$

The Grashof number becomes important only at very small velocities of flow, particularly if the motion is caused by buoyancy forces, such as in the stream which rises above a hot plate. Such flows are called *natural*, and we refer to the problem as one in *natural convection*. In such cases the flow becomes independent of the Reynolds number, and

$$\mathsf{N}_m = f(\mathsf{G}, \mathsf{P}) \quad \text{(natural convection)}\,.$$

Examples of such problems are given in Secs. e to h of the present chapter.

d. Boundary layer simplifications

It has already been stated on several occasions that it is intuitively evident that in many cases the temperature field around a hot body in a fluid stream is of the *boundary layer type*. This means that the temperature field which spreads from the body extends essentially only over a narrow zone in the immediate neighbourhood of the surface, whereas the regions at a larger distance from it are not materially affected by the higher body temperature. In particular this is the case when the conductivity, k, is small, as for gases and liquids. In such cases there is a very steep temperature gradient at right angles to the wall and the heat flux due to conduction is of the same order of magnitude as that due to convection only across a thin layer near the wall. On the other hand it is to be expected that the temperature increase near an unheated body in a fluid stream flowing at a high Reynolds number, and which is due to the generation of frictional heat, is important only in the thin boundary layer, because the quantity of mechanical energy which is transformed into heat through friction is significant only there. Hence it may be expected that in conjunction with the velocity boundary layer there will be formed a thermal boundary layer across which the temperature gradient is very large. It is, therefore, possible to take advantage of this fact and to introduce into the energy equation, which governs the temperature distribution, simplifications of a similar nature to those introduced earlier into the equations of motion (Chap. VII).

Dimensionless forms of the equations of motion and energy were given in the preceding section where a representative velocity, U_∞, a representative length,

l, as well as a representative temperature difference, $(\Delta T)_0$, were used to render the relevant quantities dimensionless. For the sake of simplicity we shall restrict ourselves to the two-dimensional case with constant fluid properties and we shall choose the x-axis along the direction of the main stream. Under these assumptions the equation of motion in the x-direction and the energy equation, eqns. (14.19) and (14.20), can be written in the following form:

$$u\,\frac{\partial u}{\partial x} + v\,\frac{\partial u}{\partial y} = -\frac{\partial p}{\partial x} + \frac{\mathsf{G}}{\mathsf{R}^2} + \frac{1}{\mathsf{R}}\left(\frac{\partial^2 u}{\partial x^2} + \frac{\partial^2 u}{\partial y^2}\right) \tag{14.31 a}$$

$$1 \quad 1 \qquad \delta_S\,\frac{1}{\delta_S} \qquad\qquad 1 \qquad\qquad \delta_S^2 \quad 1 \qquad \frac{1}{\delta_S^2}$$

$$u\,\frac{\partial T}{\partial x} + v\,\frac{\partial T}{\partial y} = \frac{1}{\mathsf{P}\,\mathsf{R}}\left(\frac{\partial^2 T}{\partial x^2} + \frac{\partial^2 T}{\partial y^2}\right) + \mathsf{E}\left(u\,\frac{\partial p}{\partial x} + v\,\frac{\partial p}{\partial y}\right) + \mathsf{E}\,\frac{1}{\mathsf{R}}\,\Phi\,. \tag{14.31 b}$$

$$1 \quad 1 \qquad \delta_S\,\frac{1}{\delta_T} \qquad \delta_T^2 \qquad 1 \qquad \frac{1}{\delta_T^2} \qquad\qquad 1 \quad 1 \qquad \delta_S\;\delta_S \qquad\qquad \delta_S^2\,\frac{1}{\delta_S^2}$$

The stars have now been omitted as superfluous. The orders of magnitude of the various terms in the two equations which have been estimated with the aid of the velocity boundary layer equation (7.1) are shown above. The essential result of the previous estimation was that the viscous forces were of the same order of magnitude as the inertia forces only if the velocity boundary layer thickness, δ_S, satisfied the condition

$$\left(\frac{\delta_S}{l}\right)^2 \sim \frac{1}{\mathsf{R}}\,. \tag{14.32}$$

As a consequence it proved to be possible to neglect $\partial^2 u/\partial x^2$ against $\partial^2 u/\partial y^2$ in the first equation of motion and the second equation of motion dropped out altogether. This was connected with the fact that the transverse pressure gradient $\partial p/\partial y \sim \delta_S$, so that the pressure could be assumed to depend on x alone. As seen from eqn. (14.31 a) the body force which is due to the buoyancy of the hotter fluid particles, i. e. to their thermal expansion, is of the same order of magnitude as the inertia and viscous forces if

$$\mathsf{G} \approx \mathsf{R}^2\,,$$

which occurs only with very small velocities and considerable temperature differences.

It is now possible to make a similar estimation of terms in the energy equation. The dimensionless group

$$\frac{k}{\varrho\, g\, c_p U_\infty l} = \frac{k}{g\, c_p\, \mu}\,\frac{1}{\mathsf{R}} = \frac{1}{\mathsf{P}}\,\frac{1}{\mathsf{R}}\,,$$

i. e. the multiplicative factor of the thermal conduction terms, is also a small quantity as far as liquids and gases are concerned if the Reynolds number is large, because the Prandtl number for gases is of the order of 1, and for liquids it ranges from 10 to 1000. Hence it is seen that the conduction terms can become of the same order of magnitude as the convection terms only if $\partial T/\partial y$ is very large i. e. only if in the vicinity of the surface of the body there is a layer with a steep transverse temperature gradient: the *thermal boundary layer*. The order of magnitude of the convectional and viscous terms can now be estimated. It is shown under the equation and the symbol δ_T denotes the thickness of the thermal boundary layer. The term $\partial^2 T/\partial x^2$ can be neglected against $\partial^2 T/\partial y^2$ and the conduction term becomes of the same order of magnitude as the convectional term only if the thickness of the thermal boundary layer is of the order

$$\left(\frac{\delta_T}{l}\right)^2 \sim \frac{1}{\mathsf{R} \cdot \mathsf{P}}. \tag{14.33}$$

In view of the previously obtained estimation for the thickness of the velocity boundary layer $\delta_S \sim 1/\sqrt{\mathsf{R}}$, we obtain

$$\frac{\delta_T}{\delta_S} \sim \frac{1}{\sqrt{\mathsf{P}}}. \tag{14.34}$$

This equation gives a very good physical interpretation of the Prandtl number, and it is seen that the thermal boundary layer in a gas may be expected to be approximately of the same order of magnitude as the velocity boundary layer, whereas for liquids it is smaller.

Estimating the remaining terms in the energy equation it is concluded that in the expression for the dissipation function only the term $(\partial u/\partial y)^2$ remains significant, and

$$\Phi = \left(\frac{\partial u}{\partial y}\right)^2 \sim \frac{1}{\delta_S^2}.$$

The heat due to friction is seen to be important only if

$$\mathsf{E} = \frac{U_\infty^2}{g\, c_p\, (\Delta T)_0} \sim 1.$$

In the case of gases the heat generated by friction becomes important only if the temperature rise due to adiabatic compression is of the same order of magnitude as the difference in temperature between the body and the fluid. The same remark applies to the heat of compression.

Reverting to dimensional quantities and taking into account the dependence of viscosity on temperature, we obtain the following simplified equations for two-dimensional compressible fluid flow:

$$\frac{\partial(\varrho u)}{\partial x} + \frac{\partial(\varrho v)}{\partial y} = 0 \tag{14.35 a}$$

$$\varrho\left(u\frac{\partial u}{\partial x} + v\frac{\partial u}{\partial y}\right) = \frac{\partial}{\partial y}\left(\mu\frac{\partial u}{\partial y}\right) - \frac{\mathrm{d}p}{\mathrm{d}x} + \varrho\, g_x\, \beta\, (T - T_\infty) \tag{14.35 b}$$

$$\varrho\, g\, c_p\left(u\frac{\partial T}{\partial x} + v\frac{\partial T}{\partial y}\right) = k\frac{\partial^2 T}{\partial y^2} + \mu\left(\frac{\partial u}{\partial y}\right)^2 + u\frac{\mathrm{d}p}{\mathrm{d}x} \tag{14.35 c}$$

$$\frac{p}{\varrho} = g\, R\, T\, ; \qquad \mu = \mu(T). \tag{14.35 d, e}$$

Since in the framework of boundary layer theory the pressure may be regarded as a given, impressed force, we have here a system of five simultaneous equations for the five unknowns ϱ, u, v, T, μ.

For the incompressible case (ϱ = const) and for constant viscosity these equations reduce to

$$\frac{\partial u}{\partial x} + \frac{\partial v}{\partial y} = 0 \tag{14.36 a}$$

$$\varrho \left(u \frac{\partial u}{\partial x} + v \frac{\partial u}{\partial y} \right) = \mu \frac{\partial^2 u}{\partial y^2} - \frac{\mathrm{d}p}{\mathrm{d}x} + \varrho\, g_x\, \beta\, (T - T_\infty) \tag{14.36 b}$$

$$\varrho\, g\, c_p \left(u \frac{\partial T}{\partial x} + v \frac{\partial T}{\partial y} \right) = k \frac{\partial^2 T}{\partial y^2} + \mu \left(\frac{\partial u}{\partial y} \right)^2 , \tag{14.36 c}$$

giving three equations for u, v, and T.

e. General properties of thermal boundary layers

1. Forced and natural flows. The differential equations for the velocity and thermal boundary layer, eqns. (14.36 b) and (14.36 c), are very similar in structure. They differ only in the last two terms in the equation of motion and in the last term in the temperature equation. In the general case the velocity field and the temperature field mutually interact which means that the temperature distribution depends on the velocity distribution and, conversely, the velocity distribution depends on the temperature distribution. In the special case when buoyancy forces may be disregarded, and when the properties of the fluid may be assumed to be independent of temperature, mutual interaction ceases, and the velocity field no longer depends on the temperature field, although the converse dependence of the temperature field on the velocity field still persists. This happens at large velocities (large Reynolds numbers) and small temperature differences, such flows being termed *forced* (*cf.* p. 299). The process of heat transfer in such flows is described as *forced convection*. Flows in which buoyancy forces are dominant are called *natural*, the respective heat transfer being known as *natural convection*. This case occurs at very small velocities of motion in the presence of large temperature differences. The state of motion which accompanies natural convection is evoked by buoyancy forces in the gravitational field of the earth, the latter being due to density differences and gradients. For example, the field of motion which exists above a vertical hot plate belongs to this class. Forced flows can be subdivided into those with moderate and those with high velocities depending on whether the heat due to friction and compression need or need not be taken into account. In both cases the temperature field depends on the field of flow. At moderate velocities, when the heat due to friction and compression may be neglected, the dependence of the temperature field on the velocity field is governed solely by the Prandtl number. To each *single* velocity field there corresponds a singly infinite family of temperature distributions with the Prandtl number as its parameter. At high velocities work due both to friction and compression must be included. Whether this is necessary or not depends on the Eckert number $\mathsf{E} = (\Delta T)_{ad}/(\Delta T)_0$ i. e. on whether it is comparable with unity. In other words the work due to friction and compression must be taken into account when the temperature increase due to friction and compression is comparable with the temperature difference prescribed as a boundary condition (temperature difference between body and fluid). If the prescribed temperature difference is of the order of the mean absolute temperature, the work due to friction and compression becomes important only if the velocity of flow is comparable with that of sound.

It is important to note that the temperature equation is linear, unlike the equation of motion. This leads to considerable simplifications in the process of integrating, and superposition of known solutions becomes possible.

2. Adiabatic wall. Finally it is necessary to mention that the variety of possible sets of boundary conditions is much greater for the temperature field than for the velocity field. The temperature on the surface of the body may be constant or variable but, moreover, it is also possible to encounter problems for which the heat flux is prescribed. In view of eqn. (14.28), this means that the temperature gradient at the wall may appear as a boundary condition. The so-called *adiabatic wall* constitutes a particular example of the latter class of cases, since it must be postulated that there is no heat flux from the wall to the fluid, i. e. the boundary condition at the wall is

$$\left(\frac{\partial T}{\partial n}\right)_{n=0} = 0 \qquad \text{(adiabatic wall)}\ .$$

This case can be visualized by imagining that the wall of the body is perfectly insulated against heat flow. The heat generated by the fluid through friction serves to heat the wall until the condition $(\partial T/\partial n)_{n=0} = 0$ is reached. Thus the temperature of the wall which we may also call the *adiabatic wall temperature* becomes higher than that of the fluid at some distance from it. Such conditions are satisfied in practice when a so-called plate thermometer is used, i. e. when the temperature of a fluid stream is measured with the aid of a flat plate which is placed parallel to the stream†. The excess temperature on the plate constitutes the error of the plate thermometer. The error must be deducted in order to obtain the true temperature of the moving fluid. This difference is sometimes called the *kinetic temperature.*

3. Analogy between heat transfer and skin friction‡. For boundary layer flow there exists a remarkable relationship between heat transfer and skin friction which was discovered by O. Reynolds [43] in 1874 and which is, therefore, known as the Reynolds analogy. As seen from eqn. (14.28), the heat flux from the body to the fluid (quantity of heat transferred per unit area and time), is given by

$$q(x) = -k\left(\frac{\partial T}{\partial y}\right)_{y=0}. \tag{14.37 a}$$

This equation is analogous to the one for local skin friction which, as seen from eqn. (1.2), has the form:

$$\tau_0(x) = \mu\left(\frac{\partial u}{\partial y}\right)_{y=0}. \tag{14.37 b}$$

† For this reason in older text-books the problem of an adiabatic wall was referred to as the plate thermometer problem.

‡ The Author is indebted to Dr. K. Gersten for the new and revised form of this section.

The total values, i. e. the quantity of heat transferred per unit time or the total skin-friction drag are obtained by integration. Thus

$$Q = b\int_0^l q(x)\,\mathrm{d}x\,; \qquad \mathrm{D}_f = b\int_0^l \tau_0(x)\,\mathrm{d}x\,,$$

where b denotes the width of the body.

Let us now consider the particularly simple case of parallel flow past a flat plate at zero incidence when $\mathrm{d}p/\mathrm{d}x = 0$, and when the temperature of the plate is uniform at a value T_w. If the buoyancy forces and frictional heat can be neglected and if the properties ϱ, μ, k, c_p of the fluid can be assumed constant, the differential equations (14.36 b) and (14.36 c) for the velocity component u and for the temperature T become identical on condition that the Prandtl number $\mathsf{P} = \mu\, g\, c_p/k$ is equal to unity. It is noted that under the conditions under consideration the differential equations as well as the boundary conditions for them are identical for $u = 0$ and $T - T_w = 0$ at the wall, and $u = U_\infty = \text{const}$ as well as $T - T_w = T_\infty - T_w = \text{const}$ at the edge of the boundary layer. It follows, therefore, that the solutions for u/U_∞ and $(T - T_w)/(T_\infty - T_w)$ must have identical algebraic forms. Consequently, the boundary layer thickness δ_S for the velocity field must be equal to the boundary layer δ_T for the temperature field. In addition it is possible to write down the relation

$$\frac{\partial}{\partial y}\left(\frac{u}{U_\infty}\right) = \frac{\partial}{\partial y}\left(\frac{T - T_w}{T_\infty - T_w}\right) \tag{14.37 c}$$

which proves that the heat flux from eqn. (14.37 a) and the skin friction from eqn. (14.37 b) are proportional to each other. Indeed, it follows from eqn. (14.37 c) that

$$q(x) = \frac{k}{\mu}\,\frac{T_w - T_\infty}{U_\infty}\,\tau_0(x)\,, \tag{14.37 d}$$

and from it, by integration, that

$$Q = \frac{k}{\mu}\,\frac{T_w - T_\infty}{U_\infty}\,D_f\,.$$

Introducing dimensionless quantities, in particular the length Nusselt number N_x from eqn. (14.29), we can modify eqn. (14.37 d) to read

$$\mathsf{N}_x = \frac{x}{\mu\, U_\infty}\cdot \tau_0(x) = \tfrac{1}{2}\,\frac{\varrho\, U_\infty\, x}{\mu}\cdot\frac{\tau_0(x)}{\tfrac{1}{2}\,\varrho\, U_\infty^{\,2}}\,.$$

Introducing, further, the length Reynolds number $\mathsf{R}_x = \varrho\, U_\infty\, x/\mu$ and the skin friction coefficient $c_f' = \tau_0(x)/\tfrac{1}{2}\,\varrho\, U_\infty^{\,2}$, we obtain

$$\boxed{\mathsf{N}_x = \tfrac{1}{2}\,\mathsf{R}_x\, c_f'} \quad \text{for } \mathsf{P} = 1\,. \tag{14.38 a}$$

Finally, integrating over a length l, an expression for the mean Nusselt number N_m can be obtained in the form

$$\mathsf{N}_m = \tfrac{1}{2}\, \mathsf{R}_l\, c_f \qquad \text{for } \mathsf{P} = 1\,.$$

The preceding relation between the coefficient of heat transfer and the skin friction coefficient is known as the Reynolds analogy. From the method of derivation it is clear that, so far, its validity is restricted to incompressible laminar flows past flat plates of constant temperature and on condition that the frictional heat is neglected. However, the validity of the analogy extends far beyond this particular case; it retains its validity in the case of turbulent flows in relation to which it is of great importance because it then affords the only theoretical basis for the calculation of rates of heat transfer in turbulent flows.

The validity of eqn. (14.38a) can be extended to the following additional cases:—

a) Flat plate without frictional heat, but for $\mathsf{P} \neq 1$.

In deriving eqn. (14.38a) it was assumed that $\mathsf{P} = 1$, but it will be shown in Sec. XIVg that the Nusselt number N_x remains proportional to the coefficient of skin friction c_f' except that the factor of proportionality depends on the Prandtl number. It will, namely, be shown there that

$$\mathsf{N}_x = \tfrac{1}{2}\, \sqrt[3]{\mathsf{P}}\, \mathsf{R}_x\, c_f'\,, \tag{14.38b}$$

or that

$$\mathsf{N}_m = \tfrac{1}{2}\, \sqrt[3]{\mathsf{P}}\, \mathsf{R}_x\, c_f\,. \tag{14.38c}$$

Since

$$c_f' = 0{\cdot}664\ \mathsf{R}_x^{-1/2} \qquad \text{and} \qquad c_f = 1{\cdot}328\ \mathsf{R}^{-1/2}\,,$$

(eqns. (7.35a) and (7.37) respectively), it is also possible to write

$$\mathsf{N}_x = 0{\cdot}332\ \sqrt[3]{\mathsf{P}}\,\sqrt{\mathsf{R}_x} \qquad \text{and} \qquad \mathsf{N}_m = 0{\cdot}664\ \sqrt[3]{\mathsf{P}}\,\sqrt{\mathsf{R}_l}\,. \tag{14.38d}$$

b) Flat plate with frictional heat and $\mathsf{P} \neq 1$.

If frictional heat is taken into account in incompressible flow, it is found that the equations remain unchanged if the Nusselt number is referred to the temperature difference $T_w - T_a$ instead of $T_w - T_\infty$, where T_a is the adiabatic wall temperature, eqn. (14.68) and footnote on p. 318.

c) Flat plate in compressible flow, $\mathsf{P} \neq 1$.

In the case of compressible laminar flow past a flat plate of constant temperature, the equations remain approximately the same, and even exactly the same in the special case when $\mathsf{P} = 1$, *cf.* eqn. (15.18), on condition that the Nusselt number is formed with the temperature difference $T_w - T_a$ as in case b), and if all remaining quantities are referred to those in the external stream. The relation is then independent of the Mach number. It is true that in compressible flows the characteristic properties of the fluid vary and that that results in considerable deviations compared with the case of constant properties. In particular, the velocity field becomes coupled to the temperature field. Since, however, as far as gases are concerned, the viscosity μ and the thermal conductivity k vary in the same way with temperature (*cf.* Table 14.1), the local Prandtl number remains nearly constant in the whole field. Consequently, the similarity between the velocity field and the temperature field remains largely preserved.

d) Turbulent flow

The analogy between heat transfer and skin friction expressed in eqn. (14.38a) is very important because it retains its validity in the case of turbulent flows and, which is even more important, it remains approximately true in cases when the pressure gradient is different from zero without being too large [31]. For example, it can be used to calculate coefficients of heat transfer in tubes from the well-known expressions for pipe friction. The Reynolds analogy gives good service in cases involving external flows too, as seen from Sec. XIXg.

f. Exact solutions for the problem of temperature distribution in a viscous flow

We shall now proceed to solve several particular problems of temperature distribution. The examples to be discussed will be selected from the large number of possible cases on the ground of mathematical simplicity. We shall begin by discussing several cases of exact solutions, as given by H. Schlichting [45], just as we have begun with the discussion of examples of exact solutions of the equations of flow with friction in Chap. V. For the case of incompressible two-dimensional flow with constant properties the system of equations for the velocity and temperature distribution in steady flow along a horizontal x, y-plane and without the boundary layer simplifications discussed in the preceding section, is (eqns. (14.15) to (14.17)):

$$\frac{\partial u}{\partial x} + \frac{\partial v}{\partial y} = 0 . \tag{14.39 a}$$

$$\varrho \left(u \frac{\partial x}{\partial u} + v \frac{\partial u}{\partial y} \right) = - \frac{\partial p}{\partial x} + \mu \left(\frac{\partial^2 u}{\partial x^2} + \frac{\partial^2 u}{\partial y^2} \right) \tag{14.39 b}$$

$$\varrho \left(u \frac{\partial v}{\partial x} + v \frac{\partial v}{\partial y} \right) = - \frac{\partial p}{\partial y} + \mu \left(\frac{\partial^2 v}{\partial x^2} + \frac{\partial^2 v}{\partial y^2} \right) \tag{14.39 c}$$

$$g \varrho c \left(u \frac{\partial T}{\partial x} + v \frac{\partial T}{\partial y} \right) = k \left(\frac{\partial^2 T}{\partial x^2} + \frac{\partial^2 T}{\partial y^2} \right) + \mu \Phi , \tag{14.40}$$

where

$$\Phi = 2 \left[\left(\frac{\partial u}{\partial x} \right)^2 + \left(\frac{\partial v}{\partial y} \right)^2 \right] + \left(\frac{\partial v}{\partial x} + \frac{\partial u}{\partial y} \right)^2 .$$

1. Couette flow. A particularly simple exact solution of this system is obtained for *Couette flow*, i. e. for the case of flow between two parallel flat walls of which one is at rest, the other moving with a constant velocity U_1 in its own plane, Fig. 14.4. The solution of the equations of motion in the absence of a pressure gradient in the x-direction is

$$u(y) = U_1 \frac{y}{h} ; \qquad v \equiv 0 ; \qquad p = \text{const} .$$

A very simple solution for the temperature distribution is obtained when it is postulated that the temperature is constant along the wall, the boundary conditions being

$$y = 0: \quad T = T_0; \qquad y = h: \quad T = T_1. \tag{14.40 a}$$

In this case the dissipation function reduces to the simple expression $\Phi = (\partial u/\partial y)^2$, and the equation for temperature distribution becomes consequently

$$g \varrho c \left(u \frac{\partial T}{\partial x} + v \frac{\partial T}{\partial y}\right) = k \left(\frac{\partial^2 T}{\partial x^2} + \frac{\partial^2 T}{\partial y^2}\right) + \mu \left(\frac{\partial u}{\partial y}\right)^2. \tag{14.40 b}$$

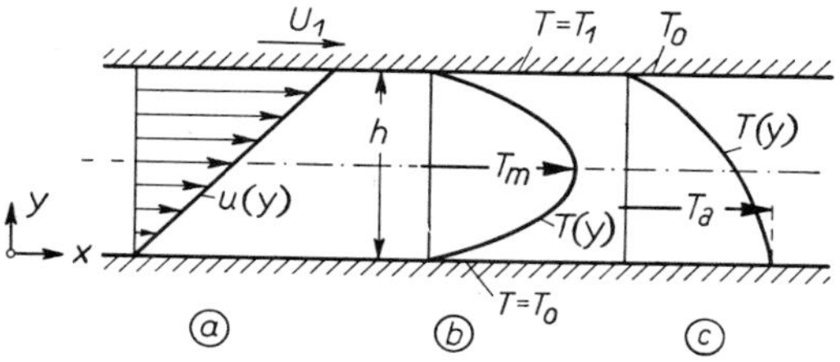

Fig. 14.4. Velocity and temperature distribution in Couette flow. a. Velocity distribution. b. Temperature distribution with heat generated by friction when the temperatures of both walls are equal. c. Temperature distribution with heat generated by friction for the case when the lower wall is non-conducting

With the boundary conditions (14.40a) the above equation has a solution which is independent of x. Since, with $v = 0$, the term $v\, \partial T/\partial y$ on the left-hand side also vanishes, all the convective terms on the left-hand side become equal to zero. The resulting temperature distribution is, therefore, due solely to the generation of heat through friction and to conduction in the transverse direction. From eqn. (14.40b) we obtain

$$k \frac{\mathrm{d}^2 T}{\mathrm{d}y^2} = -\mu \left(\frac{\mathrm{d}u}{\mathrm{d}y}\right)^2, \tag{14.40 c}$$

and, substituting $\mathrm{d}u/\mathrm{d}y$, we have

$$k \frac{\mathrm{d}^2 T}{\mathrm{d}y^2} = -\mu \frac{U_1^2}{h^2}.$$

The solution of this equation which satisfies conditions (14.40a) is

$$\frac{T - T_0}{T_1 - T_0} = \frac{y}{h} + \frac{\mu U_1^2}{2k(T_1 - T_0)} \frac{y}{h} \left(1 - \frac{y}{h}\right).$$

The dimensionless parameter

$$\frac{\mu U_1^2}{k(T_1 - T_0)}$$

can also be written as

$$\frac{\mu U_1^2}{k(T_1 - T_0)} = \frac{\mu g c_p}{k} \frac{U_1^2}{g c_p (\Delta T)_0} = \mathsf{P} \cdot \mathsf{E},$$

if we put $T_1 - T_0 = (\Delta T)_0$. It is seen that it can be expressed in terms of the Prandtl number and the Eckert number from eqn. (14.26). In the case under consideration,

i. e. when there is no convection of heat, the temperature distribution is seen to depend on the product $\mathsf{P} \times \mathsf{E}$. If, finally, the abbreviation $\eta = y/h$ is introduced, the following very simple equation for temperature distribution is obtained:

$$\frac{T - T_0}{T_1 - T_0} = \eta + \frac{1}{2} \mathsf{P} \cdot \mathsf{E}\, \eta\,(1 - \eta)\,. \tag{14.41}$$

The temperature distribution consists of a linear term which is the same as in the case of a fluid at rest with no frictional heat generated. Superimposed on it there is a parabolic distribution which is due to the heat generated through friction. The temperature distribution for various values of the product $\mathsf{P} \times \mathsf{E}$ is seen plotted in Fig. 14.5. It is worthy of note that for a given value of the temperature difference

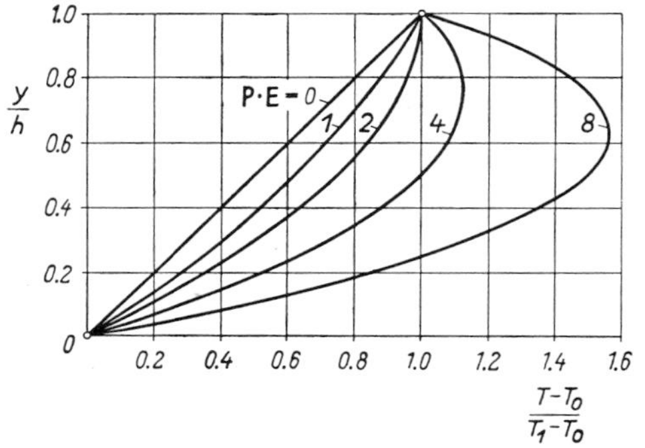

Fig. 14.5. Temperature distribution in Couette flow for various temperatures of both walls with heat generated by friction (T_0 = temperature of the lower wall, T_1 = temperature of the upper wall)

of the two walls $T_1 - T_0 > 0$ heat flows from the upper wall to the fluid only as long as the velocity U_1 of the upper wall does not exceed a certain value. A reversal of the direction of the flow of heat at the upper plate occurs when the temperature gradient at it changes sign. It is seen from eqn. (14.41) that $(\mathrm{d}T/\mathrm{d}y)_{y=h} = 0$ for $\mu\, U_1^2/2\,k = T_1 - T_0$. Hence the following rule applies to the direction of heat flow at the upper wall:

Heat from upper wall → fluid (cooling of upper wall):

$$\frac{\mu\, U_1^2}{2\,k} < T_1 - T_0 \quad \text{or} \quad \mathsf{P} \cdot \mathsf{E} < 2$$

Heat from fluid → upper wall (heating of upper wall):

$$\frac{\mu\, U_1^2}{2\,k} > T_1 - T_0 \quad \text{or} \quad \mathsf{P} \cdot \mathsf{E} > 2\,. \tag{14.42}$$

This simple example shows that the generation of heat due to friction exerts a large effect on the process of cooling and that at high velocities the warmer wall may become heated instead of being cooled. This effect is of fundamental importance for the consideration of cooling at high velocities. It will occur in the problems connected with thermal boundary layers and will be discussed later.

In the case when the two walls in Couette flow have equal temperatures ($T_1 = T_0$) eqn. (14.41) leads to a simple parabolic temperature distribution which is symmetrical with respect to the mean axis

$$T(y) - T_0 = \frac{\mu\, U_1^{\,2}}{2\,k}\,\frac{y}{h}\left(1 - \frac{y}{h}\right).$$

This distribution is seen plotted in Fig. 14.4b. The highest temperature T_m created by frictional heat occurs in the centre and has a value given by

$$T_m - T_0 = \frac{\mu\, U_1^{\,2}}{8\,k}. \qquad (14.43)$$

In the case of compressible flow for which the above solution remains valid provided that the viscosity may be assumed to be independent of temperature, eqn. (14.43) can be put in the following dimensionless form

$$\frac{T_m - T_0}{T_0} = \frac{\gamma - 1}{8}\,\mathsf{P}\cdot\mathsf{M}^2\,, \qquad (14.43\text{ a})$$

where $\mathsf{M} = U_1/c_0$ denotes the Mach number and c_0 is the velocity of sound at temperature T_0. It is remarkable that the maximum temperature does not depend on the distance between the walls. The quantity of heat generated by friction is distributed evenly between the stationary and the moving wall.

The temperature distribution in the present example is important for the flow in the clearance between a journal and its bearing and was discussed in detail by G. Vogelpohl [61]. The flow in the clearance is laminar in view of the small dimensions of the latter and of the high viscosity of the oil. The temperature rise due to friction becomes considerable even at moderate velocities, as shown by the following example: Viscosity of oil at moderate temperature (say 85° F) from Table 14.1: $\mu = 0{\cdot}01087$ lbf sec/ft²; conductivity of oil $k = 0{\cdot}0179$ lbf/sec deg F. Hence from eqn. (14.43) with $U_1 = 15$ ft/sec: $T_m - T_0 = 17$ deg F, and for $U_1 =$ $= 30$ ft/sec: $T_m - T_0 = 68$ deg F. The temperature rise in the lubricating oil is so large that its dependence on temperature becomes important. R. Nahme [38] extended the preceding solution to the case of temperature-dependent viscosity and found that the velocity distribution at right angles to the walls ceases to be linear.

A further important solution for the temperature distribution from eqn. (14.40) is obtained when it is postulated that all the heat due to friction is transferred to one of the walls only, whereas no heat transfer takes place at the other wall (adiabatic wall). Let it be assumed that the lower wall is insulated, so that the boundary conditions for temperature become:

$$y = h: \quad T = T_0\,; \qquad y = 0: \quad \frac{\mathrm{d}T}{\mathrm{d}y} = 0\,. \qquad (14.44)$$

The solution of eqn. (14.40b) with the above boundary conditions is

$$T(y) - T_0 = \mu\,\frac{U_1^{\,2}}{2\,k}\left(1 - \frac{y^2}{h^2}\right), \qquad (14.45)$$

It is seen plotted in Fig. 14.4c. Thus the temperature increase of the lower wall is given by

$$T(0) - T_0 = T_a - T_0 = \mu\, U_1{}^2/2\,k\,. \tag{14.46}$$

The value T_a is called the *adiabatic wall temperature* as already mentioned; it is equal to the reading on a thermometer in the form of a flat plate. Upon comparing eqns. (14.46) and (14.43) it is seen that the highest temperature rise in the centre of the channel for the case of equal wall temperatures is equal to one quarter of the adiabatic wall temperature rise

$$T_a - T_0 = 4\,(T_m - T_0)\,. \tag{14.47}$$

The criterion for cooling in the case of different wall temperatures given in eqn. (14.46) can be simplified if the adiabatic wall temperature T_a is introduced. We then have

$$T_1 - T_0 \gtrless T_a - T_0 : \left.\begin{matrix}\text{cooling}\\ \text{heating}\end{matrix}\right\}\ \text{of upper wall}\,. \tag{14.48}$$

H. M. de Groff [24] generalized the preceding solution for Couette motion to include the case when the viscosity of the fluid depends on temperature.

2. Poiseuille flow through a channel with flat walls. A further and very simple exact solution for temperature distribution is obtained in the case of two-dimensional flow through a channel with parallel flat walls. Using the symbols explained in Fig. 14.6 we note with Poiseuille that the velocity distribution is parabolic:

$$u(y) = u_m \left(1 - \frac{y^2}{h^2}\right).$$

Assuming, again, equal temperatures of the walls, i. e. $T = T_0$ for $y = \pm h$, we obtain from eqn. (14.40b)

$$k\,\frac{\mathrm{d}^2T}{\mathrm{d}y^2} = -\frac{4\,\mu\,u^2{}_m}{h^4}\,y^2$$

whose solution is

$$T(y) - T_0 = \frac{1}{3}\,\frac{\mu\,u^2{}_m}{k}\left[1 - \left(\frac{y}{h}\right)^4\right]. \tag{14.49}$$

The temperature distribution is represented by a parabola of the fourth degree, Fig. 14.6, and the maximum temperature rise in the centre of the channel is

$$T_m - T_0 = \frac{1}{3}\,\frac{\mu\,u^2{}_m}{k}\,. \tag{14.50}$$

An extension of this solution to the case of temperature dependent viscosity was given by H. Hausenblas [25]. The corresponding solution for a circular pipe was recently given by U. Grigull [23].

A further exact solution for the thermal boundary layer can be obtained for the flow in a convergent and a divergent channel already considered in Sec. V. 11. The solution for the velocity field due to O. Jeffery and G. Hamel quoted in that section was utilized by K. Millsaps and K. Pohlhausen [37] in order to solve the

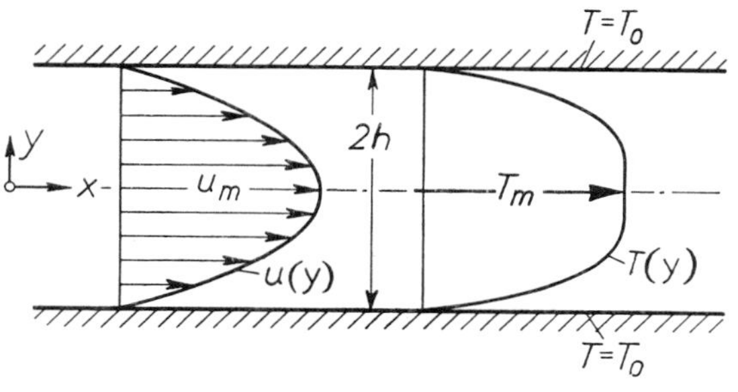

Fig. 14.6. Velocity and temperature distribution in a channel with flat walls with frictional heat taken into account

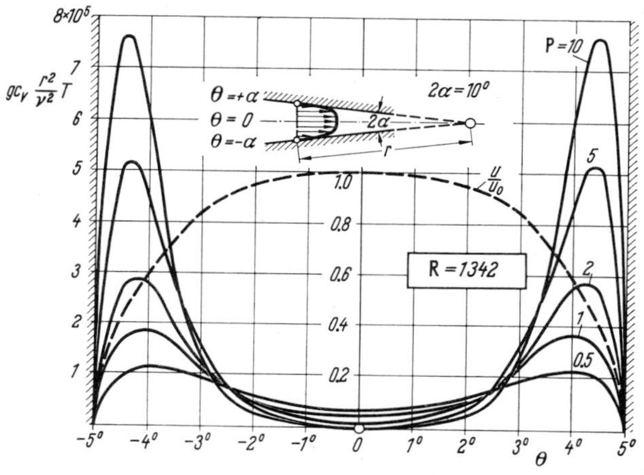

Fig. 14.7. Temperature distributions in a convergent channel of included angle $2\alpha = 10°$ at varying Prandtl numbers P, after K. Millsaps and K. Pohlhausen [37]. Reynolds number $R = 1342$ Velocity distribution from Fig. 5.15.
Owing to the dissipation of energy which is particularly large near the wall, the resulting temperature profiles acquire a pronounced "boundary layer appearance"

thermal problem. The temperature distribution across the channel is seen plotted in Fig. 14.7 for different Prandtl numbers. Owing to the dissipation of energy which is particularly large near the wall, the resulting temperature profiles acquire a pronounced "boundary layer appearance". In fact, boundary layer-like appearance becomes more pronounced as the Prandtl number increases. The velocity distribution u/u_0 from Fig. 5.15 has been plotted in Fig. 14.7 to provide a comparison.

g. Thermal boundary layers in forced flow

In the present section we shall consider several examples of thermal boundary layers in forced flow. In solving these problems, use will be made of the simplified thermal boundary layer equations. Just as in the case of a velocity boundary layer, the general problem of evaluating the thermal boundary layer for a body of arbitrary shape proves to be extremely difficult, so that we shall begin with the simpler example of the flat plate at zero incidence.

1. Parallel flow past a flat plate at zero incidence. We shall assume that the x-axis is placed in the plane of the plate in the direction of flow, the y-axis being at right angles to it and to the flow, with the origin at the leading edge. The boundary layer equations for incompressible flow and constant properties (i. e. independent of temperature) have been given in eqns. (14.36a, b, c); assuming that the buoyancy forces are equal to zero as well as that $\mathrm{d}p/\mathrm{d}x = 0$ [10, 42], we obtain

$$\frac{\partial u}{\partial x} + \frac{\partial v}{\partial y} = 0 \tag{14.51 a}$$

$$\varrho \left(u \frac{\partial u}{\partial x} + v \frac{\partial u}{\partial y} \right) = \mu \frac{\partial^2 u}{\partial y^2} \tag{14.51 b}$$

$$\varrho\, g\, c_p \left(u \frac{\partial T}{\partial x} + v \frac{\partial T}{\partial y} \right) = k \frac{\partial^2 T}{\partial y^2} + \mu \left(\frac{\partial u}{\partial y} \right)^2 . \tag{14.51 c}$$

The boundary conditions are:

$$y = 0 \;:\; u = v = 0 \;; \qquad T = T_w \quad \text{or} \quad \partial T/\partial y = 0$$

$$y = \infty \;:\; u = U_\infty \;; \qquad T = T_\infty .$$

The velocity field is independent of the temperature field so that the two flow equations (14.51 a, b) can be solved first and the result can be employed to evaluate the temperature field. An important relationship between the velocity distribution and the temperature distribution can be obtained immediately from eqns. (14.51b) and (14.51 c). If the heat of friction $\mu(\partial^2 u/\partial y^2)$ may be neglected in eqn. (14.51c) the two eqn. (14.51b) and (14.51c) become identical if T is replaced by u in the second equation and if, in addition, the properties of the fluid satisfy the equation

$$\frac{\mu}{\varrho} = \frac{k}{g\, c_p\, \varrho} \quad \text{or} \quad \nu = a, \text{ i. e. } \mathsf{P} = 1 .$$

If the frictional heat is neglected then a temperature field exists only if there is a difference in temperature between the wall and the external flow, e. g. if $T_w - T_\infty > 0$ (cooling). Hence it follows that for a flat plate at zero incidence in parallel flow and at small velocities the temperature and velocity distributions are identical provided that the Prandtl number is equal to unity:

$$\frac{T - T_w}{T_\infty - T_w} = \frac{u}{U_\infty} \quad (\mathsf{P} = 1) . \tag{14.52}$$

This result is of considerable practical importance because for all gases the Prandtl number differs but little from unity. The reader will recognize that this is a particular form of the Reynolds analogy discussed in Sec. XIV e. 3.

H. Blasius introduced new variables for the solution of the flow equations, see eqns. (7.25) and (7.26), (ψ is the stream function):

$$\eta = y \sqrt{\frac{U_\infty}{\nu x}} \;; \quad \psi = \sqrt{\nu x U_\infty}\, f(\eta) .$$

Hence

$$u = U_\infty f'(\eta) \;; \quad v = \frac{1}{2} \sqrt{\frac{\nu U_\infty}{x}} (\eta f' - f) .$$

The differential equation for $f(\eta)$, eqn. (7.29) becomes

$$f f'' + 2 f''' = 0$$

with the boundary conditions: $\eta = 0 : f = f' = 0$; $\eta = \infty : f' = 1$. The solution of these equations was given in Chap. VII, Table 7.1.

Including the effect of frictional heat, as seen from eqn. (14.51 c), the temperature distribution $T(\eta)$ is given by the equation

$$\frac{d^2T}{d\eta^2} + \frac{\mathsf{P}}{2} f \frac{dT}{d\eta} = -\mathsf{P} \frac{U_\infty^2}{g c_p} f''^2 . \qquad (14.53)$$

It is convenient to represent the general solution of eqn. (14.53) by the superposition of two solutions of the form:

$$T(\eta) - T_\infty = (T_w - T_\infty)\, \theta_1(\eta) + \frac{U_\infty^2}{2 g c_p} \theta_2(\eta) . \qquad (14.54)$$

Here $\theta_1(\eta)$ denotes the general solution of the homogeneous equation and $\theta_2(\eta)$ denotes a particular solution of the non-homogeneous equation. It is, further, convenient to choose the boundary conditions for $\theta_1(\eta)$ and $\theta_2(\eta)$ so as to make $\theta_1(\eta)$ the solution of the cooling problem with a prescribed temperature difference between the wall and the external stream $T_w - T_\infty$ with $\theta_2(\eta)$ giving the solution for the adiabatic wall. Thus $\theta_1(\eta)$ and $\theta_2(\eta)$ satisfy the following equations:

$$\theta_1'' + \tfrac{1}{2} \mathsf{P} f \theta_1' = 0 , \qquad (14.55)$$

with $\theta_1 = 1$ at $\eta = 0$ and $\theta_1 = 0$ at $\eta = \infty$ and

$$\theta_2'' + \tfrac{1}{2} \mathsf{P} f \theta_2' = -2 \mathsf{P} f''^2 \qquad (14.56)$$

with $\theta_2' = 0$ at $\eta = 0$ and $\theta_2 = 0$ at $\eta = \infty$.

Cooling problem: The solution of eqn. (14.55) was first given by E. Pohlhausen [42]. It can be written as

$$\theta_1(\eta, \mathsf{P}) = \int_{\xi=\eta}^{\infty} [f''(\xi)]^{\mathsf{P}} d\xi \Big/ \int_{\xi=0}^{\infty} [f''(\xi)]^{\mathsf{P}} d\xi . \qquad (14.57)$$

Hence for $\mathsf{P} = 1 : \theta_1(\eta) = 1 - f'(\eta) = 1 - u/U_\infty$, and for $\mathsf{P} = 1$ the temperature distribution is identical with the velocity distribution in accordance with eqn. (14.52). The temperature gradient at the wall, as calculated from eqn. (14.57) with $f''(0) = 0{\cdot}332$, becomes:

$$-\left(\frac{d\theta_1}{d\eta}\right)_0 = a_1(\mathsf{P}) = (0{\cdot}332)^{\mathsf{P}} \Big/ \int_0^{\infty} [f''(\xi)]^{\mathsf{P}} d\xi . \qquad (14.58)$$

The constant a_1 is seen to depend solely on the Prandtl number, $a_1(\mathsf{P})$. Some values calculated by E. Pohlhausen are reproduced in Table 14.2. They can be interpolated with good accuracy from the formula

$$a_1 = 0{\cdot}332 \sqrt[3]{\mathsf{P}} . \qquad (14.58\,a)$$

Table 14.2. Dimensionless coefficient of heat transfer, a_1, and dimensionless adiabatic wall temperature, b, for a flat plate at zero incidence, from eqns. (14.58) and (14.62)

P	0·6	0·7	0·8	0·9	1·0	1·1	7·0	10·0	15·0
a_1	0·276	0·293	0·307	0·320	0·332	0·344	0·645	0·730	0·835
b	0·770	0·835	0·895	0·950	1·000	1·050	2·515	2·965	3·535

The temperature distribution calculated from eqn. (14.57) is shown plotted in Fig. 14.8. As already mentioned, the curve for $\mathsf{P} = 1$ gives also the velocity distribution. For values of $\mathsf{P} > 1$ the thermal boundary layer is thinner than the velocity boundary layer. For example, for oil with a Prandtl number $\mathsf{P} = 1000$ the thermal boundary layer is only one-tenth of the velocity boundary layer.

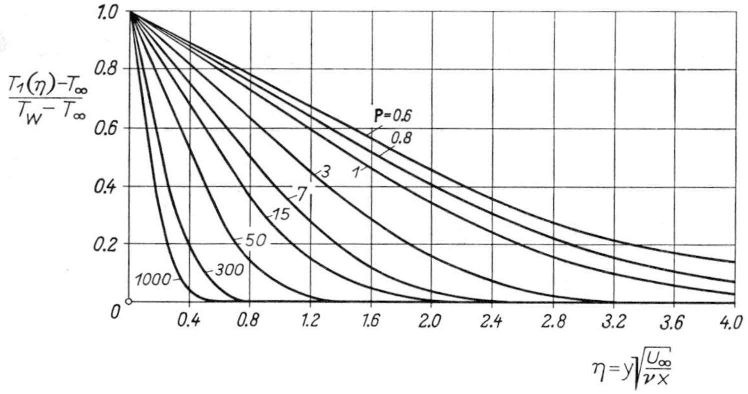

Fig. 14.8. Temperature distribution on a heated flat plate at zero incidence with small velocity plotted for various Prandtl numbers P (frictional heat neglected)

Adiabatic wall: The solution of eqn. (14.56) can be obtained by the method of 'variation of the constant'. It is

$$\theta_2(\eta,\mathsf{P}) = 2\,\mathsf{P}\int\limits_{\xi=\eta}^{\infty} [f''(\xi)]^{\mathsf{P}} \left(\int\limits_{0}^{\xi} [f''(\tau)]^{2-\mathsf{P}}\,\mathrm{d}\tau\right)\mathrm{d}\xi\,. \tag{14.59}$$

For $\mathsf{P} = 1$ we have:

$$\theta_2(\eta) = 1 - f'^2(\eta)\,. \tag{14.60}$$

The temperature which is assumed by the wall owing to frictional heat, the *adiabatic wall temperature* T_a is thus, by eqns. (14.54) and (14.59):

$$T_{2w} - T_\infty = T_a - T_\infty = \frac{U_\infty^2}{2\,g\,c_p}\,b(\mathsf{P})\,, \tag{14.61}$$

with

$$b(\mathsf{P}) = \theta_2(0,\,\mathsf{P}) \tag{14.62}$$

from eqn. (14.59). For a constant Prandtl number the adiabatic wall temperature is proportional to the adiabatic temperature rise $U_\infty{}^2/2\,g\,c_p$ which was plotted in Fig. 14.3. Some numerical values of the factor $b(\mathsf{P})$ are given in Table 14.2; for moderate Prandtl numbers these values may be interpolated with sufficient accuracy from the formula $b = \sqrt{\mathsf{P}}$. The values for larger Prandtl numbers can be inferred from Fig. 14.9. It is remarkable that for $\mathsf{P} = 1$ we have exactly $b = 1$. Thus

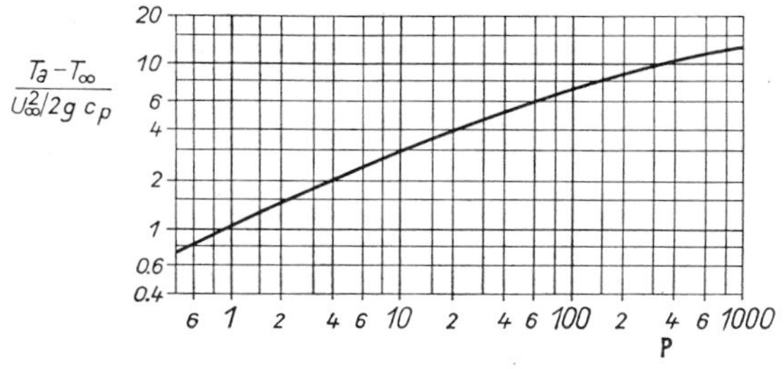

Fig. 14.9. Adiabatic wall temperature T_a of a flat plate at zero incidence with velocity U_∞ for various values of the Prandtl number; after E. Eckert and O. Drewitz [7]

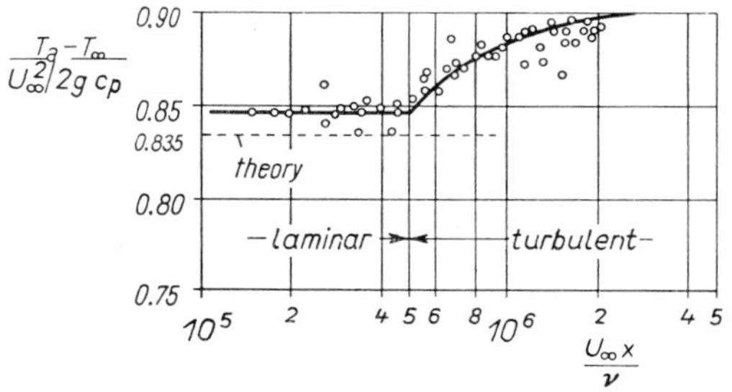

Fig. 14.10. Measurement of adiabatic wall temperature on a flat plate in a parallel air stream at zero incidence in a laminar and turbulent boundary layer; theory for laminar flow and $\mathsf{P} = 0{\cdot}73$, after Eckert and Weise [12]

for a gas with $\mathsf{P} = 1$ flowing in a parallel stream with velocity U_∞ past a flat plate at zero incidence the temperature rise due to frictional heat is equal to the adiabatic temperature, i. e. to that which occurs from velocity U_∞ to zero. The adiabatic wall temperature [8, 12] measured at various Reynolds numbers $U_\infty\,x/\nu$ is seen plotted in Fig. 14.10. The agreement is very good in the laminar region. At the point of transition from laminar to turbulent flow in the boundary layer the temperature increases suddenly. The temperature distribution for an adiabatic wall represented non-dimensionally is

$$\frac{T_2(\eta) - T_\infty}{T_{2w} - T_\infty} = \frac{T_2(\eta) - T_\infty}{T_a - T_\infty} = \frac{\theta_2(\eta,\,\mathsf{P})}{b(\mathsf{P})}$$

and is seen plotted in Fig. 14.11 for various values of the Prandtl number. By the superposition of (14.57) and (14.59), as shown in eqn. (14.54), it is possible to obtain a general solution for a prescribed temperature difference between the wall and the free stream $T_w = T_\infty$. Thus

$$T(\eta) - T_\infty = [(T_w - T_\infty) - (T_a - T_\infty)]\,\theta_1(\eta,\,\mathsf{P}) + \frac{U_\infty^2}{2\,g\,c_p}\,\theta_2(\eta,\,\mathsf{P}) \qquad (14.63)$$

with $T_a - T_\infty$ from eqn. (14.61). The dimensionless temperature distribution becomes

$$\frac{T - T_\infty}{T_w - T_\infty} = [1 - \tfrac{1}{2}\, \mathsf{E}\, b(\mathsf{P})]\, \theta_1(\eta, \mathsf{P}) + \tfrac{1}{2}\, \mathsf{E}\, \theta_2(\eta, \mathsf{P})\,. \tag{14.63a}$$

It is shown plotted in Fig. 14.12 for various values of the Eckert number $\mathsf{E} = U_\infty^2/g\, c_p (T_w - T_\infty)$ from eqn. (14.26). For $b \times \mathsf{E} > 2$ the boundary layer

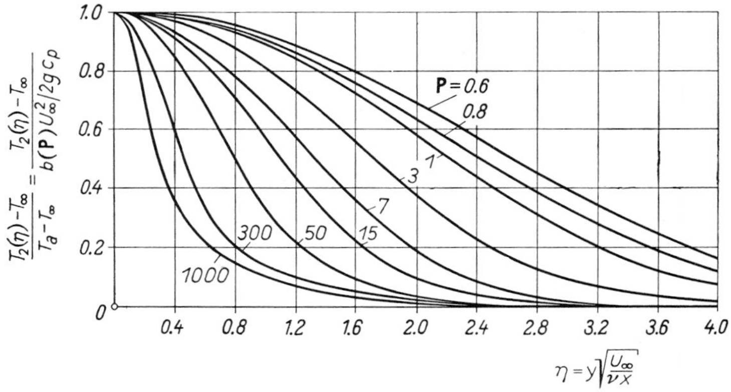

Fig. 14.11. Temperature excess in the laminar boundary layer on a flat plate at zero incidence in a parallel stream with high velocity in the *absence of heating* for various Prandtl numbers (adiabatic wall)

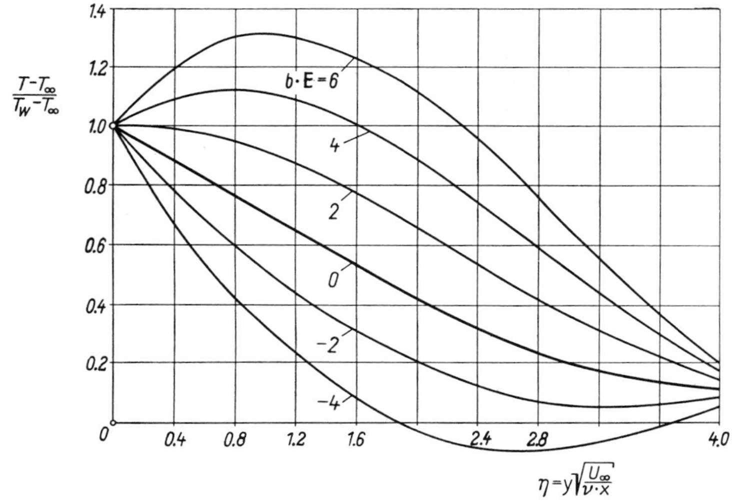

Fig. 14.12. Temperature distribution in a laminar boundary layer on a heated ($\mathsf{E} > 0$) and cooled ($\mathsf{E} < 0$) flat plate at zero incidence in a parallel stream for the case of a laminar boundary layer and with frictional heat accounted for as calculated from eqn. (14.63). Prandtl number $\mathsf{P} = 0{\cdot}7$ (air). The temperature of the wall is maintained constant at T_w. Curve $b \times \mathsf{E} = 0$ for zero frictional heat; curve $b \times \mathsf{E} = 2$ corresponds to an adiabatic wall; $\mathsf{E} = U_\infty^2/g\, c_p\, (T_w - T_\infty)$; $b = 0{\cdot}835$. For $b \times \mathsf{E} > 2$ the hot wall ceases to be cooled by the stream of cooler air, since the 'heat cushion' provided by frictional heat prevents cooling

near the wall is warmer than the wall itself owing to the generation of frictional heat. In such cases the wall will not be cooled by the stream of air flowing past it.

Heat transfer. As seen from eqn. (14.3) the heat flux from plate to fluid at station x has the value $q(x) = -k(\partial T/\partial y)_{y=0}$ or

$$q(x) = -k\sqrt{\frac{U_\infty}{\nu x}}\left(\frac{\mathrm{d}T}{\mathrm{d}\eta}\right)_{\eta=0}. \qquad (14.64)$$

The rate of heat transfer per unit time for both sides of a plate (length l, width b) is $Q = 2b\int_0^l q(x)\,\mathrm{d}x$, so that

$$Q = 4\,b\,k\sqrt{\frac{U_\infty l}{\nu}}\left(-\frac{\mathrm{d}T}{\mathrm{d}\eta}\right)_0. \qquad (14.65)$$

a) *Neglecting frictional heat:* In this case $T(\eta) - T_\infty = (T_w - T_\infty)\,\theta_1(\eta)$ by eqn. (14.57) with $(\mathrm{d}T/\mathrm{d}\eta)_0 = -a_1(T_w - T_\infty)$. With a_1 from eqn. (14.58a) we have

$$\left(\frac{\mathrm{d}T}{\mathrm{d}\eta}\right)_0 = -0{\cdot}332\,\sqrt[3]{\mathsf{P}}\,(T_w - T_\infty).$$

so that

$$\left.\begin{aligned} q(x) &= 0{\cdot}332\,k\,\sqrt[3]{\mathsf{P}}\,\sqrt{\frac{U_\infty}{\nu x}}\,(T_w - T_\infty),\\ Q &= 1{\cdot}328\,b\,k\,\sqrt[3]{\mathsf{P}}\,\sqrt{\mathsf{R}_l}\,(T_w - T_\infty).\end{aligned}\right\} \qquad (14.66)$$

Introducing dimensionless coefficients in the form of the Nusselt number from (14.29) instead of the local and total heat flux, respectively

$$q(x) = \frac{k}{x}\,\mathsf{N}_x\,(T_w - T_\infty) \quad \text{and} \quad Q = 2\,b\,l\,\frac{k}{l}\,\mathsf{N}_m\,(T_w - T_\infty),$$

we have

$$\mathsf{N}_x = 0{\cdot}332\,\sqrt[3]{\mathsf{P}}\,\sqrt{\mathsf{R}_x} \qquad (14.66\text{a})$$

$$\mathsf{N}_m = 0{\cdot}664\,\sqrt[3]{\mathsf{P}}\,\sqrt{\mathsf{R}_l} \qquad \text{(laminar)} \qquad (14.66\text{b})$$

which is identical with eqn. (14.38d) derived directly from the Reynolds analogy. The case of turbulent flow can be approximated by the equations

$$\mathsf{N}_x = 0{\cdot}0296\,\sqrt[3]{\mathsf{P}}\cdot\mathsf{R}_x^{0{\cdot}8} \qquad (14.66\text{c})$$

$$\mathsf{N}_m = 0{\cdot}037\,\sqrt[3]{\mathsf{P}}\cdot\mathsf{R}^{0{\cdot}8} \qquad \text{(turbulent)} \qquad (14.66\text{d})$$

which we quote here for completeness. The derivation of these equations can be found on p. 497, Chap. XIX. The preceding formulae for the rate of heat transfer are in good agreement with the measurements due to F. Elias [18], A. Edwards and B. N. Furber [17a] and J. Kestin, P. F. Maeder and H. E. Wang [30b].

b) *With frictional heat:* In this case with $T(\eta)$ from eqn. (14.63) we obtain

$$\left(\frac{\mathrm{d}T}{\mathrm{d}\eta}\right)_0 = -a_1 (T_w - T_a) = -0{\cdot}332 \sqrt[3]{\mathsf{P}}\,(T_w - T_a)\,,$$

where T_a is the adiabatic wall temperature. It is identical with the wall temperature in the thermometer problem and follows from the equation

$$T_a - T_\infty = b(\mathsf{P}) \frac{U_\infty^2}{2\,g\,c_p} \approx \sqrt{\mathsf{P}}\,\frac{U_\infty^2}{2\,g\,c_p}\,. \tag{14.67}$$

Here $b(\mathsf{P})$ can be taken from Table 14.2. Introducing the Mach number $\mathsf{M} = U_\infty / c_\infty$ from (14.25), T_a may also be taken from

$$T_a = T_\infty \left(1 + \frac{\gamma - 1}{2}\,\mathsf{M}^2\right) \quad \text{for} \quad \mathsf{P} = 1\,.$$

Thus we obtain the following expression for the local and total heat flux from eqns. (14.64) and (14.65) respectively

$$\left.\begin{aligned} q(x) &= 0{\cdot}332\,k \sqrt[3]{\mathsf{P}} \sqrt{\frac{U_\infty}{\nu\,x}}\,(T_w - T_a)\,,\\ Q &= 1{\cdot}328\,b\,k \sqrt[3]{\mathsf{P}} \sqrt{\mathsf{R}_l}\,(T_w - T_a)\,. \end{aligned}\right\} \tag{14.68}$$

It now ceases to be useful to base the coefficient of heat transfer $\alpha(x)$ on the temperature difference $(T_w - T_\infty)$ from eqn. (14.27) or to define the Nusselt number as in eqn. (14.29) because the heat flux is no longer proportional to that temperature difference†.

The cooling action of a stream of fluid on a wall is considerably reduced because of the heat generated by friction. In the absence of frictional heat, heat will flow from the plate to the fluid ($q > 0$) as long as $T_w > T_\infty$ but in actual fact, if frictional heat is present, a flow of heat persists only if $T_w > T_a$, eqn. (14.68). Taking into account the value deduced for T_a, we obtain the condition that heat flows from wall to fluid (upper sign) or in the reverse direction (lower sign), if

$$T_w - T_\infty \gtrless \sqrt{\mathsf{P}}\,\frac{U_\infty^2}{2\,g\,c_p}\,. \tag{14.69}$$

A numerical example may serve to illustrate the significance of eqn. (14.69): In a stream of air flowing at $U_\infty = 600$ ft/sec, $\mathsf{P} = 0{\cdot}7$, $c_p = 0{\cdot}24$ Btu/lbf deg F we obtain $\sqrt{\mathsf{P}}\,U_\infty^2/2\,g\,c_p = 25$ deg F. The wall will begin to be cooled when $T_w - T_\infty >$

† E. Eckert and W. Weise [9] have, therefore, suggested to introduce a Nusselt number N^* based on the difference $(T_w - T_a)$. We might then expect to obtain as a first approximation the same formulae for N^* as in (14.66a, b). They would, moreover be expected to be valid for incompressible and compressible flow alike. If, on the other hand, we retain the Nusselt number based on $(T_w - T_\infty)$ then eqn. (14.68) leads to the following expressions instead of (14.66a):

$$\mathsf{N}_x = 0{\cdot}332 \sqrt[3]{\mathsf{P}} \sqrt{\mathsf{R}_x}\,[1 - \tfrac{1}{2}\,\mathsf{E}\,b(\mathsf{P})]\,,$$

i. e. $\mathsf{N}_x = 0$ for $b\,\mathsf{E} = 2$ and $\mathsf{N}_x < 0$ for $b\,\mathsf{E} > 2$, see Fig. 14.12.

25 deg F. If the temperature difference between wall and stream is smaller than this value the wall will pick up a portion of the heat generated by friction. In particular this is the case when the temperature of the wall and stream are equal†.

2. Thermal boundary layers for other body shapes; theoretical results. N. Froessling [21] carried out calculations on the temperature distribution in the laminar boundary layer about a body of arbitrary shape for the two-dimensional and axially symmetrical cases. In his calculations, in which friction and compression work were neglected throughout, he assumed a power series for the potential velocity distribution around the body expanded in terms of the length of arc (Blasius series), similar to Sec. IXc, i. e. of the form:

$$U = u_1\, x + u_3\, x^3 + u_5\, x^5 + \dots .$$

The corresponding velocity distribution in the boundary layer is assumed to have the form:

$$u(x, y) = u_1\, x\, f_1(y) + u_3\, x^3\, f_3(y) + \dots .$$

Correspondingly the assumption for the temperature distribution was of the form:

$$T(x, y) = T_0 + x^2 T_2(y) + x^4 T_4(y)$$

In a manner similar to that for the velocity boundary layer in Sec. IXc it is found that the functions $T_2(y)$, $T_4(y)$,... satisfy ordinary differential equations which include the functions f_1, f_3, ... of the velocity distribution. In this case, however, the functions T_2, T_4, ... also depend on the Prandtl number. The first auxiliary functions for the two-dimensional and axially symmetrical case were evaluated numerically for a Prandtl number of 0·7. The method under consideration is somewhat cumbersome by its nature, as was the case with the velocity boundary layer, particularly for slender body forms when a large number of terms in the power expansion is required.

In the special case when $\mathsf{P} = 1$, and when the heat due to friction is neglected, the differential equation for the temperature distribution in the boundary layer around an arbitrary cylinder is identical with that for the transverse velocity component (velocity component in the direction of the generatrix of the yawed cylinder). This can be seen upon comparing eqns. (14.51c) and (10.47). The relation, which has already been discussed in Sec. Xb, was utilized by L. Goland [22] for the evaluation of the temperature distribution in the boundary layer around a cylinder of special form.

In the neighbourhood of a stagnation point where the velocity distribution is given by $U = u_1\, x$ the coefficient of heat transfer is given by

$$\alpha = A\, k \sqrt{\frac{u_1}{\nu}}\,,$$

† In this connexion attention may be drawn to the case of a prescribed *variable wall temperature* $T_w(x)$ which was discussed by D. R. Chapman and M. W. Rubesin [3]. It was also treated in a simpler manner by H. Schlichting [46]. Even if frictional heat is neglected, the magnitude of the local heat flux is by no means determined solely by the temperature difference $T_w(x) - T_\infty$. It proves to be strongly influenced by the 'past history' of the boundary layer, see p. 324.

if the heat due to compression and friction is neglected. The values of A in terms of the Prandtl number are given in Table 14.3. For a circular cylinder we have $U(x) = 2\,U_\infty \sin(x/R)$ and hence $u_1 = 4\,U_\infty/D$ in the neighbourhood of the stagnation point. Consequently the Nusselt number based on the diameter of the cylinder $\mathsf{N}_D = \alpha\,D/k$ becomes

$$\mathsf{N}_D = 2\,A\,\sqrt{\frac{U_\infty D}{\nu}}\,. \qquad (14.70)$$

Table 14.3. The constant A in the equation for the calculation of the coefficient of heat transfer in the neighbourhood of a stagnation point after Squire [56]

P	0·6	0·7	0·8	0·9	1·0	1·1	7·0	10	15
A	0·466	0·495	0·521	0·546	0·570	0·592	1·18	1·34	1·54

The above expression agrees reasonably well with the measurements performed by E. Schmidt and K. Wenner [50], Fig. 14.13. Although the general trend of the variation of the Nusselt number with the angular co-ordinate ϕ is reproduced very well by the experimental points, particularly in the neighbourhood of the stagnation point, there seems to be present a systematic influence of the Reynolds number. The curves for lower Reynolds numbers agree far better with the theoretical values than those at higher Reynolds numbers, and, for example at $\mathsf{R} = 1{\cdot}7 \times 10^5$, the measured value exceeds the theoretical one at $\phi = 0°$ by about 10—15 %. We shall revert to this point in Sec. XIV g. 4 where it will be shown that the discrepancy is due to the effect of varying free-stream turbulence, and not actually to a change in the Reynolds number.

When performing numerical calculations on thermal boundary layers, it is found that *approximate methods* are much simpler than the preceding exact methods. Such approximate methods are based on equations modelled on the integral momentum equation for the calculation of velocity boundary layers which

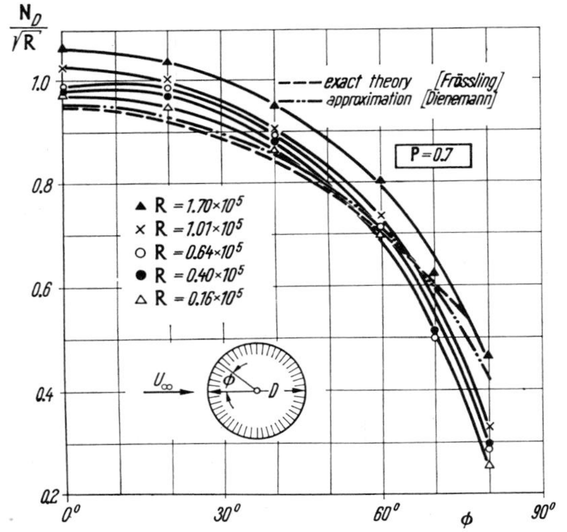

Fig. 14.13. Local rate of heat transfer around a circular cylinder. Comparison between theory and experiment. Nusselt number N_D and Reynolds number R_D referred to cylinder diameter $D = 100$ mm. Measurements performed by E. Schmidt and K. Wenner [50]. Theory due to N. Froessling [21] and W. Dienemann [4]. Systematic influence of Reynolds number due to varying free-stream turbulence, Sec. XIV g, 4

was considered in detail in Chap. XII. Neglecting frictional heat and the effects of compressibility it is possible to integrate the energy equation (14.35c) from $y = 0$ to $y = \infty$ and so to obtain the *heat flux equation*

$$\frac{\mathrm{d}}{\mathrm{d}x}\int_0^\infty [u(T-T_\infty)]\,\mathrm{d}y = -a\left(\frac{\partial T}{\partial y}\right)_{y=0}, \tag{14.71}$$

where $a = k/\varrho\, g\, c_p$ is the thermal diffusivity introduced in eqn. (14.22). The preceding equation, sometimes also called the energy integral equation†, is quite analogous to the momentum integral equation (8.35) for the velocity boundary layer.

From among the numerous procedures which are available for the solution of the heat flux equation (14.71), we propose to describe that due to H. B. Squire [57] in some detail because it is particularly simple and because it is a natural continuation of Pohlhausen's approximate method for the solution of the velocity boundary layer described in Chap. XII. In order to evaluate the integral on the left-hand side of eqn. (14.71) we introduce the variables $\eta = y/\delta$ for the velocity boundary layer and $\eta_T = y/\delta_T$ for the thermal layer. We denote, further, their ratio by $\Delta = \delta_T/\delta$, and we assume that the velocity and temperature distributions, respectively, have the forms

$$u = U(x)\,[2\,\eta - 2\,\eta^3 + \eta^4] = U(x)\,F(\eta) \tag{14.72a}$$

$$T - T_\infty = (T_w - T_\infty)\,[1 - 2\,\eta_T + 2\,\eta_T{}^3 - \eta_T{}^4] = (T_w - T_\infty)\,L(\eta_T)\,. \tag{14.72b}$$

The velocity distribution stipulated here corresponds to the Pohlhausen assumption in eqn. (12.23) and the form of the temperature distribution function is so selected as to ensure identical velocity and temperature distributions for $\delta_T = \delta$, as required by the Reynolds analogy for a flat plate at $\mathsf{P} = 1$, eqn. (14.52). On substituting eqns. (14.72a, b) into eqn. (14.71), we obtain

$$\frac{\mathrm{d}}{\mathrm{d}x}\left\{\delta_T \cdot U \cdot H(\Delta)\right\} = 2\,\frac{a}{\delta_T}\,. \tag{14.73}$$

Here $H(\Delta)$ is a universal function of $\Delta = \delta_T/\delta$ which turns out to be given by

$$H = \int_0^\infty F(\eta)\cdot L(\eta_T)\cdot \mathrm{d}\eta_T\,. \tag{14.74}$$

Performing the indicated integrations, we obtain

$$H(\Delta) = \frac{2}{15}\,\Delta - \frac{3}{140}\,\Delta^3 + \frac{1}{180}\,\Delta^4 \quad \text{for } \Delta < 1$$

$$\text{and } H(\Delta) = \frac{3}{10} - \frac{3}{10}\,\frac{1}{\Delta} + \frac{2}{15}\,\frac{1}{\Delta^2} - \frac{3}{140}\,\frac{1}{\Delta^4} + \frac{1}{180}\,\frac{1}{\Delta^5} \quad \text{for } \Delta > 1$$

Some numerical values of the function $H(\Delta)$, calculated by W. Dienemann [4], have been listed in Table 14.4.

† Not to be confused with the energy integral equation (8.38).

Table 14.4. Numerical values of the function $H(\Lambda)$

Λ	H
0·7	0·0873
0·8	0·0980
0·9	0·1080
1·0	0·1175
1·2	0·1345
1·4	0·1492

The integration of eqn. (14.73) yields

$$(\delta_T\, U \cdot H)^2 = 4\, a \int_0^x U \cdot H \cdot \mathrm{d}x\,. \tag{14.75}$$

The velocity boundary layer thickness δ can be evaluated with the aid of eqn. (12.37) when it is remembered from eqn. (12.24)† that $\delta/\theta = 315/37$. Thus

$$\delta^2 = 34\, \frac{\nu}{U^6} \int_{x=0}^{x} U^5\, \mathrm{d}x\,. \tag{14.76}$$

Upon dividing eqn. (14.75) by eqn. (14.76), we obtain

$$\Lambda^2 \cdot H(\Lambda) = \frac{2}{17}\, \frac{1}{\mathsf{P}}\, \frac{U^4 \int_0^x U\, H \cdot \mathrm{d}x}{H \int_0^x U^5\, \mathrm{d}x}\,. \tag{14.77}$$

Since $H(\Lambda)$ is a known function, Table 14.4, the preceding equation can be used to determine $\Lambda(x)$. The calculation is best performed by successive approximations, starting with the initial assumption that Λ = const. Hence we obtain

$$\Lambda^2 \cdot H(\Lambda) = \frac{2}{17}\, \frac{1}{\mathsf{P}}\, \frac{U^4 \int_0^x U\, \mathrm{d}x}{\int_0^x U^5\, \mathrm{d}x}\,. \tag{14.77 a}$$

The resulting value of Λ is now introduced into the left-hand side of eqn. (14.77) thus leading to an improved value of Λ. In general two steps in the iteration are found to be sufficient.

The local rate of heat transfer becomes

$$q(x) = -\, k \left(\frac{\partial T}{\partial y}\right)_0 = 2\,(T_w - T_\infty)\, \frac{k}{\delta_T}\,,$$

† For the sake of simplicity the calculation is based throughout on the flat plate relations ($\Lambda = 0$).

and hence the local Nusselt number referred to a characteristic length l is

$$\mathsf{N}_x = \frac{q(x)}{T_w - T_\infty} \cdot \frac{l}{k} = 2\,\frac{l}{\delta_T}\,. \tag{14.78}$$

The steps to be taken to evaluate the thermal boundary layer, and in particular, to determine the variation of the Nusselt number along a body of prescribed shape are thus the following ones: —

1. evaluate $\Delta(x)$ from eqns. (14.77) and (14.77a)
2. evaluate $\delta(x)$ from eqn. (14.76)
3. steps 1 and 2 give $\delta_T(x)$; finally, the local Nusselt number follows from eqn. (14.78).

Flat plate at zero incidence: The preceding approximate method will now be compared with the exact solution in the case of a flat plate at zero incidence. Inserting $U(x) = U_\infty$ into eqn. (14.77), we obtain

$$\Delta^2 H(\Delta) = \frac{4}{34} \cdot \frac{1}{\mathsf{P}}\,.$$

The expression $\Delta = \mathsf{P}^{-1/3}$ constitutes an approximation to the solution of this equation which is in error by not more than 5 per cent. as compared with the exact solution. The boundary layer thickness from eqn. (14.76) is

$$\delta = 5{\cdot}83 \sqrt{\nu\, x/U_\infty}\,.$$

Hence the local Nusselt number referred to the current length x along the plate, eqn. (14.78), becomes

$$\mathsf{N}_x = 0{\cdot}343 \sqrt[3]{\mathsf{P}}\, \mathsf{R}_x\,, \tag{14.79}$$

whereas the exact solution, eqn. (14.66a), showed the numerical coefficient to be equal to 0·332.

Alternative approximate procedures for the calculation of the thermal boundary layer on bodies of arbitrary shapes have been indicated by E. Eckert [11] and by E. Eckert and J. N. B. Livingood [15, 17]; the latter require a somewhat larger amount of numerical work, but their accuracy is improved. In this connection the paper by W. Dienemann [4] may be useful to the reader. A drastically simplified procedure which is applicable to axially symmetrical as well as two-dimensional cases is contained in refs. [1, 19].

E. Eckert and O. Drewitz [10] performed calculations on the temperature distribution in the boundary layer allowing for the effects of compressibility and frictional heat. In general, in gaseous motion the work of compression is of the same order of magnitude as that dissipated through viscosity. It is then no longer possible to reduce the equation for temperature distribution to a differential equation of the first order, as was the case with the flat plate, and this circumstance renders the calculation much more difficult. In particular, the preceding authors made detailed calculations for the thermal boundary layers associated with the so-called wedge-flows which correspond to $U(x) = u_1 x^m$ and whose velocity boundary layers, calculated earlier by D. R. Hartree, have been discussed in Sec. IXa. The thermal boundary layer for wedge flow is also discussed in a paper by A. N. Tifford [59]. The rate of heat transfer across a laminar boundary layer when the fluid properties are temperature-dependent was calculated by H. Schuh [52].

The case when the wall temperature varies along the body in accordance with a prescribed function $T_w(x)$ merits consideration in this connection. The case was treated, among others, by D. R. Chapman and M. W. Rubesin [3], by M. J. Lighthill [35], H. Schuh [53], S. Levy [33], and somewhat simpler by H. Schlichting [46]. The method due to H. B. Squire can be extended to include the case of variable temperature [58]. Even when frictional heat is neglected, the local rate of heat transfer ceases to be proportional to the temperature difference $T_w(x) - T_\infty$, and depends strongly on the "previous history" of the boundary layer, i. e. on the whole function $T(x)$.

3. Other body shapes; measurements. Measurements on the coefficient of heat transfer by forced convection, mostly from circular cylinders, can be found in papers by R. Hilpert [27] and E. Schmidt and K. Wenner [50]. R. Hilpert performed measurements on circular cylinders in a cross-flow of air covering a very wide range of Reynolds numbers. Fig. 14.14 contains a plot of the mean Nusselt number N_m taken for the whole circumference of the cylinder against the Reynolds number R. Both N_m and R are based on the diameter of the cylinder. As a first crude approximation it can be assumed that N_m is proportional to $\mathsf{R}^{1/2}$ as confirmed by the theoretical calculations for the flat plate at zero incidence, eqn. (14.66b), and for the flow near a stagnation point, eqn. (14.70), in laminar flow.

The local coefficient of heat transfer varies considerably over the surface of cylinders and other bodies. The local coefficient of heat transfer was measured by

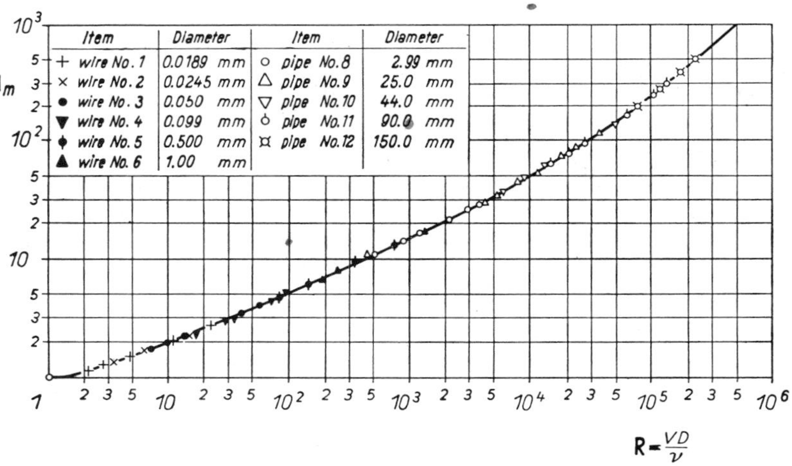

Fig. 14.14. The Nusselt number N_m in terms of the Reynolds number R for circular cylinders. Surface temperature 212° F approx; after R. Hilpert [27]

E. Schmidt and K. Wenner (Fig. 14.15). It is seen that in the laminar boundary layer the coefficient of heat transfer decreases with distance from the stagnation point and reaches a minimum in the neighbourhood of the point of separation. In turbulent flow its value near the point of separation is about equal to that at the leading edge in the laminar layer. Similar work is reported in refs. [31] and [44]. A comparison between the measured values for the forward portion of the cylinder from Fig. 14.15, i. e. for the portion where the flow is laminar, and theoretical calculations has already been given in Fig. 14.13. The theoretical curves were based on the actual, measured velocity distribution in the external flow. As is known, near the forward stagnation point the latter agrees very well with that given by potential theory. The agreement, as already stated, is satisfactory except for an apparent systematic effect of increasing Reynolds number. This is really connected with the effect of free-stream turbulence to be discussed in the succeeding section. E. Eckert and W. Weise [9, 12] published the results of their measurements on the mean and local adiabatic wall temperatures on unheated cylinders in parallel and in cross-flow covering a range of air velocities nearly up to sonic. In the case of a stream parallel to the axis of the cylinder they obtained a mean value $(T_a - T_\infty)\, 2\, g\, c_p / U_\infty^2 = 0{\cdot}84$ which was independent of the Mach number, in good agreement with the value from eqn. (14.67) for a flat plate. In cross-flow they obtained a value between 0·6 and 0·8 which was also reasonably independent of the Mach number.

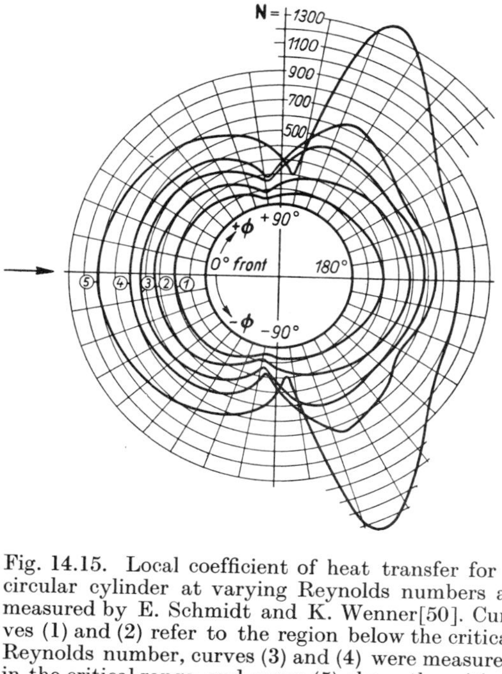

Fig. 14.15. Local coefficient of heat transfer for a circular cylinder at varying Reynolds numbers as measured by E. Schmidt and K. Wenner[50]. Curves (1) and (2) refer to the region below the critical Reynolds number, curves (3) and (4) were measured in the critical range, and curve (5) above the critical range. (1) $\mathsf{R} = 39{,}800$, (2) $\mathsf{R} = 101{,}300$, (3) $\mathsf{R} = 170{,}000$, (4) $\mathsf{R} = 257{,}600$, (5) $\mathsf{R} = 426{,}000$

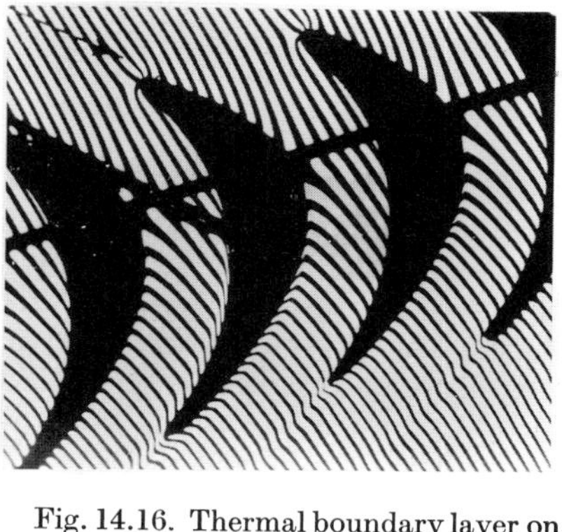

Fig. 14.16. Thermal boundary layer on a turbine cascade, made visible with the aid of the interfero- meter method, after E. Eckert. Angle of flow at inlet $\beta_1 = 40°$; Solidity $l/t = 2{\cdot}18$; Reynolds number $\mathsf{R} = 1{\cdot}97 \times 10^5$.

The shift of the interferometer lines is proportional to the change in density. The sudden kinks in the lines near the wall show the outer edge of the thermal boundary layer, since the heat of friction produces a large change in density in that region

The thermal boundary layer can be conveniently made visible with the aid of interferometric photographs. Fig. 14.16 represents the flow past a turbine cascade. The shift in the lines is a measure of the difference between the local density and that at a reference state (e. g. with respect to the undisturbed stream). The changes in density in the region of potential flow are due mainly to pressure changes, but in the boundary layer the heat due to friction contributes greatly to the change in density. Upon close examination it is possible to discern in Fig. 14.16 sudden sharp kinks in the lines. These are due to the considerable additional change in density produced by frictional heat. Thus the kinks trace the outer edge of the thermal boundary layer. In natural convection it is even easier to render the boundary layer visible as it is possible to use a Schlieren method for this purpose, first described by E. Schmidt [48], *cf.* p. 335.

4. Effect of free-stream turbulence. It has been stated in Sec. VII g that a laminar boundary layer can be associated with a turbulent as well as a laminar external stream. In the overwhelming majority of practical cases, the external stream is turbulent which means that at every point in it the velocity fluctuates, changing its magnitude and direction. When the velocity is steady on the average, there are superimposed on it three fluctuating velocity components whose time-averages over sufficiently long time intervals vanish. The effect which such oscillations have on the velocity boundary layer were mentioned in Sec. VII g and discussed in somewhat greater detail in Chap. XI in connexion with non-steady boundary layers. In the present section we shall examine the effect of such free-stream oscillations, particularly those due to turbulence, on thermal boundary layers and on rates of heat transfer, confining ourselves to the incompressible case.

It will be recognized at the outset that two turbulent, or oscillating parallel streams are not similar when the Reynolds numbers $\mathsf{R} = \overline{U}\, l/\nu$ (l = characteristic length) based on the average velocity U are identical, the condition being necessary but not sufficient. Two such streams may differ with respect to the amplitudes and frequencies of the oscillating components. In the case of turbulent streams the oscillations are random in nature and in principle no two such streams can be similar. However, it is found by experiment that certain average properties of the oscillations are adequate to establish similarity. The two important properties in question are: the intensity of turbulence T defined in Sec XVI d. 1 and the scale of turbulence L defined in Sec. XVIII e. It is found, further, that in cases when the scale of turbulence is small compared with the dimensions of the body, similarity will prevail with a sufficient degree of accuracy if the two parameters, the average Reynolds number $\mathsf{R} = U\, l/\nu$, and the intensity of turbulence T are equal. The latter is a rough measure of the amplitude of the random oscillation. Hence it must be expected that for geometrically similar isothermal bodies in parallel, isothermal, turbulent streams, the local Nusselt number N_x will be a function of these two parameters in addition to the Prandtl number,

$$\mathsf{N}_x = f_1(\mathsf{R}, \mathsf{P}, \mathsf{T}) \tag{14.80}$$

and the same is true of the average Nusselt number

$$\mathsf{N}_m = f_2(\mathsf{R}, \mathsf{P}, \mathsf{T})\,. \tag{14.80a}$$

The preceding equations supplement eqn. (14.30a) given earlier.

Owing to the impossibility of handling random fluctuations by the use of mathematical analysis, it is necessary to investigate the extent of the effect of turbulence intensity on rates of heat transfer by experimental means. The existence of such an effect can be surmised from Fig. 14.17 which compares two sets of measurements made on "infinite" circular cylinders in cross-flow. One set of measurements was performed by R. Hilpert [27] and was already illustrated in Fig. 14.14. The second set was obtained by E. Griffith and J. H. Awberry [22a]. From a description of the experimental procedures contained in the two papers it is clear that the only difference between them was the intensity of turbulence in the wind tunnel streams: it was low in Hilpert's tunnel, and rather high in the NPL tunnel used by Griffith and Awberry. It is noticed that the differences in the measured Nusselt numbers are high, and average about 70 per cent. for the higher intensity of turbulence. This is a discrepancy of an order of magnitude which exceeds the combined errors of measurement and must be attributed to the systematic influence of turbulence intensity T.

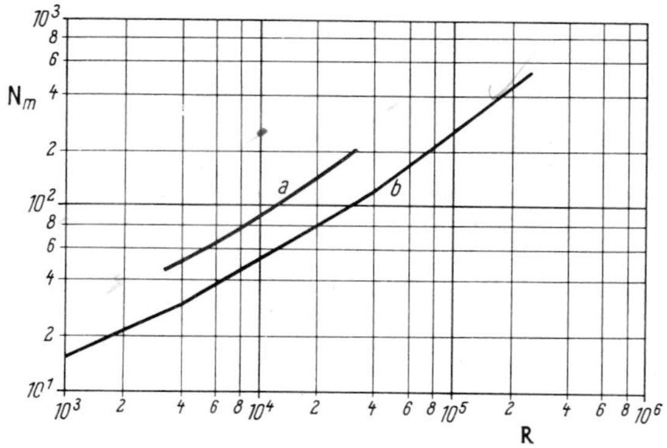

Fig. 14.17. Comparison between two sets of measurements on "infinite" circular cylinders in cross-flow. a. E. Griffith and J. H. Awberry [22a], b. R. Hilpert [27]

An increase in turbulence intensity in the free stream must have two effects which should be carefully distinguished from each other. In the case of a blunt body, such as the cylinder considered in connexion with Fig. 14.17, it will first affect the flow pattern in the boundary layer about it. At low Reynolds numbers the flow pattern consists of a laminar boundary layer in front and a wake behind caused by laminar separation (*subcritical* flow pattern). An increase in turbulence intensity will cause earlier separation and consequently the arc subtended by the laminar boundary layer will shorten in favour of the arc subtended by the separated region. This will change the Nusselt number, because the local Nusselt number is different for these two basic flow patterns. At higher Reynolds numbers the flow pattern near the cylinder consists of a laminar boundary layer, followed by a turbulent boundary layer behind the point of transition and a wake behind the point of turbulent separation (*supercritical* flow pattern). An increase in the turbulence intensity will now cause earlier transition, the effect on the point of separation being very small owing to the greater stability of a turbulent boundary layer. The Nusselt number must increase because the laminar boundary layer recedes in favour of the turbulent boundary layer. Finally, an increase in turbulence intensity in the range of critical Reynolds numbers may cause a sudden change from the subcritical to the supercritical flow pattern causing a sudden change in the value of the Nusselt number. In addition to this type of effect, and in accordance with the preceding introductory remarks, changes in turbulence intensity must affect the local Nusselt numbers for the laminar boundary layer, the turbulent boundary layer and the wake. The diagram in Fig. 14.17 shows the combined influence of all those effects for subcritical Reynolds numbers. The range of critical Reynolds numbers was covered more systematically by J. Kestin and P. F. Maeder [30a]. The resulting complex relationship between the Nusselt number and Reynolds number for varying intensities of turbulence is shown plotted in Fig. 14.18; the measurements were made in air at a substantially constant Prandtl number. The diagram in Fig. 14.18 contains Hilpert's experimental points and correlation curve in the same range of Reynolds numbers from which it can be inferred that his tunnel had the relatively low intensity of turbulence of $\mathsf{T} = 0{\cdot}9$ per cent.

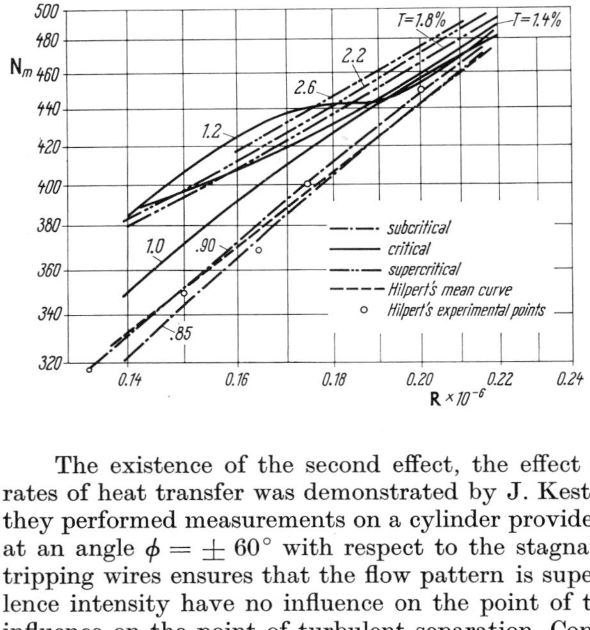

Fig. 14.18. Relation between Nusselt and Reynolds numbers at varying intensities of turbulence T for a circular cylinder in a cross-flow of air, as measured by J. Kestin and P. F. Maeder [30a]. $\mathsf{P} = 0{\cdot}7$ (air)

The existence of the second effect, the effect of turbulence intensity on local rates of heat transfer was demonstrated by J. Kestin and P. F. Maeder [30a] when they performed measurements on a cylinder provided with two tripping wires placed at an angle $\phi = \pm 60°$ with respect to the stagnation point. The use of Prandtl's tripping wires ensures that the flow pattern is supercritical. Now changes in turbulence intensity have no influence on the point of transition and only a very small influence on the point of turbulent separation. Consequently, if the local effect did not exist, the experimental points would arrange themselves on a single curve in a diagram of mean Nusselt *versus* Reynolds number, since the Prandtl number was kept constant. The experimental results are seen plotted in Fig. 14.19 which shows that the contrary is the case. It turns out that there is a strong systematic dependence on turbulence intensity, particularly when the flow pattern is subcritical. This suggests that the largest effect occurs across the laminar portion of the boundary layer which contributes a larger portion to the heat transfer rate in the subcritical than in the supercritical range. It is interesting to note that a relatively small change in turbulence from one percent to two per cent causes the Nusselt number to increase by about 20 percent (at about $\mathsf{R} = 150{,}000$).

In order to demonstrate that the influence of turbulence intensity is particularly pronounced outside a laminar boundary layer, J. Kestin, P. F. Maeder and H. H. Sogin performed (unpublished) experiments on the local rates of heat transfer from cylinders, similar to those performed by E. Schmidt and K. Wenner [50] and discussed earlier, except that they varied the intensity of turbulence of the free stream in a systematic way. The results of these measurements are seen plotted in Fig. 14.20. They have been compared with Froessling's [21] theoretical calculations which, of course, correspond to the case when $\mathsf{T} = 0$. The similarity between this diagram and that of Fig. 14.13 is complete. The explanation for it lies in the fact that the turbulence intensity in a wind tunnel varies usually with the wind velocity which

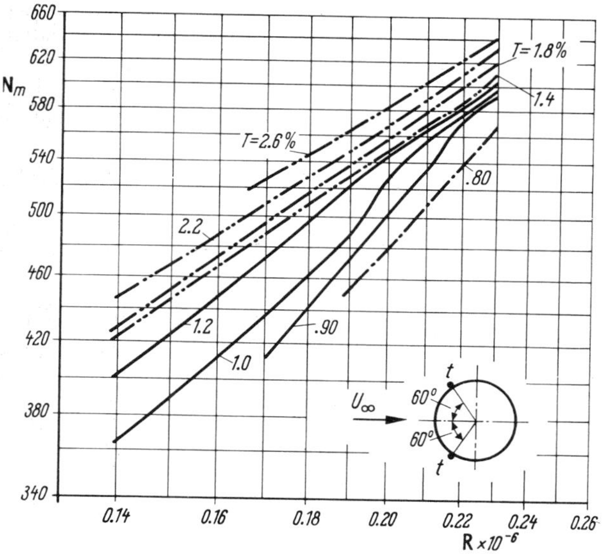

Fig. 14.19. Variation of Nusselt number N_m with Reynolds number R at varying intensities of turbulence for experiments on cylinders provided with tripping wires after J. Kestin and P. F. Maeder [30a]

— · — · —subcritical flow pattern
————critical flow pattern
— ·· — ·· — supercritical flow pattern
t— tripping wires

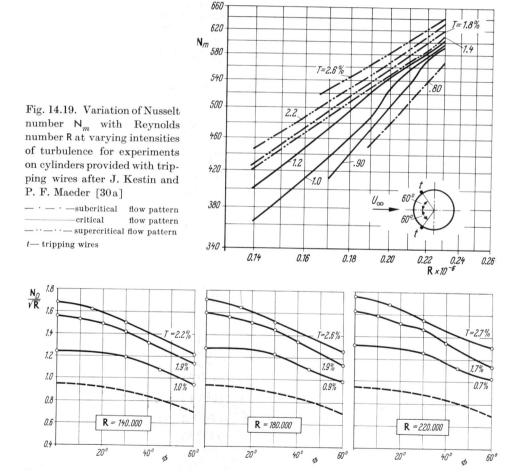

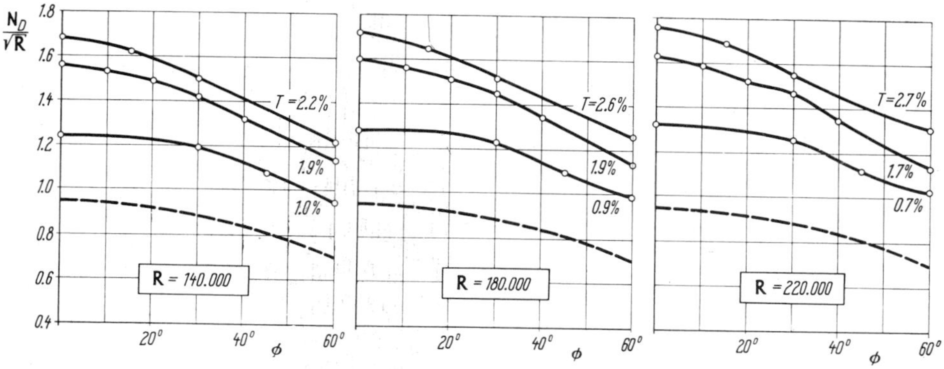

Fig. 14.20. Variation of local Nusselt number N_D on a circular cylinder with turbulence intensity T and angular co-ordinate ϕ after J. Kestin, P. F. Maeder and H. H. Sogin (Values of intensity of turbulence T approximate only) ——— Theory after N. Froessling [21]

gives the impression in Fig. 14.13 that the result depends on the Reynolds number. In reality, the curves shift upwards because of increasing turbulence intensity. A similar influence is discernible also in Fig. 14.14 which represents the results of Hilpert's experiments. On very close examination it can be seen that the mean curve through the experimental results shows slight kinks at points which correspond to a change in diameter. For two different diameters, the same Reynolds number is obtained with different velocities, that is with different intensities of turbulence. Hence two such points lie on two slightly different curves and produce a slight kink when a single correlation curve is drawn.

The influence of turbulence on the transfer of heat from flat plates at zero incidence, i. e. with a zero pressure gradient was investigated by A. Edwards and B. N. Furber [17a] who performed average measurements over the whole length of the plate, and by J. Kestin, P. F. Maeder and H. E. Wang [30c] who performed local measurements. The latter results are seen plotted in Fig. 14.21; they lead to the conclusion that a change in the intensity of turbulence affects only the position of the point of transition and has no effect on the Nusselt number. The results for a laminar boundary layer lie exactly on the theoretical line traced by Pohlhausen's solution ($\mathsf{T}=0$) discussed in Sec. XIV g irrespectively of the intensity of turbulence. The points for a turbulent boundary layer lie on Prandtl's curve, eqn. (14.66c), also irrespectively of turbulence intensity. The same conclusions can be drawn from the experiments performed by A. Edwards and B. N. Furber [17a].

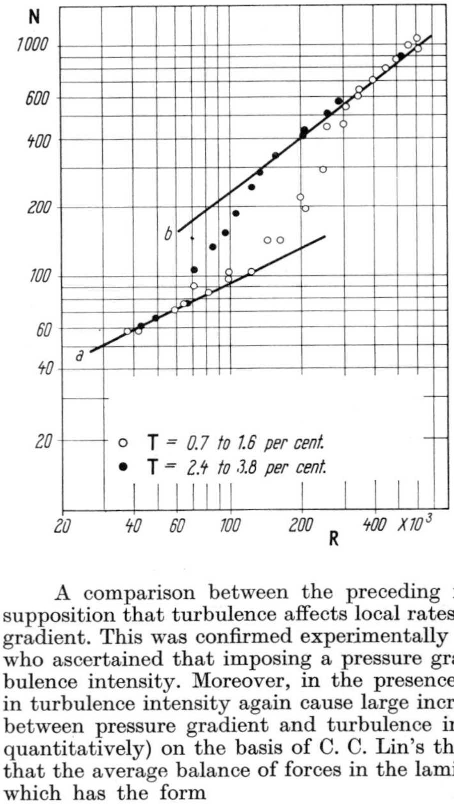

Fig. 14.21. Local Nusselt number on a flat plate in terms of Reynolds number R and turbulence intensity T after J. Kestin, P. F. Maeder and H. E. Wang [30c]

a = Pohlhausen's equation (14.66a) i. e.

$\mathsf{N}_x = 0{\cdot}295 \sqrt{\mathsf{R}}$ for laminar flow, $\mathsf{P} = 0{\cdot}7$

b = Prandt's equation (19.43d) i. e.

$\mathsf{N}_x = 0{\cdot}0236\, \mathsf{R}^{0{\cdot}8}$ for turbulent flow, $\mathsf{P} = 0{\cdot}7$

A comparison between the preceding results for cylinders and flat plates leads to the supposition that turbulence affects local rates of heat transfer only in the presence of a pressure gradient. This was confirmed experimentally by J. Kestin, P. F. Maeder and H. E. Wang [30c] who ascertained that imposing a pressure gradient on a flat plate restores the influence of turbulence intensity. Moreover, in the presence of a moderate pressure gradient, small increases in turbulence intensity again cause large increases in the Nusselt number. This interdependence between pressure gradient and turbulence intensity can be understood qualitatively (but not quantitatively) on the basis of C. C. Lin's theory discussed in Sec. XI e. 3. It was shown there that the average balance of forces in the laminar boundary layer involves an additional term $\mathfrak{F}$, which has the form

$$\mathfrak{F} = \tfrac{1}{2}\, U_0 \frac{\mathrm{d}U_0}{\mathrm{d}x}\, F\left(\frac{y}{\delta_0}\right)$$

in the case a harmonic oscillation $U_0(x)\sin nt$ superimposed on an average velocity $\overline{U}(x)$. In this example the amplitude U_0 plays the same part as the intensity of turbulence which is a measure of the r. m. s. of the amplitude of random oscillations. The term $\mathfrak{F}$ vanishes when the rate of change of amplitude $dU_0/dx = 0$. In the absence of a pressure gradient, as is known from measurements on turbulence, the intensity of turbulence changes very little along the stream. On the other hand, strong deceleration and subsequent acceleration of a stream, as in the neighbourhood of the stagnation line on a cylinder, will cause the rate of change of the intensity of turbulence along a stream-line to become large. Thus in the latter case the velocity field is strongly modified by the term $\mathcal{T}$ and this, in turn, modifies the temperature field, as seen from the energy equation (14.40). On a flat plate at zero incidence $d\mathsf{T}/dx \sim dU_0/dx \approx 0$ and the effect is absent, in good agreement with measurements.

The fact that external turbulence affects the rate of heat transfer has a bearing on the validity of the Reynolds analogy discussed in Sec. XIV e. 3. The analogy is preserved in the case of a flat plate because there is no influence from turbulence there. In other cases, the presence of a pressure gradient and the fact that the boundary condition on the (oscillating) velocity at $y = \infty$ differs from the (constant) temperature at $y = \infty$, will tend to destroy or modify the form of the analogy. So far, the exact effect of free-stream turbulence on the form of the Reynolds analogy has not been investigated in detail.

A related problem was studied analytically by J. Kestin P. F. Maeder and H. E. Wang [30b] on the example of the progressing wave discussed in Sec. XIV e. 4. Having found the solution for the velocity components u and v, eqn. (11.55), it is now possible to solve the energy equation for the temperature field, assuming a series expansion for

$$\theta = \frac{T - T_\infty}{T_w - T_\infty}$$

namely

$$\theta(x,y,t) = \theta_0(x,y) + \lambda\, \theta_1(x,y,t) + \lambda^2\, \theta_2(x,y,t) + \cdots . \tag{14.81}$$

Substituting this expression into eqn. (14.12b) with $a = k/\varrho\, g\, c$ and $\phi = 0$, we are led to a series of differential equations for θ_0, θ_1, etc. The equation for θ_0 is identical with Pohlhausen's equation, Sec. XIV g. 1. For the remaining terms we assume

$$\left.\begin{aligned}
\theta_1(x,y,t) &= \sum_1^\infty \{ K_k(\eta)\, \beta^{k-1} \cos\psi + L_k(\eta)\, \beta^{k-1} \sin\psi \} \\
\theta_2(x,y,t) &= \sum_1^\infty \{ M_k(\eta)\, \beta^{k-1} + N_k(\eta)\, \beta^{k-1} \cos 2\psi + P_k(\eta)\, \beta^{k-1} \sin 2\psi \} \\
\text{with}\quad \eta &= y \sqrt{\frac{U_0}{\nu\, x}} \\
\beta &= x\, n/U_0 \\
\psi &= n\left(\frac{x}{U_0} - t\right)
\end{aligned}\right\} \tag{14.82}$$

in strict analogy with Sec. XIV e. 4. Substitution into the equations for θ_1, θ_2, etc. leads to a set of non-linear differential equations for the functions K_k, L_k, etc. which have been solved numerically. The functions K_1 and M_1 together with their first derivatives have been plotted in Fig. 11.13. In this manner it is possible to derive that the time-averaged heat flux $\bar{q}$ is given by

$$\begin{aligned}
\bar{q} &= -k(T_w - T_\infty)\, \theta_0'(0) \sqrt{\frac{U_0}{\nu\, x}} \left\{ 1 + \lambda^2 \frac{M'(0)}{\theta_0'(0)} + O(\lambda^2 \beta^2) + O(\lambda^4) \right\} \\
&\approx q_0\, (1 - 0{\cdot}0724\, \lambda^2)
\end{aligned} \tag{14.83}$$

where q_0 denotes the heat flux in the absence of the progressing wave. Hence

$$\overline{\mathsf{N}} = \mathsf{N}_0\, (1 - 0{\cdot}0724\, \lambda^2)\,, \tag{14.83a}$$

where N_0 denotes the Nusselt number in the absence of a wave. On comparing this with the expression for the skin friction coefficient given in eqn. (11.59a) we see that the amplitude λ cannot be eliminated and remains in the equation. Thus, instead of eqn. (14.38a) we now obtain

$$\overline{\mathsf{N}} = \tfrac{1}{2} \times 0{\cdot}7\; \bar{c}_f\, \frac{1 + 0{\cdot}1777\, \lambda^2}{1 - 0{\cdot}0724\, \lambda^2}\, \overline{\mathsf{R}} \tag{14.84}$$

for $\mathsf{P} = 0{\cdot}7$. The bars over the symbols signify that the dimensionless quantities have been formed with the average velocity $\overline{U}$.

The effect of turbulence on heat transfer was also investigated by E. W. Comings, J. T. Clapp and J. F. Taylor [3a], D. S. Maisel and T. K. Sherwood [36a], W. H. Giedt [21a, b], K. Sato and B. H. Sage [44a], R. A. Seban [53a] and B. G. van der Hegge Zijnen [25a].

h. Thermal boundary layers in natural flow

Motions which are caused solely by the density gradients created by temperature differences are termed 'natural' as distinct from those 'forced' on the stream by external causes. Such a natural flow exists around a vertical hot plate or around a horizontal hot cylinder. Natural flows also display, in most cases, a boundary layer structure, particularly if the viscosity and conductivity of the fluid are small.

In the case of a *vertical hot plate*, the pressure in each horizontal plane is equal to the gravitational pressure and is thus constant. The only cause of motion is furnished by the difference between weight and buoyancy in the gravitational field of the earth. The equation of motion is obtained from eqns. (14.36a, b, c) with $\mathrm{d}p/\mathrm{d}x = 0$ and $\beta = 1/T_\infty$. Neglecting frictional heat we have

$$\frac{\partial u}{\partial x} + \frac{\partial v}{\partial y} = 0\,, \tag{14.85}$$

$$u\,\frac{\partial u}{\partial x} + v\,\frac{\partial u}{\partial y} = \nu\,\frac{\partial^2 u}{\partial y^2} + g\,\frac{T_w - T_\infty}{T_\infty}\,\theta\,, \tag{14.86}$$

$$u\,\frac{\partial \theta}{\partial x} + v\,\frac{\partial \theta}{\partial y} = a\,\frac{\partial^2 \theta}{\partial y^2}\,. \tag{14.87}$$

Here $a = k/g\,\varrho\,c_p$ is the thermal diffusivity and $\theta = (T - T_\infty)/(T_w - T_\infty)$ is the dimensionless local temperature. In a theoretical investigation concerning the experimentally determined temperature and velocity field of a case involving natural convection on a vertical hot plate due to E. Schmidt and W. Beckmann [47], E. Pohlhausen demonstrated that if a stream function is introduced by putting $u = \partial\psi/\partial y$ and $v = -\partial\psi/\partial x$, then the resulting partial differential equation for ψ can be reduced to an ordinary differential equation by the similarity transformation

$$\eta = c\,\frac{y}{\sqrt[4]{x}}\,; \qquad \psi = 4\,\nu\,c\,x^{3/4}\,\zeta(\eta)$$

where

$$c = \sqrt[4]{\frac{g\,(T_w - T_\infty)}{4\,\nu^2\,T_\infty}}\,. \tag{14.88}$$

The velocity components now become

$$u = 4\,\nu\,x^{1/2}\,c^2\,\zeta'\,; \qquad v = \nu\,c\,x^{-1/4}\,(\eta\,\zeta' - 3\,\zeta)$$

and the temperature distribution is determined by the function $\theta(\eta)$. Equations (14.86), (14.87) and (14.88) lead to the following differential equations

$$\zeta''' + 3\,\zeta\,\zeta'' - 2\,\zeta'^2 + \theta = 0\,, \qquad \theta'' + 3\,\mathsf{P}\,\zeta\,\theta' = 0$$

with the boundary conditions $\zeta = \zeta' = 0$ and $\theta = 1$ at $\eta = 0$ and $\zeta' = 0$, $\theta = 0$ at $\eta = \infty$. Figs. 14.22 and 14.23 illustrate the solutions of these equations for various values of P. Figs. 14.24 and 14.25 contain a comparison between the calculated velocity and temperature distribution and those measured by E. Schmidt and W. Beckmann [47]. The agreement is seen to be very good. It is seen, further, that the velocity and thermal boundary layer thickness are proportional to $x^{1/4}$. See also ref. [41].

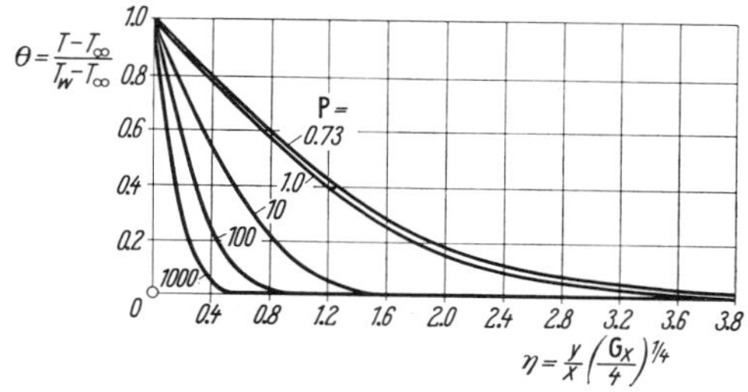

Fig. 14.22. Temperature distribution in the laminar boundary layer on a hot vertical flat plate in natural convection. Theoretical curves, for $\mathsf{P} = 0{\cdot}73$ after E. Pohlhausen [42] and S. Ostrach [41]

$$\mathsf{G}_x = \frac{g\,x^3}{\nu^2}\,\frac{T_w - T_\infty}{T_\infty} = \text{Grashof number}$$

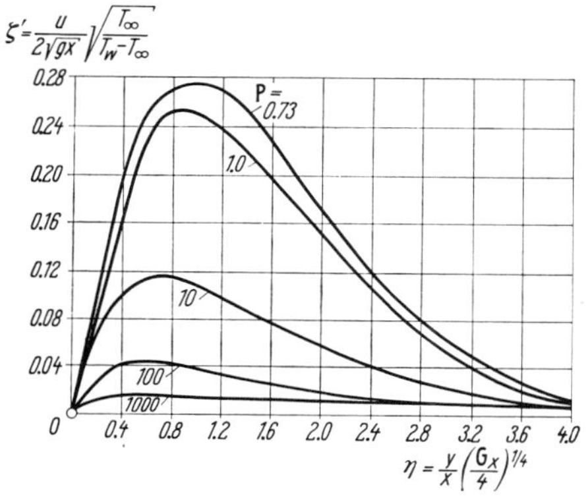

Fig. 14.23. Velocity distribution in the laminar boundary layer on a hot vertical flat plate in natural convection (see also Fig. 14.22)

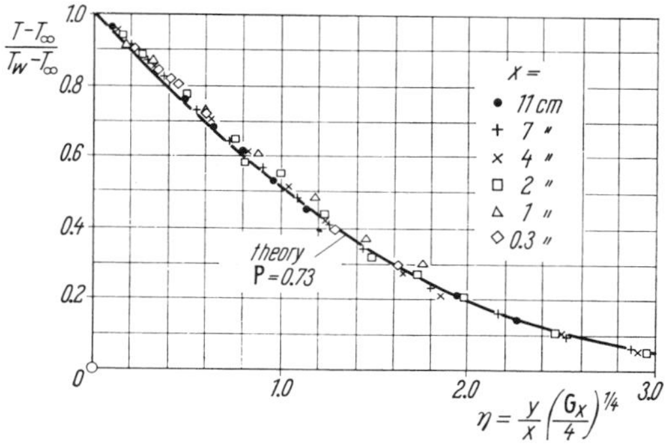

Fig. 14.24. Temperature distribution in the laminar boundary layer on a hot vertical flat plate in natural convection in air, as measured by E. Schmidt and W. Beckmann [47]; x = distance from the lower edge of the plate

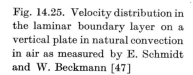

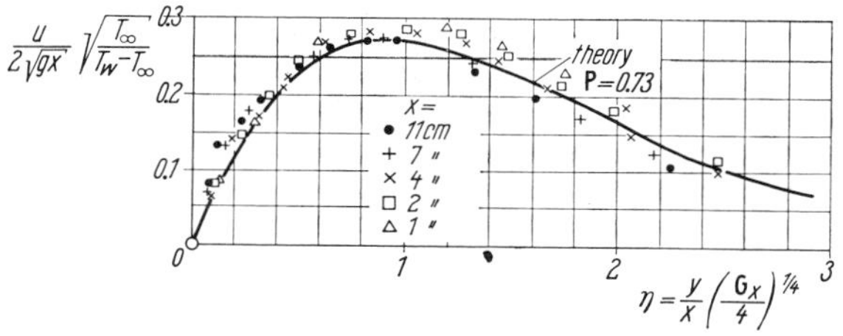

Fig. 14.25. Velocity distribution in the laminar boundary layer on a vertical plate in natural convection in air as measured by E. Schmidt and W. Beckmann [47]

Heat transfer: The quantity of heat $q(x) = -k(\partial T/\partial y)_0$ transferred per unit time and area from the plate to the fluid at section x becomes

$$q(x) = -k\,c\,x^{-1/4}\left(\frac{d\theta}{d\eta}\right)_0 (T_w - T_\infty)\,,$$

with $(\partial\theta/\partial\eta)_0 = -0{\cdot}508$ for $\mathsf{P} = 0{\cdot}733$. The total heat transferred by a plate of length l and width b is $Q = b\int_0^l q(x)\,dx$, and hence

$$Q = \tfrac{4}{3} \times 0{\cdot}508\, b\, l^{3/4}\, c\, k(T_w - T_\infty)\,.$$

The mean Nusselt number defined by $Q = b\,k\,\mathsf{N}_m\,(T_w - T_\infty)$ thus becomes $\mathsf{N}_m = 0{\cdot}677\,c\,l^{3/4}$, or, inserting the value of c from eqn. (14.88):

$$\mathsf{N}_m = 0{\cdot}478\,\mathsf{G}^{1/4}\,, \tag{14.89}$$

where

$$\mathsf{G} = \frac{g\,l^3\,(T_w - T_\infty)}{\nu^2\,T_\infty} \tag{14.90}$$

is the Grashof number. It can also be written as $\mathsf{G} = g\,l^3\,\beta(T_w - T_\infty)/\nu^2$ in the case of liquids.

The diagram in Fig. 14.26 gives a comparison between theoretical results on free convection with measurements on heated vertical cylinders and flat plates performed by E. R. G. Eckert and T. W. Jackson [14]. When the product $\mathsf{GP} < 10^8$, the flow is laminar, and for $\mathsf{GP} > 10^{10}$ the flow is turbulent. The agreement between theory and experiment is excellent.

E. Pohlhausen's calculations have been extended by H. Schuh [51] to the case of large Prandtl numbers such as exist in oils. The values of the coefficient of heat transfer calculated by him are given in Table 14.5.

Measurements on a vertical hot plate in oil performed by H. H. Lorenz [36] gave the value $\mathsf{N}_m = 0{\cdot}555\,(\mathsf{G} \times \mathsf{P})^{1/4}$ which constitutes very satisfactory agreement with theoretical calculations if it is considered that the theory does not take into account the dependence of viscosity on temperature and which is important precisely in the case of oils.

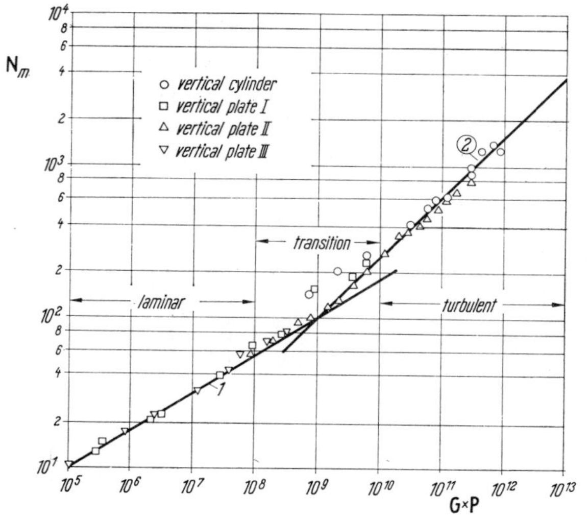

Fig. 14.26. Average Nusselt number for free convection on vertical plates and cylinders after E. R. G. Eckert and T. W. Jackson [14]

Curve (1) laminar:

$\mathsf{N}_m = 0{\cdot}555\,(\mathsf{GP})^{1/4}$; $\mathsf{GP} < 10^9$

Curve (2) turbulent:

$\mathsf{N}_m = 0{\cdot}0210\,(\mathsf{GP})^{2/5}$; $\mathsf{GP} > 10^9$

Table 14.5. Coefficients of heat transfer for a vertical plate in natural convection (laminar) after E. Pohlhausen [42] and H. Schuh [51]

P	$\frac{N_m}{G^{1/4}}$	$\frac{N_m}{(G \times P)^{1/4}}$
0·73	0·478	0·517
10	1·09	0·612
100	2·06	0·652
1000	3·67	0·653

The laminar thermal boundary layer around heated bodies in natural convection can be conveniently made visible with the aid of a Schlieren method devised by E. Schmidt [48]. A parallel beam of light is passed through the boundary layer in a direction parallel to the plate and produces shadows on a screen placed at a large distance from the body. The density gradient in the air at right angles to the surface causes the rays of light to be deflected outwards. The deflexion is largest at points where the density gradient is steep, i. e. near the body. With a sufficiently large distance between screen and body the space taken up by the heated layer remains dark so that in the Schlieren picture the shadow of the body is surrounded by a shadow due to the thermal boundary layer. The rays of light which are deflected out of the temperature field create an illuminated zone around the dark shadow. The outer edge of this zone of light is formed by the rays which just skirt the surface; consequently their deflexion is proportional to the density gradient at the surface, i. e. to the local coefficient of heat transfer. Fig. 14.27 represents a Schlieren photograph taken on a heated vertical flat plate. The contour of the plate is shown by a broken white line. It is easy to recognize on the shadow that

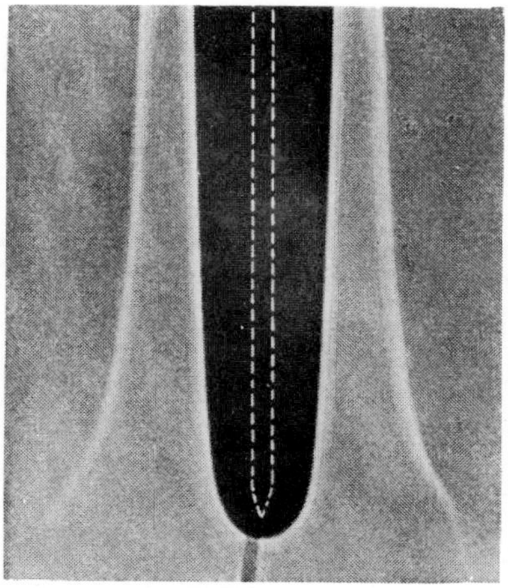

Fig. 14.27. Schlieren photograph of the thermal boundary layer on a heated vertical flat plate after E. Schmidt [48]

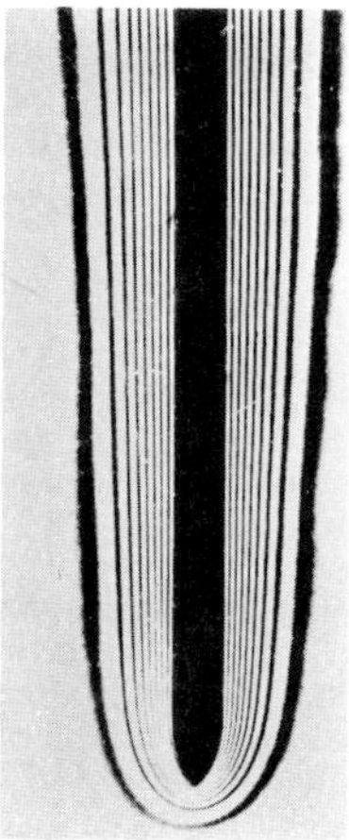

Fig. 14.28. Interferogram of a thermal boundary layer on a vertical, heated, flat plate, after E. R. G. Eckert and E. Soehngen [6]

the boundary layer thickness increases with $x^{1/4}$. The edge of the zone of light shows that the local coefficient of heat transfer is proportional to $x^{-1/4}$. The picture in Fig. 14.28 gives an interferogram for the same type of boundary layer; it was obtained by E. R. G. Eckert and E. Soehngen [6].

Other shapes: The motion due to natural convection around a horizontal heated circular cylinder was treated in an analogous way by R. Hermann [26]. He found for $\mathsf{P} = 0{\cdot}7$ a mean heat transfer coefficient $\mathsf{N}_m = 0{\cdot}372\, \mathsf{G}^{1/4}$, where G is based on the diameter. Measurements in air performed by K. Jodlbauer [30] gave $\mathsf{N}_m = 0{\cdot}395\, \mathsf{G}^{1/4}$ at $\mathsf{G} = 10^5$ which shows a satisfactory agreement with theory. Measurements on vertical cylinders [60] in water and ethylene glycol gave ($\mathsf{P} \times \mathsf{G} = 2 \times 10^8$ to 4×10^{10}): $\mathsf{N} = 0{\cdot}726\, (\mathsf{P} \times \mathsf{G})^{1/4}$ for laminar flow, and ($\mathsf{P} \times \mathsf{G} = 4 \times 10^{10}$ to 9×10^{11}): $\mathsf{N} = 0{\cdot}0674\, (\mathsf{G} \times \mathsf{P}^{1{\cdot}29})^{-1/3}$ for turbulent flow.

For the sphere J. I. Shell [55] calculated $\mathsf{N}_m = 0{\cdot}429\, \mathsf{G}^{1/4}$, which was confirmed by measurements in air.

References

[1] H. J. Allen and B. C. Look, A method of calculating heat transfer in the laminar flow regions of bodies. NACA Report 764 (1943).

[2] M. Ten Bosch, Die Wärmeübertragung, Berlin, 1936.

[3] D. R. Chapman and M. W. Rubesin, Temperature and velocity profiles in the compressible laminar boundary layer with arbitrary distribution of surface temperature. J. Aero. Sci., **16**, 547 (1949).

[3a] E. W. Comings, J. T. Clapp and J. F. Taylor, Air turbulence and transfer processes; flow normal to cylinders. Ind. and Eng'g. Chemistry **40**, 1076—1082 (1948).

[4] W. Dienemann, Berechnung des Wärmeüberganges an laminar umströmten Körpern mit konstanter und ortsveränderlicher Wandtemperatur. Thesis, Braunschweig 1951, ZAMM **33**, 89—109 (1953); see also extract in J. Aero. Sci. **18**, 64 (1951).

[5] P. L. Donoughe and J. N. B. Livingood, Exact solutions of laminar-boundary layer equations with constant property values for porous wall with variable temperature. NACA Rep. 1229, (1955).

[6] E. R. G. Eckert and E. Soehngen, Interferometric studies on free convection heat transfer. US Air Force Techn. Rep. 4748.

[7] E. R. G. Eckert and O. Drewitz, Der Wärmeübergang an eine mit großer Geschwindigkeit längsangeströmte Platte. Forsch. Ing.-Wes. **11**, 116 (1940).

[8] E. R. G. Eckert, Temperaturmessungen in schnell strömenden Gasen. Z. VDI **84**, 813 (1940).

[9] E. R. G. Eckert and W. Weise, Die Temperatur unbeheizter Körper in einem Gasstrom hoher Geschwindigkeit. Forsch. Ing.-Wes. **12**, 40 (1941).

[10] E. R. G. Eckert and O. Drewitz, Die Berechnung des Temperaturfeldes in der laminaren Grenzschicht schnell angeströmter unbeheizter Körper. Luftfahrtforschung **19**, 189 (1942).

[11] E. R. G. Eckert, Die Berechnung des Wärmeüberganges in der laminaren Grenzschicht umströmter Körper. VDI-Forschungsheft 416 (1942).

[12] E. R. G. Eckert and W. Weise, Messung der Temperaturverteilung auf der Oberfläche schnell angeströmter unbeheizter Körper. Forsch. Ing.-Wes. **13**, 246, (1942).

[13] E. R. G. Eckert, Einführung in den Wärme- und Stoffaustausch. 2nd ed., Berlin 1959. Also E. R. G. Eckert and R. M. Drake. Jr., Heat and mass transfer. McGraw-Hill 1959.

[14] E. R. G. Eckert and T. W. Jackson, Analysis of turbulent free convection boundary layer on a flat plate. NACA Rep. 1015 (1951).

[15] E. R. G. Eckert and J. N. B. Livingood, Method for calculation of laminar heat transfer in air flow around cylinders of arbitrary cross-section (including large temperature differences and transpiration cooling). NACA Rep. 1118 (1953).

[16] E. R. G. Eckert and A. J. Diagula, Experimental investigation of free-convection heat transfer in vertical tube at large Grashof numbers. NACA Rep. 1211 (1955).

[17] E. R. G. ECKERT and J. N. B. LIVINGOOD, Calculations of laminar heat transfer around cylinders of arbitrary cross-section and transpiration cooled walls with application to turbine blade cooling. NACA Rep. 1220 (1955).
[17a] A. EDWARDS and B. N. FURBER, The influence of free-stream turbulence on heat transfer by convection from an isolated region of a plane surface in parallel air flow. Proc. Inst. Mech. Eng. **170**, 941 (1956).
[18] F. ELIAS, Reports of the Aero. Inst. Aachen, No. 9 (1930); ZAMM **9**, 434 (1929) and 10, 1 (1930).
[19] C. W. FRICK and G. M. MCCULLOUGH, A method for determining the rate of heat transfer from a wing or a streamline body. NACA Rep. 830 (1945).
[20] A. F. FRITSCHE, M. BODNARESCU, O. KIRSCHER and H. ESDORN, Probleme der Wärmeübertragung. VDI Forschungsheft 450 (1955).
[21] N. FROESSLING, Verdunstung, Wärmeübertragung und Geschwindigkeitsverteilung bei zweidimensionaler und rotationssymmetrischer Grenzschichtströmung. Lunds Universitets Arsskrift. N. F. Avd. 2, **36**, No. 4 (1940).
[21a] W. H. GIEDT, Investigation of variation of point unit heat-transfer coefficient around a cylinder normal to an air stream. Trans. ASME **71**, 375—381 (1949).
[21b] W. H. GIEDT, Effect of turbulence level of incident air stream on local heat transfer and skin friction on a cylinder. J. Aero. Sci. **18**, 725—730, 766 (1951).
[22] L. GOLAND, A theoretical investigation of heat transfer in the laminar flow regions of airfoils. J. Aero. Sci. **17**, 436 (1950).
[22a] E. GRIFFITH and J. H. AWBERRY, Heat transfer between metal pipes and a stream of air. Proc. Inst. Mech. Engrs. (London), **125**, 319—382 (1933).
[23] U. GRIGULL, Wärmeübertragung in laminarer Strömung mit Reibungswärme. Chemie-Ingenieur-Technik, pp. 480—483 (1955).
[23a] GRÖBER/ERK/GRIGULL, Die Grundgesetze der Wärmeübertragung, 3rd. ed., Berlin 1955.
[24] H. M. DE GROFF, On viscous heating. J. Aero. Sci. **23**, 395—396 (1956).
[25] H. HAUSENBLAS, Die nicht isotherme Strömung einer zähen Flüssigkeit durch enge Spalte und Kapillarröhren. Ing.-Arch. **18**, 151 (1950).
[25a] B. G. VAN DER HEGGE ZIJNEN, Heat transfer from horizontal cylinders to a turbulent air flow. Appl. Sci. Res. A **7**, 205—223 (1957).
[26] R. HERMANN, Wärmeübertragung bei freier Strömung am waagerechten Zylinder in zwei-atomigen Gasen. VDI-Forschungsheft No. 379 (1936).
[27] R. HILPERT, Wärmeabgabe von geheizten Drähten und Rohren im Luftstrom. Forsch. Ing.-Wes. **4**, 215 (1933).
[28] L. HOWARTH, Velocity and temperature distribution for a flow along a flat plate. Proc. Roy. Soc. London, A **154**, 364 (1936).
[29] M. JAKOB, Heat transfer, vols. I and II, New York 1949 and 1957.
[30] K. JODLBAUER, Das Temperatur- und Geschwindigkeitsfeld um ein geheiztes Rohr bei freier Konvektion. Forsch. Ing.-Wes. **4**, 157 (1933).
[30a] J. KESTIN and P. F. MAEDER, Influence of turbulence on transfer of heat from cylinders, NACA TN 4018 (1954).
[30b] J. KESTIN, P. F. MAEDER and H. E. WANG, On boundary layers associated with oscillating streams. To be published.
[30c] J. KESTIN, P. F. MAEDER and H. E. WANG, Influence of turbulence on the transfer of heat from plates with and without a pressure gradient. To be published.
[31] J. G. KNUDSEN and D. L. KATZ, Fluid dynamics and heat transfer. McGraw-Hill, 1958.
[32] G. KROUJILIN, The heat transfer of a circular cylinder in a transverse airflow in the range of $Re = 6000$—425000. Techn. Physics USSR **5**, 289—297 (1938).
[33] S. LEVY, Heat transfer to constant property laminar boundary flows with power-function free-stream velocity and wall temperature variation. Jour. Aero. Sci. **19**, 341 (1952).
[34] A. F. LIETZKE, Theoretical and experimental investigation of heat transfer by laminar natural convection between parallel plates. NACA Rep. 1223 (1955).
[35] M. J. LIGHTHILL, Contributions to the theory of heat transfer through a laminar boundary layer. Proc. Roy. Soc. London, A **202**, 359—377 (1950).
[36] H. H. LORENZ, Die Wärmeübertragung an einer ebenen senkrechten Platte an Öl bei natürlicher Konvektion. Z. techn. Physik 362 (1934).
[36a] D. S. MAISEL and T. K. SHERWOOD, Evaporation of liquids into turbulent gas streams, Chem. Eng. Progr. **46**, 131—138 (1950).

[37] K. MILLSAPS and K. POHLHAUSEN, Thermal distribution in Jeffery-Hamel flows between nonparellel plane walls. Jour. Aero. Sci. **20**, 187—196 (1953).
[38] R. NAHME, Beiträge zur hydrodynamischen Theorie der Lagerreibung. Ing.-Arch. **11**, 191 (1940).
[39] W. NUSSELT, Das Grundgesetz des Wärmeüberganges. Ges. Ing. **38**, 477 (1915).
[40] J. G. OLDROYD, Calculations concerning theoretical values of boundary layer thickness and coefficients of friction and heat transfer for steady two-dimensional flow in an incompressible boundary layer with main stream velocity $U \sim x^m$ or $U \sim e^x$. Phil. Mag. **36**, 587 (1945).
[41] S. OSTRACH, An analysis of laminar free-convection flow and heat transfer about a flat plate parallel to the direction of the generating body force. NACA Report 1111 (1953).
[42] E. POHLHAUSEN, Der Wärmeaustausch zwischen festen Körpern und Flüssigkeiten mit kleiner Reibung und kleiner Wärmeleitung. ZAMM **1**, 115 (1921).
[43] O. REYNOLDS, On the extent and action of the heating surface for steam boilers. Proc. Manchester Lit. Phil. Soc. **14**, 7—12 (1874).
[44] E. G. RICHARDSON, The aerodynamic characteristics of a cylinder having a heated boundary layer. Phil. Mag. **23**, 681 (1937).
[44a] K. SATO and B. H. SAGE, Thermal transfer in turbulent gas streams; — Effect of turbulence on macroscopic transport from spheres. Trans. ASME **80**, 1380 (1958).
[45] H. SCHLICHTING, Einige exakte Lösungen für die Temperaturverteilung in einer laminaren Strömung. ZAMM **31**, 78—83 (1951).
[46] H. SCHLICHTING, Der Wärmeübergang an einer längsangeströmten Platte mit veränderlicher Wandtemperatur. Forsch. Ing.-Wes. **17**, 1 (1951).
[47] E. SCHMIDT and W. BECKMANN, Das Temperatur- und Geschwindigkeitsfeld von einer Wärme abgebenden senkrechten Platte bei natürlicher Konvektion. Forsch. Ing.-Wes. **1**, 391 (1930).
[48] E. SCHMIDT, Schlierenaufnahmen der Temperaturfelder in der Nähe wärmeabgebender Körper. Forsch. Ing.-Wes. **3**, 181 (1932).
[49] E. SCHMIDT, Einführung in die technische Thermodynamik und in die Grundlagen der chemischen Thermodynamik. 7th ed. Berlin 1958.
[49′] E. SCHMIDT, transl. J. Kestin. Thermodynamics. Clarendon Press, Oxford, 1949.
[50] E. SCHMIDT and K. WENNER, Wärmeabgabe über den Umfang eines angeblasenen geheizten Zylinders. Forsch. Ing.-Wes. **12**, 65 (1941). Engl. transl. NACA TM 1050 (1943).
[51] H. SCHUH, Einige Probleme bei freier Strömung zäher Flüssigkeiten (unpublished); see Göttinger Monographien vol. B, Grenzschichten, 1946.
[52] H. SCHUH, Über die Lösung der laminaren Grenzschichtgleichung an einer ebenen Platte für Geschwindigkeits- und Temperaturfeld bei veränderlichen Stoffwerten und für das Diffusionsfeld bei höheren Konzentrationen. ZAMM **25/27**, 54 (1947).
[53] H. SCHUH, Ein neues Verfahren zum Berechnen des Wärmeübergangs in ebenen und rotationssymmetrischen laminaren Grenzschichten bei konstanter und veränderlicher Wandtemperatur. Forschung Ing.-Wes. **37** (1954).
[53a] R. A. SEBAN, The influence of free-stream turbulence on the local heat transfer from cylinders. Trans. ASME, preprint paper No. 59-HT. 3, 1959.
[54] W. Y. SHAO, Heat transfer in laminar compressible boundary layer on a porous flat plate with fluid injection. J. Aero. Sci. **16**, 741 (1949).
[55] J. I. SHELL, Die Wärmeübergangszahl von Kugelflächen. Bull. Acad. Sci. Nat. Belgrade, 4, 189, (1938).
[56] H. B. SQUIRE, Section in "Modern Developments in Fluid Dynamics", edited by S. Goldstein, Oxford **II**, 623 (1938).
[57] H. B. SQUIRE, Heat transfer calculation for aerofoils. ARC R & M 1986 (1942).
[58] H. B. SQUIRE, Note on the effect of variable wall temperature on heat transfer. ARC R & M 2753 (1953).
[59] A. N. TIFFORD, The thermodynamics of the laminar boundary layer of a heated body in a high speed gas flow field. J. Aero. Sci. **12**, 241 (1945).
[60] Y. S. TOULOUKIAN, G. A. HAWKINS and M. JAKOB, Heat transfer by free convection from heated vertical surfaces to liquids. Trans. ASME **70**, 13 (1948).
[61] G. VOGELPOHL, Der Übergang der Reibungswärme von Lagern aus der Schmierschicht in die Gleitflächen. — Temperaturverteilung und thermische Anlaufstrecke in parallelen Schmierschichten bei Erwärmung durch innere Reibung. VDI-Forschungsheft 425 (1949).

CHAPTER XV

Boundary layers in compressible flow

a. Introductory remarks

The development of the theory of boundary layer flow in compressible streams was stimulated by the progress in aeronautical engineering and rocket research because of the very high velocities of flight attained in modern times. In incompressible flow it was possible to separate the calculation of the velocity boundary layer from that of the thermal boundary layer, but this is no longer the case with compressible streams. The velocity and thermal boundary layers interact intimately so that, consequently, both must be considered simultaneously. This follows from the fact that at high velocities of flow heat due to friction as well as temperature changes due to compression must be taken into account. In addition it is necessary to include the effects of the variation of viscosity with temperature in connexion with the large temperature variations which occur in the flow. The relation $\mu(T)$ must be found by experiment, and the extensive body of data available [27a, 34a] leads to the conclusion that the functional relationship is a complex one and that no single correlation function can be found to apply to all gases. Alternatively, the dependence of viscosity on temperature can be calculated with the aid of the methods of statistical mechanics [27b] but, as yet, no completely satisfactory theory has been evolved. These calculations, too, lead to complex expressions for the function $\mu(T)$. In order not to complicate the already difficult problem of calculating compressible boundary layers it is necessary to compromise and to adopt reasonably simple, if not extremely precise, semi-empirical relations. In the case of air, as shown by E. R. van Driest [15], it is possible to use an interpolation formula based on D. M. Sutherland's theory of viscosity. This can be written

$$\frac{\mu}{\mu_0} = \left(\frac{T}{T_0}\right)^{\frac{3}{2}} \frac{T_0 + S}{T + S}, \tag{15.1}$$

where μ_0 denotes the viscosity at the reference temperature, T_0, and S is a constant which for air assumes the value

$$S = 110^\circ \text{ K}.$$

The preceding relation between the viscosity μ of air and the temperature, T, is seen plotted as curve (1) in Fig. 15.1. Since the relation (15.1) is still too complicated, it is customary to approximate it in theoretical calculations by the simpler power law

$$\frac{\mu}{\mu_0} = \left(\frac{T}{T_0}\right)^{\omega} \quad \text{with} \quad 0{\cdot}5 < \omega < 1. \tag{15.2}$$

The curves corresponding to $\omega = 0{\cdot}5, 0{\cdot}75$ and $1{\cdot}0$ are also shown plotted in Fig. 15.1. It is seen from the graph that Sutherland's formula (15.1) can be approximated at high temperatures by adopting values of ω between $0{\cdot}5$ and $0{\cdot}75$, whereas at lower temperatures the value $\omega = 1{\cdot}0$ appears to be adequate. Frequently, curve (1) in Fig. 15.1 is approximated piece-wise by straight lines, care being taken to make sure that the value of the viscosity at the wall agrees with that from eqn. (15.1). The specific heat, c_p, and the Prandtl number, P, can both be assumed to be constant even at large temperature differences, with a satisfactory degree of approximation as seen from Table 14.1 on p. 294.

The phenomena under consideration become, naturally, very complicated because of the interaction between the velocity and the thermal boundary layers. As compared with incompressible flow there are at least four additional quantities which must be taken into account in the calculation of compressible boundary layers:

1. The Mach number
2. The Prandtl number
3. The viscosity function $\mu(T)$ [exponent ω in eqn. (15.2)]
4. Boundary condition for temperature distribution (heat transfer or adiabatic wall).

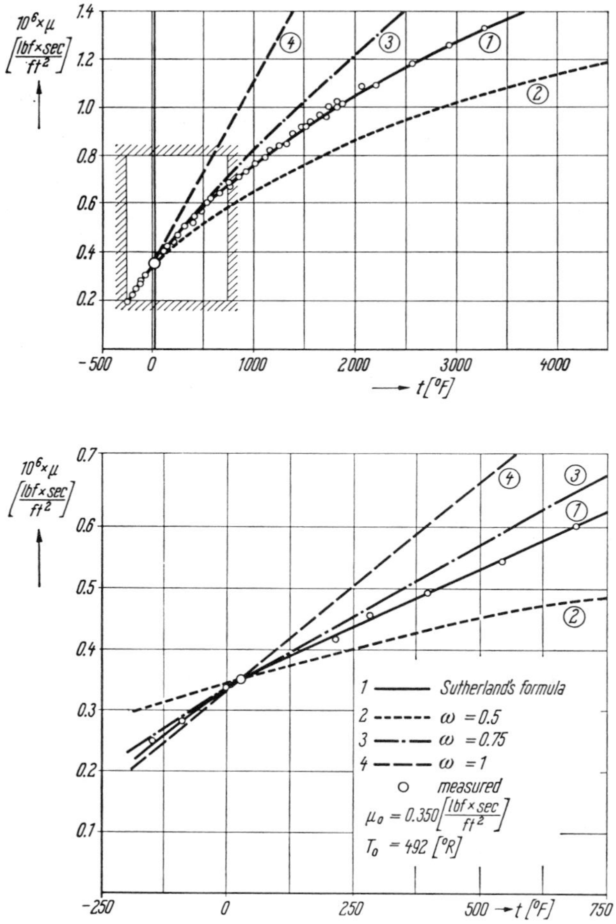

Fig. 15.1. The dynamic viscosity, μ, of air in terms of the temperature T

Curve (1) Measurements and interpolation formula (15.1) based on Sutherland's equation. Curves (2), (3), and (4) power laws, eqn. (15.2), with different values of the exponent ω

It is clear that the large number of additional parameters, compared with incompressible flow, causes the number of cases likely to occur in practice to become almost intractable as a consequence.

Comprehensive reviews of the numerous papers concerned with compressible boundary layers were given by G. Kuerti [35] and A. D. Young [60].

b. Relation between the velocity and the temperature fields

In the case of two-dimensional flow, and irrespective of the shape of the body, there exists a remarkably simple relation between the fields of velocity and temperature. In the particular case when $\mathsf{P} = 1$, the integration of the differential equations becomes much easier. The corresponding proposition was first used by A. Busemann [6] when he calculated the compressible boundary layer on a plate. It can be stated simply by asserting that irrespective of the form of the viscosity function $\mu(T)$, the temperature T depends solely on the velocity component u taken parallel to the wall, i. e. $T = T(u)$. Thus curves of constant velocity ($u =$ const) are identical with the isotherms ($T =$ const).

This remarkable theorem can be easily deduced from the boundary layer equations. Neglecting the buoyancy forces but taking into account the temperature dependence of the properties μ and k, we can rewrite the boundary layer equations (14.35a, b,c) as:

$$\frac{\partial(\varrho u)}{\partial x} + \frac{\partial(\varrho v)}{\partial y} = 0 \tag{15.3}$$

$$\varrho\left(u\frac{\partial u}{\partial x} + v\frac{\partial u}{\partial y}\right) = -\frac{\mathrm{d}p}{\mathrm{d}x} + \frac{\partial}{\partial y}\left(\mu\frac{\partial u}{\partial y}\right) \tag{15.4}$$

$$\varrho\, g\, c_p\left(u\frac{\partial T}{\partial x} + v\frac{\partial T}{\partial y}\right) = u\frac{\mathrm{d}p}{\mathrm{d}x} + \frac{\partial}{\partial y}\left(k\frac{\partial T}{\partial y}\right) + \mu\left(\frac{\partial u}{\partial y}\right)^2 \tag{15.5}$$

$$p = \varrho\, g\, R\, T\,. \tag{15.6}$$

The pressure gradient, as was the case with incompressible flow, is now also determined by the frictionless external flow:

$$\frac{\mathrm{d}p}{\mathrm{d}x} = -\varrho_1 U\frac{\mathrm{d}U}{\mathrm{d}x} = \varrho_1 g\, c_p\frac{\mathrm{d}T_1}{\mathrm{d}x} \tag{15.7}$$

with $\varrho_1(x)$ and $T_1(x)$ denoting the density and temperature respectively, at the outer edge of the boundary layer. Since $\partial p/\partial y = 0$ at any point x along the flow, the temperature and density satisfy the relation

$$\varrho(x,y)\cdot T(x,y) = \varrho_1(x)\cdot T_1(x)\,. \tag{15.8}$$

Making the assumption in eqns. (15.3) to (15.5) that the temperature depends on the single variable u, i. e. that

$$T = T(u)\,,$$

we can deduce from eqn. (15.5) that

$$\varrho\, g\, c_p\, T_u \left(u \frac{\partial u}{\partial x} + v \frac{\partial u}{\partial y}\right) = u \frac{\mathrm{d}p}{\mathrm{d}x} + \frac{\partial}{\partial y}\left(k T_u \frac{\partial u}{\partial y}\right) + \mu \left(\frac{\partial u}{\partial y}\right)^2,$$

where differentiation with respect to u is denoted by the subscript, so that $T_u = \mathrm{d}T/\mathrm{d}u$. Eliminating the left-hand side with the aid of eqn. (15.4), we have

$$g\, c_p\, T_u \left[-\frac{\mathrm{d}p}{\mathrm{d}x} + \frac{\partial}{\partial y}\left(\mu \frac{\partial u}{\partial y}\right)\right] = u \frac{\mathrm{d}p}{\mathrm{d}x} + T_u \frac{\partial}{\partial y}\left(k \frac{\partial u}{\partial y}\right) + (T_{uu}\, k + \mu)\left(\frac{\partial u}{\partial y}\right)^2$$

or

$$-\frac{\mathrm{d}p}{\mathrm{d}x}(g\, c_p\, T_u + u) + T_u \left[g c_p \frac{\partial}{\partial y}\left(\mu \frac{\partial u}{\partial y}\right) - \frac{\partial}{\partial y}\left(k \frac{\partial u}{\partial y}\right)\right] = (T_{uu}\, k + \mu)\left(\frac{\partial u}{\partial y}\right)^2.$$

Introducing the Prandtl number $\mathsf{P} = \mu\, g\, c_p/k$, which may be assumed independent of temperature as far as gases are concerned (*cf.* Table 14.1), we obtain

$$-\frac{\mathrm{d}p}{\mathrm{d}x}(g\, c_p\, T_u + u) + g\, c_p\, \frac{\mathsf{P}-1}{\mathsf{P}}\, T_u \frac{\partial}{\partial y}\left(\mu \frac{\partial u}{\partial y}\right) = (T_{uu}\, k + \mu)\left(\frac{\partial u}{\partial y}\right)^2.$$

It is clear from this form that $T = T(u)$ is a solution of the system of equations (15.3) to (15.5) if, simultaneously,

$$\frac{\mathrm{d}p}{\mathrm{d}x} = 0 : \mathsf{P} = 1 \quad \text{and} \quad T_u = -\frac{\mu}{k} = -\frac{1}{g c_p} \tag{15.9}$$

or, if

$$\frac{\mathrm{d}p}{\mathrm{d}x} \neq 0: \text{ in addition } T_u = 0 \text{ at } y = 0\,. \tag{15.9a}$$

This proves our proposition.

The actual function which describes the relation between temperature and velocity is obtained by integration. Thus from eqn. (15.9) we have the general solution

$$T(u) = -\frac{u^2}{2\, g\, c_p} + C_1\, u + C_2\,.$$

The constants of integration C_1 and C_2 can now be determined from the boundary conditions. For $\mathrm{d}p/\mathrm{d}x \neq 0$ we have $C_1 = 0$.

I. Adiabatic wall:

The boundary conditions are

$$y = 0 : u = 0; \quad \frac{\partial T}{\partial y} = 0\,, \text{ and hence } \frac{\mathrm{d}T}{\mathrm{d}u} = 0\,.$$

$$y = \infty : u = U; \quad T = T_1\,.$$

Here $T_1(x)$ denotes the temperature at the outer edge of the boundary layer, and the solution becomes

$$T = T_1 + \frac{1}{2\, g\, c_p}(U^2 - u^2)\,. \tag{15.10}$$

Consequently the adiabatic wall temperature $T = T_{ad}$ for $u = 0$ is given by

$$T_{ad} = T_1 + \frac{U^2}{2\,g\,c_p}\,. \tag{15.10a}$$

Introducing the Mach number $\mathsf{M} = U/c_1$ where $c_1^2 = (\gamma - 1)\,g\,c_p\,T_1$ we can re-write eqn. (15.7a) in the form

$$T_{ad} = T_1\left(1 + \frac{\gamma - 1}{2}\,\mathsf{M}^2\right), \quad (\mathsf{P} = 1). \tag{15.10b}$$

The quantity $T_{ad} - T_1$ represents the temperature increase of an adiabatic wall which is due to frictional heat. It is independent of the exponent of the viscosity function.

II. Heat transfer (Flat plate, $dp/dx = 0$):

We assume that the temperature of the wall is kept constant and equal to T_w. Thus the boundary conditions are

$$y = 0 : u = 0\,; \quad T = T_w; \quad y = \infty : u = U_\infty\,; \quad T = T_\infty\,,$$

which gives the solution

$$\frac{T - T_w}{T_\infty} = \left(1 - \frac{T_w}{T_\infty}\right)\frac{u}{U_\infty} + \frac{U_\infty^2}{2\,g\,c_p\,T_\infty}\,\frac{u}{U_\infty}\left(1 - \frac{u}{U_\infty}\right). \tag{15.11}$$

Expressing it in terms of the Mach number $\mathsf{M}_\infty = U_\infty/c_\infty$, we obtain

$$\frac{T - T_w}{T_\infty} = \left(1 - \frac{T_w}{T_\infty}\right)\frac{u}{U_\infty} + \frac{\gamma - 1}{2}\,\mathsf{M}_\infty^2\,\frac{u}{U_\infty}\left(1 - \frac{u}{U_\infty}\right). \tag{15.11a}$$

In the limiting case when $\mathsf{M}_\infty \to 0$, eqn. (15.11a) assumes the form of eqn. (14.52) which was obtained earlier for incompressible flow.

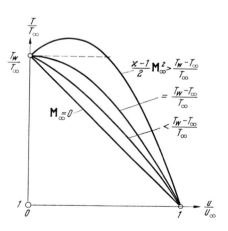

Fig. 15.2. Relationship between velocity and temperature distribution for the compressible laminar boundary layer on a flat plate including frictional heat from eqn. (15.11)

Prandtl number $\mathsf{P} = 1$. T_w = wall temperature; T_∞ = free stream temperature. For $\frac{1}{2}\,(\gamma - 1)\,\mathsf{M}^2 > (T_w - T_\infty)/\,T_\infty$ we have $(\partial T/\partial y)_{wall} > 0$, and heat is transferred to the wall owing to the large quantity of heat generated by friction, although $T_w > T_\infty$

The relation between the velocity and temperature distribution given in eqn. (15.11) is seen plotted in Fig. 15.2. The direction of heat flow can be deduced at once from the temperature gradient at the wall. Since $(\partial u/\partial y)_w > 0$, the direction of the heat flow is determined by the gradient $(\mathrm{d}T/\mathrm{d}u)_w$ at the wall. In fact, we can deduce from eqn. (15.11) that

$$\frac{U_\infty}{T_\infty}\left(\frac{\mathrm{d}T}{\mathrm{d}u}\right)_w = 1 - \frac{T_w}{T_\infty} + \frac{U_\infty^2}{2\,g\,c_p\,T_\infty}\,, \tag{15.12}$$

so that for $(\mathrm{d}T/\mathrm{d}u)_w < 0$ there is a flow of heat from the wall to the fluid, and conversely, for $(\mathrm{d}T/\mathrm{d}u)_w > 0$ heat flows from the fluid to the wall. In this manner

$$T_w - T_\infty \gtrless \frac{U_\infty^2}{2\,g\,c_p} \quad \text{or} \quad \frac{T_w - T_\infty}{T_\infty} \gtrless \frac{\gamma-1}{2}\,\mathsf{M}_\infty^2 : \tag{15.13}$$

Heat flux wall $\rightleftarrows$ fluid, valid for $\mathsf{P} = 1$.

c. The flat plate at zero incidence

The boundary layer on a flat plate at zero incidence has been studied extensively in numerous publications, and we propose to begin with a more detailed discussion of this case. First we shall deduce the relation between the velocity and temperature distribution on a flat plate from the preceding general proposition.

In the case of an *adiabatic wall* (flat-plate thermometer) we substitute $T_1 = T_\infty$ and $U = U_\infty$ into eqn. (15.10), so that the temperature distribution in the boundary layer on a flat plate becomes

$$T = T_\infty + \frac{1}{2g\,c_p}\,(U_\infty^2 - u^2) \tag{15.14}$$

and the adiabatic wall temperature is

$$T_{ad} = T_\infty + \frac{U_\infty^2}{2\,g\,c_p} = T_\infty\left(1 + \frac{\gamma-1}{2}\,\mathsf{M}_\infty^2\right) \quad (\mathsf{P} = 1)\,, \tag{15.15}$$

which follows with $\mathsf{M}_\infty = U_\infty/c_\infty$, and $c^2_\infty = (\gamma-1)\,g\,c_p\,T_\infty$. It is worth noting that the temperature of a wall in compressible flow given by eqn. (15.15) is identical with that for an incompressible fluid from eqn. (14.67) provided that in the former case $\mathsf{P} = 1$. H. W. Emmons and J. G. Brainerd [19] have shown that in the case of Prandtl numbers which differ from unity the deviations in wall temperature caused by compressibility effects, as compared with the incompressible equation (14.67), are only very slight. Thus the adiabatic wall temperature equation

$$T_{ad} = T_\infty + \sqrt{\mathsf{P}}\,\frac{U_\infty^2}{2g\,c_p} = T_\infty\left(1 + \sqrt{\mathsf{P}}\,\frac{\gamma-1}{2}\,\mathsf{M}_\infty^2\right) \tag{15.16}$$

remains valid for compressible flows with a very good degree of approximation. For air, with $\gamma = 1{\cdot}4$ and $\mathsf{P} = 0{\cdot}723$, we obtain

$$T_{ad} = T_\infty\,(1 + 0{\cdot}169\ \mathsf{M}_\infty^2)\,. \tag{15.16 a}$$

The resulting dependence of the adiabatic wall temperature on the Mach number has been represented graphically by the plot in Fig. 15.3. For example, at a Mach number $\mathsf{M}_\infty = 1$ the wall becomes heated by 45° C (or 80° F) in round figures. At $\mathsf{M}_\infty = 3$, the temperature increase becomes as high as 400° C (or 720° F), and at $\mathsf{M}_\infty = 5$, it is as much as 1200° C (or 2200° F).

It has now become customary to write eqn. (15.16) in the more general form

$$T_{ad} = T_\infty + r\,\frac{U_\infty^2}{2\,g\,c_p} = T_\infty\left(1 + r\,\frac{\gamma - 1}{2}\,\mathsf{M}_\infty^2\right). \tag{15.17}$$

The *recovery factor* r then represents the ratio of the frictional temperature increase of the plate, $(T_{ad} - T_\infty)$, to that due to adiabatic compression

$$\Delta T_{ad} = \frac{U_\infty^2}{2\,g\,c_p}$$

from eqn. (14.14). On comparing eqns. (15.16) and (15.17) it is seen that the recovery factor has the value

$$r = \sqrt{\mathsf{P}} \qquad \text{(laminar)}\,. \tag{15.17a}$$

Hence for air

$$r = \sqrt{0{\cdot}723} = 0{\cdot}851 \qquad \text{(laminar)}\,. \tag{15.17b}$$

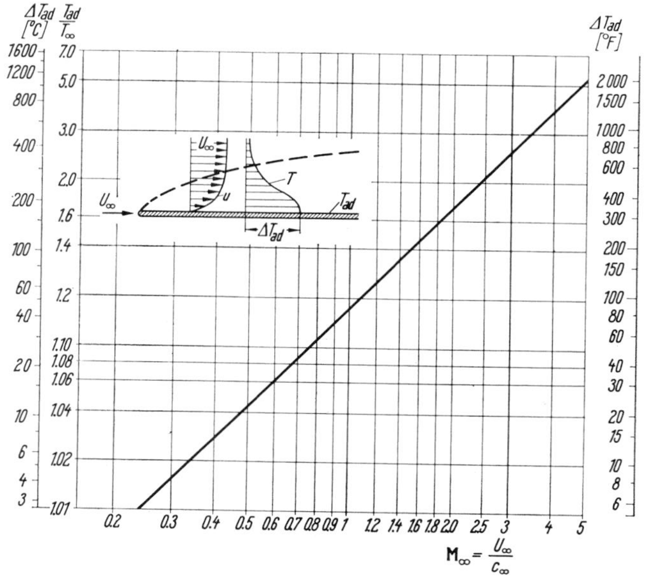

Fig. 15.3. Increase in the temperature of a flat wall owing to frictional heat when the wall is *adiabatic*, in terms of the Mach number, for air, from eqn. (15.16b)

Prandtl number, $\mathsf{P} = 0{\cdot}7$; Adiabatic wall temperature $= T_{ad}$; External temperature $= T_\infty$; Increase in wall temperature, $(\Delta T)_{ad} = T_{ad} - T_\infty$; $T_\infty = 273°$ K (492° R)

The diagrams in Fig. 15.4 represent the results of measurements on the recovery factor in the case of laminar boundary layers on cones in supersonic streams performed by G. R. Eber [17]. The theoretical relation $r = \sqrt{\mathsf{P}}$ is seen to be confirmed by these measurements.

In the general case, with heat transfer present, the relation between the velocity and temperature distribution can be deduced from eqn. (15.11 a). When $\mathsf{P} = 1$, it can be written

$$\frac{T}{T_\infty} = 1 + \frac{\gamma - 1}{2}\,\mathsf{M}_\infty^2\left[1 - \left(\frac{u}{U_\infty}\right)^2\right] + \frac{T_w - T_{ad}}{T_\infty}\left[1 - \frac{u}{U_\infty}\right] \quad (\mathsf{P} = 1) \qquad (15.18)$$

where T_{ad} is given by eqn. (15.15). The preceding equation can be extended to Prandtl numbers differing from unity by the introduction of the recovery factor, when we obtain

$$\frac{T}{T_\infty} = 1 + r\,\frac{\gamma - 1}{2}\,\mathsf{M}_\infty^2\left[1 - \left(\frac{u}{U_\infty}\right)^2\right] + \frac{T_w - T_{ad}}{T_\infty}\left[1 - \left(\frac{u}{U_\infty}\right)\right]. \qquad (15.19)$$

In this equation, the adiabatic wall temperature should be calculated from eqn. (15.16), but it must be realized that this is only an approximation. The direction in which heat is transferred can be deduced from eqn. (15.16) and written

$$T_w - T_\infty \gtrless \sqrt{\mathsf{P}}\;\frac{U_\infty^2}{2\,g\,c_p} \quad : \text{Heat wall} \rightleftarrows \text{gas} \qquad (15.20)$$

in complete agreement with eqn. (14.69) for incompressible flow.

Velocity and temperature distributions: Two papers by W. Hantzsche and H. Wendt [25, 27] and a paper by L. Crocco [12] contain explicit formulae for the calculation of the velocity and temperature distribution in a number of specific cases. Fig. 15.5 contains plots of the velocity distribution in the boundary layer for

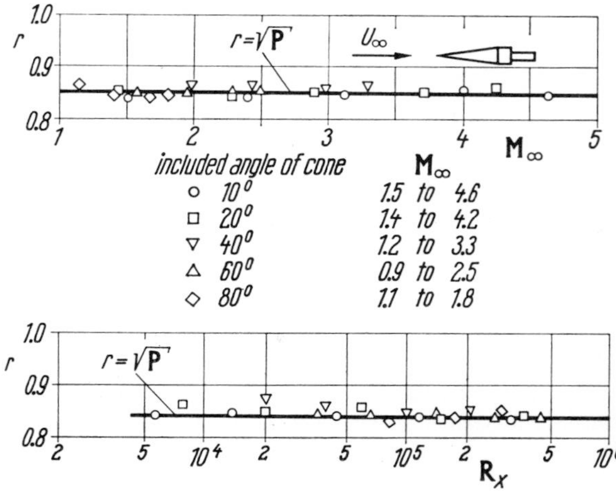

Fig. 15.4. Measured recovery factors, r, for laminar boundary layers on cones at supersonic velocities for different Mach numbers and Reynolds numbers, after G. R. Eber [17]; comparison with theoretical values from eqn. (15.17 a)

several Mach numbers. It represents Crocco's calculations for a boundary layer on an *adiabatic flat plate* on the assumption of a viscosity law with $\omega = 1$ and for $\mathsf{P} = 1$. The distance from the wall has been made dimensionless with reference to $\sqrt{\nu_\infty x / U_\infty}$ where ν_∞ denotes the kinematic viscosity in the external flow. It is seen that for increasing Mach numbers there is a considerable thickening of the boundary layer and that for very large Mach numbers the velocity distribution is approximately linear over its whole thickness.

The temperature distribution is shown in Fig. 15.5, and it is seen that the frictional increase in the temperature in the boundary layer assumes large values for large Mach numbers. The paper by W. Hantzsche and H. Wendt [25], quoted earlier, contains calculations for $\mathsf{P} = 0{\cdot}7$ (air) for the case of a heat-conducting plate. It is shown that the velocity distribution u/U_∞ plotted in terms of $y\sqrt{U_\infty/x\,\nu_w}$ deviates considerably from that for $\mathsf{P} = 1$ when the Mach number assumes larger values. The velocity profiles shown in Fig. 15.5 can be made nearly to coincide

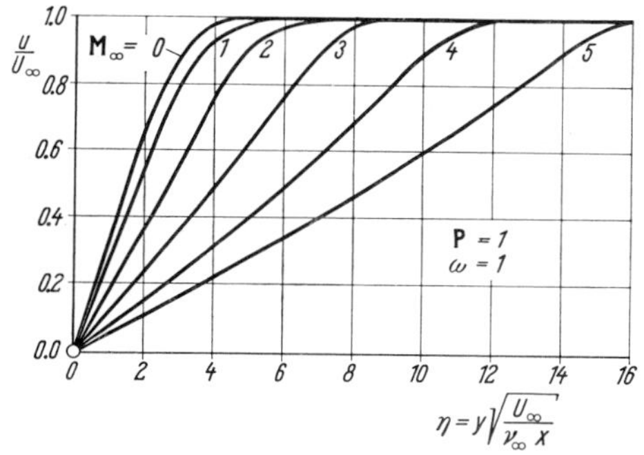

◀ Fig. 15.5. Velocity and temperature distribution in compressible, laminar boundary layer on adiabatic flat plate, after Crocco [12]

Prandtl number $\mathsf{P} = 1$, $\omega = 1$, $\gamma = 1.4$. Distance from wall referred to $\sqrt{\nu_\infty x/U_\infty}$

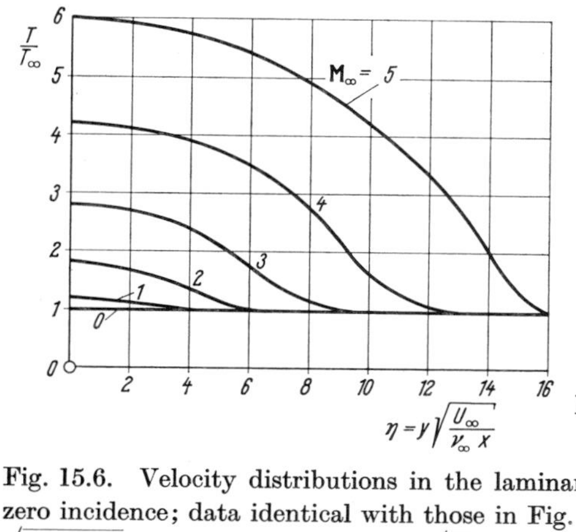

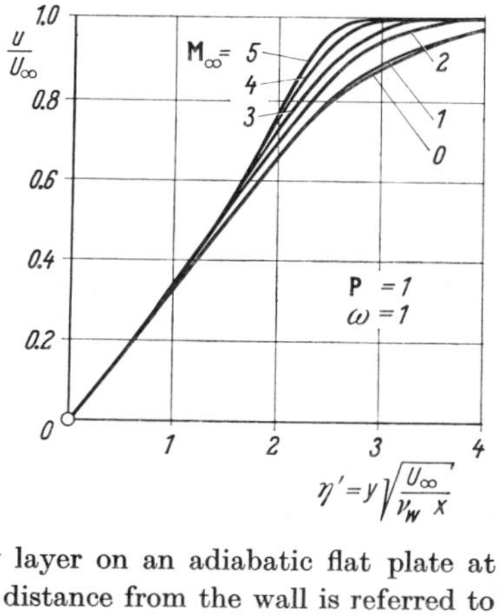

Fig.15.6 ▶

Fig. 15.6. Velocity distributions in the laminar boundary layer on an adiabatic flat plate at zero incidence; data identical with those in Fig. 15.5. The distance from the wall is referred to $\sqrt{\nu_w x/U_\infty}$. For $\omega = 1$, we have $\sqrt{\nu_w/\nu_\infty} = T_w/T_\infty$

In this method of plotting, the curves for different Mach numbers have been made nearly to coincide. It is possible to conclude from this that the large increase in the boundary layer thickness with Mach number is mainly due to the increase in volume which is associated with the increase in temperature of the air near the wall when the distance from the wall, y, is made dimensionless with reference to $\sqrt{\nu_w\, x/U_\infty}$, Fig. 15.6, where ν_w denotes the kinematic viscosity of the air at the wall. This circumstance denotes physically that the increase in boundary layer thickness with Mach number (at constant Reynolds number) is mainly due to the increase in volume which is associated with the increase in the temperature of the air near the wall. This fact was first noticed by A. N. Tifford [56].

Coefficient of skin friction: The coefficient of skin friction for an adiabatic wall, as calculated by W. Hantzsche and H. Wendt, has been plotted in terms of the Mach number in Fig. 15.7. For $\omega = 1$ the product $c_f\sqrt{\mathsf{R}}$ is independent of the Mach number, but for different values of ω the coefficient of skin friction decreases with increasing Mach number, the rate of decrease being larger for smaller values of ω. Figure 15.8 contains a comparison between the values of the coefficient of skin friction for an adiabatic flat plate obtained by several authors, i. e. for different values of the Prandtl number, P, and of the exponent in the viscosity function. The plot shows that the Prandtl number exerts a much smaller influence on the coefficient of skin friction than the exponent ω.

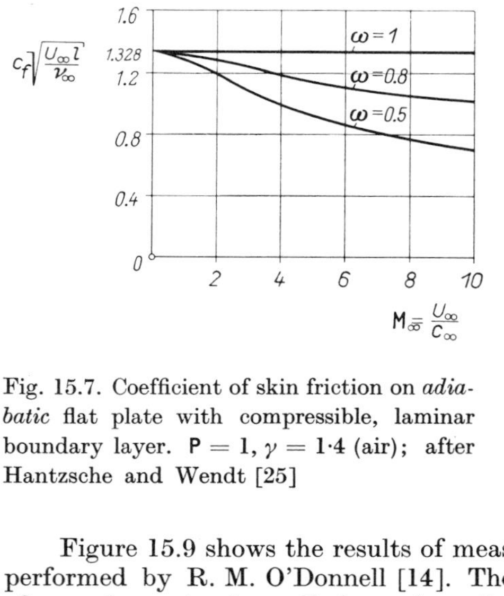

Fig. 15.7. Coefficient of skin friction on *adiabatic* flat plate with compressible, laminar boundary layer. $\mathsf{P} = 1$, $\gamma = 1{\cdot}4$ (air); after Hantzsche and Wendt [25]

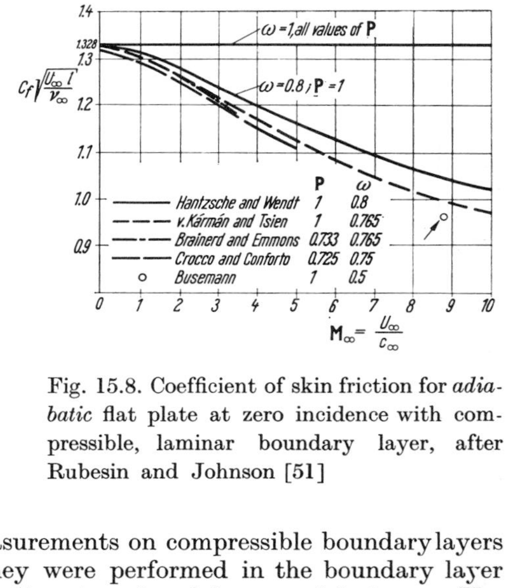

Fig. 15.8. Coefficient of skin friction for *adiabatic* flat plate at zero incidence with compressible, laminar boundary layer, after Rubesin and Johnson [51]

Figure 15.9 shows the results of measurements on compressible boundary layers performed by R. M. O'Donnell [14]. They were performed in the boundary layer of very long circular cylinders of small diameter placed in an axial stream. The Mach number was kept constant at $\mathsf{M}_\infty = 2{\cdot}4$ but the Reynolds number was varied. The velocity distribution has been plotted against y/θ, where θ denotes the momentum thickness from eqn. (15.52). It is seen that the velocity profiles at different distances from the leading edge are similar to each other and there is good agreement with the theory due to D. R. Chapman and M. W. Rubesin [9].

As already mentioned, the second paper by W. Hantzsche and H. Wendt contains numerous examples for the case of the *heat-conducting wall.* Some results are seen plotted in Fig. 15.10. They refer to the case when the temperature of the

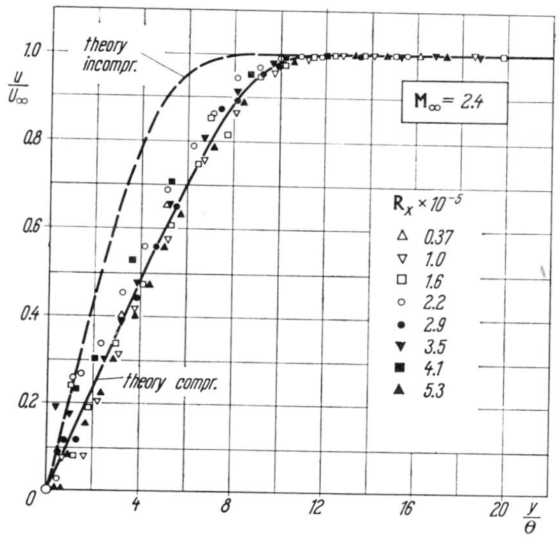

Fig. 15.9. Measurements on velocity distribution in *laminar* boundary layer with supersonic velocity past adiabatic flat plate. θ = momentum thickness. Mach number $M_\infty = 2{\cdot}4$, after R. M. O'Donnell [14], theory from [9]

walls is reduced by cooling to that in the free stream ($T_w = T_\infty$). A comparison of the velocity distributions in Figs. 15.10 and 15.5 shows that the boundary layer on a heat-conducting wall is considerably smaller than on an adiabatic one. The temperature profiles show that in the case under consideration the highest temperature increase in the boundary layer attains a value of about 20 per cent. of that due to adiabatic compression irrespective of the Mach number.

Since for $\omega = 1$ the coefficient of skin friction is independent of the Mach number (Fig. 15.7), the rate at which heat is transferred becomes equal to that in an incompressible stream, eqn. (14.68). A survey of heat transfer coefficients and recovery factors for laminar and turbulent flow at high Mach numbers can be found in a paper by J. Kaye [34]. In this connexion ref. [58] may also be mentioned.

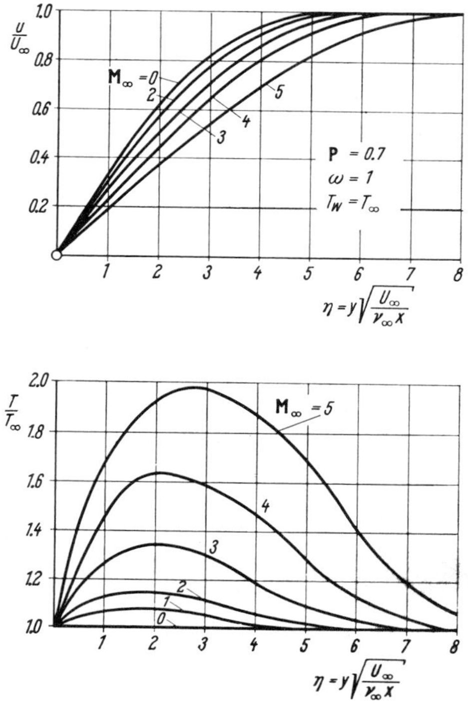

Fig. 15.10. Velocity and temperature distribution in compressible laminar boundary layer on flat plate at zero incidence *with heat transfer*, after Hantzsche and Wendt [25]

Wall temperature = free stream temperature, $T_w = T_\infty$; $P = 0{\cdot}7$, $\omega = 1$; $\gamma = 1{\cdot}4$

The case when the temperature varies along the wall, i. e. when $T_w(x)$, has been studied by D. R. Chapman and M. W. Rubesin [9] on the assumption of a viscosity function $\mu/\mu_0 = C\, T/T_0$. The analysis shows that the local heat flux (quantity of heat transferred per unit area and time) cannot be determined from the temperature difference $T_w(x) - T_{ad}$ alone but that it depends to a large degree on the previous 'history' of the boundary layer, i. e. on the conditions which prevail upstream of the section under consideration. The local Nusselt number loses its significance in cases when the wall temperature varies along the flow, because its use implies that the local heat flux is proportional to $T_w - T_\infty$, eqn. (14.29), or, taking into account the heat generated by friction, that it is proportional to $T_w - T_{ad}$.

Calculations concerning compressible boundary layers on flat plates which are based on the momentum integral equation (Chap. XII) have been performed by Th. von Kármán and H. S. Tsien [33]; see also Fig. 15.8. The asymptotic solution for a flat plate at zero incidence with uniform suction given in Chap. XIII has been extended by A. D. Young [57] and H. G. Lew [37] to compressible flow along an adiabatic wall. Further details about compressible boundary layers with suction can be found in Chap. XIII.

d. Boundary layer with non-zero pressure gradient

1. Exact solutions. The calculations concerning boundary layers with non-zero pressure gradients are more difficult than those concerning flat plates, owing to the large number of independent variables. L. Crocco [12] discovered quite early a transformation which simplifies the task of integrating the equations for the cases when either (1) $\mathsf{P} = 1$, and the viscosity function $\mu(T)$ is arbitrary, or (2) when the Prandtl number has an arbitrary value but $\mu/T = \text{const}$ (i. e. when $\omega = 1$). The transformation is applicable to adiabatic as well as to heat-conducting walls. In the special cases of an adiabatic wall with $\mathsf{P} = 1$ and $\omega = 1$, L. Howarth [29] and K. Stewartson [53] discovered a transformation which reduces the compressible boundary layer equations to almost the same form as that valid for incompressible flow. Consequently, all methods which have been developed for the latter case can be used in the former. In addition, both exact solutions as well as numerous approximate methods have been developed. In the group of exact solutions, the class of similar solutions occupies an important position. In the field of incompressible flow, solutions were considered to be similar, when velocity profiles $u(x, y)$ at two different positions x differed only by scale factors in u and y (Sec. VIII b), and it was shown that such similar solutions existed only for definite external streams $U(x)$. When this was the case, the partial differential equation for the stream function reduced itself to an ordinary differential equation. The latter is, naturally, easier to solve exactly or numerically, than the former.

Investigations into the existence of similar compressible boundary layers are contained in numerous papers for example refs. [29, 30, 31]. T. Y. Li and H. T. Nagamatsu continued this work in a series of meritorious papers [38, 39] and succeeded in showing that similar boundary layers exist in compressible flows too. Similarity prevails with regard to the longitudinal velocity component, u, as was the case with incompressible flows; as far as the temperature profile is concerned, similarity prevails with respect to the stagnation enthalphy

$$h = g\, c_p\, T + \tfrac{1}{2}\, u^2 \, . \tag{15.21}$$

The system of partial differential equations for u, v, and T reduces itself now to two coupled ordinary differential equations, one for the stream function, and one for the stagnation enthalpy.

Similar solutions of compressible boundary-layer flows are of considerable importance, first because they are interesting in themselves, and secondly, being exact, they can serve as testing grounds for approximate methods. We shall, therefore, now proceed to give a more detailed account of what is involved. Regarding the properties of the gas, we shall assume that

$$\mathsf{P} = 1 \quad \text{and} \quad \omega = 1 \, .$$

The wall will be assumed to be heat-conducting, so that T_w/T_1 or T_w/T_0 together with the stagnation temperature, T_0, constitute the relevant parameters for the thermal boundary layer. The external flow is isentropic, and the stagnation enthalpy is constant:

$$h_1 = g\, c_p\, T + \tfrac{1}{2}\, U^2 = g\, c_p\, T_0 = h_0 = \text{const} \, , \tag{15.22}$$

where T_0 is the stagnation temperature.

According to eqn. (15.10), in the special case of an *adiabatic wall,* we have

$$h(x, y) = g\, c_p\, T + \tfrac{1}{2}\, u^2 = g\, c_p\, T_1 + \tfrac{1}{2}\, U_1{}^2 = h_1 = \text{const} \tag{15.23}$$

which shows that the stagnation enthalpy remains constant over the whole width of the boundary layer as well as in the external flow. Thus, the similarity of the stagnation enthalpy profiles becomes trivial. In the case of a *heat-conducting* flat plate ($\mathrm{d}p/\mathrm{d}x = 0$) the velocity distribution and the temperature distribution satisfy the simple relation in eqn. (15.11). The latter can also be written

$$h - h_1 = (h_w - h_1)\left(1 - \frac{u}{U}\right) , \tag{15.24}$$

when the stagnation enthalpy h from eqn. (15.21) is introduced into it together with $h_w = c_p\, T_w$, in analogy with eqn. (14.52). The above equation shows that the profiles of stagnation enthalpy (flow over plate with heat transfer and $\mathsf{P} = 1$) are identical with the velocity profiles. This is an extension of the theorem, discussed in Sec. XIV. 2, which asserts that temperature and velocity profiles are identical in incompressible flow, eqn. (14.52). In what follows, we shall obtain a further extension of eqn. (15.24) to the case of compressible flow with pressure gradient and heat transfer at the wall.

In order to obtain the similar solutions for compressible boundary layers with pressure gradient, it is convenient, as mentioned in ref. [39], to introduce the stagnation enthalpy, h, defined in eqn. (15.21) into the fundamental equations (15.3) to (15.5). These can be easily shown to assume the forms:

$$\frac{\partial}{\partial x}\left(\frac{u}{T}\right) + \frac{\partial}{\partial y}\left(\frac{v}{T}\right) = -\frac{c_p}{RT_1}\frac{u}{T}\frac{\mathrm{d}T_1}{\mathrm{d}x}, \tag{15.25}$$

$$\frac{u}{T}\frac{\partial u}{\partial x} + \frac{v}{T}\frac{\partial u}{\partial y} = -\frac{g\,c_p}{T_1}\frac{\mathrm{d}T_1}{\mathrm{d}x} + \frac{Rg}{p_1}\frac{\mu_0}{T_0}\frac{\partial}{\partial y}\left(T\frac{\partial u}{\partial y}\right), \tag{15.26}$$

$$\frac{u}{T}\frac{\partial h}{\partial x} + \frac{v}{T}\frac{\partial h}{\partial y} = \frac{Rg}{p_1}\frac{\mu_0}{T_0}\frac{\partial}{\partial y}\left(T\frac{\partial h}{\partial y}\right). \tag{15.27}$$

Introducing a stream function

$$\psi(x,y) = \int_0^y \frac{u}{T}\,\mathrm{d}y \quad \text{so that} \quad \frac{u}{T} = \frac{\partial \psi}{\partial y}, \tag{15.28}$$

we obtain

$$\frac{\partial \psi}{\partial x} + \frac{v}{T} + \frac{c_p}{RT_1}\frac{\mathrm{d}T_1}{\mathrm{d}x}\psi = 0, \tag{15.29}$$

$$\frac{\partial \psi}{\partial y}\frac{\partial u}{\partial x} - \frac{\partial u}{\partial y}\left(\frac{c_p}{RT_1}\frac{\mathrm{d}T_1}{\mathrm{d}x}\psi + \frac{\partial \psi}{\partial x}\right) = -\frac{g\,c_p}{T_1}\frac{\mathrm{d}T_1}{\mathrm{d}x} + \frac{Rg}{p_1}\frac{\mu_0}{T_0}\frac{\partial}{\partial y}\left(T\frac{\partial u}{\partial y}\right), \tag{15.30}$$

$$\frac{\partial \psi}{\partial y}\frac{\partial h}{\partial x} - \frac{\partial h}{\partial y}\left(\frac{c_p}{RT_1}\frac{\mathrm{d}T_1}{\mathrm{d}x}\psi + \frac{\partial \psi}{\partial x}\right) = \frac{Rg}{p_1}\frac{\mu_0}{T_0}\frac{\partial}{\partial y}\left(T\frac{\partial h}{\partial y}\right). \tag{15.31}$$

The succeeding calculation aims at obtaining similar solutions for the three variables ψ, u, h from the above system of equations. In order to achieve this it is necessary to introduce a similarity variable η in analogy with the incrompessible case discussed in Chap. VIII, and to assume

$$\psi(x,y) = N(x)\cdot K(\eta) \tag{15.32}$$

$$u(x,y) = U(x)\cdot F(\eta) \tag{15.33}$$

$$h(x,y) = h_1\cdot G(\eta). \tag{15.34}$$

Evaluating u from eqn. (15.28) together with (15.32) and comparing with eqn. (15.33) we obtain the following equation for the similarity parameter η:

$$\frac{\partial \eta}{\partial y} = \frac{U(x)\cdot F(\eta)}{N(x)\cdot K'(\eta)}\cdot\frac{1}{T(x,y)}.$$

Choosing

$$K'(\eta) = F(\eta), \tag{15.35}$$

we have

$$\eta = \int_0^y \frac{U(x)}{N(x)}\frac{\mathrm{d}y}{T(x,y)}. \tag{15.36}$$

Equations (15.32) to (15.34) define only two new functions because of the relation in eqn. (15.35) between two of the three. We shall consider that $K(\eta)$ and $G(\eta)$ are the new functions.

It is now necessary to introduce the assumed forms from eqns. (15.32) to (15.34) into the differential equation of motion in the x-direction, eqn. (15.30), and into the energy equation (15.31). Having done this we investigate the conditions under which the external flow $U(x)$ and the scale factor $N(x)$ will lead to a transformation of the resulting partial differential equations into two ordinary coupled differential equations.

After some rearrangement, eqn. (15.30) can be given the form

$$\left(1+\frac{\gamma-1}{2}\mathsf{M}^2\right)(K'^2-G)=\frac{U}{U'}\left(\frac{c_p}{R}\frac{T_1'}{T_1}+\frac{N'}{N}\right)KK''+\frac{Rg}{p_1}\frac{\mu_0}{T_0}\frac{U^2}{N^2U'}K''' \tag{15.37}$$

and eqn. (15.31) becomes

$$-\left(\frac{c_p}{R}\frac{T_1'}{T_1}+\frac{N'}{N}\right)K\,G'=\frac{Rg}{p_1}\frac{\mu_0}{T_0}\frac{U}{N^2}G'' \tag{15.38}$$

where $\mathsf{M}=U/c_1$ is the local Mach number of the external flow. In order to be in a position to cancel the coefficients which depend on x it is necessary to impose the following conditions:

$$\frac{c_p}{R}\frac{T_1'}{T_1}+\frac{N'}{N}=\frac{Rg}{p_1}\frac{\mu_0}{T_0}\frac{U}{N^2} \tag{15.39}$$

and

$$\frac{c_p}{R}\frac{T_1'}{T_1}+\frac{N'}{N}=m\,\frac{U'}{U}\left(1+\frac{\gamma-1}{2}\mathsf{M}^2\right). \tag{15.40}$$

Here m denotes a still undefined constant. It is seen at once that the coefficients of eqn. (15.38) cancel simultaneously.

Equations (15.39) and (15.40) constitute two coupled ordinary differential equations which determine the external flow $U(x)$ and the scale factor $N(x)$. Thus eqns. (15.37) and (15.38) reduce to the following two ordinary differential equations:

$$K'''+K\cdot K''=\frac{1}{m}(K'^2-G), \tag{15.41}$$

$$G''+K\,G'=0 \tag{15.42}$$

with the boundary conditions

$$\left.\begin{aligned}\eta=0\ &:\quad K=K'=0\,;\quad G=G_w=T_w/T_0\,;\\ \eta=\infty &:\qquad\quad K'=1\,;\quad G=1\,.\end{aligned}\right\} \tag{15.43}$$

Integration of eqn. (15.40) leads to the following relation between $U(x)$ and the scale factor $N(x)$:

$$N(x)=N_0\{U(x)\}^m\,c_1^{\frac{m-(m+2)\gamma}{\gamma-1}}. \tag{15.44}$$

Here c_1 denotes local velocity of sound of the external flow and the arbitrary constant of integration, N_0, is determined by the condition

$$N_0^2=\frac{Rg_0}{T_0}.$$

Thus the corresponding external flow can be determined. The ensuing tedious calculation results in simple expressions for $U(x)$ only for special values of the free parameter m. If it is assumed that

$$m = -\frac{2\gamma - 1}{\gamma - 1}, \tag{15.45}$$

it is found that

$$U(x) = \left(\frac{2\gamma - 1}{5\gamma - 3}\, p_0\right)^{\frac{\gamma-1}{5\gamma-3}} \cdot c_0^{\frac{2}{3-5\gamma}} \cdot (x + x_0)^{\frac{\gamma-1}{3-5\gamma}} \tag{15.46}$$

The external flow turns out to be given by a power of x, and the values of m as well as those of the exponent of $(x + x_0)$ have been listed below for three different values of γ, each corresponding to a monatomic, a diatomic and tri-atomic molecule, respectively:

Gas	γ	m	$\frac{\gamma - 1}{3 - 5\gamma}$
monatomic	$\frac{9}{7}$	$-\frac{11}{2}$	$-\frac{1}{12}$
diatomic	$\frac{7}{5}$	$-\frac{9}{2}$	$-\frac{1}{10}$
triatomic	$\frac{5}{3}$	$-\frac{7}{2}$	$-\frac{1}{8}$

The resulting flow is retarded for the three types of gases considered.

As shown earlier, eqn. (15.23), the stagnation enthalpy remains constant over the boundary layer thickness when the wall is adiabatic. Consequently in eqn. (15.34) we have $h(x, y) = h = \text{const}$, or $G = 1$. Equation (15.42) becomes an identity, and eqn. (15.41) is reduced to

$$K''' + K \cdot K'' = \beta(K'^2 - 1) \tag{15.41 a}$$

where we have put $\beta = 1/m$. This equation is identical with the incompressible equation for wedge flow, eqn. (9.8), which was investigated by D. R. Hartree with different values of β. It was found that separation occurs for all values $\beta < -0{\cdot}199$, Fig. 9.1. Consequently at least the last two preceding values of m will lead to separation when the wall is adiabatic.

The system of equations (15.41) to (15.43) was solved numerically by T. Y. Li and H. T. Nagamatsu [39] who considered a large number of values of the parameters $\beta = 1/m$ and T_w/T_0. The resulting velocity and enthalpy distributions are shown plotted in Fig. 15.11 for a set of values of the parameter β for the case of a heated wall with $T_w/T_0 = 2$ (heat transfer from wall to boundary layer). The velocity distribution is affected by the pressure gradient to a much greater extent than the enthalpy distribution.

From the remaining examples considered by the previous authors [39], not discussed here, it is possible to derive the following conclusions regarding the influence of heat transfer on separation:

1. When the wall is adiabatic, separation occurs for the same value of β as in incompressible flow, namely $\beta = -0{\cdot}199$.
2. A transfer of heat from the wall to the stream favours separation, or, in other words, separation occurs with a lower adverse pressure gradient than is the case with an adiabatic wall.

Further numerical results concerning similar compressible boundary layers have been given by C. B. Cohen and E. Reshotko [11]. Assumptions which lead to an exact procedure valid for arbitrary pressure distributions in the presence of heat transfer have been given by K. W. Mangler [44a].

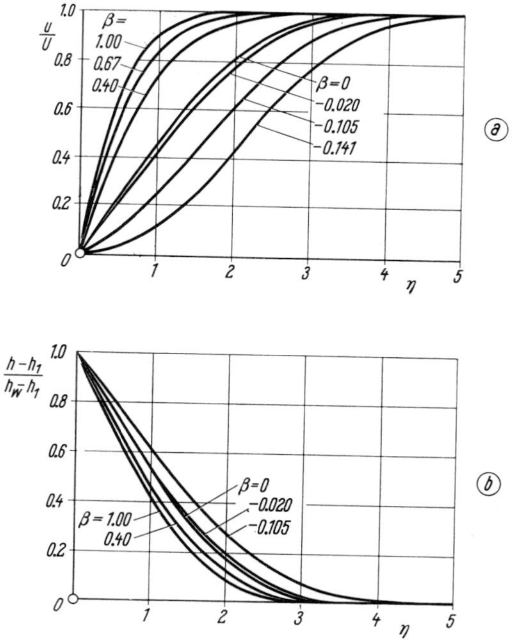

Fig. 15.11. Velocity and enthalpy distribution in similar solutions of the differential equations for compressible boundary layers with pressure gradient and heat transfer, after T. Y. Li and H. T. Nagamatsu [39], eqns. (15.41) and (15.42)

$T_w = 2\,T_0$ with $T_0 = T_1 + U^2/2\,g\,c_p$ being the stagnation temperature Prandtl number $\mathsf{P} = 1$; $\omega = 1$,

a) Velocity distributions $u/U = K'$;
b) Enthalpy distribution from eqn. (15.42)

$$\frac{h-h_1}{h_w-h_1} = \frac{G-1}{\dfrac{T_w}{T_0}-1} = G-1$$

2. Approximate methods. The numerous approximate methods which have been devised for the calculation of compressible laminar boundary layers are based, in most cases, on the momentum and energy integral equations of the boundary layer. The reader will recall that this was also the case with incompressible boundary layers. All these approximate methods have the common feature that they lead to much more involved procedures than the ones applicable to incompressible flows which were discussed in Chap. XII. The number of alternative procedures is much larger in the case of compressible than incompressible boundary layers as would be expected from the increased number of variables. In this connexion the surveys written by A. D. Young [60] and M. Morduchow [47] may be consulted.

An earlier method, devised by L. Howarth [29] and modified somewhat by H. Schlichting [52], is applicable to the case of an adiabatic wall with $\mathsf{P} = 1$ and $\omega = 1$.

The method due to E. Gruschwitz [24] is also applicable to adiabatic walls with $\omega = 1$, but there are no restrictions concerning the Prandtl number. The method developed by I. Ginzel [23] is concerned with the case of a heat-conducting wall. D. N. Morris and J. W. Smith [48] developed a very general method which is applicable to adiabatic and to heat-conducting walls, places no restrictions on the Prandtl number or on the viscosity function, and includes the case when the wall temperature varies along the surface of the body.

We now propose to devote some time to a somewhat more detailed description of one of these approximate methods. We shall choose that due to E. Gruschwitz, because it is comparatively simple in its numerical calculation and because its applicability to practical problems is not restricted to any particular Prandtl number. Furthermore, on passing to the limiting case of incompressible flow Gruschwitz's method reduces directly to the method due to K. Pohlhausen and Holstein-Bohlen, which was discussed in detail in Chap. XII.

We begin with the fundamental equations of compressible boundary layer flow, as given in eqns. (15.3) to (15.6). Introducing the enthalpy

$$h = g\, c_p\, T \tag{15.47}$$

we can rewrite the energy equation (15.5) in the form:

$$\varrho \left(u \frac{\partial h}{\partial x} + v \frac{\partial h}{\partial y}\right) = u \frac{\mathrm{d}p}{\mathrm{d}x} + \mu \left(\frac{\partial u}{\partial y}\right)^2 + \frac{\partial}{\partial y}\left(\frac{\mu}{\mathsf{P}} \frac{\partial h}{\partial y}\right). \tag{15.48}$$

The boundary conditions are

$$\left.\begin{array}{llll} y = 0: & u = v = 0; & \dfrac{\partial h}{\partial y} = 0 & \text{(adiabatic wall)} \\ y = \infty: & u = U(x); & h = h_1 . & \end{array}\right\} \tag{15.49}$$

Equations (15.3), (15.4), (15.5) and (15.48) together with the boundary conditions (15.49) constitute a system of four equations for the variables u, v, ϱ and h. The pressure $p(x)$ is known from Bernoulli's equation and is given by eqn. (15.7); it remains constant over the thickness of the boundary layer, i. e. $\partial p/\partial y = 0$. Since the pressure remains constant across the layer, we have

$$\frac{h}{h_1} = \frac{T}{T_1} = \frac{\varrho_1}{\varrho}, \tag{15.50}$$

where h_1, T_1, ϱ_1 denote the values of enthalpy, temperature, and density, respectively, at the outer edge of the boundary layer. We now introduce a displacement thickness, a momentum thickness and an energy dissipation thickness in the same way as in incompressible flow (Chaps. VIII and XII) and several additional quantities defined with the aid of enthalpy. In this connexion the former parameters are so defined as to reduce to the respective quantities for incompressible flow, eqns. (8.33), (8.34), and (8.37), when ϱ = const is substituted in the definitions. Denoting the boundary layer thickness of the velocity layer by δ, we introduce the definitions:

$$\delta^* = \int_0^\delta \left(1 - \frac{\varrho u}{\varrho_1 U}\right) dy \qquad \text{(displacement thickness)} \tag{15.51}$$

$$\theta = \int_0^\delta \frac{\varrho u}{\varrho_1 U}\left(1 - \frac{u}{U}\right) dy \quad \text{(momentum thickness)} \tag{15.52}$$

$$\theta_E = \int_0^\delta \frac{\varrho u}{\varrho_1 U}\left(1 - \frac{u^2}{U^2}\right) dy \quad \text{(energy dissipation thickness)} \tag{15.53}$$

$$\theta_H = \int_0^\delta \frac{\varrho u}{\varrho_1 U}\left(\frac{h}{h_1} - 1\right) dy \quad \text{(enthalpy thickness)} \tag{15.54}$$

$$\delta_u = \int_0^\delta \left(1 - \frac{u}{U}\right) dy \qquad \text{(velocity thickness)}\,. \tag{15.55}$$

It is easy to verify from eqns. (15.50), (15.51), (15.54) and (15.55) that the parameters δ^*, θ_H and δ_u satisfy the relation

$$\delta^* - \delta_u = \theta_H\,. \tag{15.56}$$

The energy dissipation thickness θ_E and the enthalpy thickness θ_H also satisfy a relation which follows from the energy equation in its form (15.10). On comparing eqn. (15.10) with eqn. (15.47), we obtain

$$\tfrac{1}{2}\int_0^\delta \varrho u\,(U^2 - u^2)\,dy = \int_0^\delta \varrho u\,(h - h_1)\,dy$$

so that in view of eqns. (15.53) and (15.54)

$$\tfrac{1}{2}\,U^2\,\theta_E = h_1\,\theta_H\,. \tag{15.57}$$

Introducing the velocity of sound $c_1^2 = \gamma\, g\, R\, T_1$ at state T_1 at the edge of the plate, we have

$$h_1 = g\, c_p\, T_1 = \frac{c_1^2}{\gamma - 1}$$

so that eqn. (15.57) becomes

$$\theta_H = \frac{\gamma - 1}{2}\,\mathsf{M}^2\,\theta_E\,, \tag{15.58}$$

where $\mathsf{M} = U/c_1$ denotes the local Mach number at the outer edge of the boundary layer.

Integrating the momentum equation (15.4) and the energy equation (15.48) over y, in the same way as was done for incompressible flow, we can obtain the momentum and energy integral equation for compressible flow.

Taking into account that

$$\frac{1}{\varrho_1}\frac{\mathrm{d}\varrho_1}{\mathrm{d}x} = -\frac{\mathsf{M}^2}{U}\frac{\mathrm{d}U}{\mathrm{d}x}$$

we obtain the *momentum integral equation* in the form

$$\frac{\mathrm{d}\theta}{\mathrm{d}x} + \frac{\theta}{U}\frac{\mathrm{d}U}{dx}\left(2 + \frac{\delta^*}{\theta} - \mathsf{M}^2\right) = \frac{\mu_w}{\varrho_1 U^2}\left(\frac{\partial u}{\partial y}\right)_w \tag{15.59}$$

as an integral of eqn. (15.4). From eqn. (15.48) we first obtain the energy integral equation in the form

$$\frac{\mathrm{d}}{\mathrm{d}x}(\varrho_1 U h_1 \theta_H) + \varrho_1 U^2 \frac{\mathrm{d}U}{\mathrm{d}x}(\delta^* - \delta_u) = \int_0^\delta \mu \left(\frac{\partial u}{\partial y}\right)^2 \mathrm{d}y\,.$$

Taking into account the relations (15.56) and (15.58) we obtain the final form of the *energy integral equation:*

$$\frac{\mathrm{d}\theta_E}{\mathrm{d}x} + \frac{\theta_E}{U}\frac{\mathrm{d}U}{\mathrm{d}x}[3-(2-\gamma)\,\mathsf{M}^2] = \frac{2}{\varrho_1 U^3}\int_0^\delta \mu\left(\frac{\partial u}{\partial y}\right)^2 \mathrm{d}y\,. \tag{15.60}$$

Equations (15.59) and (15.60) which represent, respectively, the integral forms of the momentum and energy equation constitute the basis for further calculation. For incompressible flow, $\mathsf{M} \to 0$, eqns. (15.59) and (15.60), respectively, transform into the corresponding equations for incompressible flow, as already given in (8.35) and (8.36). It is necessary to note, however, that eqns. (15.58) and (15.60) are valid for adiabatic walls only, because eqn. (15.10) was used in their derivation. On the other hand, eqn. (15.59) is not subject to this limitation.

In order to proceed with the evaluation of the momentum integral equation (15.59) and the energy integral equation (15.60), it is possible to assume polynomials for the velocity and enthalpy distributions, in a manner similar to that explained in Chap. XII. In this connexion use is made of the dimensionless wall distance η, defined by

$$\eta = \frac{1}{\delta_1}\int_0^y \frac{\varrho}{\varrho_1}\,\mathrm{d}y\;,$$

where

$$\delta_1(x) = \int_0^{\delta(x)} \frac{\varrho}{\varrho_1}\,\mathrm{d}y$$

and $\delta(x)$ denotes a finite distance from the wall across which the boundary layer flow goes over into the external free stream. It will be noted that $\eta = 0$ for $y = 0$ and $\eta = 1$ for $y = \delta$, and that for incompressible flow we have $\eta = y/\delta(x)$ as in eqn. (12.19).

The *velocity distribution* will be represented by a polynomial of the fourth degree, as in eqn. (12.19). Thus

$$\frac{u}{U} = c_1\,\eta + c_2\,\eta^2 + c_3\,\eta^3 + c_4\,\eta^4\,.$$

Using the same boundary conditions as in incompressible flow, eqn. (12.20), it is seen that the coefficients satisfy the relations:

$$c_1 = 2 + \frac{1}{6}\,\Lambda\,; \qquad c_2 = -\frac{1}{2}\,\Lambda\,; \qquad c_3 = \frac{1}{2}\,\Lambda - 2\,; \qquad c_4 = 1 - \frac{1}{6}\,\Lambda\,,$$

where

$$\Lambda = \frac{\varrho_1}{\varrho_w}\,\frac{\delta_1{}^2}{\nu_1}\,\frac{\mathrm{d}U}{\mathrm{d}x} \tag{15.61}$$

denotes the shape factor of the velocity profile, to be determined from the momentum integral equation.

Instead of assuming a polynomial for the enthalpy it is more convenient to do this for the quantity

$$\left(1 - \frac{u}{U}\right)\frac{\varrho_1}{\varrho}\,,$$

because the density appears only in such a combination. Thus, we assume

$$\left(1 - \frac{u}{U}\right)\frac{\varrho_1}{\varrho} = b_0 + b_1\,\eta + b_2\,\eta^2 + b_3\,\eta^3 + b_4\,\eta^4 + b_5\,\eta^5\,.$$

The six coefficients $b_0, \ldots, b_5$ must satisfy five boundary conditions so that one of them remains undetermined and must be deduced from the energy integral equation. We shall choose

$$b_0 = \frac{\varrho_1}{\varrho_w} = \frac{T_w}{T_1}\,, \tag{15.62}$$

i. e. the ratio of wall temperature to that at the edge of the boundary layer, as the temporarily free coefficient. It is now convenient to introduce the parameter

$$K = \Lambda\left(\frac{\theta}{\delta_1}\right)^2 = b_0\,\frac{\theta^2}{\nu_1}\,\frac{\mathrm{d}U}{\mathrm{d}x} \tag{15.63}$$

in the same way as was done by Holstein and Bohlen for incompressible flow, eqn. (12.27). The two shape factors K and Λ satisfy the same relation as in incompressible flow, eqn. (12.30).

The momentum thickness and the energy dissipation thickness can each be represented as a function of Λ, again in complete analogy with the incompressible case. Hence

$$\frac{\theta}{\delta_1} = \frac{37}{315} - \frac{1}{945}\,\Lambda - \frac{1}{9072}\,\Lambda^2,$$

$$\frac{\theta_E}{\delta_1} = \frac{798{,}048 - 4{,}656\,\Lambda - 758\,\Lambda^2 - 7\,\Lambda^3}{4{,}324{,}320}\,.$$

Finally, we introduce the universal functions

$$F_1(K) = 2\,\frac{\theta}{\delta_1}\left(1 - \frac{1}{15}\Lambda + \frac{1}{240}\Lambda^2\right) \tag{15.64}$$

$$F_2(K) = 1 - \frac{\gamma-1}{2}\,\frac{\delta_1}{\theta}\left(\frac{\theta_E}{\delta_1} - \mathsf{P}\,\frac{(12+\Lambda)^2}{2160}\right) \tag{15.65}$$

$$F_3(K) = \frac{\gamma-1}{2}\left[2 - \frac{\delta_1}{\theta}\left(\frac{\theta_E}{\delta_1} - \mathsf{P}\,\frac{(12+\Lambda)^2}{2160}\right)\right] \tag{15.66}$$

$$F_4(K) = \frac{\gamma-1}{2}\left[2 - \frac{\delta_1}{\theta}\left(\frac{\theta_E}{\delta_1} - \frac{(12+\Lambda)^2}{2160}\right)\right], \tag{15.67}$$

and after a lengthy calculation we obtain the following two equations from the momentum equation (15.59) and the energy equation (15.60):

$$\frac{\theta U}{\nu_1}\,\frac{\mathrm{d}\theta}{\mathrm{d}x} = F_1(K) - \frac{K}{b_0}\left[2 - \mathsf{M}^2 F_2(K)\right], \tag{15.68}$$

$$b_0 = \left(1 + \frac{\gamma-1}{2}\,\mathsf{M}^2\right)\frac{1 + \mathsf{M}^2 F_3(K)}{1 + \mathsf{M}^2 F_4(K)}\,. \tag{15.69}$$

The functions $F_1(K)$, $F_2(K)$, $F_3(K)$, and $F_4(K)$ have been tabulated by E. Gruschwitz and the result is shown in Table 15.1.

The point of separation is determined by the same values as in incompressible flow, i. e. by

$$\Lambda = -12 \quad \text{and} \quad K = -0{\cdot}1567 \quad \text{(separation)} \tag{15.70}$$

and the shearing stress at the wall is given by

$$\frac{\tau_w}{\varrho_1 U^2} = \frac{\nu_1}{U\,\delta_1}\left(2 + \frac{1}{6}\Lambda\right). \tag{15.71}$$

The quantities $U(x)$, $\mathrm{d}U/\mathrm{d}x$, $\nu_1(x)$ as well as $\mathsf{M} = U/c_1$ and P are to be considered given. Thus equations (15.68) and (15.69) together with eqn. (15.63) constitute a system of three differential equations for the three variables, namely the momentum thickness $\theta(x)$, the wall temperature $b_0 = T_w(x)/T_1(x)$, and the shape factor K.

The process of integration of eqn. (15.68) is the same as that explained in Chap. XII in connexion with incompressible flow. The initial values at the stagnation point are also obtained in the same way as before. With $K_0 = 0{\cdot}0770$, we have

$$\theta_0 = \sqrt{K_0\,\nu_1 \Big/ \left(\frac{\mathrm{d}U}{\mathrm{d}x}\right)_0}$$

and

$$\left(\frac{\mathrm{d}\theta}{\mathrm{d}x}\right)_0 = -0{\cdot}424\,\theta_0\left(\frac{\mathrm{d}^2U}{\mathrm{d}x^2}\right)_0 \Big/ \left(\frac{\mathrm{d}U}{\mathrm{d}x}\right)_0$$

(*cf.* eqn. (12.36a)).

Table 15.1. Universal functions for the calculation of compressible laminar boundary layers, after E. Gruschwitz [24]; $\mathsf{P} = 0{\cdot}725$, $\gamma = 1{\cdot}405$ (air)

K	Λ	F_1	F_2	F_3	F_4
0·0948	12·00	0·1422	1·115	0·518	0·685
0·090	9·44	0·1449	0·993	0·399	0·519
0·085	8·34	0·1482	0·952	0·358	0·463
0·080	7·49	0·1518	0·925	0·330	0·424
0·077	7·052	0·1540	0·911	0·316	0·405
0·075	6·77	0·1556	0·903	0·308	0·394
0·070	6·135	0·1597	0·885	0·290	0·370
0·065	5·554	0·1640	0·870	0·275	0·349
0·060	5·015	0·1685	0·857	0·262	0·330
0·055	4·509	0·1732	0·845	0·250	0·314
0·050	4·029	0·1781	0·835	0·240	0·299
0·045	3·570	0·1831	0·825	0·230	0·286
0·040	3·129	0·1882	0·816	0·221	0·274
0·035	2·703	0·1935	0·808	0·213	0·262
0·030	2·290	0·1990	0·801	0·206	0·252
0·025	1·888	0·2046	0·794	0·199	0·242
0·020	1·496	0·2103	0·787	0·193	0·233
0·015	1·112	0·2162	0·782	0·186	0·224
0·010	0·735	0·2223	0·776	0·181	0·216
0·005	0·365	0·2285	0·771	0·175	0·209
0	0	0·2349	0·765	0·170	0·202
—0·005	— 0·360	0·2414	0·760	0·166	0·195
—0·010	— 0·716	0·2481	0·756	0·161	0·188
—0·015	— 1·069	0·2549	0·751	0·156	0·182
—0·020	— 1·419	0·2619	0·747	0·152	0·177
—0·025	— 1·766	0·2690	0·743	0·148	0·171
—0·030	— 2·111	0·2764	0·739	0·145	0·166
—0·035	— 2·455	0·2839	0·736	0·141	0·161
—0·040	— 2·798	0·2916	0·732	0·138	0·156
—0·045	— 3·141	0·2993	0·729	0·134	0·151
—0·050	— 3·483	0·3073	0·726	0·131	0·147
—0·055	— 3·826	0·3155	0·723	0·128	0·143
—0·060	— 4·170	0·3240	0·720	0·126	0·139
—0·065	— 4·515	0·3326	0·718	0·123	0·135
—0·070	— 4·861	0·3414	0·715	0·120	0·131
—0·075	— 5·210	0·3505	0·713	0·118	0·128
—0·080	— 5·562	0·3599	0·710	0·115	0·125
—0·085	— 5·916	0·3694	0·708	0·113	0·121
—0·090	— 6·275	0·3792	0·706	0·111	0·118
—0·095	— 6·638	0·3892	0·704	0·109	0·115
—0·100	— 7·007	0·3995	0·702	0·107	0·113
—0·105	— 7·382	0·4102	0·701	0·106	0·110
—0·110	— 7·764	0·4212	0·699	0·104	0·108
—0·115	— 8·154	0·4323	0·697	0·102	0·105
—0·120	— 8·553	0·4439	0·695	0·101	0·103
—0·125	— 8·964	0·4561	0·694	0·099	0·101
—0·130	— 9·387	0·4689	0·693	0·098	0·100
—0·135	— 9·826	0·4822	0·692	0·097	0·098
—0·140	—10·282	0·4962	0·691	0·096	0·097
—0·145	—10·760	0·5108	0·691	0·096	0·096
—0·150	—11·265	0·5263	0·690	0·095	0·095
—0·155	—11·80	0·5436	0·690	0·095	0·095
—0·157	—12·00	0·5485	0·690	0·095	0·095

The calculation is simpler with the assumption of $\mathsf{P} = 1$, when $F_3 = F_4$, so that

$$b_0 = \frac{T_w}{T_1} = 1 + \frac{\gamma - 1}{2} \mathsf{M}^2 \tag{15.72}$$

as seen from eqn. (15.69). This is identical with eqn. (15.10b). In this manner it is now only necessary to solve eqn. (15.68).

In the case of incompressible flow, when $\mathsf{M} = 0$, eqn. (15.69) yields $b_0 = 1$, i.e. $T_w = T_1$, and eqn. (15.68) transforms into eqn. (12.36), because $F_1(K) - 2K = \frac{1}{2} F(K)$, if $F(K)$ is taken from eqn. (12.35).

The preceding method due to E. Gruschwitz was recently subjected to a thorough discussion by E. A. Eichelbrenner [18].

Example:

The above approximate method will now be applied to the case of flow past an aerofoil† (NACA 8410).

The potential pressure distributions for the suction side of the aerofoil in question are seen plotted in Fig. 15.12 for three Mach numbers: $\mathsf{M}_\infty = 0$; 0·6; and 0·8 and for an angle of incidence $\alpha = 0$. The diagrams also include plots of the temperature T_1 outside the boundary layer. The results of the calculation are shown in Figs. 15.13 and 15.14. The graph in Fig. 15.13 shows the variation of the momentum thickness θ, the displacement thickness δ^*, as well as the shearing stress τ_w along

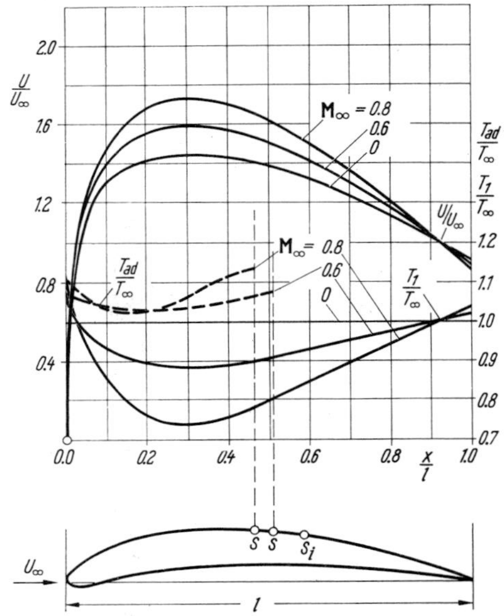

Figs. 15.12. to 15.14. Laminar boundary layer in compressible subsonic flow for the suction side of the NACA 8410 aerofoil on the assumption of an adiabatic wall. Angle of incidence $\alpha = 0°$. Mach number $M_\infty = U_\infty / c_\infty$; Prandtl number $\mathsf{P} = 0{\cdot}725$. Calculation based on E. Gruschwitz's [24] approximate method

S = point of separation

Fig. 15.12. Potential velocity distribution U/U_∞ at the outer edge of the boundary layer, the corresponding temperature distribution T_1/T_∞, and the variation in the wall temperature, T_{ad}/T_∞

† The author is indebted to Mr. F. Moser for working out this example. Since Gruschwitz's method does not lead to reasonable temperatures, as already noticed in ref. [18], the present temperature profiles have been calculated on the basis of ref. [21].

the suction side. As the Mach number is increased, the point of laminar separation moves slightly forward. The variation of the momentum thickness and shearing stress depends only little on the Mach number, whereas the displacement thickness δ^* increases considerably as the Mach number is increased. Finally, Fig. 15.14 displays the velocity and temperature distributions at several positions along the contour of the aerofoil. The velocity profiles do not change much with the Mach number, but the temperature profiles show large increases in the wall temperature with increasing Mach number. This is to be expected, because the wall was assumed to be adiabatic. The wall temperatures T_{ad} are also shown plotted in Fig. 15.12.

The case of a circular cone in an axial supersonic stream calculated by W. Hantzsche and H. Wendt [26] constitutes an example of an axially symmetrical boundary layer. The boundary layer on a yawed circular cone in a supersonic stream was considered by F. K. Moore [48a].

The proposition due to Mangler, described in Chap. VIII, permits us to reduce the calculation of axially symmetrical boundary layers on arbitrary bodies of revolution to that in two-dimensional flow. It remains valid in the field of compressible fluid flow.

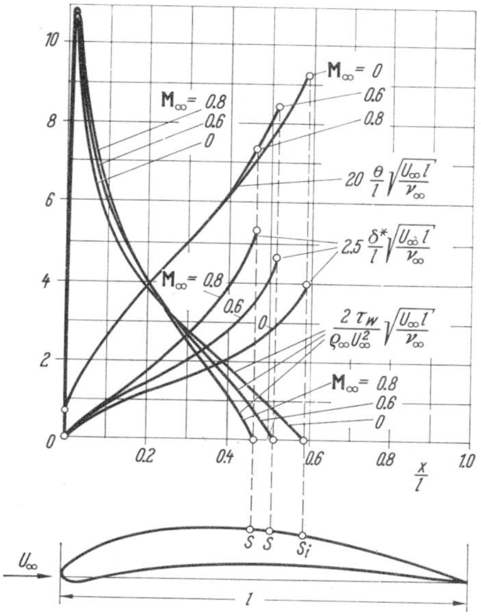

Fig. 15.13. Momentum thickness θ, displacement thickness δ^*, and shearing stress τ_w for different Mach numbers

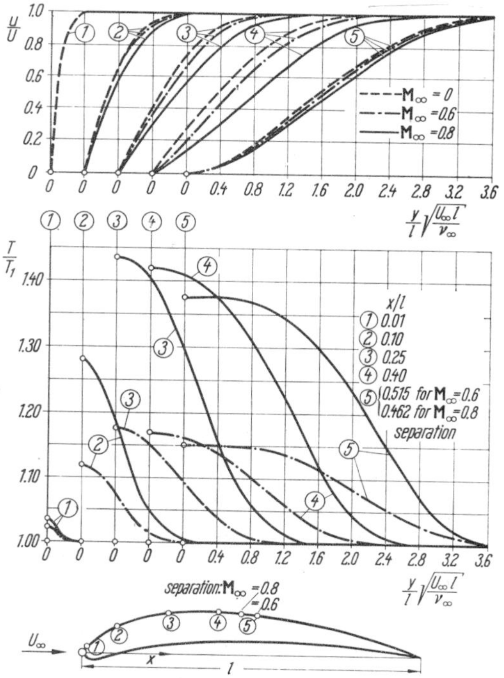

Fig. 15.14. a) Velocity distributions and b) temperature distributions in the boundary layer at different Mach numbers

e. Interaction between shock wave and boundary layer

When a solid body is placed in a stream whose velocity is high, or when it flies through air with a high velocity, local regions of supersonic velocity can be formed in its neighbourhood. The transition from supersonic velocity to subsonic velocity against the adjoining adverse pressure gradient will usually take place through a shock wave. On crossing the very thin shock wave, the pressure, density and temperature of the fluid change at extremely high rates. The rates of change are so high that the transition can be regarded as being discontinuous, except for the immediate neighbourhood of the wall. The existence of shock waves is of fundamental importance for the drag of the body as they often cause the boundary layer to separate. The theoretical calculation of shock waves and associated flow fields is very difficult, and we do not propose to discuss this topic here. Experiments show that the processes of shock and boundary layer formation interact strongly with each other. This leads to phenomena of great complexity because the behaviour of the boundary layer depends mainly on the Reynolds number, whereas the conditions in a wave are primarily dependent on the Mach number. Systematic investigations in which these two influences have been clearly separated have been put to hand only recently. J. Ackeret, F. Feldmann and N. Rott [1], H. W. Liepmann [41] and W. Holder and G. E. Gadd [28] varied in their experiments the Reynolds and Mach numbers independently of each other and so succeeded in providing some clarification of this complex interaction. The most important results obtained in the above three investigations are described in this section.

The pressure increase along the boundary layer must ultimately be the same as that in the external flow because the stream-line which separates the two regions must become parallel to the contour of the body after the shock. In the boundary layer, by its nature, the particles near the wall move with subsonic velocities but shock waves can only occur in supersonic streams. It is, therefore, clear that a shock wave which originates in the external stream cannot reach right up to the wall, and it follows that the pressure gradient parallel to the wall must be much more

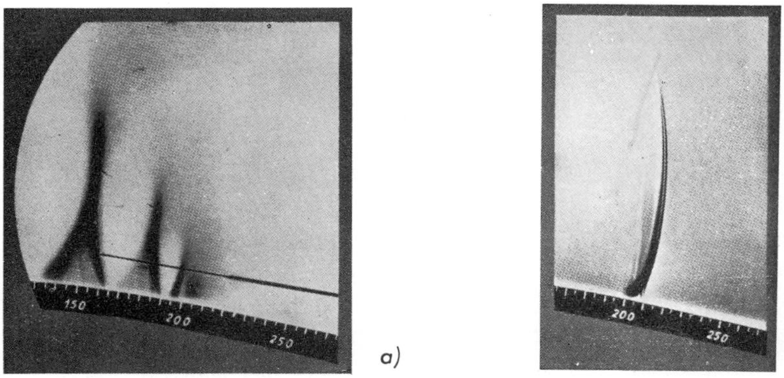

a) b)

Fig. 15.15. Schlieren photograph of shock wave; direction of flow from left to right, after Ackeret, Feldman and Rott [1] a) laminar boundary layer; multiple λ-shock, $\mathsf{M} = 1{\cdot}92$, $\mathsf{R}_\theta = 390$; b) turbulent boundary layer; normal shock, $\mathsf{M} = 1{\cdot}28$, $\mathsf{R}_\theta = 1159$

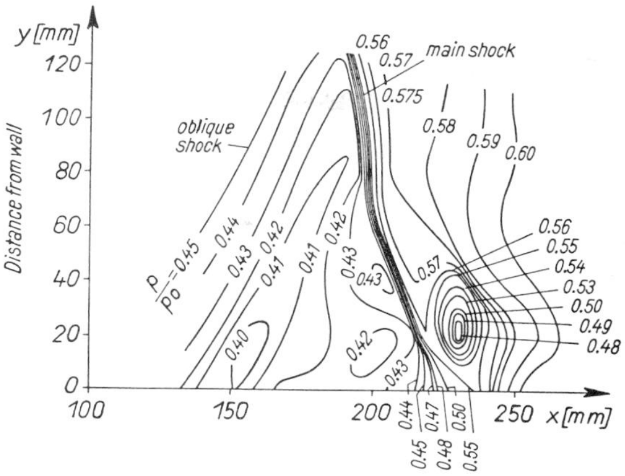

Fig. 15.16. Isobars in a shock region in laminar flow (λ-shock), after Ackeret, Feldmann and Rott [1]

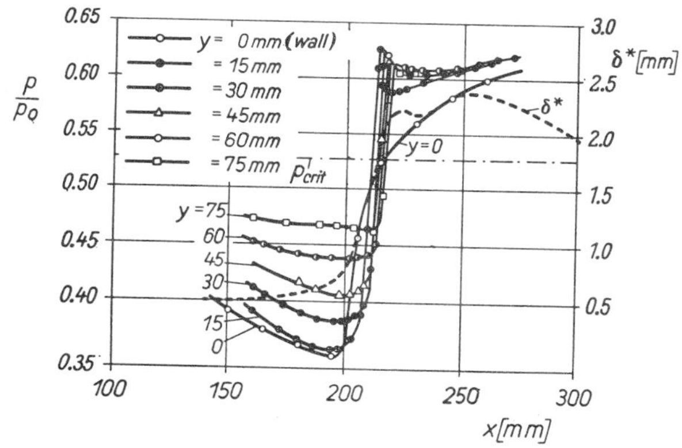

Fig. 15.17. Turbulent boundary layer in a shock region; pressure distribution at various distances from wall, after Ackeret, Feldmann and Rott [1]

gradual in the neighbourhood of the wall than in the external stream. Near the point where the shock wave reaches towards the wall the rates of change of $\partial u/\partial x$ and $\partial u/\partial y$ become of the same order of magnitude and transverse pressure gradients can also occur there. Both conditions render the well-known assumptions of boundary layer theory invalid.

The appearance of the shock wave is fundamentally different depending on whether the boundary layer is laminar or turbulent, Fig. 15.15. A short distance ahead of the point where the essentially perpendicular shock wave impinges on a laminar boundary layer, there appears a short leg forming a so-called λ-shock, Fig. 15.15a. In general, when the boundary layer is turbulent, the normal shock does not split and no λ-shocks are formed, Fig. 15.15b. An *oblique* shock which impinges on a laminar boundary layer from the outside becomes reflected from it in the form of a fan of expansion waves, Fig. 15.24a. However, when the boundary layer is turbulent, the reflexion appears in the form of a more concentrated expansion wave.

The plot of isobaric curves in Fig. 15.16 and the pressure curves in Fig. 15.17 show that the rate of pressure increase along a laminar or a turbulent boundary layer is more gradual than in the external stream. This flattening of the pressure gradient in the boundary layer is described by stating that the pressure distribution "diffuses" near the wall. It is observed that diffusion is much more pronounced for a laminar than for a turbulent boundary layer. The difference between laminar and turbulent shock diffusion can also be recognized from Fig. 15.18 which represents the pressure variation along a flat plate placed parallel to a supersonic stream. The measurements were performed by H. W. Liepmann, A. Roshko and S. Dhawan [42]. The pressure plots have been taken near the point on the plate where the oblique shock produced by a wedge interacts with the boundary layer. The pressure gradient is considerably steeper for the turbulent than for the laminar boundary layer. The width of diffusion is equal to about 100 δ in the case of interaction with a laminar boundary layer, but decreases to about 10 δ for a turbulent boundary layer; the symbol δ denotes here the boundary layer thickness in the shock region. The higher degree of diffusion which is characteristic of laminar boundary layers can be understood if it is noted that the subsonic region of flow extends further away from the wall in a laminar than in a turbulent boundary layer.

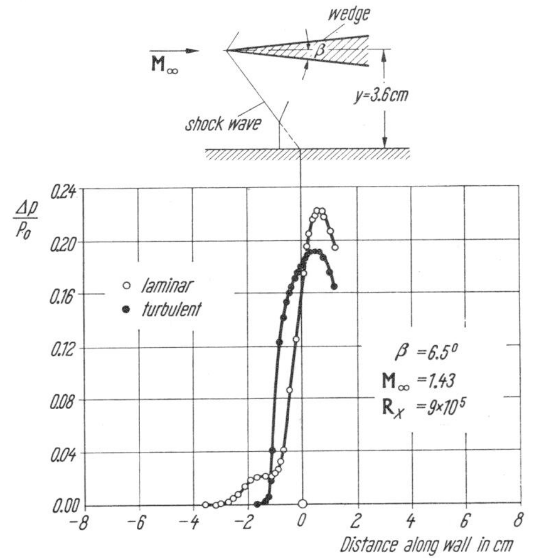

Fig. 15.18. Pressure distribution along a flat plate at supersonic velocity in the neighbourhood of the region of reflexion of a shock wave from laminar and turbulent boundary layer, after Liepmann, Roshko and Dhawan [42]

boundary layer thickness: laminar $\delta_l \approx 0{\cdot}7$ mm (0·028 in), turbulent $\delta_t \approx 1{\cdot}4$ mm (0·056 in)

Irrespective of whether separation does or does not occur, the boundary layer thickness increases ahead of the point of arrival of the shock wave. The pressure increase at the outer edge of the boundary layer, and hence also inside the boundary layer, corresponds to the curved stream-line which is convex in the direction of the wall and which separates the external from the boundary layer flow. Even in the domain of influence of the expansion waves which appear in the reflexion of an oblique shock wave, the slight decrease in pressure in the boundary layer, Fig. 15.18, corresponds to the fact that the curvature of the dividing stream-line is concave towards the wall. A laminar boundary layer which has not separated can support only very small pressure rises because the external flow impresses on it the pressure gradient exclusively through viscous forces. A non-separated turbulent

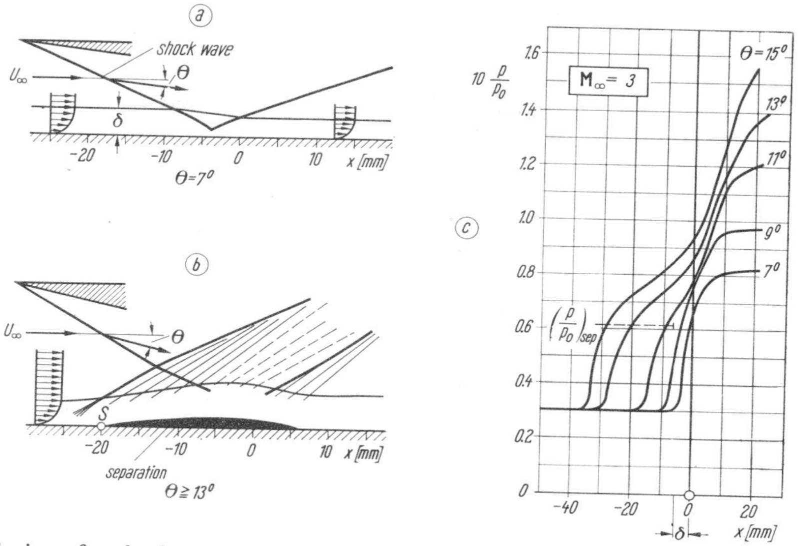

Fig. 15.19. Reflexion of a shock wave from a turbulent boundary layer on a flat wall, after S. M. Bogdonoff and C. E. Kepler [4]. Boundary layer thickness ahead of shock wave $\delta \approx 3$ mm (0.12 in). a) Weak shock, deflexion angle $\Theta = 7°$. Reflexion similar to that in frictionless flow; no boundary layer separation; b) Strong shock; deflexion angle $\Theta \geq 13°$. Reflexion in form of a system of compression and expansion waves; boundary layer separation; c) Pressure distributions at different deflexion angles Θ. Separation occurs at $p_{sep}/p_\infty = 2$ approx

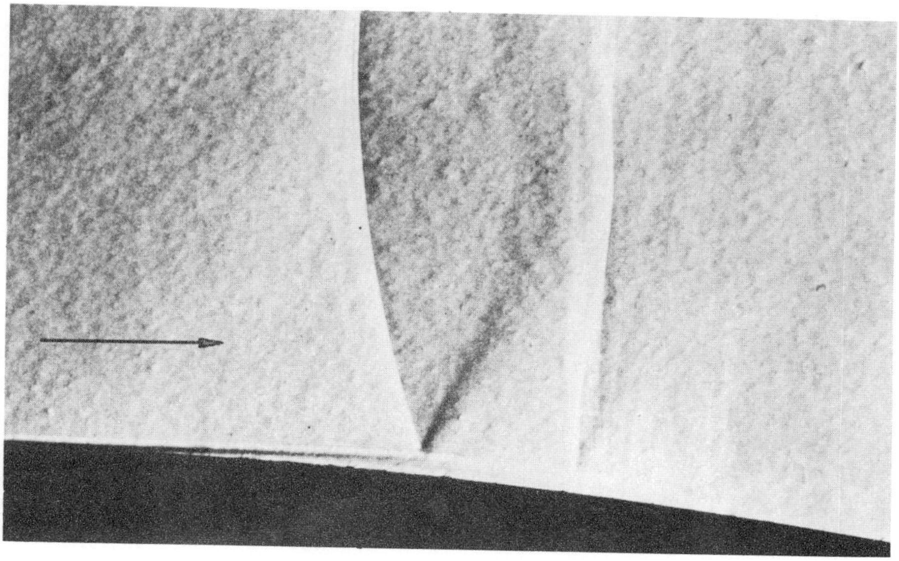

Fig. 15.20. Schlieren photograph of the flow past an aerofoil. Shock wave and boundary layer interaction. Case (2): Laminar boundary layer with separation ahead of the shock, but reattaching behind shock. $\mathsf{M} = 0{\cdot}84$, $\mathsf{R} = 8{\cdot}45 \times 10^5$, after Liepmann [41]

boundary layer can take up much larger pressure gradients because now the turbulent mixing motion aids the process. Both laminar and turbulent boundary layers are in a position to support the large pressure increases of strong shocks if they separate. In particular, in the turbulent case the dead-water vortex between the separated boundary layer and the wall can create considerable velocities which carry the inner edge of the boundary layer against the pressure rise by the action of viscosity. The sketch in Fig. 15.19 shows how the boundary layer and the dead-water region thicken ahead of the shock front and become thinner behind it. Finally, as shown in Fig. 15.19, the boundary layer re-attaches itself completely. The same phenomenon is also visible in Fig. 15.20.

The sketches in Fig. 15.19 reproduce the results of some measurements performed by S. M. Bogdonoff and C. Kepler [4] in connexion with their investigations into the reflexion of oblique shock waves from a flat wall carrying a turbulent boundary layer at a Mach number $\mathsf{M}_\infty = 3$ in the external stream. The sketches in Figs. 15.19a and b show the reflexions of a weak and a strong shock, respectively, their strength being regulated by the magnitude of the deflection angle Θ. When the shock is weak ($\Theta = 7°$), the reflected shock presents a pattern which would be

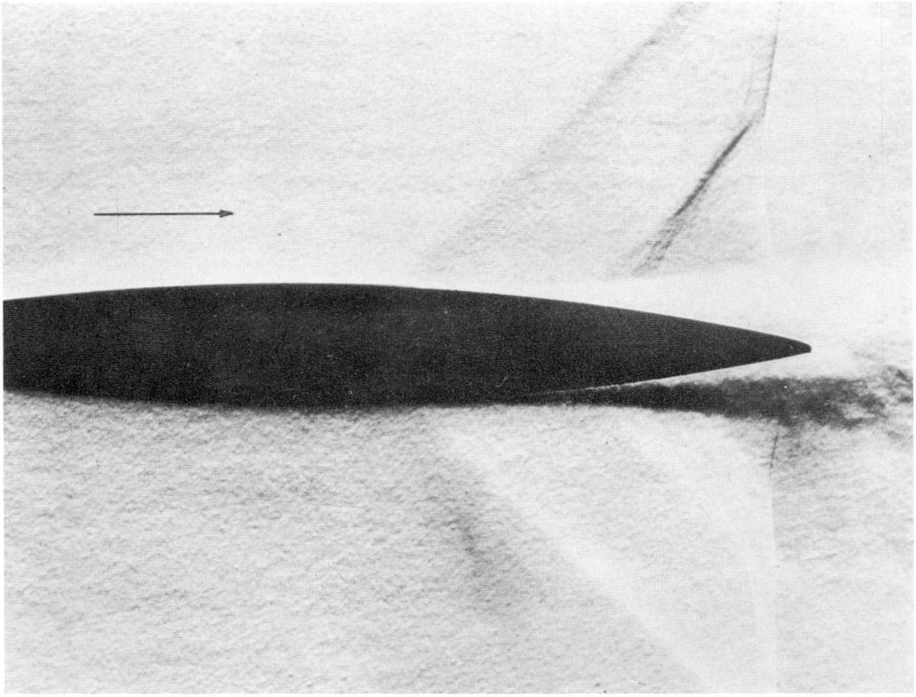

Fig. 15.21. Schlieren photograph of the flow past an aerofoil. Shock wave and boundary layer interaction. Case (3): Laminar boundary layer with separation behind shock. $\mathsf{M} = 0{\cdot}90$, $\mathsf{R} = 8{\cdot}74 \times 10^5$, after Liepmann [41]

expected on the basis of ideal-flow theory, and the boundary layer does not separate. When the strength of the shock is increased ($\Theta = 13°$), the reflected pattern contains a system of compression and expansion waves. The boundary layer exhibits a large local thickening which leads to separation. The boundary layer is thicker behind the reflected than ahead of the incident shock. The corresponding pressure distributions along the wall are shown plotted in Fig. 15.19c for different deflexion angles (and hence different shock strengths). Separation occurs for $\Theta > 9°$. The pressure rise which leads to separation is independent of the deflexion angle and has a value of about $p_A/p_\infty = 2$. In the domain of reflected expansion waves, the course of the pressure distribution curves is very flat. In a more recent paper, E. A. Mueller [49] attempted to give an analytic study of the problem of reflexion. The system of reflected expansion waves obtained theoretically shows qualitative agreement with the pattern observed by S. M. Bogdonoff, Fig. 15.19.

The incidence of transition and separation in the neighbourhood of an impinging shock wave are governed principally by the Reynolds number of the boundary layer and by the Mach number of the external stream. When the shock is weak and the Reynolds number is very small, the boundary layer remains laminar through-

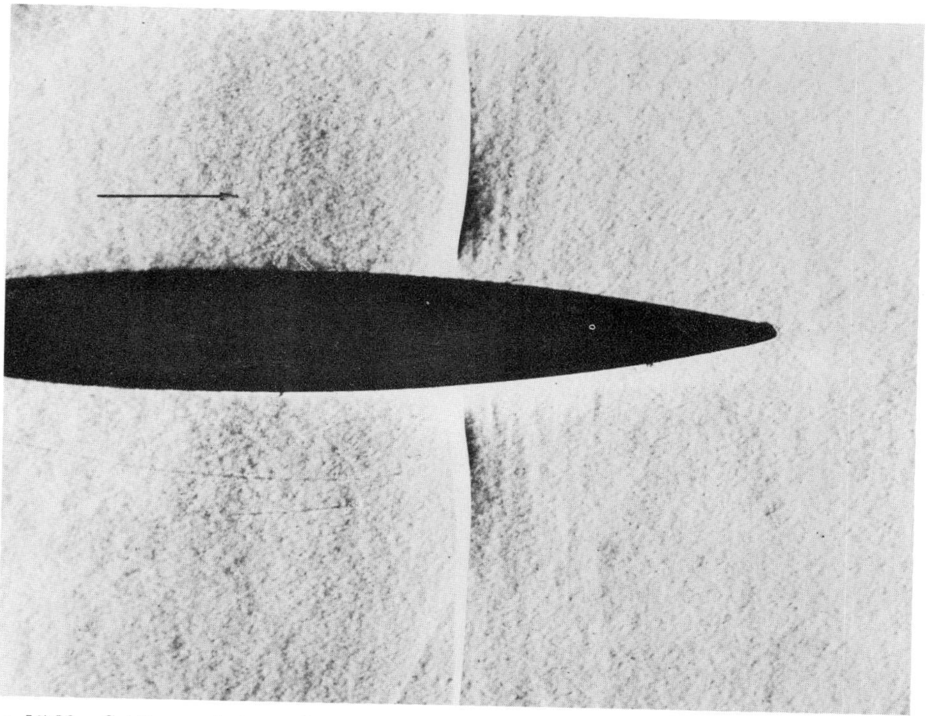

Fig. 15.22. Schlieren photograph of the flow past an aerofoil. Shock wave and boundary layer interaction. Case (4): Boundary layer turbulent ahead of shock, no separation. $\mathsf{M} = 0{\cdot}85$, $\mathsf{R} = 1{\cdot}69 \times 10^6$, after Liepmann [41]

out. Increasing the Reynolds number at a fixed, small Mach number, causes transition to occur at the point of impingement. When the shock is strong (large Mach number) and the Reynolds number is small, the laminar boundary layer will separate ahead of the shock front owing to pressure diffusion; it may also undergo transition ahead of the shock front. When the Reynolds number is large enough, transition in the boundary layer occurs ahead of the shock, whether the boundary layer has separated or not. According to observations made by A. Fage and R. Sargent [20], turbulent boundary layers do not separate when the pressure ratio p_2/p_1 is smaller than 1·8 which corresponds to a Mach number $\mathsf{M}_\infty < 1{\cdot}3$ for a normal shock wave. Further experimental results on the interaction between shock waves and boundary layers can be found in the publications by W. A. Mair [44], N. H. Johannesen [32], O. Bardsley and W. A. Mair [2], and J. Lukasiewicz and J. K. Royle [43].

The various effects of shocks impinging on a boundary layer will now be illustrated with reference to Schlieren photographs. As pointed out by A. D. Young [60], it is possible to distinguish the following cases:

(1) The approaching boundary layer is laminar and remains so beyond the shock without separation.

(2) The approaching boundary layer is laminar, but separates ahead of the shock because of the adverse pressure gradient and then returns to the surface in either a laminar or turbulent state, Fig. 15.20 †.

Fig. 15.23. Schlieren photograph of the flow past an aerofoil. Shock wave and boundary layer interaction. Case (5): Turbulent boundary layer with strong separation behind shock. $\mathsf{M} = 0{\cdot}90$, $\mathsf{R} = 1{\cdot}75 \times 10^6$, after Liepmann [41]

† Thanks are due to Professor H. W. Liepmann of the California Institute of Technology for his permission to use the photographs in Figs. 15.20 to 15.24 and for his kindness in supplying the original prints for publication.

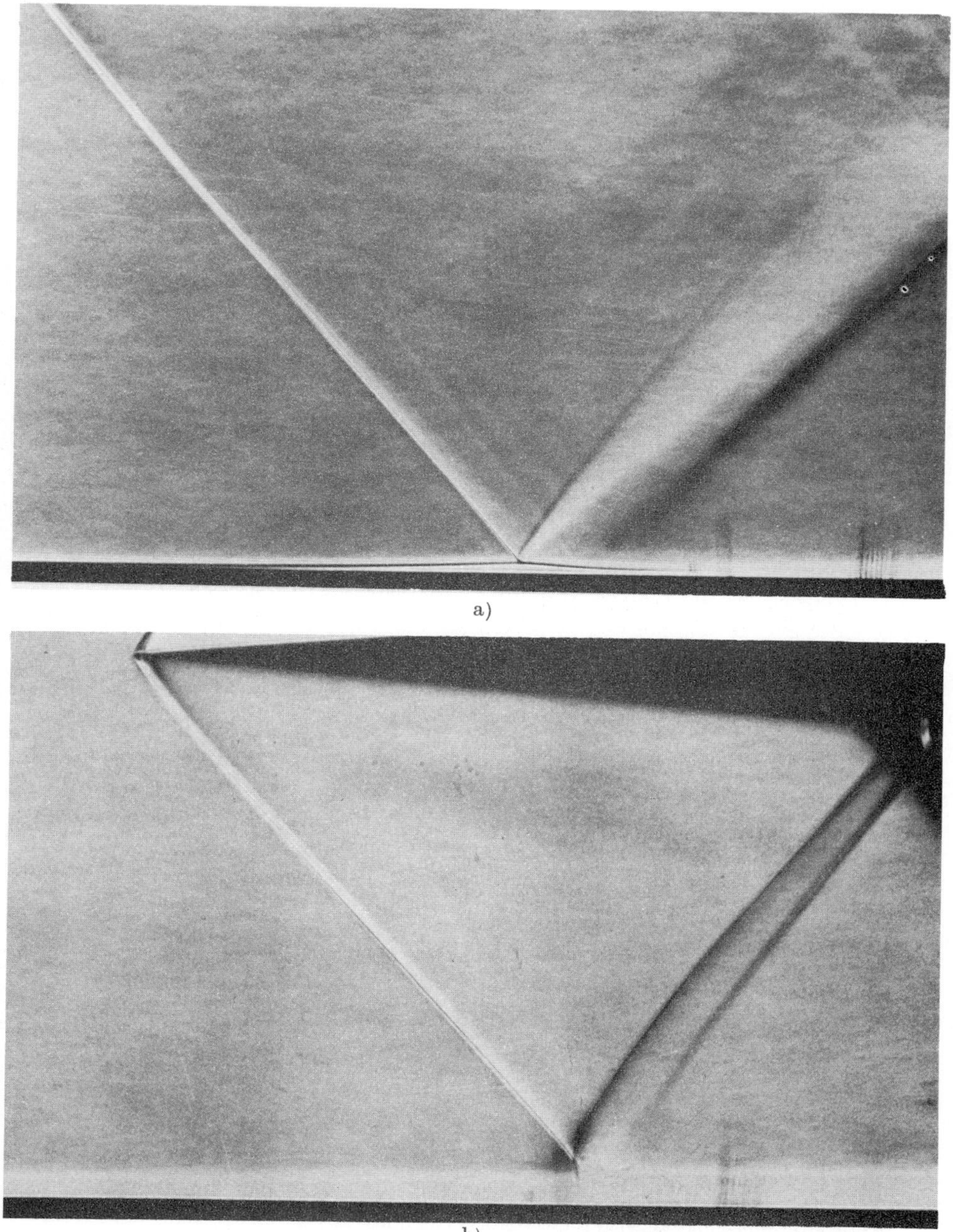

a)

b)

Fig. 15.24 a, b. Reflexion of oblique shock from flat plate with boundary layer, after Liepmann, Roshko and Dhawan [42]. a) Laminar boundary layer; b) Turbulent boundary layer

(3) The approaching boundary layer is laminar, separates completely from the surface ahead of the shock, and does not re-attach itself to the surface, Fig. 15.21; the shock is normal and sprouts a λ-limb.
(4) The approaching boundary layer is turbulent and does not separate from the surface, Fig. 15.22.
(5) The approaching boundary layer is turbulent and separates from the surface, Fig. 15.23.

Some time ago, A. Busemann [7] published observations on boundary layer separation in supersonic flow. Supersonic tunnels are usually equipped with a diffuser which serves to recover pressure from the high wind velocity. These diffusers are made in the shape of convergent-divergent channels through which the stream flows with an adverse pressure gradient in both the convergent and the divergent portion. A. Busemann observed that at all Mach numbers separation did not depend on either the angle of convergence or on the angle of divergence, but that it could always be associated with the adverse pressure gradient. In this connexion it should be realized that the change in the character of the flow which occurs at higher Mach numbers is linked with changed conditions for the adverse pressure gradients.

References

[1] J. Ackeret, F. Feldmann and N. Rott, Untersuchungen an Verdichtungsstößen und Grenzschichten in schnell bewegten Gasen. Report No. 10 of the Inst. Aero. ETH Zürich 1946; see also NACA Tech. Memo. 1113 (1947).

[2] O. Bardsley and W. A. Mair, Separation of the boundary layer at a slightly blunt leading edge in supersonic flow. Phil. Mag. **43**, 338, 344—352 (1952).

[3] F. W. Barry, A. H. Shapiro and E. P. Neumann, Some experiments on the interaction of shock waves with boundary layers on a flat plate. Jour. Appl. Mech. **17**, 126 (1950).

[4] S. M. Bogdonoff and C. E. Kepler, Separation of a supersonic turbulent boundary layer. Jour. Aero. Sci. **22**, pp. 414—424 (1955).

[5] W. S. Bradfield, D. G. Decoursin and C. B. Blumer, The effect of leading-edge bluntness on a laminar supersonic boundary layer. Jour. Aero. Sci. **21**, pp. 373—382 and 398 (1954).

[6] A. Busemann, Gasströmung mit laminarer Grenzschicht entlang einer Platte. ZAMM **15**, 23—25 (1935).

[7] A. Busemann, Das Abreißen der Grenzschicht bei Annäherung an die Schallgeschwindigkeit. Jahrbuch d. deutschen Luftfahrtforschung I, 539—541 (1940).

[8] L. F. Byran, Experiments on aerodynamic cooling. Report No. 18 of the Aero. Inst. ETH Zürich, 1951.

[9] D. R. Chapman and M. W. Rubesin, Temperature and velocity profiles in the compressible laminar boundary layer with arbitrary distribution of surface temperature. Jour. Aero. Sci. **16**, 547—565 (1949).

[10] W. F. Cope and D. R. Hartree, The laminar boundary layer in a compressible flow. Phil. Trans. Roy. Soc. A, **241**, 1 (1948).

[11] C. B. Cohen and E. Reshotko, Similar solutions for the compressible laminar boundary layer with heat transfer and pressure gradient. NACA TN 3325 (1955) and NACA Rep. No. 1293 (1956).

[12] L. Crocco, Sullo strato limite laminare nei gas lungo una lamina plana, Rend. Mat. Univ. Roma V 2, 138 (1941).

[13] L. Crocco and C. B. Cohen, Compressible laminar boundary layer with heat transfer and pressure gradient. "Fifty Years of Boundary Layer Research", Braunschweig (1955), pp. 280—293, see also NACA Rep. No. 1294 (1956).

[14] R. M. O'Donnel, Experimental investigation at Mach number of 2.41 of average skin friction coefficients and velocity profiles for laminar and turbulent boundary layers and assessment of probe effects. NACA TN 3122 (1954).

[15] E. R. van Driest, Investigation of laminar boundary layer in compressible fluids using the Crocco-Method. NACA TN 2597 (1952).

[16] E. R. VAN DRIEST, The problem of aerodynamic heating. Aero. Eng. Review, **15**, pp. 26—41, (1956).

[17] G. R. EBER, Recent investigations of temperature recovery and heat transmission on cones and cylinders in axial flow in the NOL Aeroballistics Wind Tunnel. Jour. Aero. Sci. **19**, pp. 1—6 (1952).

[18] E. A. EICHELBRENNER, Méthodes de calcul de la couche limite laminaire bidimensionelle en régime compressible. Office National d'Etudes et de Recherche Aéronautiques (ONERA). Publication No. 83 (1956).

[19] H. W. EMMONS and J. G. BRAINERD, Temperature effects in a laminar compressible fluid boundary layer along a flat plat e. J. Appl. Mech. **8**, A 105 (1941) and J. Appl. Mech. **9**, A 1 (1942).

[20] A. FAGE and R. SARGENT, Shock wave and boundary layer phenomena near a flat plate surface. Proc. Roy. Soc. A **190**, 1—20 (1947).

[21] I. FLÜGGE-LOTZ and A. F. JOHNSON, Laminar compressible boundary layer along a curved insulated surface. Jour. Aero. Sci. **22**, 7, pp. 445—454 (1955).

[22] G. E. GADD, Some aspects of laminar boundary layer separation in compressible flow with no heat transfer to the wall. Aero. Quarterly **IV**, p. 123 (1953).

[23] I. GINZEL, Ein Pohlhausen-Verfahren zur Berechnung laminarer kompressibler Grenzschichten. ZAMM **29**, 6—8 (1949), and I. GINZEL, Ein Pohlhausen-Verfahren zur Berechnung laminarer kompressibler Grenzschichten an einer geheizten Wand. ZAMM **29**, 321 — 337 (1949).

[24] E. GRUSCHWITZ, Calcul approché de la couche limite laminaire en écoulement compressible sur une paroi non-conductrice de la chaleur. ONERA (Office National d'Etudes et de Recherche Aéronautiques), Publication No. 47, Paris 1950.

[25] W. HANTZSCHE and H. WENDT, Zum Kompressibilitätseinfluß bei der laminaren Grenzschicht der ebenen Platte. Jb. d. dt. Luftfahrtforschung I, 517—521 (1940).

[26] W. HANTZSCHE and H. WENDT, Die laminare Grenzschicht an einem mit Überschallgeschwindigkeit angeströmten nicht angestellten Kreiskegel. Jahrbuch d. deutschen Luftfahrtforschung I, 76—77 (1941).

[27] W. HANTZSCHE and H. WENDT, Die laminare Grenzschicht an der ebenen Platte mit und ohne Wärmeübergang unter Berücksichtigung der Kompressibilität. Jb. d. dt. Luftfahrtforschung I, 40—50 (1942).

[27a] J. HILSENRATH, Sources of transport coefficients and correlations of transport data in selected combustion problems II, Butterworths Sci. Publ., London 1956.

[27b] J. O. HIRSCHFELDER, C. CURTIS and R. BIRD, The molecular theory of gases and liquids, Wiley, New York, 1954.

[28] G. E. GADD, D. W. HOLDER and J. D. REGAN, An experimental investigation of the interaction between shock waves and boundary layers. Proc. Roy. Soc. London, A. **226**, 227—253 (1954).

[29] L. HOWARTH, Concerning the effect of compressibility on laminar boundary layers and their separation. Proc. Roy. Soc. London, A **194**, 16 (1948).

[30] C. R. ILLINGWORTH, The laminar boundary layer associated with the retarded flow of a compressible fluid. ARC R & M 2590 (1946).

[31] C. R. ILLINGWORTH, Steady flow in the laminar boundary layer of a gas. Proc. Roy. Soc. London, A **199**, 533 (1949).

[32] N. H. JOHANNESEN, Experiments on two-dimensional supersonic flow in corners and over concave surfaces. Phil. Mag. **43**, 340, 568—580 (1952).

[33] TH. VON KÁRMÁN and H. S. TSIEN, Boundary layer in compressible fluid. Jour. Aero. Sci. **5**, 227—232 (1938); see also TH. VON KÁRMÁN, Report on Volta Congress, Rome 1935.

[34] J. KAYE, Survey of friction coefficients, recovery factors and heat transfer coefficients for supersonic flow. Jour. Aero. Sci. **21**, 117—129 (1954).

[34a] J. KESTIN, Viscosity of gases, article in Amer. Inst. of Phys. Handbook, McGraw-Hill, New York, 1957, p. 2—201.

[35] G. KUERTI, The laminar boundary layer in compressible flow. Advances in Applied Mechanics, vol. **II**, 21—92 (1951).

[36] L. LEES, Influence of the leading-edge shock wave on the laminar boundary layer at hypersonic speeds. Jour. Aero. Sci. **23**, pp. 594—600 and 612 (1956).

[37] H. G. LEW, On the compressible boundary layer over a flat plate with uniform suction. Reissner Annivers. Vol., Contr. Appl. Mech., Ann. Arbor, Mich. 43—60 (1949).

[38] T. Y. LI and H. T. NAGAMATSU, Similar solutions of compressible boundary layer equations. Jour. Aero. Sci. **20**, p. 653 (1953).
[39] T. Y. LI and H. T. NAGAMATSU, Similar solutions of compressible boundary layer equations. Jour. Aero. Sci. **22**, pp. 607—616 (1955).
[40] P. A. LIBBY and M. MORDUCHOW, Method for calculation of compressible laminar boundary layer with axial pressure gradient and heat transfer. NACA TN 3157 (1954).
[41] H. W. LIEPMANN, The interaction between boundary layer and shock waves in transonic flow. Jour. Aero. Sci. **13**, 623—637 (1946).
[42] H. W. LIEPMANN, A. ROSHKO and S. DHAWAN, On reflection of shock waves from boundary layers. NACA Rep. No. 1100 (1952).
[43] J. LUKASIEWICZ and J. K. ROYLE, Boundary layer and wake investigation in supersonic flow. ARC R & M 2613 (1952).
[44] W. A. MAIR, Experiments on separation of boundary layers on probes in a supersonic airstream. Phil. Mag. **43**, 342, 695—716 (1952).
[44a] K. W. MANGLER, Ein Verfahren zur Berechnung der laminaren Grenzschicht mit beliebiger Druckverteilung und Wärmeübergang für alle Mach-Zahlen. Zeitschr. f. Flugwiss. **4**, 63—66 (1956).
[45] R. C. MAYDEW and C. C. PAPPAS, Experimental investigation of the local and average skin friction in the laminar boundary layer on a flat plate at a Mach number of 2·4. NACA TN 2740 (1952).
[46] D. MEKSYN, Integration of the boundary layer equations for a plane in a compressible fluid. Proc. Roy. Soc. London, A **195**, 180 (1948).
[47] M. MORDUCHOW, Analysis and calculation by integral methods of laminar compressible boundary layer with heat transfer and with and without pressure gradient. NACA Report No. 1245 (1955).
[48] D. N. MORRIS and J. W. SMITH, The compressible laminar boundary layer with arbitrary pressure and surface temperature gradients. Jour. Aero. Sci. **20**, 805—818 (1953). See also D. N. MORRIS and J. W. SMITH, Ein Näherungsverfahren für die Integration der laminaren kompressiblen Grenzschichtgleichungen. ZAMM **34**, 193—194 (1954).
[48a] F. K. MOORE, Three-dimensional laminar boundary layer flow. Jour. Aero. Sci. **20**, pp. 525—534 (1953).
[49] E. A. MÜLLER, Theoretische Untersuchungen über die Wechselwirkung zwischen einem einfallenden schwachen Verdichtungsstoß und der laminaren Grenzschicht in einer Überschallströmung. "Fifty years of boundary layer research", Braunschweig 1955, pp. 343 — 363.
[50] S. I. PAI and S. F. SHEN, Hypersonic viscous flow over an inclined wedge with heat transfer. "Fifty years of boundary layer research", Braunschweig 1955, pp. 112—121.
[51] M. W. RUBESIN and H. A. JOHNSON, A critical review of skin friction and heat transfer solutions of the laminar boundary layer of a flat plate. Trans. ASME **71**, 383—388 (1949).
[52] H. SCHLICHTING, Zur Berechnung der laminaren Reibungsschicht bei Überschallgeschwindigkeit. Proc. Braunschw. Wiss. Gesellschaft **3**, 239—264 (1951).
[53] K. STEWARTSON, Correlated compressible and incompressible boundary layers. Proc. Roy. Soc. London, A **200**, 84 (1949).
[54] K. STEWARTSON, On the interaction between shock waves and boundary layers. Proc. Cambr. Phil. Soc. **47**, p. 545—553 (1951).
[55] I. TANI, On the approximate solution of the laminar boundary-layer equations. Jour. Aero. Sci. **21**, 487—495 (1954).
[56] A. N. TIFFORD, Simplified compressible laminar boundary layer theory. Jour. Aero. Sci. **18**, 358—359 (1951).
[57] A. D. YOUNG, Note on the velocity and temperature distributions attained with suction on a flat plate of infinite extent in compressible flow. Quarterly Journ. of Mech. and Appl. Math. I, 70 (1948).
[58] A. D. YOUNG, Skin friction in the laminar boundary layer of a compressible flow. Aero. Quarterly I, 137 (1949).
[59] A. D. YOUNG, Boundary layers and skin friction in high speed flow. Jour. Roy. Aero. Soc. **55**, 285 (1951).
[60] A. D. YOUNG, Section on "Boundary Layers" in "Modern Developments in Fluid Mechanics, High Speed Flow", ed. by L. HOWARTH; vol. **I**, 375—475, Oxford, Clarendon Press 1953.
[61] J. A. ZAAT, A one-parameter method for the calculation of laminar compressible boundary-layer flow with a pressure gradient. Nat. Luchtv. Lab. Amsterdam, Rep. F 141 (1953).

Part C. Transition

CHAPTER XVI

The origin of turbulence I

Some experimental results; foundations of the stability theory and experimental verification for the boundary layer on the flat plate

a. Some experimental results on transition from laminar to turbulent flow

1. Transition in pipe flow. Very often the flows of real fluids differ from the laminar flows considered in the preceding chapters. They exhibit a characteristic feature which is termed *turbulence*. When the Reynolds number is increased, internal flows in boundary layers formed on solid bodies undergo a remarkable transition from the laminar to the turbulent regime. The origin of turbulence and the accompanying transition from laminar to turbulent flow is of fundamental importance for the whole science of fluid mechanics. The incidence of turbulence was first recognised in relation to flows through straight pipes and channels. In a flow at very low Reynolds number through a straight pipe of uniform cross-section and smooth walls, every fluid particle moves with a uniform velocity along a straight path. Viscous forces slow down the particles near the wall in relation to those in the external core. The flow is well-ordered and particles travel along neighbouring layers (laminar flow), Fig. 2.18a. However, observation shows that this orderly pattern of flow ceases to exist at higher Reynolds numbers, Fig. 2.18b, and that strong mixing of all the particles occurs. This mixing process can be made visible in a flow through a pipe, as first shown by O. Reynolds [42], by feeding into it a thin thread of liquid dye. As long as the flow is laminar the thread maintains sharply defined boundaries all along the stream. As soon as the flow becomes turbulent the thread diffuses into the stream and the fluid appears uniformly coloured at a short distance downstream. In this case there is superimposed on the main motion in the direction of the axis of the pipe a subsidiary motion at right angles to it which effects mixing. The pattern of streamlines at a fixed point becomes subjected to continuous fluctuations and the subsidiary motion causes an exchange of momentum in a transverse direction because each particle substantially retains its forward momentum while mixing is taking place. As a consequence, the velocity distribution over the cross-section is considerably more uniform in turbulent than in laminar flow. The measured velocity distribution for these two types of flow is shown in Fig. 16.1, where the mass flow is the same for both cases. In laminar flow, according to the Hagen-Poiseuille solution given in Chap. I, the velocity distribution over the cross-section is parabolic (see also Fig. 1.2), but in turbulent flow, owing to the transfer of momentum in the transverse direction, it becomes considerably more uniform. On closer investigation it appears that the most essential feature of a turbulent flow is the fact that at a given point in it, the velocity and the pressure are not constant in time but exhibit very irregular, high-frequency fluctuations, Fig. 16.17. The velocity at a given point can only be considered constant on the average and over a longer period of time (quasi-steady flow).

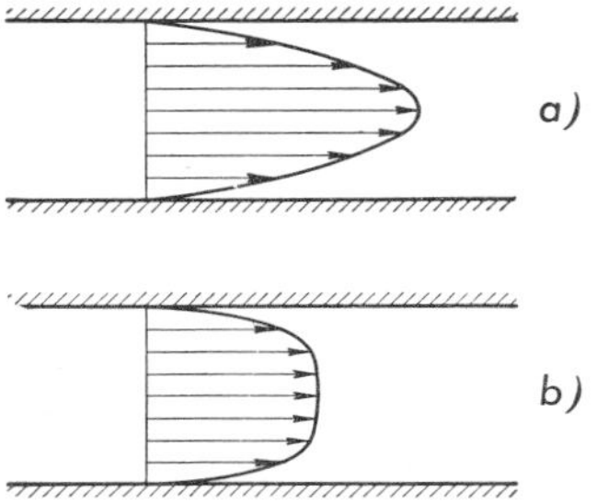

Fig. 16.1. Velocity distribution in pipe; a) laminar; b) turbulent

The first systematic investigation into these two fundamentally different patterns of flow were conducted by O. Reynolds [42]. O. Reynolds was also the first to investigate in greater detail the circumstances of the transition from laminar to turbulent flow. The previously mentioned dye experiment was used by him in this connexion, and he discovered the law of similarity, which now bears his name, and which states that transition from laminar to turbulent flow always occurs at nearly the same Reynolds number $\overline{w}\, d/\nu$, where $\overline{w} = Q/A$ is the mean flow velocity (Q = volume rate of flow, A = cross-sectional area). The numerical value of the Reynolds number at which transition occurs (critical Reynolds number) was established as being approximately

$$\mathsf{R}_{crit} = \left(\frac{\overline{w}\, d}{\nu}\right)_{crit} = 2300\,. \tag{16.1}$$

Accordingly, flows for which the Reynolds number $\mathsf{R} < \mathsf{R}_{crit}$, are supposed to be laminar, and flows for which $\mathsf{R} > \mathsf{R}_{crit}$, are expected to be turbulent. The numerical value of the critical Reynolds number depends very strongly on the conditions which prevail in the initial pipe length as well as in the approach to it. Even Reynolds thought that the critical Reynolds number increases as the disturbances in the flow before the pipe are decreased. This fact was confirmed experimentally by H. T. Barnes and E. G. Coker [1], and later by L. Schiller [49] who reached critical values of the Reynolds number of up to 20,000. V. W. Ekman [14] succeeded in maintaining laminar flow up to a critical Reynolds number of 40,000 by providing an inlet which was made exceptionally free from disturbances. The upper limit to which the critical Reynolds number can be driven if extreme care is taken to free the inlet from disturbances is not known at present. There exists, however, as demonstrated by numerous experiments, a lower bound for R_{crit} which is approximately at 2000. Below this value, the flow remains laminar even in the presence of very strong disturbances.

Transition from laminar to turbulent flow is accompanied by a noticeable change in the law of resistance. In laminar flow, the longitudinal pressure gradient which maintains the motion is proportional to the first power of the velocity (*cf.* Sec. Id); by contrast, in turbulent flow this pressure gradient becomes nearly proportional to the square of the mean velocity of flow. The increase in the resistance to flow has its origin in the turbulent mixing motion. This change in the law of pipe friction can be inferred from Fig. 20.1.

More recent, detailed investigations of the process of transition reveal that in a certain range of Reynolds numbers around the critical the flow becomes "intermittent" which means that it alternates in time between being laminar or turbulent. The variation of the velocity of flow with time in this range is shown graphically in Fig. 16.2 which represents the results of measurements performed by J. Rotta [45] at different distances along a pipe radius. The velocity plots demonstrate that periods of laminar and turbulent flow succeed each other in a random sequence. At positions closer to the centre line, the velocity in the laminar intervals exceeds the temporal mean value of the velocity of flow in the turbulent intervals; at positions closer to the pipe wall, conditions are reversed. Since during the experiments care was taken to maintain a constant rate of flow over long intervals of time, it is concluded that in the region of intermittent flow the velocity distribution alternates between a corresponding developed laminar distribution, and a corresponding fully developed turbulent distribution, as shown in Figs. 16.1a and 16.1b respectively. The physical nature of this flow can be aptly described with

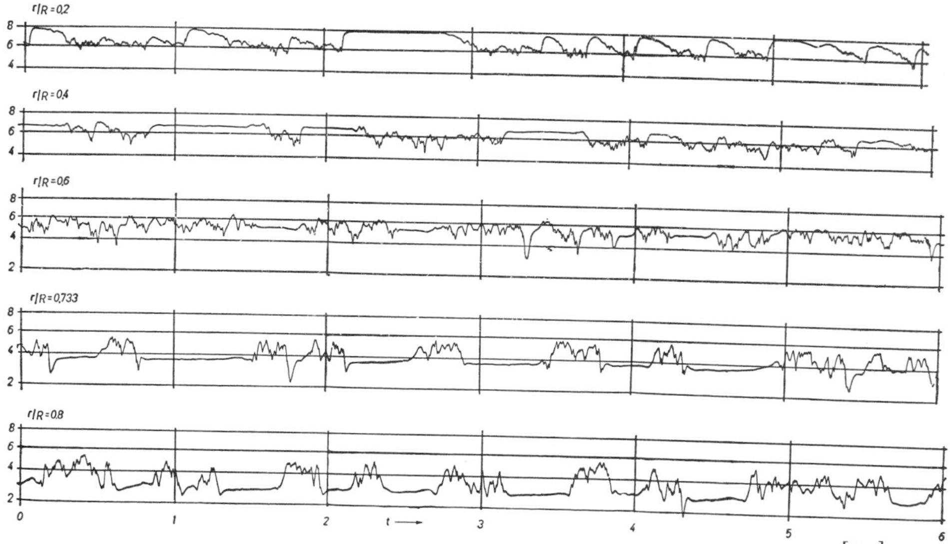

Fig. 16.2. Variation of flow velocity in a pipe in the transition range at different distances r from pipe axis, as measured by J. Rotta [45]

Reynolds number $\mathsf{R} = \overline{w}d/\nu = 2550$; axial distance $x/d = 322$; $\overline{w} = 4{\cdot}27$ m/sec ($= 14{\cdot}0$ ft/sec); velocities given in m/sec. These velocity plots, obtained with the aid of a hot-wire anemometer, demonstrate the intermittent nature of the flow in that periods of laminar and turbulent flow succeed each other in time

the aid of the intermittency factor γ, which is defined as that fraction of time during which the flow at a given position remains turbulent. Hence $\gamma = 1$ corresponds to continuous turbulent flow, and $\gamma = 0$ denotes continuous laminar flow. The intermittency factor is shown plotted in Fig. 16.3 for various Reynolds numbers in terms of the axial distance x. At a constant Reynolds number, the intermittency factor increases continuously with the distance. The Reynolds numbers cover the range from $\mathsf{R} = 2300$ to 2600 over which transition is completed. At Reynolds numbers near the lower limit, the process of transition to fully developed turbulent flow extends over very large distances measured in thousands of diameters.

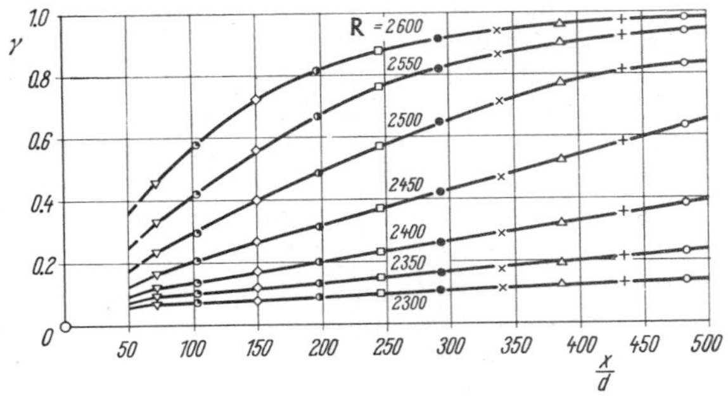

Fig. 16.3. Intermittency factor γ for pipe flow in the transition range in terms of the axial distance x for different Reynolds numbers R as measured by J. Rotta [45]

Here $\gamma = 1$ denotes continuously turbulent, and $\gamma = 0$ continuously laminar flow

2. Transition in the boundary layer on a solid body. As already stated, the flow in a boundary layer can also undergo transition, a fact which was discovered much later than transition in a pipe. The whole field of flow about a body immersed in a stream, and in particular, the force exerted on it, are strongly dependent on whether the flow in the boundary layer is laminar or turbulent. Transition in a boundary layer on a solid body in a stream is affected by many parameters, the most important ones being the pressure distribution in the external flow, the nature of the wall (roughness) and the nature of the disturbances in the free flow (intensity of turbulence).

Blunt Bodies: A particularly remarkable phenomenon connected with transition in the boundary layer occurs with blunt bodies, for example spheres or circular cylinders. It is seen from Figs. 1.4 and 1.5 that the drag coefficient of a sphere or cylinder decreases abruptly at Reynolds numbers $\mathsf{R} = VD/\nu$ of about 3×10^5. This abrupt drop in the drag coefficient, noticed first by G. Eiffel [13] in relation to spheres, is a consequence of transition in the boundary layer. Transition causes the point of separation to move downstream which considerably decreases the width of the wake. The truth of this explanation was demonstrated by L. Prandtl [36] who mounted a thin wire hoop somewhat ahead of the equator of a sphere. This causes artificially the boundary layer to become turbulent at a lower Reynolds number and produces the same drop in drag as occurs when the Reynolds number is made to increase. The smoke photographs in Figs. 2.20 and 2.21 show clearly the extent of the wake on a sphere: in the sub-critical flow regime the wake is wide and the drag is large, and in the super-critical regime it is narrow and the drag is small. The latter flow regime was here created with the aid of Prandtl's "tripping wire".

These experiments show conclusively that the jump in the drag curve of a sphere is due to a boundary layer effect and is caused by transition.

Flat plate: The process of transition on a flat plate at zero incidence is somewhat simpler to understand than that on a blunt body. The process of transition in the boundary layer on a flat plate was first studied by J. M. Burgers [2], B. G. van der Hegge Zijnen [25] and later by M. Hansen and, in greater detail, by H. L. Dryden [7, 8, 9]. According to Chap. VII, the boundary layer thickness on a flat plate increases in proportion to $\sqrt{x}$, where x denotes the distance from the leading edge. Near the leading edge the boundary layer is always laminar†, becoming turbulent further downstream. On a plate with a sharp leading edge and in a normal air stream (i. e. of intensity of turbulence $T \approx 0.5\%$) transition takes place at a distance x from it, as determined by

$$\mathsf{R}_{x,crit} = \left(\frac{U_\infty x}{\nu}\right)_{crit} = 3.5 \times 10^5 \text{ to } 10^6 .$$

On a flat plate, in the same way as in a pipe, the critical Reynolds number can be increased by providing for a disturbance-free external flow (very low intensity of turbulence).

Transition is easiest to perceive by a study of the velocity distribution in the boundary layer. As seen from Fig. 2.19, transition is shown prominently by a sudden increase in the boundary layer thickness. In a laminar boundary layer the dimensionless boundary layer thickness, $\delta/\sqrt{\nu x/U_\infty}$, remains constant and equal, approximately, to 5. The dimensionless boundary layer thickness is seen plotted against the length Reynolds number $\mathsf{R}_x = U_\infty x/\nu$ in Fig. 2.19 already mentioned; at $\mathsf{R}_x > 3.2 \times 10^5$ a sudden increase in the boundary layer thickness is clearly visible. Transition also involves a noticeable change in the shape of the velocity distribution curve. The changes in the velocity profiles in the transition region have

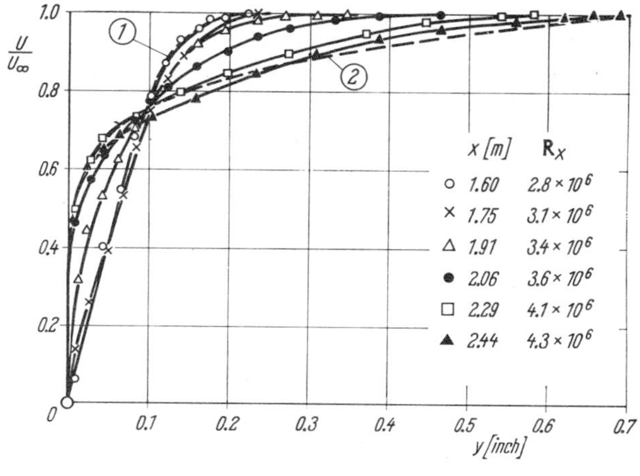

Fig. 16.4. Velocity profiles in a boundary layer on a flat plate in the transition region as measured by Schubauer and Klebanoff [52]

(1) laminar, Blasius profile; (2) turbulent, $^1/_7$-th power law, $\delta = 17$ mm (= 1·36 in), external velocity $U_\infty = 27$ m/sec (89 ft/sec); turbulence intensity $T = 0.03\%$

x [m]	R_x
o 1.60	2.8×10^6
× 1.75	3.1×10^6
△ 1.91	3.4×10^6
● 2.06	3.6×10^6
□ 2.29	4.1×10^6
▲ 2.44	4.3×10^6

† Except for leading edge separation which may occur on a flat plate of finite thickness — if no precautions have been taken to suppress it, as explained later.

been plotted in Fig. 16.4. They are based on measurements performed by G. B. Schubauer and P. S. Klebanoff [52] in a stream of very low turbulence intensity and it is seen that in this case the transition region extends over a range of Reynolds numbers from about $\mathsf{R}_x = 3 \times 10^6$ to 4×10^6. In this range, the boundary layer profile changes from that of fully developed laminar flow, as calculated by Blasius, to fully developed turbulent flow (see Chap. XXI). The process of transition involves a large decrease in the shape factor $H = \delta^*/\theta$, as seen from Fig. 16.5; here δ^* denotes the displacement thickness and θ is the momentum thickness. In the case of a flat plate, the shape factor decreases from $H \approx 2{\cdot}6$ in the laminar regime to $H \approx 1{\cdot}4$ in the turbulent regime.

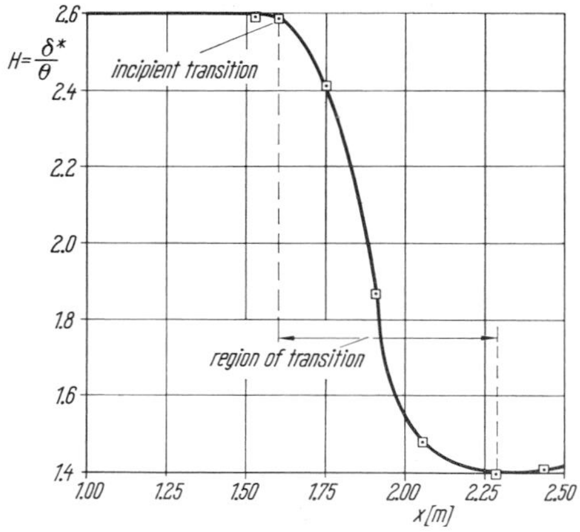

Fig. 16.5. Change in the shape factor $H = \delta^*/\theta$ for a flat plate in the transition region as measured by Schubauer and Klebanoff [52] quoted from [35a]

This change in the velocity distribution in the transition region can be utilized for the convenient determination of the point of transition, or, rather, of the transition region. The principle is explained with the aid of Fig. 16.6. A total-head tube or a Pitot tube is moved parallel to the wall at a distance which corresponds to the maximum difference between the velocities in the laminar and turbulent regimes. On being moved downstream across the transition region, the tube shows a fairly sudden increase in the total or dynamic pressure.

Transition on a flat plate also involves a large change in the resistance to flow, in this case in the skin friction. In laminar flow the skin friction is proportional to the 1·5 power of velocity, eqn. (7.36), whereas in turbulent flow the power increases to about 1·85, as shown a long time ago by W. Froude [20] who performed towing experiments with plates at very high Reynolds numbers. In this connexion the reader may also wish to consult Fig. 21.2 on p. 538.

More recent experiments performed by H. W. Emmons [15], G. B. Schubauer and P. S. Klebanoff [52] have shown that in the case of a flat plate the process of transition is also intermittent and consists of an irregular sequence of laminar and turbulent regions. As explained in Fig. 16.7, at a given point in the boundary layer there occurs suddenly a small turbulent area ("turbulent spot"), irregular in shape, which then travels downstream in a wedge-shaped region, as shown. Such turbulent spots appear at irregular intervals of time and at different, randomly

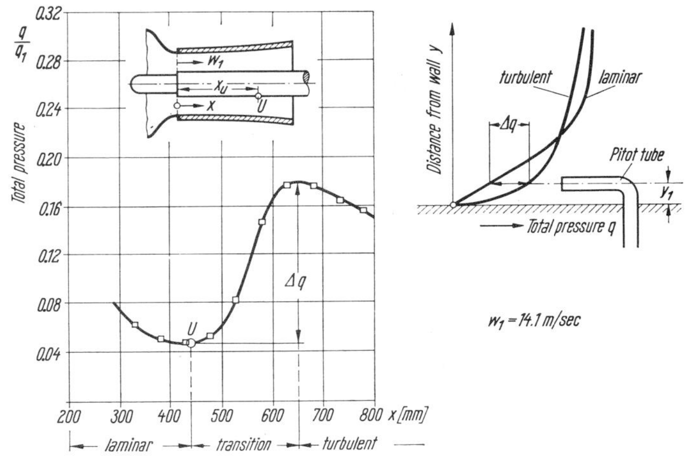

Fig. 16.6. Explanation of the method of determining the position of the point of transition with the aid of a total-head tube or a Pitot tube

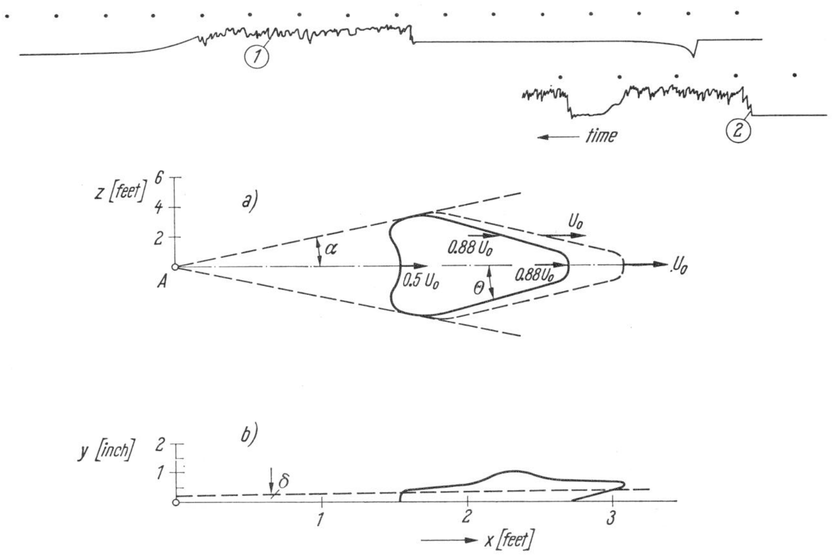

Fig. 16.7. Growth of an artificial turbulent spot in a laminar boundary layer on a flat plate at zero incidence as measured by G. B. Schubauer and P. S. Klebanoff [52], quoted from [11]

(a) plan; (b) side view of a turbulent spot artificially created at A when it is at a distance of about 2·4 ft from the point of origin. The point A is at a distance of 2·3 ft from the leading edge. $\alpha = 11{\cdot}3°$, $\Theta = 15{\cdot}3°$, δ = boundary layer thickness, $U_\infty \approx 10$ m/ sec (velocity). (1) and (2) represent oscillograms obtained with the aid of a hot-wire anemometer when an artificial or natural turbulent spot swims by. Time interval between marker traces is $^1/_{60}$ sec

distributed points on the plate. In the interior of the wedge-like domain the flow is predominantly turbulent, whereas in the adjoining regions it alternates continuously between being laminar and turbulent.

Slender bodies: It has been established that the pressure gradient along a wall exerts an important influence on the position of the point of transition in the boundary layer. In ranges of decreasing pressure (accelerated flow), the boundary layer remains, generally speaking, laminar, whereas even a very small pressure increase almost always brings transition with it. Making use of this fact, it is always possible to reduce the skin friction on slender bodies (aerofoils, stream-line bodies) by displacing the point of transition as far downstream as possible; this is achieved by a suitable choice of shape or profile and of the corresponding pressure distribution. The skin friction of bodies possessing such long laminar initial lengths of boundary layer (laminar profiles) can be reduced to as little as half or less of what it would be on a more normal shape.

The position of the point of transition and hence the magnitude of the skin friction can be strongly affected by other means also, for example by sucking away the boundary layer.

b. Principles of the theory of stability of laminar flows

1. Introductory remarks. Efforts to clarify and to explain theoretically the remarkable process of transition just described were initiated many decades ago; they have led to success only in the last thirty years. These theoretical investigations are based on the assumption that laminar flows are affected by certain small disturbances; in the case of pipe flow these disturbances may originate, for example, in the inlet, whereas in the case of a boundary layer on a solid body placed in a stream they may also be due to wall roughness or to irregularities in the external flow. The theory endeavours to follow up in time the behaviour of such disturbances when they are superimposed on the main flow, bearing in mind that their exact form still remains to be determined in particular cases. The decisive question to answer in this connexion is whether the disturbances increase or die out with time. If the disturbances decay with time, the main flow is considered stable; on the other hand, if the disturbances increase with time the flow is considered unstable, and there exists the possibility of transition to a turbulent pattern. In this way a *theory of stability* is created, and its object is to predict the value of the critical Reynolds number for a prescribed main flow. The basis of the theory of stability can be traced to O. Reynolds [43] who supposed that the laminar pattern, being a solution of the differential equations of fluid dynamics, always represents a possible type of flow, but becomes unstable above a definite limit (precisely above the critical Reynolds number) and changes into the turbulent pattern.

Much work has been done on the mathematical foundations of Reynolds' hypothesis during many decades, first by O. Reynolds himself and later, notably, by Lord Rayleigh [41]. These efforts, which led to very complicated calculations have remained for a long time devoid of achievement. About 1930, L. Prandtl and his collaborators succeeded in attaining the initial object of predicting the value of the critical Reynolds number in a satisfactory way. The experimental verification of the stability theory came some ten years later when H. L. Dryden with his co-workers were able to obtain brilliant agreement between theory and experiment. Comprehensive accounts of the theory of stability were given by H. Schlichting [48, 48a] and by C. C. Lin [32, 32a].

2. Foundation of the method of small disturbances. The theory of stability of laminar flows decomposes the motion into a mean flow (whose stability constitutes the subject of the investigation) and into a disturbance superimposed on it. Let the mean flow, which may be regarded as steady, be described by its Cartesian velocity components, U, V, W and its pressure P. The corresponding quantities for the non-steady disturbance will be denoted by u', v', w', and p' respectively. Hence, in the resultant motion the velocity components are

$$u = U + u' , \qquad v = V + v' , \qquad w = W + w' , \tag{16.2}$$

and the pressure is

$$p = P + p' . \tag{16.3}$$

In most cases it is assumed that the quantities related to the disturbance are small compared with the corresponding quantities of the main flow.

The investigation of the stability of such a disturbed flow can be carried out with the aid of either of two different methods. The first method (*energy method*) consists merely in the calculation of the variation of the energy of the disturbances with time. Conclusions are drawn depending on whether the energy decreases or increases as time goes on. The theory admits an arbitrary form of the superimposed motion and demands only that it should be compatible with the equation of continuity. The energy method was developed mainly by H. A. Lorentz [33] and did not prove successful; we shall, therefore, refrain from considering it in detail.

The second method accepts only flows which are consistent with the equations of motion and analyzes the manner in which they develop in the flow, by reference to the appropriate differential equations. This is the *method of small disturbances*. This second method has led to complete success and will, for this reason, be described with some detail.

We shall now consider a two-dimensional incompressible mean flow and an equally two-dimensional disturbance. The resulting motion, described by eqns. (16.2) and (16.3), satisfies the two-dimensional form of the Navier-Stokes equations as given in eqns. (4.4a, b, c). We shall further simplify the problem by stipulating that the mean velocity U depends only on y, i. e. $U = U(y)$, whereas the remaining two components are supposed to be zero everywhere, or $V \equiv W \equiv 0$†. We have encountered such flows earlier, describing them as *parallel flows*. In the case of a channel with parallel walls or a pipe, such a flow is reproduced with great accuracy at a sufficient distance from the inlet section. The flow in the boundary layer can also be regarded as a good approximation to parallel flow because the dependence

† There are reasons to suppose, as shown by G. B. Schubauer and P. S. Klebanoff, that these components are always present in real flows, particularly in flows past flat plates. Their magnitude is negligible for most purposes, but they seem to play a part, not yet fully elucidated, in the process of transition.

of the velocity U in the main flow on the x-co-ordinate is very much smaller than that on y. As far as the pressure in the main flow is concerned, it is obviously necessary to assume a dependence on x as well as on y, i. e. $P(x, y)$, because the pressure gradient $\partial P/\partial x$ maintains the flow. Thus we assume a mean flow with

$$U(y)\,, \qquad V \equiv W \equiv 0\,; \qquad P(x,y)\,. \tag{16.4}$$

Upon the mean flow we assume superimposed a two-dimensional disturbance which is a function of time and space. Its velocity components and pressure are, respectively,

$$u'(x,y,t)\,, \qquad v'(x,y,t)\,, \qquad p'(x,y,t)\,. \tag{16.5}$$

Hence the resultant motion, according to eqns. (16.2) and (16.3), is described by

$$u = U + u'\,; \qquad v = v'\,; \qquad w = 0\,; \qquad p = P + p'\,. \tag{16.6}$$

It is assumed that the mean flow, eqn. (16.4), is a solution of the Navier-Stokes equations, and it is required that the resultant motion, eqn. (16.3), must also satisfy the Navier-Stokes equations. The superimposed fluctuating velocities from eqn. (16.5) are taken to be "small" in the sense that all quadratic terms in the fluctuating components may be neglected with respect to the linear terms. The succeeding section will contain a more detailed description of the form of the disturbance. Now, the task of the stability theory consists in determining whether the disturbance is amplified or whether it decays for a given mean motion; the flow is considered stable or unstable depending on whether the former or the latter is the case.

Substituting into the Navier-Stokes eqns. (3.29) and neglecting quadratic terms in the disturbance velocity components, we obtain

$$\frac{\partial u'}{\partial t} + U\frac{\partial u'}{\partial x} + v'\frac{\mathrm{d}U}{\mathrm{d}y} + \frac{1}{\varrho}\frac{\partial P}{\partial x} + \frac{1}{\varrho}\frac{\partial p'}{\partial x} = \nu\left(\frac{\mathrm{d}^2 U}{\mathrm{d}y^2} + \nabla^2 u'\right),$$

$$\frac{\partial v'}{\partial t} + U\frac{\partial v'}{\partial x} + \frac{1}{\varrho}\frac{\partial P}{\partial y} + \frac{1}{\varrho}\frac{\partial p'}{\partial y} = \nu\,\nabla^2 v',$$

$$\frac{\partial u'}{\partial x} + \frac{\partial v'}{\partial y} = 0$$

where ∇^2 denotes the Laplacian operator $\partial^2/\partial x^2 + \partial^2/\partial y^2$.

If it is considered that the mean flow itself satisfies the Navier-Stokes equations, the above equations can be simplified to

$$\frac{\partial u'}{\partial t} + U\frac{\partial u'}{\partial x} + v'\frac{\mathrm{d}U}{\mathrm{d}y} + \frac{1}{\varrho}\frac{\partial p'}{\partial x} = \nu\,\nabla^2 u', \tag{16.7}$$

$$\frac{\partial v'}{\partial t} + U\frac{\partial v'}{\partial x} + \frac{1}{\varrho}\frac{\partial p'}{\partial y} = \nu\,\nabla^2 v', \tag{16.8}$$

$$\frac{\partial u'}{\partial x} + \frac{\partial v'}{\partial y} = 0\,. \tag{16.9}$$

We have obtained three equations for u', v' and p'. The boundary conditions specify that the turbulent velocity components u' and v' vanish on the walls (no slip condition). The pressure p' can be easily eliminated from the two equations, (16.7) and (16.8), so that together with the equation of continuity there are two equations for u' and v'. It is possible to criticize the assumed form of the mean flow, eqn. (16.4), on the ground that the variation of the component U of the velocity with x as well as the normal component V have been neglected. In this connection, however, J. Pretsch [39] proved that the resulting terms in the equations are unimportant for the stability of a boundary layer (see also S. J. Cheng [3]).

3. Mathematical form of the disturbance. The mean laminar flow in the x-direction with a velocity $U(y)$ is assumed to be influenced by a disturbance which is composed of a number of discrete partial fluctuations, each of which is said to consist of a wave which is propagated in the x-direction. As it has already been assumed that the perturbation is two-dimensional, it is possible to introduce a stream function $\psi(x,y,t)$ thus integrating the equation of continuity (16.9). The stream function representing a single oscillation of the disturbance is assumed to be of the form

$$\psi(x, y, t) = \phi(y)\, e^{i(\alpha x - \beta t)} . \qquad (16.10)\dagger$$

Any arbitrary two-dimensional disturbance is assumed expanded in a Fourier series, each of whose terms represents such a partial oscillation. In eqn. (16.10) α is a real quantity and $\lambda = 2\pi/\alpha$ is the wavelength of the disturbance. The quantity β is complex,

$$\beta = \beta_r + i\, \beta_i ,$$

where β_r is the circular frequency of the partial oscillation, whereas β_i (amplification factor) determines the degree of amplification or damping. The disturbances are damped if $\beta_i < 0$ and the laminar mean flow is stable, whereas for $\beta_i > 0$ instability sets in. Apart from α and β it is convenient to introduce their ratio

$$c = \frac{\beta}{\alpha} = c_r + i\, c_i . \qquad (16.11)$$

Here c_r denotes the velocity of propagation of the wave in the x-direction (phase velocity) whereas c_i again determines the degree of damping or amplification depending on its sign. The amplitude function, ϕ, of the fluctuation is assumed to depend on y only because the mean flow depends on y alone. From eqn. (16.10) it is possible to obtain the components of the perturbation velocity

$$u' = \frac{\partial \psi}{\partial y} = \phi'(y)\, e^{i(\alpha x - \beta t)} \qquad (16.12)$$

$$v' = -\frac{\partial \psi}{\partial x} = -i\, \alpha\, \phi(y)\, e^{i(\alpha x - \beta t)} . \qquad (16.13)$$

† The convenient complex notation is used here. Physical meaning is attached only to the real part of the stream function, thus

$$\mathrm{Re}(\psi) = e^{\beta_i t} [\phi_r \cos(\alpha x - \beta_r t) - \phi_i \sin(\alpha x - \beta_r t)]$$

where $\phi = \phi_r + i\, \phi_i$ is the complex amplitude.

Introducing these values into eqns. (16.7) and (16.8), we obtain, after the elimination of pressure, the following, ordinary, fourth-order, differential equation for the amplitude $\phi(y)$:

$$(U - c)(\phi'' - \alpha^2 \phi) - U'' \phi = - \frac{i\nu}{\alpha \mathsf{R}} (\phi'''' - 2\alpha^2 \phi'' + \alpha^4 \phi) . \qquad (16.14)$$

This is the fundamental *differential equation for the disturbance (stability equation)* which forms the point of departure for the stability theory of laminar flows. It is commonly referred to as the *Orr-Sommerfeld equation.* Equation (16.14) has been cast in dimensionless form in that all lengths have been divided by a suitable reference length b or δ (width of channel or boundary layer thickness), and velocities have been divided by the maximum velocity U_m of the main flow. The dashes denote here differentiation with respect to the dimensionless co-ordinates y/δ or y/b, and

$$\mathsf{R} = \frac{U_m b}{\nu} \qquad \text{or} \qquad \mathsf{R} = \frac{U_m \delta}{\nu}$$

denotes the Reynolds number which is a characteristic of the mean flow. The terms on the left-hand side of eqn. (16.14) are derived from the inertia terms, and those on the right-hand side from the viscous terms in the equations of motion. By way of example, the boundary conditions for a boundary-layer flow demand that the components of the perturbation velocity must vanish at the wall ($y = 0$) and at a large distance from it (free stream). Thus:

$$y = 0: \quad u' = v' = 0: \quad \phi = 0, \quad \phi' = 0 \qquad (16.15)$$

$$y = \infty: \quad u' = v' = 0: \quad \phi = 0, \quad \phi' = 0 .$$

At this stage it is possible to raise the objection that disturbances superimposed on a two-dimensional flow pattern need not be two-dimensional, if a complete analysis of the question of stability is to be achieved. This objection was removed by H. B. Squire [55] who proved, by assuming disturbances which were periodic also in the z-direction, that a two-dimensional flow pattern becomes unstable at a higher Reynolds number when the disturbance is assumed three-dimensional than when it is supposed to be two-dimensional. In this sense two-dimensional disturbances are "more dangerous" for two-dimensional flows than three-dimensional disturbances. Hence the value of the critical Reynolds number, or, more precisely, of the lowest limit of stability, is obtained by considering two-dimensional disturbances.

4. The eigen-value problem. The problem of stability has now been reduced to an eigen-value problem of eqn. (16.14) with the boundary conditions (16.15). When the mean flow $U(y)$ is specified, eqn. (16.14) contains four parameters, namely α, R, c_r and c_i. Of these the Reynolds number of the mean flow is likewise specified and, further, the wavelength $\lambda = 2\pi/\alpha$ of the disturbance is to be considered given. In this case the differential equation (16.14), together with the boundary conditions (16.15), furnish one eigen-function $\phi(y)$ and one complex eigenvalue $c = c_r + i c_i$ for each pair of values α, R. Here c_r represents the phase velocity of the prescribed disturbance whereas the sign of c_i determines whether the wave is amplified ($c_i > 0$) or damped ($c_i < 0$)†. For $c_i < 0$ the corresponding flow (U, R) is stable for the given value of α, whereas $c_i > 0$ denotes instability. The limiting case $c_i = 0$ corresponds to neutral (indifferent) disturbances.

The result of such an analysis for a prescribed laminar flow $U(y)$ can be represented graphically in an α, R diagram because every point of this plane corresponds to a pair of values of c_r and c_i. In particular, the locus $c_i = 0$ separates the region of stable from that of unstable disturbances. This locus is called the *curve of neutral stability* (Fig. 16.8). The point on this curve at which the Reynolds number has its smallest value (tangent parallel to the α-axis) is of greatest interest since it indicates that value of the Reynolds number below which all individual oscillations decay, whereas above that value at least some are amplified. This smallest Reynolds number is the *critical Reynolds number* or *limit of stability* with respect to the type of laminar flow under consideration.

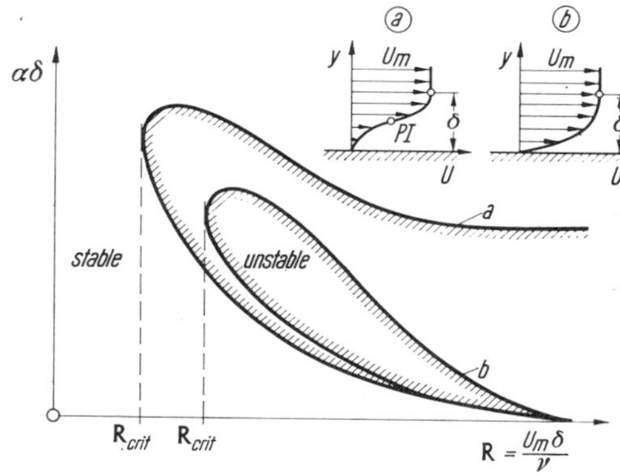

Fig. 16.8. Curves of neutral stability for a two-dimensional boundary layer with two-dimensional disturbances

(a) "non-viscous" instability; in the case of velocity profiles of type a *with* point of inflexion *PI*, the curve of neutral stability is of type a

(b) "viscous" instability; in the case of velocity profiles of type b *without* point of inflexion, the curve of neutral stability is of type b

The asymptotes for the curve of neutral stability a at $R \to \infty$ are obtained from the "frictionless" stability equation (16.16)

The experimental evidence concerning transition from laminar to turbulent flow referred to previously leads us to expect that, at small Reynolds numbers for which laminar flow is observed, all wavelengths would produce only stable disturbances, whereas at larger Reynolds numbers, for which turbulent flow is observed, unstable disturbances ought to correspond to at least some wavelengths. However, it is necessary to remark at this point that the critical Reynolds number calculated from stability considerations cannot be expected to be equal to the Reynolds number observed at the point of transition. If attention is fixed on the flow in the boundary layer along a wall, then the theoretical critical Reynolds number indicates the point on the wall at which amplification of some individual disturbances begins and proceeds downstream of it. The transformation of such amplified disturbances into turbulence takes up some time, and the unstable disturbance has had a chance

† On the other hand, it is also possible to regard R and the circular frequency β_r as fixed. In this case the eigenvalue problem determines a corresponding value of α (the wavelength) and the coefficient of amplification, β_i. These were the conditions satisfied by the experiments carried out by H. L. Dryden and his collaborators, as described in Sec. XVIe, when an artificial disturbance of a definite frequency was superimposed on a laminar flow with the aid of a suitably excited strip.

to travel some distance in the downstream direction. It must, therefore, be expected that the observed position of the point of transition will be downstream of the calculated, theoretical limit of stability, or, in other words, that the experimental critical Reynolds number exceeds its theoretical value. This remark, evidently, applies to Reynolds numbers based on the current length as well as to those based on the boundary layer thickness. In order to distinguish between these two values it is usual to call the theoretical critical Reynolds number (limit of stability) the *point of instability* whereas the experimental critical Reynolds number is called the *point of transition* †.

The stability problem, briefly described in the preceding paragraphs, leads to extremely difficult mathematical considerations. Owing to these, success in the calculation of the critical Reynolds number eluded the workers in this field for several decades, in spite of the greatest efforts directed towards this goal. Consequently, in what follows we shall be unable to provide a complete presentation of the stability theory and will be forced to restrict ourselves to giving an account of the most important results only.

5. General properties of the disturbance differential equation. Since from experimental evidence the limit of stability $c_i = 0$ is expected to occur for large values of the Reynolds number, it is natural to simplify the equation by omitting the viscous terms on the right-hand side of it, as compared with the inertia terms, because of the smallness of the coefficient $1/\mathsf{R}$. The resulting differential equation is known as the *frictionless disturbance* (or *stability*) *equation:*

$$(U-c)\,(\phi'' - \alpha^2\,\phi) - U''\,\phi = 0\,. \tag{16.16}$$

It is important to note here that of the four boundary conditions (16.15) of the complete equation it is now possible to satisfy only two, because the frictionless stability equation is of the second order. The remaining boundary condition to be satisfied is the vanishing of the normal components of velocity near the wall of a channel, or, in boundary layer flow, their vanishing at the wall and at infinity. Thus, in the latter case, we have

$$y = 0:\quad \phi = 0;\qquad y = \infty:\quad \phi = 0\,. \tag{16.17}$$

The omission of the viscous terms constitutes a drastic simplification, because the order of the equation is reduced from four to two, and this may result in a loss of important properties of the general solution of the complete equation, as compared with its simplified version. Here we may repeat the remarks noted previously in Chap. IV in connexion with the transition from the Navier-Stokes equations of a viscous fluid to those for a frictionless fluid.

The majority of earlier papers on the theory of stability used the frictionless equation (16.16) as their point of departure. In this manner, evidently, no critical Reynolds number can be obtained but it is possible to answer the question of

† As already explained in Sec. XVIa, recent experimental results (H. W. Emmons [15], and Schubauer and Klebanoff [52]) indicate that there is no well-defined point of transition but that the process of transition from laminar to fully developed turbulent flow extends over a finite distance.

whether a given laminar flow is stable or not†. The complete equation (16.14) was analyzed much later when, after many failures, critical Reynolds numbers were at last successfully evaluated

Starting with the above frictionless stability equation, eqn. (16.16), Lord Rayleigh [40] succeeded in deriving several important, general theorems concerning the stability of laminar velocity profiles. The validity of these has later been confirmed also for the case when the effect of viscosity is taken into account.

Theorem I: The first important, general theorem of this kind, the so-called *point-of-inflexion criterion,* asserts that velocity profiles which possess a point of inflexion are unstable.

Lord Rayleigh was able only to prove that the existence of a point of inflexion constitutes a *necessary condition* for the occurrence of instability. Much later, W. Tollmien [60] succeeded in showing that this constitutes also a *sufficient condition* for the amplification of disturbances. The point-of-inflexion criterion is of fundamental importance for the theory of stability because it provides — except for a correction due to the omission of the influence of viscosity — a first, rough classification of all laminar flows. From the practical point of view, this criterion is important owing to the direct connexion between the existence of a point of inflexion and the presence of a pressure gradient. In the case of convergent channel flow with a favourable pressure gradient, as seen from Fig. 5.15, the velocity profiles are very full and possess no points of inflexion. In contradistinction, in a divergent channel with an adverse pressure gradient, the velocity profiles are pointed and points of inflexion are present. Identical differences in the geometrical form of the velocity profiles occur in the laminar boundary layer on a body immersed in a stream. According to boundary layer theory, the velocity profiles in the interval where the pressure decreases are free from points of inflexion, whereas those in the interval where the pressure increases always possess them, see Sec. VIIc. Hence, the point-of-inflexion criterion becomes equivalent to a statement about the effect of the pressure gradient in the external flow on the stability of the respective boundary layers. As applied to boundary layer flow, it amounts to this: a favourable pressure gradient stabilizes the flow, whereas an adverse pressure gradient enhances instability. It follows that the position of the point of minimum pressure on a body placed in a stream is decisive for the position of the point of transition, and, roughly speaking, we can say that the position of the point of minimum pressure determines that of the point of transition and causes the latter to lie close behind the former.

The influence of viscosity on the solution of the stability equation, which has been neglected up to this point, changes the preceding conclusions only very slightly. The preceding instability of velocity profiles with points of inflexion is usually referred to as "frictionless instability" because the laminar mean flow proves to be unstable even without taking into account the effect of viscosity on the oscillating motion. In the diagram of Fig. 16.8, the case of frictionless instability corresponds to the curve of type *a*. Even at $\mathsf{R} = \infty$ there exists already a certain unstable range of wavelengths; in the direction of decreasing Reynolds numbers, this range is separated from the stable range by the curve of neutral stability.

† With the reservation that the influence of viscosity on the disturbance itself has been left out of consideration.

In contrast with the preceding case, *viscous instability* is associated with a curve of neutral stability of shape b, also shown in Fig. 16.8, and with boundary layer profiles possessing no point of inflexion. At Reynolds numbers tending to infinity, the range of unstable wavelengths is contracted to a point and domains of unstable oscillations are seen to exist only for finite Reynolds numbers. Generally speaking, the amount of amplification is much larger in the case of frictionless instability than in the case of viscous instability.

The existence of viscous instability can be discovered only in connexion with a discussion of the full Orr-Sommerfeld equation; it constitutes, therefore, the more difficult analytical case. The simplest case of flow, namely that along a flat plate with zero pressure gradient belongs to the kind for which only viscous instability does occur; it was successfully tackled only comparatively recently.

Theorem II: The second important general theorem states that the velocity of propagation of neutral disturbances ($c_i = 0$) in a boundary layer is smaller than the maximum velocity of the mean flow, i. e. that $c_r < U_m$.

This theorem was also first proved by Lord Rayleigh [40], albeit under some restrictive assumptions; it was proved again by W. Tollmien [61] for more general conditions. It asserts that in the interior of the flow there exists a layer where $U - c = 0$ for neutral disturbances. This fact, too, is of fundamental importance in the theory of stability. The layer for which $U - c = 0$ corresponds, namely, to a singular point of the frictionless stability equation (16.16). At this point ϕ'' becomes infinite if U'' does not vanish there simultaneously. The distance $y = y_K$ where $U = c$, is called the *critical layer* of the mean flow. If $U_K'' \neq 0$, then ϕ'' tends to infinity as

$$\frac{U''_K}{U'_K} \frac{1}{y - y_K}$$

in the neighbourhood of the critical layer where it is permissible to put $U - c = U_K'(y - y_K)$ approximately; consequently the x-component of the velocity can be written as

$$u' = \phi' \sim \frac{U''_K}{U'_K} \cdot \ln(y - y_K) . \tag{16.18}$$

Thus, according to the frictionless stability equation, the component u' of the velocity which is parallel to the wall becomes infinite if the curvature of the velocity profile at the critical layer does not vanish simultaneously. This mathematical singularity in the frictionless stability equation points to the fact that the effect of viscosity on the equation of motion must not be neglected in the neighbourhood of the critical layer. The inclusion of the effect of viscosity removes this physically absurd singularity of the frictionless stability equation. The analysis of the effect of this so-called viscous correction on the solution of the stability equation plays a fundamental part in the discussion of stability.

The two theorems due to Lord Rayleigh show that the curvature of the velocity profile affects stability in a fundamental way. Simultaneously it has been demonstrated that the calculation of velocity profiles in laminar boundary layers must proceed with very high accuracy for the investigation of stability to be possible: it is not enough to evaluate $U(y)$ with a sufficient degree of accuracy but its second derivative d^2U/dy^2 must also be accurately known.

c. Results of the theory of stability as they apply to the boundary layer on a flat plate at zero incidence

1. Some older investigations into stability. The earlier investigations undertaken as a continuation of Lord Rayleigh's work limited themselves at first to the consideration of Couette flow, i. e. to the case of linear velocity distribution in a flow between two parallel walls, Fig. 1.1. The very exhaustive discussion of the case which included the full effect of viscosity provided by A. Sommerfeld [54], R. von Mises [34] and L. Hopf [29] led to the conclusion that this type of flow remains stable at all Reynolds numbers and at all wavelengths. For a time, after this negative result had been obtained, it was thought that the method of small oscillations was unsuitable for the theoretical solution of the problem of transition. It transpired later that this view was not justified, because Couette flow is a very special and restricted example. Moreover, as shown earlier, the curvature of the velocity profile plays an essential physical role in the flow, and it is not permissible to leave it out of account.

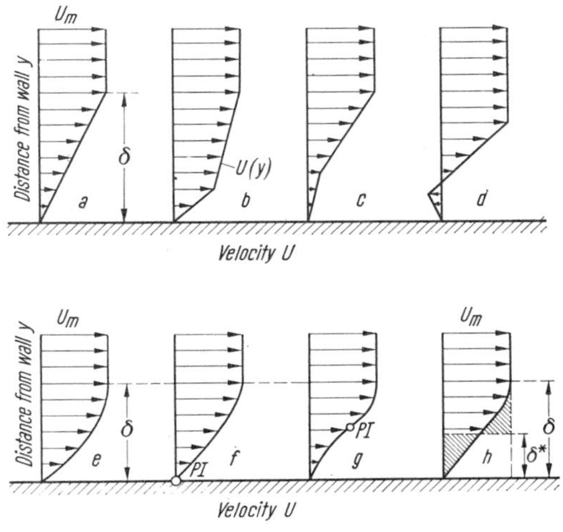

Fig. 16.9. Velocity profiles illustrating the study of the stability of laminar boundary layers

$U(y)$ = velocity distribution; U_m = velocity in the free stream; δ = boundary layer thickness; δ^* = displacement thickness; PI = point of inflexion of the velocity profile. For $\mathsf{R} \to \infty$ the profiles of type a, b, e, and f are stable; profiles of type c, d, g are unstable; profiles of type e exist in a favourable pressure gradient; type f corresponds to constant pressures; type g exists in an adverse pressure gradient

In the year 1921 L. Prandtl [37] reverted to the attempt to examine the problem of stability by theoretical methods. In order to consider the stability of a laminar boundary layer on a flat plate without undue mathematical complications, velocity profiles with straight segments were used, Figs. 16.9a, b, c, d in the same way as was done previously by Lord Rayleigh. A calculation performed by O. Tietjens [58] on the basis of the frictionless stability equation showed that in the case of boundary layer profiles, the existence of convex corners Figs. 16.9a, b, ensures stability, whereas concave corners, Figs. 16.9c, d, always lead to instability. This investigation made it plausible to suppose that velocity profiles with points of inflexion, Fig. 16.9g, are unstable. The truth of this supposition was later demonstrated by W. Tollmien [60], as already stated in Sec. XVIb, Theorem I.

In order to obtain a limit of stability expressed in terms of a Reynolds number for unstable velocity profiles (Figs. 16.9c and d), the largest viscous terms appearing in the complete stability equation (16.14) were taken into account, and it was expected that they will promote damping. The influence of viscosity on the disturbances extended here only over a very small region of the whole velocity profile, being located in the immediate neighbourhood of the wall, in order to satisfy the no-slip condition. The calculations performed by O. Tietjens led to the very unexpected result that the introduction of a small value of viscosity into the equations did not produce damping but amplification for all Reynolds numbers, and for all wavelengths of the disturbances. Moreover, this result was obtained not only for unstable velocity profiles (Figs. 16.9c, d) but also for the profiles of type a and b in Fig. 16.9, which have been shown to be stable when viscosity was neglected.

2. Tollmien's method for the calculation of the curve of neutral stability. A satisfactory explanation of the above paradox was supplied by W. Tollmien [59] in the year 1929. He demonstrated that the influence of viscosity on disturbances must be taken into account not only in the immediate neighbourhood of the wall, as supposed by O. Tietjens, but that, in addition, it must be accounted for also in the neighbourhood of the critical layer, where the velocity of wave propagation of the disturbances becomes equal to the velocity of the main flow and where, as shown in Sec. XVI b. 5, the component u' becomes infinite according to the simplified, frictionless theory, the curvature of the profile being different from zero. The existence of viscosity causes large changes in this *critical layer*, while it is also evident that in reality u' remains finite there. However, the influence of viscosity becomes evident only if the curvature of the velocity profile is not left out of account. These considerations demonstrated that it was necessary to study the behaviour of small disturbances with respect to curved velocity profiles ($\mathrm{d}^2U/\mathrm{d}y^2 \neq 0$), and with viscosity taken into account both in the neighbourhood of the wall and in the critical layer. This programme was carried out by W. Tollmien in the paper quoted earlier, and as a result, he was able to find a limit of stability (critical Reynolds number) for the example of the flow in the boundary layer on a flat plate at zero incidence which agreed well with experiments. The method developed by W. Tollmien became the basis for further progress in modern times, and it seems appropriate to examine it a little more closely.

In order to formulate the boundary value problem for the complete stability equation (16.14), together with the boundary conditions (16.15), it is necessary to write down a fundamental system ϕ_1, ϕ_2, ϕ_3, ϕ_4 for this differential equation. Since the evaluation of four particular solutions of the Orr-Sommerfeld stability equation (16.14) is still a very difficult task, the method consists in finding two solutions ϕ_1 and ϕ_2 from the frictionless stability equation (16.16); the second pair, ϕ_3 and ϕ_4, is then deduced from a new subsidiary equation. The subsidiary equation is derived from the full equation (16.14) by retaining only the most important viscous term.

The frictionless solutions: We shall suppose that the basic flow $U(y)$ has one of the profiles of Fig. 16.9 and that at a finite distance δ from the wall its velocity merges into the free stream $U = U_m = \text{const.}$ In the region of the free stream

($y > \delta$) it is possible at once to write down the solution of the frictionless equation (16.16); taking into account the boundary condition at $y = \infty$, we obtain

$$\phi = e^{-\alpha y} . \tag{16.19}$$

As shown previously in Sec. XVIb, 5, Theorem II, for the neutral disturbances there exists a point where $U - c_r = 0$ at the critical layer and whose distance was denoted by $y = y_K$. The pair of solutions ϕ_1, ϕ_2 of the frictionless equation (16.16) can be expanded into power series in $(y - y_K)$ and the following two forms are obtained:

$$\begin{aligned} \phi_1 &= (y - y_K)\, P_1 , \\ \phi_2 &= P_2 + \frac{U''_K}{U'_K} (y - y_K)\, P_1 \cdot \ln (y - y_K) . \end{aligned} \tag{16.20}$$

Here P_1 and P_2 denote two power series in $(y - y_K)$ and U_K' and U_K'' denote the values of dU/dy and d^2U/dy^2, respectively, at the point $y = y_K$. Since ϕ_2' becomes infinite at $y = y_K$, the corresponding x-component of the fluctuation velocity also becomes infinite, and the solution for ϕ_2 requires the application of a viscous correction in the neighbourhood of $y = y_K$.

The viscous correction: In order to evaluate the viscous correction term for ϕ_2 as well as the second pair of solutions ϕ_3, ϕ_4, we deduce a simplified stability equation which is obtained from eqn. (16.14) by retaining only the largest viscous terms. It is convenient to introduce a new variable η defined as

$$\eta = \frac{y - y_K}{\varepsilon}$$

where

$$\varepsilon = (\alpha \mathsf{R}\, U'_K)^{-1/3} . \tag{16.21}$$

Generally speaking ε will be small for neutral disturbances. Thus $\phi(\eta)$ satisfies the equation

$$i\, \phi'''' + \eta\, \phi'' = \varepsilon \frac{U''_K}{U'_K} . \tag{16.22}$$

Putting

$$\phi_2^{(1)} = 1 + \varepsilon\, \phi_{21} ,$$

we obtain the following differential equation for $\phi_{21}(\eta)$:

$$i \frac{d^4 \phi_{21}}{d \eta^4} + \eta \frac{d^2 \phi_{21}}{d\eta^2} = \frac{U''_K}{U'_K} .$$

For large values of η it is necessary to match this solution to the frictionless solution ϕ_2. W. Tollmien discussed this solution in detail and found that, if the logarithm in eqn. (16.20) is taken as being real for $(y - y_K) > 0$, then for $(y - y_K) < 0$ it is necessary to take $\ln | y - y_K | - i \pi$.

This means that for $(y - y_K) > 0$ the component u' of the disturbance becomes

$$\frac{U''_K}{U'_K} \ln (y - y_K) \cdot \cos (\alpha x - \beta t) , \tag{16.23}$$

and for $(y - y_K) < 0$ it is

$$\frac{U''_K}{U'_K} \ln | y - y_K | \cdot \cos (\alpha x - \beta t) + \pi \frac{U''_K}{U'_K} \sin (\alpha x - \beta t) . \tag{16.24}$$

It has thus been shown that on crossing the critical layer there is a *jump* in the *phase* of the component u' which persists when passing to the limit of very large Reynolds numbers. This phase jump comes to light only when the influence of viscosity on the disturbances is taken into account in a proper manner in the neighbourhood of the critical layer, and if the calculation is carried out for a velocity profile with non-zero curvature. This phase jump is of fundamental importance for the mechanism of propagation of disturbances.

The viscous solutions: The second pair of solutions, the so-called viscous solutions ϕ_3 and ϕ_4, are obtained from eqn. (16.22) by equating its right-hand side to zero, i. e. from

$$\mathrm{i}\, \phi'''' + \eta\, \phi'' = 0 . \tag{16.25}$$

The pair of solutions ϕ_3 and ϕ_4 is seen to be completely independent of the mean flow $U(y)$, and can be calculated once and for all. In view of the boundary conditions, of the two solutions ϕ''_3 and ϕ''_4 only that one is relevant which decreases rapidly for large values of η. We shall denote it by ϕ_3. Thus the solution of eqn. (16.25) becomes

$$\phi_3 = \int_\infty^\eta \int_\infty^{\eta'} \eta'^{1/2} H^{(1)}_{1/3}\left[\tfrac{2}{3} (\mathrm{i}\, \eta')^{3/2}\right] \mathrm{d}\eta\, \mathrm{d}\eta' ,$$

where $H^{(1)}{}_{1/3}$ denotes the Hankel function of the first kind. This function was first tabulated by Tietjens [58]; the numerical values have later been tabulated with great accuracy by H. Holstein [28].

The eigen-value problem: With these introductory remarks we are now in a position to give a very simple formulation of the eigen-value problem. We begin by assuming that the mean flow is a boundary layer flow which joins the uniform external flow at $y = \delta$. Hence the solution given in eqn. (16.19) is valid for $y > \delta$, i.e. $\phi' + \alpha\, \phi = 0$ for $y \geq \delta$. The general solution of the complete stability equation is now seen to be the sum of three particular solutions, as follows:

$$\phi = C_1\, \phi_1 + C_2\, \phi_2 + C_3\, \phi_3 .$$

Since the solution ϕ_3 decreases rapidly for large values of y, it is not necessary to take it into account at $y = \delta$. Thus the first boundary condition becomes

$$C_1\, \Phi_{1\delta} + C_2\, \Phi_{2\delta} = 0 ,$$

where the abbreviation $\Phi_{\nu\delta} = \phi'_{\nu\delta} + \alpha\, \phi_{\nu\delta}$ has been used. At this point it is necessary to include the viscous term ϕ_3, and consequently

$$C_1\, \phi_{1w} + C_2\, \phi_{2w} + C_3\, \phi_{3w} = 0$$
$$C_1\, \phi'_{1w} + C_2\, \phi'_{2w} + C_3\, \phi'_{3w} = 0\,.$$

The preceding three homogeneous equations for C_1, C_2 and C_3 lead to the condition

$$\begin{vmatrix} \phi_{1w} & \phi_{2w} & \phi_{3w} \\ \phi'_{1w} & \phi'_{2w} & \phi'_{3w} \\ \Phi_{1\delta} & \Phi_{2\delta} & 0 \end{vmatrix} = 0$$

or, in expanded form

$$\frac{\phi_{3w}}{\phi'_{3w}} = \frac{\phi_{2w}\, \Phi_{1\delta} - \phi_{1w}\, \Phi_{2\delta}}{\phi'_{2w}\, \Phi_{1\delta} - \phi'_{1w}\, \Phi_{2\delta}}\,. \tag{16.26}$$

On putting, further,

$$\phi_{3w}/\phi'_{3w} = -\,\varepsilon \cdot D(\eta_w) \quad \text{and} \quad \eta_w = -\,y_K/\varepsilon$$

in accordance with eqn. (16.21), and introducing the additional contraction

$$-\frac{1}{y_K}\, \frac{\phi_{2w}\, \Phi_{1\delta} - \phi_{1w}\, \Phi_{2\delta}}{\phi'_{2w}\, \Phi_{1\delta} - \phi'_{1w}\, \Phi_{2\delta}} = E\,(\alpha, c)\,,$$

it is possible to write the eigen-value problem from eqn. (16.26) in the form

$$-\,\frac{D(\eta_w)}{\eta_w} = E\,(\alpha, c)\,. \tag{16.27}$$

It is now necessary to determine the related eigen-values, namely the wavelength of the disturbance $\lambda = 2\,\pi/\alpha$, the propagation velocity c_r, and the Reynolds number $\mathsf{R} = U_m\, \delta/\nu$ for a neutral disturbance. This can be done numerically or graphically. The right-hand side of this last equation contains only the frictionless solutions and is, therefore, a function of α and c_r only. The left-hand side contains only the viscous solution ϕ_3 and is a function of η_w alone. In order to solve the complex equation (16.27) we use a graphical method. Representing real values along the axis of abscissae, and imaginary values along the axis of ordinates (Argand, or polar diagram) we draw the curve $-\,D(\eta_w)/\eta_w$. On the same diagram we now plot E as a function of α at constant values of c_r (Fig. 16.10). From the two points of intersection of the two curves it is now possible to determine α and η_w for the co-ordinates of the curve of neutral stability. The values of η_w, together with the selected value of c_r and the corresponding wall distance y_K, determine values of ε and hence the Reynolds number R from eqn. (16.21). The two points of intersection correspond to one point each on the upper and lower branches of the neutral stability curve in Fig. 16.11.

At a later time, W. Tollmien [62] supplemented the asymptotic estimates of the approximate solutions given in his 1929 paper with a detailed assessment of the errors and the result turned out to be entirely satisfactory. In this connexion the reader may wish to consult a paper by D. Grohne [22]. See also W. Tollmien [62a].

3. Results for the flat plate. As a first application, W. Tollmien [95] employed the preceding method to the investigation of the stability of the boundary layer on a flat plate at zero incidence. The velocity profile of such a boundary layer (Blasius profile) is shown in Fig. 7.8. The profiles at different stations along the plate are similar which means that they can be made to coincide when they are plotted against $y/\delta(x)$. Here $\delta(x)$ denotes the boundary thickness which has been shown in eqn. (7.38) to be given by $\delta = 5{\cdot}1 \sqrt{\nu\, x/U_\infty}$. The velocity profile possesses a point of inflexion at the wall and corresponds to the one shown in Fig. 16.9f. Thus, in the light of the point-of-inflexion criterion which we stated in Sec. XVIb. 5, it is seen that this profile lies just on the border-line between profiles with no point of inflexion, which are stable according to the frictionless theory, and profiles with a point of inflexion, which are unstable.

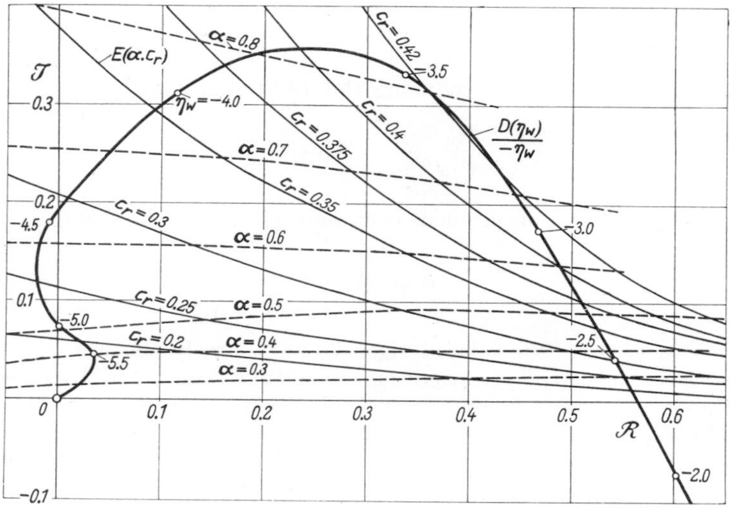

Fig. 16.10. Argand diagram for the solution of the eigenvalue problem in eqn. (16.26). Example: Boundary layer velocity profile on a flat plate at zero incidence. R real part, I imaginary part of E and $-D(\eta_w)/\eta_w$ respectively

The results of stability calculations performed in accordance with the method described in the preceding section are shown in Figs. 16.11 and 16.12. The state-points along the curves themselves represent neutral disturbances; the region embraced by the curve corresponds to unstable disturbances, and that outside it contains stable points. The two branches of the curve of neutral stability tend towards zero at very large Reynolds numbers. The smallest Reynolds number, for which one indifferent disturbance still exists, represents the critical Reynolds number and is given by

$$\left(\frac{U_\infty \delta^*}{\nu}\right)_{crit} = \mathsf{R}_{crit} = 420 \quad \text{(point of instability)}.$$

This is the point of instability for the boundary layer on a flat plate. It is remarkable that only a comparatively narrow range of wavelengths and frequencies is "dangerous" for the laminar boundary layer. On the one hand, there is a *lower* limit for the Reynolds number, on the other, there is an *upper* limit for the characteristic magnitudes of the disturbances. Once the latter are exceeded no instability is caused. The numerical values are:

$$\frac{c_r}{U_\infty} = 0{\cdot}42\ ; \quad \alpha\,\delta^* = 0{\cdot}36\ ; \quad \frac{\beta_r\,\delta^*}{U_\infty} = 0{\cdot}15\,.$$

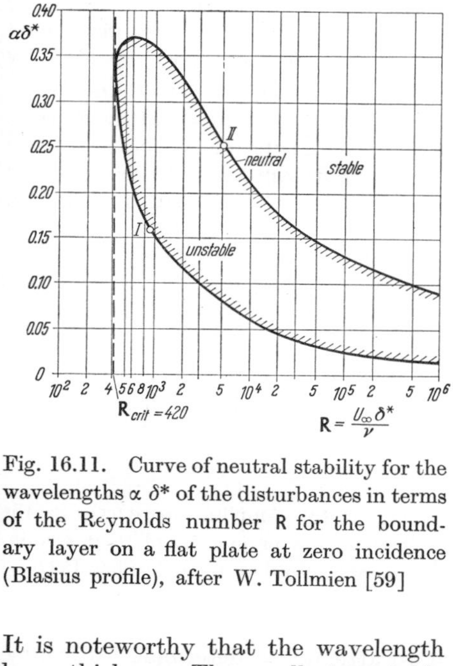

Fig. 16.11. Curve of neutral stability for the wavelengths $\alpha\ \delta^*$ of the disturbances in terms of the Reynolds number R for the boundary layer on a flat plate at zero incidence (Blasius profile), after W. Tollmien [59]

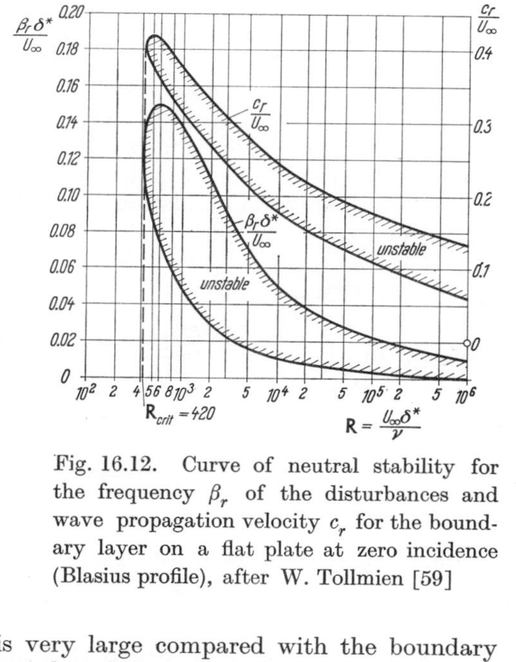

Fig. 16.12. Curve of neutral stability for the frequency β_r of the disturbances and wave propagation velocity c_r for the boundary layer on a flat plate at zero incidence (Blasius profile), after W. Tollmien [59]

It is noteworthy that the wavelength is very large compared with the boundary layer thickness. The smallest unstable wavelength is

$$\lambda_{min} = \frac{2\pi}{0{\cdot}36}\,\delta^* = 17{\cdot}5\,\delta^* \approx 6\,\delta\,.$$

A detailed comparison between the preceding theoretical results and experiment will be given in the next chapter. Here we shall only remark that the position where the boundary layer becomes first unstable according to theory (point of instability) must always be expected to lie upstream of the experimentally observed point of transition because actual turbulence is created along the path from the point of instability to the point of transition owing to the amplification of the unstable disturbances. This condition is satisfied in the case under consideration. We have already said in Sec. XVI a. that according to older measurements the point of transition occurs at $(U_\infty x/\nu)_{crit} = 3{\cdot}5 \times 10^5$ to 10^6. Using the value of $\delta^* = 1{\cdot}72 \sqrt{\nu x/U_\infty}$ from eqn. (7.40) we cand find that this corresponds to a critical Reynolds number

$$\left(\frac{U_\infty \delta^*}{\nu}\right)_{crit} = 950 \quad \text{(point of transition)}\,,$$

which is considerably larger than the value of 420 which we quoted earlier for the point of instability.

The distance between the point of instability and the point of transition depends on the *degree of amplification* and the kind of disturbances present in the external stream (intensity of turbulence), but the actual mechanism of amplification can be obtained from the study of the magnitudes of the parameters in the interior of the curve of neutral stability, $\beta_i > 0$. Calculations of this kind were first performed by H. Schlichting [46] for the flat plate; they have been recently repeated by S. F. Shen [53]. The result of such calculations can be seen plotted in Fig. 16.13.

In order to gain a clearer insight into the mechanics of the oscillating motion, H. Schlichting [47] determined the eigen-functions $\phi(y)$ for several neutral disturbances. This enabled him to draw the pattern of stream-lines of the disturbed motion for the neutral oscillations. An example of such a pattern can be found in Fig. 16.14.

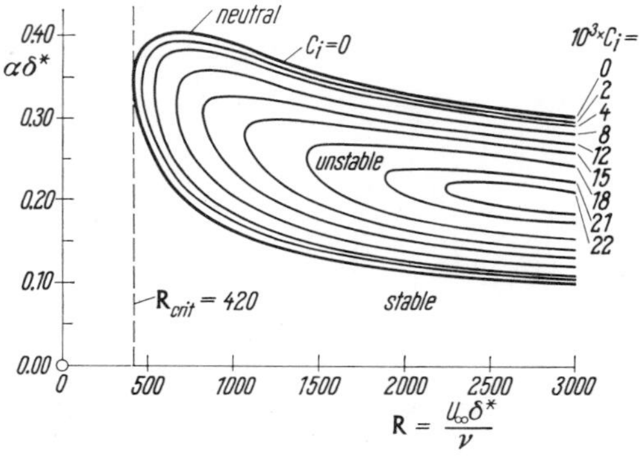

Fig. 16.13. Amplification curves for the boundary layer on a flat plate at zero incidence according to S. F. Shen [53]

In recent times, J. T. Stuart [56] made an attempt to determine the course of the amplification of unstable disturbances taking into account the effect of the non-linear terms in the equations. In this connexion it is important to realize that the amplification of the unstable disturbances causes the mean flow to contract. This, in turn, causes a change in the transfer of energy from the main motion to the oscillating motion, since it is proportional to $\mathrm{d}U/\mathrm{d}y$. The main effect of this is that at a later stage the unstable disturbances no longer amplify in proportion to exp $(\beta_i t)$ but tend to a finite value which is independent of the initial value. In this connexion the reader may also refer to [5b].

More than a decade was to elapse before an experimental verification of the above theory of stability could be obtained. This was brilliantly achieved by G. B. Schubauer and H. K. Skramstad and we shall give an account of their

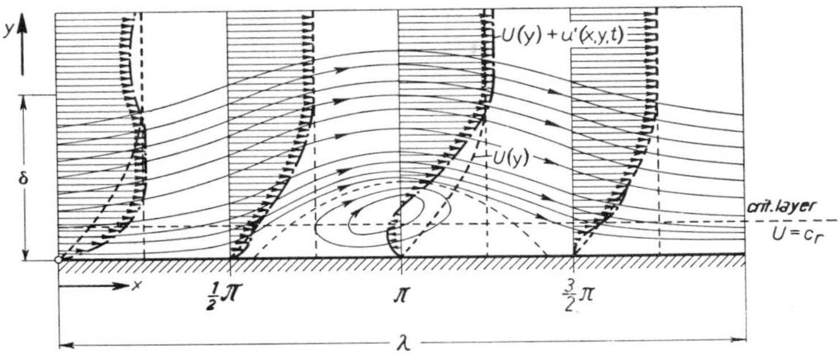

Fig. 16.14. Patterns of stream-lines and velocity distribution for a neutral disturbance in the boundary layer on a flat plate at zero incidence (disturbance I in Fig. 16.11)

$U(y)$ = mean flow; $U(y) + u'(x, y, t)$ = disturbed velocity distribution; $U_\infty \delta^*/\nu = 793$ = Reynolds number; $\lambda = 40\, \delta^*$ = wavelength of disturbance; $c_r = 0{\cdot}35\, U_\infty$ = wave propagation velocity;

$\int_0^\delta \sqrt{\overline{u'^2}}\, dy = 0{\cdot}172\; U_\infty\, \delta$ = intensity of disturbance

work in the succeeding section. At a time when these experimental results were already known, C. C. Lin [31] repeated all the calculations required in the development of the theory; his calculations agreed at all essential points with those due to W. Tollmien and H. Schlichting. On this occasion C. C. Lin also performed stability calculations in relation to the two-dimensional parabolic velocity profile shown in Fig. 5.1. The critical Reynolds number, formed with the maximum velocity U_m and half of the channel width, b, turned out to have the value

$$\mathsf{R}_{crit} = \left(\frac{U_m\, b}{\nu}\right)_{crit} = 5314\,.$$

C. C. Lin's calculations were later checked and confirmed by L. H. Thomas [63].

d. Comparison of the theory of stability with experiment

1. Older measurements of transition. The preceding results were the first solutions of the theory of small disturbances which led to the evaluation of a critical Reynolds number of the same order of magnitude as that measured experimentally. In accordance with the theory, small disturbances which fall within a certain range of frequency and wavelength are amplified, whereas disturbances of smaller or larger wavelengths are damped, provided that the Reynolds number exceeds a certain limiting value. The theory shows that disturbances whose wavelengths are large and equal to a multiple of the boundary layer thickness are particularly "dangerous". It is further assumed that the amplification of disturbances eventually effects the transition from laminar to turbulent flow. The process of amplification represents, so to say, the link between the stability theory and the experimentally established fact of the existence of transition.

Some time before the first successes of the theory of stability had been achieved, L. Schiller [50] carried out extensive experimental investigations into the phenomenon of transition, particularly as it occurs in pipes. These led to the development of a semi-empirical theory of transition which was based on the premise that, essentially, transition is due to finite disturbances which originate in the inlet to the pipe, or, in the case of boundary layer flow, in the external free stream. These ideas were further developed theoretically, particularly by G. I. Taylor [57].

The decision as to which of the two theories should be adopted had to be left to experiment. Even before the stability theory was established, transition on a flat plate had been investigated experimentally and in detail by J. M. Burgers [2], B. G. van der Hegge Zijnen [25] and M. Hansen. These measurements led to the result that the critical Reynolds number was contained in the range

$$\left(\frac{U_\infty x}{\nu}\right)_{crit} = 3{\cdot}5 \text{ to } 5 \times 10^5 .$$

Soon after, H. L. Dryden [7, 8] and his collaborators undertook a very thorough and careful investigation of this type of flow. During the course of these investigations extensive data on the velocity distribution were carefully plotted with the aid of hot-wire anemometers in terms of space co-ordinates and time. However, the selective amplification of disturbances predicted by the theory could not be detected.

At about the same time, experiments carried out at Goettingen on a flat plate in a water channel yielded a qualitative confirmation of the theory of stability. The photographs in Fig. 16.15 depict a turbulent region which originated from a disturbance of long wavelength. The similarity between these photographs and the theoretical pattern of streamlines of a neutral disturbance shown in Fig. 16.14 is irrefutable.

Fig. 16.15. Flow along a flat plate; turbulence originating from a disturbance of long wavelength, after L. Prandtl [38]
The photographs were taken with the aid of a slow motion-picture camera, which travelled on a trolley along with the flow; consequently, the camera is trained on the same group of vortices all the time. The flow is made visible by sprinkling aluminium dust on the water surface

In discussing transition it is necessary to introduce one very important parameter which measures the "degree of disturbance" in the external stream. Its importance was first recognised when measurements of the drag of spheres were performed in different wind tunnels. In this connexion it was discovered that the critical Reynolds number of a sphere, that is that value of the Reynolds number which corresponds to the abrupt decrease in the drag coefficient shown in Fig. 1.5, depends very markedly on the strength of the disturbances in the free stream. This can be measured quantitatively with the aid of the time-average of the oscillating, turbulent velocities as they occur, for example, behind a screen (see also Chap. XVIII). Denoting this time-average of the three components by $\overline{u'^2}$, $\overline{v'^2}$, $\overline{w'^2}$, we define the *intensity* (or *level*) *of turbulence* of a stream as

$$\mathsf{T} = \sqrt{\tfrac{1}{3}(\overline{u'^2} + \overline{v'^2} + \overline{w'^2})} \Big/ U_\infty \,,$$

where U_∞ denotes the mean velocity of the flow. In general, at a certain distance from the screens or honeycombs, the turbulence in a wind tunnel becomes *isotropic*, i. e. one for which the mean oscillations in the three components are equal:

$$\overline{u'^2} = \overline{v'^2} = \overline{w'^2} \,.$$

In this case it is sufficient to restrict oneself to the oscillation u' in the direction of flow, and to put

$$\mathsf{T} = \sqrt{\overline{u'^2}} \Big/ U_\infty \,.$$

This simpler definition of turbulence intensity is very often used in practice even in cases when the turbulence is not isotropic. Measurements in different wind tunnels show that the critical Reynolds number of a sphere depends very strongly on the turbulence intensity, T, the value of R_{crit} increasing fast as T decreases. In older wind tunnels, the intensity of turbulence was of the order of 0·01.

2. Verification of the theory of stability by experiment. In 1940, H. L. Dryden, assisted by G. B. Schubauer and H. K. Skramstad of the National Bureau of Standards in Washington, undertook a new and extensive experimental programme of investigation into the phenomenon of transition from laminar to turbulent flow [10, 51]. In the meantime it became accepted that the intensity of turbulence exerts a decisive influence on the process of transition. Consequently a special wind tunnel was constructed for these investigations, and by the use of a large number of suitable screens and a very large contraction ratio, the intensity of turbulence was reduced to the extremely low, and never previously attained, value

$$\mathsf{T} = \sqrt{\overline{u'^2}} \Big/ U_\infty = 0{\cdot}0002 \,.$$

The stream was then used for the thorough investigation of the laminar boundary layer on a flat plate at zero incidence, when it was discovered that at very low turbulence intensities, i. e. of the order of $\mathsf{T} < 0{\cdot}001$, the previously established value of the critical Reynolds number of $\mathsf{R}_{crit} = 3{\cdot}5$ to 5×10^5 was increased to

$$\left(\frac{U\,x}{\nu}\right)_{crit} \approx 2{\cdot}8 \times 10^6 \,,$$

see Fig. 16.16. It was further discovered, as revealed by Fig. 16.16, that a decrease in the intensity of turbulence causes the critical Reynolds number to increase, at first quite fast; after a value of about $\mathsf{T} = 0{\cdot}0008$ has been reached, a critical Reynolds number of $\mathsf{R}_{crit} = 2{\cdot}8 \times 10^6$ is retained at lower turbulence intensities. This demonstrates the existence of an upper limit of the critical Reynolds number on a flat plate. A measured point obtained earlier by A. A. Hall and G. S. Hislop [23] fits quite well into the graph of Fig. 16.16.

All the measurements which we are about to discuss were carried out at an intensity of turbulence of $\mathsf{T} = 0{\cdot}0003$. Velocities were measured with the aid of a hot-wire anemometer and a cathode-ray oscillograph. The measurement consisted in the determination of the variation of the velocity with time at several stations along the plate; these were undertaken first under normal conditions (i. e. in the presence of natural disturbances), and then with artificially produced disturbances.

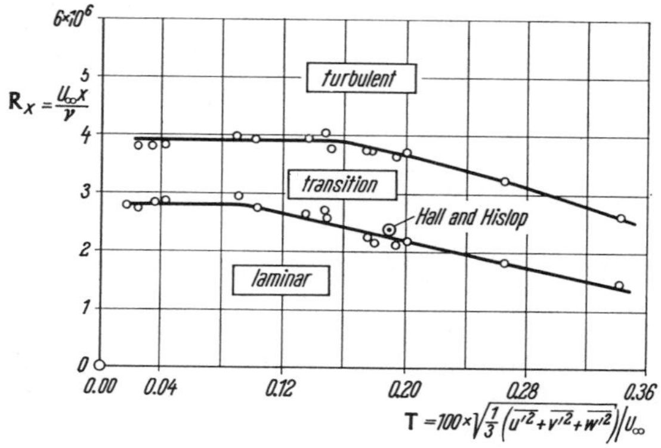

Fig. 16.16. Influence of intensity of turbulence on critical Reynolds number on flat plate at zero incidence, as measured by Schubauer and Skramstad [51]

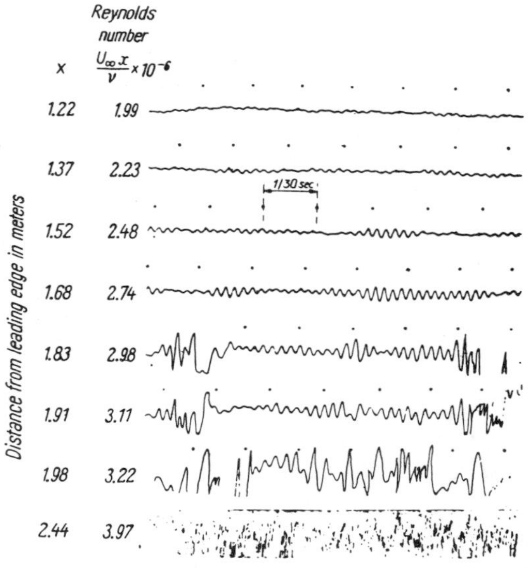

Fig. 16.17. Oscillogram of the u' component of fluctuations caused by random ("natural") disturbances in the laminar boundary layer on a flat plate in a stream of air. Measurements on transition from laminar to turbulent flow due to Schubauer and Skramstad [51]

Distance from wall: 0·57 mm; free-stream velocity $U_\infty = 24$ m/sec, interval between time marks: $^1/_{30}$ sec

Such artificial disturbances of a definite frequency were created with the aid of a thin metal strip which was placed at a distance of 0·15 mm from the wall and in which oscillations were excited electromagnetically. The existence of amplified sinusoidal disturbances could be clearly demonstrated even in the presence of *natural oscillations* (i. e. with no excitation), see Fig. 16.17. Owing to the extremely low intensity of turbulence, there are hardly any irregular oscillations left in the boundary layer, but, as the point of transition is approached, there appear almost purely sinusoidal oscillations; their amplitude is at first small and increases rapidly in the downstream direction. A short distance ahead of the point of transition, oscillations of very high amplitude make their appearance. At the point of transition, these regular oscillations break down and are suddenly transformed into the irregular patterns of high frequency which are characteristic of turbulent motion.

The measurements under consideration also threw light on the question as to why such amplified sinusoidal oscillation escaped detection during earlier experiments. It turns out, namely, that transition is caused directly by the random disturbances and is not preceded by a selective amplification of sinusoidal oscillations if the intensity of turbulence is increased, as already mentioned, from the above value of $\mathsf{T} = 0{\cdot}0003$ to $\mathsf{T} = 0{\cdot}01$, i. e. to a value commonly encountered in previous measurements.

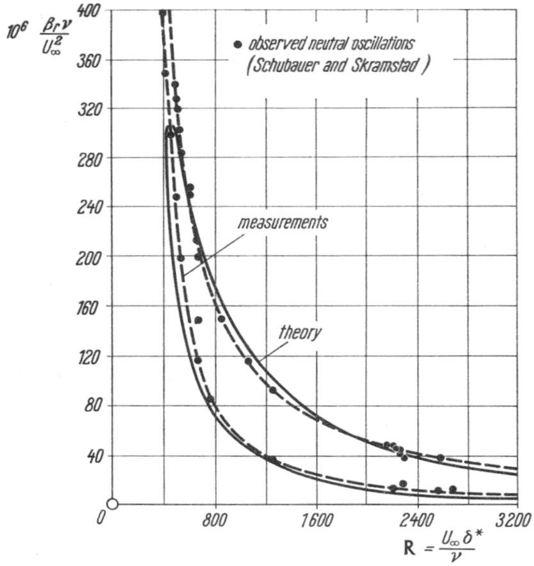

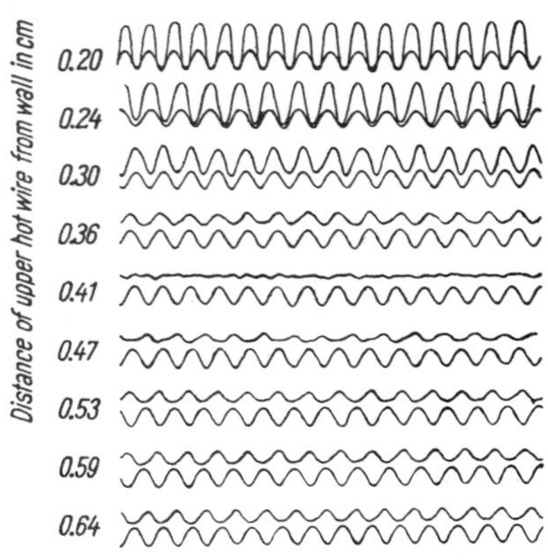

Fig. 16.19

Fig. 16.18. Curves of neutral stability for neutral frequencies of disturbances on a flat plate at zero incidence. Measurements due to Schubauer and Skramstad [51]. Theory due to Tollmien [59]

Fig. 16.19. Measurements on oscillations in the laminar boundary layer performed by Schubauer and Skramstad [51]

The above oscillograms display the phase reversal of the u'-component in fluctuations which are produced by an oscillating strip in the boundary layer ("artificial" disturbances). Simultaneous recording of velocity with the aid of two hot-wire anemometers placed at a distance of 30 cm behind the strip. The lower curve corresponds to a hot-wire placed at a distance of 1·4 mm from the wall; the upper curve corresponds to a hot-wire placed at varying distances from the wall as indicated. The strip was placed at a distance of 90 cm behind the leading edge of the plate. Frequency 70 sec^{-1}. Velocity $U_\infty = 13$ m/sec

During the experiments with *artificial disturbances* a thin metal strip extending over a width of about 30 cm, 0·05 mm thick and 2·5 mm deep was placed at a distance of 0·15 mm from the wall and was excited by a magnetic field induced with the aid of an alternating current. In this way it was possible to induce two-dimensional disturbances of prescribed frequency, as stipulated by the theory. This gave rise to amplified, damped and neutral oscillations simultaneously. They were again measured with the aid of a hot-wire anemometer. Results of such measurements are shown plotted in Fig. 16.18. The experimental points, which are joined by a broken line, represent measured neutral oscillations. The theoretical curve of neutral stability from Fig. 16.12 has been drawn-in for comparison, and the agreement is seen to be very good.

In order to gain more insight into the mechanism of transition, measurements of the amplitude of the u'-component were carried out for several neutral disturbances at varying distance from the wall. Fig. 16.19 shows oscillograms of the sinusoidal motion for the component u'. Each oscillogram contains two simultaneous curves, one of which was always taken at the same distance from the wall, the other having been taken at various distances. As the distance of the second station from the wall increases, there appears a 180° phase shift between the two fluctuations.

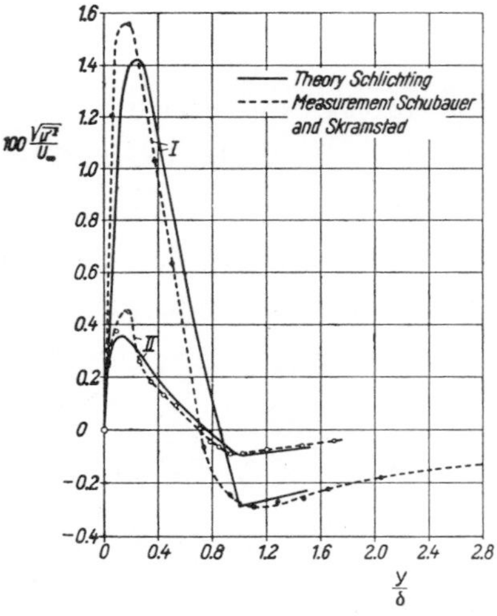

Fig. 16.20. Variation of amplitude of the u'-fluctuation for two neutral disturbances in a laminar boundary layer on flat plate at zero incidence. Measurements due to Schubauer and Skramstad [51]. Theory due to Schlichting [47]

The curves labelled I and II correspond to the two neutral disturbances I and II in Fig. 16.11

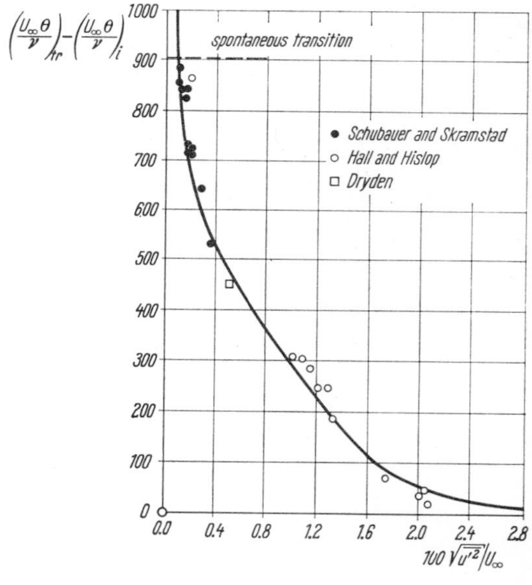

Fig. 16.21. Measurements on transition of a flat plate after P. S. Granville [21]. Difference between the Reynolds numbers at the points of transition and instability in terms of turbulence intensity. As turbulence intensity increases, the point of transition moves closer to the point of instability

This is the 180° phase-jump which occurs at the edge of the critical layer. Moreover, the variation of the amplitude of u' of the two neutral disturbances shown in Fig. 16.11, over the boundary layer thickness, Fig. 16.20, agrees completely with the theory due to H. Schlichting [47].

We have already remarked earlier that the experimental verification of the stability theory was first made possible when a stream of very low turbulence intensity could be produced. The older experiments which were performed at a turbulence intensity of $\mathsf{T} = 0{\cdot}01$ confirmed the expectation that the observed point of transition lies downstream of the point of instability predicted by theory. However, the distance between the points of instability and transition depends to a marked degree on turbulence intensity. It is to be expected that this distance should decrease as the intensity of turbulence is increased because in the presence of high turbulence a small amount of amplification suffices to produce turbulence from the unstable disturbances. The graph due to P. S. Granville [21] and shown in Fig. 16.21 illustrates this point in relation to the boundary layer on a flat plate. The difference between the Reynolds numbers formed with the momentum thickness at the points of transition an instability, namely

$$\left(\frac{U_\infty \theta}{\nu}\right)_{tr} - \left(\frac{U_\infty \theta}{\nu}\right)_i$$

has been used as a measure of this distance and has been plotted against the intensity of turbulence. For the point of instability of a flat plate the value

$$\left(\frac{U_\infty \theta}{\nu}\right)_i = \frac{1}{2{\cdot}6}\left(\frac{U_\infty \delta}{\nu}\right)_i = \frac{420}{2{\cdot}6} = 163$$

was used.

The preceding diagram correlates Schubauer and Skramstad's [51] more recent measurements performed at very low turbulence intensities as well as the older measurements due to Hall and Hislop and performed at higher turbulence intensities. All experimental points trace a *single* curve. The point of transition does not coincide with the point of instability until very high turbulence intensities of about $\mathsf{T} = 0{\cdot}02$ to $0{\cdot}03$ have been reached.

Very recently, F. X. Wortmann [66] succeeded in confirming the results of the stability theory with respect to the flow in the boundary layer along a flat plate in water by the use of the tellurium method.

It may be remarked at this stage that the theorem on the instability of velocity profiles possessing a point of inflexion, which is due to Lord Rayleigh and W. Tollmien, had already been subjected to an experimental investigation by G. Rosenbrook [44]. He was also able to report complete agreement between theoretical predictions and measurement. A paper by S. Hollingdale [27] contains a contribution to the study of the stability of velocity profiles in the wake of a solid body. The stability of laminar jets was studied by N. Curle [5a].

The experimental results reported in this chapter show such complete agreement with the theory of stability of laminar flows that the latter may now be regarded as a verified component of fluid mechanics. The hypothesis — that the process of transition from laminar to turbulent flow is the consequence of an instability in the laminar flow, enunciated by O. Reynolds, is hereby completely vindicated.

It certainly represents a *possible* and *observable* mechanism of transition. The question as to whether it paints a complete picture of the process and whether it constitutes the *only* mechanism encountered in nature is still at present an open one. The latter questions now occupy the attention of many research workers and in this connection the reader may wish to consult a review paper by M. V. Morkovin [34a].

References

[1] H. T. Barnes, E. G. Coker, The flow of water through pipes. Proc. Roy. Soc. London, A **74**, 341 (1905).
[2] J. M. Burgers, The motion of a fluid in the boundary layer along a plane smooth surface. Proc. of the First Internat. Congress for Applied Mechanics 113, Delft (1924).
[3] S. J. Cheng, On the stability of laminar boundary layer flow. Quarterly Appl. Math. **11,** pp. 346—350 (1953).
[4] P. Chiarulli and J. Freeman, Stability of the boundary layer. Brown University, Hdqtrs Air. Mat. Comm. Dayton, Tech. Rep. Nr. F-TR-1197-IA, Aug. 1948.
[5] M. Couette, Ann. chim. phys. **21**, 433 (1890).
[5a] N. Curle, Hydrodynamic stability in unlimited fields of viscous flow. Proc. Roy. Soc. London, A **238**, 489—501 (1957).
[5b] S. Dhawan and R. Narasimha, Some properties of boundary layer flow during transition from laminar to turbulent motion. J. Fluid Mechanics, **3** 418—436 (1958).
[6] H. Doetsch, Untersuchungen an einigen Profilen mit geringem Widerstand im Bereich kleiner c_a-Werte. Jb. d. dt. Luftfahrtforschung I, 54 (1940).
[7] H. L. Dryden, Boundary layer flow near flat plates. Proc. Fourth Internat. Congress for Applied Mechanics, Cambridge, 1934, p. 175.
[8] H. L. Dryden, Airflow in the boundary layer near a plate. NACA Report No. 562 (1936).
[9] H. L. Dryden, Turbulence and the boundary layer. J. Aero. Sci. **6**, 85 and 101 (1939).
[10] H. L. Dryden, Some recent contributions to the study of transition and turbulent boundary layers (Papers presented at the Sixth Intern. Congress for Appl . Mech., Paris, Sept. 1946; NACA TN 1168 (1947); see also: "Recent Advances in the mechanics of boundary layer flow. Advances in Appl. Mech." New York **I**, p. 2 (1948).
[11] H. L. Dryden, Recent investigation of the problem of transition. ZFW **4**, 89—95 (1956).
[12] W. Dubs, Über den Einfluß laminarer und turbulenter Strömung auf das Röntgenbild von Wasser und Nitrobenzol. Ein röntgenographischer Beitrag zum Turbulenzproblem. Helv. phys. Acta **12**, 169—228 (1939).
[13] G. Eiffel, Comptes Rendus, **155**, 1597 (1912).
[14] V. W. Ekman, Archiv für Math. Astr. och Fys. **VI**, No. 12 (1910).
[15] H. W. Emmons and A. E. Bryson, The laminar-turbulent transition in a boundary layer. Part I: Jour. Aero. Sci. **18**, 490—498 (1951); Part II, Proc. First US National Congress Appl. Mech., pp. 859—868 (1952).
[16] A. Fage, Fluid motion transition from laminar to turbulent flow in a boundary layer. Phys. Soc. Repts. on Progress in Physics **6**, 270 (1939).
[17] A. Fage, Experiments on the breakdown of laminar flow. J. Aero. Sci. **7**, 513 (1940).
[18] A. Fage and J. H. Preston, Experiments on transition from laminar to turbulent flow in the boundary layer. Proc. Roy. Soc. London A **178**, 201 (1941).
[19] A. Fage, Transition in the boundary layer caused by turbulence. ARCR & M. 1896 (1942).
[20] W. Froude, Experiments on the surface friction. Brit. Ass. Rep. 1872.
[21] P. S. Granville, The calculations of viscous drag of bodies of revolution. Navy Department. The David Taylor Model Basin; Report No. 849 (1953).
[22] D. Grohne, Über das Spektrum bei Eigenschwingungen ebener Laminarströmungen. ZAMM **34**, 344—357 (1954).
[23] A. A. Hall and G. S. Hislop, Experiments on the transition of the laminar boundary layer on a flat plate. ARC R & M 1843 (1938).
[24] G. Hamel, Göttinger Nachrichten (1911).

[25] B. G. VAN DER HEGGE ZIJNEN, Measurements of the velocity distribution in the boundary layer along a plane surface. Thesis, Delft 1924.
[26] W. HEISENBERG, Über Stabilität und Turbulenz von Flüssigkeitsströmen. Ann. d. Physik **24**, 577 (1924).
[27] S. HOLLINGDALE, Stability and configuration of the wakes produced by solid bodies moving through fluids. Phil. Mag., VII **29**, 209 (1940).
[28] H. HOLSTEIN, Über die äußere und innere Reibungsschicht bei Störungen laminarer Strömungen. ZAMM **30**, 25 (1950).
[29] L. HOPF, Ann. d. Phys. **44**, 1 (1914) and **59**, 538 (1919); see also comprehensive review by F. NOETHER, ZAMM **1**, 125 (1921).
[30] G. W. LEWIS, J. Roy. Aero. Soc. May 1939 (27th. Wilbur Wright Memorial Lecture). German Summary in "Luftfahrtschrifttum des Auslandes in Übersetzungen" **5**, 153 (1939).
[31] C. C. LIN, On the stability of two-dimensional parallel flows. Quartely Appl. Math. **3**, 117—142 (July 1945); **3**, 218—234 (Oct. 1945); **3**, 277—301 (Jan. 1946).
[32] C. C. LIN, The theory of hydrodynamic stability. Cambridge University Press 1955.
[32a] C. C. LIN, Stability of laminar flows. Appl. Mech. Reviews **10**, 1—3 (1957).
[33] H. A. LORENTZ, Abhandlung über theoretische Physik **I**, 43, Leipzig (1907); new version of earlier paper Akad. v. Wet. Amsterdam **6**, 28 (1897); see also L. PRANDTL. The mechanics of viscous fluid, in F. DURAND, Aerodynamic Theory **III**, 178 (1935).
[34] R. von MISES, HEINRLICH WEBER anniversary volume 1912; Jahresbericht d. dt. Math.Vereinigung 1912.
[34a] M. V. MORKOVIN, Transition from laminar to turbulent shear flow. A review of some recent advances in its understanding. Trans. ASME. **80**, 1121 (1958).
[35] W. M. F. ORR, Proc. Royal Irish Academy **17** (A), 124 (1907).
[35a] J. PERSH, A study of boundary-layer transition from laminar to turbulent flow. U. S. Naval Ordnance Lab. Report No. 4339 (1956).
[36] L. PRANDTL, Über den Luftwiderstand von Kugeln. Göttinger Nachrichten 177 (1914).
[37] L. PRANDTL, Bemerkungen über die Entstehung der Turbulenz. ZAMM **1**, 431 (1921) and Phys. Z. **23**, 19 (1922).
[38] L. PRANDTL, Neuere Ergebnisse der Turbulenzforschung. ZVDI **77**, 105 (1933).
[39] J. PRETSCH, Die Stabilität einer ebenen Laminarströmung bei Druckgefälle und Druckanstieg. Jahrb. d. dt. Luftfahrtforschung I, p. 58 (1941).
[40] LORD RAYLEIGH, Sci. Papers **I**, 474 (1880); **III**, 17 (1887); **IV**, 197 (1913).
[41] LORD RAYLEIGH, On the stability of certain fluid motions. Proc. London, Math. Soc. **11**, 57 (1880), and **19**, 67 (1887); Scientific Papers **I**, 474, and **III**, 17; see also Scientific Papers **IV**, 203 (1895) and **VI**, 197 (1913).
[42] O. REYNOLDS, Phil. Trans. Roy. Soc (1883) or Collected Papers **II**, 51.
[43] O. REYNOLDS, Sci. Papers **2** (1883) and also: On the dynamic theory of incompressible viscous fluids and the determination of the criterion. Phil. Trans. Roy. Soc. (1895).
[44] G. ROSENBROOK, Instabilität der Gleitschichten im schwach divergenten Kanal. ZAMM **17**, 8 (1937).
[45] J. ROTTA, Experimenteller Beitrag zur Entstehung turbulenter Strömung im Rohr. Ing-. Arch. **24**, 258—281 (1956).
[46] H. SCHLICHTING, Zur Entstehung der Turbulenz bei der Plattenströmung. Nachr. Ges. Wiss. Göttingen, Math. Phys. Klasse 182—208 (1933); see also ZAMM **13**, 171 (1933).
[47] H. SCHLICHTING, Amplitudenverteilung und Energiebilanz der kleinen Störungen bei der Plattenströmung. Nachr. Ges. Wiss. Göttingen, Math. Phys. Klasse, Fachgruppe I, **1**, 47—78 (1935).
[48] H. SCHLICHTING, Über die Theorie der Turbulenzentstehung, zusammenfassender Bericht. (Summary review). Forschung a. d. Gebiet des Ingenieurwesens **16**, 65 (1950).
[48a] H. SCHLICHTING, Entstehung der Turbulenz, article in "Handbuch der Physik", ed. by S. FLÜGGE, vol. VIII/I, pp. 351—450.
[49] L. SCHILLER, Untersuchungen über laminare und turbulente Strömung. Forschung Ing.-Wesen, Heft 248 (1922), or ZAMM **2**, 96 (1922), also Physikal. Zeitschrift **23**, 14 (1922).
[50] L. SCHILLER, Neue quantitative Versuche zur Turbulenzentstehung. ZAMM **14**, 36 (1934).
[51] G. B. SCHUBAUER and H. K. SKRAMSTAD, Laminar boundary layer oscillations and stability of laminar flow. National Bureau of Standards Research Paper 1772. (Reprint of a classified NACA Report first published in April 1943, and later released as NACA War-time Report W-8), and J. Aero. Sci. **14**, 69 (1947); see also NACA Rep. No. 909.

[52] G. B. Schubauer and P. S. Klebanoff, Contributions on the mechanics of boundary layer transition. NACA TN 3489 (1955) and NACA Rep. No. 1289 (1956); see also Proc. Symposium on Boundary Layer Theory, Nat. Phys. Lab. England 1955.
[53] S. F. Shen, Calculated amplified oscillations in plane Poiseuille and Blasius flows. Jour. Aero. Sci. **21**, 62—64 (1954).
[54] A. Sommerfeld, Atti del congr. internat. dei Mat. Rome 1908.
[55] H. B. Squire, On the stability of three-dimensional distribution of viscous fluid between parallel walls. Proc. Roy. Soc. London, A **142** (1933).
[56] J. T. Stuart, On the effects of the Reynolds stress on hydrodynamic stability. ZAMM Sonderheft (Special issue) 32—38 (1956).
[57] G. I. Taylor, Some recent developments on the study of turbulence. Proc. of the Fifth Int. Congr. for Applied Mechanics, New York, 294 (1938); see also: Statistical Theory of Turbulence V. Effect of turbulence on boundary layers. Proc. Roy. Soc. London, A **156**, 307 (1936).
[58] O. Tietjens, Beiträge zur Entstehung der Turbulenz. Diss. Göttingen 1922 and ZAMM **5**, 200 (1925).
[59] W. Tollmien, Über die Entstehung der Turbulenz. 1. Mitteilung, Nachr. Wiss. Göttingen, Math. Phys. Klasse 21—44 (1929); Engl. transl. in NACA Tech. Memo. No. 609 (1931).
[60] W. Tollmien, Ein allgemeines Kriterium der Instabilität laminarer Geschwindigkeitsverteilungen. Nachr. Ges. Wiss. Göttingen Math. Phys. Klasse, Fachgruppe I, 1, 79—114 (1935); Engl. transl. in NACA Tech. Memo. No. 792 (1936).
[61] W. Tollmien, Göttinger Monographie über Grenzschichten, Pt. B 3, 1946.
[62] W. Tollmien, Asymptotische Integration der Störungsdifferentialgleichung ebener laminarer Strömungen bei hohen Reynoldschen Zahlen. ZAMM **25/27**, 33 (1947).
[62a] W. Tollmien, Miscellen aus der Turbulenzforschung, Centro Internaziole di Matematica Estivo (CIME), Corso sulla teoria della turbulenza varenna, 1—10 Sept. 1957, vol. 2. Torino (no year of publ. indicated).
[63] L. H. Thomas, The stability of plane Poiseuille flow. The Physical Review, Vol. **86**, p. 812 (1952).
[64] H. C. H. Townsend, Note on boundary layer transition. ARC R & M 1873 (1939).
[65] C. Wieselberger, Der Luftwiderstand von Kugeln. ZFM **5**, 140—144 (1914).
[66] F. X. Wortmann, Untersuchungen instabiler Grenzschichtschwingungen in einem Wasserkanal mittels der Tellur-Methode. "Fifty years of boundary layer research", Braunschweig (1955), pp. 460—470.

CHAPTER XVII

Origin of turbulence II

Effect of pressure gradient, suction, compressibility, heat transfer, and roughness on transition

Introductory remark

The results described in Chap. XVI have demonstrated, in principle, the applicability of the method of small disturbances to the study of the phenomenon of transition from laminar to turbulent flow. We may, therefore, expect that this theory should also supply us with information concerning the other parameters which exert an important influence on transition, in addition to the single one, the Reynolds number, discussed so far. We have already briefly reported in Sec. XVI b that the pressure gradient in the external flow has a great influence on the stability of the boundary layer, and hence on transition, in the sense that a favourable pressure gradient stabilizes the flow and an adverse pressure gradient renders it less stable. Body forces, such as the centrifugal force in a curved stream and the buoyancy in a non-homogeneous stream, are also very important for transition. In more modern times problems connected with boundary layer control through suction or blowing and their effect on transition have become important (*cf.* Chap. XIII). Suction exerts a stabilizing effect, but blowing promotes instability. In the case of flows which occur at very high speeds, when the fluid must be regarded as being compressible, the presence of heat transfer from or to the wall (heating or cooling) affects transition to an important degree. The transfer of heat from the fluid to the wall has a highly stabilizing effect but if the flow of heat is from the wall to the fluid the effect is reversed. Finally, problems connected with the influence of roughness on transition are of great practical importance.

The present chapter will contain a review of all these diverse problems, and we shall begin with the study of the effect of pressure gradients because of its great importance in practical applications.

a. Effect of pressure gradients on transition in boundary layer along flat walls

The boundary layer on a flat plate at zero incidence whose stability was investigated in Chap. XVI has the peculiar characteristic that its velocity profiles at different distances from the leading edge are similar to each other (*cf.* Chap. VII). In this case similarity results from the absence of a pressure gradient in the external flow.

On the other hand, in the case of a cylindrical body of arbitrary shape when the pressure gradient along the wall changes from point to point, the resulting velocity profiles are not, generally speaking, similar to each other. In the ranges where the pressure decreases downstream, the velocity profiles have no points of inflexion and are of the type shown in Fig. 16.9e whereas in regions where the pressure increases downstream they are of the type shown in Fig. 16.9g and do possess points of inflexion. In the case of a flat plate all velocity profiles have the same limit of stability, namely $\mathsf{R}_{crit} = (U_\infty \delta^*/\nu)_{crit} = 420$; in contrast with that, in the case of an arbitrary body shape, the individual velocity profiles have markedly different limits of stability, higher than for a flat plate with favourable pressure gradients, and lower with adverse pressure gradients. Consequently, in order to determine the position of the point of instability for a body of a given, prescribed shape, it is necessary to perform the following calculations:

1. Determination of the pressure distribution along the contour of the body for frictionless flow. 2. Determination of the laminar boundary layer for that pressure distribution. 3. Determination of the limits of stability for these individual velocity profiles. The problem of determining the pressure distribution belongs to potential theory which supplies convenient methods of computation as, for example, described by T. Theodorsen and J. E. Garrick [115] and F. Riegels [88]. Convenient methods for the calculation of laminar boundary layers were given in Chap. XII. The third step, the stability calculation, will now be discussed in detail.

It is known from the theory of laminar boundary layers, Chap. XII, that, generally speaking, the curvature of the wall has little influence on the development of the boundary layer on a cylindrical body; this is true as long as the radius of curvature of the wall is much larger than the boundary layer thickness, which amounts to saying that the effect of the centrifugal force may be neglected when analyzing the formation of a boundary layer on such bodies. Hence the boundary layer is seen to develop in the same way as on a *flat* wall, but under the influence of that pressure gradient which is determined by the potential flow past the body. The same applies to the determination of the limit of stability of a boundary layer with a pressure gradient which is different from zero.

In contrast with the case of a flat plate, where the external flow is uniform at $U_\infty = \text{const}$, we now have to contend with an external stream whose velocity $U_m(x)$ is a function of the length co-ordinate. The velocity $U_m(x)$ is related to the pressure gradient $\mathrm{d}p/\mathrm{d}x$ through the Bernoulli equation

$$\frac{\mathrm{d}p}{\mathrm{d}x} = -\varrho\, U_m \frac{\mathrm{d}U_m}{\mathrm{d}x}\,. \tag{17.1}$$

In spite of the dependence of the external velocity on the length co-ordinate, it is possible, as shown by J. Pretsch [84], to analyze the stability of laminar flows with a pressure gradient in the same way as in its absence (Chap. XVI); it is again possible to work with a mean flow whose velocity $U(y)$ depends only on the transverse co-ordinate y. The influence of the pressure gradient on stability manifests itself through the form of the velocity profile given by $U(y)$. We have already said in Sec. XVIb that the limit of stability of a velocity profile depends strongly on its shape, profiles with a point of inflexion possessing considerably lower limits of stability than those without one (point-of-inflexion criterion). Now, since the pressure gradient controls the curvature of the velocity profile in accordance with eqn. (7.18)

$$\mu \left(\frac{d^2U}{dy^2}\right)_{wall} = \frac{dp}{dx}, \tag{17.2}$$

the strong dependence of the limit of stability on the shape of the velocity profile amounts to a large influence of the pressure gradient on stability. It is, therefore, true to say that accelerated flows ($dp/dx < 0$, $dU_m/dx > 0$, favourable pressure gradient) are considerably more stable than decelerated flows ($dp/dx > 0$, $dU_m/dx < 0$, adverse pressure gradient.)

The strong influence of the pressure gradient on stability and on the amplification of small disturbances predicted by the present theory was confirmed experimentally by G. B. Schubauer and H. K. Skramstad, Sec. XVId. The graphs in Fig. 17.1 represent oscillograms of the velocity oscillations on a flat wall with a pressure gradient. The upper half of the diagram shows that a pressure drop which amounts to 10 per cent of the dynamic pressure causes a complete damping out of the oscillations, whereas the pressure increase which succeeds it and which amounts to only 5 per cent of the dynamic pressure, causes not only strong amplification but produces transition at once. (In this connection attention is drawn to the reduced scale of the last two oscillograms!)

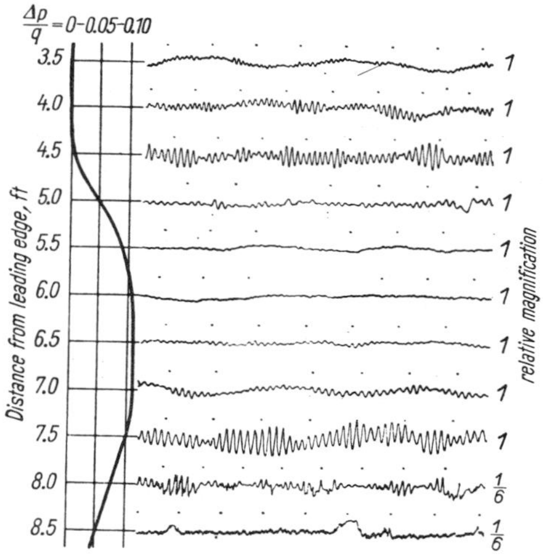

Fig. 17.1. Oscillogram of velocity fluctuations in laminar boundary layer with pressure gradient as measured by G. B. Schubauer and H. K. Skramstad. Decreasing pressure produces damping; increasing pressure causes strong amplification and produces transition

Distance of measuring station from wall — 0·5 mm. Velocity U_∞ = 29 m/sec

An account of an investigation into transition in a separated laminar boundary layer is available in a paper by H. Sato [89a].

In the evaluation of stability, it appears to be convenient to express the influence of a pressure gradient by the use of a shape factor of the velocity profile and to stipulate, for the sake of simplicity, a one-parameter family of laminar velocity profiles. An example of such a one-parameter family of velocity profiles, which, moreover, constitute exact solutions of the boundary layer equations, is represented by Hartree's wedge flows. Their free-stream velocity is given by

$$U_m(x) = u_1 \cdot x^m ,$$

and the associated velocity profiles can be found plotted in Fig. 9.1. Here m denotes the shape factor of the profiles and the wedge angle is $\beta = 2\,m/(m+1)$. When $m < 0$ (increasing pressure), the velocity profiles have a point of inflexion; when $m > 0$ (decreasing pressure), there is no point of inflexion. J. Pretsch [83] carried out the stability calculation for a series of profiles of this one-parameter family, and the result can be seen reproduced in Table 17.1.

Table 17.1. Critical Reynolds number and maximum amplification factor in terms of the shape factor β of the velocity profile for flows with a pressure gradient as calculated by J. Pretsch [83, 84]. Velocity profiles from Fig. 9.1

β	-0.10	0	0·2	0·4	0·6	1·0
$m = \frac{x}{U}\frac{\mathrm{d}U}{\mathrm{d}x}$	-0.048	0	0·111	0·25	0·43	1·0
$\left(\frac{U_m\,\delta^*}{\nu}\right)_{crit}$	126	660	3200	5000	8300	12600
$\left(\frac{\beta_i\,\delta^*}{U_m}\right)_{max} \cdot 10^4$	155	34·5	14·6	—	9·1	7·3

The preceding calculation showed a strong dependence of the critical Reynolds number on the shape factor m. In a further paper J. Pretsch [84] calculated the amplification of unstable disturbances for the same velocity profiles. Maximum values of the amplification coefficient β_i for several velocity profiles have been included in Table 17.1. As expected, the amplification is much greater in the presence of an adverse rather than a favourable pressure gradient. At an earlier date H. Schlichting [94] performed stability calculations in relation to the velocity profiles in a convergent or a divergent channel which belong to the potential flow given by $U_m(x) = U_0 - ax$ (Sec. IXd); these have also shown a strong dependence of the critical Reynolds number on the pressure gradient.

K. Pohlhausen's approximate method described in Chap. XII is the most convenient one for the calculation of laminar velocity profiles and it is, therefore, useful to investigate the stability of the associated velocity profiles. The shape of the velocity profiles is determined by the dimensionless shape factor

$$\Lambda = \frac{\delta^2}{\nu}\frac{\mathrm{d}U_m}{\mathrm{d}x} . \tag{17.3}$$

The velocity profiles were shown in Fig. 12.4. The shape factor Λ assumes values between $\Lambda = +12$ and -12, the latter value corresponding to separation; at the forward stagnation point it is equal to $\Lambda = +7.05$ and at the point of minimum pressure we have $\Lambda = 0$. For $\Lambda > 0$ the pressure decreases and $\Lambda < 0$ corresponds to an increase in pressure. The velocity profiles for $\Lambda < 0$ each possess a point of inflexion.

H. Schlichting and A. Ulrich [95] carried out stability calculations for this family of velocity profiles†. The curves of neutral stability are shown in Fig. 17.2. Both branches of the curves of neutral stability for all velocity profiles with a decreasing pressure ($\Lambda > 0$) tend to zero as $\mathsf{R} \to \infty$, just as was the case for the flat plate, $\Lambda = 0$. On the other hand the upper branches of curves corresponding to profiles with adverse pressure gradients ($\Lambda < 0$) tend to an asymptote which differs from zero so that even for $\mathsf{R} \to \infty$ there exists a finite region of wavelengths at which disturbances are always amplified. The velocity profiles in the region of favourable pressure gradient ($\Lambda > 0$) as well as the profile for constant pressure ($\Lambda = 0$) belong to the type of "viscous" instability (curve b in Fig. 16.8), whereas the profiles in the range of adverse pressure gradient ($\Lambda < 0$) are of the type characteristic of "frictionless' instability (curve a in Fig. 16.8). It is seen from Fig. 17.2 that the region of unstable wavelengths enclosed by the curve of neutral stability is much greater for boundary layers with adverse pressure gradients than for accelerated flows. The dependence of the critical Reynolds number on the shape factor Λ which follows from Fig. 17.2 has been plotted in Fig. 17.3‡. It varies with the value of the shape factor Λ, and hence with the pressure gradient, very strongly.

The preceding results will enable us to calculate in the following section the position of the point of instability for the case of two-dimensional flow past a body of arbitrary shape.

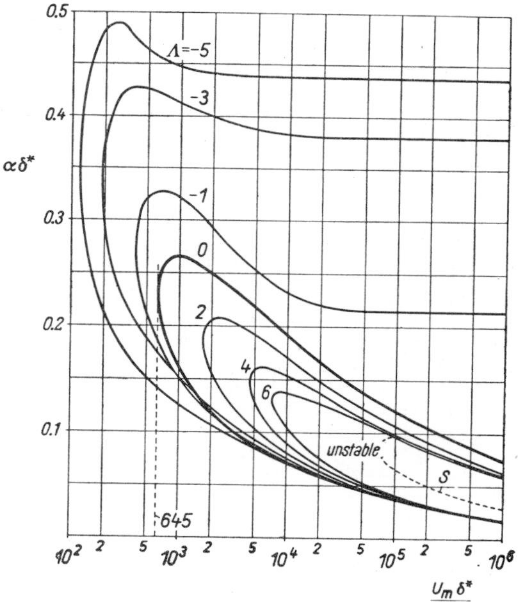

Fig. 17.2. Curves of neutral stability for laminar boundary layer profiles with pressure decrease ($\Lambda > 0$) and pressure increase ($\Lambda < 0$). The shape factor of the velocity profile is defined as

$$\Lambda = \frac{\delta^2}{\nu}\frac{\mathrm{d}U}{\mathrm{d}x}\,,\ \text{see also Fig. 12.4}$$

S = curve for boundary layer with suction, see Fig. 17.15

† The stability calculations were not based on the velocity profiles represented by a fourth degree polynomial (P 4 method), because their curvature $U''(y)$, being essential for stability calculations, is not sufficiently accurate compared with exact solutions. The original assumption was replaced by a polynomial of sixth degree (P 6 method) and a method analogous to the original Pohlhausen approximation was developed for the purpose. Thus the curvature $U''(y)$ is obtained with a satisfactory degree of accuracy. The velocity profiles of the P 4 and the P 6 methods were linked together in a simple manner, i. e. by prescribing equal momentum thickness at all points of the wetted contour.

‡ The value $\mathsf{R}_{crit} = 645$ given here for $\Lambda = 0$ differs somewhat from the value 420 given previously in Fig. 16.11. This is due to the difference between the exact Blasius velocity profile used previously and the approximate one employed in the P 6 method for Fig. 17.2.

b. Determination of the position of the point of instability for prescribed body shape

The determination of the position of the point of transition for prescribed body shapes (in two-dimensional flow) becomes very easy if use is made of the results contained in Figs. 17.2 and 17.3. The essential advantage of the method to be described here consists in the fact that no further laborious calculations are required, the tedious part of the work having been completed once and for all when computing the diagrams in Fig. 17.2.

We begin with the evaluation of the laminar boundary layer from the potential velocity distribution $U_m(x)/U_\infty$, which is regarded as known, by the use of Pohlhausen's approximate method outlined in Chap. XII. Such a calculation furnishes values of the shape factor Λ and the displacement thickness δ^* in terms of the length of arc x, measured from the forward stagnation point. On proceeding along the laminar boundary layer from the forward stagnation point in a down stream direction at an assumed constant body Reynolds number $U_\infty l/\nu$ (l—length of body), it is noticed that, at the beginning, the limit of stability, $(U_m\delta^*/\nu)_{crit}$, is very high owing to the sharp pressure decrease. On the other hand the boundary layer is thin and consequently the local Reynolds number $U_m\delta^*/\nu$ is certain to be smaller than the critical value, $(U_m\delta^*/\nu)_{crit}$, and the boundary layer is stable. Further downstream the rate of pressure decrease becomes smaller and is followed by a pressure increase behind the point of minimum pressure so that the local limit of stability, $(U_m\delta^*/\nu)_{crit}$,

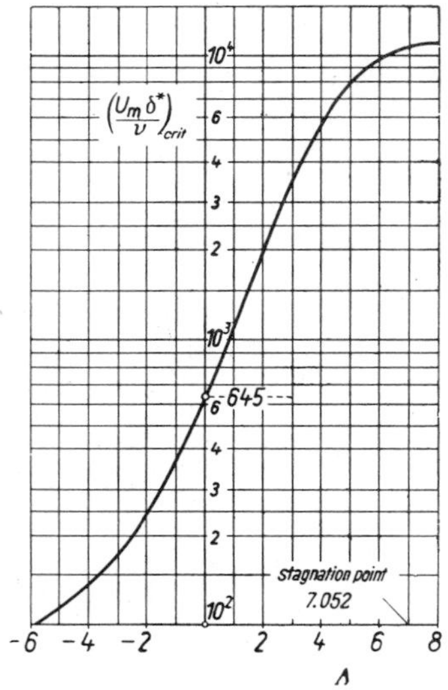

Fig. 17.3. Critical Reynolds number of boundary layer velocity profiles with pressure gradient as a function of the shape factor Λ

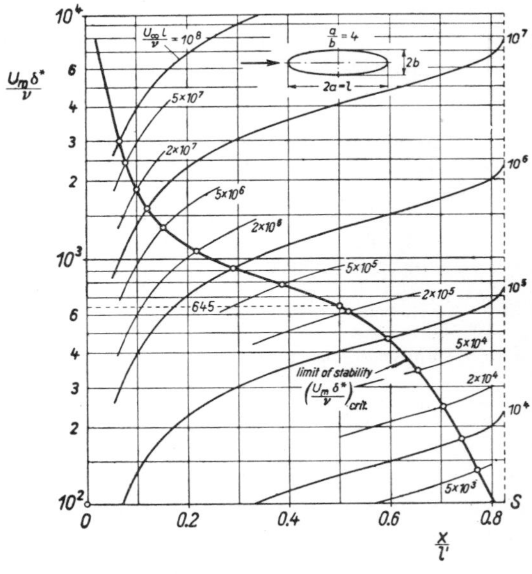

Fig. 17.4. Calculation of the position of the point of instability in terms of the Reynolds number $U_\infty l/\nu$ for an elliptic cylinder with slenderness ratio $a/b = 4$

$2l'$ = circumference

decreases in the downstream direction, whereas the boundary layer thickness and, with it, the local Reynolds number, $(U_m\delta^*/\nu)$, increase. At a certain point the two become equal:

$$\frac{U_m\,\delta^*}{\nu} = \left(\frac{U_m\,\delta^*}{\nu}\right)_{crit} \quad \text{(point of instability)}\,, \qquad (17.4)$$

and from that point onwards the boundary layer is unstable. The point defined by eqn. (17.4) will be referred to as the *point of instability* and its position does, evidently, depend on the body Reynolds number, $(U_\infty\, l/\nu)$, because the local boundary layer thickness is influenced by it.

The calculation of the position of the point of instability in terms of the Reynolds number sketched in the preceding paragraph can be conveniently performed with the aid of the diagrams in Fig. 17.4. It will be developed in more detail for the example of an elliptic cylinder whose major axis a is related to its minor axis b by the ratio $a/b = 4$. The flow will be assumed parallel to the major axis. The potential velocity distribution function for such a cylinder was already given in Fig. 12.10, and the results of the calculations pertaining to the boundary layer are shown in Fig. 12.11 and 12.12. From the variation of the shape factor Λ with x, Fig. 12.11b and with the aid of Fig. 17.3 it is now possible to plot the variation of the local critical Reynolds number, $\mathsf{R}_{crit} = (U_m\delta^*/\nu)_{crit}$, as shown by the curve marked *limit of stability* in Fig. 17.4. From the calculation of the laminar boundary layer we can also take the variation of the dimensionless displacement thickness (δ^*/l) $(\sqrt{U_\infty\, l/\nu})$, as shown in Fig. 12.11a. For a given body Reynolds number $U_\infty\, l/\nu$, it is now possible to evaluate the local Reynolds number, $U_m\delta^*/\nu$, based on the displacement thickness, since

$$\frac{U_m\,\delta^*}{\nu} = \left(\frac{\delta^*}{l}\sqrt{\frac{U_\infty l}{\nu}}\right)\sqrt{\frac{U_\infty l}{\nu}}\,\frac{U_m}{U_\infty}\,. \qquad (17.5)$$

where the value of $U_m(x)/U_\infty$ is known from the potential velocity-function. The points of intersection of these curves with the *limit of stability* give the position of the point of instability for the respective value of the Reynolds number†. The points of instability for a family of elliptic cylinders of slenderness ratios $a/b = 1$, 2, 4, 8 are shown in Fig. 17.5. It is remarkable that the shift of the point of instability with an increasing Reynolds number is very small for the case of a circular cylinder. This shift becomes more pronounced as the slenderness ratio is increased.

The position of the point of instability for an aerofoil can be easily calculated in a similar manner. In this connexion it is particularly important to determine the dependence on the angle of incidence in addition to that on the Reynolds number. The results of such calculations for the case of a symmetrical Joukovsky aerofoil at varying angles of incidence and lift coefficients are shown in Fig. 17.6. It is seen that, as the angle of incidence increases, the minimum of pressure on the suction side becomes more and more prominent and moves forward, whereas that

† The curves $U_m\,\delta^*/\nu$ for various values of $U_\infty\, l/\nu$ can be drawn from each other by translating them in a direction parallel to the axis of ordinates, if a logarithmic scale is used for the latter. This is a very convenient simplification to use when a graphical method is employed.

on the pressure side becomes flatter and moves to the rear. This causes the point of instability to move upstream on the suction side and downstream on the pressure side as the angle of incidence is increased. Simultaneously the point of instability on the suction side closes up towards the point of minimum pressure for all Reynolds numbers because of the steep course of the curve near the minimum; the opposite effect occurs on the pressure side, where the curves are flat near the minimum causing the points of instability to diverge. In any case the diagram in Fig. 17.6 displays very clearly the dominating influence of the pressure distribution on the position of the point of instability and hence on that of the point of transition. Even at high Reynolds numbers the point of instability (and hence the point of transition) hardly moves in front of the point of minimum pressure, whereas behind the point of minimum pressure instability and, consequently, transition sets in almost at once even at low Reynolds numbers. Fig. 17.7 shows, further, the position of the point of transition, as determined experimentally for an NACA aerofoil, which possessed an almost identical pressure distribution with that of the Joukovsky aerofoil under consideration. It is seen that the point of transition lies behind the point of instability but in front of the point of laminar separation for all values of Reynolds number and lift coefficient as expected from theoretical considerations. Secondly, the shift of the point of transition with a varying Reynolds number and lift coefficient follows that of the point of instability. Results of systematic calculations on the position of the point of transition for aerofoils of varying thickness and camber can be found in a report by K. Bussmann and A. Ulrich [8].

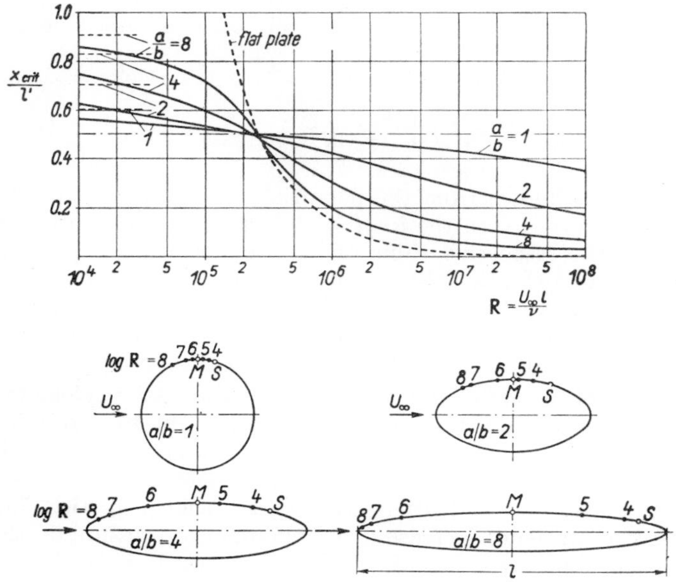

Fig. 17.5. Position of points of instability for elliptic cylinders of slenderness ratio $a/b = 1, 2, 4, 8, \infty$ (flat plate) plotted against the body Reynolds number R

$2\,l'$ — circumference; S — point of laminar separation; M — point of minimum pressure

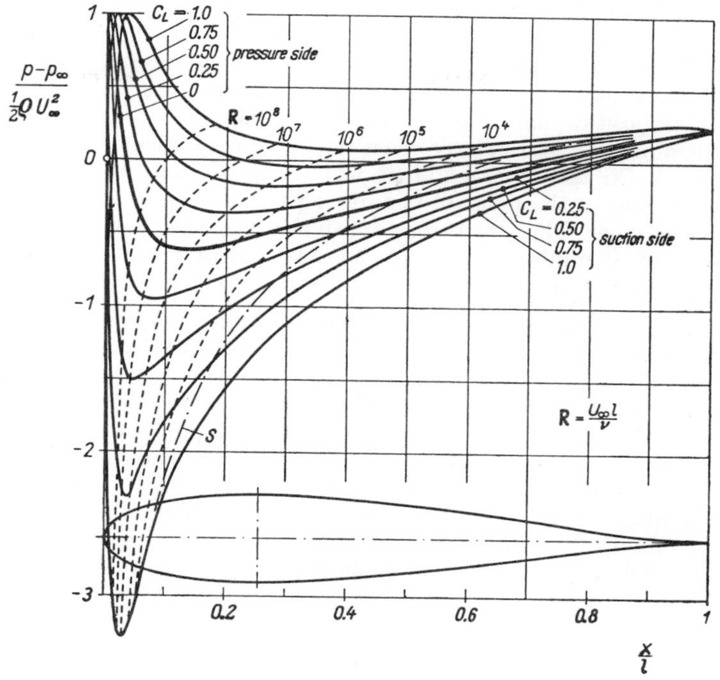

Fig. 17.6. Pressure distribution ——, position of point of instability ---- on a symmetrical Joukovsky aerofoil at varying lift coefficients

S = position of point of laminar separation

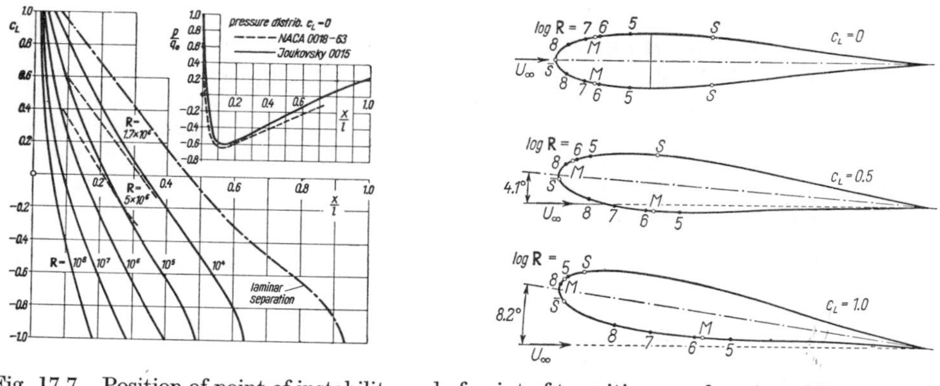

Fig. 17.7. Position of point of instability and of point of transition as a function of lift coefficient and Reynolds number. —— theoretical point of instability: J 0015; ---- measured point of transition: NACA 0018

$\bar{S}$ = stagnation point; M = point of minimum pressure; S = point of laminar separation

As a rough guide in approximate calculations it is possible to deduce the rule that the point of transition almost coincides with the point of minimum pressure of the potential flow in the range of Reynolds numbers from 10^6 to 10^7. At very large Reynolds numbers the point of transition may lie a short distance in front of that position and it may move a considerable distance behind it at small Reynolds numbers, particularly when the pressure gradient, whether positive or negative, is small. On the other hand, it will be noted that the point of transition always lies in front of the point of laminar separation irrespective of the value of the Reynolds number. Thus we can establish the rule that the point of transition lies behind the point of minimum pressure but in front of the point of laminar separation, at all except very large Reynolds numbers.

The precise distance between the point of transition and the point of instability depends on the rate of amplification of the unstable disturbances and on the intensity of turbulence in the free stream. In turn, the rate of amplification is strongly influenced by the pressure gradient. R. Michel [74a] discovered a remarkably simple, purely empirical relationship between the rate of amplification and the distance between the theoretical position of the point of instability and the experimentally determined position of the point of transition. Recently, A. M. O. Smith [104] succeeded in confirming this relation on the basis of the stability theory. As it enters the region of instability, Fig. 17.2, every unstable disturbance which travels downstream suffers an amplification which is proportional to $\exp(\beta_i t)$, or to

$$\exp\left(\int \beta_i \, \mathrm{d}t\right), \tag{17.6}$$

if β_i depends on time. Here the integral should extend over the range of unstable disturbances which is traversed by the disturbance after it had entered the region of instability. The amplification diagrams of $\beta_i = \text{const}$ (of the kind shown in Fig. 16.14) which are associated with different pressure gradients have been evaluated by J. Pretsch [84]. A. M. O. Smith utilized these diagrams and performed a large number of calculations for aerofoils and bodies of revolution for which experimental determinations of the point of transition were available. He calculated the amplification rate from eqn. (17.6) extending the integration over the path from the theoretical limit of stability to the experimental point of transition. The result of his calculations is shown in Fig. 17.8. The result of these calculations which related to many different measurements performed at very low turbulence intensities in the free stream and with very smooth surfaces leads to the conclusion that the amplification rate of unstable disturbances integrated along the path from the point of instability to the point of transition has a value of

$$\exp\left(\int \beta_i \, \mathrm{d}t\right) = \exp 9 \, . \tag{17.7}$$

This discovery was also confirmed by J. L. van Ingen [52].

The distance between the point of instability and the point of transition can be represented in the form of the difference between the Reynolds numbers formed with the aid of the momentum thickness at these two points, as was already done in Fig. 16.21, that is, as $(U\theta/\nu)_{tr} - (U\theta/\nu)_i$. Fig. 17.9 shows a plot of this quantity in terms of the mean Pohlhausen parameter $\bar{K}$ and is based on the values found by P. S. Granville [42]. Here we have

$$\bar{K} = \frac{1}{x_{tr} - x_i} \int_{x_i}^{x_{tr}} \frac{\theta^2}{\nu} \frac{dU_m}{dx} dx = \frac{1}{x_{tr} - x_i} \int_{x_i}^{x_{tr}} K(x) dx, \qquad (17.8)$$

and K is defined in eqn. (12.27).

The measurements which have been taken into account in the above calculation were all performed at very low turbulence intensities (free-flight measurements and

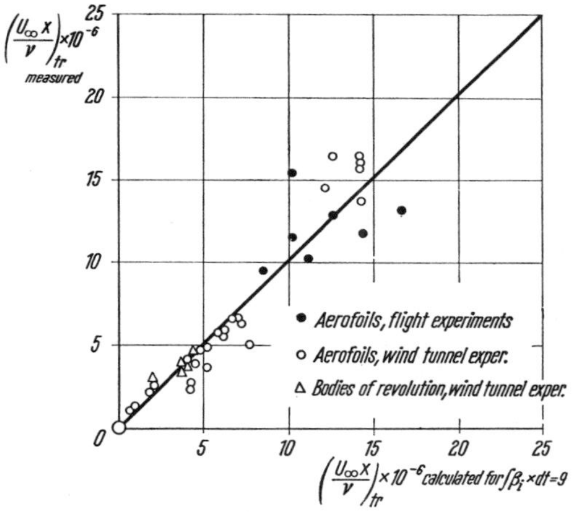

Fig. 17.8

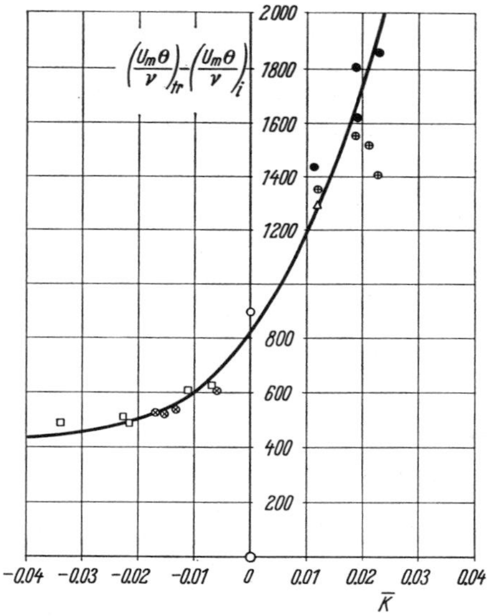

Fig. 17.9

Fig. 17.8. Determination of the amplification rate $\exp \int \beta_i\, dt$ for unstable disturbances extended over the path from the theoretical limit of stability to the experimental point of transition, after A. M. O. Smith [104]

Fig. 17.9. Measurements on the point of transition in boundary layers with pressure gradient after Granville [42]. Difference between the Reynolds numbers at the point of transition, $R_{\theta, tr} = (U_m \theta/\nu)_{tr}$, and at the point of instability, $R_{\theta, i} = (U_m \theta/\nu)_i$ as a function of the mean pressure gradient $\bar{K}$ from eqn. (17.8). $\bar{K} > 0$ corresponds to accelerated and $\bar{K} < 0$ to decelerated flows

○ Flat plate, Schubauer and Skramstad [98]
⊠ NACA aerofoil 0012, von Doenhoff [13]
● Suction side } Aerofoil NACA 65 (215)—114, Braslow and Visconti [5]
⊕ Pressure side }
□ Aerofoil of 8 % thickness ratio, B. M. Jones [56]
△ Laminar aerofoil of 14.7 % thickness ratio, Zalovcik and Skoog [124]; [5, 13, 98] measurements in low-turbulence wind tunnel; [42, 124] free-flight measurements

measurements in low-turbulence wind tunnels). The diagram in Fig. 17.9 shows that the results due to many experimenters arrange themselves satisfactorily on a single curve. The difference $R_{\theta,tr} - R_{\theta,i}$ is considerably larger for favourable pressure gradients ($\overline{K} > 0$) than for adverse ones ($\overline{K} < 0$). At constant pressure ($\overline{K} = 0$) this difference attains a value of about 800 which agrees well with that given in Fig. 16.21 for a flat plate at very small turbulence intensity.

Laminar aerofoils: The stability calculations summarized in Figs. 17.5 and 17.6 demonstrate very convincingly that the pressure gradient has a decisive influence on stability and transition in complete agreement with measurements. The design of *laminar aerofoils* is based on the same circumstance. The small skin friction of such aerofoils is achieved by designing for long stretches of laminar boundary layer. This aim is achieved by moving the point of maximum thickness, and hence the point of minimum pressure, a considerable distance towards the trailing edge. In any case the desired shift in the position of pressure minimum can only be attained in a certain narrow range of angles of incidence.

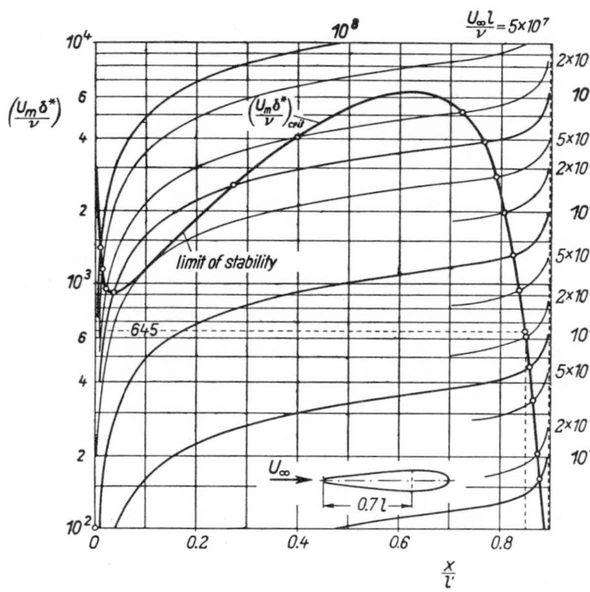

Fig. 17.10. Determination of position of point of instability for a laminar aerofoil with maximum thickness at 70 per cent. chord

It has been observed that the point of transition of such aerofoils sometimes moves forward with a jump as the Reynolds number is increased. This phenomenon can also be shown to be a consequence of the present theory, as seen from stability calculations illustrated in Fig. 17.10. This shows the results for a symmetrical aerofoil of 15 per cent thickness ratio whose maximum thickness is at 70 per cent chord and which is kept at zero incidence. The *limit of stability* $(U_m\delta^*/\nu)_{crit}$ shows a minimum far in front followed by a maximum. This course of the curve is determined by a corresponding variation in the shape factor Λ and leads to three points of intersection with the curve $U_m\delta^*/\nu$ in a certain range of Reynolds numbers $U_\infty l/\nu$.

For example for Reynolds numbers up to $U_\infty l/\nu = 5 \times 10^6$ there is only one point of instability far along the aerofoil. When the Reynolds number is only slightly increased there appears suddenly an additional point of instability at a station quite near the leading edge. Observing the boundary layer from the stagnation point onwards at a Reynolds number of, say, $U_\infty l/\nu = 10^7$ it is noticed that it becomes unstable for the first time at $x/l' = 0{\cdot}035$, turns stable at $x/l' = 0{\cdot}275$ and becomes again, and finally, unstable at $x/l' = 0{\cdot}767$. It is, however, impossible to decide whether the first zone of instability is sufficient to effect transition without analyzing the process of amplification. If we, nevertheless, interpret this first point of intersection as the point of instability, we obtain the diagram in Fig. 17.11 in which the position of the point of instability is plotted against the free-stream Rey-

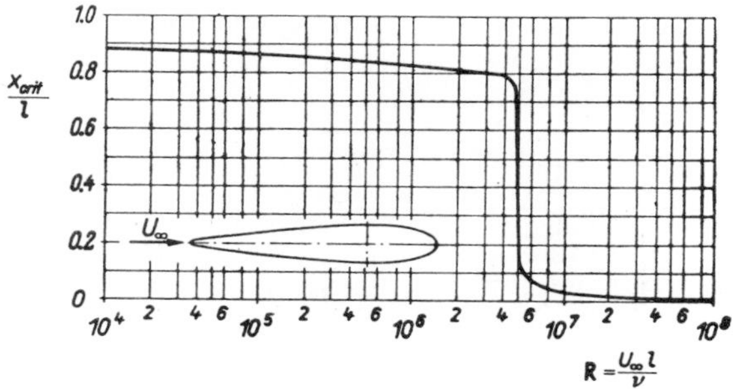

Fig. 17.11. Position of point of instability plotted against Reynolds number for the laminar aerofoil in Fig. 17.10

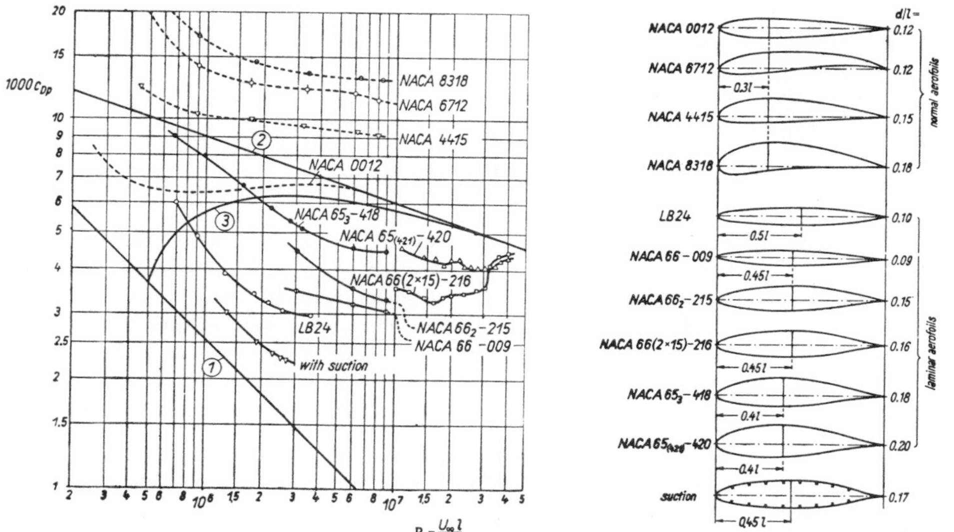

Fig. 17.12. Drag coefficient for laminar aerofoil and "normal" aerofoils from refs. [1] and [54]. LB 24 — Japanese laminar aerofoil. Aerofoil with suction after W. Pfenninger

Curves (1), (2) and (3) represent coefficient of skin friction of flat plate at zero incidence in (1) laminar flow, (2) completely turbulent flow, and, (3) transition from laminar to turbulent flow

nolds number. It is seen that the point of instability jumps suddenly forward from $x_{crit}/l = 0{\cdot}8$ to $x_{crit}/l = 0{\cdot}1$ at a Reynolds number of $U_\infty l/\nu = 5 \times 10^6$.

Very extensive measurements on laminar aerofoils were carried out during the second world war in the United States [1]. H. Doetsch [14] published the first experimental results on laminar aerofoils as early as in 1939, but B. M. Jones [56] had previously observed remarkably long stretches of laminar boundary layers during experiments in flight. Fig. 17.12 shows the amount of saving in drag that can be attained with laminar aerofoils. The saving due to the "laminar effect" reaches values of 30 to 50 per cent. of the drag of normal aerofoils in the interval of Reynolds numbers $\mathsf{R} = 2 \times 10^6$ to 3×10^7. At very large Reynolds numbers, say $\mathsf{R} > 5 \times 10^7$, the laminar effect is lost because the point of transition on the aerofoil shifts suddenly forward as demanded by the stability theory. The pressure distribution curves for some of the aerofoils are shown in Fig. 17.13. The measured

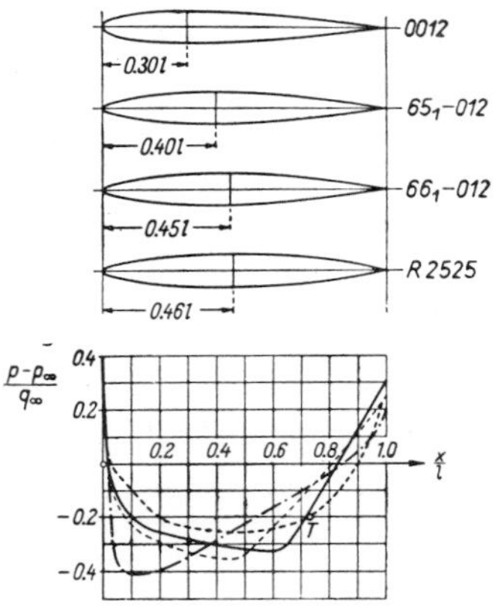

Fig. 17.13. Pressure distribution for laminar aerofoils at zero incidence ($c_L = 0$). Aerofoils 0012, 65_1—012, 66_1— 012 from ref. [5]; aerofoil R 2525 after Doetsch [14]

T = position of point of transition for $\mathsf{R} = 3{\cdot}5 \times 10^6$

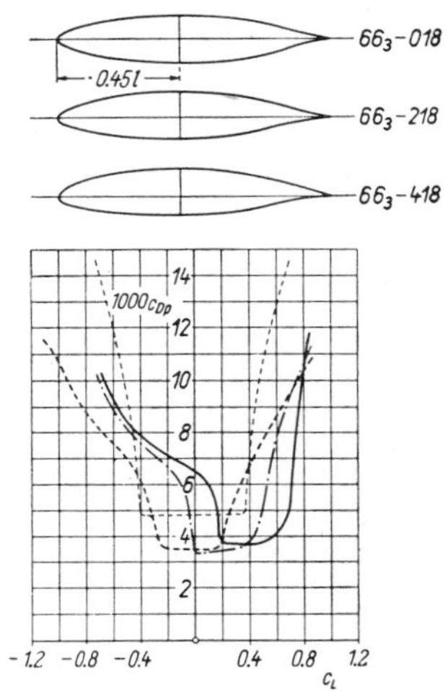

Fig. 17.14. Coefficients of profile drag, c_{Dp}, plotted against lift coefficient, c_L, for three laminar aerofoils with varying camber, $\mathsf{R} = 9 \times 10^6$, from ref. [5]. The region of small drag moves towards higher lift coefficients, c_L, as camber increases

position of the point of transition is shown in addition for aerofoil R 2525. It is seen that transition occurs shortly after pressure minimum in complete agreement with the theoretical results in Fig. 17.6. Fig. 17.14 shows, further, plots of drag coefficients in terms of the lift coefficient for three aerofoils of equal thickness but varying camber. It should be noted that by increasing the camber it is possible to cause a shift in the region of very small drag in the direction of higher values of lift, but even so, the region of reduced drag still extends over a definite width only. At this point it is necessary to remark that certain circumstances cause considerable difficulties in the practical application of laminar aerofoils. Principally these are due to the great demands on the smoothness of the surfaces in order to exclude premature transition owing to roughness.

The discussion in this section may be summarized as follows:

1. The theory of stability shows that the pressure gradient exerts an overwhelming influence on the stability of the laminar boundary layer; a decrease in pressure in the downstream direction has a stabilizing effect, whereas increasing pressure leads to instability.
2. In consequence the position of the point of maximum velocity of the potential velocity distribution function (= point of minimum pressure) influences decisively the position of the point of instability and of the point of transition. It can be assumed, as a rough guiding rule, that at medium Reynolds numbers ($\mathsf{R} = 10^6$ to 10^7) the point of instability coincides with the point of minimum pressure and that the point of transition follows shortly afterwards.
3. As the angle of incidence of an aerofoil is increased at a constant Reynolds number, the points of instability and transition move forwards on the suction side and rearwards on the pressure side.
4. As the Reynolds number is increased at constant incidence the points of instability and transition move forwards.
5. At very high Reynolds numbers and with a flat pressure minimum, the point of instability may, under certain circumstances, slightly precede the point of minimum pressure.
6. Even at low Reynolds numbers ($\mathsf{R} = 10^5$ to 10^6) the points of instability and transition precede the point of laminar separation; under certain circumstances the laminar boundary layer may become separated and may re-attach as a turbulent boundary layer.

c. Effect of suction on transition in a boundary layer

It has already been pointed out in Chap. XIII that the application of suction to a laminar boundary layer is an effective means of reducing drag. The effect of suction is to stabilize the boundary layer in a way similar to the effect of the pressure gradient discussed in the preceding section, and the reduction in drag is achieved by preventing transition from laminar to turbulent flow. A more detailed analysis reveals that the influence of suction is due to two effects. First, suction reduces the boundary layer thickness and a thinner boundary layer is less prone to become turbulent. Secondly, suction creates a laminar velocity profile which possesses a higher limit of stability (critical Reynolds number) than a velocity profile with no suction.

So far only continuous suction can be treated mathematically and several solutions of such cases have already been given in Chap. XIII. In connexion with the problem of maintaining laminar flow it is important to estimate the quantity of fluid to be removed. It is possible to obtain any desired reduction in boundary layer thickness, and hence to keep the Reynolds number below the limit of stability, provided that enough fluid is sucked away. However, a large suction volume is uneconomical because a large proportion of the saving in power due to the reduction in drag is then used to drive the suction pump. It is, therefore, important to determine the *minimum suction volume* which is required in order to maintain laminar flow.

The saving in drag achieved through suction is greatest when this minimum value is used because any higher suction volume will lead to a thinner boundary layer and to an increase in shearing stress at the wall.

As shown in Chap. XIII the solution of the boundary layer equations with suction included is particularly simple for the case of a flat plate at zero incidence with uniform suction (velocity of suction denoted by $-v_0$†). It will be recalled that the velocity profile, and hence the boundary layer thickness, become independent of the current co-ordinate from a certain distance from the leading edge onwards. As shown in eqn. (13.7) the displacement thickness of this *asymptotic suction profile* is given by

$$\delta^* = \frac{\nu}{-v_0} . \tag{17.9}$$

K. Bussmann and H. Muenz [7] carried out an investigation into the stability of this profile (Fig. 13.6) on the lines of the method explained in Chap. XVI. As seen from eqn. (13.6), the velocity profile is decribed by the equation

$$u(y) = U_\infty \left[1 - \exp\left(v_0 y/\nu\right)\right] ,$$

for which the critical Reynolds number has the very large value of

$$\left(\frac{U_\infty \delta^*}{\nu}\right)_{crit} = 70{,}000 . \tag{17.10}$$

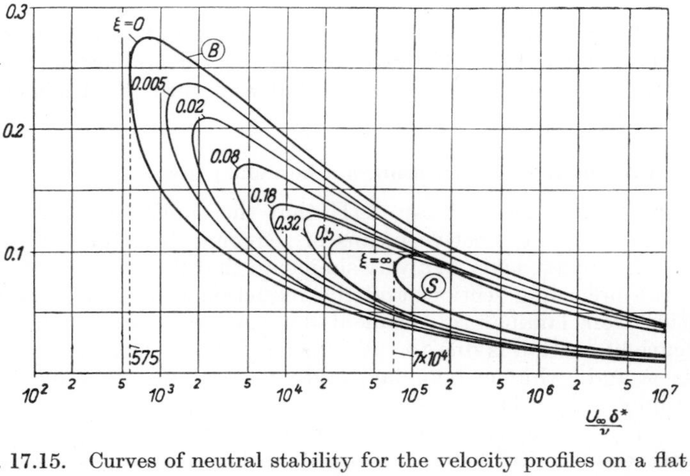

Curve A: asymptotic suction profile
Curve B: profile with no suction

Fig. 17.15. Curves of neutral stability for the velocity profiles on a flat plate at zero incidence with uniform suction; $\xi = \left(\frac{-v_0}{U_\infty}\right)^2 \frac{U_\infty x}{\nu}$ denotes dimensionless inlet length

Thus the critical Reynolds number of the asymptotic suction profile is seen to be more than one hundred times larger than on a flat plate at zero incidence and in the absence of a pressure gradient or suction. This value demonstrates the highly

† Here $v_0 < 0$ denotes suction and $v_0 > 0$ denotes blowing

stabilizing effect of suction. Furthermore the preceding argument shows that laminar flow is maintained not only owing to the reduction in boundary layer thickness but also, and in particular, owing to a large increase in the limit of stability of the velocity profile. The curve of neutral stability for the asymptotic suction profile is shown in Fig. 17.15 ($\xi = \infty$). It should be noted that the limit of stability is increased as compared with the case with no suction and that, in addition, the range of unstable disturbance wavelengths circumscribed by the curve of neutral stability is reduced considerably.

The preceding results allow us now to find an answer to the important question of how much fluid must be removed in order to maintain laminar flow. Assuming, by the way of simplification, that the asymptotic profile already exists at the leading edge of the flat plate to which uniform suction has been applied, we conclude that a laminar boundary layer which is stable along the whole plate exists if the value of the displacement thickness Reynolds number is smaller than the limit of stability given by eqn. (17.10). Hence

$$\text{condition of stability:}\ \frac{U_\infty \delta^*}{\nu} < \left(\frac{U_\infty \delta^*}{\nu}\right)_{crit} = 70{,}000\,.$$

Using the value of δ^* for the asymptotic profile from eqn. (17.9) we have

$$\text{condition of stability:}\ \frac{(-v_0)}{U_\infty} = c_Q > \frac{1}{70{,}000}\,. \tag{17.11}$$

According to this result the boundary layer would be stable if the volume coefficient of suction had the extremely low value of $1/70{,}000 = 1{\cdot}4 \times 10^{-5}$.

It might be remarked here that a more accurate calculation would presumably lead to a higher value of the volume coefficient. This is due to the fact that the asymptotic velocity profile, on whose existence the above calculation was based, develops only at a certain distance from the leading edge. The velocity profiles between that point and the leading edge are of different shapes, changing gradually from the Blasius form with no suction at short distances behind the leading edge to the above asymptotic form. The profile shapes in this initial, starting length for the laminar boundary layer with suction have been plotted in detail in Fig. 13.8. All these velocity profiles have lower limits of stability than the asymptotic one, and it follows that the quantity of fluid to be removed over the initial length must be larger than the value given in eqn. (17.11), if laminar flow is to be maintained.

In order to analyze this matter in greater detail it is necessary to repeat the stability calculation for the series of velocity profiles in the starting length taking suction into account. These profiles constitute a one-parameter family of curves as shown in Fig. 13.8, the parameter being given by

$$\xi = c_Q^{\,2} \cdot \frac{U_\infty x}{\nu}\,,$$

and changing from $\xi = 0$ at the leading edge to $\xi = \infty$ for the asymptotic profile. In practice, however, it may be assumed that the starting length ends with $\xi = 4$. The resulting critical Reynolds numbers have been computed by A. Ulrich [117] and are given in Table 17.2; the corresponding curves of neutral stability have been plotted in Fig. 17.15. The amplification of unstable disturbances for the asymptotic profile has been calculated by J. Pretsch [85]. The highest degree of amplification obtained in this calculation was about 10 times smaller than that for the flat plate (Blasius flow) in Fig. 16.17. With the results of this calculation it is now easy to determine the volume coefficient of suction which is sufficient to ensure stability over the starting length. It can be obtained from Fig. 17.16 in which the limit of stability from Table 17.2 and the variation of the dimensionless displacement thickness

$$\frac{U_\infty \delta^*}{\nu} = \frac{-v_0\, \delta^*}{\nu}\,\frac{1}{c_Q}$$

for a prescribed value of $c_Q = (-v_0)/U_\infty$ have been plotted against the dimensionless length co-ordinate. Here $(-v_0)\,\delta^*/\nu$ is known in terms of ξ from the calculation of the boundary layer, Table 13.1. It is seen from Fig. 17.16 that the limit of stability is not crossed at any point over the whole length only if the volume coefficient is kept at a value larger than 1/8,500. Hence the critical value of the volume coefficient becomes

$$c_{Q\,crit} = 1{\cdot}18 \times 10^{-4}\,. \tag{17.12}$$

Table 17.2. Dependence of critical Reynolds number of velocity profiles with suction on dimensionless suction volume factor ξ, after Ulrich [117]

$\xi = c_Q{}^2\,\dfrac{U_\infty x}{\nu}$	0	0·005	0·02	0·08	0·18	0·32	0·5	∞
$\left(\dfrac{U_\infty \delta^*}{\nu}\right)_{crit}$	575	1120	1820	3940	7590	13500	21900	70000

We are now in a position to answer the question which was left open in Chap. XIII, namely that concerning the actual decrease in the drag on a flat plate at zero incidence whose boundary layer is kept laminar by suction. Fig. 13.9 contained a plot of the coefficient of skin friction

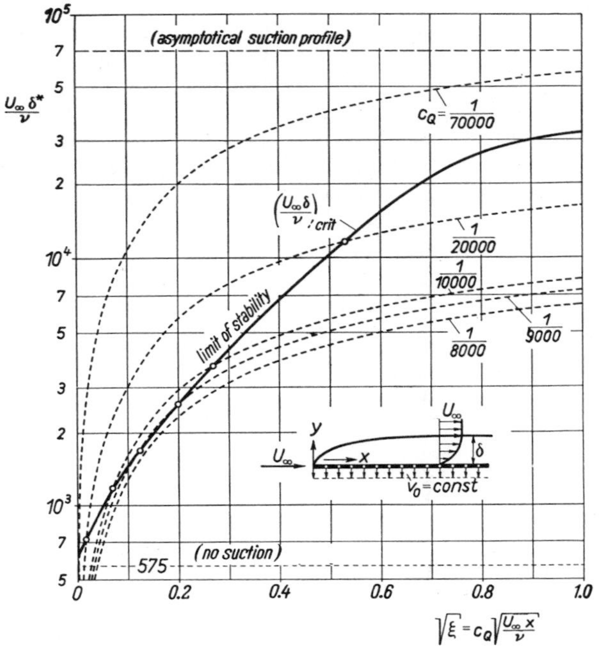

Fig. 17.16. Determination of critical value of volume coefficient for maintenance of laminar flow through suction for boundary layer on flat plate

under these conditions expressed in terms of the Reynolds number with the volume coefficient c_Q appearing as a parameter. If the curve which corresponds to $c_{Q\,crit}$ from eqn. (17.12) is now plotted in the diagram, it is possible to deduce the variation of the coefficient of skin friction for a flat plate under conditions of *optimum suction*, as shown in Fig. 17.17. The distance between the curve marked 'optimum suction' and that marked 'turbulent' corresponds to the saving in drag effected by the application of suction.

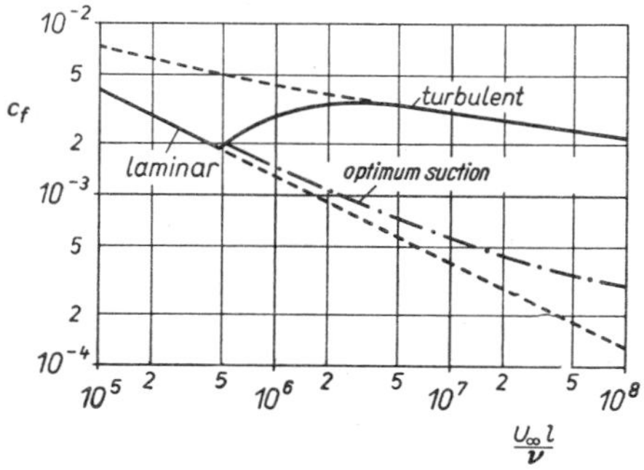

Fig. 17.17. Coefficient of skin friction of a flat plate at zero incidence. *Optimum suction* denotes smallest volume coefficient $c_{Q\,crit} = 1{\cdot}2 \times 10^{-4}$ which just suffices to maintain laminar flow

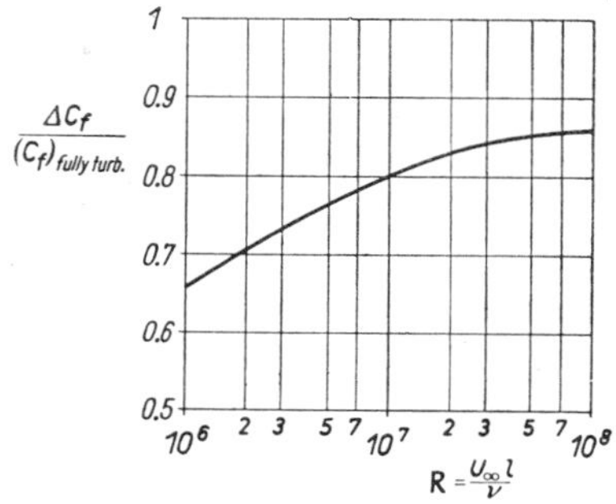

Fig. 17.18. Relative saving in drag on flat plate at zero incidence with suction maintaining laminar flow at *optimum suction* from Fig. 17.17

$\Delta c_f = c_{f\,turb} - c_{f\,laminar\ with\ suction}$

The relative saving in drag calculated with respect to turbulent drag increases somewhat as the Reynolds number is increased, Fig. 17.18. It varies from 65 to 85 per cent. in a range of Reynolds numbers $R = 10^6$ to 10^8. Experimental results concerning boundary layer control have already been discussed in Chap. XIII. These theoretical results concerning the saving of drag due to suction have found an excellent confirmation in the experiments carried out in flight and in a wind tunnel [49, 57, 58], see also Fig. 13.12.

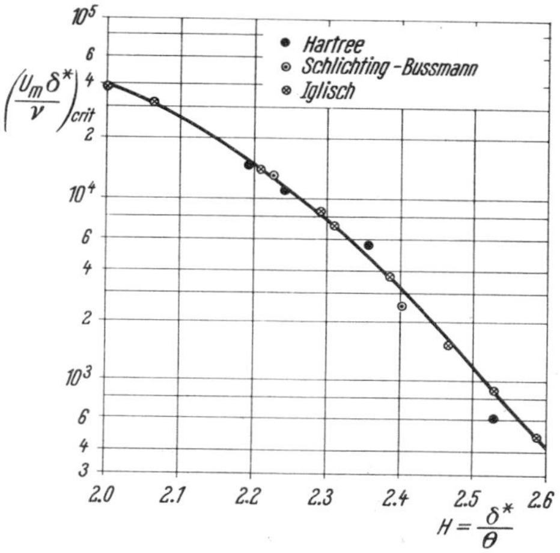

Fig. 17.19. The critical Reynolds number for laminar velocity profiles with suction, and with a pressure gradient plotted as a function of the shape factor $H = \delta^*/\theta$

The effect of suction on the limit of stability together with that of a pressure gradient can be represented graphically by plotting the critical Reynolds number against the shape factor $H = \delta^*/\theta$ of the boundary layer profile, as was done in Fig. 17.19. The critical Reynolds numbers for a flat plate with zero pressure gradient and uniform suction (Iglisch profiles, Fig. 13.8), those for a plate with suction described by $v_0 \sim 1/\sqrt{x}$ (Bussmann profiles, Fig. 13.12) as well as those for the case with no suction but with a pressure gradient (Hartree profiles) place themselves well on a single curve. For the asymptotic suction profile we have $H = 2$ and for the plate with no suction the value is $H = 2{\cdot}59$.

A paper by H. Krueger [61] contains calculations of the critical Reynolds number for several examples involving *wing sections*. W. Wuest [122, 123] proved analytically that the stabilizing effect of several single slits placed one behind the other is markedly smaller than that produced by uniform suction.

d. Effect of body forces on transition

1. Boundary layers on convex walls (centrifugal forces). There are cases when transition from laminar to turbulent flow is materially affected by external forces impressed on the boundary layer. The flow in the annulus between two rotating concentric cylinders affords an example of such a case. When the inner cylinder is at rest and the outer cylinder rotates uniformly, the velocity in the annulus increases practically linearly from zero at the inner wall to the peripheral velocity of the outer wall. A fluid particle from an outer layer opposes a tendency to being moved inwards because its centrifugal force exceeds that on a particle nearer the axis of the cylinder and shows a tendency to being thrown outwards. Equally, motion outwards is made more difficult because the centrifugal force acting on an inner particle is smaller than that on a particle further away from the axis so that, consequently, particles are acted upon by what might be termed a 'centripetal lift'. Hence it can be appreciated that transverse motions which are characteristic of turbulent flow are impeded by centrifugal forces. Thus in this case the centrifugal forces have a stabilizing effect.

All stability calculations described so far were confined to flat plates. H. Goertler [37] generalized Tollmien's stability criterion for profiles with a point of inflexion to include the influence of wall curvature, this case being of great practical importance. Tollmien's theorem for plane walls which states that in the limiting case of very large Reynolds number velocity profiles with a change in sign of $\mathrm{d}^2U/\mathrm{d}y^2$ become unstable, see Sec. XVIb, must be modified by stating that a change in the sign of the expression

$$\left(\frac{\mathrm{d}^2 U}{\mathrm{d}y^2} + \frac{1}{R}\frac{\mathrm{d}U}{\mathrm{d}y}\right) = 0 \tag{17.13}$$

causes frictionless instability in the case of curved walls. Here R denotes the radius of curvature of the wall with $R > 0$ denoting a convex and $R < 0$ denoting a concave region of the wall. Since the left-hand side of eqn. (17.13) represents the pressure gradient, except for a constant factor, it is seen that instability with respect to two-dimensional disturbances occurs on convex walls, just as on flat walls, exactly at the pressure minimum. However, on the whole, the influence of wall curvature is very small if the ratio of boundary layer thickness δ to the radius of curvature satisfies the conditions that $\delta/|R| \ll 1$. With concave walls a different kind of instability, namely that with respect to certain three-dimensional disturbances, to be discussed in Sec. f of this chapter, becomes of far greater importance.

H. Schlichting [91] carried out a thorough investigation into the stability of two-dimensional flows past curved walls on the example of the flow inside a rotating cylinder: In the case of steady-state flow in the annulus between two concentric cylinders with the inner cylinder at rest and the outer cylinder rotating about its axis no limit of stability can exist in analogy with Couette flow, ($\mathsf{R}_{crit} = \infty$, *cf.* Sec. XVIc). For this reason the investigation was extended to include velocity profiles which occur when the outer cylinder is set in motion impulsively. The velocity profiles which develop in this case belong to the kind shown in Fig. 5.5, but they are slightly modified by the wall curvature. It was assumed that there is no inner cylinder in order to simplify the calculations. The result of these stability calculations is shown in Fig. 17.20 which shows a plot of the critical Reynolds number based on the displacement thickness δ^* and on the peripheral velocity, U_m, against the ratio δ^*/R, where R denotes the radius of the cylinder. Owing to the stabilizing effect of centrifugal forces, the critical Reynolds number increases steeply as δ^*/R increases. The results are shown in Table 17.3, which also lists the values of the critical Reynolds number based on the radius of the cylinder, R. The latter passes through a minimum at

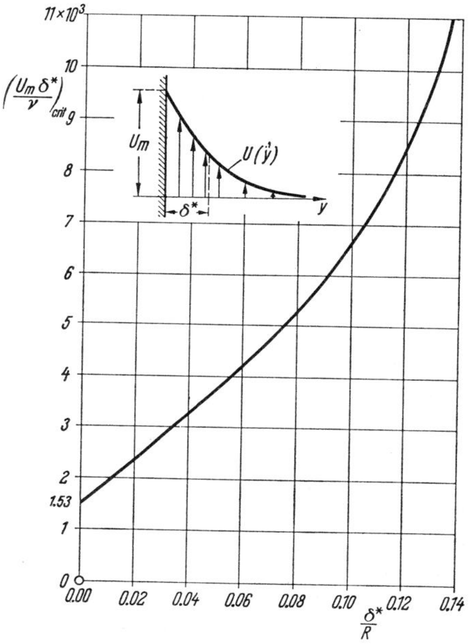

Fig. 17.20. Critical Reynolds number for the velocity profiles which occur on a rotating cylinder during impulsive acceleration

R — radius of cylinder

U_m — peripheral velocity of the cylinder

$$\left(\frac{U_m R}{\nu}\right)_{crit} = 66{,}000\,.$$

In order to compare this result with experimental values it is necessary to choose examples where the inner cylinder is at rest, and the outer cylinder rotates, in which case the critical Reynolds number depends further on the ratio of annulus width to external radius. Some experimental results [73, 114, 119] are seen plotted in Fig. 17.21. The preceding theoretical value corresponds to $s/R = 1$. Extrapolation of measured values to $s/R = 1$ gives $(U_m R/\nu) = 200{,}000$ which can be considered as being in satisfactory agreement with experiment if it is recalled that the ideal case assumes the existence of just one neutral disturbance wavelength, whereas the occurrence of transition requires the amplification of a larger range of wavelengths.

A further confirmation of these theoretical results was recently supplied by F. Schultz-Grunow [98a] who was able to prove quite rigorously that the flow between two concentric cylinders of which the outer rotates and the inner is at rest is completely stable. Since, as mentioned before, the flow becomes eventually turbulent under those conditions, the explanation was sought in a study of the

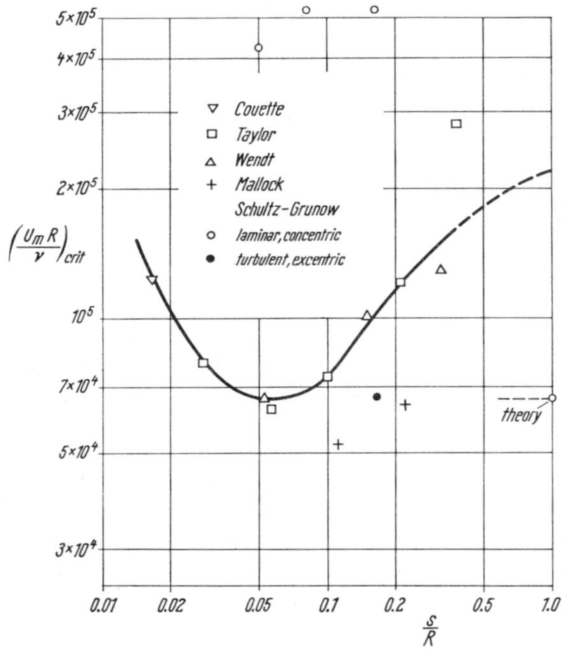

R — radius of outer cylinder
s — width of annular gap
○ Schultz-Grunow, laminar, perfect concentricity
● Schultz-Grunow, turbulent, slight eccentricity

Fig. 17.21. Critical Reynolds number for flow in annulus between two concentric, rotating cylinders; inner cylinder is at rest, outer cylinder rotating. Older measurements (Couette, Taylor, Wendt, Mallock) show the existence of a critical Reynolds number. More recent measurements by F. Schultz-Grunow [98a] show complete stability (open circles) with perfect concentricity and transition (blackened circle) with eccentric arrangement

Table 17.3. Critical Reynolds number of velocity profiles occuring, when cylinder is impulsively set in rotation about axis, after Schlichting [91]

$\frac{\delta^*}{R}$	0	0·011	0·027	0·055	0·073	0·109	0·136
$\left(\frac{U_m \delta^*}{\nu}\right)_{crit} \times 10^{-3}$	1·53	1·96	2·65	3·96	4·90	7·32	10·8
$\left(\frac{U_m R}{\nu}\right)_{crit} \times 10^{-4}$	∞	17·9	9·69	7·24	6·72	6·74	7·89

starting process but the fact that turbulence persisted into the steady-state remained unexplained. In addition to the analytical investigation, Schultz-Grunow performed experiments with an arrangement in which particular attention was paid to making sure that the cylinders were exactly concentric and free from vibrations induced by imperfect balancing. It was established that although transition does occur during the starting process, the flow reverts to a laminar pattern when a steady-state has been established. This occured even at the highest speeds which the installation was capable to develop and laminar flows were observed at Reynolds numbers which exceeded those for which transition had been observed previously by factors of 5 to 8, as shown in Fig. 17.21 by the open circles. The flow behaved differently, and turbulence persisted, as in older experiments, when a controlled amount of eccentricity was built into the arrangement, Fig. 17.21, black circles. It has thus been confirmed that the persistence of turbulence into the steady-state regime was caused by imperfections in the geometrical shape and did not signify that the theory had failed.

When the inner cylinder rotates and the outer one is at rest the motion may become unstable with respect to three-dimensional disturbances in analogy with the boundary layer on a concave wall. We shall deal with this case in Sec. XVIIf.

2. The flow of non-homogeneous fluids (stratification). The influence of vertical *density variations* on the stability of flow past a flat horizontal wall is in a sense related to the case of centrifugal forces occurring in a homogeneous fluid flowing along a curved wall. When the density decreases upwards, the arrangement is stable, and it becomes unstable when the density variation is reversed. In the latter case there is instability even without flow, when the fluid is heated from below. The fluid then becomes unstable in that the horizontal layers of fluid become honeycombed into regular hexagonal eddy patterns [2a, 54, 86]. In the case of flow with stable density stratification, turbulent mixing in the vertical direction is impeded because heavier particles must be lifted and lighter particles must be depressed against hydrostatic forces. Turbulence can even be completely suppressed if the density gradient is strong enough, the phenomenon being of some importance in certain meteorological processes. It is, for example, possible to observe that on cool summer evenings damp meadows are blanketed in sharply outlined mists with a gentle wind blowing. This is a sign that the wind ceased to be turbulent so that layers of air slide over each other in laminar motion and without turbulent mixing. The cause of this phenomenon lies in the pronounced temperature gradient which is formed in the air as the earth cools in the evening and prevents mixing of the warmer, and therefore lighter, upper layers of the atmosphere with the colder and heavier layers near the ground. The "falling off" of the wind which can sometimes be observed towards the evening is due to the same effect. The wind prevails in all its force at higher altitudes but the suppression of turbulence near the ground on cooling greatly reduces its speed. Furthermore, the streaming of sweet over salt water which occurs e. g. in the Kattegat, as well as the remarkable stability of Bjerknes' polar fronts, when the cold masses of air form a wedge under the warm air, belong to this group of phenomena.

L. Prandtl [77] analysed the phenomena connected with density gradients as well as with the previously discussed flows over curved surfaces involving the influence of centrifugal forces with the aid of an energy method. He has shown that the stability of stratified flows depends on the stratification parameter

$$\mathsf{R}_i = \frac{-\frac{g}{\varrho}\frac{\mathrm{d}\varrho}{\mathrm{d}y}}{\left(\frac{\mathrm{d}U}{\mathrm{d}y}\right)_w^2} \tag{17.14}$$

known as the Richardson number, in addition to the usual dependence on Reynolds number. Here g denotes the acceleration due to gravity, ϱ the density and the positive direction of y is measured vertically upwards. The subscript w refers to the value of the velocity gradient at the wall, and $\mathsf{R}_i = 0$ corresponds to a homogeneous fluid, $\mathsf{R}_i > 0$ denoting stable, and $\mathsf{R}_i < 0$ unstable stratification. The energy method used by L. F. Richardson [87] and L. Prandtl has shown that turbulence may be expected to disappear at $\mathsf{R}_i > 2$. G. I. Taylor [112] refined Prandtl's reasoning and obtained $\mathsf{R}_i \geq 1$ as the limit of stability. H. Ertel [28] supplied a thermodynamic justification for this criterion.

G. I. Taylor [112] and S. Goldstein [35] were the first ones to apply the method of small disturbances to this problem. Assuming a continuous density distribution and a linear velocity profile in an infinite fluid they found the limit of stability to be at $\mathsf{R}_i = \frac{1}{4}$. The influence of viscosity and of curvature in the velocity profile have been neglected in this connexion. H. Schlichting [93] investigated the stability of flows with density stratification with the aid of Tollmien's theory. The calculation was based on the assumption of a Blasius profile for a flat plate with a density gradient in the boundary layer and constant density outside it. It was found that the critical Reynolds number increased rapidly as the Richardson number increased, Fig. 17.22, changing its value from $\mathsf{R}_{crit} = 575$ for $\mathsf{R}_i = 0$ (homogeneous flow) to $\mathsf{R}_{crit} = \infty$ for $\mathsf{R}_i = 1/24$. Thus for

$$\mathsf{R}_i > 0{\cdot}0417 \quad \text{(stable)}$$

the flow remains stable everywhere on the flat plate. It is seen that the present limit of stability is considerably smaller than that given by previous theories.

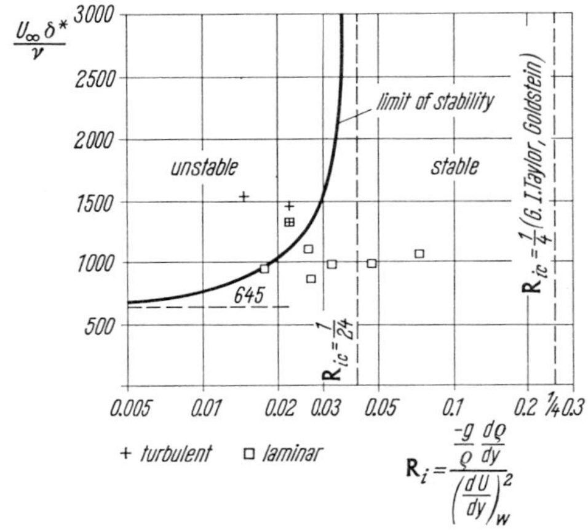

Fig. 17.22. Critical Reynolds number for the boundary layer on a flat plate at zero incidence in flow with density gradient as a function of the Richardson number R_i

A comparison between theory and the experimental results due to H. Reichardt [78] is given in Fig. 17.22; measurements were performed in a special rectangular channel in Goettingen. The air was passed through the channel whose upper wall was heated with the aid of steam, the bottom wall being cooled with water. It is seen that all observed laminar flows fall within the stable region, whereas all turbulent flows fall within the unstable region. Agreement is, therefore, excellent.

G. I. Taylor [113] observed turbulent flow in ocean currents at considerably higher values of the Richardson number and it appears that this phenomenon is due to the absence of walls.

Recently J. T. Stuart [107] investigated theoretically the effect of a magnetic field on transition. It turned out that the critical Reynolds number increases considerably for the case of laminar flow between two parallel flat walls when the lines of the magnetic field are parallel to the walls.

e. Effects due to heat transfer and compressibility

1. Introductory remark. The theoretical and experimental results concerning transition described in the preceding sections are valid only for flows at moderate speeds (incompressible flow). The effect of the compressibility of the fluid on transition has recently been exhaustively investigated under the stimulus from aeronautical engineering. In the case of compressible flows, apart from the Mach number, it is necessary to take into account one additional, important parameter which is connected with the rate of heat transferred between the fluid and the wall. When the fluid is incompressible, heat can be exchanged between the wall and the fluid only if the temperature of the wall is higher or lower than that of the fluid flowing past it. In the case of a compressible fluid, the heat evolved in the boundary layer produces an additional, important influence, as already shown in Chap. XV. In either case a thermal boundary layer develops in addition to the velocity boundary layer and plays its part in the determination of the stability of the latter. The theoretical and experimental considerations which we are about to discuss will show that the transfer of heat from the boundary layer to the wall exerts a stabilizing influence by causing the critical Reynolds number to increase. The opposite flow of heat from the wall to the fluid has the reverse effect and promotes instability by reducing the critical Reynolds number.

2. The effect of the transfer of heat. The main features of the effect of the transfer of heat from the wall to the fluid on the stability of a laminar boundary layer can be readily recognised even in the case when the flow is incompressible. We shall, therefore, explain it first in this simplified form. The first experimental investigation on the influence of heat transfer on transition were performed quite some time ago by W. Linke [71]. W. Linke measured the drag on a vertical heated plate placed in a horizontal stream in a range of length Reynolds numbers $\mathsf{R}_l = 10^5$ to 10^6 and observed that heating caused it to increase by a large amount. He concluded from this, quite rightly, that the heating of the plate causes the critical Reynolds number to decrease so that, consequently, in the above range of Reynolds numbers which, evidently, corresponds to the transition region, a large increase in drag is observed.

With the aid of the point-of-inflexion criterion which was discussed in Chap. XVI it is easy to show that when $T_w > T_\infty$, the transfer of heat from the wall to the fluid in incompressible flow depresses the limit of stability, whereas the transfer of heat from the fluid to the wall at $T_w < T_\infty$ causes it to become larger. In essence, the stabilizing or de-stabilizing effect due to the transfer of heat is a consequence of the dependence of the viscosity μ of the fluid on the temperature T. According to eqn. (15.1), the viscosity of gases increases with temperature. When the temperature-dependence of the viscosity is taken into account, the curvature of the velocity profile $U(y)$ of the main flow is given, according to eqn. (15.4), by

$$\frac{\mathrm{d}}{\mathrm{d}y}\left(\mu \frac{\mathrm{d}U}{\mathrm{d}y}\right)_w = \frac{\mathrm{d}p}{\mathrm{d}x} \tag{17.15}$$

so that in the case of a flat plate at zero incidence, we have

$$\frac{\mathrm{d}}{\mathrm{d}y}\left(\mu \frac{\mathrm{d}U}{\mathrm{d}y}\right)_w = 0 . \tag{17.16}$$

Carrying out the indicated differentiation, we obtain

$$\mu_w \left(\frac{\mathrm{d}^2 U}{\mathrm{d}y^2}\right)_w + \left(\frac{\mathrm{d}\mu}{\mathrm{d}y}\right)_w \left(\frac{\mathrm{d}U}{\mathrm{d}y}\right)_w = 0 ,$$

and the curvature of the velocity profile at the wall becomes

$$\left(\frac{\mathrm{d}^2 U}{\mathrm{d}y^2}\right)_w = -\frac{1}{\mu_w}\left(\frac{\mathrm{d}\mu}{\mathrm{d}y}\right)_w \left(\frac{\mathrm{d}U}{\mathrm{d}y}\right)_w . \tag{17.17}$$

Now, if the wall is hotter than the gas in the free stream, we have $T_w > T_\infty$ and the temperature gradient at the wall is negative: $(\partial T/\partial y)_w < 0$. Since the viscosity is an increasing function of temperature, we must have $(\partial \mu/\partial y)_w < 0$, and since the velocity gradient is positive at the wall, it follows from eqn. (17.17) that

$$T_w \gtrless T_\infty \quad \text{implies} \quad \left(\frac{\mathrm{d}^2 U}{\mathrm{d}y^2}\right)_w \gtrless 0 . \tag{17.18}$$

Thus for a heated wall when $T_w > T_\infty$, the curvature of the velocity profile at the wall is positive and for a cooled wall it is negative. Further, it follows immediately that in the case of a heated wall there must exist within the boundary layer a point at which the curvature vanishes (point of inflexion), i. e. one for which we have $\mathrm{d}^2U/\mathrm{d}y^2 = 0$, because the curvature is vanishingly small but negative at $y = \infty$ (*cf.* Fig. 7.5). This means that the velocity profile for a heated wall possesses a point of inflexion and so becomes highly unstable by the criterion given in Chap. XVI. The transfer of heat from the wall into the fluid flowing past it renders the boundary layer highly unstable in a manner analogous to a pressure increase in the downstream direction, whereas a cooling effect renders it stable and acts like a favourable pressure gradient.

Since the viscosity of a liquid decreases as the temperature is increased, the effect would, presumably, be reversed in that case, but no direct measurements to confirm this statement seem to be available.

The de-stabilizing effect of heating was fully confirmed by the measurements performed by H. W. Liepmann and G. H. Fila [70] on a vertical flat plate at zero incidence, as shown in Fig. 17.23. It is seen from it that the critical Reynolds number decreases as the wall temperature increases, the decrease being steeper for higher turbulence intensities of the free stream. This effect is to be expected from the consideration of the influence of turbulence intensity on transition given in Sec. XVI. In this connexion comparison may be made with the measurements performed by R. W. Higgins and C. C. Pappas [44].

The stability of the boundary layer on a flat plate with free and forced convection was investigated experimentally by E. R. G. Eckert [26, 27].

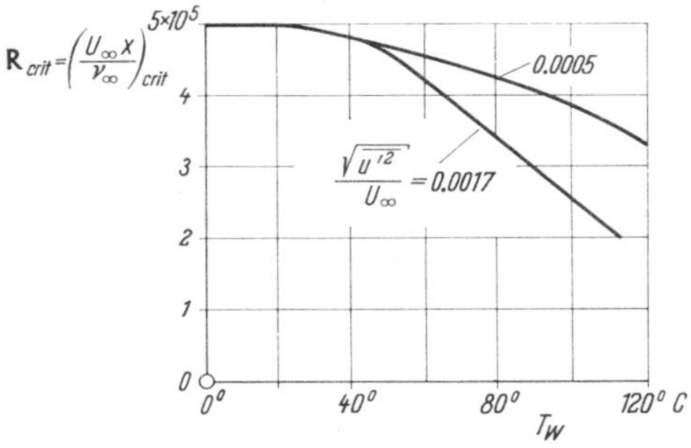

Fig. 17.23. The critical Reynolds number of a heated flat plate at zero incidence in an incompressible air stream. Measurements performed by H. W. Liepmann and G. H. Fila [70]

T_w — wall temperature ;

$\sqrt{\overline{u'^2}}/U_\infty$ — turbulence intensity in external flow

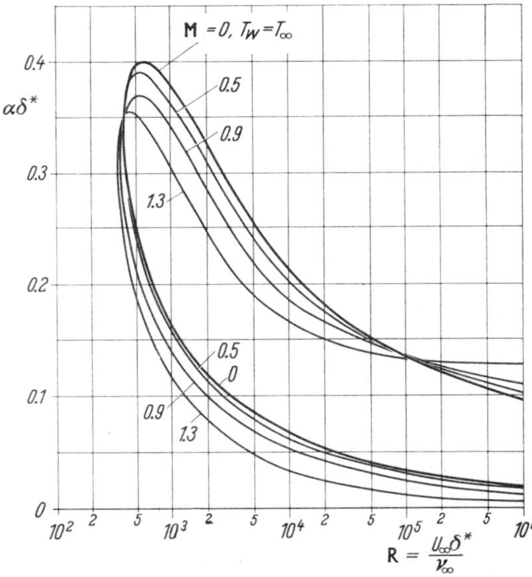

Fig. 17.24. Curves of neutral stability for laminar boundary layer on a flat plate at zero incidence in a compressible stream. Wall made of *adiabatic material*. Results due to Lees and Lin [65]

Prandtl number P = 1

3. The effect of compressibility. The stability of compressible laminar layers was first analyzed with the aid of the method of small oscillations by D. Kuechemann [62] in his thesis presented to the University of Goettingen. In order to simplify the calculation he assumed a linear velocity distribution, as shown in Fig. 16.9a. The influence of friction on the propagation of disturbances was neglected. The work discussed neutral disturbances in the form of progressing waves described in Sec. XVIb on the one hand and forced oscillations on the other. The latter were assumed in the form of oblique waves which are characteristic of supersonic flow and which, coming from the outside, are reflected in the boundary layer, see Figs. 15.24a, b.

Kuechemann obtained eigen-values for neutral oscillations but, naturally, no critical Reynolds numbers because he neglected the effect of viscosity. In more recent times these investigations have been extended by E. A. Mueller, as described in Chap. XV [49]; the reader may also wish to consult the comprehensive review given by W. Tollmien [116].

An analysis of the stability of compressible laminar boundary layers including the influence of velocity profile curvature and friction was first carried out by L. Lees and C. C. Lin [64]†. In the case of an *adiabatic* wall, the effect of compressibility on the stability of the boundary layers is fairly insignificant at low Mach numbers. This can be inferred from Fig. 17.24 which shows curves of neutral stability for different Mach numbers and the boundary layer on a flat plate at zero incidence. As the Mach number is increased, the critical Reynolds number based on the displacement thickness decreases only very slightly.

By contrast, in the case of a *heat-conducting* wall the effect of heat transfer on stability is very large in the compressible case too. Some results concerning this case can be seen plotted in Fig. 17.25. They, again, refer to a flat plate at a moderate Mach number ($\mathsf{M}_\infty = 0.7$). A study of the curves of neutral stability for different values of T_w/T_∞ shows that the extraction of heat from the boundary layer with $T_w < T_\infty$ causes a large increase in the limit of stability, whereas the addition of heat with $T_w > T_\infty$ reduces it considerably. It should be noted that the curve of neutral stability has a shape typical for frictionless instability and is similar to the one encountered in the case of boundary layers with an adverse pressure gradient in Sec. XVIIa (see also Fig. 16.8), when $T_w/T_\infty > 1$.

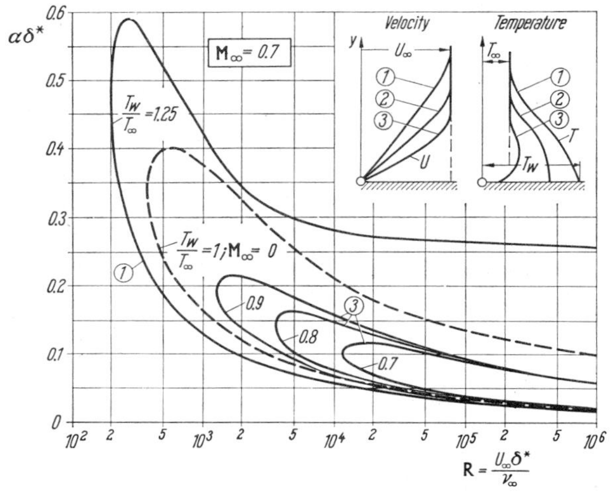

Prandtl number $\mathsf{P} = 1$; Mach number $\mathsf{M}_\infty = 0{\cdot}7$

(1) Addition of heat to boundary layer with *heat transfer from wall to gas* ($T_w > T_\infty$) lowers the limit of stability
(2) adiabatic wall
(3) extraction of heat from boundary layer with *heat transfer from gas to wall* ($T_w < T_\infty$) raises the limit of stability

Fig. 17.25. Curves of neutral stability for the laminar boundary layer on a flat plate at zero incidence in compressible flow and with *heat transfer*, after L. Lees and C. C. Lin [65]

† Attention is drawn to the discussion in [3] and [4].

The effects become particularly striking when the influence of a large heat flux is considered at a high Mach number. Calculations performed by E. R. van Driest [16, 17] show that under certain conditions the boundary layer becomes stable for arbitrarily large Reynolds numbers ($\mathsf{R}_{crit} \to \infty$). This fact is illustrated in Fig. 17.26 which contains a plot of the critical Reynolds number as a function

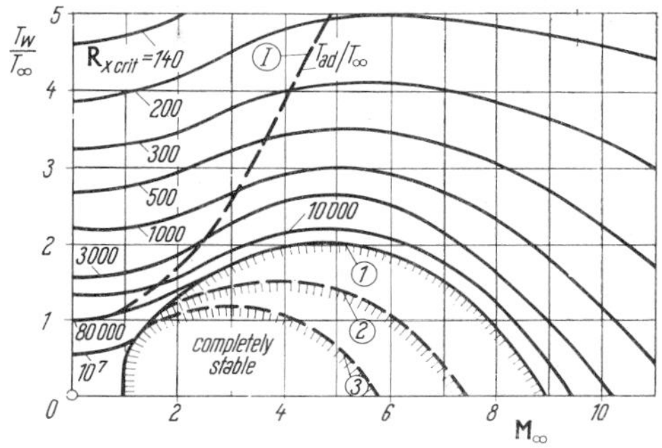

Fig. 17.26. Effect of Mach number and wall temperature on the critical Reynolds number on a flat plate at zero incidence as calculated by E. R. van Driest [17]. Reynolds number defined as $\mathsf{R}_x = U_\infty\, x/\nu_\infty$. In the shaded region the boundary layer is stable for all Reynolds numbers ($\mathsf{R}_{x\,crit} = \infty$)

The boundary of this region depends on the viscosity-temperature law: curve (1), $\mathsf{P} = 0{\cdot}75$, Sutherland's equation (15.1); curve (2), $\mathsf{P} = 0{\cdot}75$, $\omega = 1$; curve (3) $\mathsf{P} = 1$, $\omega = 1$

of Mach number and the temperature ratio T_w/T_∞. The curve denoted by (I) indicates the limit between heating and cooling; it represents the adiabatic wall temperature evaluated in accordance with eqn. (15.16a). In the region to the left of this curve the boundary is heated by the wall, the remaining region corresponding to cooling. It is seen from Fig 17.26 that for a sufficiently large amount of cooling, say for $T_w/T_\infty < 0.75$, there exists a range of supersonic Mach numbers within which no increase in the Reynolds number leads to instability. The existence of this region of "complete stabilization" was first discovered by L. Lees; it was later investigated in greater detail by E. R. van Driest. The boundary of this region depends to a certain extent on the Prandtl number and on the empirical law $\mu(T)$ given in eqn. (15.1) which describes the dependence of viscosity on temperature. The above investigations have recently been further developed by D. W. Dunn and C. C. Lin [23] who have taken into account the influence of pressure gradients and of three-dimensional disturbances; the latter will be discussed in Sec. XVIIf. The region of complete stabilization remains, in essence, preserved under those conditions. Additional, clarifying remarks about the effect of pressure gradients in the external flow on the stability of a compressible boundary layer are contained in papers by H. Weil [118] and G. M. Low [72]†.

The experimental results plotted in Fig. 17.27 show good qualitative agreement with the theoretical results from Figs. 17.25 and 17.26. The diagram in this figure gives a plot showing the dependence of the critical Reynolds number on a flat plate at zero incidence on the dimensionless temperature difference

$$\frac{T_w - T_a}{U_\infty{}^2/2\,g\,c_p}$$

† Note added in proof. Recently some doubts have arisen as to the validity of the numerical results leading to the diagram in Fig. 17.26. In particular, it is not certain that improved calculations will confirm the existence of a completely stable region.

whose sign determines the direction of heat flow in accordance with eqn. (15.20). It is seen from Fig. 17.27 that the critical Reynolds number falls with an increasing Mach number and that it decreases sharply when the difference $T_w = T_a$ decreases, in agreement with theory. The considerable difference between the position of the point of transition determined experimentally and the theoretical point of instability is here also conditioned by the process of amplification of unstable disturbances. In a series of measurements whose description we propose to omit here, K. R. Czarnecki and A. R. Sinclair [11] attained a very large critical value of the Reynolds number, namely $\mathsf{R}_{x\,crit} = 28 \times 10^6$, in a wind tunnel at a Mach number of $\mathsf{M} = 1{\cdot}6$ and with cooling. In flight measurements on the V 2 rocket [106] the much higher value of $\mathsf{R}_{x\,crit} = 90 \times 10^6$ was attained. The pressure distribution along the wall exerts a large influence on the position of the point of transition in the region of supersonic flow too [50]. A remarkably strong stabilization of a laminar

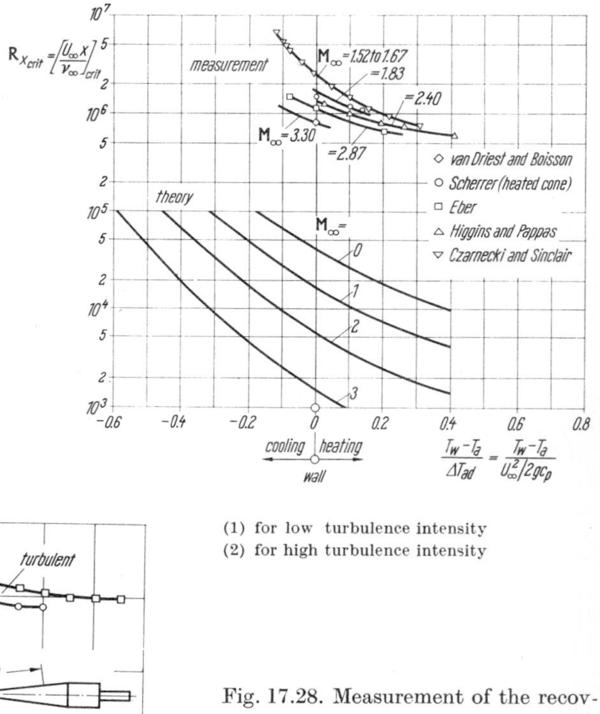

Fig. 17.27. Effect of heating and cooling the boundary layer on the critical Reynolds number on a flat plate at zero incidence. Theory due to E. R. van Driest [17], R. F. Probstein and C. C. Lin. Measurements performed by different workers [11, 17, 25, 44, 90]

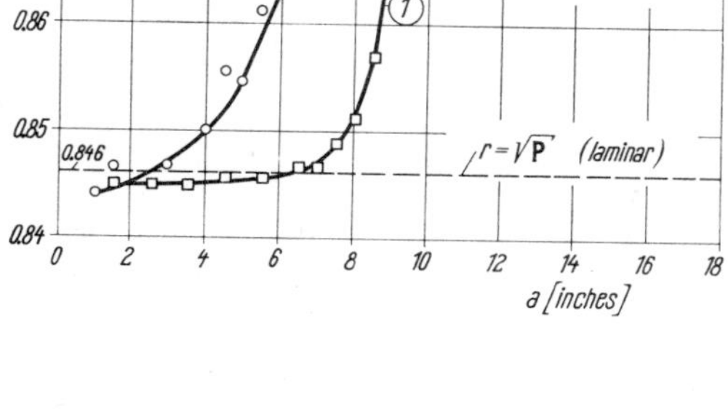

(1) for low turbulence intensity
(2) for high turbulence intensity

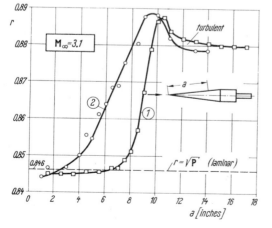

Fig. 17.28. Measurement of the recovery factor on a cone in supersonic flow ($\mathsf{M} = 3{\cdot}1$) for the purpose of determining the point of transition, after J. C. Evvard and M. Tucker [30]

In laminar flow we have $r = \sqrt{\mathsf{P}} = 0{\cdot}846$ in accordance with eqn. (15.17b). The steep increase in the plot of the recovery factor against distance from vertex indicates the position of the point of transition

boundary layer occurs behind a rarefaction wave which emanates from a convex corner in supersonic flow. A description of the respective measurements is available in a paper by A. H. Lange and R. E. Lee [63].

Generally speaking, it is impossible to determine the position of the point of transition in supersonic flow with the aid of a hot-wire anenometer or a total-pressure tube, but it can be done conveniently with the aid of measurements of the increase in the temperature of the wall due to frictional heating. Transition causes a fairly steep increase in the wall temperature and hence of the recovery factor defined in eqn. (15.17) because heating is more vigorous in turbulent than in laminar flow. An example of such a measurement, performed by J. C. Evvard [29] on a cone at zero incidence, is shown in Fig. 17.28. The steep gradient in the curve showing the variation of the recovery factor with current length indicates the position of the point of transition. The two curves in the diagram refer to two different turbulence intensities in the external flow. In the presence of a high intensity of turbulence, the point of transition lies further upstream than is the case with low turbulence. Further experiments of this kind are described in ref. [89].

f. Stability of a boundary layer in the presence of three-dimensional disturbances

1. Flow between concentric rotating cylinders. In all examples discussed so far the basic flow under consideration was two-dimensional and its stability was investigated on the assumption that the disturbance superimposed on it was also two-dimensional. Moreover the disturbance was assumed to be in the form of a plane wave which progressed in the direction of the main flow. As far as flows along a flat plate are concerned, this scheme leads to the lowest limit of stability because, as noticed by H. B. Squire (see p. 386), three-dimensional disturbances will always lead to a higher limit of stability.

When flows along curved walls are considered, it is found that a different kind of instability must be taken into account. The case of flow between two rotating concentric cylinders of which the inner cylinder is in motion and the outer cylinder is at rest affords an example of an unstable stratification caused by centrifugal forces. The fluid particles near the inner wall experience a higher centrifugal force and show a tendency to being propelled outwards. G. I. Taylor [114] was the first to prove that when a certain Reynolds number has been exceeded, there appear in the flow vortices whose axes are located along the circumference and which have alternately opposite directions. The pattern of streamlines for one such vortex is shown in Fig. 17.29 which was drawn in a plane intersecting the vortex at right angles to its axis. The conditions for the occurrence of such cellular vortices have been

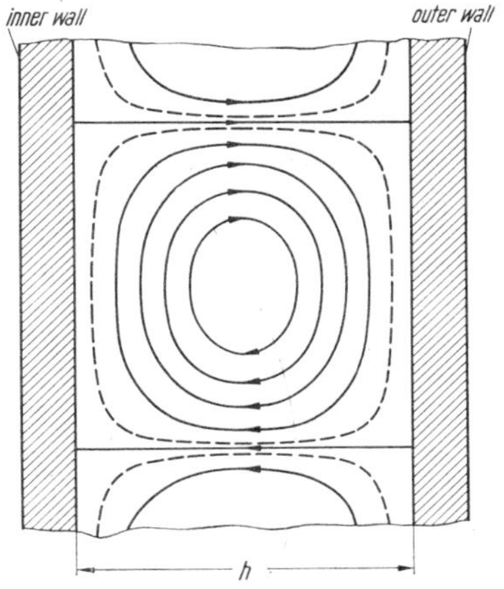

Fig. 17.29. Pattern of stream-lines of secondary flow between two concentric rotating cylinders, the outer cylinder being at rest and the inner cylinder rotating, after G. I. Taylor [114]

investigated in great detail by G. I. Taylor who was also able to establish excellent agreement between theory and measurement. According to L. Prandtl [79], the condition for the onset of vortex formation can be written

$$\frac{U_i h}{\nu} \sqrt{\frac{h}{R_i}} > 41{\cdot}3 \tag{17.19}$$

where h denotes the width of the gap, R_i the inner radius, and U_i the peripheral velocity of the inner cylinder. Measurements show that the cellular vortices remain completely stable in a fairly wide range of Reynolds numbers above the limit given in eqn. (17.19). They become unstable at a much higher Reynolds number when the flow turns turbulent. This can be seen clearly in the pictures of such Taylor vortices which have been published recently by F. Schultz-Grunow and H. Hein [99] and some of which can be seen in Fig. 17.30. The experimental arrangement used by them had a gap $h = 4$ mm and an inner radius $R_i = 21$ mm so that the theoretical limit for vortex formation given in eqn. (17.19) leads to the value $\mathsf{R} = U_i\, h/\nu = 94{\cdot}5$. The first appearance of vortices was observed at precisely this value, Fig. 17.30a, but the flow remained laminar at the much higher Reynolds numbers of $\mathsf{R} = 322$ and $\mathsf{R} = 865$, Figs. 17.30b, c. Turbulent flow did not become developed until a Reynolds number $\mathsf{R} = 3960$ had been reached, Fig. 17.30d. S. Goldstein [34] extended the investigation to include the case when the fluid between the cylinders has an axial velocity component.

It is worth stressing here that the initial occurrence of neutral vortices at the theoretical limit of stability and of amplified vortices at somewhat higher Reynolds numbers does not at all signify that the flow is becoming turbulent. On the contrary, the flow remains well ordered and laminar, and turbulence sets in only at much higher Reynolds numbers when a larger range of wavelengths becomes considerably amplified. Similar behaviour prevails in the case of Goertler vortices described in the next section.

2. Boundary layers on concave walls. A similar kind of instability with respect to three-dimensional disturbances occurs in flows along concave walls. In a boundary layer formed on a convex wall the centrifugal forces exert a stabilizing effect whose magnitude, however, is numerically small, as was already shown in Sec. XVIId. In contrast with that, the de-stabilizing effect of centrifugal forces on concave walls leads to a type of instability which resembles the pattern of Taylor vortices shown in Fig. 17.29. The existence of the latter effect was first demonstrated by H. Goertler [38]. Considering a basic flow in the x—direction given by $U(x)$ (y—distance from the wall, x—measured at right angles to flow direction in the plane of the wall, Fig. 17.31) it is assumed that there is superimposed on it a three-dimensional disturbance of the form

$$\left.\begin{aligned} u' &= u_1\,(y)\,\{\cos\,(\alpha z)\} \times e^{\beta t} \\ v' &= v_1\,(y)\,\{\cos\,(\alpha z)\} \times e^{\beta t} \\ w' &= w_1(y)\,\{\sin\,(\alpha z)\} \times e^{\beta t}\,. \end{aligned}\right\} \tag{17.20}$$

Here β is real and denotes the amplification factor, whereas $\lambda = 2\,\pi/\alpha$ represents the wavelength of the disturbance at right angles to the principal flow direction. The vortices have the shape shown in Fig. 17.31, their axes being parallel to the

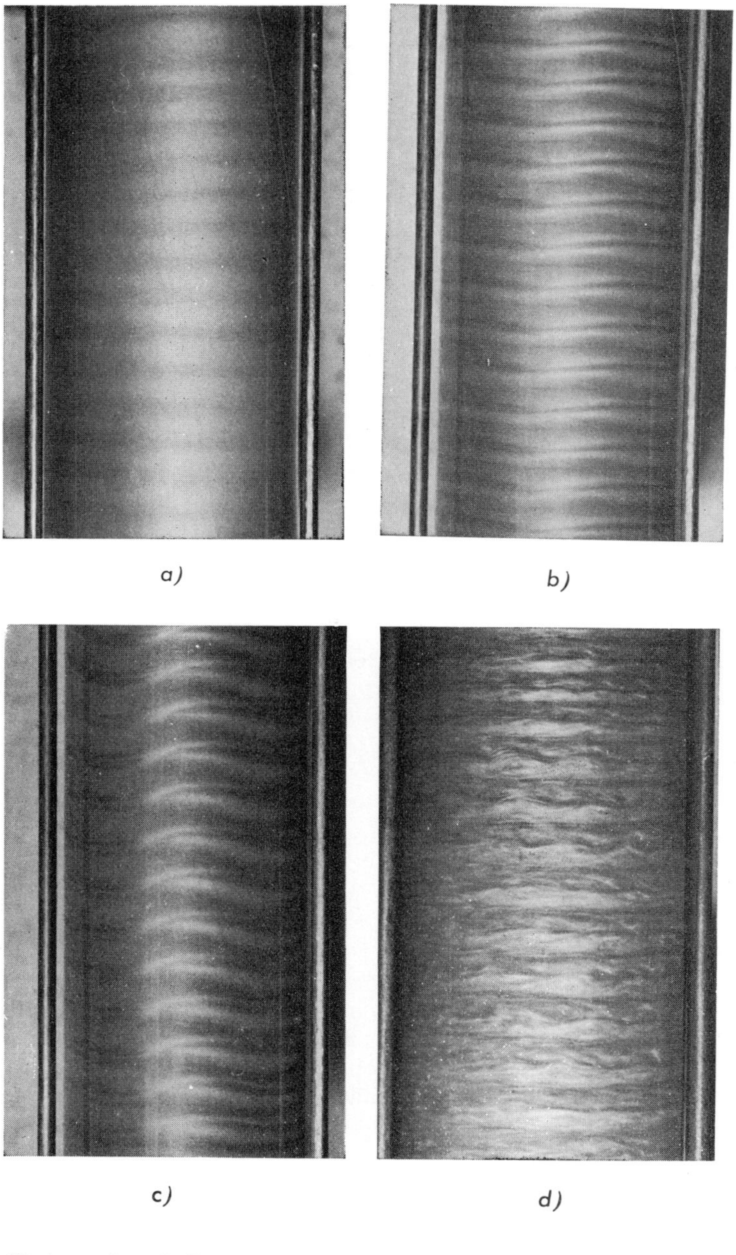

Fig. 17.30. Photographs of Taylor vortices from Fig. 17.29 for flow between concentric rotating cylinders, after F. Schultz-Grunow and H. Hein [99]. a) $\mathsf{R} = 94{\cdot}5$: laminar, onset of vortex formation; b) $\mathsf{R} = 322$: still laminar; c) $\mathsf{R} = 868$: still laminar; d) $\mathsf{R} = 3960$: turbulent

basic flow direction. The present problem is concerned with standing waves (cellular vortices) which are known as Taylor-Goertler vortices, and are distinct from the travelling waves discussed in Chap. XVI.

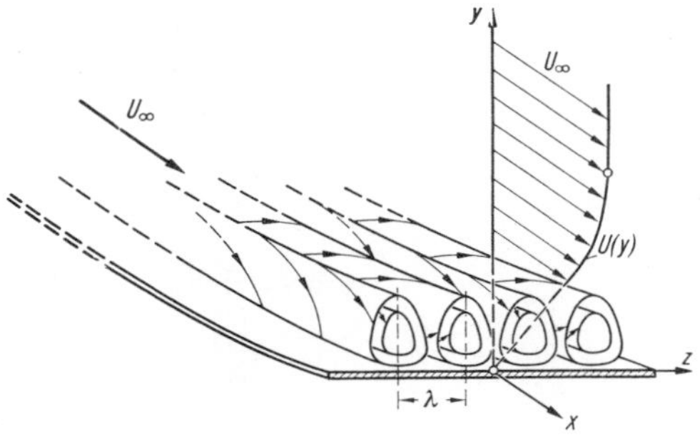

Fig. 17.31. Vortices caused by three-dimensional disturbances in the flow along a concave wall, after H. Goertler [38]. $U(y)$ = main flow

The calculation of the amplification of these vortices with time based on the method of small disturbances leads to an eigen-value problem in a manner similar to that discussed in connexion with two-dimensional disturbances (Chap. XVI). The influence of viscosity was taken into account in the investigation under discussion. As distinct from the case of two-dimensional flow, it turns out that the limit of stability is influenced only very slightly by the assumed velocity profile of the principal flow. The resulting limit of stability, i. e. the locus of the values which correspond to the first appearance of the vortices, is shown in Fig. 17.32 and has the form of the curve denoted as $\beta = 0$. Vortices first occur for every wavelength α when the characteristic parameter formed with the boundary layer thickness δ and the radius of curvature of the wall, R, exceeds a certain limit, namely

$$\frac{U_\infty \delta}{\nu}\sqrt{\frac{\delta}{R}} > 16 .$$

The first approximate solution to this rather difficult eigen-value problem was given by H. Goertler [38]. A check-calculation performed by D. Meksyn [74] showed large deviations from Goertler's values. Subsequently G. Haemmerlin [45] found an exact solution to the eigen-value problem which provided a good confirmation of Goertler's approximation. The preceding results have more recently been again confirmed by an extensive numerical analysis performed by A. M. O. Smith [103].

The results of the preceding theory have been subjected to experimental verification through measurements on bodies provided with external concave walls and placed in a stream. In this connection it is necessary to bear in mind that the point of transition can be expected to appear only a considerable distance downstream of the limit of stability owing to the finite time required for amplification, in analogy with the two-dimensional, travelling Tollmien-Schlichting waves discussed in Sec. XVIb†. Experiments on the process of transition as it occurs on curved walls have been carried out by L. M. Clauser and F. Clauser [9] and, later, by H. W. Liepmann [67, 69]. The results obtained by H. W. Liepmann with concave as well as with convex walls have been reproduced in Fig. 17.33. The plot in Fig. 17.33a confirms the theoretical prediction that the effect of curvature on the critical Reynolds number in the case of convex walls is very slight and that it is smaller for concave than for convex walls. Fig. 17.33b shows a plot of the critical Reynolds number

$$\frac{U_\infty \theta_{tr}}{\nu} \sqrt{\frac{\theta_{tr}}{R}}$$

against θ/R as suggested by Goertler's theory. According to the experiments plotted in the diagram, transition occurs at a value

$$\mathsf{R}_{\theta tr} \sqrt{\frac{\theta_{tr}}{R}} > 7 \qquad (17.21)$$

which exceeds the limit of stability in Fig. 17.32 by a factor of twenty. According to H. L. Dryden [19], the numerical value in (17.21) depends, in addition, on the intensity of turbulence; its value is contained between 6 and 9 where the lower

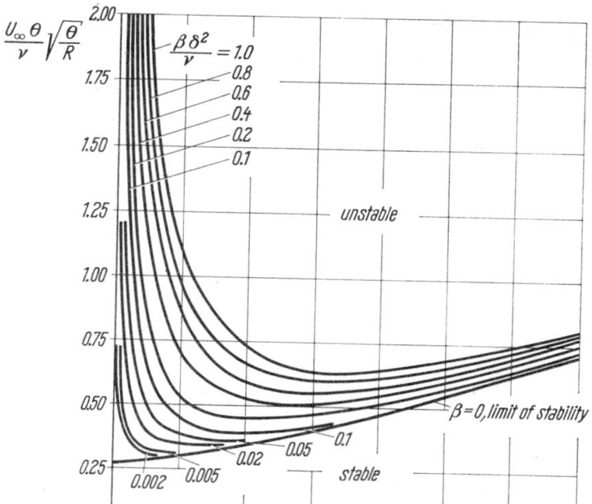

Fig. 17.32. Stability curves for flow along a concave wall, as calculated by H. Goertler [38] and G. Haemmerlin [45]

θ = momentum thickness; δ = boundary layer thickness; β = amplification factor from eqn. (17.20); R = radius of curvature of wall

† In contrast with that, it must be expected that the appearance of Taylor vortices in the Couette experiment should nearly coincide numerically with the theoretical Reynolds numbers. When the angular velocity is constant, the amplification proceeds at a constant Reynolds number, and the amplification factor attains the required magnitude simply by extending the experiment over a sufficiently long period of time. This is confirmed by the photograph in Fig. 17.30a and by eqn. (17.19).

limit corresponds to an external intensity of turbulence of $\mathsf{T} = 0{\cdot}003$, the higher value corresponding to a considerably lower intensity†.

Recently H. Goertler drew attention to the fact that the same type of instability can occur near the forward stagnation point of a bluff body in a stream.

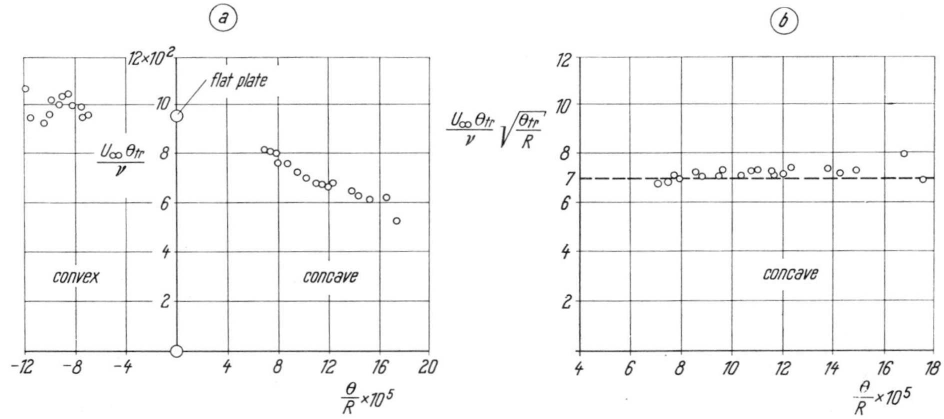

Fig. 17.33. Measurements on the point of transition of slightly concave walls, after H. W. Liepmann [67, 68]. (a) critical Reynolds number $\frac{U_\infty \theta_{tr}}{\nu}$ *versus* $\frac{\theta}{R}$; (b) the characteristic quantity $\frac{U_\infty \theta_{tr}}{\nu}\sqrt{\frac{\theta_{tr}}{R}}$ *versus* $\frac{\theta}{R}$

θ = momentum thickness; R = radius of curvature of wall

The necessary condition that the streamlines must be concave in the direction of increasing velocity is here present. So far, the calculations performed by H. Goertler [39] and G. Haemmerlin [46] for the case of two-dimensional stagnation flow represented in Fig. 5.10 have shown the existence of unstable disturbances, but no limit of stability in the form of a critical Reynolds number has yet been obtained. Experiments performed by N. A. V. Piercy and E. G. Richardson [75, 76] suggest that the flow in the neighbourhood of the forward stagnation point on a circular cylinder does indeed become unstable.

A review of three-dimensional effects in the theory of stability was recently given by H. Goertler [40].

The considerations contained in the present section together with those in Chap. XVI and Secs. XVIIa, b lead to the following picture of transition in the boundary layer of a solid body (e. g. an aerofoil): transition on flat and convex walls is governed by the instability of travelling, two-dimensional Tollmien-Schlichting waves whereas that on concave walls is governed by the stationary Taylor-Goertler vortices.

† In the paper already quoted, A. M. O. Smith evaluated the amplification factor for the distance between the theoretical limit of stability and the measured point of transition for the case of Taylor-Goertler vortices. It is astonishing to find that the resulting value of exp 10 is of the same order of magnitude as the value of exp 9 quoted in Chap. XVI for Tollmien-Schlichting waves.

3. Stability of three-dimensional boundary layers. The details of the process of transition in a three-dimensional boundary layer appear to be entirely different from those associated with the two-dimensional flows considered earlier. One example of this type of transition is afforded by the case of a disk rotating in a fluid at rest for which the details of the laminar layer are known from Sec. Vb. A photograph illustrating the process of transition on a rotating disk and taken by N. Gregory, and W. S. Walker [43] is seen reproduced in Fig. 17.34. The photograph shows

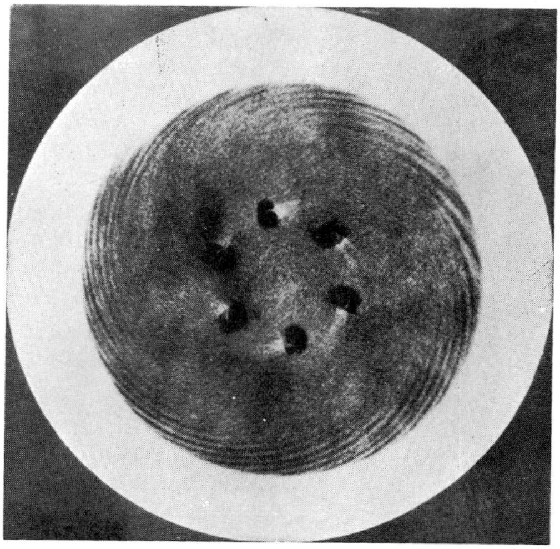

Fig. 17.34. Photograph illustrating transition in the boundary layer on a disk rotating in a fluid at rest after N. Gregory, J. T. Stuart and W. S. Walker [43]. Direction of rotation is counter-clockwise; speed $n = 3200$ rpm; radius of disk $= 15$ cm

Stationary vortices are seen forming in an annular region of inner radius $R_i = 8{\cdot}7$ cm and outer radius $R_0 = 10{\cdot}1$. The inner radius constitutes the limit of stability, with $\mathsf{R}_i = R_i\ \omega^2/\nu = 1{\cdot}9 \times 10^5$. Transition occurs at the outer radius where $\mathsf{R}_0 = R_0\ \omega^2/\nu = 2{\cdot}8 \times 10^5$

that in an annular region there appear stationary vortices which assume the shape of logarithmic spirals. The inner radius of this region marks the onset of instability and transition occurs at the outer radius. The inner radius corresponds to a Reynolds number of $\mathsf{R}_i = R_i^2\ \omega/\nu = 1{\cdot}9 \times 10^5$ and at the outer radius we have $\mathsf{R}_o = R_o^2\ \omega/\nu = 2{\cdot}8 \times 10^5$. J. T. Stuart complemented the experimental work with an analytic study of the stability of such a motion. In it, he assumed the existence of three-dimensional periodic disturbances whose forms included as special cases the progressing Tollmien-Schlichting waves as well as the stationary three-dimensional Taylor-Goertler vortices. The results of his calculations showed qualitative agreement with the experimental results of Fig. 17.34.

g. The influence of roughness on transition

1. Introductory remark. The problem which we are about to examine in this section, namely the question of how the process of transition depends on the roughness of the solid walls, is one of considerable practical importance; so far, however, it has not been possible to analyze it theoretically. The problem under consideration has gained in importance in the recent past, particularly since the advent of laminar aerofoils in aeronautical applications. The very extensive experimental material collected up-to-date includes information on the effect of cylindrical (two-dimensional roughness elements), point-like (three-dimensional, single roughness elements) and distributed roughness elements. Many of the investigations include additional data on the influence of pressure gradients, turbulence intensity or Mach number.

Generally speaking, the presence of roughness favours transition in the sense that under otherwise identical conditions transition occurs at a lower Reynolds number on a rough wall than on a smooth wall. That this should be so follows clearly from the theory of stability: the existence of roughness elements gives rise to additional disturbances in the laminar stream which have to be added to those generated by turbulence and already present in the boundary layer. If the disturbances created by roughness are bigger than those due to turbulence, we must expect that a lower degree of amplification will be sufficient to effect transition. On the other hand, if the roughness elements are very small, the resulting disturbances should lie below the 'threshold' which is characteristic of those generated by the turbulence of the free stream. In this case, the presence of roughness would be expected to have no effect on transition. The preceding considerations show complete agreement with experiment. When the roughness elements are very large, transition will occur at the points where they are present themselves, as is, for example, the case with the tripping wire on the sphere shown in Fig. 2.21. In this connexion the reader may wish to consult the paper by J. Stueper [108].

The earlier papers which addressed themselves to this problem, namely those by L. Schiller [97], I. Tani, J. Hama and S. Mituisi [109], S. Goldstein [33], and A. Fage and J. H. Preston [31], assumed that the point of transition was located at the position of roughness elements, when they were large, or that their presence had no influence at all when they were small. However, A. Fage has shown recently that the point of transition moves continuously upstream as the height of the roughness elements is increased until it ultimately reaches the position of the roughness elements themselves. Consequently, in discussing the influence of roughness on transition, it is necessary to provide answers to the following three questions:

1. What is the maximum height of roughness elements below which no influence on transition exists? (Critical height of roughness elements in laminar flow).
2. What is the (larger) limiting height of a roughness element which causes transition to occur at the element itself?
3. How is it possible to describe the position of the point of transition in the range intermediate between these two limits?

2. Single cylindrical roughness elements. A single, cylindrical (or two-dimensional) roughness element usually takes the form of, say, a wire which is attached to the wall at right angles to the stream direction. For this type of roughness element, S. Goldstein deduced from older measurements, that the *critical height*, i. e. the height which just does not affect transition, can be represented by

$$\frac{u_k^* \, k_{crit}}{\nu} = 7 \, . \qquad (17.22)$$

Here $u_k^* = \sqrt{\tau_{0k}/\varrho}$ denotes the friction velocity and τ_{0k} is the shearing stress at the wall in the laminar boundary layer at the position of the roughness element. According to I. Tani and his co-workers [109] the minimum height for which transition occurs at the element itself can be found from the relation $u_k^* \, k_{crit}/\nu = 15$, whereas A. Fage and J. H. Preston [31] quote

$$\frac{u_k^* \, k_{crit}}{\nu} = 20. \tag{17.23}$$

The preceding characteristic values apply to circular wires. In the case of flat and cupped cross-sections or for grooves the values are considerably larger, whereas for sharp elements they become smaller.

H. L. Dryden [20] provided an argument of a dimensional nature which leads to an empirical law which determines the position of the point of transition, x_{tr}, in terms of the height k of the roughness element and its position, x_k. Dryden discovered that in incompressible flow all experimental points for the case when transition does not occur at the roughness element itself, i. e. when $x_{tr} > x_k$, arrange themselves on a *single* curve in a plot of the Reynolds number $\mathsf{R}_{tr}^* = U \, \delta_{tr}^*/\nu$ formed with the displacement thickness δ_{tr}^* of the boundary layer at the point of transition against the ratio k/δ_k^*, where δ_k^* denotes the displacement thickness at the position

$\mathsf{R}_{tr,\,0}^* = \dfrac{U \, \delta_{tr}^*}{\nu}$ and

$\mathsf{R}_{x,\,tr,\,0} = \dfrac{U \, x_{tr}}{\nu}$ denote the critical Reynolds numbers for a smooth plate

- - - - calculated from eqn. (17.25),
○ □ ◇ △ ▽ ▷ × + $x_{tr} \geq x_k$, $\mathsf{R}_{x,\,tr,\,0} = 1{\cdot}7 \times 10^6$, p = const, after [32];

▲ $\mathsf{R}_{x,\,tr,\,0} = 1{\cdot}7 \times 10^6$, p = const, after I. Tani;

● $\mathsf{R}_{x,\,tr,\,0} = 2{\cdot}7 \times 10^6$, p = const, after I. Tani;

◆ $\mathsf{R}_{x,\,tr,\,0} = 2{\cdot}7 \times 10^6$, pressure decrease $(p_1 - p_{tr}) \Big/ \frac{1}{2} \varrho U_1^2 = 0{\cdot}2$ to $0{\cdot}8$ after [111];

▼ p = const, after Schubauer, [98];

■ $\mathsf{R}_{x,\,tr,\,0} = 6 \times 10^5$, p = const, after [111]; (full points refer to experimental results at $x_{tr} > x_k$)

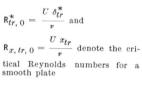

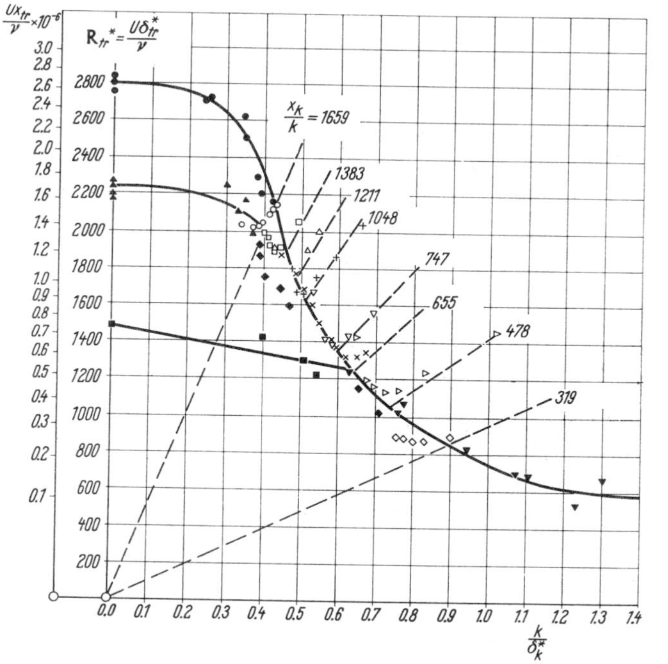

Fig. 17.35. Critical Reynolds number of laminar boundary layer as a function of the ratio of roughness height to boundary layer thickness for two-dimensional, single roughness elements in incompressible flow

of the roughness element, Fig. 17.35. The diagram in Fig. 17.35 contains an auxiliary scale of $\mathsf{R}_{x,\,tr} = U\,x_{tr}/\nu$†. Hence we can write

$$\frac{U\,x_{tr}}{\nu} = \mathrm{f}\left(\frac{k}{\delta_k^*}\right) \text{ for } x_{tr} > x_k\,. \tag{17.24}$$

As the height k is increased, the position of the point of transition x_{tr} moves closer to the roughness element which means that the curve representing eqn. (17.24) in Fig. 17.35 is traversed from left to right. The experimental points begin to deviate from this curve upwards as soon as the point of transition has reached the roughness element, i. e. when $x_{tr} = x_k$. They then lie along the family of straight lines which contain x_k/k as a parameter and is given by

$$\frac{U\delta_{tr}^*}{\nu} = 3{\cdot}0\,\frac{k}{\delta_k^*}\,\frac{x_k}{k}\,; \tag{17.25}$$

it is also shown in Fig. 17.35. According to recent Japanese measurements, the hyperbola-like branch of the curves in Fig. 17.35 possesses universal validity, both for flows with different, weak pressure gradients, and with different intensities of turbulence. Increased turbulence causes merely an earlier deviation of the curve to the left, in the direction of the turbulence-dependent critical Reynolds number of a flat plate, $(\mathsf{R}_{x,\,tr})_{k=0} = \mathsf{R}_{x,\,tr,\,o}$. According to Dryden [21], it is possible to take into account the variation in the turbulence intensity by plotting the ratio of the critical Reynolds number for a rough wall to that for a smooth wall, namely $(\mathsf{R}_{x,\,tr})_{rough}/(\mathsf{R}_{x,\,tr})_{smooth}$, as a function of k/δ_k^*, Fig. 17.36. When plotted in this system of co-ordinates, the results of measurements with different intensities of

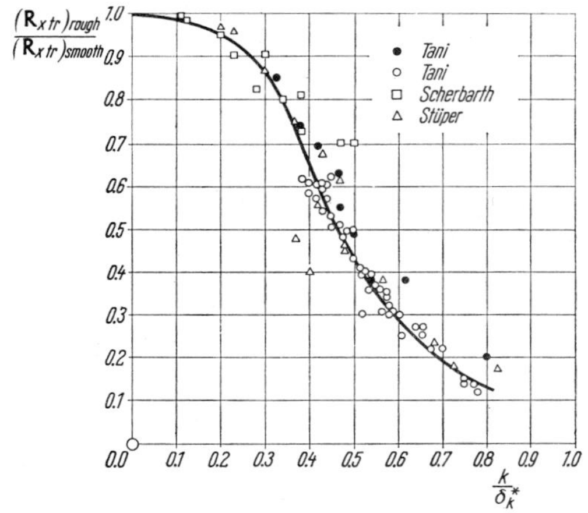

Fig. 17.36. Ratio of the critical Reynolds number on a flat plate at zero incidence with a single roughness element to that of a smooth plate, after Dryden [20]

$\mathsf{R}_{x,\,tr} = U\,x_{tr}/\nu$

k—height of roughness element δ^*_k — displacement thickness of the boundary layer at the roughness element. Measurement due to Tani [109] and others

† The two Reynolds numbers on the axis of ordinates are related through the equation

$$\mathsf{R}_{tr}^* = \frac{U\delta_{tr}^*}{\nu} = 1{\cdot}72\sqrt{\frac{U x_{tr}}{\nu}} = 1{\cdot}72\sqrt{\mathsf{R}_{x,\,tr}}\,.$$

turbulence fall on a single curve which means that the ratio $(\mathsf{R}_{x,\,tr})_{rough}/(\mathsf{R}_{x,\,tr})_{smooth}$ is a function of the single parameter k/δ_k^*. The three questions posed at the end of the last section can now be easily answered with the aid of the two graphs of Figs. 17.35 and 17.36.

The influence of roughness on transition is considerably smaller in compressible than in incompressible flow. This fact can be deduced from Fig. 17.37 which refers to a flat plate at zero incidence and which, as far as the results for compressible flow are concerned, is based on the measurements performed by P. F. Brinich [6].

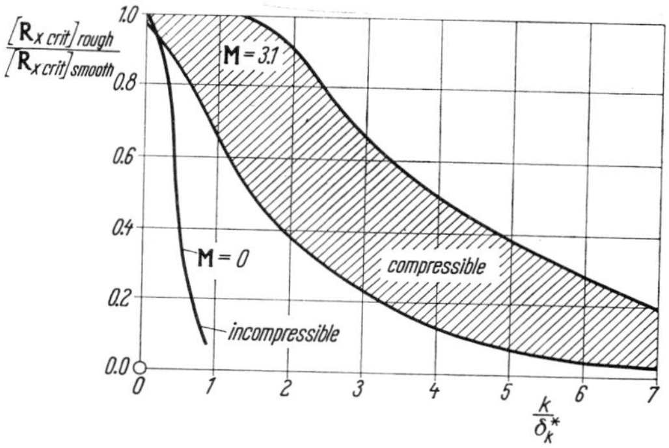

Fig. 17.37. Influence of single, two-dimensional roughness elements on the critical Reynolds number on a flat plate in compressible flow, as measured by P. F. Brinich [6]

k — height of single roughness element;
δ^*_k — displacement thickness of boundary layer at roughness element

The measurements were performed with the aid of cylindrical roughness elements of circular cross-section at a Mach number $\mathsf{M} = 3{\cdot}1$; when plotted in the co-ordinates of Fig. 17.37, they arrange themselves in a family of curves which covers the shaded area in the diagram, but which still strongly depends on the position x_k of the roughness element. The curve for incompressible flow, shown in Fig. 17.37 for the purpose of comparison, illustrates the fact that at high Mach numbers the boundary layer can 'tolerate' a considerably larger roughness element than in incompressible flow. According to the graph, the critical height of a roughness element is some 3 to 7 times larger than in incompressible flow. Experiments performed by R. H. Korgeki [59] at the even higher Mach number of $\mathsf{M} = 5{\cdot}8$ showed that at such large Mach numbers a tripping wire produces no turbulence at all. On the other hand, the blowing of air seems to be effective in promoting transition even in compressible flow.

3. Distributed roughness. There exist only scant results concerning measurements on transition in the presence of distributed roughness [10]. A paper by E. G. Feindt [32] contains a brief description of an investigation into the influence of a pressure gradient and grain size, k_S, in the presence of sand roughness. The measurements were performed in a convergent and a divergent channel of circular cross-section with a cylinder covered with sand placed axially in them. The walls of the channels were smooth and their slope controlled the pressure gradient. The graph in Fig. 17.38 represents the relation between the critical Reynolds number $U_1 x_{tr}/\nu$ formed with the coordinate of the point of transition and the Reynolds number $U_1 k_S/\nu$ formed with the sand grain size, k_S, for different pressure gradients measured by E. G. Feindt. The values for a smooth wall ranged from $U_1 x_{tr}/\nu = 2 \times 10^5$ to

8×10^5 at different pressure gradients, corresponding to the strongly stabilizing or de-stabilizing influence of the pressure gradient. It is seen that the measurements under consideration lead to the conclusion that when $U_1 k_S/\nu$ increases, at first there is no change in the critical Reynolds number. The critical Reynolds number decreases steeply, but only after the value

$$\frac{U_1 k_S}{\nu} = 120 \tag{17.26}$$

has been exceeded. Hence this value determines the critical roughness and answers Question 1 posed earlier. Roughness is seen to exert an influence comparable to that of the pressure gradient at values exceeding this limit.

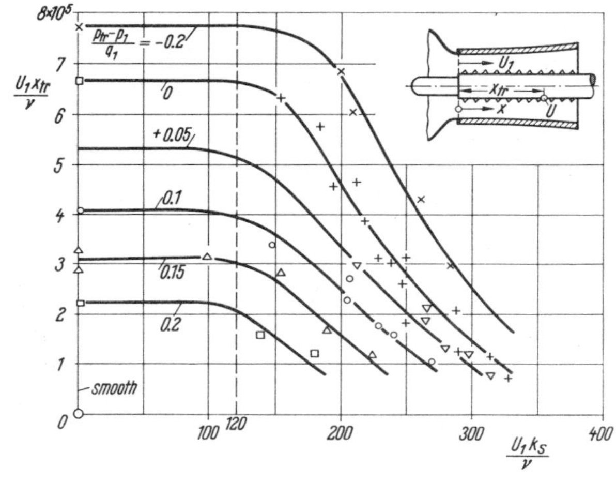

Fig. 17.38. Influence of pressure gradient and surface roughness on sand-covered wall on position of point of transition for incompressible flow as measured by E. G. Feindt [32]

k_S — sand-grain size. The sand roughness has no influence on transition when $U_1 k_S/\nu < 120$

h. Axially-symmetrical flows

The most important case of an axially-symmetrical flow is that existing in a straight pipe i. e. when the velocity profile is parabolic. This case was investigated very early by Th. Sexl [99a] who was unable to discover any instability; he was equally unable, however, to prove the existence of stability for all Reynolds numbers. Some time later, J. Pretsch [82] succeeded in proving that the analysis of the stability of these parabolic velocity profiles can be reduced to that of plane Couette flow (i. e. pure shear flow). Since the latter is stable at all Reynolds numbers, the same is seen to be true about the parabolic velocity profiles in a pipe.

The same conclusion was reached by G. M. Corcos and T. R. Sellars [9a] and by C. L. Pekeris [74b]; it was finally confirmed by Th. Sexl and K. Spielberg [99b]. This fact is surprising for two reasons. First, because flows in pipes do undergo transition. In fact, as the reader will recall, the earliest experiments on transition have been performed by O. Reynolds on pipes. Secondly, it is difficult to visualize the fact that parabolic velocity profiles in channels can — but parabolic velocity profiles in pipes cannot — be made unstable by very small disturbances. For these reasons attemps are being made to investigate this matter still further, both analytically and experimentally. In this connexion it may be noted that R. J. Leite [66a] failed to observe any amplification of small, axi-symmetrical disturbances travelling downstream in a circular pipe at Reynolds numbers as high as $\mathsf{R} = 13000$. Th. Sexl and K. Spielberg [99b] established that in relation to axially symmetrical flows, Squire's theorem mentioned on p. 386 no longer holds and that symmetrical plane waves are, therefore, no longer more critical for the flow, than disturbances of a three-dimensional nature. Since no theoretical studies on the behaviour of such more general disturbances superimposed on a Poiseuille flow are available, it is necessary to study them experimentally.

J. Rotta, whose work was discussed in detail in Sec. XVIa, performed measurements on the intermittency factor of large disturbances propagated downstream in the inlet section of a pipe. Similar experiments were performed by E. R. Lindgren [70a] who made the disturbance visible by the use of polarized light and a bi-refringent, weak solution of bentonite. E. R. Lindgreen was able to show that even strong initial disturbances decay in the inlet length when the Reynolds number of the flow (based on the pipe diameter) is small. At Reynolds numbers from about $\mathsf{R} = 2600$ upwards the process of transition begins. It is characterized by an amplification of the initial disturbances and by the appearance of self-sustaining turbulent flashes which emanate from fluid layers near the wall along the tube.

The preceding peculiarities of laminar flows through pipes force us to re-consider the relation between the theory of small disturbances and transition and, in particular, to pose the question as to whether transition can *always* be said to be due to an amplification of *small* disturbances. No conclusive answer to this question can at present be given without further work on the behaviour of small, three-dimensional disturbances. In this connexion it should also be remembered that the limit of stability for plane Poiseuille flow which lies at $\mathsf{R}_{crit} = 5314$ as stated on p. 399, considerably exceeds the critical Reynolds number for transition observed in channels. This is inconsistent with the theory which asserts that the limit of stability must always occur at a lower Reynolds number than transition itself. However, at the present stage of knowledge, and in the face of the present interest in the subject, judgement must be reserved until further results become available.

The stability of a laminar boundary layer on a body of revolution was also investigated by J. Pretsch. In cases when the ratio of boundary layer thickness to curvature is very small compared with unity, the resulting stability equation for the axially symmetrical becomes identical with that for the plane case. Hence all results obtained for the latter can be extended to apply to the former without reservation.

References

[1] J. H. Abbott, A. E. von Doenhoff and L. S. Stivers, Summary of airfoil data. NACA Rep. 824 (1954).

[2] ARC R & M 2499, Transition and drag measurements on the Boulton Paul sample of laminar flow wing construction.
Part I: by J. H. Preston, N. Gregory
Part II: by K. W. Kimber
Part III: Joint Discussion.

[2a] H. BERNARD, Ann. Chimie Phys. **23**, 62 (1901).
[3] M. BLOOM, The effect of surface cooling on laminar boundary layer stability. Jour. Aero. Sci. **18**, 635—636 (1951).
[4] M. BLOOM, Further comments on "The effect of surface cooling on laminar boundary-layer stability". Jour. Aero. Sci. **19**, 359 (1952).
[5] A. L. BRASLOW and F. VISCONTI, Investigation of boundary layer Reynolds-number for transition on an NACA $65_{(215)}$ —114 airfoil in the Langley two-dimensional low-turbulence pressure tunnel. NACA Tech. Note No. 1704 (1948).
[6] P. F. BRINICH, Boundary layer transition at Mach 3.12 with and without single roughness element. NACA Tech. Note 3267 (1954).
[7] K. BUSSMANN and H. MÜNZ, Die Stabilität der laminaren Reibungsschicht mit Absaugung. Jb. d. dt. Luftfahrtforschung I, 36 (1942).
[8] K. BUSSMANN and A. ULRICH, Systematische Untersuchungen über den Einfluß der Profilform auf die Lage des Umschlagpunktes. Preprint of Jahrbuch 1943 d. deutschen Luftfahrtforschung in Techn. Berichte, Vol. **10**, Part 9 (1943).
[9] L. M. CLAUSER and F. CLAUSER, The effect of curvature on the transition from laminar to turbulent boundary layer. NACA TN 613 (1937).
[9a] G. M. CORCAS and J. R. SELLARS, On the stability of fully developed flow in a pipe. J. Fl. Mech. **5**, 97 (1959).
[10] K. R. CZARNECKI, R. B. ROBINSON and J. H. HILTON jr., Investigation of distributed surface roughness on a body of revolution at a Mach number of 1·61. NACA Tech. Note 3230 (1954).
[11] K. R. CZARNECKI and A. R. SINCLAIR, An investigation of the effects of heat transfer on boundary-layer transition on a parabolic body of revolution (NACA RM-10) at a Mach Number of 1·61. NACA Rep. No. 1240 (1955).
[12] A. E. VON DOENHOFF, Preliminary investigation of boundary layer transition along a flat plate with adverse pressure gradient. NACA TN 639 (1938).
[13] A. E. VON DOENHOFF, Investigation of the boundary layer about a symmetrical airfoil in a wind tunnel of low turbulence. NACA Wartime Report L-507 (1940).
[14] H. DOETSCH, Untersuchungen an einigen Profilen mit geringem Widerstand im Bereich kleiner c_a-Werte. Jb. d. dt. Luftfahrtforschung I, 54 (1940).
[15] E. R. VAN DRIEST, Cooling required to stabilize the laminar boundary layer on a flat plate. Jour. Aero. Sci. **18**, 698—699 (1951).
[16] E. R. VAN DRIEST, Calculation of the stability of the laminar boundary layer in a compressible fluid on a flat plate with heat transfer. Jour. Aero. Sci. **19**, 801—813 (1952).
[17] E. R. VAN DRIEST and J. C. BOISON, Boundary layer stabilization by surface cooling in supersonic flow. Jour. Aero. Sci. **22**, 70 (1955).
[18] H. L. DRYDEN, Recent investigations on the problem of transition. Z. f. Flugwiss. **4**, 89—95 (1956).
[19] H. L. DRYDEN, "Recent advances in the mechanics of boundary layer flow" ed. by R. von Mises and Th. von Kármán, "Advances in Appl. Mech." **I**, 1—40, New York (1948).
[20] H. L. DRYDEN, Review of published data on the effect of roughness on transition from laminar to turbulent flow. Jour. Aero. Sci. **20**, 477—482 (1953).
[21] H. L. DRYDEN, Effects of roughness and suction on transition from laminar to turbulent flow. Publications Scientifiques et Techn. de Ministère de l'Air, Paris (SDJT) 49—60 (1954).
[22] H. L. DRYDEN, Transition from laminar to turbulent flow at subsonic and supersonic speeds. Proc. Conference on High-Speed Aeronautics. Polytechnic Institute of Brooklyn, New York 1955.
[23] D. W. DUNN and C. C. LIN, On the stability of the laminar boundary layer in a compressible fluid. Jour. Aero. Sci. **22**, 455—477 (1955); see also Jour. Aero. Sci. **20**, 577 (1953) and **19**, 491 (1952).
[24] R. W. DUNNING and E. F. ULMANN, Effects of sweep and angle of attack on boundary layer transition on wings at Mach number 4·04. NACA Tech. Note 3473 (1955).
[25] G. R. EBER, Recent investigation of temperature recovery and heat transmission on cones and cylinders in axial flow at the NOL Aeroballistics Wind Tunnel. Jour. Aero. Sci. **19**, (1952).
[26] E. R. G. ECKERT, Heat Transfer and Fluid Mechanics Institute. Berkeley, Cal., publ. by ASME 181—190 (1949).

[27] E. R. G. Eckert, Interferometric studies on the stability and transition to turbulence of a free-convection boundary layer. Proc. of the General Discussion on Heat Transfer, Sept. 1951, publ. by Inst. Mech. Eng. London.
[28] H. Ertel, Thermodynamische Begründung des Richardsonschen Turbulenzkriteriums. Meteorol. Z. **56**, 109 (1939).
[29] J. C. Evvard, M. Tucker and W. C. Burgess, Transition point fluctuations in supersonic flow. Jour. Aero. Sci. **21**, 731—738 (1954).
[30] J. C. Evvard, M. Tucker and W. C. Burgess, Statistical study of transition point fluctuations in supersonic flow. NACA Tech. Note 3100 (1954).
[31] A. Fage and J. H. Preston, On transition from laminar to turbulent flow in the boundary layer, Proc. Roy. Soc. London, A **178**, 201—227 (1941).
[32] E. G. Feindt, Untersuchungen über die Abhängigkeit des Umschlages laminar-turbulent von der Oberflächenrauhigkeit und der Druckverteilung. Thesis Braunschweig 1956; Jahrbuch 1956 der Schiffbautechnischen Gesellschaft, **50**, 180—203 (1957).
[33] S. Goldstein, A note on roughness. ARC R & M 1763 (1936).
[34] S. Goldstein, The stability of viscous fluids between rotating cylinders. Proc. Cambridge Phil. Soc. **33**, 41 (1937).
[35] S. Goldstein, On the stability of superposed streams of fluids of different densities. Proc. Roy. Soc. London, A **132**, 523 (1939).
[36] S. Goldstein, Low-Drag and Suction Airfoils. (11th Wright Brothers Lecture) J. Aero. Sci. **15**, 189 (1948).
[37] H. Görtler, Über den Einfluß der Wandkrümmung auf die Entstehung der Turbulenz. ZAMM **20**, 138—147 (1940).
[38] H. Görtler, Über eine dreidimensionale Instabilität laminarer Grenzschichten an konkaven Wänden. Nachr. Wiss. Ges. Göttingen, Math. Phys. Klasse, New Series **2**, No. 1 (1940); see also ZAMM **21**, 250—252 (1941).
[39] H. Görtler, Dreidimensionale Instabilität der ebenen Staupunktströmung gegenüber wirbelartigen Störungen. "Fifty years of boundary layer research", Braunschweig 304—314, 1955.
[40] H. Görtler, Dreidimensionales zur Stabilitätstheorie laminarer Grenzschichten. ZAMM **35**, 362—364 (1955).
[41] N. Gregory and S. Walker, The effect on transition of isolated surface excrescences in the boundary layer. ARC R & M **13**, 436 (1950).
[42] P. S. Granville, The calculation of viscous drag of bodies of revolution. Navy Department. The David Taylor Model Basin. Report No. 849 (1953).
[43] N. Gregory, J. T. Stuart and W. S. Walker, On the stability of three-dimensional boundary layers with application to the flow due to a rotating disk. Phil. Trans. Roy. Soc., London, A **248**, 155—199 (1955).
[44] R. W. Higgins and C. C. Pappas, An experimental investigation of the effect of surface heating on boundary layer transition on a flat plate in supersonic flow. NACA Tech. Note 2351 (1951).
[45] G. Hämmerlin, Über das Eigenwertproblem der dreidimensionalen Instabilität laminarer Grenzschichten an konkaven Wänden. Diss. Freiburg 1954. Jour. Rat. Mech. and Anal. **4**, 279—321 (1955); see also ZAMM **35**, 366—367 (1955).
[46] G. Hämmerlin, Zur Instabilitätstheorie der ebenen Staupunktströmung. "Fifty years of boundary layer research", Braunschweig 315—327, 1955.
[47] E. N. Harrin, A flight investigation of laminar and turbulent boundary layers passing through shock waves at full-scale Reynolds-numbers. NACA Tech. Note 3056 (1953).
[48] W. Hausammann, Flugwehr und Technik, Zürich **4**, 179 (1942).
[49] M. R. Head, The boundary layer with distributed suction. ARC R & M 2783 (1955).
[50] J. H. Hilton and K. R. Czarnecki, An exploratory investigation of skin friction and transition on three bodies of revolution at a Mach-Number of 1·61. NACA Tech. Note 3193 (1954).
[51] H. Holstein, Messungen zur Laminarhaltung der Reibungsschicht. Report S 10 of the Lilienthal-Gesellschaft für Luftfahrtforschung 17 (1940).
[52] J. L. van Ingen, A suggested semi-empirical method for the calculation of the boundary layer transition region. Dept. Aero. Eng., Inst. of Technology, Delft, Report V. T. H. 74 (1956).
[53] J. R. Jack and N. S. Diaconis, Variation of boundary-layer transition with heat transfer on two bodies of revolution at a Mach number of 3·12. NACA Tech. Note 3562 (1955).

[54] E. N. Jacobs and A. Sherman, Airfoil section characteristics as affected by variations of the Reynolds number. NACA Tech. Rep. 586 (1937).
[55] H. Jeffreys, Phil. Mag **2**, 833 (1926) and Proc. Soc. London A. **118**, 195 (1918).
[56] B. M. Jones, Flight experiments on the boundary layer. J. Aero. Sci. **5**, 81 (1938) (Wright Brothers Lecture), also Aircraft Engng. **10**, 135 (1938).
[57] B. M. Jones and M. R. Head, The reduction of drag by distributed suction. Proc. Third Anglo-American Aero. Conference, Brighton pp. 199—230, 1951.
[58] J. M. Kay, Boundary layer flow along a flat plate with uniform suction. ARC R & M 2628 (1948).
[59] R. H. Korkegi, Transition studies and skin-friction measurements on an insulated flat plate at a hypersonic Wind Tunnel. Memorandum No. 17 (1954).
[60] R. H. Korkegi, Transition studies and skin-friction measurements on a insulated flat plate at a Mach number of 5·8. Jour. Aero. Sci. **23**, 87 (1956).
[61] H. Krüger, Über den Einfluß der Absaugung auf die Lage der Umschlagstelle an Tragflügelprofilen. Ing. Arch. **19**, 384—387 (1951).
[62] D. Küchemann, Störungsbewegungen in einer Gasströmung mit Grenzschicht. ZAMM **18**, 207 (1938); see also remark by H. Görtler, ZAMM **23**, 179 (1943).
[63] A. H. Lange and R. E. Lee, Note on boundary layer transition in supersonic flow. Reader's Forum J. Aero. Sci. **21**, 1, 58 (1954) and **22**, 4, 282 (1955).
[64] L. Lees and C. C. Lin, Investigation of the stability of the laminar boundary layer in a compressible fluid. NACA TN 1115 (1946).
[65] L. Lees, The stability of the laminar boundary layer in a compressible flow. NACA TN 1360 (1947) and NACA Rep. 875 (1947).
[66] L. Lees, Comments on the "Effect of surface cooling on laminar boundary-layer stability". Jour. Aero. Sci. **18**, 844 (1951).
[66a] R. J. Leite, An experimental investigation of the stability of Poiseuille flow, J. Fl. Mech. **5**, 81 (1959).
[67] H. W. Liepmann, Investigations on laminar boundary layer stability and transition on curved boundaries. NACA Wartime Report W-107 (1943).
[68] H. W. Liepmann, Investigations on laminar boundary layer stability and transition on curved boundaries. ARC R & M 7302 (1943).
[69] H. W. Liepmann, Investigation of boundary layer transition on concave walls. NACA Wartime Report W-87 (1945).
[70] H. W. Liepmann and G. H. Fila, Investigations of effect of surface temperature and single roughness elements on boundary layer transition. NACA TN 1196 (1947) and NACA Rep. No. 890 (1947).
[70a] E. R. Lindgren, Liquid flow in tubes I, II and III, Arkiv för Fysik **15**, 97 (1959); **15**, 503 (1959); **15**, 103 (1959).
[71] W. Linke, Über den Strömungswiderstand einer beheizten ebenen Platte, Luftfahrtforschung **19**, 157—160 (1942).
[72] G. M. Low, Cooling requirement for stability of laminar boundary layer with small pressure gradient at supersonic speeds. NACA Tech. Note 3103 (1954); see also Jour. Aero. Sci. **22**, 329 (1955).
[73] Mallock, Phil. Trans., A **41** (1896).
[74] D. Meksyn, Stability of viscous flow over concave cylindrical surfaces. Proc. Roy. Soc. London, A, **203**, 253—265 (1950).
[74a] R. Michel, Etude de la transition sur les profiles d'aile; établissement d'un critère de determination du point de transition et calcul de la traînée de profil en incompressible. ONERA Rapport 1/1578 A (1951).
[74b] C. L. Pekeris, Stability of the laminar flow through a straight pipe in infinitesimal disturbances which are symmetrical about the axis of the pipe, Proc. Nat. Acad. Sci. Wash., **34**, 285 (1948).
[75] N. A. V. Piercy and E. G. Richardson, The variation of velocity amplitude close to the surface of a cylinder moving through a viscous fluid. Phil. Mag. **6**, 970—976 (1928).
[76] N. A. V. Piercy and E. G. Richardson, The turbulence in front of a body moving through a viscous fluid. Phil. Mag. **9**, 1038—1041 (1930).
[77] L. Prandtl, Einfluß stabilisierender Kräfte auf die Turbulenz. Vorträge aus d. Geb. d. Aerodyn. u. verwandter Gebiete, Aachen 1929, 1; Springer Berlin 1930.
[78] L. Prandtl and H. Reichardt, Einfluß von Wärmeschichtung auf die Eigenschaften einer turbulenten Strömung. Deutsche Forschung, No. 21, 110 (1934).

[79] L. Prandtl, Abriß der Strömungslehre. 2. ed. Braunschweig, p. 100 (1935).
[80] L. Prandtl, Bericht über neuere Untersuchungen über das Verhalten der laminaren Reibungsschicht, insbesondere den laminar-turbulenten Umschlag. Mitt. deutsch. Akad. Luftfahrtforsch. **2**, 141 (1942).
[81] J. Pretsch, Über die Stabilität der Laminarströmung um eine Kugel. Luftfahrtforschung **18**, 341 (1941).
[82] J. Pretsch, Über die Stabilität der Laminarströmung in einem geraden Rohr mit kreisförmigem Querschnitt. ZAMM **21**, 204—217 (1941).
[83] J. Pretsch, Die Stabilität einer ebenen Laminarströmung bei Druckgefälle und Druckanstieg. Jb. d. dt. Luftfahrtforschung I, 58 (1941).
[84] J. Pretsch, Die Anfachung instabiler Störungen in einer laminaren Reibungsschicht. Jb. d. dt. Luftfahrtforschung I, 54—71 (1942).
[85] J. Pretsch, Umschlagbeginn und Absaugung. Jb. d. dt. Luftfahrtforschung I, 1—7 (1942).
[86] Lord Rayleigh, On convection currents in a horizontal layer of fluid, when the higher temperature is on the underside. Phil. Mag. **32**, 529 (1916) or Scientific Papers **6**, 432.
[87] L. F. Richardson, The supply of energy from and to atmospheric eddies. Proc. Roy. Soc. London, A **97**, 354 (1926).
[88] F. Riegels, Das Umströmungsproblem bei inkompressiblen Potentialströmungen. Ing. Arch. **16**, 373 (1948) and **17**, 94 (1949).
[89] A. O. Ross, Determination of boundary layer transition Reynolds numbers by surface-temperature measurements of a 10° cone in various NACA supersonic wind tunnels. NACA Tech. Note 3020 (1953).
[89a] H. Sato, Experimental investigation on the transition of laminar separated layer. Jour. Phys. Soc. Japan, **11**, 6, 702—709 (1956).
[90] R. Scherrer, Comparison of theoretical and experimental heat transfer characteristics of bodies of revolution at supersonic speeds. NACA Report No. 1055 (1951).
[91] H. Schlichting, Über die Entstehung der Turbulenz in einem rotierenden Zylinder. Nachr. Ges. d. Wiss., Göttingen, Math. Phys. Klasse, 160 (1932).
[92] H. Schlichting, Über die Stabilität der Couette-Strömung. Ann. d. Phys. **V**, 905 (1932).
[93] H. Schlichting, Turbulenz bei Wärmeschichtung. ZAMM **15**, 313 (1935), also Proc. Fourth Int. Congr. Appl. Mech., Cambridge, p. 245, 1935.
[94] H. Schlichting, Über die theoretische Berechnung der kritischen Reynoldschen Zahl einer Reibungsschicht in beschleunigter und verzögerter Strömung. Jb. d. dt. Luftfahrtforschung I, 97 (1940).
[95] H. Schlichting and A. Ulrich, Zur Berechnung des Umschlages laminar-turbulent. Jahrbuch d. dt. Luftfahrtforschung I, 8 (1942). Extensive treatment in Rep. S 10 of the Lilienthal-Gesellschaft 75—135 (1940).
[96] H. Schlichting, Die Beeinflussung der Grenzschicht durch Absaugung und Ausblasen. Jb. d. dt. Akad. d. Luftfahrtforschung 90 (1943/44).
[97] L. Schiller, Handbuch der Experimental-Physik **4**, 189—192, Leipzig (1932).
[98] G. B. Schubauer and H. K. Skramstad, Laminar boundary layer oscillations and stability of laminar flow. National Bureau of Standards Research Paper 1772. (Reprint of a classified NACA Rep. dated April 1943, later released as NACA Wartime Report W-8), and J. Aero. Sci. **14**, 69 (1947); see also NACA Report 909.
[98a] F. Schultz-Grunow, Zur Stabilität der Couette-Strömung, ZAMM **39**, 101 (1959).
[99] F. Schultz-Grunow and H. Hein, Beitrag zur Couetteströmung. Zeitschr. f. Flugwiss. **4**, 28—30 (1956).
[99a] Th. Sexl, Zur Stabilitätsfrage der Poiseuilleschen und der Couette-Strömung. Ann. Phys. IV. Series **83**, 835 (1927).
[99b] Th. Sexl and K. Spielberg, Zum Stabilitätsproblem der Poiseuille-Strömung, Acta Phys. Austriaca, **12**, 9 (1958).
[100] A. H. Shapiro, Effects of pressure gradient and heat transfer on the stability of the compressible laminar boundary layers. Jour. Aero. Sci. **23**, 81 (1956).
[101] S. Shen and J. Persh, The limiting wall temperature ratios required for complete stabilization of laminar boundary layers with blowing. Jour. Aero. Sci. **23**, 286—287 (1956).
[102] A. Silverstein and J. V. Becker, Determination of boundary layer transition on three symmetrical airfoils in the NACA full-scale wind tunnel. NACA Rep. 637 (1938).
[103] A. M. O. Smith, On the growth of Taylor-Görtler vortices along highly concave walls. Quarterly Appl. Math. **XIII**, 3 (1955).

[104] A. M. O. SMITH, Transition pressure gradient and stability theory. Proc. 9th. Intern. Congress of Appl. Mech., Brussels, 1957 v. 4, p. 234; see also Report No. ES 26388 of the Douglas Aircraft Comp., El Segundo, Cal. USA 1956.
[105] J. R. STALDER, M. W. RUBESIN and T. H. TENDELAND, A determination of the laminar, transitional and turbulent boundary-layer temperature-recovery factors on a flat plate in supersonic flow. NACA Tech. Note 2077 (1950).
[105a] W. STENDER, Laminarprofil-Messungen des NACA, eine Auswertung zur Gewinnung allgemeiner Erkenntnisse über Laminarprofile. Luftfahrttechnik **2**, 218—227 (1956).
[106] J. STERNBERG, A free-flight investigation of the possibility of high Reynolds Number supersonic laminar boundary layers. Jour. Aero. Sci. **19**, 721—733 (1952).
[107] J. T. STUART, On the stability of viscous flow between parallel planes in the presence of a coplanar magnetic field. Proc. Roy. Soc. London A **221**, 189—206 (1954).
[108] J. STÜPER, Der Einfluß eines Stolperdrahtes auf den Umschlag der Grenzschicht an einer ebenen Platte. Zeitschr. f. Flugwiss. **4**, 30—34 (1956).
[109] J. TANI, R. HAMA and S. MITUISI, On the permissible roughness in the laminar boundary layer. Rep. Aero. Res. Inst., Tokyo Imp. Univ. No. 199 (1940).
[110] J. TANI and S. MITUISI, Contributions to the design of aerofoils suitable for high speeds. Aero. Research Inst. Tokyo Imperial Univ. Rep. 198 (1940).
[111] J. TANI, M. JUCHI and K. YAMAMOTO, Further experiments on the effect of a single roughness element on boundary transition. Rep. Inst. Sci. and Technol. Tokyo Univ., Vol. **8**, Aug. 1954.
[111a] J. TANI and F. R. HAMA, Some experiments on the effects of a single roughness element on boundary layer transition. Jour. Aero. Sci. 20, 289—290 (1953).
[112] G. I. TAYLOR, Effects of variation in density on the stability of superposed streams of fluid. Proc. Roy. Soc. London, A **132**, 499 (1931).
[113] G. I. TAYLOR, Internal waves and turbulence in a fluid of variable density. Rapp. Proc. Verb. Cons. Internat. pour l'Exploration de la Mer. LXVI Kopenhagen, 20 (1931).
[114] G. I. TAYLOR, Stability of a viscous liquid contained between two rotating cylinders. Phil. Trans. A **223**, 289 (1923); see also Proc. Roy. Soc. London A, **151**, 494 (1935) and **157**, 546 or 565 (1936).
[115] T. THEODORSEN and J. GARRICK, General potential theory of arbitrary wing section. NACA Tech. Report 452 (1933).
[116] W. TOLLMIEN, Über Stabilitätsprobleme gasförmiger Grenzschichten. Jahrbuch d. Wiss. Ges. f. Luftfahrt 215—224 (1953).
[117] A. ULRICH, Theoretische Untersuchungen über die Widerstandsersparnis durch Laminarhaltung mit Absaugung. Schriften d. dt. Akad. d. Luftfahrtforschung, 8 **B**, No. 2 (1944).
[118] H. WEIL, Effects of pressure gradient on stability and skin friction in laminar boundary layers in compressible fluids. Jour. Aero. Sci. **18**, 311—318 (1951).
[119] F. WENDT, Turbulente Strömung zwischen zwei rotierenden koaxialen Zylindern. Ing.-Arch. **4**, 577 (1933).
[120] H. WIJKER, On the determination of the transition point from measurements of the static pressure along a surface. Holl. Ber. A 1210 (1951).
[121] H. WIJKER, Survey of transition point measurements at the NLL, mainly for two-dimensional flow over a NACA 0018 profile. Holl. Ber. A 1269 (1951).
[122] W. WUEST, Näherungsweise Berechnung und Stabilitätsverhalten von laminaren Grenzschichten mit Absaugung durch Einzelschlitze. Ing.-Arch. **21**, 90—103 (1953).
[123] W. WUEST, Stabilitätsmindernde Einflüsse der Absaugegrenzschichten. Zeitschr. f. Flugwiss. **4**, 81—84 (1956).
[124] J. A. ZALOVCIK and R. B. SKOOG, Flight investigation of boundary layer transition and profile drag of an experimental low-drag wing installed on a fighter-type airplane. NACA Wartime-Report L-94 (1945).

Part D. Turbulent boundary layers

CHAPTER XVIII

Fundamentals of turbulent flow

Introductory remarks

Most flows which occur in practical applications are turbulent, and this term denotes a motion in which an irregular fluctuation (mixing, or eddying motion) is superimposed on the main stream. Several photographs of turbulent flows in an open water channel are shown in Figs. 18.1 a, b, c, and d in order to illustrate the type of motion under consideration, the pattern having been made visible by sprinkling the free surface with powder. The velocity of flow was the same in all pictures but the camera was moved at different speeds along the axis of the channel. It is easy to deduce from each picture whether the longitudinal velocity of the fluid particles was smaller than or exceeded that of the camera and their appearance gives a very impressive idea of the complexity of turbulent motion.

The fluctuation which is superimposed on the principal motion is so hopelessly complex in its details that it seems to be inaccessible to mathematical treatment, but it must be realized that the resulting mixing motion is very important for the course of the flow and for the equilibrium of forces. The effects caused by it are as if the viscosity were increased by factors of one hundred, ten thousand, or even more. At large Reynolds numbers there exists a continuous transport of energy from the main flow into the large eddies. However, energy is dissipated preponderantly by the small eddies, and the process occurs in a narrow strip inside the boundary layer, in the neighbourhood of the wall, as shown in detail in ref. [14].

Mixing is responsible for the large resistance experienced by turbulent flow in pipes, for the drag encountered by ships and aeroplanes and for the losses in turbines and turbocompressors, yet, on the other hand, turbulence enables us to achieve greater pressure increases in diffusers or along aeroplane wings and compressor blades. These devices would all show separation, if the flow were laminar and free of turbulence, and consequently the degree of energy recovery in a diffuser would be small and wings and blades would operate in an unsatisfactory manner.

In the succeeding chapter we shall discuss the first of the fundamental problems stated in Sec. XVI b, namely that involving *fully developed turbulent motion.* In this connexion we are forced to restrict ourselves to the consideration of time-averages of turbulent motion, because a complete theoretical formulation has so far proved impossible, owing to the complexity of turbulent fluctuations.

In following this path it has at least proved possible to establish certain theoretical principles which allow us to introduce a measure of order into the experimental material. Moreover in many cases it proved possible to predict these mean values under the assumption of certain plausible hypotheses and so to obtain good agreement with experiment. The following chapters will give an account of such a semi-empirical theory of turbulent flow†.

The present chapter will be devoted to the study of the influence of fluctuations on the mean flow. The succeeding chapter will be concerned with the semi-empirical assumptions used in the calculation of turbulent motion; most of them are linked with the concept of *mixing length* due to Prandtl. The remaining chapters will then deal with specific groups of turbulent motions on this basis and will include the flow through pipes, along plates, in turbulent boundary layers with pressure gradients, and free turbulent flow, i. e. the flow in jets and wakes where no restricting walls are present.

a. Mean motion and fluctuations

Upon close investigation it appears that the most striking feature of turbulent motion consists in the fact that the velocity and pressure at a fixed point in space do not remain constant with time but perform very irregular fluctuations of high frequency (see Fig. 16.17). The lumps of fluid which perform such fluctuations in the direction of flow and at right angles to it do not consist of single molecules as assumed in the kinetic theory of gases; they are macroscopic fluid balls of varying small size. It may be noted, by the way of example, that although the velocity fluctuation in channel flow does not exceed several per cent, it nevertheless has a decisive influence on the whole course of the motion. The fluctuations under consideration may be visualized by realizing that certain bigger portions of the fluid have their own intrinsic motion which is superimposed on the main flow. Such *fluid balls* or *lumps*, are clearly visible in the photographs, Figs. 18.1 b, c, d. The size of such fluid balls, which continually agglomerate and disintegrate, determines the *scale of turbulence*; their size is determined by the external conditions associated with the flow, that is, for example, by the mesh of a screen or honeycomb through which the stream had passed. Serval quantitative measurements of the magnitudes associated with such fluctuations will be given in Sec. XVIII d.

In natural winds these fluctuations manifest themselves very clearly in the form of squalliness and often attain a magnitude of 50 per cent. of the mean wind speed. The size of turbulence elements in the atmosphere can be judged, for example, by observing the eddying of a corn field.

It has already been pointed out in Chap. XVI that in describing a turbulent flow in mathematical terms it is convenient to separate it into a *mean motion* and

† Several workers, in particular M. J. Burgers, Th. von Kármán and G. I. Taylor quite early developed a theory which exceeds these limits and which is based on statistical concepts. However this theory has not so far been able to solve the fundamental problem mentioned earlier. We do not propose to consider this statistical theory of turbulence in the remainder of this book and refer the reader to the comprehensive reviews by K. Wieghardt [35], J. M. Burgers [2], Th. von Kármán [12], W. Tollmien [29], and to the books written by G. K. Batchelor [1] and Hinze [10a]

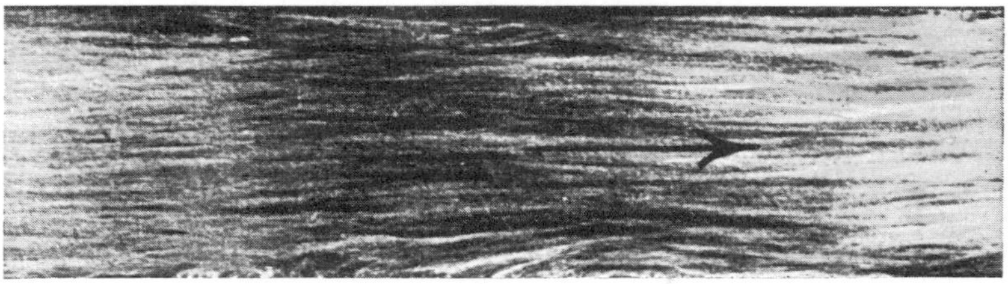

Fig. 18.1 a. Camera velocity 12·15 cm/sec

Fig. 18.1 b. Camera velocity 20 cm/sec

Fig. 18.1 c. Camera velocity 25 cm/sec

Fig. 18.1 d. Camera velocity 27·6 cm/sec

Figs. 18.1 a, b, c, d. Turbulent flow in a water channel 6 cm wide, photographed with varying camera speeds. Photographs taken by Nikuradse [19] and published by Tollmien [29]

into a *fluctuation*, or *eddying motion*. Denoting the time-average of the u-component of velocity by $\bar{u}$ and its velocity of fluctuation by u', we can write down the following relations for the velocity components and pressure:

$$u = \bar{u} + u'; \quad v = \bar{v} + v'; \quad w = \bar{w} + w'; \quad p = \bar{p} + p', \tag{18.1}$$

as indicated in eqn. (16.2). The time-averages are formed at a fixed point in space and are given e.g. by

$$\bar{u} = \frac{1}{T} \int\limits_{t_0}^{t_0+T} u \, dt. \tag{18.2}$$

In this connexion it is understood that the mean values are taken over a sufficiently long interval of time, T, for them to be completely independent of time. Thus, by definition, the time-averages of all quantities describing the fluctuations are equal to zero:

$$\overline{u'} = 0; \quad \overline{v'} = 0; \quad \overline{w'} = 0; \quad \overline{p'} = 0. \tag{18.3}$$

The feature which is of fundamental importance for the course of turbulent motion consists in the circumstance that the fluctuations u', v', w' influence the mean motion $\bar{u}$, $\bar{v}$, $\bar{w}$ in such a way that the latter exhibits an apparent increase in the resistance to deformation. In other words, the presence of fluctuations manifests itself in an apparent increase in the viscosity of the fundamental flow. This increased *apparent viscosity* of the mean stream forms the central concept of all theoretical considerations of turbulent motion. We shall begin, therefore, by endeavouring to obtain a closer insight into these relations.

It is useful to list here several rules of operating on mean time-averages, as they will be required for reference. If f and g are two dependent variables whose mean values are to be formed and if s denotes any one of the independent variables x, y, z, t then the following rules apply:

$$\left.\begin{aligned} \bar{\bar{f}} = \bar{f}; \qquad & \overline{f+g} = \bar{f} + \bar{g}, \\ \overline{\bar{f} \cdot g} & = \bar{f} \cdot \bar{g}, \\ \overline{\frac{\partial f}{\partial s}} = \frac{\partial \bar{f}}{\partial s}; \qquad & \overline{\int f \, ds} = \int \bar{f} \, ds. \end{aligned}\right\} \tag{18.4}$$

b. Additional, "apparent" turbulent stresses

Before deducing the relation between the mean motion and the apparent stresses caused by the fluctuations we shall give a physical explanation which will illustrate their occurrence. The argument will be based on the momentum theorem.

Let us now consider an elementary area dA in a turbulent stream whose velocity components are u, v, w. The normal to the area is imagined parallel to the x-axis and the directions y and z are in the plane of dA. The mass of fluid passing through this area in time dt is given by $dA \cdot \varrho u \cdot dt$ and hence the flux of momentum in the

x-direction is $dJ_x = dA \cdot \varrho\, u^2 \cdot dt$; correspondingly the fluxes in the y and z-directions are $dJ_y = dA \cdot \varrho\, u\, v \cdot dt$ and $dJz = dA \cdot \varrho\, u\, w \cdot dt$, respectively. Remembering that the density is constant we can calculate the following time-averages for the fluxes of momentum per unit time:

$$\overline{dJ_x} = dA \cdot \varrho\, \overline{u^2}; \qquad \overline{dJ_y} = dA \cdot \varrho\, \overline{u\, v}; \qquad \overline{dJ_z} = dA \cdot \varrho \cdot \overline{u\, w}\,.$$

By eqn. (18.1) we find that, e. g.

$$u^2 = (\bar{u} + u')^2 = \bar{u}^2 + 2\, \bar{u}\, u' + u'^2$$

and applying the rules in eqns. (18.3) and (18.4) we find that

$$\overline{u^2} = \bar{u}^2 + \overline{u'^2}$$

and that, similarly

$$\overline{u \cdot v} = \bar{u} \cdot \bar{v} + \overline{u'\, v'}; \qquad \overline{u \cdot w} = \bar{u} \cdot \bar{w} + \overline{u'\, w'}\,.$$

Hence the expressions for the momentum fluxes per unit time become

$$\overline{dJ_x} = dA \cdot \varrho\, (\bar{u}^2 + \overline{u'^2})\,; \qquad \overline{dJ_y} = dA \cdot \varrho\, (\bar{u} \cdot \bar{v} + \overline{u'\, v'})\,;$$

$$\overline{dJ_z} = dA \cdot \varrho\, (\bar{u} \cdot \bar{w} + \overline{u'\, w'})\,.$$

These quantities, denoting the rate of change of momentum, have the dimension of forces on the elementary area dA, and upon dividing by it we obtain forces per unit area, i. e. stresses. Since the flux of momentum per unit time through an area is always equivalent to an equal and opposite force exerted on the area by the surroundings, we conclude that the area under consideration, which is normal to the x-axis, is acted upon by the stresses $-\varrho\, (\bar{u}^2 + \overline{u'^2})$ in the x-direction, $-\varrho\, (\bar{u}\, \bar{v} + \overline{u'\, v'})$ in the y-direction and $-\varrho\, (\bar{u}\, \bar{w} + \overline{u'\, w'})$ in the z-direction. The first of the three is a normal stress and the latter two are shearing stresses. It is thus seen that the superposition of fluctuations on the mean motion gives rise to three additional stresses

$$\sigma_x = -\varrho\, \overline{u'^2}; \qquad \tau_{yx} = -\varrho\, \overline{u'\, v'}; \qquad \tau_{xz} = -\varrho\, \overline{u'\, w'} \tag{18.5}$$

acting on the elementary surface. They are termed "apparent" or Reynolds stresses of turbulent flow and must be added to the stresses caused by the steady flow as explained earlier in connexion with laminar flow. Corresponding expressions apply in the case of elementary areas normal to the two remaining axes y and z. They form together a complete *stress tensor of turbulent flow*. Equations (18.5) were first deduced by O. Reynolds [22] from the equations of motion of fluid dynamics (see also the next section).

It is easy to visualize that the time-averages of the mixed products of velocity fluctuations, such as e. g. $\overline{u'\, v'}$ do, in fact, differ from zero. The stress component $\tau_{xy} = \tau_{yx} = -\varrho\, \overline{u'\, v'}$ can be interpreted as the transport of x-momentum through a surface normal to the y-axis. Considering, for example, a mean flow given by $\bar{u} =$

$= \bar{u}(y)$, $\bar{v} = \bar{w} = 0$ with $d\bar{u}/dy > 0$, Fig. 18.2, we can see that the mean product $\overline{u' v'}$ is different from zero: The particles which travel upwards in view of the turbulent fluctuation ($v' > 0$) arrive at a layer y from a region where a smaller mean velocity $\bar{u}$ prevails. Since they do, on the whole, preserve their original velocity $\bar{u}$, they give rise to a negative component u' in a layer y. Conversely the particles which arrive from above the layer ($v' < 0$) give rise to a positive u' in it. On the average, therefore, a positive v' is "mostly" associated with a negative u' and a negative v' is "mostly" associated with a positive u'. We may thus expect that the time-average $\overline{u' v'}$ is not only different from zero but also negative. The shearing stress $\tau_{xy} = - \varrho \overline{u' v'}$ is positive in this case and has the same sign as the relevant laminar shearing stress $\tau_l = \mu \, du/dy$. This fact is also expressed by stating that there exists a *correlation* between the longitudinal and transverse fluctuation of velocity at a given point.

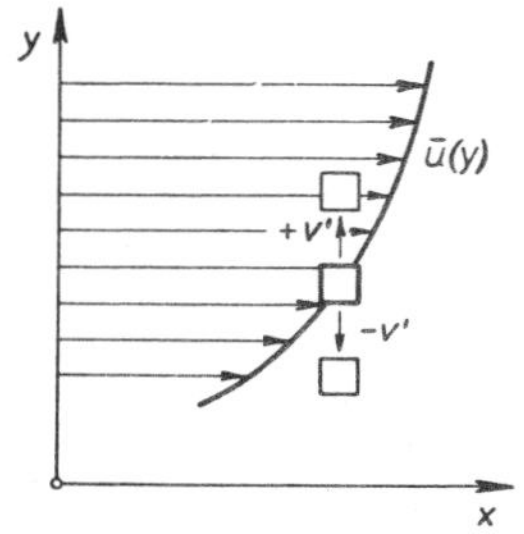

Fig. 18.2. Transport of momentum due to turbulent velocity fluctuation

c. Derivation of the stress tensor of apparent turbulent friction from the Navier-Stokes equations

Having illustrated the origin of the additional forces caused by turbulent fluctuation with the aid of a physical argument we shall now proceed to derive the same expression in a more formal way and directly from the Navier-Stokes equations. The object of the succeeding argument is to derive the equations of motion which must be satisfied by the time-averages of the velocity components $\bar{u}, \bar{v}, \bar{w}$ and of the pressure $\bar{p}$. The Navier-Stokes equations (3.29) for incompressible flow can be rewritten in the form

$$\varrho \left\{ \frac{\partial u}{\partial t} + \frac{\partial (u^2)}{\partial x} + \frac{\partial (uv)}{\partial y} + \frac{\partial (uw)}{\partial z} \right\} = - \frac{\partial p}{\partial x} + \mu \nabla^2 u, \tag{18.6a}$$

$$\varrho \left\{ \frac{\partial v}{\partial t} + \frac{\partial (vu)}{\partial x} + \frac{\partial (v^2)}{\partial y} + \frac{\partial (vw)}{\partial z} \right\} = - \frac{\partial p}{\partial y} + \mu \nabla^2 v, \tag{18.6b}$$

$$\varrho \left\{ \frac{\partial w}{\partial t} + \frac{\partial (wu)}{\partial x} + \frac{\partial (wv)}{\partial y} + \frac{\partial (w^2)}{\partial z} \right\} = - \frac{\partial p}{\partial z} + \mu \nabla^2 w, \tag{18.6c}$$

$$\frac{\partial u}{\partial x} + \frac{\partial v}{\partial y} + \frac{\partial w}{\partial z} = 0, \tag{18.6d}$$

where ∇^2 denotes Laplace's operator. We now introduce the hypotheses regarding the decomposition of velocity components and pressure into their time-averages and fluctuation terms from eqn. (18.1) and form time-averages in the resulting equations term by term, taking into account the rules from eqn. (18.4). Since $\partial \overline{u'}/\partial x = 0$ etc. the equation of continuity becomes

$$\frac{\partial \bar{u}}{\partial x} + \frac{\partial \bar{v}}{\partial y} + \frac{\partial \bar{w}}{\partial z} = 0 . \tag{18.7}$$

From eqns. (18.7) and (18.6d) we obtain also that

$$\frac{\partial u'}{\partial x} + \frac{\partial v'}{\partial y} + \frac{\partial w'}{\partial z} = 0 .$$

It is seen that the time-averaged velocity components and the fluctuating components each satisfy the incompressible equation of continuity.

Introducing the assumptions from eqn. (18.1) into the equations of motion (18.6 a, b, c) we obtain expressions similar to those given in the preceding section. Upon forming averages and considering the rules in eqn. (18.4) it is noticed that the quadratic terms in the mean values remain unaltered because they are already constant in time. The terms which are linear in the turbulent components such as e. g. $\partial u'/\partial t$ and $\partial^2 u'/\partial x^2$ vanish in view of eqn. (18.3). The same is true of the mixed terms such as e. g. $\bar{u} \cdot u'$, but the quadratic terms in the fluctuating components remain in the equations. Upon averaging they assume the form $\overline{u'^2}$, $\overline{u'\,v'}$ etc. Hence if the averaging process is carried out on eqns. (18.6) and if simplifications arising from the continuity equation (18.7) are introduced, the following system of equations results

$$\left.\begin{aligned}
\varrho\left(\bar{u}\frac{\partial \bar{u}}{\partial x} + \bar{v}\frac{\partial \bar{u}}{\partial y} + \bar{w}\frac{\partial \bar{u}}{\partial z}\right) &= -\frac{\partial \bar{p}}{\partial x} + \mu\,\nabla^2 \bar{u} - \varrho\left[\frac{\partial \overline{u'^2}}{\partial x} + \frac{\partial \overline{u'\,v'}}{\partial y} + \frac{\partial \overline{u'\,w'}}{\partial z}\right]\\
\varrho\left(\bar{u}\frac{\partial \bar{v}}{\partial x} + \bar{v}\frac{\partial \bar{v}}{\partial y} + \bar{w}\frac{\partial \bar{v}}{\partial z}\right) &= -\frac{\partial \bar{p}}{\partial y} + \mu\,\nabla^2 \bar{v} - \varrho\left[\frac{\partial \overline{u'v'}}{\partial x} + \frac{\partial \overline{v'^2}}{\partial y} + \frac{\partial \overline{v'\,w'}}{\partial z}\right]\\
\varrho\left(\bar{u}\frac{\partial \bar{w}}{\partial x} + \bar{v}\frac{\partial \bar{w}}{\partial y} + \bar{w}\frac{\partial \bar{w}}{\partial z}\right) &= -\frac{\partial \bar{p}}{\partial z} + \mu\,\nabla^2 \bar{w} - \varrho\left[\frac{\partial \overline{u'\,w'}}{\partial x} + \frac{\partial \overline{v'w'}}{\partial y} + \frac{\partial \overline{w'^2}}{\partial z}\right].
\end{aligned}\right\} \tag{18.8}$$

The quadratic terms in turbulent velocity components have been transferred to the right-hand side for a reason which will soon become apparent. Eqns. (18.8) together with the equation of continuity, eqn. (18.7), determine the problem under consideration. The left-hand sides of eqns. (18.8) are formally identical with the steady-state Navier-Stokes equations (3.29), if the velocity components u, v, w are replaced by their time-averages, and the same is true of the pressure and friction terms on the right-hand side. In addition the equations contain terms which depend on the turbulent fluctuation of the stream.

Comparing eqns. (18.8) with eqns. (3.10) it is seen that the additional terms on the right-hand side of eqns. (18.8) can be interpreted as components of a stress tensor. By eqn. (3.9a) the resultant surface force per unit area due to the additional terms is seen to be

$$\boldsymbol{P} = \boldsymbol{i}\left(\frac{\partial \sigma_x}{\partial x} + \frac{\partial \tau_{xy}}{\partial y} + \frac{\partial \tau_{xz}}{\partial z}\right) + \boldsymbol{j}\left(\frac{\partial \tau_{xy}}{\partial x} + \frac{\partial \sigma_y}{\partial y} + \frac{\partial \tau_{yz}}{\partial z}\right) + \boldsymbol{k}\left(\frac{\partial \tau_{xz}}{\partial x} + \frac{\partial \tau_{yz}}{\partial y} + \frac{\partial \sigma_z}{\partial z}\right).$$

Carrying the analogy with eqns. (3.10) still further we can rewrite eqns. (18.8) in the form

$$\left.\begin{aligned}
\varrho\left(\bar{u}\frac{\partial\bar{u}}{\partial x}+\bar{v}\frac{\partial\bar{u}}{\partial y}+\bar{w}\frac{\partial\bar{u}}{\partial z}\right) &= -\frac{\partial\bar{p}}{\partial x}+\mu\nabla^2\bar{u}+\left(\frac{\partial\sigma_x}{\partial x}+\frac{\partial\tau_{xy}}{\partial y}+\frac{\partial\tau_{xz}}{\partial z}\right)\\
\varrho\left(\bar{u}\frac{\partial\bar{v}}{\partial x}+\bar{v}\frac{\partial\bar{v}}{\partial y}+\bar{w}\frac{\partial\bar{v}}{\partial z}\right) &= -\frac{\partial\bar{p}}{\partial y}+\mu\nabla^2\bar{v}+\left(\frac{\partial\tau_{xy}}{\partial x}+\frac{\partial\sigma_y}{\partial y}+\frac{\partial\tau_{yz}}{\partial z}\right)\\
\varrho\left(\bar{u}\frac{\partial\bar{w}}{\partial x}+\bar{v}\frac{\partial\bar{w}}{\partial y}+\bar{w}\frac{\partial\bar{w}}{\partial z}\right) &= -\frac{\partial\bar{p}}{\partial z}+\mu\nabla^2\bar{w}+\left(\frac{\partial\tau_{xz}}{\partial x}+\frac{\partial\tau_{yz}}{\partial y}+\frac{\partial\sigma_z}{\partial z}\right)
\end{aligned}\right\}\qquad(18.9)$$

and upon comparing eqns. (18.9) with (18.8) we can see that the components of the stress tensor due to the turbulent velocity components of the flow are:

$$\begin{pmatrix}\sigma_x & \tau_{xy} & \tau_{xz}\\ \tau_{xy} & \sigma_y & \tau_{yz}\\ \tau_{xz} & \tau_{yz} & \sigma_z\end{pmatrix} = -\begin{pmatrix}\varrho\,\overline{u'^2} & \varrho\,\overline{u'v'} & \varrho\,\overline{u'w'}\\ \varrho\,\overline{u'v'} & \varrho\,\overline{v'^2} & \varrho\,\overline{v'w'}\\ \varrho\,\overline{u'w'} & \varrho\,\overline{v'w'} & \varrho\,\overline{w'^2}\end{pmatrix}. \qquad (18.10)$$

This stress tensor is identical with the one obtained in eqn. (18.5) with the aid of the momentum equation.

From the preceding argument it can be concluded that the components of the mean velocity of turbulent flow satisfy the same equations, i. e. eqns. (18.9), as those satisfied by laminar flow, except that the laminar stresses must be increased by additional stresses which are given by the stress tensor in eqn. (18.10). These additional stresses are known as *apparent*, or *virtual stresses of turbulent flow* or *Reynolds stresses*. They are due to turbulent fluctuation and are given by the time-mean values of the quadratic terms in the turbulent components. Since these stresses are added to the ordinary viscous terms in laminar flow and have a similar influence on the course of the flow, it is often said that they are caused by *eddy viscosity*. The total stresses are the sums of the viscous stresses from eqn. (3.22) and of these apparent stresses, so that e. g.

$$\left.\begin{aligned}
\sigma_x &= -p+2\mu\frac{\partial\bar{u}}{\partial x}-\varrho\,\overline{u'^2},\\
\tau_{xy} &= \mu\left(\frac{\partial\bar{u}}{\partial y}+\frac{\partial\bar{v}}{\partial x}\right)-\varrho\,\overline{u'v'},\ \ldots\,.
\end{aligned}\right.\qquad(18.11)$$

Generally speaking, the apparent stresses far outweigh the viscous components and, consequently, the latter may be omitted in many actual cases with a good degree of approximation.

Boundary conditions: The boundary conditions to be satisfied by the mean velocity components in eqns. (18.9) are the same as in ordinary laminar flow, namely they all vanish at solid walls (no-slip condition). Moreover all turbulent components must vanish at the walls and they are very small in their immediate neighbourhood. It follows, therefore, that all components of the tensor of apparent stresses vanish at the solid walls and the only stresses which act near them are the viscous stresses of laminar flow as they, generally speaking, do not vanish there. Furthermore it is seen that in the immediate neighbourhood of a wall the apparent stresses are small compared with the viscous stresses and it follows that in every turbulent flow there exists a very thin layer next to the wall which, in essence, behaves like one in laminar motion. It is known as the *laminar sub-layer* and its velocities are so small that the viscous forces dominate over the inertia forces. Thus no turbulence can exist in it. The laminar sub-layer joins a transitional layer in which the velocity fluctuations are so large that they give rise to turbulent shearing stresses which are, in turn, comparable with the viscous stresses. At still larger distances from the wall the turbulent stresses eventually completely outweigh the viscous stresses. This is the actual turbulent boundary layer. The thickness of the laminar sub-layer is so small, in most cases, that it is impossible, or very difficult, to observe it under experimental conditions. Nevertheless it is of decisive importance for the flow under consideration because it is the seat of phenomena by which the shearing at the wall and hence the viscous drag are determined. We shall revert to this point later in the book.

Equations (18.9) and (18.10) constitute the starting point for the mathematical treatment of turbulent flow problems, or, more precisely, for the calculation of the time-averages of the magnitudes which describe the flow. The time-averaged values of the turbulent velocity components can be interpreted as the components of a stress tensor but it must be borne in mind that such an interpretation does not in itself lead to very much. Eqns. (18.9) and (18.10) cannot be used for a rational evaluation of the mean flow as long as the relation between the mean and the turbulent components is not known. Such a relation can only be obtained empirically and forms the essential contents of all the hypotheses concerning turbulence which will be discussed in the succeeding chapter.

d. Account of some measurements on fluctuating turbulent velocities

In experimental work on turbulent flow it is usual to measure only the mean values of pressure and velocity because they are the only quantities which can be measured conveniently. The measurement of the turbulent, fluctuating components u' v', . . . themselves, or of their mean values such as $\overline{u'^2}$, $\overline{u'\,v'}$, . . . is rather difficult and requires elaborate equipment. Reliable measurements of the fluctuation velocity components have been obtained with the aid of hot-wire anemometers. The measurement of the mean values is quite sufficient for most practical applications, but only through the actual measurement of the fluctuating components is it possible to gain a deeper understanding of the mechanism of turbulent flow. We now propose to give a short account of some experimental work on the measurement of the fluctuating velocity components in order to present a more vivid physical picture of the phenomena and in order to give some justification to the preceding mathematical argument.

H. Reichardt [21] carried out such measurements in a wind tunnel with a rectangular test section 1 m wide and 24·4 cm high. The variation of the mean velocity over the height of the tunnel, $\bar{u}(y)$, is seen plotted in Fig. 18.3; measurements were made in the central section of the tunnel. It is seen to be a typical turbulent velocity profile with a steep increase near the wall and a fairly uniform velocity near the centre-line. The maximum velocity was $U = 100$ cm/sec. The same diagram contains also plots of the root-mean-square values of the longitudinal and transverse components $\sqrt{\overline{u'^2}}$ and $\sqrt{\overline{v'^2}}$ respectively. The transverse fluctuation does not vary greatly over the height of the channel and its average value is about 4 per cent. of U, but the longitudinal turbulent component exhibits a pronounced steep maximum of 0·13 U very close to the wall. It is clearly seen from the diagram that both turbulent components decrease to zero at the wall, as stated earlier. Fig. 18.4 shows a plot of the mean value of the product $-\overline{u'\,v'}$, which is equal to the turbulent shearing stress except for a factor ϱ. The value of $-\overline{u'\,v'}$ falls to zero in the centre of the test section for reasons of symmetry, whereas its maximum occurs near the wall

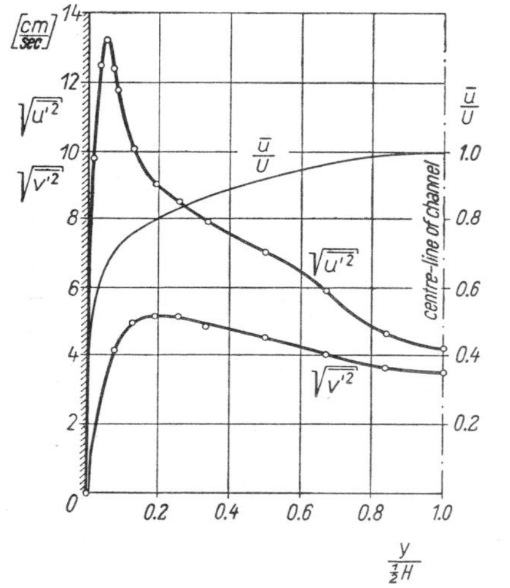

Fig. 18.3. Measurement of fluctuating turbulent components in a wind tunnel after Reichardt [21]

Root-mean-square of longitudinal fluctuation $\sqrt{\overline{u'^2}}$, transverse fluctuation $\sqrt{\overline{v'^2}}$, mean velocity $\bar{u}$ at maximum velocity $U = 100$ cm/sec

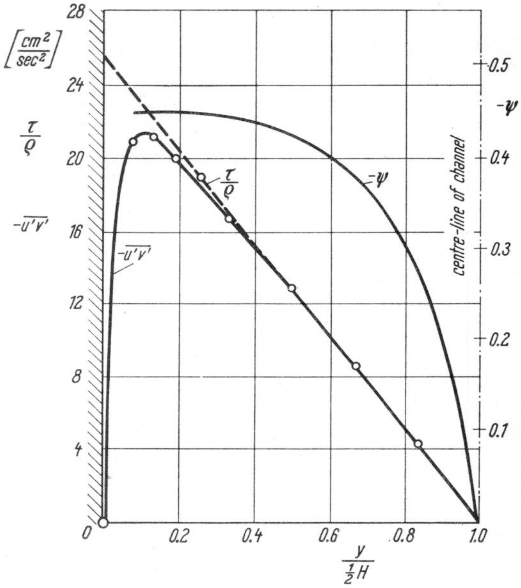

Fig. 18.4. Measurement of fluctuating components in a channel after Reichardt [21]

The product $\overline{u'\,v'}$, the shearing stress τ/ϱ and the correlation coefficient ψ

showing that turbulent friction has its largest value there. The broken line τ/ϱ shows the variation of shearing stress which was obtained from the measured pressure distribution and independently of the measurement of velocity. The two curves nearly coincide over the major portion of the height of the test section, and this may be interpreted as a good check on the measurements; it also shows that almost all of the shearing stress is due to turbulence. The two curves under consideration diverge near the wall, the curve of $-\overline{u'\,v'}$ decreasing to zero, because turbulent fluctuations die out near the wall. The difference between the two curves gives laminar friction.

Finally Fig. 18.4 contains values of the *correlation coefficient*, ψ, between the longitudinal and transverse fluctuation at the same point; it is defined by

$$\psi = \frac{\overline{u' v'}}{\sqrt{\overline{u'^2}} \cdot \sqrt{\overline{v'^2}}} \,. \tag{18.12}$$

The correlation coefficient† ranges over values up to $\psi = -0{\cdot}45$.

More recently, extensive measurements on the turbulent fluctuations have also been performed in the boundary layer of a flat plate at zero incidence. Fig. 18.5 reproduces some of the results obtained by P. S. Klebanoff [14] in a boundary layer associated with a stream of the very low turbulence intensity of 0·02 % (*cf.* Secs. XVId and XVIIIe) at a Reynolds number $\mathsf{R}_x = U_\infty x/\nu = 4 \cdot 2 \times 10^6$. The profile of the temporal mean of the velocity, $\bar{u}$, exhibits a shape which is very much like that in a channel, Fig. 18.3. The variation of the longitudinal fluctuation $\sqrt{\overline{u'^2}}$

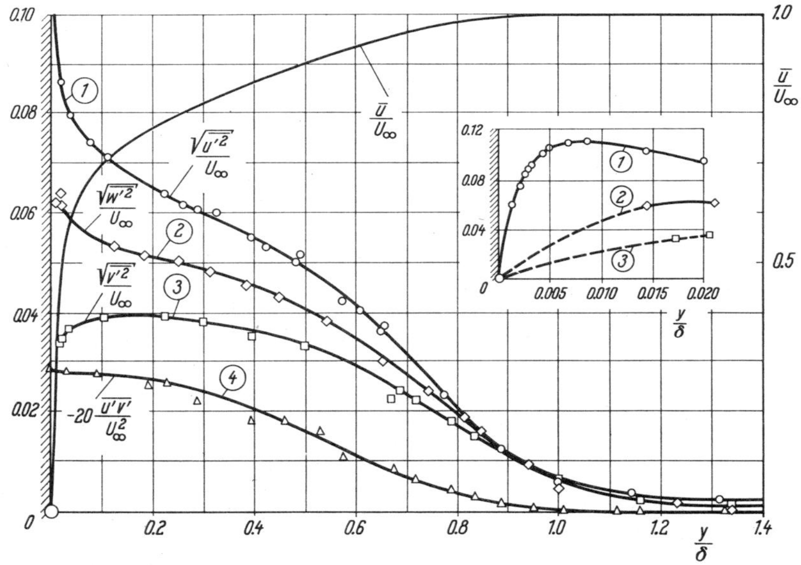

Fig. 18.5. Variation of the fluctuating turbulent velocity components in the boundary layer on a flat plate at zero incidence, as measured by P. S. Klebanoff [14]

Curve (1), longitudinal oscillation: $\sqrt{\overline{u'^2}}$

Curve (2), transverse oscillation parallel to wall: $\sqrt{\overline{w'^2}}$

Curve (3), transverse oscillation at right angles to wall: $\sqrt{\overline{v'^2}}$

Curve (4), turbulent shearing stress: $\overline{u' v'} = -\tau/\varrho$; $\bar{u}$ denotes mean velocity

† It may be remarked here in passing that the existence of an apparent shearing stress due to velocity fluctuations always implies a correlation between the turbulent velocity components in two different directions. Such a correlation also exists in the case of the disturbances which have been investigated in connexion with the theory of stability of laminar motion; see ref. [30]

with its pronounced maximum in close proximity of the wall as well as the flatter course of the curve of transverse oscillation at right angles to the wall, $\sqrt{\overline{v'^2}}$, closely resemble those obtained in the channel, Fig. 18.3. It is remarkable that in the boundary layer on a flat plate, Fig. 18.5, the transverse oscillation parallel to the wall, $\sqrt{\overline{w'^2}}$, also attains considerable values, values which, moreover, exceed those attained by $\sqrt{\overline{v'^2}}$. The turbulent shearing stress at the wall has the value $\tau/\varrho\, U^2_\infty = -\overline{u'\,v'}/U^2_\infty \approx 0{\cdot}0015$ which agrees with the local value of the skin friction coefficient $\frac{1}{2}\,c'_f$ in the diagram of Fig. 21.2. A comparison between Figs. 18.3 and 18.4 for the channel and Fig. 18.5 for the boundary layer reveals that the turbulent fluctuations are very similar in both cases. They provide a justification for the application of the laws of turbulent flow deduced from the study of flows through channels and pipes to the description of the flow in a boundary layer. We shall make use of this possibility in Chap. XXI.

G. B. Schubauer and P. S. Klebanoff [26] performed also very careful measurements of the fluctuations of the turbulent velocity components and of the correlation coefficient in a turbulent boundary layer on a flat wall with a *favourable* and an *adverse* pressure gradient.

J. Laufer [16] performed extensive measurements on the fluctuating components in *pipe flow*. Earlier measurements performed by P. S. Klebanoff and Z. W. Diehl [13] on an artificially thickened boundary layer on a flat plate demonstrated that it behaves substantially like an ordinary boundary layer with a correspondingly increased inlet length. Detailed results on turbulent flow through a channel can be found described in a paper by J. Laufer [15]. A paper by J. C. Laurence [16a] contains the results of his investigations of the intensity of turbulence in free jets.

The investigations into turbulent oscillations in the boundary layer of a flat plate described in ref. [14] have shown, further, that the turbulence at the outer edge of the boundary layer is intermittent and resembles in this respect the flow in the inlet length of a pipe described in Sec. XVIa and Figs. 16.2 and 16.3. Oscillograms of the oscillating turbulent velocity components demonstrate that the position of the fairly sharp boundaries between the highly turbulent flow in the boundary layer and the nearly turbulence-free external stream fluctuates strongly with time. The variation of the intermittency factor γ over the width of the boundary layer is shown plotted in Fig. 18.6. The value $\gamma = 1$ signifies that the flow is turbulent at all times and $\gamma = 0$ corresponds to a flow which remains laminar. It can be inferred

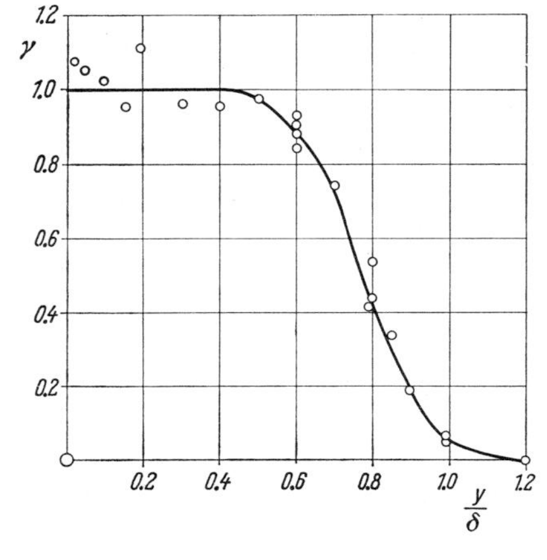

Fig. 18.6. Variation of the intermittency factor γ in a turbulent boundary layer on a flat plate at zero incidence as measured by P. S. Klebanoff [14]

from the diagram that the boundary layer is intermittent in that respect from $y = 0{\cdot}5\,\delta$ to $y = 1{\cdot}2\,\delta$. Turbulent streams and wakes behave in a similar manner.

The mechanism of turbulent motion creates a continuous flow of energy from the mean or main motion to the secondary or eddy motion which is in turn dissipated into heat by friction. In this connexion it is important to study the spectral

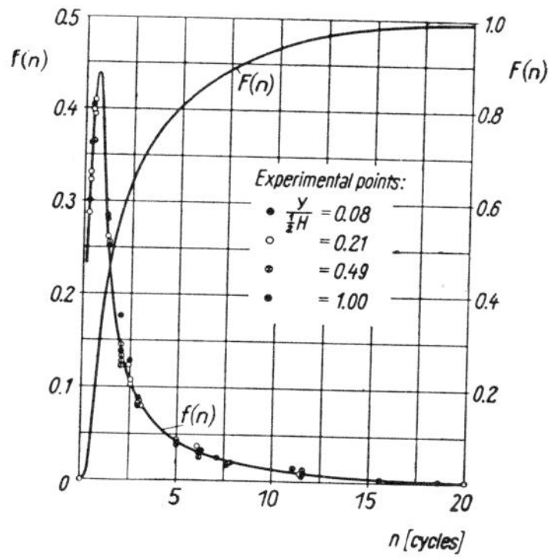

Fig. 18.7. Spectral distribution of the energy of longitudinal fluctuations $\overline{u'^2}$ for channel flow as in Fig. 18.3, after Reichardt and Motzfeld [18]

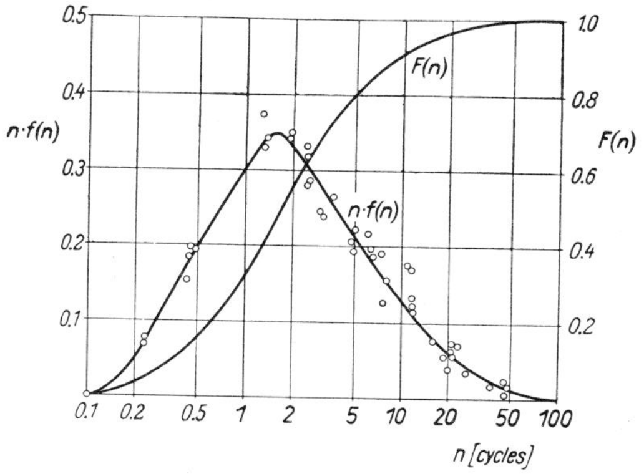

Fig. 18.8. Logarithmic representation of spectral distribution of longitudinal fluctuation from Fig. 18.7

distribution of the energy of the secondary motion over the frequency range. If n denotes frequency and $f(n)$ the percentage of energy contained between frequency n and $n + dn$, then the curve $f(n)$ represents the spectral distribution of the energy in the eddy motion. Consequently, the energy contained in the frequency range 0 to n is, by definition:

$$F(n) = \int_0^n f(n)\,dn \qquad (18.13)$$

and

$$F(\infty) = \int_0^\infty f(n)\,dn = 1\,.$$

The spectral distribution of the energy of longitudinal fluctuation $\overline{u'^2}$ was measured by H. Reichardt and H. Motzfeld [18] and their results are shown in Fig. 18.7. The measurements relate to the same channel as the curves in Fig. 18.3. Since the curve $f(n)$ is very steep in the range of small frequencies, it was re-plotted on a logarithmic diagram shown in Fig. 18.8. In this connexion the product $n \cdot f(n)$ has been chosen as the ordinate in order again to obtain $F(n)$ as the area under the curve. The most striking result of these measurements is that the spectral energy distribution is practically the same for all wall distances, (*cf.* refs. [14] and [16]). The maximum of the energy spectrum occurs at about $n = 1$ cycle. L. F. G. Simmons and C. Salter [27] and H. L. Dryden [7] measured the energy spectrum behind a screen in a wind tunnel.

e. Wind tunnel turbulence

The relative magnitude of the fluctuations of velocity is a very important variable in wind tunnel measurements; it determines the degree to which measurements performed on a model can be applied to the full-scale structure as well as how measurements performed in different tunnels can be compared among themselves. We have already mentioned in Sec. XVId that, in particular, transition from laminar to turbulent flow strongly depends on the magnitude of the oscillating velocity component. The magnitude of the fluctuations in a given tunnel is determined by the mesh of its screens, grids or honeycombs. At a certain distance from the screens there is *isotropic turbulence* which means that the mean velocity fluctuations in the three co-ordinate directions are equal to each other:

$$\overline{u'^2} = \overline{v'^2} = \overline{w'^2} .$$

In such cases the *level, degree* or *intensity of turbulence* can be described by the quantity $\sqrt{\overline{u'^2}}/U_\infty$ which is then identical with

$$\sqrt{\tfrac{1}{3}\left(\overline{u'^2} + \overline{v'^2} + \overline{w'^2}\right)} \Big/ U_\infty .$$

The degree of turbulence of a wind tunnel expressed as $\sqrt{\overline{u'^2}}/U_\infty$ can be reduced to values as low as 0·1 per cent., if a sufficient number of fine-mesh screens or honeycombs is used, see Fig. 16.16†.

The experimentally verified fact that the critical Reynolds number of a sphere for which the drag coefficient decreases steeply (Fig. 1.5) depends strongly on the degree of turbulence of the wind tunnel, is of great practical importance. The value of the critical Reynolds number is of the order of $(V\,D/\nu)_{crit} = 1{\cdot}5$ to 4×10^5 and decreases with an increasing intensity of turbulence. This fact is evident on physical grounds because a high intensity of turbulence in the free stream leads to transition at low Reynolds numbers so that the point of separation is shifted downstream causing the wake to decrease, and this, in turn, reduces drag. On the other hand free-flight measurements on a sphere performed by C. B. Millikan and A. L. Klein [17] gave the surprising result that in the free atmosphere the critical Reynolds number of the sphere is independent of the structure of turbulence which varies with the weather. Free-flight measurements gave a critical Reynolds number of $\mathsf{R}_{crit} = 3{\cdot}85 \times 10^5$, which is larger than that for most wind tunnels, although measurements in low-turbulence tunnels approach the value in free flight.

† H. L. Dryden and G. B. Schubauer [9] undertook extensive measurements on the effect of placing fine mesh screens in a wind tunnel on its turbulence level. The addition of a single screen reduces the intensity of turbulence in the ratio $1/\sqrt{1+c}$, where c denotes the resistance coefficient of the screen; hence when n screens are used, the reduction in turbulence intensity is in the ratio $\{1/(1+c)\}^{(1/2)n}$. Consequently, for a given pressure loss the reduction in turbulence intensity is greater when a large number of screens of small resistance is chosen in preference to a single screen of large resistance. According to ref. [14a], the addition of a contraction cone to the tunnel brings with it a great reduction of the absolute value of the longitudinal oscillating component. On the other hand, the transverse components either remain constant or even increase.

The fact that the critical Reynolds number measured in free flight is independent of the weather is explained by the circumstance that the turbulent eddies in the atmosphere are so large that they cannot affect the phenomena in the thin boundary layer on a sphere. In any case these measurements lead to the conclusion that it is necessary to design wind tunnels of low turbulence intensity if model measurements are to be applicable to the design of full-scale aircraft. This is particularly important when measurements are performed on low-drag aerofoils whose boundary layers remain laminar over long stretches (laminar aerofoils, Sec. XVII b). The characteristics of such aerofoils can be successfully measured only in low-turbulence tunnels, i. e. in tunnels whose intensity of turbulence is extremely small ($\mathsf{T} \approx 0{\cdot}0005$; *cf* [10]). Reference [3] contains a summary of measurements on the intensity of turbulence of a large number of wind tunnels.

Since the direct measurement of the velocity fluctuation $\sqrt{\overline{u'^2}}/U_\infty$ is quite difficult, attempts were made to regard the critical Reynolds number on a sphere as the parameter which describes the intensity of turbulence in a wind-tunnel. This critical Reynolds number for a sphere can be determined either by measuring the drag† as suggested by H. L. Dryden [4,5], or by measuring the pressure difference between the forward stagnation point and a point at the rear of the sphere, as suggested by S. Hoerner [11]‡. The latter method was extensively used by R. C. Platt [20]. H. L. Dryden and A. M. Kuethe [4] correlated the critical Reynolds number for a sphere with the mean longitudinal fluctuation, Fig. 18.9, and discovered that these two quantities satisfy a unique functional relationship. The value of the critical Reynolds number, $\mathsf{R}_{crit} = 3{\cdot}85 \times 10^5$, measured on a sphere in free flight corresponds to a vanishingly small intensity of turbulence, $\mathsf{T} \to 0$.

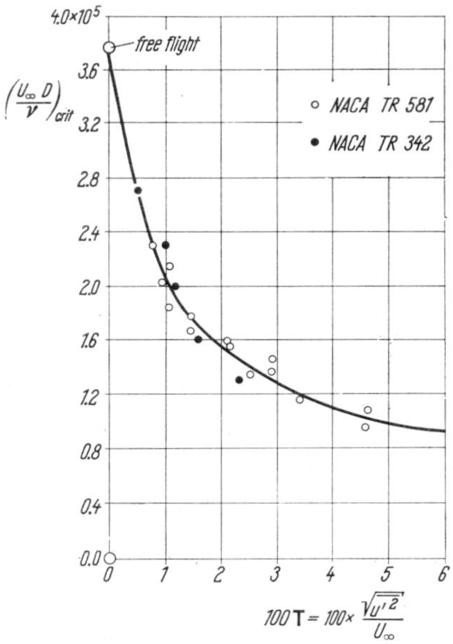

Fig. 18.9. Relation between the critical Reynolds number of a sphere and the intensity of turbulence of the tunnel, after H. L. Dryden and A. M. Kuethe [4, 6]

Bodies of other than spherical shapes also exhibit some influence of the intensity of turbulence on their drag. This has been demonstrated by the measurements on flat plates placed at right angles to the stream which have been performed by G. B. Schubauer and H. L. Dryden [25].

† It has been agreed to define the critical Reynolds number of a sphere as that number for which the drag coefficient has the conventional value $C_D = 0{\cdot}3$.

‡ To the conventional value of $C_D = 0{\cdot}3$ there corresponds a pressure difference between the forward stagnation point and a point at the rear of the sphere of $\Delta p = 1{\cdot}22\, q$, where q denotes the dynamic pressure in the free stream.

More detailed investigations which were carried out by H. L. Dryden [7] and his co-workers have, however, led to the conclusion that the structure of the turbulence present in a wind tunnel cannot be adequately described by specifying the magnitude of the fluctuation of the velocity components alone. It is also necessary to specify a characteristic length which is a measure of the *magnitude of turbulent eddies*, i. e. *the scale of turbulence*. This characteristic length is also determined by the mesh of the screens etc. used in the tunnel. H. L. Dryden [6] found that it can be determined experimentally by measuring the correlation coefficient of longitudinal fluctuations u_1' and u_2' at two points whose transverse distance is y or, in other words, by specifying the quantity

$$R(y) = \frac{\overline{u_1' u_2'}}{\sqrt{\overline{u_1'^2}} \cdot \sqrt{\overline{u_2'^2}}}\,. \tag{18.14}$$

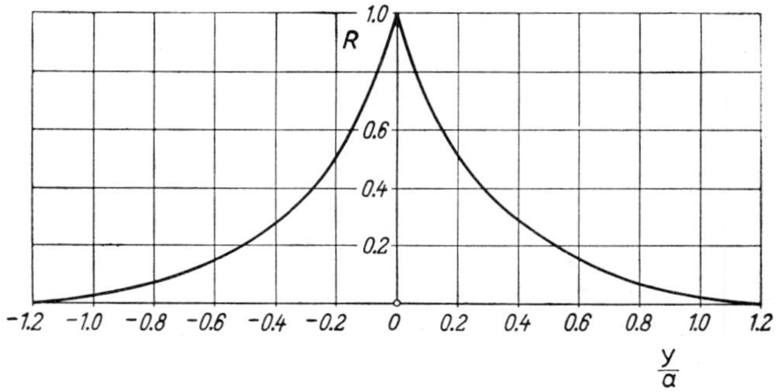

Fig. 18.10. Correlation coefficient $R(y)$ of longitudinal fluctuation from eqn. (18.14) for two points at a transverse distance y; distance behind screen equal to $40\,a$, where a is the mesh width

The results of measurements taken behind a screen of mesh-width a in a region of isotropic turbulence are seen plotted in Fig. 18.10 against the transverse distance y. The correlation coefficient decreases fast to zero with increasing y and the quantity which is characteristic of the scale of turbulence is given by

$$L = \int_0^\infty R(y)\,\mathrm{d}y\,.$$

It is a measure of the magnitude of the lumps of fluid which move together as a unit and thus describes the size of individual *eddies*. Measurements performed by H. L. Dryden have shown that L depends on the width a of the mesh of the screen and on the distance from it. The critical Reynolds number of a sphere depends on a parameter given by

$$\frac{\sqrt{\overline{u'^2}}}{U_\infty}\left(\frac{D}{L}\right)^{\frac{1}{5}}$$

where D denotes the diameter of the sphere. G. I. Taylor [28, 34, 35] supplied a theoretical explanation of this effect. A theoretical investigation of wind-tunnel turbulence based on the Navier-Stokes equations was given by W. Tollmien and M. Schaefer [31]; the reader may also wish to consult a paper by W. Tollmien [33].

References

[1] G. K. BATCHELOR, The theory of homogeneous turbulence. Cambridge University Press 1953.

[2] J. M. BURGERS, A mathematical model illustrating the theory of turbulence. "Advances in Applied Mechanics", Vol. I, ed. by R. VON MISES and TH. VON KÁRMÁN, New York 1948.

[3] R. D. COOPER and M. P. TULIN, Turbulence measurements with the hot-wire anemometer. AGARDograph No. 12 (1955).

[4] H. L. DRYDEN and A. M. KUETHE, Effect of turbulence in wind tunnel measurements. NACA Rep. No. 342 (1929).

[5] H. L. DRYDEN, Reduction of turbulence in wind-tunnels. NACA Rep. 392 (1931).

[6] H. L. DRYDEN, G. B. SCHUBAUER, W. C. MOCK and H. K. SKRAMSTAD, Measurements of intensity and scale of wind-tunnel turbulence and their relation to the critical Reynolds Number of spheres. NACA Rep. No. 581 (1937).

[7] H. L. DRYDEN, Turbulence investigations at the National Bureau of Standards. Proc. Fifth Intern. Congress of Applied Mech. 362 (1938).

[8] H. L. DRYDEN, Turbulence and the boundary layer. Jour. Aero. Sci. **6**, 85 (1939).

[9] H. L. DRYDEN and G. B. SCHUBAUER, The use of damping screens for the reduction of wind tunnel turbulence. Jour. Aero. Sci. **14**, 221—228 (1947).

[10] H. L. DRYDEN and J. H. ABBOTT, The design of low turbulence wind-tunnels. NACA Tech. Note 1755 (1948).

[10a] J. O. HINZE, Turbulence. An introduction to its mechanism and theory. McGraw-Hill, New York, 1959.

[11] S. HOERNER, Versuche mit Kugeln betreffend Kennzahl, Turbulenz und Oberflächenbeschaffenheit. Luftfahrtforschung **12**, 42 (1934).

[12] TH. VON KÁRMÁN, Progress in the statistical theory of turbulence. Proc. Nat. Acad. Sci. Washington **34**, 530 (1948).

[13] P. S. KLEBANOFF and Z. W. DIEHL, Some features of artifically thickened fully developed turbulent boundary layers with zero pressure gradient. NACA Rep. No. 1110 (1952).

[14] P. S. KLEBANOFF, Characteristics of turbulence in a boundary layer with zero pressure gradient. NACA Rep. No. 1247 (1955).

[14a] L. S. G. KOVASZNAY, Turbulence Measurements. Sec. F of "Physical Measurements in Gasdynamics and Combustion". Vol. IX. of "High Speed Aerodynamics and Jet Propulsion", ed. by W. R. LADENBURG, Princeton University Press 1954, pp. 213—285 (Princeton series).

[15] J. LAUFER, Investigation of turbulent flow in a two-dimensional channel. NACA Rep. No. 1053 (1951).

[16] J. LAUFER, The structure of turbulence in fully developed pipe flow. NACA Rep. No. 1174 (1954).

[16a] J. C. LAURENCE, Intensity, scale, and spectra of turbulence in mixing region of free subsonic jet. NACA Report No. 1292 (1956).

[16b] C. C. LIN, Aspects of the problem of turbulent motion. J. Aero. Sci. **23**, 453—461 and 506 (1956).

[17] C. B. MILLIKAN and A. L. KLEIN, The effect of turbulence. Aircraft Eng'g 169, Aug. (1933).

[18] H. MOTZFELD, Frequenzanalyse turbulenter Schwankungen. ZAMM **18**, 362 (1938).

[19] J. NIKURADSE, Kinematographische Aufnahme einer turbulenten Strömung. ZAMM **9**, 495 (1929).

[20] R. C. PLATT, Turbulence factors of NACA wind tunnels as determined by sphere tests. NACA Rep. No. 558 (1936).

[21] H. REICHARDT, Messungen turbulenter Schwankungen. Naturwissenschaften 404 (1938); see also ZAMM **13**, 177 (1933) and ZAMM **18**, 358 (1938).

[22] O. REYNOLDS, Phil. Trans. Roy. Soc. T. **186** A. 123, or Sci. Papers **I**, 355.

[22a] H. S. RIBNER and M. TUCKER, Spectrum of turbulence in a contracting stream. NACA Rep. No. 1113 (1953).

[23] H. SCHLICHTING, Neuere Untersuchungen über die Turbulenzentstehung. Die Naturwissenschaften, **22**, 376 (1934).

[24] H. SCHLICHTING, Amplitudenverteilung und Energiebilanz der kleinen Störungen bei der Plattenströmung. Nach. Ges. d. Wiss. Göttingen, Math. Phys. Klasse, New series **1**, 4, 47 (1935).

[25] G. B. SCHUBAUER and H. L. DRYDEN, The effect of turbulence on the drag of flat plates. NACA Rep. No. 546 (1935).

[26] G. B. SCHUBAUER and P. S. KLEBANOFF, Investigation of separation of the turbulent boundary layer. NACA Rep. 1030 (1951).
[27] L. F. G. SIMMONS and C. SALTER, An experimental determination of spectrum of turbulence. Proc. Roy. Soc. London, A. **165**, 73—89 (1938).
[28] G. I. TAYLOR, Statistical theory of turbulence. V. Effect of turbulence on boundary layer. Theoretical discussion of relationship between scale of turbulence and critical resistance of spheres. Proc. Roy. Soc. London, A **151**, 421, 873 (1935); see also J. Aero. Sci. **4**, 311 (1937).
[29] W. TOLLMIEN, Turbulente Strömungen. Handbuch der Experimentalphysik, Vol. **4**, Pt. I, 291 (1931).
[30] W. TOLLMIEN, Über die Korrelation der Geschwindigkeitskomponenten in periodisch schwankenden Wirbelverteilungen. ZAMM **15**, 96 (1935).
[31] W. TOLLMIEN and M. SCHÄFER, Zur Theorie der Windkanalturbulenz. ZAMM **21**, 1 (1941).
[32] W. TOLLMIEN, Fortschritte der Turbulenzforschung. Zusammenfassender Bericht. ZAMM **33**, 200—211 (1953).
[33] W. TOLLMIEN, Abnahme der Windkanalturbulenz nach dem Heisenbergschen Austauschansatz als Anfangswertproblem. Wiss. Zschr. T. H. Dresden **2**, 443—448 (1952/53).
[34] K. WIEGHARDT, Über die Wirkung der Turbulenz auf den Umschlagpunkt. ZAMM **20**, 58 (1940).
[35] K. WIEGHARDT, Zusammenfassender Bericht über Arbeiten zur statistischen Turbulenztheorie. Luftfahrtforschung **18**, 1—7 (1941).

CHAPTER XIX

Theoretical assumptions for the calculation of turbulent flows

a. Fundamental equations

It is not very likely that science will ever achieve a complete understanding of the mechanism of turbulence because of its extremely complicated nature. The main variables which are of practical interest are the mean velocities, but so far no rational theory which would enable us to determine them by calculation has been formulated. For this reason many attempts have been made to create a mathematical basis for the investigation of turbulent motion with the aid of semi-empirical hypotheses. The empirical assumptions advanced in the past have been developed into more or less complete theories but none of them succeeded in fully analyzing even a single case of turbulent flow. It is necessary to supplement the original hypothesis with additional hypotheses which vary from case to case, and the form of certain functions, or at least certain numerical values, must be derived experimentally. The aim which underlies such empirical theories of turbulence is to deduce the still missing fundamental physical ideas from results of experimental measurements.

The turbulent mixing motion is responsible not only for an exchange of momentum but it also enhances the transfer of heat and mass in fields of flow associated with non-uniform distributions of temperature or concentration. The methods for the calculation of turbulent flow, temperature, and concentration fields developed so far are based on empirical hypotheses which endeavour to establish a relationship between the Reynolds stresses produced by the mixing motion, and the mean values of the velocity components together with suitable hypotheses concerning heat and mass transfer. By this means the apparent stresses are given a mathematical form which, upon substitution into eqns. (18.8), as well as into the differential equation for the temperature field (not quoted), leads to differential equations containing only mean values of pressure and velocity. These transformed differential equations constitute then the starting point for the calculation of the mean flow.

J. Boussinesq [6, 18] was the first to work on the problem stated in the preceding section. In analogy with the coefficient of viscosity in Stokes' law for laminar flow

$$\tau_l = \mu \frac{\partial u}{\partial y},$$

he introduced a *mixing coefficient*, A_τ, for the Reynolds stress in turbulent flow by putting

$$\tau_t = A_\tau \frac{\partial \overline{u}}{\partial y} \qquad (19.1)$$

and similar expressions for the remaining turbulent stress components. As far as the transfer of heat is concerned, it is customary to make an assumption which is modelled on Fourier's law for laminar flow, namely

$$q_l = - k \frac{\partial \overline{T}}{\partial y}$$

and to put

$$q_t = - A_q \, c_p \, g \frac{\partial \overline{T}}{\partial y} \tag{19.2}$$

for the case of turbulent heat transfer. Here $\overline{u}$ and $c_p \, g \, T$ represent the momentum and enthalpy per unit mass, respectively, and τ and q denote the corresponding fluxes (rates of flow per unit time and area). The turbulent mixing coefficient, A_τ, corresponds to the viscosity, μ, in laminar flow and is, therefore, often called "apparent" or "virtual" (also "eddy") viscosity. Correspondingly, the turbulent mixing coefficient A_q is referred to as the "apparent", "virtual" (or "eddy") conductivity. The two coefficients are, in general, different from each other, because the mechanisms for momentum and thermal energy transport are not identical.

The assumptions in equations (19.1) and (19.2) have the great disadvantage that the eddy viscosity, A_τ, and the eddy conductivity, A_q, are not properties of the fluid like μ and k, but depend themselves on the mean velocity $\overline{u}$. This can be recognized if it is noted that viscous forces in turbulent flow are approximately proportional to the square of the mean velocity rather than to its first power as in laminar flow. According to equation (19.1) this would imply that A_q is approximately proportional to the first power of the mean velocity.

Often use is made of the apparent (virtual or eddy) kinematic viscosity $\varepsilon = A_\tau / \varrho$ which is analogous to the kinematic viscosity $\nu = \mu / \varrho$. If this is done, the equations for the shearing stress are rewritten

$$\tau_l = \varrho \cdot \nu \frac{\mathrm{d}u}{\mathrm{d}y}$$

and

$$\tau_t = \varrho \cdot \varepsilon \frac{\mathrm{d}\overline{u}}{\mathrm{d}y} \, .$$

It is now possible to introduce into the Navier-Stokes equations for the mean flow, eqn. (18.9), the boundary layer simplifications. In the case of the velocity boundary layer these will be similar to the considerations discussed in Sec. VIIa in connection with laminar boundary layers. The simplifications applicable to the equation of the thermal boundary layer were given in Sec. XIVd. In the case of two-dimensional, incompressible turbulent flow, with due regard being given to equations (19.1) and (19.2), we obtain the following system of differential equations for the velocity- and thermal boundary layers:

$$\frac{\partial \overline{u}}{\partial x} + \frac{\partial \overline{v}}{\partial y} = 0 \tag{19.3a}$$

$$\varrho \left(\overline{u} \frac{\partial \overline{u}}{\partial x} + \overline{v} \frac{\partial \overline{u}}{\partial y} \right) = - \frac{\mathrm{d}\overline{p}}{\mathrm{d}x} + \frac{\partial}{\partial y} \left[(\mu + A_\tau) \frac{\partial \overline{u}}{\partial y} \right] \tag{19.3b}$$

$$\varrho \, g \, c_p \left(\overline{u} \frac{\partial \overline{T}}{\partial x} + \overline{v} \frac{\partial \overline{T}}{\partial y} \right) = \frac{\partial}{\partial y} \left[(k + A_q \, c_p g) \frac{\partial \overline{T}}{\partial y} \right] + (\mu + A_\tau) \left(\frac{\partial \overline{u}}{\partial y} \right)^2 . \tag{19.3c}$$

The preceding set of equations corresponds to equations (14.36a) to (14.36c) for laminar flow, and the boundary conditions for the velocity components and the temperature are identical with those in the laminar case, Sec. XIVd. It will be recognized that in contrast with the remarks made in Secs. XI and XIV, the resulting system of equations does not contain terms which account for the difference between the average velocity- and temperature profiles in quasi-steady flow directly, and that the averaging process has been extended to include the boundary conditions. The effect of the oscillation has been introduced in a heuristic way and is contained in the terms multiplying the eddy coefficients A_τ and A_q.

b. Prandtl's mixing length theory

The hypotheses in equations (19.1) and (19.2) cannot be used for the calculation of actual examples if nothing is known about the dependence of A_τ and A_q on velocity. In order to develop the preceding method (initiated by Boussinesq) it is necessary to find empirical relations between the coefficients and the mean velocity. In discussing these, we shall confine ourselves in the present section to the velocity field in incompressible flow because the latter is then independent of the temperature field. The calculation of temperature fields, and, in particular, of the rates of heat transfer in turbulent motion, will be taken up in detail in Sec. XIXg.

In 1925 L. Prandtl [12] made an important advance in this direction. In developing his hypothesis we shall refer to the simplest case of two-dimensional parallel flow in which the velocity varies only from stream-line to stream-line. The principal direction of flow is assumed parallel to the x-axis and we have

$$\overline{u} = \overline{u}(y) \; ; \qquad \overline{v} = 0 \; ; \qquad \overline{w} = 0 \, .$$

The preceding type of flow is realized in a rectangular channel for which the results of measurement on turbulent velocity components were given in Figs. 18.3 and 18.4. In the present case only the shearing stress

$$\tau_{xy} = \tau = -\varrho\, \overline{u' v'} = \varrho\, \varepsilon \frac{d\overline{u}}{dy} \tag{19.4}$$

remains different from zero.

With L. Prandtl we can now visualize the following simplified mechanism of the motion: as the fluid passes along the wall in turbulent motion, fluid particles coalesce into lumps which move bodily and which cling together for a given traversed length, both in the longitudinal and in the transverse direction, retaining their momentum parallel to x. It will now be assumed that such a lump of fluid, which comes, say, from a layer at $(y_1 - l)$ and has a velocity $\overline{u}(y_1 - l)$, is displaced over a distance l in the transverse direction, Fig. 19.1. This distance l is known as *Prandtl's mixing length*†. As the lump of fluid retains its original momentum, its velocity in the new lamina at y_1 is smaller than the velocity prevailing there. The difference in velocities is then

$$\Delta u_1 = \overline{u}(y_1) - \overline{u}(y_1 - l) = l \left(\frac{d\overline{u}}{dy}\right)_1 .$$

† The term *mixture length* has also been used.

The last expression is obtained by developing the function $u(y_1 - l)$ in a Taylor series and neglecting all higher order terms. In this transverse motion we have $v' > 0$. Similarly a lump of fluid which arrives at y_1 from the lamina at $y_1 + l$ possesses a velocity which exceeds that around it, the difference being

$$\Delta u_2 = \overline{u}(y_1 + l) - \overline{u}(y_1) = l \left(\frac{d\overline{u}}{dy}\right)_1 .$$

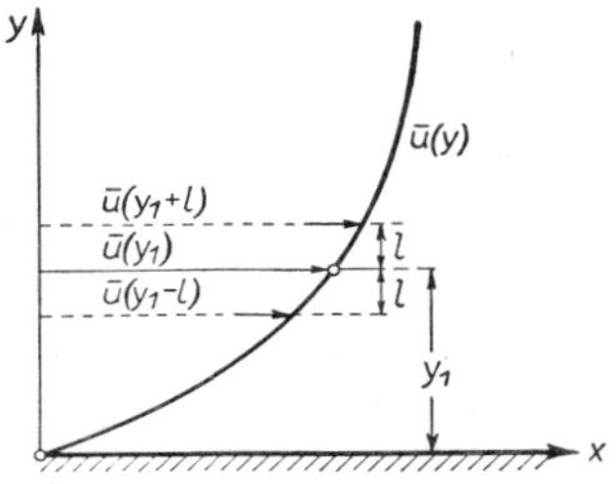

Fig. 19.1. Explanation of the mixing length concept

Here $v' < 0$. The velocity differences caused by the transverse motion can be regarded as the turbulent velocity components at y_1. Hence we can calculate the time-average of the absolute value of this fluctuation and we obtain

$$\overline{|u'|} = \tfrac{1}{2}(|\Delta u_1| + |\Delta u_2|) = l \left|\left(\frac{d\overline{u}}{dy}\right)_1\right| . \tag{19.4a}$$

Equation (19.4a) leads to the following physical interpretation of the mixing length l. The mixing length is that distance in the transverse direction which must be covered by an agglomeration of fluid particles travelling with its original mean velocity in order to make the difference between its velocity and the velocity in the new lamina equal to the mean transverse fluctuation in turbulent flow. The question as to whether the lump of fluid completely retains the velocity of its original lamina as it moves in a transverse direction, or whether it partly assumes the velocity of the crossed lamina and continues beyond it in a transverse direction, is here left entirely open. Prandtl's concept of a mixing length is analogous, up to a certain point, with the mean free path in the kinetic theory of gases, the main difference being that the latter concerns itself with the microscopic motion of molecules, whereas the present concept deals with the macroscopic motion of large agglomerations of fluid particles †.

† In analogy with eqn. (19.4a) we can write

$$u' = l' \frac{d\overline{u}}{dy}, \tag{19.4b}$$

for the variation of the longitudinal, turbulent component u' with time. Here l' denotes a length which varies with time and which may assume both positive and negative values. Hence from eqn. (19.4) we obtain

$$\tau = -\varrho\, \overline{v' l'} \frac{d\overline{u}}{dy} = \varrho\, \varepsilon \frac{d\overline{u}}{dy}, \tag{19.4c}$$

and the virtual kinematic viscosity becomes

$$\varepsilon = -\overline{v' l'} . \tag{19.4d}$$

It may be imagined that the transverse velocity fluctuation originates in the following way: Consider two lumps of fluid meeting in a lamina at a distance y_1, the slower one from $(y_1 - l)$ preceding the faster one from $(y_1 + l)$. Under these circumstances the lumps will collide with a velocity $2\,u'$ and will diverge sideways. This is equivalent to the existence of a transverse velocity component in both directions with respect to the layer at y_1. If the two lumps appear in the reverse order they will move apart at a velocity $2\,u'$ and the empty space between them will be filled from the surrounding fluid, again giving rise to a transverse velocity component in the two directions at y_1. This argument implies that the transverse component v' is of the same order of magnitude as u' and we put

$$\overline{|v'|} = \text{const} \times \overline{|u'|} = \text{const} \times l \frac{\mathrm{d}\bar{u}}{\mathrm{d}y} \,. \tag{19.5}$$

In order to find an expression for the shearing stress from eqn. (19.4) it is necessary to investigate the mean value $\overline{u'\,v'}$ a little closer. It follows from the preceding representation that the lumps which arrive at layer y_1 with a positive value of v' (upwards from below in Fig. 19.1) give rise "mostly" to a negative u' so that their product $u'\,v'$ is negative. The lumps with a negative value of v' (downwards from above in Fig. 19.1) are "mostly" associated with a positive u' and the product $u'\,v'$ is again negative. The qualifying word "mostly" in the above context expresses the fact that the appearance of particles for which u' has the opposite sign to the above is not completely excluded but is, nevertheless, much less frequent. Thus the temporal average $\overline{u'\,v'}$ is different from zero and negative. Hence we assume

$$\overline{u'\,v'} = -\,c\,\overline{|u'|}\cdot\overline{|v'|}\,, \tag{19.5a}$$

with $0 < c < 1$ $(c \neq 0)$. Nothing is known about the numerical factor c but, in essence, it appears to be identical with the correlation factor defined in eqn. (18.12). The experimental results plotted in Fig. 18.4 give some idea as to its behaviour. Combining eqns. (19.4a) and (19.5) we now obtain

$$\overline{u'\,v'} = -\,\text{const} \times l^2 \left(\frac{\mathrm{d}\bar{u}}{\mathrm{d}y}\right)^2 .$$

It should be noted that the constant in the above equation is different from that in eqn. (19.5), as the former also contains the factor c from eqn. (19.5a). The constant can now be included with the still unknown mixing length, and we may write

$$\overline{u'\,v'} = -\,l^2 \left(\frac{\mathrm{d}\bar{u}}{\mathrm{d}y}\right)^2 .$$

Consequently the shearing stress from eqn. (19.4) can be written as

$$\tau = \varrho\, l^2 \left(\frac{\mathrm{d}\bar{u}}{\mathrm{d}y}\right)^2 .$$

Taking into account that the sign of τ must change with that of $\mathrm{d}\bar{u}/\mathrm{d}y$, it is found that it is more correct to write

$$\boxed{\tau = \varrho\, l^2 \left|\frac{\mathrm{d}\bar{u}}{\mathrm{d}y}\right| \frac{\mathrm{d}\bar{u}}{\mathrm{d}y}} \ . \tag{19.6}$$

This is *Prandtl's mixing length hypothesis*. It will be shown later that it is very useful in the calculation of turbulent flows.

Comparing eqn. (19.6) with the Boussinesq hypothesis in eqn. (19.1), we find the following expressions for the virtual viscosity

$$A_\tau = \varrho\, l^2 \left|\frac{\mathrm{d}\bar{u}}{\mathrm{d}y}\right| \tag{19.7a}$$

and for the virtual kinematic viscosity

$$\varepsilon = l^2 \left|\frac{\mathrm{d}\bar{u}}{\mathrm{d}y}\right| \ . \tag{19.7b}$$

On comparing Prandtl's equation (19.6) with J. Boussinesq's equation (19.1) it might be thought that little has been gained because the unknown ε (virtual kinematic viscosity) has been replaced by the equally unknown quantity l (mixing length). However, upon reflexion, it will be concluded that Prandtl's equation (19.6) is far more suitable for the calculation of turbulent motion than the older formula (19.1). It is known from experimental evidence that turbulent drag is roughly proportional to the square of velocity and the same result is obtained from eqn. (19.6), if the mixing length is assumed to be independent of the magnitude of velocity. The mixing length, unlike viscosity in Stoke's law, is still not a property of the fluid, but it is, at least, a purely local function. Furthermore, it is far simpler to make plausible assumptions concerning the mixing length l than for the virtual kinematic viscosity ε. This constitutes the essential superiority of Prandtl's equation over that due to Boussinesq.

In numerous cases it is possible to establish a simple relation between the mixing length, l, and a characteristic length of the respective flow. For example in flows along smooth walls l must vanish at the wall itself, because transverse motions are inhibited by its presence. In flows along rough walls the mixing length near the wall must tend to a value of the same order of magnitude as the solid protrusions.

Prandtl's equation (19.6) has been successfully applied to the study of *turbulent motion along walls* (pipe, channel, plate) and to the problem of so-called *free turbulent flow*. The latter term refers to flows without solid walls, such as the mixing of a jet with the surrounding still air. Examples of such applications will be given in Chaps. XX, XXI, and XXIII.

c. Two further assumptions for the turbulent shearing stress

Prandtl's equation (19.6) for shearing stress in turbulent flow is still unsatisfactory in that the apparent kinematic viscosity ε, eqn. (19.7b), vanishes at points where $\mathrm{d}\bar{u}/\mathrm{d}y$ is equal to zero, i. e. at points of maximum or minimum velocity. This is certainly not the case because turbulent mixing does not vanish at points of maximum velocity (centre of channel). The latter view is confirmed by Reichardt's measurements on turbulent fluctuations, Fig. 18.3, which show that in the centre of the channel the longitudinal and transverse fluctuations both differ from zero. Following L. Prandtl it is possible to account for this fact by assuming that the apparent kinematic viscosity is proportional to a statistical mean of $|\mathrm{d}\bar{u}/\mathrm{d}y|$ in the neighbourhood of a velocity maximum, where $\mathrm{d}\bar{u}/\mathrm{d}y$ varies sharply. The mean is taken over a small neighbourhood of the point under consideration; in other words ε is taken to be proportional to $\sqrt{\overline{(\mathrm{d}\bar{u}/\mathrm{d}y)^2}}$, where the bar above the derivative denotes a local mean. This local mean can also be written as

$$\sqrt{\left(\frac{\mathrm{d}\bar{u}}{\mathrm{d}y}\right)^2 + l_1^2\left(\frac{\mathrm{d}^2\bar{u}}{\mathrm{d}y^2}\right)^2}\,,$$

where l_1 denotes a new length which, again, must be derived from experimental measurements. According to this more general assumption the apparent kinematic viscosity may be written as

$$\varepsilon = l^2\sqrt{\left(\frac{\mathrm{d}\bar{u}}{\mathrm{d}y}\right)^2 + l_1^2\left(\frac{\mathrm{d}^2\bar{u}}{\mathrm{d}y^2}\right)^2}$$

and the shearing stress becomes

$$\tau = \varrho\, l^2 \frac{\mathrm{d}\bar{u}}{\mathrm{d}y}\sqrt{\left(\frac{\mathrm{d}\bar{u}}{\mathrm{d}y}\right)^2 + l_1^2\left(\frac{\mathrm{d}^2\bar{u}}{\mathrm{d}y^2}\right)^2}\,. \qquad (19.8)$$

Equation (19.8) is very inconvenient because of the square root and has been used only occasionally, see Chap. XXIII.

In order to counter these difficulties L. Prandtl [14] established a considerably simpler equation for the apparent kinematic viscosity. It is valid only in the case of free turbulent flow and was derived from extensive experimental data on free turbulent flow due to H. Reichardt [15]. In setting up this new hypothesis L. Prandtl assumed that the dimensions of the lumps of fluid which move in a transverse direction during turbulent mixing are of the same order of magnitude as the width of the mixing zone. It will be recalled that the previous hypothesis implied that they were small compared with the transverse dimensions of the region of flow. The virtual kinematic viscosity, ε, is now formed by multiplying the maximum difference in the time-mean flow velocity with a length which is assumed to be proportional to the width, b, of the mixing zone. Thus

$$\varepsilon = \varkappa_1\, b\,(\bar{u}_{\max} - \bar{u}_{\min})\,. \qquad (19.9)\dagger$$

Here $\varkappa_1$ denotes a dimensionless number to be determined experimentally. It follows from eqn. (19.9) that ε remains constant over the whole width of every cross-section,

† On comparing this equation with eqn. (19.4d), it is seen that according to the present hypothesis the transverse fluctuation v' is proportional to $\bar{u}_{max} - \bar{u}_{min}$, and that the mixing length l' is proportional to the width b. An alternative hypothesis which relates to the apparent kinematic viscosity ε and is very similar to that in eqn. (19.9) was formulated by H. Reichardt [15].

whereas the previous hypothesis (19.7) implied that it varied even if the mixing length were assumed to be constant. From eqns. (19.9) and (19.1) we obtain that the turbulent shearing stress is given by

$$\tau = \varrho\, \varkappa_1\, b\, (\bar{u}_{\max} - \bar{u}_{\min})\, \frac{\mathrm{d}\bar{u}}{\mathrm{d}y}\,. \tag{19.10}$$

Examples of the application of this hypothesis are also given in Chap. XXIII.

So far attention has been centred only on the component τ_{xy} of the tensor of apparent turbulent stress. However, the preceding considerations can be suitably extended, and it is possible to make an equivalent hypothesis for the complete stress tensor. In analogy with Stokes' law, eqn. (3.22), the tensor of apparent turbulent stress is obtained by replacing the ordinary viscosity μ by $\varrho\, \varepsilon$. Thus, for two-dimensional flow we have

$$\begin{pmatrix} \sigma_x & \tau_{xy} \\ \tau_{xy} & \sigma_y \end{pmatrix} = \varrho\, \varepsilon \begin{pmatrix} 2\,\dfrac{\partial \bar{u}}{\partial x} & \dfrac{\partial \bar{u}}{\partial y} + \dfrac{\partial \bar{v}}{\partial x} \\ \dfrac{\partial \bar{u}}{\partial y} + \dfrac{\partial \bar{v}}{\partial x} & 2\,\dfrac{\partial \bar{v}}{\partial y} \end{pmatrix}. \tag{19.11}$$

In the above expression ε may be replaced either by its value from the mixing length theory, eqn. (19.7), or from the new hypothesis, eqn. (19.9). In most practical applications the normal turbulent components σ_x and σ_y are small compared with the mean pressure and may be neglected.

d. G. I. Taylor's vorticity transfer theory

In the argument which led to the establishment of Prandtl's mixing length, equation (19.6), it was assumed that lumps of fluid, on the whole, preserve their velocity in turbulent motion, and hence their momentum in the principal flow direction. In this sense Prandtl's theory can be described as the *momentum transport*, or *momentum transfer theory*. Equations (19.1) and (19.6) for shearing stress in turbulent flow can be regarded as equations describing the transfer of momentum in the x-direction across an element of surface normal to the y-direction and taken per unit area and time. In a flow, apart from momentum, we can visualize the transfer of other quantities, such as heat or chemical characteristics. Assuming that the mixing length remains the same, we can write, for example, for heat transfer (heat flux q = quantity of heat per unit area and time)

$$q = c\, \varrho\, \varepsilon\, \frac{\mathrm{d}T}{\mathrm{d}y} = c\, \varrho\, l^2 \left| \frac{\mathrm{d}\bar{u}}{\mathrm{d}y} \right| \frac{\mathrm{d}T}{\mathrm{d}y}\,. \tag{19.12}$$

Here c denotes the specific heat per unit mass and T is the temperature. H. Reichardt [16] conducted a thorough investigation into this matter and his work will be more fully discussed later (Chap. XXIII), but it is worth noting here that he found that the mixing length for momentum and heat transfer respectively are not exactly equal.

On comparing the transfer of momentum with that of heat, G. I. Taylor [19] pointed out that the relation between them will be fundamentally different in free turbulence and in that created near a wall, respectively. In a flow along a wall temperature differences and velocities (momentum) are propagated in accordance with the same law. On the other hand in free turbulence the propagation of temperature corresponds to the propagation of vorticity in the mean flow. It is possible to give a theoretical explanation of this statement by assuming that in a flow along a wall, vortices whose axes are parallel to the direction of flow predominate, whereas in free turbulence the dominating vortices have axes which are normal to the main flow direction and to the direction of the velocity gradient.

If it is assumed that *all* vortices present in the stream have such a direction, the flow is thereby assumed to be two-dimensional. If we assume, further, that the viscosity is negligible the vortices will obey Helmholtz' law and the vorticity of each particle will remain constant. This is the fundamental assumption of G. I. Taylor's *vorticity transport*, or *vorticity transfer theory* which asserts that the vorticity remains constant throughout the process of turbulent mixing. From this assumption it is possible to derive an expression for the turbulent shearing stress. We now propose to indicate briefly the argument in question.

Let us now denote by u, v and p, respectively, as before, the values of the velocity components and pressure, all quantities being variable with time. The quantity

$$\omega = \frac{1}{2}\left(\frac{\partial u}{\partial y} - \frac{\partial v}{\partial x}\right)$$

denotes the vorticity which also varies with time. Owing to the assumption that the viscosity is negligible, we may use Euler's equation of motion

$$\frac{\partial u}{\partial t} + u\frac{\partial u}{\partial x} + v\frac{\partial u}{\partial y} = -\frac{1}{\varrho}\frac{\partial p}{\partial x},$$

which can be modified and put in the form:

$$\frac{\partial u}{\partial t} + \frac{\partial}{\partial x}\left(\frac{u^2+v^2}{2}\right) + 2\,v\,\omega = -\frac{1}{\varrho}\frac{\partial p}{\partial x}. \tag{19.13}$$

The mean motion is, once more, assumed to be of the form:

$$\overline{u} = \overline{u}(y)\,; \qquad \overline{v} = 0\,.$$

It is now necessary to form temporal averages of the quantities in eqn. (19.13). Assuming fully developed motion, e. g. flow through a pipe or a rectangular channel, which does not vary with x, we find that the time-mean values of $\partial(u^2+v^2)/\partial x$ and $\partial u/\partial t$ are equal to zero. On the other hand the temporal averages of $\partial p/\partial x$ and of $2\,v\,\omega$ are different from zero. The calculation of the time-mean value of $2\,v\,\omega$ requires particular attention. The temporal average of $2\,\omega$ is, evidently, equal to $\mathrm{d}\overline{u}/\mathrm{d}y$. The fluctuation in ω can be expressed with the aid of a mixing length L, in the same way as that in u, so that for the total time-variable $2\,\omega$ we may write

$$2\,\omega = \frac{\mathrm{d}\overline{u}}{\mathrm{d}y} + L\,\frac{\mathrm{d}^2\overline{u}}{\mathrm{d}y^2}\,.$$

It should be noted that here, as distinct from Prandtl's theory, the new mixing length L depends on time. It varies from lump of fluid to lump of fluid and assumes both positive and negative values. Introducing this into eqn. (19.13) and bearing in mind that $v = v'$, we obtain

$$-\frac{1}{\varrho}\frac{\partial \bar{p}}{\partial x} = \overline{v' L}\,\frac{\mathrm{d}^2\bar{u}}{\mathrm{d}y^2} \tag{19.14}$$

The time-mean of $v'\,L$ is different from zero, because for the lumps which arrive from below (Fig. 19.1) v' is positive and L is negative, the opposite being true for those arriving from above. Thus the product $v'\,L$ is "mostly" negative. The transverse velocity component, v', can be written as

$$v' = L_1\,\frac{\mathrm{d}\bar{u}}{\mathrm{d}y}\,,$$

in analogy with eqn. (19.5). Consequently the time-mean becomes:

$$\overline{v' L} = -\left|\,\overline{L \cdot L_1}\,\frac{\mathrm{d}\bar{u}}{\mathrm{d}y}\right|\,.$$

Inserting this value into eqn. (19.14) and putting $\overline{L\,L_1} = l_w^{\,2}$ we obtain

$$\frac{1}{\varrho}\frac{\partial \bar{p}}{\partial x} = l_w^{\,2}\left|\frac{\mathrm{d}\bar{u}}{\mathrm{d}y}\right|\frac{\mathrm{d}^2\bar{u}}{\mathrm{d}y^2}\,.$$

We can now again introduce an apparent shearing stress, as in eqn. (18.9); considering that

$$-\frac{\partial \bar{p}}{\partial x} + \frac{\partial \tau}{\partial y} = 0\,,$$

we see that the right-hand side of the last equation becomes equal to $(1/\varrho)\cdot(\partial\tau/\partial y)$, and we have

$$\frac{\partial \tau}{\partial y} = \varrho\, l_w^{\,2}\left|\frac{\mathrm{d}\bar{u}}{\mathrm{d}y}\right|\frac{\mathrm{d}^2\bar{u}}{\mathrm{d}y^2}\,.$$

Assuming that l_w is independent of y, we can integrate this equation. We then obtain

$$\tau = \frac{1}{2}\,\varrho\, l_w^{\,2}\left|\frac{\mathrm{d}\bar{u}}{\mathrm{d}y}\right|\frac{\mathrm{d}\bar{u}}{\mathrm{d}y}\,. \tag{19.15}$$

This result differs from Prandtl's equation (19.6) merely by the factor $\frac{1}{2}$, which means that the mixing length of G. I. Taylor's vorticity transfer theory is larger by a factor $\sqrt{2}$ than that in L. Prandtl's momentum transfer theory. Thus $l_w = \sqrt{2}\,l$.

The preceding argument leads to the following conclusions: By way of example we shall now compare the temperature and velocity distribution in the wake behind a heated bar, i. e. we shall consider a problem in free turbulence. According to Prandtl's momentum transfer theory both curves should be identical. Taylor's vorticity transfer theory leads to the same velocity distribution as Prandtl's theory, if the mixing length in Taylor's equation (19.15) is made larger than that in Prandtl's equation (19.6) by a factor $\sqrt{2}$, as already mentioned. However, Taylor's theory would predict a different temperature curve. Since Taylor's virtual viscosity, $l_w^2\,|d\bar{u}/dy|$, is larger than Prandtl's, $l^2\,|d\bar{u}/dy|$, the temperature curve corresponding to the former would be wider. Such a temperature distribution has, indeed, been measured by A. Fage and V. M. Falkner, and their results have been quoted in G. I. Taylor's paper.

It must, however, be stressed once more that Taylor's vorticity transfer theory finds its application only to problems of free turbulence. Experiments show that it is not applicable to turbulent streams along walls.

e. Von Kármán's similarity hypothesis

It would be very convenient to possess a rule which allowed us to determine the dependence of mixing length on space co-ordinates. Th. von Kármán [9] made an attempt to establish such a rule assuming that turbulent fluctuations are similar at all points of the field of flow (*similarity rule*), i. e. that they differ from point to point only by time and length scale factors. The units of time and length can be replaced by time and velocity as fundamental units. It appears that the mixing length l can be chosen as the characteristic linear dimension for the fluctuation and further support for the choice will be given in the following argument. A velocity which is characteristic of the turbulent, fluctuating motion can be formed with the aid of the turbulent shearing stress by defining it, with the aid of eqn. (19.4), as follows:

$$v_* = \sqrt{\frac{|\tau|}{\varrho}} = \sqrt{|\overline{u'v'}|}\,. \tag{19.16}$$

The quantity v_* is called the *friction velocity* and is a measure of the intensity of turbulent eddying and of the transfer of momentum due to these fluctuations.

In order to obtain the similarity rule under consideration we shall imagine a two-dimensional mean flow in the x-direction, such that $\bar{u} = \bar{u}\,(y)$ and $\bar{v} = 0$ (parallel flow), and an auxiliary motion which is also two-dimensional, and which can be described by a stream function $\psi(x, y)$, eqn. (4.10):

$$\frac{\partial \nabla^2 \psi}{\partial t} + \left(\bar{u} + \frac{\partial \psi}{\partial y}\right)\frac{\partial \nabla^2 \psi}{\partial x} - \frac{\partial \psi}{\partial x}\left(\frac{d^2\bar{u}}{dy^2} + \frac{\partial \nabla^2 \psi}{\partial y}\right) = 0\,.$$

The symbol $\nabla^2 = \partial^2/\partial x^2 + \partial^2/\partial y^2$ denotes, as usual, the Laplace operator. We now fix our attention on the neighbourhood of a point x_0, y_0, where the velocity is $\bar{u}_0$. The mean flow will now be expanded in a Taylor series in the neighbourhood of this point, so that

$$\bar{u} = \bar{u}_0 + \left(\frac{d\bar{u}}{dy}\right)_0 (y - y_0) + \frac{1}{2}\left(\frac{d^2\bar{u}}{dy^2}\right)_0 (y - y_0)^2 + \ldots\,. \tag{19.17}$$

Further, we introduce a system of co-ordinates moving with a velocity $\bar{u}_0$ and we assume that the auxiliary motion is steady with respect to such a system. Thus the equation of motion for the auxiliary flow can be written:

$$(y - y_0)\left(\frac{\mathrm{d}\bar{u}}{\mathrm{d}y}\right)_0 \frac{\partial \nabla^2 \psi}{\partial x} - \left(\frac{\mathrm{d}^2\bar{u}}{\mathrm{d}y^2}\right)_0 \frac{\partial \psi}{\partial x} + \frac{\partial \psi}{\partial y}\frac{\partial \nabla^2 \psi}{\partial x} - \frac{\partial \psi}{\partial x}\frac{\partial \nabla^2 \psi}{\partial y} = 0\,. \tag{19.18}$$

According to the similarity hypothesis the stream function of the auxiliary motion must be of a form which depends only on the scale of length and velocity at point x_0, y_0. These will be denoted by l for length and by B for velocity, the two quantities being characteristic of the point. We now introduce the quantities ξ, η, and f for the amplitude of the auxiliary motion by the definitions:

$$\left.\begin{aligned} x - x_0 &= l\,\xi\,, \\ y - y_0 &= l\,\eta\,, \\ \psi &= B\,l\,f\,(\xi, \eta)\,. \end{aligned}\right\} \tag{19.19}$$

Inserting these values into eqn. (19.18) and dividing by $(B/l) \cdot (\mathrm{d}\bar{u}/\mathrm{d}y)_0$, we find the following differential equation for f:

$$\eta\,\frac{\partial \nabla^2 f}{\partial \xi} - \frac{(\mathrm{d}^2\bar{u}/\mathrm{d}y^2)_0}{l(\mathrm{d}\bar{u}/\mathrm{d}y)_0}\frac{\partial f}{\partial \xi} + \frac{B}{l(\mathrm{d}\bar{u}/\mathrm{d}y)_0}\left(\frac{\partial f}{\partial \eta}\frac{\partial \nabla^2 f}{\partial \xi} - \frac{\partial f}{\partial \xi}\frac{\partial \nabla^2 f}{\partial \eta}\right) = 0\,.$$

where, again, $\nabla^2 = \partial^2/\partial\xi^2 + \partial^2/\partial\eta^2$ is the Laplace operator. In accordance with the hypothesis under consideration the last equation must be independent of the quantities l, B, $(\mathrm{d}\bar{u}/\mathrm{d}y)_0$, and $(\mathrm{d}^2\bar{u}/\mathrm{d}y^2)_0$, as they are local functions. This requirement leads to the following two equations:

$$\frac{(\mathrm{d}^2\bar{u}/\mathrm{d}y^2)_0}{l(\mathrm{d}\bar{u}/\mathrm{d}y)_0} = \text{const}\,, \qquad \frac{B}{l(\mathrm{d}\bar{u}/\mathrm{d}y)_0} = \text{const}\,.$$

Thus the scales of length and velocity are given by

$$B \sim l\left(\frac{\mathrm{d}\bar{u}}{\mathrm{d}y}\right)_0; \qquad l \sim \left(\frac{\mathrm{d}\bar{u}/\mathrm{d}y}{\mathrm{d}^2\bar{u}/\mathrm{d}y^2}\right)_0. \tag{19.20}$$

Introducing an empirical dimensionless constant $\varkappa$, von Kármán made the assumption that the mixing length satisfies the equation:

$$l = \varkappa \left|\frac{\mathrm{d}\bar{u}/\mathrm{d}y}{\mathrm{d}^2\bar{u}/\mathrm{d}y^2}\right|. \tag{19.21}$$

In accordance with the above hypothesis, the mixing length, l, is independent of the magnitude of velocity, being a function of the velocity distribution only. The mixing length becomes a purely local function as already required earlier, and the constant $\varkappa$ in eqn. (19.21) can only be determined empirically. It is a universal dimensionless constant which must have the same value for all turbulent flows, provided that the assumptions made previously are satisfied (parallel flow).

The turbulent shearing stress, τ, is determined by the temporal average of $\varrho \cdot (\partial\psi/\partial x) \cdot (\partial\psi/\partial y)$ which, in accordance with eqn. (19.19), is proportional to $\varrho\,(B\,l)^2/l^2 = \varrho\,B^2$ and, in accordance with eqn. (19.20), to $\varrho\,l^2\,(\mathrm{d}\bar{u}/\mathrm{d}y)^2$. Consequently von Kármán's similarity hypothesis gives the following expression for turbulent shearing stress:

$$\tau = \varrho\,l^2 \left|\frac{\mathrm{d}\bar{u}}{\mathrm{d}y}\right| \frac{\mathrm{d}\bar{u}}{\mathrm{d}y}\,, \tag{19.22}$$

which is identical with the one derived from Prandtl's mixing length theory, eqn. (19.6). In addition, the present argument leads to the result that the velocity scale, B, is proportional to the friction velocity v_* from eqn. (19.16), as already stated at the beginning of this section. That this is so, follows from the fact that $\tau \sim \varrho\,B^2$, i. e. $B \sim \sqrt{\tau/\varrho}$.

Introducing finally, eqn. (19.21) into eqn. (19.22), we find that the turbulent shearing stress is

$$\tau = \varrho\,\varkappa^2\,\frac{(\mathrm{d}\bar{u}/\mathrm{d}y)^4}{(\mathrm{d}^2\bar{u}/\mathrm{d}y^2)^2}\,. \tag{19.23}$$

A. Betz [4] gave a very lucid derivation of eqn. (19.21). A rigorous deduction of von Kármán's similarity rule was given by G. Hamel [7]. A remark concerning eqn. (19.23) made by O. Bjorgum [5] may also be of interest. In recent times von Kármán's hypothesis has been extended to include compressible turbulent flows too, [11].

f. Universal velocity distribution law

Both von Kármán's law of turbulent friction, eqn. (19.23), and Prandtl's law, eqn. (19.6), are easily applied to the problem of finding the velocity distribution in a rectangular channel. Since this universal law is of fundamental importance for the considerations in the succeeding chapters, and since it is applicable to circular channels as well, we shall devote a little space to its derivation.

The channel will be assumed to have a width $2\,h$ and the x-axis will be placed along its centre-line, the co-ordinate y being measured from the latter. We shall assume a constant pressure gradient along the axis, putting $\partial\bar{p}/\partial x = C$. Since $-\,\partial\bar{p}/\partial x + \partial\tau/\partial y = 0$, the shearing stress is a linear function of the width of the channel, i. e.

$$\tau = \tau_0\,\frac{y}{h}\,, \tag{19.24}$$

where τ_0 denotes the stress at the wall.

1. Von Kármán's velocity distribution law. Applying von Kármán's similarity rule, eqn. (19.23), to eqn. (19.24), we obtain

$$\frac{\tau_0}{\varrho}\,\frac{y}{h} = \varkappa^2\,\frac{(\mathrm{d}\bar{u}/\mathrm{d}y)^4}{(\mathrm{d}^2\bar{u}/\mathrm{d}y^2)^2}\,.$$

Integrating twice and determining the constants of integration from the condition that $\overline{u} = \overline{u}_{max}$ at $y = 0$, we have

$$\overline{u} = \overline{u}_{max} + \frac{1}{\varkappa}\sqrt{\frac{\tau_0}{\varrho}}\left\{\ln\left[1-\sqrt{\frac{y}{h}}\right] + \sqrt{\frac{y}{h}}\right\}.$$

Introducing the frictional velocity at the wall, $v_{*0} = \sqrt{\tau_0/\varrho}$, we can rewrite the last equation in dimensionless form

$$\frac{\bar{u}_{max} - \bar{u}}{v_{*0}} = -\frac{1}{\varkappa}\left\{\ln\left[1-\sqrt{\frac{y}{h}}\right] + \sqrt{\frac{y}{h}}\right\}; (y = \text{distance from centre-line}). \quad (19.25)$$

This is the form in which the universal velocity distribution law was deduced by Th. von Kármán. It is shown as curve (2) in Fig. 19.2. The predicted velocity distribution curve has a kink near the centre-line of the channel which is due to the fact that the requirement of similarity cannot be satisfied here, because, in accordance with eqn. (19.21), the mixing length becomes equal to zero at the centre. At the wall, for $y = h$, eqn. (19.25) leads to an infinitely large velocity which is explained by the fact that molecular friction has been neglected in comparison with the apparent, turbulent friction. This assumption breaks down in the neighbourhood of the wall where the turbulent boundary layer goes over into the laminar sublayer. We are thus led to additional considerations which will be given later. In what follows we shall, therefore, exclude from consideration a small region near the centre-line and a small region near the wall. It is particularly remarkable that the universal velocity distribution law in its form given by eqn. (19.25) does not contain either the roughness or the Reynolds number explicitly†. The velocity distribution law in eqn. (19.25) can be expressed in words as follows: The velocity distribution curves for a rectangular channel can be made to coincide if the difference $\overline{u}_{max} - \overline{u}$ is made dimensionless with the aid of the friction velocity at the wall, v_{*0}, and plotted against y/h. This result, which turns out to be valid for circular pipes as well, will be compared with experimental measurements in Chap. XX.

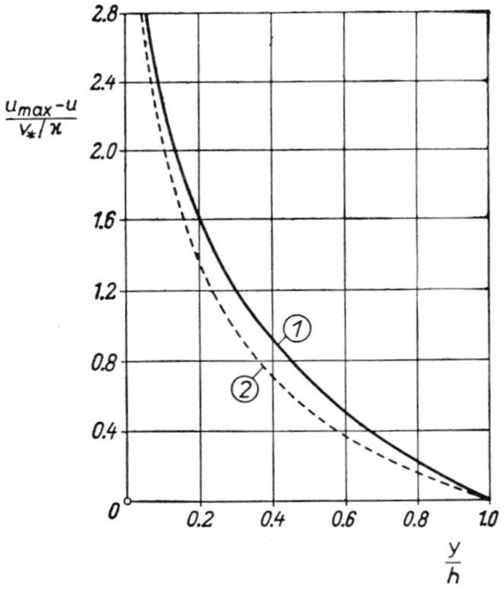

Fig. 19.2. Universal velocity distribution law for turbulent channel flow after von Kármán and Prandtl [9,12]

Curve (1) corresponds to eqn. (19.28); Curve (2) corresponds to eqn. (19.25). y — distance from wall

2. Velocity distribution from Prandtl's theory. A similar velocity distribution law can also be deduced from Prandtl's hypothesis for the turbulent shearing stress, eqn. (19.6). In the process of deriving the relevant expression we shall gain more

† They are, of course, contained implicitly in the wall stress τ_0.

insight into the conditions which prevail in the immediate neighbourhood of the wall and which we were forced to exclude from the preceding argument. We shall consider a turbulent stream along a smooth flat wall and we shall denote the distance from the wall by the symbol y, with $\overline{u}(y)$ denoting the velocity. In the neighbourhood of the wall we shall assume proportionality between mixing length and wall distance, so that

$$l = \varkappa \cdot y \,. \tag{19.26}$$

Here $\varkappa$ denotes a dimensionless constant which must be deduced from experiment. This assumption is reasonable, because the turbulent shearing stress at the wall is zero owing to the disappearance of the fluctuations. Hence, according to Prandtl's assumption, the turbulent shearing stress becomes

$$\tau = \varrho\, \varkappa^2\, y^2 \left(\frac{\mathrm{d}\bar{u}}{\mathrm{d}y}\right)^2 .$$

At this stage Prandtl introduced an additional, far-reaching assumption, namely that the shearing stress remains constant, i. e. that $\tau = \tau_0$, where τ_0 denotes the shearing stress at the wall. Introducing once more the friction velocity

$$v_{*0} = \sqrt{\frac{\tau_0}{\varrho}}$$

we obtain

$$v_{*0}^{\,2} = \varkappa^2\, y^2 \left(\frac{\mathrm{d}\bar{u}}{\mathrm{d}y}\right)^2$$

or

$$\frac{\mathrm{d}\bar{u}}{\mathrm{d}y} = \frac{v_{*0}}{\varkappa\, y} \,.$$

On integrating we have

$$\overline{u} = \frac{v_{*0}}{\varkappa} \ln y + C \,. \tag{19.27}$$

Here the constant of integration, C, must be determined from the condition at the wall and serves to fit the turbulent velocity distribution to that in the laminar sublayer. However, even without determining C it is possible to deduce from eqn. (19.27) a law analogous to that in eqn. (19.25). In spite of the fact that eqn. (19.27) is valid only in the neighbourhood of the wall, because of the assumption that $\tau =$ const., we shall attempt to use it for the whole region, i. e. up to $y = h$. Since at $y = h$ we have $\overline{u} = \overline{u}_{max}$, we obtain

$$\overline{u}_{max} = \frac{v_{*0}}{\varkappa} \ln h + C \,,$$

and hence, by forming the velocity difference, we deduce

$$\frac{\bar{u}_{max} - \bar{u}}{v_{*0}} = \frac{1}{\varkappa} \ln \frac{h}{y} \,; \quad (y = \text{distance from wall}) \,. \tag{19.28}$$

This universal velocity distribution law due to Prandtl is shown plotted as curve (1) in Fig. 19.2. In the preceding argument we succeeded in deriving a universal velocity distribution law from Prandtl's law of friction in complete analogy with that in eqn. (19.25), which was obtained from von Kármán's similarity rule. The only difference is in the form of the functions of y/h which appear on the right-hand side of eqns. (19.25) and (19.28) respectively. On reflexion this will not appear incomprehensible, if we take into account the difference in the assumptions concerning the shearing stress. Von Kármán assumed a linear shearing stress distribution, the mixing length being $l \sim \bar{u}'/\bar{u}''$. On the other hand, Prandtl assumed a constant shearing stress and $l \sim y$. Fig. 19.2 contains a comparison between these two laws. A further comparison with experiment is deferred to Chap. XX.

It may be worth noting in passing that it is possible to obtain the simple result that $l = \varkappa y$ from the velocity distribution law (19.27), together with von Kármán's equation for mixing length. This may be easily verified by the reader. Finally, it should be noted that the preceding argument proves that the coefficients $\varkappa$ in eqns. (19.26) and (19.21) are identical.

We shall now revert to the problem of determining the constant of integration, C, in eqn. (19.27). As already mentioned, the constant should be determined from the condition that the turbulent velocity distribution must join the laminar velocity distribution in the immediate neighbourhood of the wall where the laminar and turbulent shearing stresses are of the same order of magnitude. We determine the constant of integration C from the condition that $\bar{u} = 0$ at a certain distance y_0 from the wall. In this manner

$$\bar{u} = \frac{v_{*0}}{\varkappa} (\ln y - \ln y_0) \,. \tag{19.29}$$

The distance y_0 is of the order of magnitude of the thickness of the laminar sub-layer. Using a dimensional argument we find that this distance y_0 is proportional to the ratio ν/v_{*0} of the kinematic viscosity, ν, and the friction velocity, v_{*0}, as its dimension is that of a length. We may thus put

$$y_0 = \beta \frac{\nu}{v_{*0}} \,, \tag{19.30}$$

where β denotes a dimensionless constant. Substituting into eqn. (19.29) we obtain

$$\frac{\bar{u}}{v_{*0}} = \frac{1}{\varkappa} \left(\ln \frac{y\, v_{*0}}{\nu} - \ln \beta \right) , \tag{19.29a}$$

which is the dimensionless, logarithmic, universal velocity distribution law, and asserts that the velocity, referred to the friction velocity v_{*0}, is a function of the dimensionless wall distance, $y\, v_{*0}/\nu$. The latter is a kind of Reynolds number based on the wall distance, y, and on the friction velocity at the wall. Equation (19.29a) contains the two empirical constants, $\varkappa$ and β. In accordance with the previous reasoning we may expect that the constant $\varkappa$ is independent of the nature of the wall (whether smooth or rough) and that it is, moreover, a universal constant of turbulent flow. Experimental results, to be discussed in greater detail in the succeeding chapter, give a value of $\varkappa = 0{\cdot}4$. The second constant, β, depends on the nature of the wall surface; relevant numerical values will be given in Chap. XX.

Introducing the abbreviations

$$\frac{\bar{u}}{v_{*0}} = \phi\,, \tag{19.31}$$

$$\frac{y\, v_{*0}}{\nu} = \eta \tag{19.32}$$

we can shorten eqn. (19.29a) to read

$$\phi(\eta) = A_1 \ln \eta + D_1\,, \tag{19.33}$$

where

$$A_1 = \frac{1}{\varkappa} = 2{\cdot}5\,; \qquad D_1 = -\frac{1}{\varkappa} \ln \beta\,. \tag{19.34}$$

The universal velocity distribution law, eqn. (19.33), which has now been derived for the case of a flat wall (rectangular channel) retains its fundamental importance for flows through circular pipes, as will be seen in the next chapter. We may now state in anticipation that it leads to good agreement with experiment.

In concluding this chapter it may be worth stressing once again that the two universal velocity distribution laws in eqns. (19.27) and (19.33) were obtained for turbulent flow, and took into account, apart from the small sub-layer near the wall, only turbulent shearing stresses, and it should be realized that such an assumption is satisfied at large Reynolds numbers only. Consequently the velocity distribution law, particularly that in eqn. (19.33), must be regarded as an asymptotic law applicable to very large Reynolds numbers. For smaller Reynolds numbers, when laminar friction exerts some influence outside the very thin sub-layer, experiment leads to a power law of the form

$$\phi(\eta) = C\, \eta^n \tag{19.35}$$

or

$$\frac{\bar{u}}{v_{*0}} = C \left(\frac{y\, v_{*0}}{\nu}\right)^n,$$

where the exponent n is approximately equal to $\frac{1}{7}$, but varies somewhat with the Reynolds number. This point will also be taken up again in the succeeding chapter.

The case of so-called Couette flow between two parallel flat plates which are displaced relative to each other (Fig. 1.1) constitutes a very simple example of a flow in which the shearing stress remains constant. The shearing stress τ remains rigorously constant in turbulent as well as in laminar flow, and is equal to that at the wall, τ_0. H. Reichardt [17] carried out an extensive investigation of this case; some of his results can be inferred from Fig. 19.3 which shows several velocity profiles observed in Couette flow. The flow remains laminar as long as the Reynolds number $\mathsf{R} < 1500$ and the velocity distribution is then linear to a good degree of approximation. When the Reynolds number R exceeds the value 1500 the flow is turbulent. The turbulent velocity profiles are very flat near the centre and become very steep near the walls. A profile of this kind is to be excepted in turbulent flow if it is remembered that the shearing stress consists of a laminar contribution

$$\tau_l = \mu \left(\frac{\mathrm{d}u}{\mathrm{d}y}\right)$$

and a turbulent contribution

$$\tau_t = A_\tau \left(\frac{d\bar{u}}{dy}\right)$$

due to turbulent mixing. Hence

$$\tau = \tau_0 = (\mu + A_\tau)\,\frac{d\bar{u}}{dy}\,,$$

where A_τ denotes the mixing coefficient defined in eqn. (19.1). In this manner the velocity gradient turns out to be proportional to $1/(\mu + A)$. Since A varies from zero at the wall to its maximum in the centre of the channel, the velocity profile must become steep at the wall and flat at the centre, as confirmed by the plots in Fig. 19.3. The turbulent mixing coefficient increases with an increasing Reynolds number and the curvature of the velocity profile becomes, correspondingly, more pronounced.

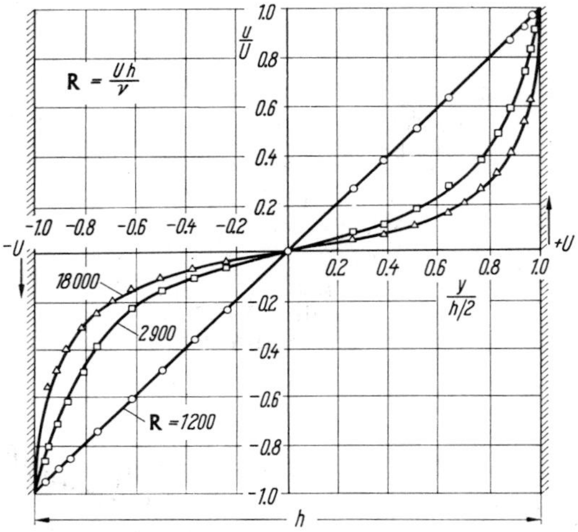

Fig. 19.3. Velocity profiles in parallel Couette flow between two parallel plates moving in opposite directions, after H. Reichardt [17]

At R = 1200 the flow is laminar; at R = 2900 and 18,000 the flow is turbulent

g. Heat transfer in turbulent flow†

The oscillatory motion in a turbulent stream causes a vigorous exchange of momentum between layers moving at different velocities and leads to a large value of apparent viscosity. This, however, is not the only effect caused by turbulent mixing. In addition to exchanging momentum, turbulent mixing enhances the transfer of heat and mass in flow fields with non-uniform distributions of temperature and concentration. It follows, consequently, that the phenomena of heat and momentum transfer, and so the values of the rate of heat transfer and skin friction at the wall are most closely related to each other. This close relation between the phenomena of momentum and heat transfer was first noticed by O. Reynolds [17b] and is now known under the name of the *Reynolds analogy*. The existence of

† The Author is indebted to Dr. K. Gersten for the present section.

this analogy allows us to derive relations for heat transfer from the known relations for skin friction in turbulent flow.

It will be recalled that the shearing stress τ in a turbulent stream is composed of a laminar contribution which corresponds to the exchange of momentum on a molecular scale, and of a turbulent contribution which corresponds to the exchange of momentum caused by the turbulent oscillations. The same is true also of the heat flux q, and we can write

$$\left.\begin{aligned} \tau &= (\mu + A_\tau)\,\frac{\mathrm{d}\bar{u}}{\mathrm{d}y} \\ q &= -\,c_p\,g\left(\frac{k}{c_p\,g} + A_q\right)\frac{\mathrm{d}\bar{T}}{\mathrm{d}y}\,. \end{aligned}\right\} \tag{19.36}$$

Here A_τ and A_q denote the eddy coefficients for momentum and heat intrcduced in Sec. XIXa. They have the same physical dimension as viscosity, namely $\mathrm{FL^{-2}T}$, and can be combined into a turbulent, dimensionless Prandtl number

$$\mathsf{P}_t = \frac{A_\tau}{A_q} \tag{19.37}$$

which is analogous to the usual Prandtl number $\mathsf{P} = g\,c_p\,\mu/k$. With the aid of the former, we can rewrite equations (19.36) to read

$$\left.\begin{aligned} \tau &= (\mu + A_\tau)\,\frac{\mathrm{d}\bar{u}}{\mathrm{d}y} \\ \frac{q}{c_p\,g} &= -\left(\frac{\mu}{\mathsf{P}} + \frac{A_\tau}{\mathsf{P}_t}\right)\frac{\mathrm{d}\bar{T}}{\mathrm{d}y}\,. \end{aligned}\right\} \tag{19.38}$$

It was shown in Sec. XIXa. that the equations of motion for the temporal mean values in turbulent flow can be obtained from those valid in laminar flow if the viscosity μ is replaced by $(\mu + A_\tau)$ and if the ratio $k/c_p\,g$ is replaced by $(k/c_p\,g + A_q)$. Further, it was shown in Chap. XIV that the velocity and temperature profiles are identical in the case of laminar flow past a flat plate at zero indicence on condition that frictional heat is neglected and that the Prandtl number is equal to unity. The same can be asserted in relation to turbulent flow, on condition that $\mathsf{P}_t = 1$ as well as $\mathsf{P} = 1$. This implies physically that it is assumed that the same mechanism causes the exchange of momentum as well as of heat. Since the velocity and temperature profiles are identical, we can then write, in analogy with equation (14.37d), that

$$q(x) = \frac{k}{\mu}\,\frac{T_w - T_\infty}{T_w}\,\tau_0(x)\,. \tag{19.39}$$

The preceding equation can be easily re-arranged to the form

$$\mathsf{N}_x = \tfrac{1}{2}\,\mathsf{R}_x\,c_f' \qquad \text{(Reynolds, } \mathsf{P} = \mathsf{P}_t = 1\text{)} \tag{19.40}$$

described earlier as the Reynolds analogy. It is seen that the relation of direct proportionality between the Nusselt number and the coefficient of skin friction which was derived in Chapter XIV for the case of laminar flow past a flat plate at zero incidence, (*cf.* equation (14.38a) remains valid in the turbulent case. Equation (19.40) retains its validity in the presence of compressibility, just as was the case with laminar flow, on condition that the Nusselt number is now formed with the temperature difference $T_w - T_a$.

As already mentioned before, the principal difficulty in studying turbulent boundary layers and turbulent heat transfer problems stems from the fact that the eddy coefficients A_τ and A_q are not properties of the fluid, unlike the viscosity μ or the thermal conductivity k, but that they depend on the distance from the wall inside the boundary layer. At a sufficiently large distance from the wall they assume values which are many times larger than the molecular coefficients μ and k, so much so, in fact, that in most cases the latter can be neglected with respect to the former. By contrast, in the immediate neighbourhood of the wall, i. e. in the laminar sub-layer, the eddy coefficients vanish because in it turbulent fluctuations and hence turbulent mixing are no longer possible. Nevertheless, the rate of heat transfer between the stream and the wall depends precisely on the phenomena in the laminar sub-layer and so on the molecular coefficients μ and k. It is fortunate that eqn. (19.40) remains valid throughout, regardless of the existence of a laminar sub-layer, because when $\mathsf{P} = 1$, as shown in Section XIVg, the velocity and temperature distribution in the laminar sub-layer remain identical. The assumption that $\mathsf{P}_t = 1$ in turbulent boundary layers corresponds to reality with a high degree of precision, as is known from the measurements performed by H. Ludwieg [11a]; by contrast, the Prandtl number in the laminar sub-layer can differ appreciably from unity, as is the case, for example, with liquids. When this is the case, eqn. (19.40) loses its validity. Extensions of the Reynolds analogy to cases when $\mathsf{P} \neq 1$ have been formulated by many authors, among them L. Prandtl [14a], G. I. Taylor [19a] and Th. von Kármán [10a].

L. Prandtl assumed that $\mathsf{P}_t = 1$ and divided the boundary layer into two zones: the laminar sublayer in which the eddy coefficients vanish, and the turbulent, external boundary layer, in which the molecular coefficients μ and k can be neglected. Under these assumptions, eqn. (19.36) written for the laminar sub-layer will assume the form

$$\frac{q}{\tau} = -\frac{k}{\mu}\frac{\mathrm{d}\overline{T}}{\mathrm{d}\bar{u}}$$

whereas in the turbulent layer it will lead to

$$\frac{q}{\tau} = -c_p\, g\, \frac{\mathrm{d}\overline{T}}{\mathrm{d}\bar{u}}\,.$$

Remembering that at the wall $\overline{u} = 0$, assuming that the temperature at the wall, is constant and equal to T_w, and denoting the velocity and temperature, respectively, at the outer edge of the laminar sub-layer by $\overline{u}_l$ and T_l, and in the free stream by $\overline{U}_\infty$, T_∞, Prandtl introduced the assumption that the ratio q/τ remains constant across the whole width of the boundary layer†. Integration over the laminar sub-layer will then lead to

$$\frac{q}{\tau} = -\frac{k}{\mu}\frac{T_l - T_w}{\bar{u}_l} = -\frac{k}{\mu\,\bar{U}_\infty} \cdot \frac{T_l - T_w}{\left(\frac{\bar{u}_l}{\bar{U}_\infty}\right)} . \qquad (19.41)$$

Similarly, integration over the turbulent zone will lead to

$$\frac{q}{\tau} = -c_p\, g\, \frac{T_l - T_\infty}{\bar{u}_l - \bar{U}_\infty} . \qquad (19.41\,\text{a})$$

Equating the two right-hand sides of equation (19.41) and (19.41 a), we obtain

$$\mathsf{P}\,(T_w - T_\infty) = -\frac{\bar{U}_\infty}{\bar{u}_l}\left[1 + \frac{\bar{u}_l}{\bar{U}_\infty}(\mathsf{P}-1)\right](T_l - T_w) .$$

Hence, the local coefficient of heat transfer becomes

$$\alpha = \frac{q}{T_w - T_\infty} = -\frac{\mathsf{P}}{1 + \frac{\bar{u}_l}{\bar{U}_\infty}(\mathsf{P}-1)} \cdot \frac{q\,\frac{\bar{u}_l}{\bar{U}_\infty}}{T_l - T_w} .$$

On introducing eqn. (19.41) we have

$$\alpha = \frac{1}{1 + \frac{\bar{u}_l}{\bar{U}_\infty}(\mathsf{P}-1)} \cdot \frac{g\, c_p\, \tau}{\bar{U}_\infty} .$$

We can express this result in terms of the Nusselt number and are led in this way to the extension of the Reynolds analogy which was derived independently by L. Prandtl and G. I. Taylor:

$$\mathsf{N}_x = \frac{\tfrac{1}{2} c_f{}'\, \mathsf{R}_x\, \mathsf{P}}{1 + \left(\frac{\bar{u}_l}{\bar{U}_\infty}\right)(\mathsf{P}-1)} \qquad (\text{Prandtl-Taylor, } \mathsf{P}_t = 1). \qquad (19.42)$$

In order to apply the preceding equation to particular cases it is still necessary to make a suitable assumption about the ratio of the mean velocity at the outer

† This condition is satisfied exactly for the flat plate because then

$$\bar{u}/\bar{U}_\infty = (T - T_w)/(T_\infty - T_w).$$

edge of the laminar sub-layer to that in the free stream †. In the particular case when $\mathsf{P} = 1$, the Prandtl-Taylor equation (19.42) reduces to Reynolds' equation (19.40).

In deriving the Prandtl-Taylor equation (19.42) it was supposed that the boundary layer could be sharply divided into a turbulent layer and a laminar sub-layer. In actual fact one merges into the other in a continuous way and it is possible to discern the existence of an intermediate, or buffer layer in which the magnitudes of the molecular and turbulent exchange are comparable. Th. von Kármán [10a] subdivided the boundary layer into three zones and derived a similar formula for the relation between the coefficients of heat transfer and skin friction. This is of the form

$$\mathsf{N}_x = \frac{\frac{1}{2}\,\mathsf{R}_x\,\mathsf{P}\,c_f'}{1 + 5\sqrt{\frac{1}{2}c_f'}\,\{(\mathsf{P}-1) + \ln[1 + \frac{5}{6}(\mathsf{P}-1)]\}} \qquad (\text{von Kármán}, \ \mathsf{P}_t = 1)\,. \quad (19.43)$$

Von Kármán's equation (19.43) also reduces to Reynolds' equation (19.40) in the special case when $\mathsf{P} = 1$‡. The relation between the local Nusselt number N_x and the Reynolds number R_x is seen plotted in Fig. 19.4 for the case of a flat plate and for three values of the Prandtl number, namely $\mathsf{P} = 10$, 1 and 0·01. The curves (b) and (c) represent, respectively, the plots from equations (19.42) and (19.43) for $\mathsf{P}_t = 1$. Fig. 19.5 shows the dependence of the local Nusselt number on the Prandtl number according to the analogy relations of Reynolds, Prandtl, and v. Kármán.

† In the case of turbulent flow in a pipe, the ratio of the velocity at the outer edge of the laminar sub-layer to the velocity $\overline{U}$ on the axis is given by

$$\bar{u}_l/\overline{U} = 5\sqrt{\tau/\varrho\,\overline{U}^2} = 5\sqrt{\tfrac{1}{2}c_f'}\,,$$

as shown in Chap. XX, eqn. (20.15). With this approximation Prandtl's equation becomes

$$\mathsf{N}_x = \frac{\frac{1}{2}\,\mathsf{R}_x\,\mathsf{P}\,c_f'}{1 + 5\sqrt{\frac{1}{2}c_f'}\,(\mathsf{P}-1)}\,.$$

Referring c_f' to the mean pipe velocity $\bar{u}$, we would have

$$\frac{\bar{u}_l}{\bar{u}} = 5\sqrt{\frac{1}{2}\,c_f'}\,.$$

‡ Many authors prefer to express the coefficient of heat transfer in the form of the so-called Stanton number

$$\mathsf{S}_x = \frac{\mathsf{N}_x}{\mathsf{R}_x\,\mathsf{P}} = \frac{\alpha}{\varrho\,g\,c_p\,\overline{U}_\infty}\,.$$

Reynolds' analogy reduces itself then to the very simple expression

$$\mathsf{S}_x = \tfrac{1}{2}\,c_f'\,.$$

The remaining equations can be similarly transformed.

It can be seen, that near $\mathsf{P} = 1$ the curves can be approximated with good accuracy by the function $\mathsf{P}^{-2/3}$. Hence we get the approximate formula

$$\mathsf{N}_x = \tfrac{1}{2}\, c_f'\, \mathsf{P}^{1/3}\, \mathsf{R}_x\,. \qquad (19.43\,\text{a})$$

Introducing the value $\frac{1}{2} c_f' = 0{\cdot}0296\ \mathsf{R}^{-0\cdot 2}$ for a flat plate as given in Chapter XXI, eqn. (21.12), we obtain

$$\mathsf{N}_x = 0{\cdot}0296\ \sqrt[3]{\mathsf{P}}\ \mathsf{R}_x^{0\cdot 8} \qquad (19.43\,\text{b})$$

and especially for air ($\mathsf{P} = 0{\cdot}7$)

$$\mathsf{N}_x = 0{\cdot}0263\ \mathsf{R}_x^{0\cdot 8} \quad (\text{flat plate, } \mathsf{P} = 0{\cdot}7)\,. \qquad (19.43\,\text{c})$$

From the more accurate formula of Prandtl, eqn. (19.42), and von Kármán, eqn. (19.43), we obtain

$$\mathsf{N}_x = 0{\cdot}0236\ \mathsf{R}_x^{0\cdot 8} \quad (\text{Prandtl-Taylor, flat plate, } \mathsf{P} = 0{\cdot}7) \qquad (19.43\,\text{d})$$

and

$$\mathsf{N}_x = 0{\cdot}0241\ \mathsf{R}_x^{0\cdot 8} \quad (\text{von Kármán, flat plate, } \mathsf{P} = 0{\cdot}7). \qquad (19.43\,\text{e})$$

The analogy relations between the rate of heat transfer and skin friction in turbulent flow are of great practical importance because their application is not restricted to flows past flat plates. They can be used for arbitrary turbulent flows and thus enjoy much more general applicability. The latter statement has been confirmed by numerous measurements.

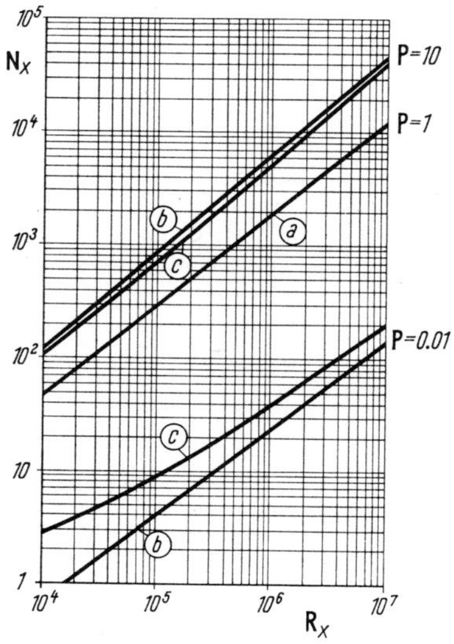

Fig. 19.4. Variation of Nusselt number with Reynolds number at different Prandtl numbers in the case of turbulent heat transfer on a flat plate (Reynolds analogy)

(a) Reynolds, eqn. (19.40)
(b) L. Prandtl and G. I. Taylor, eqn. (19.42)
(c) Th. von Kármán, eqn. (19.43)

It has been assumed that $\mathsf{P}_t = 1$,

$c_f' = 0{\cdot}0592\ \mathsf{R}_x^{-0\cdot 2}$, eqn, (21.12)

$$\frac{\bar{u}_l}{\bar{U}_\infty} = 5 \sqrt{\frac{1}{2} c_f'}$$

The equations under consideration have turned out to be valid when applied to the calculation of heat transfer from slender bodies in parallel streams, that is in cases when the pressure gradients outside the bodies are not unduly large. In particular, C. C. Pappas [11 d] and A. Seiff [18 a] were able to show that the analogy carries over to compressible flows when it remains independent of the Mach number. All of the forms of the Reynolds analogy quoted earlier remain valid when they are applied to internal flows in circular pipes. It is, furthermore, possible to replace the current length, x, in the expression for the Nusselt and Reynolds numbers by the diameter D of the pipe, and the velocity and temperature of the external stream, respectively, can be replaced by the mean velocity and the mean temperature of the fluid in the pipe. W. Nunner [11 c] succeeded in extending the validity of the analogy to rough pipes. Instead of equation (19.42), Nunner obtained the equation

$$\mathsf{N}_D = \frac{\frac{1}{2}\,\mathsf{R}_D\,\mathsf{P}\,c_f'}{\left(\frac{\bar{u}_l}{\bar{u}}\right)\left(\frac{c_f'}{c_{fo}'}\,\mathsf{P}-1\right)} \qquad (\text{Nunner},\ \mathsf{P}=1)\,, \tag{19.44}$$

where c_f'/c_{fo}' denotes the ratio of the coefficients of skin friction outside a rough and a smooth wall, respectively †. The ratio $\overline{u}_l/\overline{u}$ is most often replaced by its empirical value given by E. Hofmann [8 b].

$$\frac{\bar{u}_l}{\bar{u}} = 1{\cdot}5\ \mathsf{R}^{-1/8}\ \mathsf{P}^{-1/6}\,. \tag{19.45}$$

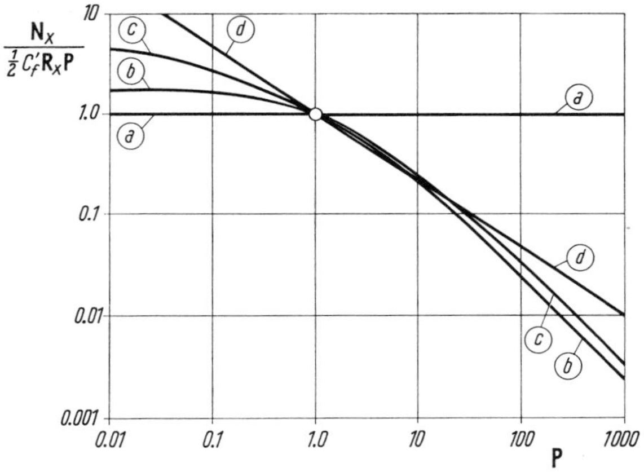

Fig. 19.5. Dependence of heat transfer rate on Prandtl number according to different analogic relations

(a) Reynolds, eqn. (19.40)
(b) Prandtl-Taylor, eqn. 19.42)
(c) v. Kármán, eqn. (19.43)
(d) approximation, eqn. (19.43 a)

In all preceding derivations we have assumed that the turbulent Prandtl number $\mathsf{P}_t = 1$. In other words, it has been assumed that the eddy coefficients for momentum and thermal energy transfer are equal. It is, however, known from measurements that the value of this ratio differs from unity. M. W. Rubesin [17 c]

† It will be shown in eqn. (20.4) (see also equations preceding eqn. (21.10)) that the skin friction coefficent c_f' is related to the dimensionless coefficient of resistance in a pipe, λ, used in hydraulics by the simple equation

$$c_f' = \tfrac{1}{4}\,\lambda\,.$$

and E. R. van Driest [8a] modified the equations due to Prandtl-Taylor and von Kármán to take this circumstance into account. They obtained

$$\mathsf{N}_x = \frac{\frac{1}{2}\frac{\mathsf{P}}{\mathsf{P}_t}\mathsf{R}_x c_f'}{1 + \frac{\bar{u}_l}{\bar{U}_\infty}\left(\frac{\mathsf{P}}{\mathsf{P}_t} - 1\right)} \qquad \text{(Rubesin)} \qquad (19.46)$$

and

$$\mathsf{N}_x = \frac{\frac{1}{2}\frac{\mathsf{P}}{\mathsf{P}_t}\mathsf{R}_x c_f'}{1 + 5\sqrt{\frac{1}{2}c_f'}\left\{\left(\frac{\mathsf{P}}{\mathsf{P}_t} - 1\right) + \ln\left[1 + \frac{5}{6}\left(\frac{\mathsf{P}}{\mathsf{P}_t} - 1\right)\right]\right\}} \,. \qquad \text{(van Driest)} \qquad (19.47)$$

Careful measurements carried out by H. Ludwieg [11a] demonstrated that the ratio $A_q/A_\tau = 1/\mathsf{P}_t$ varies not only across the boundary layer but also in a transverse direction. The variation of this quantity in turbulent flow in a cross-section of a pipe is seen plotted in Fig. 19.6; the values indicated were measured by H. Ludwieg. Close to the wall, the curve begins with a value close to unity and ascends away from it to a value of about 1·5, always remaining independent of the Mach number. A. Fage and V. M. Falkner [19] made measurements in the wake of a cylinder, and H. Reichardt [17a] made measurements in a free jet which yielded values as high as $A_q/A_\tau = 2$. It follows that owing to the influence of the wall, the ratio A_q/A_τ is smaller near it than in so-called free turbulence. It is plausible to suppose, therefore, that at a wall $A_q/A_\tau = 1$ (or $= 1{\cdot}08$ according to H. Ludwieg) increasing to $A_q/A_\tau = 2$ far away from it. In practice, it is advisable to use the value $A_q/A_\tau = 1$ or, even perhaps a suitable mean value, say $A_q/A_\tau = 1{\cdot}3$ (that is $\mathsf{P}_t = 0{\cdot}78$).

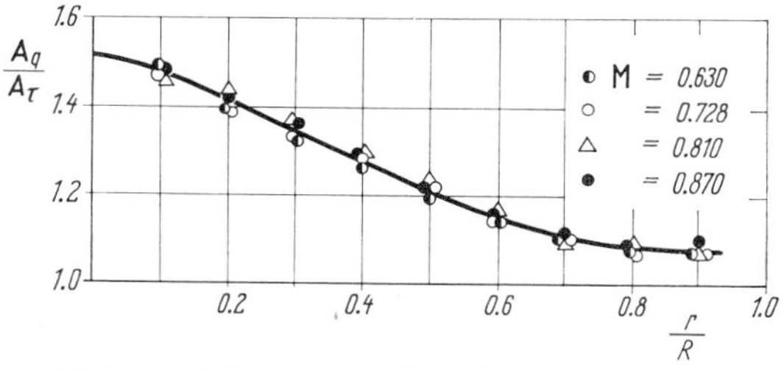

Fig. 19.6. Variation of the ratio of eddy coefficients A_q/A_τ in turbulent flow along the radius of a pipe, after H. Ludwieg [11a]. Reynolds number $\mathsf{R} = 3{\cdot}2 \times 10^5$ to $3{\cdot}7 \times 10^5$

The relation between heat transfer and skin friction was utilized by H. Ludwieg [11b] to determine experimentally the shearing stress at a wall by measuring the heat transferred from a small element built into it. The element was heated to a temperature slightly exceeding that in the free stream. In this connection it should be remembered, as stated in Section XIVh, that the validity of this relation is strongly affected by the intensity of turbulence in the free stream in the presence of even small pressure gradients, at least outside laminar boundary layers. The effect exerted by the intensity of turbulence of the free stream outside a turbulent boundary layer has not yet been explored fully.

The analogy between the transfer of momentum and thermal energy in so-called free turbulence will be discussed in Sec. XXIIIe.

h. Further development of theoretical hypotheses

The calculation of turbulent flows on the basis of the different semi-empirical hypotheses discussed previously, and carried out in detail in the succeeding chapters, is not satisfactory insofar as it is still impossible to analyze different kinds of turbulent flow with the aid of the same hypothesis concerning turbulent friction. For example Prandtl's hypothesis on the mixing length, eqn. (19.6), fails completely in the case of so-called isotropic turbulence as it exists behind a screen of fine mesh, because in this case the velocity gradient of the basic flow is equal to zero everywhere. The hypotheses for the calculation of developed turbulent flow, discussed in Secs. XIXb and c, have been considerably extended by L. Prandtl [13] in an attempt to derive a universally valid system of equations (turbulent flow near wall, free turbulent flow, isotropic turbulence). L. Prandtl based this new development on the consideration of the kinetic energy of turbulent fluctuation, $E = \frac{1}{2}\,\varrho(u'^2 + v'^2 + w'^2)$, and calculated the change of the energy of the subsidiary motion with time, $\mathrm{D}E/\mathrm{D}t$, for a particle which moves with the basic stream. This is composed of three terms: of the decrease in energy due to internal friction in the motion of the lumps of fluid, of the transfer of energy from the basic motion to the subsidiary motion — this term being proportional to $(\mathrm{d}U/\mathrm{d}y)^2$ — and, finally, of the transfer of kinetic energy from the more turbulent to the less turbulent zones. The energy balance between these three terms leads to a differential equation for the energy of the turbulent subsidiary motion which must be added to the system of differential equations for the mean motion. L. Prandtl referred to it as to the first fundamental equation; it contained three free constants (each corresponding to one of the three terms above) to be determined empirically. A second equation relates the turbulent shearing stress with the velocity gradient of the mean flow and is analogous to the old mixing equation (19.6), but also contains the energy of the turbulent subsidiary motion. In the case of isotropic turbulence, such as exists behind a screen, only the first of the three energy terms has a non-zero value and, consequently, the turbulence is found to decay downstream. In the case of a rectangular channel all three terms differ from zero but the third term (transfer of kinetic energy from more to less turbulent regions) is significant only near the wall where, owing to the vigorous creation of new turbulence by wall friction, there exists a zone of particularly high turbulence (*cf.* Fig. 18.3), and near the centre, where no turbulence is created and where the flow is, therefore, much less turbulent. A preliminary determination of the constants from measurements on isotropic turbulence as well as on a rectangular and a circular channel led to satisfactory agreement as regards numerical values for different cases. A more searching verification of these new formulae is still outstanding.

Two theoretical papers by C. F. von Weizsaecker [20] and W. Heisenberg [8] are concerned with the spectral distribution of turbulent energy. We are not in a position to discuss them here, as well as additional and numerous English and American papers [1, 2, 10], in particular the books written by G. K. Batchelor [3] and J. O. Hinze [8c].

References

[1] G. K. Batchelor, Energy decay and self-preserving correlation functions in isotropic turbulence. Quarterly Applied Mathematics **6**, 97—116 (1948).

[2] G. K. Batchelor and A. A. Townsend, The nature of turbulent motion at large wave-numbers. Proc. Roy. Soc. London, A **199**, 238—255 (1949).

[3] G. K. Batchelor, The theory of homogeneous turbulence. Cambridge University Press (1953).

[4] A. Betz, Die von Kármánsche Ähnlichkeitsüberlegung für turbulente Vorgänge in physikalischer Auffassung. ZAMM **11**, 397 (1931).

[5] O. Bjorgum, On the steady turbulent flow along an infinitely long smooth and plane wall. Universitetet i Bergen, Arbok (1951). Naturvitenskapelig rekke No. 7.

[6] J. Boussinesq, Theory de l'ecoulement tourbillant. Mem. Pre. par. div. Sav. **XXIII**, Paris (1877).

[7] G. Hamel, Streifenmethode und Ähnlichkeitsbetrachtungen zur turbulenten Bewegung. Abhdlg. preuß. Akad. Wiss. math. naturwiss. Klasse, No. 8 (1943).

[8] W. Heisenberg, Zur statistischen Theorie der Turbulenz. Z. Phys. **124**, 628—657 (1948).

[8a] E. R. van Driest, The turbulent boundary layer with variable Prandtl number. Jahrb. 1954 der Wiss. Ges. f. Luftfahrt, 66. See also memorial volume "Fifty Years of Boundary Layer Research", pp. 257—271.

[8b] E. Hofmann, Der Wärmeübergang bei der Strömung im Rohr. Z. Ges. Kälte-Ind. **44** (1937), 99—107.

[8c] J. O. Hinze, Turbulence. An introduction to its mechanism and theory. McGraw-Hill. New York, 1959.

[9] Th. von Kármán, Mechanische Ähnlichkeit und Turbulenz. Nach. Ges. Wiss. Göttingen, Math. Phys. Klasse, 58 (1930) and Proc. 3rd. Intern. Congress Appl. Mech., Stockholm, Pt. I, 85 (1930); NACA TM 611, (1931).

[10] Th. von Kármán, Progress in the statistical theory of turbulence. Proc. Nat. Acad. Sci. Washington, **34**, 530—539 (1948).

[10a] Th. von Kármán, The analogy between fluid friction and heat transfer. Trans. ASME **61** (1939), 705—710.

[11] C. C. Lin and S. F. Shen, Studies of von Kármáns similarity theory and its extension to compressible flows. A similarity theory for turbulent boundary layer over a flat plate in compressible flow. NACA TN 2542 (1951); see also NACA TN 2543 (1951).

[11a] H. Ludwieg, Bestimmung des Verhältnisses der Austauschkoeffizienten für Wärme und Impuls bei turbulenten Grenzschichten. Zeitschr. f. Flugwiss. **4** (1956), 73—81.

[11b] H. Ludwieg, Ein Gerät zur Messung der Wandschubspannung turbulenter Reibungsschichten. Ing.-Arch. **17** (1949), 207—218.

[11c] W. Nunner, Wärmeübergang und Druckabfall in rauhen Rohren. VDI-Forschungsheft 455 (1956).

[11d] C. C. Pappas, Measurement of heat transfer in the turbulent boundary layer on a flat plate in supersonic flow and comparison with skin friction results. NACA TN 3222 (1954).

[12] L. Prandtl, Über die ausgebildete Turbulenz. ZAMM **5**, 136 (1925) and Proc. 2nd. Intern. Congr. Appl. Mech., Zürich 1926.

[13] L. Prandtl, Über ein neues Formelsystem der ausgebildeten Turbulenz. Nachr. Akad. Wiss. Göttingen 6—19 (1945).

[14] L. Prandtl, Bemerkungen zur Theorie der freien Turbulenz. ZAMM **22**, 241—243 (1942).

[14a] L. Prandtl, Eine Beziehung zwischen Wärmeaustausch und Strömungswiderstand der Flüssigkeiten. Phys. Zeitschr. 11 (1910), 1072—1078.

[15] H. Reichardt, Gesetzmäßigkeiten der freien Turbulenz. VDI-Forschungsheft 414, lst. ed., Berlin 1942; 2nd. ed., Berlin 1951.

[16] H. Reichardt, Die Wärmeübertragung in turbulenten Reibungsschichten. ZAMM **20**, 297 (1940); see also ZAMM **24**, 268 (1944); NACA TM 1047 (1943).

[17] H. Reichardt, Über die Geschwindigkeitsverteilung in einer geradlinigen turbulenten Couette-Strömung. ZAMM **36**, Sonderheft (special issue) pp. 26—29 (1956); see also Rep. No. 9 of the Max-Planck-Inst. für Strömungsforschung, Göttingen 1954.

[17a] H. Reichardt, Impuls- und Wärmeaustausch bei freier Turbulenz. ZAMM **24** (1944), 268—272.

[17b] O. Reynolds, On the extent and action of the heating surface for steam boilers. Proc. Manchester Lit. Phil. Soc. **14** (1874), 7—12.

[17c] M. W. Rubesin, A modified Reynolds analogy for the compressible turbulent boundary layer on a flat plate, NACA TN 2917 (1953).

[18] W. Schmidt, Der Massenaustausch in freier Luft und verwandte Erscheinungen, Hamburg 1925.

[18a] A. Seiff, Examination of the existing data on the heat transfer of turbulent boundary layers at supersonic speeds from the point of view of Reynolds' analogy. NACA TN 3284. (1954).

[19] G. I. Taylor, The transport of vorticity and heat through fluids in turbulent motion. Appendix by A. Fage and V. M. Faulkner, Proc. Roy. Soc. London, A **135** (1932), 685; see also Phil. Trans. A **215** (1915), 1.

[19a] G. I. Taylor, Conditions at the surface of a hot body exposed to the wind. ARC R & M. 272 (1919).

[20] C. F. v. Weizsaecker, Das Spektrum der Turbulenz bei großen Reynoldsschen Zahlen. Z. Phys. **124**, 614—627 (1948).

CHAPTER XX

Turbulent flow through pipes

a. Experimental results for smooth pipes

The case of turbulent flow through pipes was investigated very thoroughly in the past because of its great practical importance [17, 20, 32, 33, 41, 43, 44, 50, 51]†. Moreover, the results arrived at are important not only for pipe flow; they also contribute to the extension of our fundamental knowledge of turbulent flow in general. Methods of dealing with other turbulent flows, such as the flow along a flat plate or a streamline body, could be devised only on the basis of the detailed experimental results obtained with pipe flow.

When a fluid is allowed to enter a circular pipe from a large container, the velocity distribution in the cross-sections of the *inlet length* varies with the distance from the initial cross-section. In sections close to that at entrance the velocity distribution is nearly uniform. Further downstream the velocity distribution changes, owing to the influence of friction, until a fully developed velocity profile is attained at a given cross-section and remains constant downstream of it. The variation of the velocity profile in the inlet length of a pipe in *laminar* flow was described in Sec. XIIe (Fig. 12.14). Its length is approximately $l_I = 0{\cdot}03\, d \times \mathsf{R}$ so that for $\mathsf{R} = 5{,}000$ to $10{,}000$ it ranges from 150 to 300 pipe-diameters. The inlet length in *turbulent* flow is considerably shorter than in laminar flow. According to the measurements performed by H. Kirsten [22] its length is about 50 to 100 diameters, but J. Nikuradse determined that the fully formed velocity profile exists already after an inlet length of 25 to 40 diameters; the reader may also consult ref. [54].

In what follows we shall concern ourselves mainly with fully developed turbulent flow through a straight pipe of circular cross-section. The radial co-cordinate measured outwards from the axis will be denoted by y' and we shall consider a fluid cylinder of length L and radius y' in *fully developed* turbulent flow. The cylinder is not acted upon by any inertia forces, so that in accordance with eqn. (1.9) we can write down the condition of equilibrium between the force due to shearing stress τ on the circumference, and the pressure difference $p_1 - p_2$‡ on the end faces in the form

$$\tau = \frac{p_1 - p_2}{L} \frac{y'}{2}\,, \tag{20.1}$$

† The following description is largely based on the experimental results reported by J. Nikuradse [29, 30].

‡ From this point onwards we shall omit the bar above the symbol to denote time-averages as confusion with time-dependent quantities is no longer possible.

the relation being equally valid for laminar and turbulent motion. In the present analysis τ denotes the sum of laminar and turbulent shearing stress. Thus the shearing stress distribution over a cross-section is linear, and its largest value, τ_0, occurs at the wall, where

$$\tau_0 = \frac{p_1 - p_2}{L} \frac{R}{2} . \tag{20.2}$$

It is seen that the shearing stress at the wall, τ_0, can be determined directly by measuring the pressure gradient along the pipe.

The relationship between the pressure gradient and the rate of flow $Q = \pi R^2 \bar{u}$ could be determined theoretically for the case of laminar flow and the result agreed with experiment. In the case of turbulent flow such a relationship can only be obtained empirically†, because attempts to perform a purely theoretical analysis of turbulent flow, even for one particular case, have so far been entirely unsuccessful. This relation is usually given by so-called *laws of friction* or *laws of resistance*. Available papers contain a large number of empirical equations for the law of friction in pipes. Furthermore, the older equations were often given in a form which depended on the respective system of units and did not satisfy Reynolds' law of similitude. In order to make use of dimensionless variables it is now common to use the dimensionless coefficient of resistance, λ, and to define it (see also eqn. (5.10)) as

$$\frac{p_1 - p_2}{L} = \frac{\lambda}{d} \frac{1}{2} \varrho \bar{u}^2 , \tag{20.3}$$

where $d = 2R$ denotes the diameter of the cross-section. Comparing eqn. (20.2) with (20.3) we can deduce the relation

$$\tau_0 = \frac{1}{8} \lambda \varrho \bar{u}^2 , \tag{20.4}$$

which will be required later. In 1911 H. Blasius made a critical survey of the then existing and already numerous experimental results and arranged them in dimensionless form in accordance with Reynolds' law of similarity. He was able to establish the following empirical equation

$$\lambda = 0{\cdot}3164 \left(\frac{\bar{u}\, d}{\nu}\right)^{-\frac{1}{4}} = 0{\cdot}3164/\mathsf{R}^{0.25} , \tag{20.5}$$

which is valid for the frictional resistance of *smooth pipes* of circular cross-section and which is known as the *Blasius formula*. Here $\bar{u}\, d/\nu = \mathsf{R}$ denotes the Reynolds number calculated with the mean flow velocity $\bar{u}$ and the diameter of the pipe. According to this result the dimensionless coefficient of resistance in a pipe is a function of the Reynolds number only. It is found that the Blasius formula is valid in the range of Reynolds numbers $\mathsf{R} = \bar{u}\, d/\nu \leq 100{,}000$. Consequently the pressure drop in turbulent flow in that range is seen to be proportional to $\bar{u}^{7/4}$. At the time when Blasius established eqn. (20.5), measurements for higher Reynolds numbers were

† The mean velocity of flow through a pipe, $\bar{u}$, will be defined as $\bar{u} = Q/\pi R^2$ and U will denote the maximum velocity in the cross-section.

not available. In Fig. 20.1, the Blasius formula, eqn. (20.5), is seen compared with experimental results; it reproduces them very accurately for Reynolds numbers up to $\mathsf{R} = 100{,}000$. However, points obtained at $\mathsf{R} > 100{,}000$ deviate considerably upwards, as seen from Fig. 20.1 in relation to experimental values reported by J. Nikuradse [29].

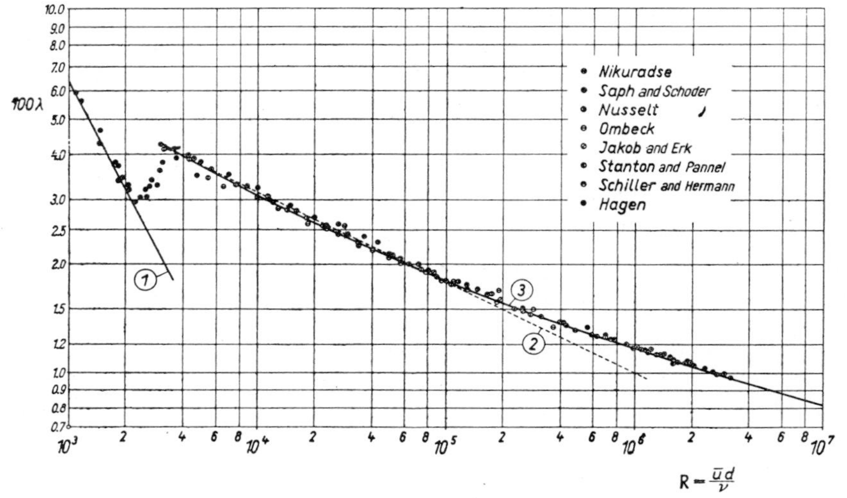

Fig. 20.1. Frictional resistance in a smooth pipe

Curve (1) from eqn. (5.11) after Hagen-Poiseuille for laminar flow; curve (2) from eqn. (20.5) after Blasius for turbulent flow; curve (3) from eqn. (20.30) after Prandtl [35] for turbulent flow

J. Nikuradse carried out a very thorough experimental investigation into the law of friction and velocity profiles in smooth pipes in a very wide range of Reynolds numbers $4 \times 10^3 \leq \mathsf{R} \leq 3{\cdot}2 \times 10^6$. Velocity profiles for several Reynolds numbers are seen plotted in Fig. 20.2. They are given in dimensionless form in that u/U has been plotted against y/R. It will be noticed that the velocity profile becomes fuller as the Reynolds number increases. It is possible to represent it by the empirical equation

$$\frac{u}{U} = \left(\frac{y}{R}\right)^{\frac{1}{n}}, \tag{20.6}$$

where the exponent n varies slightly with the Reynolds number. The plots in Fig. 20.3 show that the assumption of a simple $1/n$-th-power law agrees well with experiment as the graphs of $(u/U)^n$ against y/R, fall on straight lines, when a suitable choice for n has been made. The value of the exponent n is $n = 6$ at the lowest Reynolds number $\mathsf{R} = 4 \times 10^3$; it increases to $n = 7$ at $\mathsf{R} = 110 \times 10^3$ and to $n = 10$ at the highest Reynolds number, $\mathsf{R} = 3240 \times 10^3$, attained in this investigation.

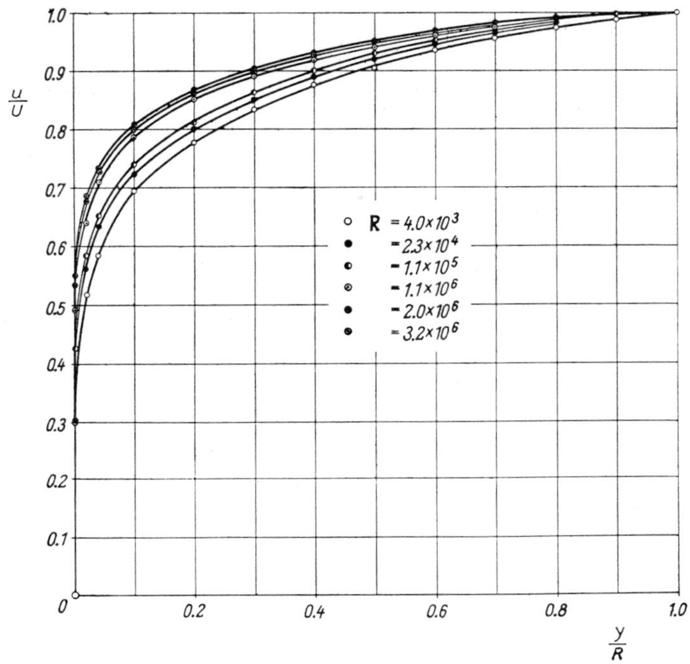

Fig. 20.2. Velocity distribution in smooth pipes for varying Reynolds number, after Nikuradse [29]

We shall note here for further reference the expression for the ratio of the mean to the maximum velocity $\bar{u}/U$ which can be easily derived from eqn. (20.6). It is found that

$$\frac{\bar{u}}{U} = \frac{2n^2}{(n+1)(2n+1)}, \tag{20.7}$$

and the respective numerical values are given in Table 20.1.

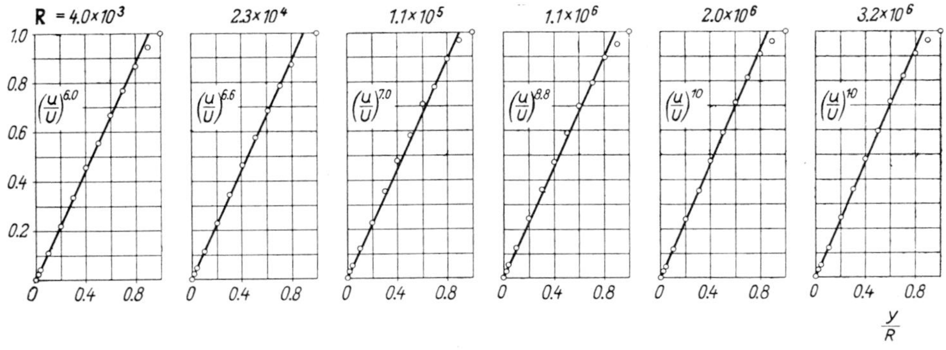

Fig. 20.3. Velocity distribution in smooth pipes. Verification of the assumption in eqn. (20.6)

Table 20.1. Ratio of mean to maximum velocity in pipe flow in terms of the exponent n of the velocity distribution, according to eqn. (20.6)

n	6	7	8	9	10
$\bar{u}/U$	0·791	0·817	0·837	0·852	0·865

b. Relation between law of friction and velocity distribution

The equation for the velocity distribution (20.6) is related to Blasius' law of friction in eqn. (20.5) and this relation, first discovered by L. Prandtl [34], is of fundamental importance in the theory of turbulent flow; it allows us to draw conclusions from pipe experiments which are valid for the flat plate [21]; use of them will be made in Chap. XXI.

On substituting the value of λ from eqn. (20.5) into eqn. (20.4) we obtain the following expression for the shearing stress at the wall:

$$\tau_0 = 0{\cdot}03955\, \varrho\, \bar{u}^{7/4}\, \nu^{1/4}\, d^{-1/4} .$$

Introducing the radius R instead of the diameter d it is necessary to divide the numerical factor in the above equation by $2^{1/4} = 1{\cdot}19$. Thus we obtain.

$$\tau_0 = 0{\cdot}03325\, \varrho\, \bar{u}^{7/4}\, \nu^{1/4}\, R^{-1/4} = \varrho\, v_*^{\,2} , \tag{20.8}$$

where $v_* = \sqrt{\tau_0/\varrho}$ denotes the friction velocity introduced in Chap. XXI. If we split $v_*^{\,2}$ into $v_*^{\,7/4}$ and $v_*^{\,1/4}$, we obtain

$$\left(\frac{\bar{u}}{v_*}\right)^{\frac{7}{4}} = \frac{1}{0{\cdot}03325}\left(\frac{v_*\, R}{\nu}\right)^{\frac{1}{4}} \qquad \text{or} \qquad \left(\frac{\bar{u}}{v_*}\right) = 6{\cdot}99\left(\frac{v_*\, R}{\nu}\right)^{\frac{1}{7}},$$

and if we eliminate the mean velocity $\bar{u}$ with the aid of the maximum velocity U by putting $\bar{u}/U = 0{\cdot}8$ which, as seen from Table 20.1, corresponds approximately to an exponent $n = 7$, i. e. to a Reynolds number $\mathsf{R} = 10^5$, we have

$$\frac{U}{v_*} = 8{\cdot}74\left(\frac{v_*\, R}{\nu}\right)^{\frac{1}{7}} . \tag{20.9}$$

It is now natural to assume that this equation is valid for any wall distance y, and not only for the pipe axis (wall distance $y = R$). Hence we obtain from eqn. (20.9)

$$\frac{u}{v_*} = 8{\cdot}74\left(\frac{y\, v_*}{\nu}\right)^{\frac{1}{7}} . \tag{20.10}$$

The preceding argument shows that the $\frac{1}{7}$*-th-power velocity distribution law* can be derived from Blasius' resistance formula. It has already been shown before that such a law agrees with experiment over a certain range of Reynolds numbers and it is seen that there exists a relation between Blasius' law of friction and the

n-th-power velocity distribution law. Introducing the abbreviations $u/v_* = \phi$ and $y\, v_*/\nu = \eta$, which were already used in eqns. (19.31) and (19.32), we can transform eqn. (20.10) to

$$\phi = 8{\cdot}74\; \eta^{1/7}\,. \qquad (20.11)\dagger$$

Thus we have once more deduced eqn. (19.35) which was first obtained from considerations of similarity, except that the numerical values of the constants C and n, which then remained undetermined, are now known from the law of pipe friction. Equation (20.11) has been compared with J. Nikuradse's experiments in Fig. 20.4, curve (4). It is seen that the $\frac{1}{7}$-th-power law agrees well with experiment up to a Reynolds number of about $\mathsf{R} = 100{,}000$. No better agreement can be expected because Blasius' equation (20.5) from which it was derived is valid only to that limit, Fig. 20.1.

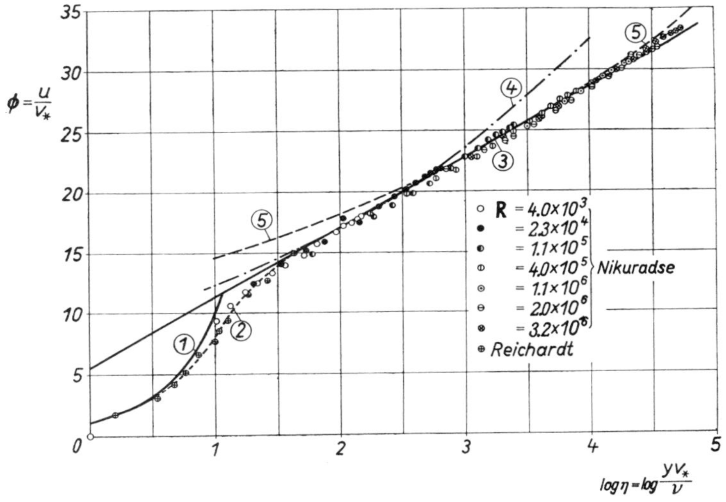

Fig. 20.4. The universal velocity distribution law for smooth pipes

(1) $\phi = \eta$ laminar; (2) transition from laminar to turbulent; (3) eqn. (20.14), turbulent, all Reynolds numbers; (4) eqn. (20.11), turbulent, $\mathsf{R} < 10^5$; (5) $\phi = 11{\cdot}5\, \eta^{1/10}$

In order to obtain better agreement it would be necessary to introduce a smaller exponent into Blasius' equation, say $\frac{1}{5}$ or $\frac{1}{6}$ instead of $\frac{1}{4}$. Performing corresponding calculations it is found that the exponent $\frac{1}{7}$ in the velocity distribution law would have to be replaced by $\frac{1}{8}$, $\frac{1}{9}$, etc., respectively, in agreement with measured values. The relation $\phi = C \times \eta^{1/10}$ has been plotted as curve (5) in Fig. 20.4, and it is

† Upon generalizing for other exponents, we obtain, with K. Wieghardt [58], $u/v_* = C(n) \times (y\, v_*/\nu)^{1/n}$ and the following numerical values:

n	7	8	9	10
$C(n)$	8·74	9·71	10·6	11·5

seen that it does, in fact, reproduce the experimental values at higher Reynolds numbers with a good measure of agreement, but that the fit is inferior at lower Reynolds numbers.

For future reference we now propose to write down an expression for the friction velocity v_* from eqn. (20.10). We obtain

$$v_* = 0{\cdot}150\, u^{\frac{7}{8}} \left(\frac{\nu}{y}\right)^{\frac{1}{8}}$$

and

$$\tau_0 = \varrho\, {v_*}^2 = 0{\cdot}0225\, \varrho\, u^{\frac{7}{4}} \left(\frac{\nu}{y}\right)^{\frac{1}{4}} \tag{20.12}$$

or

$$\tau_0 = 0{\cdot}0225\, \varrho\, U^{\frac{7}{4}} \left(\frac{\nu}{R}\right)^{\frac{1}{4}} . \tag{20.12 a}$$

This relation will be used later.

c. Universal velocity distribution laws for very large Reynolds numbers

The fact that the exponent in the law of pipe resistance as well as in the expression for velocity distribution decreases with increasing Reynolds numbers suggests that both must tend asymptotically to some expressions which are valid for very high Reynolds numbers and which must contain the logarithm of the independent variable, as it is the limit of a polynomial for very small values of the exponent. A detailed examination of experimental results for very large Reynolds numbers shows that such logarithmic laws do, in fact, exist. Physically such asymptotic laws are characterized by the fact that laminar friction becomes completely negligible compared with turbulent friction. The great advantage of such logarithmic laws, as compared with the $1/n$-th-power laws, consists in their being asymptotic expressions for very large Reynolds numbers; they may, therefore, be extrapolated to arbitrarily large values beyond the range covered by experiment. On the other hand, when the $1/n$-th-power laws are used the value of the exponent n changes, as the range of Reynolds numbers is extended.

Such an asymptotic logarithmic law has already been given in eqn. (19.33) for the case of flow along a flat plate. It was deduced from Prandtl's equation (19.6) for turbulent shearing stress under the assumption that the mixing length is proportional to the distance from the wall, $l = \varkappa\, y$, and was valid for small wall distances y. This equation has the form:

$$\phi = A \ln \eta + D\,, \tag{20.13}$$ †

† H. Reichardt [38] indicated a refined expression for the velocity distribution. It covers the whole range of distances, from the wall of the pipe at $y = 0$ to the centre-line at $y = R$, i.e. it is also true for the laminar sub-layer, to which eqn. (20.13) does not apply. It is also valid in the neighbourhood of the centre-line, where measured velocity distribution curves show systematic deviations from eqn. (20.13). In particular, the transition region shown as curve (2) in Fig. 20.4 is well reproduced by the formula. This universal velocity distribution law was deduced with the aid of theoretical estimations and very careful measurements of the turbulent mixing coefficient A defined by eqn. (19.1). Compare also a paper by W. Szablewski [53].

with $A = 1/\varkappa$ and $D = -(1/\varkappa) \cdot \ln \beta$ as free constants. We shall apply this equation without change to pipe flow. Comparing it with the measurements performed by J. Nikuradse, as shown by curve (3) in Fig. 20.4, it is seen that excellent agreement is obtained not only for points near the wall but for the whole range up to the axis of the pipe. The numerical values of the constants are found to be

$$A = 2{\cdot}5; \qquad D = 5{\cdot}5.$$

This gives the following values of $\varkappa$ and β:

$$\varkappa = 0{\cdot}4; \qquad \beta = 0{\cdot}111.$$

Hence the universal velocity distribution law for very large Reynolds numbers has the form†

$$\left.\begin{aligned} \phi &= 2{\cdot}5 \ln \eta + 5{\cdot}5 \\ \text{or} \quad \phi &= 5{\cdot}75 \log \eta + 5{\cdot}5 . \end{aligned}\right\} \quad \text{(smooth)} \tag{20.14}$$

By a reasoning similar to the one given in the preceding section it is possible to arrive at a corresponding universal asymptotic resistance formula from the above universal velocity distribution equation.

Equation (20.14), being one for turbulent flow, is valid only in regions where the laminar shearing stress can be neglected in comparison with the turbulent stress. In the immediate neighbourhood of the wall, where the turbulent shearing stress decreases to zero and laminar stresses predominate, deviations from this law must be expected. H. Reichardt [37] extended this kind of measurement to include very small distances from the wall in a flow in a channel. Curve (2) in Fig. 20.4 represents the transition from the laminar sub-layer (*cf.* Sec. XVIII c, p. 465) to the turbulent boundary layer. The curve denoted by (1) in the above diagram corresponds to laminar flow for which $\tau_0 = \mu\, u/y$. With $\tau_0 = \varrho\, v_*^2$ we obtain $u/v_* = y\, v_*/\nu$, or

$$\phi = \eta \quad \text{(laminar)} .$$

From this it can be seen that for values $y\, v_*/\nu < 5$ the contribution from turbulent friction may be completely neglected compared with laminar friction. In the range $5 < y\, v_*/\nu < 70$ both contributions are of the same order of magnitude, whereas for $y\, v_*/\nu > 70$ the laminar contribution is negligible compared with turbulent friction. Thus:

$$\left.\begin{aligned} \frac{y\, v_*}{\nu} &< 5: && \text{purely laminar friction} \\ 5 < \frac{y\, v_*}{\nu} &< 70: && \text{laminar-turbulent friction} \\ \frac{y\, v_*}{\nu} &> 70: && \text{purely turbulent friction} . \end{aligned}\right\} \tag{20.15}$$

Hence the thickness of the laminar sub-layer is seen to be equal to

$$\delta_l \approx 5 \frac{\nu}{v_*} . \tag{20.15a}$$

† In the following equations ln denotes the natural logarithm and log the logarithm to base 10.

We now propose to compare the experimental results on velocity distribution measurements in pipe flow with the alternative universal equation, which was deduced in Chap. XIX in the form $(U - u)/v^* = f(y/R)$. It will be recalled that it followed both from von Kármán's similarity theory and from Prandtl's assumption about the shearing stress, together with the relation $l = \varkappa\, y$ for the mixing length. In the first case we obtained eqn. (19.25) and in the second case eqn. (19.28) was obtained.

Since the simpler assumption on the mixing length, $l = \varkappa\, y$, does not seem to be suitable for the whole pipe diameter, it appears preferable to deduce the dependence of mixing length on distance directly from experiment and then to apply Prandtl's hypothesis

$$\tau = \varrho\, l^2 \left(\frac{\mathrm{d}u}{\mathrm{d}y}\right)^2 \tag{20.16}$$

to calculate the velocity distribution from a linear shearing stress distribution

$$\tau = \tau_0 \left(1 - \frac{y}{R}\right) . \tag{20.17}$$

It is now possible to calculate the variation of mixing length with y/R directly from eqns. (20.16) and (20.17) together with the measured velocity distribution $u(y)$. This calculation was carried out by J. Nikuradse [29], who obtained the remarkable result shown in Fig. 20.5; it represents the variation of mixing length over the diameter of the pipe for the case of smooth pipes and it seen that it is independent of the Reynolds number, when values below 10^5 are excluded. This function can be represented by the empirical relation

$$\frac{l}{R} = 0{\cdot}14 - 0{\cdot}08 \left(1 - \frac{y}{R}\right)^2 - 0{\cdot}06 \left(1 - \frac{y}{R}\right)^4 . \tag{20.18}$$

In the neighbourhood of the wall this equation can be simplified to

$$l = 0{\cdot}4\, y - 0{\cdot}44 \frac{y^2}{R} + \ldots \tag{20.18a}$$

which shows that Prandtl's hypothesis is confirmed for small distances from the wall, where $l = \varkappa\, y$ with

$$\varkappa = 0{\cdot}4 . \tag{20.19}$$

It can be shown, further, that the variation of mixing length with wall distance given in eqn. (20.18) remains valid for rough and not only for smooth pipes. Fig. 20.6 represents the results of J. Nikuradse's [30] measurements on pipes artificially roughened with sand of different grain size, and the preceding statement is seen to be confirmed. Furthermore, it may now be expected that the velocity distribution calculated from the mixing length from eqn. (20.18) will be valid for rough as well as for smooth pipes.

For the sake of simplicity the expression for the mixing length can be written as

$$l = \varkappa\, y \cdot f\left(\frac{y}{R}\right) , \tag{20.20}$$

where $f(y/R) \to 1$ for $y/R \to 0$. Introducing $v_* = \sqrt{\tau_0/\varrho}$ into eqn. (20.17) and combining with eqn. (20.16) we obtain the following differential equation for the velocity distribution

$$\frac{\mathrm{d}u}{\mathrm{d}y} = \frac{1}{l}\sqrt{\frac{\tau}{\varrho}} = \frac{v_*}{\varkappa}\,\frac{\sqrt{1-\frac{y}{R}}}{y f\left(\frac{y}{R}\right)}$$

whence, by integration

$$u = \frac{v_*}{\varkappa}\int\limits_{y_0/R}^{y/R} \frac{\sqrt{1-\frac{y}{R}}\,\mathrm{d}\left(\frac{y}{R}\right)}{\frac{y}{R}\, f\left(\frac{y}{R}\right)}\,. \tag{20.21}$$

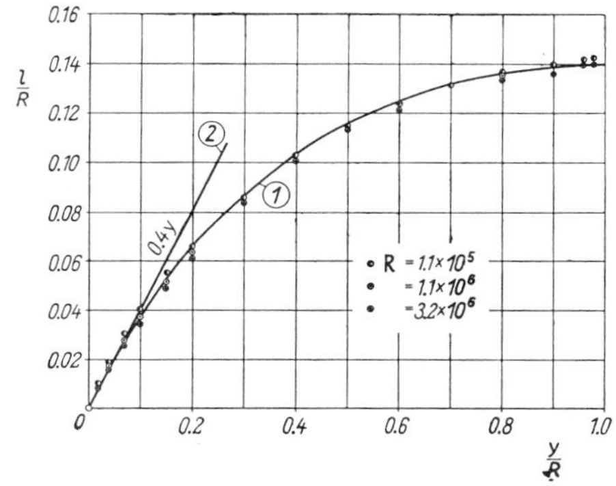

Fig. 20.5. Variation of mixing length over pipe diameter for smooth pipes at different Reynolds numbers
Curve (1) from eqn. (20.18)

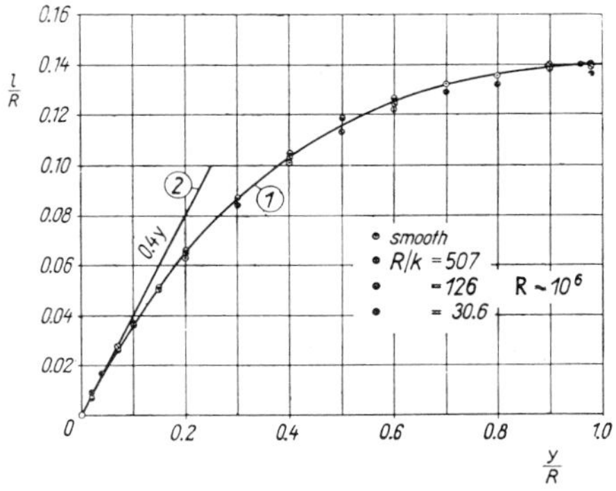

Fig. 20.6. Variation of mixing length over pipe diameter for rough pipes
Curve (1) from eqn. (20.18)

Here the lower limit of integration at y_0, where the velocity is equal to zero, is of the order of the thickness of the laminar sub-layer and, therefore, proportional to ν/v_* as seen from eqn. (20.15a). Thus $y_0/R = F_1(v_* R/\nu)$. The maximum velocity U in the centre of the pipe can be deduced from eqn. (20.21) and becomes

$$U = \frac{v_*}{\varkappa}\int\limits_{y_0/R}^{1} \frac{\sqrt{1-\frac{y}{R}}\,\mathrm{d}\left(\frac{y}{R}\right)}{\frac{y}{R}\, f\left(\frac{y}{R}\right)}\,. \tag{20.21 a}$$

By eqns. (20.21) and (20.21 a) we now have

$$\boxed{U - u = v_*\, F\left(\frac{y}{R}\right).} \tag{20.22}$$

Thus we have again been led to the universal velocity distribution law, eqn. (19.28). The essential generalization which has now been achieved consists in the fact that the universal law in eqn. (20.22) is valid for rough as well as for smooth pipes, the function $F(y/R)$ being the same in both cases. Equation (20.22) asserts that curves of velocity distribution plotted over the pipe radius contract into a single curve for *all* values of Reynolds number and for *all* degrees of roughness, if $(U - u)/v_*$ is plotted in terms of y/R, Fig. 20.7. It may be noted that the above form of the velocity distribution law was first deduced by T. E. Stanton [51]. An explicit expression for $F(y/R)$ could be obtained by evaluating the integral in eqn. (20.21); it is, however, simpler to make use of the already known form of the velocity distribution law for smooth pipes as given in eqn. (20.14). From eqn. (20.14) we have

$$U - u = 2{\cdot}5\, v_* \ln \frac{R}{y} = 5{\cdot}75\, v_* \log \frac{R}{y}$$

and hence

$$\frac{U-u}{v_*} = 5{\cdot}75 \log \frac{R}{y}. \qquad (20.23)$$

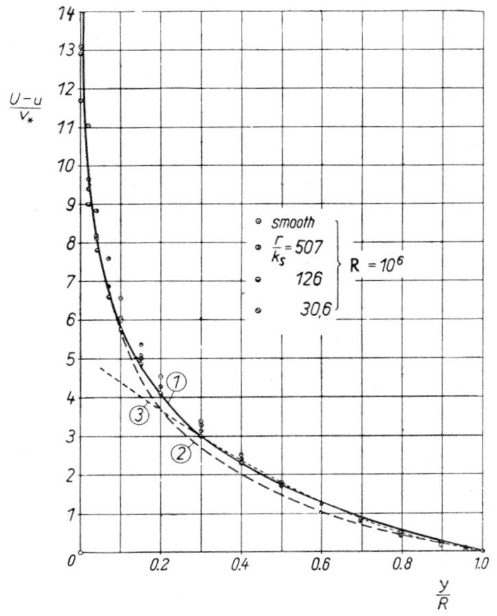

Fig. 20.7. Universal velocity distribution law for smooth and rough pipes

Curve (1) from eqn. (20.23), Prandtl; curve (2) from eqn. (20.24), von Kármán; curve (3) from eqn. (20.25), Darcy

This equation is seen plotted in Fig. 20.7 as curve (1) and compared with experimental results for smooth and rough pipes. It contains the empirical constant $\varkappa$, whose numerical value $\varkappa = 0{\cdot}4$ was already given in eqn. (20.19). The agreement between theory and experiment is very good.

The universal velocity distribution law can be deduced also from von Kármán's similarity law, eqn. (19.25), whence we obtain

$$\frac{U-u}{v_*} = -\frac{1}{\varkappa}\left\{\ln\left[1-\sqrt{1-\frac{y}{R}}\right]+\sqrt{1-\frac{y}{R}}\right\}, \qquad (20.24)$$

with y denoting the distance from the wall. This equation, shown as curve (2) in Fig. 20.7, also agrees well with the experimental values, if $\varkappa = 0{\cdot}36$ is chosen. Fig. 20.7 contains an additional curve (3) which is based on H. Darcy's [6] empirical equation. Darcy deduced it in 1855 from his very careful measurements on velocity distribution and in our present notation it can be written as

$$\frac{U-u}{v_*} = 5{\cdot}08\left(1-\frac{y}{R}\right)^{\frac{3}{2}}. \qquad (20.25)$$

Darcy's formula gives good agreement at all points except those near the wall with $y/R < 0{\cdot}25$.

It is worth pointing out here that both universal velocity distribution laws, eqn. (20.23) and (20.24), have been obtained, as seen from the argument in the preceding chapter, for two-dimensional flow in a channel. The fact that they nevertheless agree well with the experimental results for the case of pipe flow with axial symmetry can be taken as proof that there is far-reaching similarity between the velocity distribution in the two-dimensional and axially symmetrical cases. It will be recalled that in laminar flow the velocity distribution is parabolic in both cases.

Starting with G. I. Taylor's vorticity transfer theory it is also possible to deduce a universal velocity distribution law of the form of eqn. (20.22) but, evidently, with a function $F(y/R)$ which differs from those appearing in Prandtl's or von Kármán's calculations. A comparison between the results obtained from G. I. Taylor's vorticity transfer theory and from L. Prandtl's momentum transfer theory is contained in papers by S. Goldstein [14] and G. I. Taylor [55]. No unequivocal decision in favour of either of the two theories could, however, be obtained.

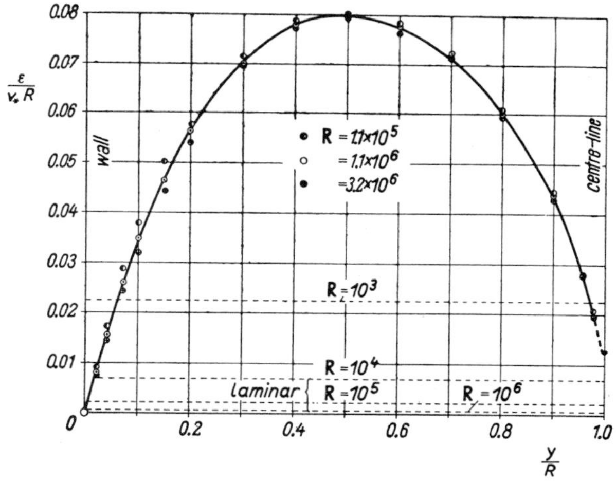

Fig. 20.8. Dimensionless virtual kinematic viscosity for smooth pipes plotted from Nikuradse's [29] experimental results

Good insight into the physical aspects of flow through a pipe can be gained by considering the variation of the apparent kinematic viscosity, ε, over the cross-section of the pipe which is seen plotted in Fig. 20.8 on the basis of J. Nikuradse's experimental results. Starting with $\tau = \varrho\, \varepsilon (\mathrm{d}u/\mathrm{d}y)$ from eqn. (19.1) we can insert the value of τ from eqn. (20.17), and hence we can obtain the variation of ε from the measured velocity distribution. The apparent kinematic viscosity is independent of the Reynolds number, just as was the case with the mixing length. However, the type of variation of ε is much more complex than that of l, Fig. 20.5. The maximum of ε falls half-way between the wall and the axis, and on the axis ε becomes very small but does not reduce to zero. Considering the diagram in Fig. 20.8 it must be conceded that it would be much more difficult to find a plausible hypothesis describing its variation than was the case with the mixing length, l. This circumstance was advanced earlier (Sec. XIX b) as a reason in favour of introducing the mixing length into the equations rather than the apparent viscosity, and this view is seen to be borne out by experimental results. In order to compare laminar with turbulent friction, Fig. 20.8 contains respective values for Poiseuille flow.

The latter are, of course, identical with ν. Since $v_* = (\sqrt{\tfrac{1}{8}\lambda})\,\bar{u}$, as seen from eqn.(20.4), and since for laminar flow $\lambda = 64/\mathsf{R}$, as seen from eqn. (5.11), we find that

$$\frac{\varepsilon_{lam}}{v_* R} = \frac{\nu}{v_* R} = \frac{1}{\sqrt{2\mathsf{R}}}\,.$$

This shows that turbulent friction is much larger than laminar friction, particularly at high Reynolds numbers.

d. Universal resistance law for smooth pipes at very large Reynolds numbers

Retracing the steps in the argument of Sec. XXb, which has led us from Blasius' resistance formula to the $\frac{1}{7}$-th-power velocity distribution law, we can now derive a new pipe resistance formula from the universal logarithmic velocity distribution law. The logarithmic velocity distribution law in eqn. (20.23) was derived under the assumption that laminar friction was negligible compared with turbulent friction which meant that it could be extrapolated to arbitrarily large Reynolds numbers. The same may now be expected to be true of the resistance law about to be deduced. The following reasoning will be based on a paper by L. Prandtl [35].

Upon integrating eqn. (20.23) over the cross-sectional area we obtain the mean velocity of flow

$$\bar{u} = U - 3{\cdot}75\, v_*\,. \tag{20.26}$$

Nikuradse's experiments show that the constant 3·75 must be adjusted slightly, so that

$$\bar{u} = U - 4{\cdot}07\, v_*\,. \tag{20.27}$$

From eqn. (20.4), we obtain

$$\lambda = 8\left(\frac{v_*}{\bar{u}}\right)^2, \tag{20.28}$$

and from the universal velocity distribution law, eqn. (20.14), we have

$$U = v_* \left\{ 2{\cdot}5 \ln \frac{R\, v_*}{\nu} + 5{\cdot}5 \right\}$$

which combined with eqn. (20.26) gives

$$\bar{u} = v_* \left\{ 2{\cdot}5 \ln \frac{R\, v^*}{\nu} + 1{\cdot}75 \right\}. \tag{20.29}$$

We can introduce the Reynolds number from

$$\frac{R\, v_*}{\nu} = \frac{1}{2}\,\frac{\bar{u}\, d}{\nu}\,\frac{v_*}{\bar{u}} = \frac{\bar{u}\, d}{\nu}\,\frac{\sqrt{\lambda}}{4\sqrt{2}}\,,$$

so that we obtain from eqns. (20.28) and (20.29)

$$\lambda = \frac{8}{\left\{2{,}5 \ln\left(\frac{\bar{u}\,d}{\nu}\sqrt{\lambda}\right) - 2{\cdot}5 \ln 4\sqrt{2} + 1{\cdot}75\right\}^2} = \frac{1}{\left\{2{\cdot}035 \log\left(\frac{\bar{u}\,d}{\nu}\sqrt{\lambda}\right) - 0{\cdot}91\right\}^2}$$

or

$$\frac{1}{\sqrt{\lambda}} = 2{\cdot}035 \log\left(\frac{\bar{u}\,d}{\nu}\sqrt{\lambda}\right) - 0{\cdot}91 \,.$$

According to this result the universal law of friction for a smooth pipe should give a straight line if $1/\sqrt{\lambda}$ is plotted against $\log (\mathsf{R}\sqrt{\lambda})$. This feature agrees extremely well with experiment, as seen from Fig. 20.9, where the results of measurements of

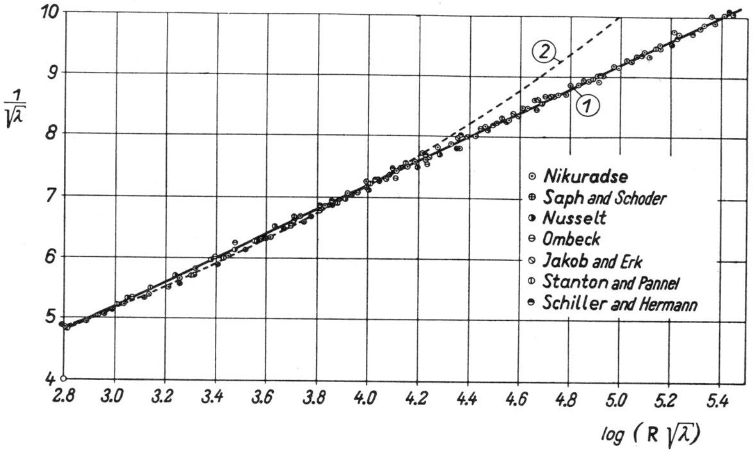

Fig. 20.9. Universal law of friction for a smooth pipe
Curve (1) from eqn. (20.30), Prandtl; curve (2) from eqn. (20.5), Blasius

many authors have been plotted. The numerical coefficients for the averaged curve passing through the experimental results differ only very little from the preceding, derived values. The straight line (1) passing through the experimental points in Fig. (20.9) can be represented by the equation

$$\boxed{\frac{1}{\sqrt{\lambda}} = 2{\cdot}0 \log\left(\frac{\bar{u}\,d}{\nu}\sqrt{\lambda}\right) - 0{\cdot}8} \qquad \text{(smooth)}\,. \qquad (20.30)$$

This is *Prandtl's universal law of friction for smooth pipes*. It has been verified by J. Nikuradse's [29] experiments up to a Reynolds number of $3{\cdot}4 \times 10^6$ and the agreement is seen to be excellent. From its derivation it is clear that it may be extrapolated to arbitrarily large Reynolds numbers, and it may be stated that measurements with higher Reynolds numbers are, therefore, not required. Values computed from eqn. (20.30) are given in Table 20.2.

Table 20.2. Coefficient of resistance for smooth pipes in terms of the Reynolds number; see also Fig. 20.9

	Prandtl, eqn. (20.30)	Blasius, eqn. (20.5)
$\mathsf{R} = \frac{\bar{u}\, d}{\nu}$	λ	λ
10^3	(0·0622)	(0·0567)
$2 \cdot 10^3$	(0·0494)	(0·0473)
$5 \cdot 10^3$	0·0374	0·0376
10^4	0·0309	0·0316
$2 \cdot 10^4$	0·0259	0·0266
$5 \cdot 10^4$	0·0209	0·0212
10^5	0·0180	0·0178
$2 \cdot 10^5$	0·0156	0·0150
$5 \cdot 10^5$	0·0131	—
10^6	0·0116	(0·0100)
$2 \cdot 10^6$	0·0104	—
$5 \cdot 10^6$	0·0090	—
10^7	0·0081	(0·0056)

The universal equation agrees well with Blasius' equation (20.5) up to $\mathsf{R} = 10^5$, but at higher values Blasius' equation deviates progressively more from the results of measurement, whereas eqn. (20.30) maintains good agreement.

The flow of gases through smooth pipes at very high velocities was investigated by W. Froessel [12]. The variation in pressure along a pipe for different mass flow rates is represented in Fig. 20.10. The numbers shown against the curves indicate the fraction of maximum mass flow through a nozzle of equal diameter and with equal stagnation pressure. The curves which fall off to the right refer to subsonic flow, whereas the increasing curves apply to supersonic flow. The latter curves include jumps to higher pressures and subsonic flow effected by a shock. The coefficients of resistance are not markedly different from those in incompressible flow, as seen from Fig. 20.11. The straight line shown for comparison corresponds to eqn. (20.30).

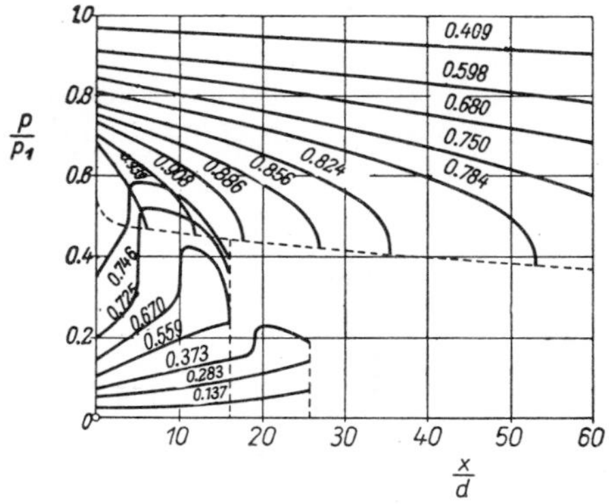

Fig. 20.10. Pressure distribution along a pipe in compressible flow, after Froessel [12]

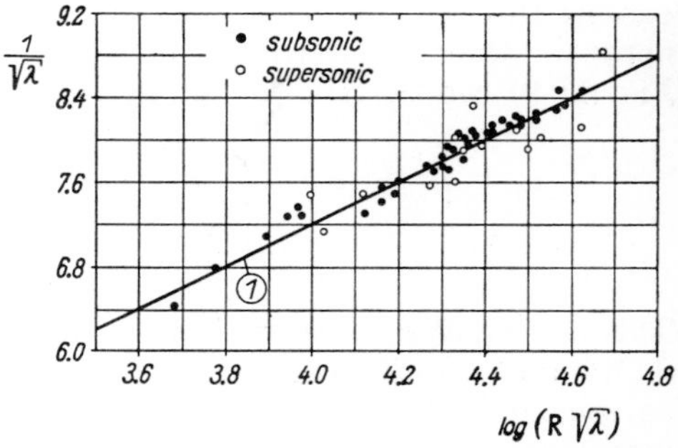

Fig. 20.11. Law of resistance for smooth pipes in compressible flow. Curve (1) from eqn. (20.30)

e. Pipes of non-circular cross-section

Turbulent flow through pipes of non-circular cross-section was investigated by L. Schiller [42] and J. Nikuradse [28], who have determined the law of friction and the velocity distribution for pipes of rectangular, triangular, and trapezoidal cross-section, as well as for circular pipes with notches. It is convenient to introduce a coefficient of resistance to flow which is referred to the *hydraulic radius* R_h:

$$\frac{p_1 - p_2}{L} = \frac{1}{2}\,\frac{\lambda'}{R_h}\,\varrho\,\bar{u}^2\,,$$

where

$$R_h = \frac{2A}{C}$$

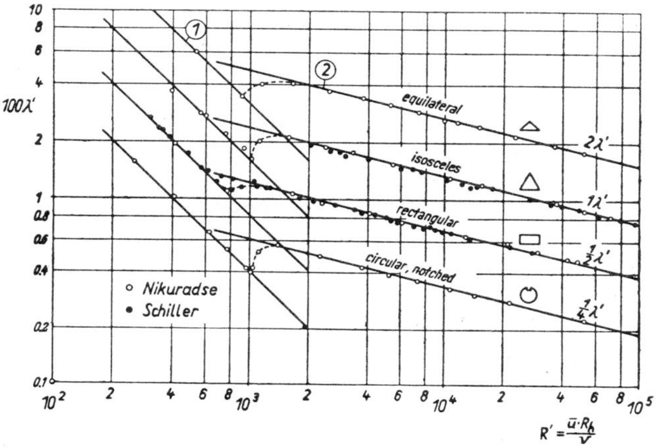

Fig. 20.12. Resistance formula for smooth pipes of non-circular cross-section

and A denotes the cross-sectional area, C denoting the wetted perimeter. In the case of a circular cross-section the hydraulic radius is equal to the radius of the circle. Hence for circular cross-sections $\lambda' = \frac{1}{2}\lambda$, where λ denotes the frictional coefficient from eqn. (20.3), related to the diameter. If the Reynolds number is also related to the radius, $\mathsf{R}' = \bar{u}\,R_h/\nu$, then for laminar flow we have $\lambda' = 16/\mathsf{R}'$, and Blasius' equation for turbulent flow can be written as $\lambda' = 0{\cdot}133\,(\mathsf{R}')^{-1/4}$.

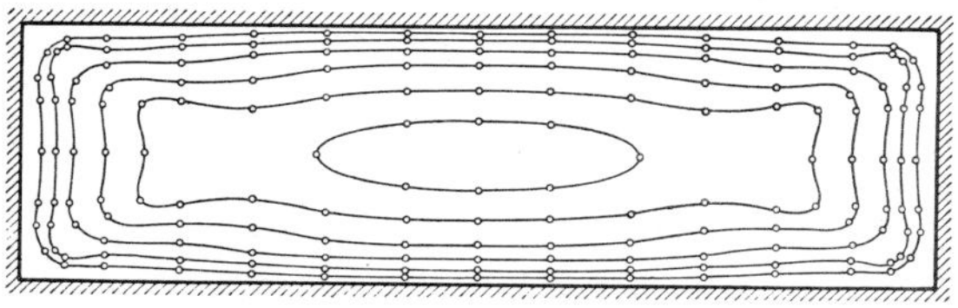

Fig. 20.13. Curves of constant velocity for pipe of rectangular cross-section, after Nikuradse [27]

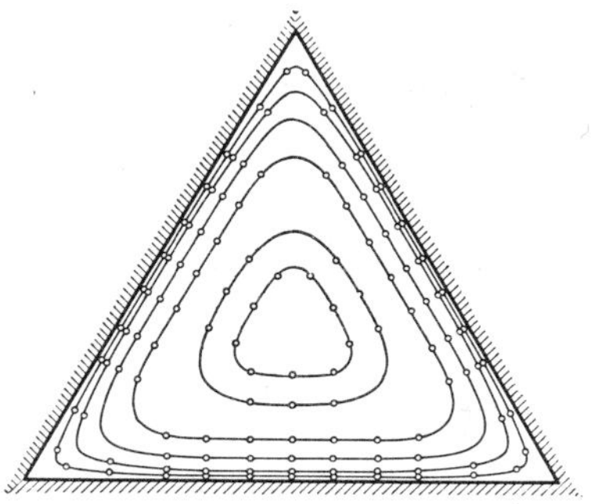

Fig. 20.14. Curves of constant velocity for a pipe of equilateral triangular cross-section after Nikuradse [28]

Figure 20.12 contains plots of λ' against R' for a series of cross-sectional shapes. It is seen that all of them completely agree with the law for circular pipes which is represented by curve (1) in the laminar and by curve (2) in the turbulent region. The applicability of the concept of the hydraulic radius has been verified by experiments [26] up to a Mach number $\mathsf{M} = 1$. The velocity distribution curves in such pipes are particularly noteworthy. The curves of constant velocity for rectangular and triangular cross-section obtained by J. Nikuradse [27] are shown in Figs. 20.13 and 20.14. In all cases the velocities at the corners are comparatively very large which stems from the fact that in all straight pipes of non-circular cross-section there exist secondary flows. These are such that the fluid flows towards the corner along the bisectrix of the angle and then outwards in both directions. The secondary flows continuously transport momentum from the centre to the corners and generate high velocities there. Schematic diagrams of secondary flows in triangular and rectangular pipes are shown in Fig. 20.15. It is seen that the secondary flow in the rectangular cross-section which proceeds from the wall inwards in the neighbourhood of the ends of the larger sides and of the middle of the shorter sides creates zones of low velocity. They appear very clearly in the picture of curves of constant velocity in Fig. 20.13. Such secondary flows come into play also in open channels, as evidenced by the pattern of curves of constant velocity in Fig. 20.16. The maximum velocity does not occur near the free surface but at about one fifth of the depth down, and the flow in the free surface

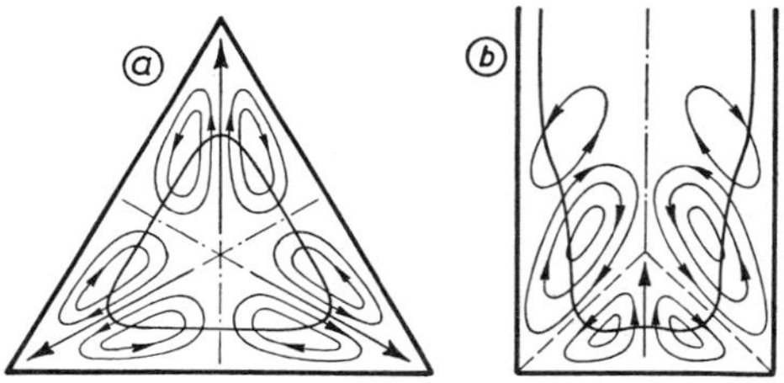

Fig. 20.15. Secondary flows in pipes of triangular and rectangular cross-section (schematic)

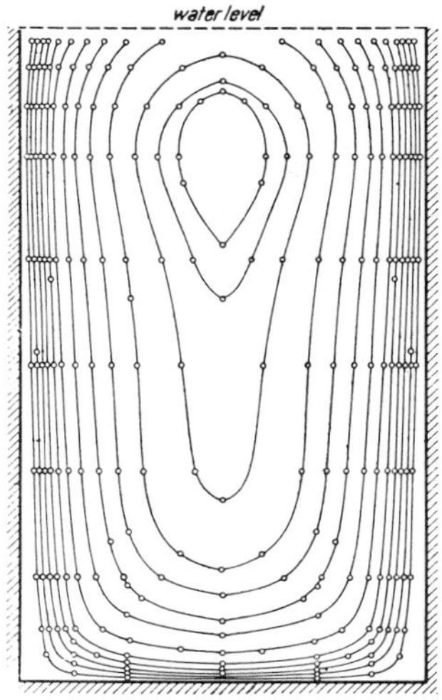

Fig. 20.16. Curves of constant velocity for a rectangular open channel after Nikuradse [27]

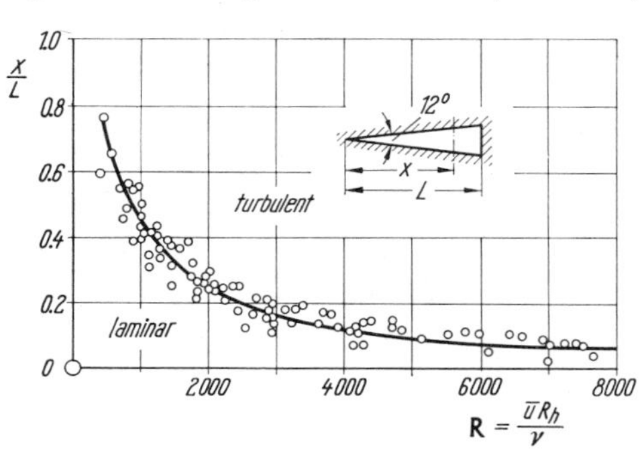

Fig. 20.17. Boundary between laminar and turbulent flow in an acute, triangular channel, determined visually by the use of smoke injection after E. R. G. Eckert and T. E. Irvine [9]
R_h — hydraulic radius

is not at all two-dimensional as might have been expected. When the cross-section of the channel contains a narrow region, transition does not occur simultaneously over the whole of the flow. For example, in the region within an acute angle of a triangular cross-section, the flow remains laminar to very large Reynolds numbers whereas in the bulk it had turned turbulent long ago. Such a state of affairs is seen illustrated with the aid of Fig. 20.17 which represents the results of measurements performed by E. R. G. Eckert and T. E. Irvine [9]. At a Reynolds number of $\mathsf{R} = 1000$, the flow remains laminar over 40 per cent. of the height of the triangle, the region of laminar flow decreasing as the Reynolds number is increased.

E. Meyer [23] investigated the pressure and velocity distribution in a flow through a straight channel with a cross-section whose shape varied but whose cross-sectional area remained constant. He used a channel in which a circular cross-section was gradually transformed into a rectangle with its sides in the ratio 1 : 2. Transition was effected in both directions over two different lengths, and it was discovered that the pressure loss in the portion with transition from circle to rectangle considerably exceeded that in the opposite direction.

f. Rough pipes and equivalent sand roughness

Most pipes used in engineering structures cannot be regarded as being hydraulically smooth, at least at higher Reynolds numbers. The resistance to flow offered by rough walls is larger than that implied by the preceding equations for smooth pipes. Consequently the laws of friction in rough pipes are of great practical importance and experimental work on them began very early. The desire to explore the laws of friction of rough pipes in a systematic way is frustrated by the fundamental difficulty that the number of parameters describing roughness is extraordinarily large owing to the great diversity of geometric forms. If we consider, for example, a wall with identical protrusions we must come to the conclusion that its drag depends on the density of distribution of such roughnesses, i. e. on their number per unit area as well as on their shape and height and, finally, also on the way in which they are distributed over its surface. It took, therefore, a long time to formulate clear and simple laws which describe the flow of fluids through rough pipes. L. Hopf [18] made a comprehensive review of the numerous earlier experimental results and found two types of roughness in relation to the resistance formula for rough pipes and open channels. The first kind of roughness causes a resistance which is proportional to the square of the velocity; this means that the coefficient of resistance is independent of the Reynolds number and corresponds to relatively coarse and tightly spaced roughness elements such as for example coarse sand grains glued on the surface, cement, or rough cast iron. In such cases the nature of the roughness can be expressed with the aid of a single roughness parameter k/R, the so-called *relative roughness*, where k is the height of a protrusion and R denotes the radius or the hydraulic radius of the cross-section. From considerations of similitude we may conclude that in this case the resistance coefficient depends on the relative roughness only. The actual relation can be determined experimentally by performing measurements on pipes or channels of differing hydraulic radii but of the same absolute roughness. Such measurements were carried out by K. Fromm [11] and W. Fritsch [10], who found that for geometrically similar roughnesses λ is proportional to $(k/R_h)^{0{\cdot}314}$.

The second type of resistance formula occurs when the protrusions are more gentle or when a small number of them is distributed over a relatively large area, such as those in wooden or commercial steel pipes. In such cases the resistance coefficient depends both on the Reynolds number and on the relative roughness.

From the physical point of view it must be concluded that the ratio of the height of protrusions to the boundary layer thickness should be the determining factor. In particular, the phenomenon is expected to depend on the thickness of the laminar sub-layer δ_l, so that k/δ_l must be regarded as an important dimensionless number which is characteristic of the kind of roughness. It is clear that roughness will cause no increase in resistance in cases where the protrusions are so small (or the boundary layer is so thick) that they are all contained within the laminar sublayer, i. e. if $k < \delta_l$, and the wall may be considered hydraulically smooth. This is similar to the absence of the influence of roughness on resistance in Hagen-Poiseuille flow. Recalling our considerations in Sec. XIXf we find that the thickness of the laminar sublayer is given by $\delta_l = \text{const} \times \nu/v_*$ and that the dimensionless roughness factor is

$$k/\delta_l \sim k\, v_*/\nu \; .$$

This is a Reynolds number which is formed with the grain size of roughness and the friction velocity v_*.

Very systematic, extensive, and careful measurements on rough pipes have been carried out by J. Nikuradse [30]†, who used circular pipes covered on the inside as tightly as possible with sand of a definite grain size glued on to the wall. By choosing pipes of varying diameters and by changing the size of grain, he was able to vary the relative roughness k_S/R from about 1/500 to 1/15. The regularities of behaviour discovered during the course of these measurements can be correlated with those for smooth pipes in a simple manner.

We shall begin by describing Nikuradse's measurements and we shall then show that the relation between the resistance formula and the velocity distribution, which we found earlier in the case of smooth pipes, can be extended to the case of rough pipes in a natural way.

Resistance formula: Fig. 20.18 represents the law of friction for pipes roughened with sand. In the region of laminar flow all rough pipes have the same resistance as a smooth pipe. The critical Reynolds number is equally independent of roughness, and in the turbulent region there is a range of Reynolds numbers over which pipes of a given relative roughness behave in the same way as smooth pipes. The rough pipe can, therefore, be said to be *hydraulically smooth* in this range and λ depends on R alone. Beginning with a definite Reynolds number whose magnitude increases as k_S/R decreases, the resistance curve for a rough pipe deviates from that for a smooth pipe and reaches the region of the quadratic resistance law at some higher value of Reynolds number, where λ depends on k_S/R only. Hence it is necessary to consider *three regimes*.

† In what follows we shall use the symbol k_S to denote the grain size in Nikuradse's sand roughness, reserving the symbol k for any other kind of roughness.

1. *hydraulically smooth*† *regime:*

$$0 \leq \frac{k_S v_*}{\nu} \leq 5: \quad \lambda = \lambda\,(\mathsf{R})\,.$$

The size of the roughness is so small that all protrusions are contained within the laminar sub-layer.

2. *transition regime:*

$$5 \leq \frac{k_S\, v_*}{\nu} \leq 70: \quad \lambda = \lambda \left(\frac{k_S}{R}, \mathsf{R}\right).$$

Protrusions extend partly outside the laminar sub-layer and the additional resistance, as compared with a smooth pipe, is mainly due to the form drag experienced by the protrusions in the boundary layer.

3. *completely rough regime:*

$$\frac{k_S\, v_*}{\nu} > 70: \quad \lambda = \lambda\,(k_S/R)\,.$$

All protrusions reach outside the laminar sub-layer and by far the largest part of the resistance to flow is due to the form drag which acts on them. For this reason the law of resistance becomes quadratic.

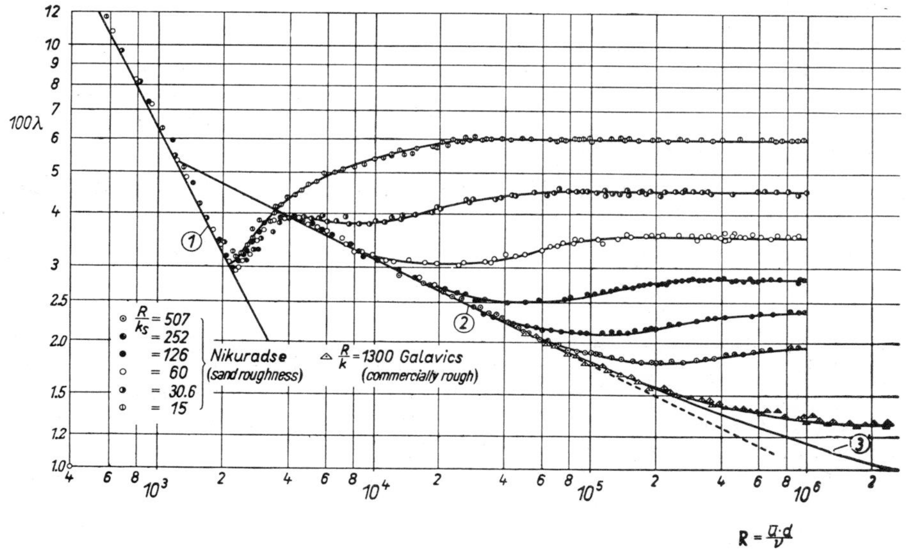

Fig. 20.18. Resistance formula for rough pipes

Curve (1) from eqn. (5.11), laminar; curve (2) from eqn. (20.5), turbulent, smooth; curve (3) from eqn. (20.30), turbulent, smooth

† The numerical values of $v^* k_S/\nu$ quoted here will be derived later from the velocity distribution law. They are valid only for roughnesses obtained with sand.

Velocity distribution: The velocity gradient near a rough wall is less steep than that near a smooth one, as can be seen from Fig. 20.19, in which the velocity ratio u/U has been plotted against the distance ratio y/R for a smooth and for several rough pipes, all having been measured within the range of validity of the square resistance law. Expressing the velocity distribution function again by a power formula we obtain exponents of $\frac{1}{4}$ to $\frac{1}{5}$. The variation of mixing length over the cross-section calculated from these curves has already been plotted in Fig. 20.6 from which it is seen that it is exactly the same for rough and for smooth pipes. It can be represented by the empirical equation (20.18). In particular in the neighbourhood of the wall we have $l = \varkappa\, y = 0{\cdot}4\, y$.

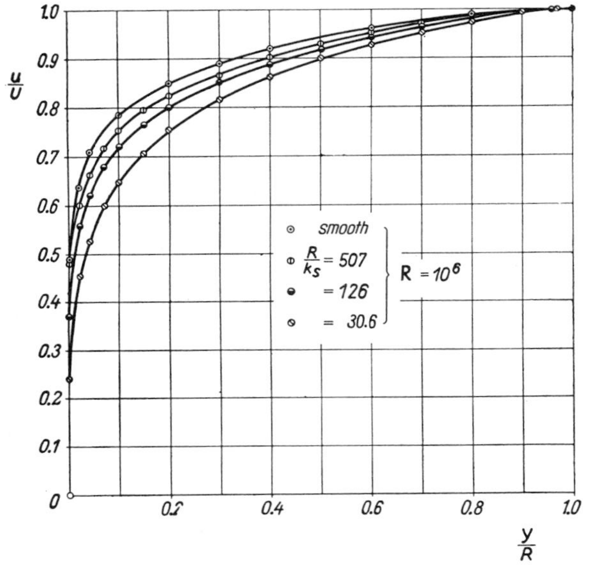

Fig. 20.19. Velocity distribution in rough pipes after Nikuradse [30]

It follows, therefore, that the logarithmic law for velocity distribution, eqn. (19.29), remains valid for rough pipes, except that the constant of integration, y_0, must be given a different numerical value. Furthermore, it is natural to make it proportional to the roughness height k_S, i. e. to put $y_0 = \gamma\, k_S$, so that eqn. (19.29) now becomes

$$\frac{u}{v_*} = \frac{1}{\varkappa}\left(\ln\frac{y}{k_S} - \ln\gamma\right), \tag{20.31}$$

the constant γ still depending on the nature of the particular roughness. Comparing this equation with J. Nikuradse's measurements we find that they can, in fact, be represented by an equation of the form:

$$\frac{u}{v_*} = 2{\cdot}5\ln\frac{y}{k_S} + B\,, \tag{20.32}$$

where the constant $2{\cdot}5 = 1/\varkappa = 1/0{\cdot}4$, whereas B assumes different values for the three ranges of roughness discussed previously. In the range of the completely rough regime, we have $B = 8{\cdot}5$, so that in this region

$$\frac{u}{v_*} = 5{\cdot}75 \log \frac{y}{k_S} + 8{\cdot}5 \quad \text{(completely rough)}\,. \tag{20.32a}$$

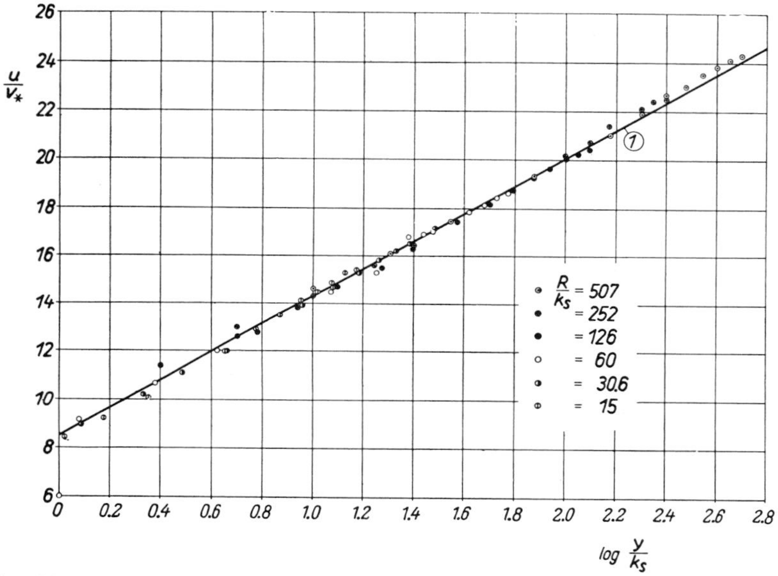

Fig. 20.20 Universal velocity distribution in rough pipes Curve (1) from eqn. (20.32a)

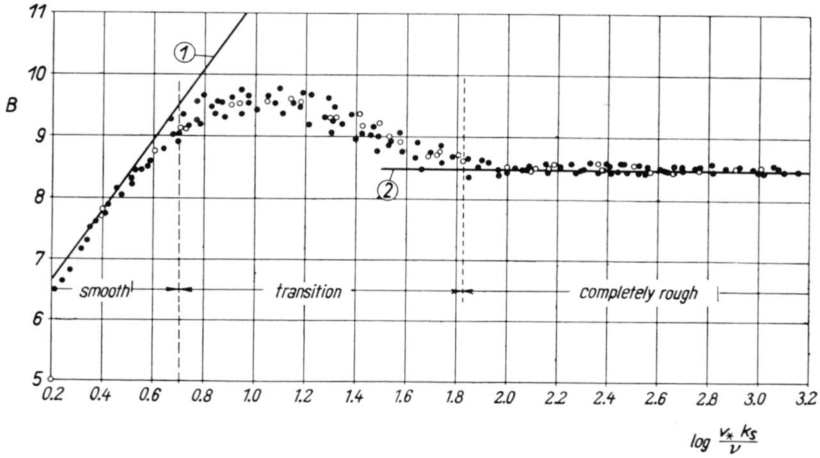

Fig. 20.21. Roughness function B in terms of $v_* k_S/\nu$ for Nikuradse's sand roughness
Curve (1): hydraulically smooth, eqn. (20.33); curve (2): $B = 8{\cdot}5$; completely rough

The corresponding straight line is seen to agree well with the results of measurement, Fig. 20.20. Generally speaking B is a function of the roughness Reynolds number $v_* k_S/\nu$. The value which corresponds to hydraulically smooth flow follows at once from eqns. (20.32) and (20.14), and is

$$B = 5{\cdot}5 + 2{\cdot}5 \ln \frac{v_* k_S}{\nu}\,, \quad \text{(hydraulically smooth)}\,. \tag{20.33}$$

The values of B in the transition region from hydraulically smooth flow to completely rough flow are shown plotted against $v_* k_S/\nu$ in Fig. 20.21; the points are seen to arrange themselves exceedingly well on one curve.

Writing eqn. (20.32) for the axis of the pipe $y = R$, $u = U$ and forming the difference $U - u$, we obtain the equation

$$\frac{U-u}{v_*} = 2{\cdot}5 \ln \frac{R}{y} = 5{\cdot}75 \log \frac{R}{y}\,, \tag{20.23}$$

once more. It has been found to apply to smooth pipes in connexion with Fig. 20.7. In order more clearly to see the connexion between the velocity distributions for smooth and rough pipes, it is useful to re-plot the results for rough pipes in the form of a relation between the dimensionless velocity $u/v_* = \phi$ and the Reynolds number $y\,v_*/\nu = \eta$, as was done in eqn. (20.13) and Fig. 20.4 in relation to smooth pipes. Writing eqn. (20.32a) for the rough pipe in the form

$$\frac{u}{v_*} = 5{\cdot}75 \log \frac{y v_*}{\nu} + D_1\,, \quad \text{(completely rough)} \tag{20.33a}$$

and comparing it with eqns. (20.33a) and (20.32a), we obtain

$$D_1 = 8{\cdot}5 - 5{\cdot}75 \log \frac{k_S v_*}{\nu} \quad \text{(completely rough)}\,. \tag{20.33b}$$

This velocity distribution is seen plotted in Fig. 20.22 after N. Scholz [46]; it represents the velocity distribution for smooth pipes as well as that for rough pipes, in accordance with eqn. (20.33a). The diagram consists of a family of parallel straight

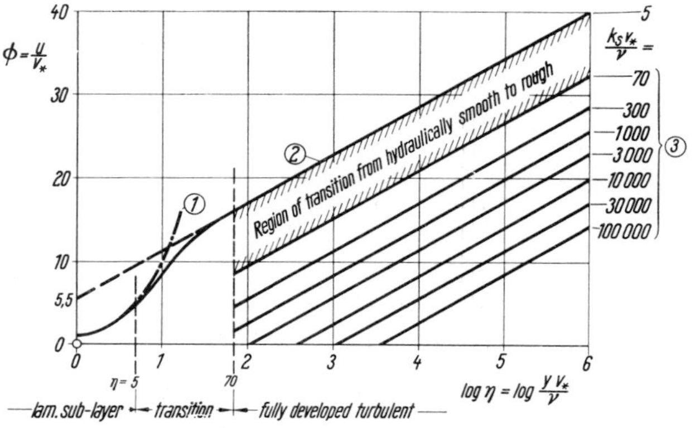

Fig. 20.22. Universal velocity profile for turbulent flows through pipes which is valid for smooth as well as for rough walls after N. Scholz [46]

(1) smooth, laminar sub-layer, $\phi = \eta$
(2) smooth, turbulent, eqn. (20.14)
(3) rough, turbulent, eqn. (20.33a) with D_1 from eqn. (20.33b)

lines with $v_* k_S/\nu$ playing the part of a parameter. The value of $v_* k_S/\nu = 5$ corresponds to hydraulically smooth walls, the range between $v_* k_S/\nu = 5$ to 70 corresponds to transition from the hydraulically smooth to the completely rough regime, and for $v_* k_S/\nu > 70$ the flow is completely rough, as mentioned previously. In particular, the diagram shows clearly that the laminar sub-layer which reaches as far as $y\, v_*/\nu = 5$ in hydraulically smooth pipes, has no importance for completely rough walls.

Relation between resistance formula and velocity distribution: This type of relation exists for rough pipes also and can be deduced in the same manner as was done in Sec. XXd for the case of smooth pipes. The relation is simplest for the *completely rough regime*. We begin by calculating the mean velocity from eqn. (20.23) in the same way as in eqn. (20.26):

$$\bar{u} = U - 3{\cdot}75\, v_* \,. \tag{20.34}$$

Substituting $U = v_* (2{\cdot}5 \ln R/k_S + 8{\cdot}5)$ from eqn. (20.32a) we have

$$\bar{u}/v_* = 2{\cdot}5 \ln (R/k_S) + 4{\cdot}75 \quad \text{or} \quad \lambda/8 = (v_*/\bar{u})^2 = [2{\cdot}5 \ln (R/k_S) + 4{\cdot}75]^{-2}$$

i. e.

$$\lambda = [2 \log (R/k_S) + 1{\cdot}68]^{-2} \,,$$

which is the quadratic resistance formula for completely rough flow. It was first derived by Th. von Kármán (Chap. XIX [9]) from the similarity law. A comparison with J. Nikuradse's experimental results (Fig. 20.23) shows that closer agreement can be obtained, if the constant 1·68 is replaced by 1·74. Hence the *resistance formula for the completely rough regime* becomes

$$\lambda = \frac{1}{\left(2 \log \frac{R}{k_S} + 1{\cdot}74\right)^2} \,. \tag{20.35}$$ †

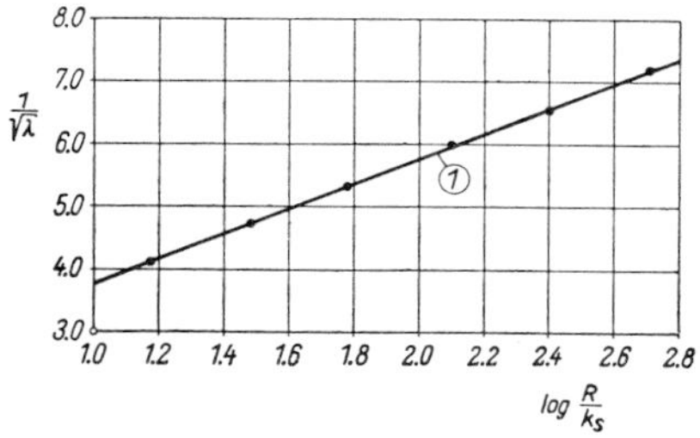

Fig. 20.23. Resistance formula of sand-roughened pipes in completely rough regime

Curve (1) from eqn. (20.35)

† An equation which correlates the whole transition region from hydraulically smooth to completely rough flow was established by Colebrook and White [5]:

$$\frac{1}{\sqrt{\lambda}} = 1{\cdot}74 - 2 \log \left(\frac{k_S}{R} + \frac{18{\cdot}7}{\mathsf{R} \sqrt{\lambda}}\right). \tag{20.35a}$$

For $k_S \to 0$ this equation transforms into eqn. (20.30), valid for hydraulically smooth pipes. For $\mathsf{R} \to \infty$, it transforms into eqn. (20.35) for the completely rough regime. In the transition region eqn. (20.35a) plots λ against R in a way which resembles the curve labelled "commercially rough" in Figs. 20.18 and 20.25.

The experimental results lie very close to a straight line in a plot of $1/\sqrt{\lambda}$ against $\log(R/k_S)$ and it is worth noting that eqn. (20.35) may be applied to pipes with non-circular cross-sectional areas, if R is replaced by the hydraulic radius $R_h = 2\,A/C$ (A = area; C = wetted perimeter).

It is also easy to derive the relation between the resistance law and the velocity distribution in the *transition region*. From eqn. (20.32) we have

$$B = \frac{u}{v_*} - 2{\cdot}5 \ln \frac{y}{k_S} = \frac{U}{v_*} - 2{\cdot}5 \ln \frac{R}{k_S}\,.$$

On the other hand, from eqn. (20.34) we obtain

$$\frac{U}{v_*} = \frac{\overline{u}}{v_*} + 3{\cdot}75 = \frac{2\sqrt{2}}{\sqrt{\lambda}} + 3{\cdot}75\,,$$

and the preceding equation gives

$$B\left(\frac{v_*\,k_S}{\nu}\right) = \frac{u}{v_*} - 2{\cdot}5 \ln \frac{y}{k_S} = \frac{2\sqrt{2}}{\sqrt{\lambda}} + 3{\cdot}75 - 2{\cdot}5 \ln \frac{R}{k_S}\,. \tag{20.36}$$

The last equation determines the value of the resistance coefficient λ if the constant B is known from the velocity distribution. On the other hand, eqn. (20.36) can be used to determine the constant B as a function of $v_*\,k_S/\nu$ either from the velocity distribution or from the resistance formula. The plot in Fig. 20.21 agrees well with the results from either of these methods and proves that the calculation of the velocity distribution from the resistance formula is permissible for rough pipes too.

The limits between the three regimes, namely those of hydraulically smooth flow, the transitional regime, and the completely rough regime, which have been given earlier, can now be taken directly from Fig. 20.21. We have

$$\left.\begin{array}{ll} \text{hydraulically smooth:} & \dfrac{v_*\,k_S}{\nu} < 5\,, \\[2ex] \text{transition:} & 5 < \dfrac{v_*\,k_S}{\nu} < 70\,, \\[2ex] \text{completely rough:} & \dfrac{v_*\,k_S}{\nu} > 70\,. \end{array}\right\} \tag{20.37}$$

These limits are in complete accord with the velocity distribution in the boundary layer in the immediate neighbourhood of a smooth wall measured by H. Reichardt and plotted in Fig. 20.4. The limit of the hydraulically smooth regime $v_*\,k_S/\nu = 5$ gives the thickness of the laminar sub-layer and coincides with the limit of the range in which the Hagen-Poiseuille, purely laminar velocity distribution law retains its validity. The limit of $v_*\,k_S/\nu = 70$ for the transitional regime also coincides with the point, where the measured velocity distribution goes over tangentially into the logarithmic formula (20.14) in fully turbulent friction.

S. Goldstein [13] succeeded in deducing the limit of $v_*\,k_S/\nu = 5$ for the hydraulically smooth regime from the criterion that at that point a von Kármán vortex street is about to begin to form on an individual protrusion. According to measurements on circular cylinders performed by F. Homann this occurs at a Reynolds number of 60 to 100, where the Reynolds number is formed with the diameter and the free-stream velocity (Fig. 1.6). In a more recent investigation J. Rotta [40] found that the thickness of the laminar sub-layer is smaller for a rough wall than for a smooth one to which eqn. (20.15a) was found to apply.

g. Other types of roughness

The roughness obtained by Nikuradse with sand can be said to be of maximum density, because the grains of sand were glued to the wall as closely to each other as possible. In many practical applications the roughness density of the walls is considerably smaller and such roughnesses can no longer be described by the indication of the height of a protrusion, k, or by the relative measure k/R only. It is convenient to arrange such roughnesses on a scale of *standard roughness* and to adopt Nikuradse's sand roughness for correlation because it has been investigated in a very large range of values of R and k_S/R. The correlation is simplest in the completely rough regime when, according to what was said previously, the resistance coefficient is given by eqn. (20.35). It is convenient to correlate any given roughness with its *equivalent sand roughness* and to define it as that value which gives the actual coefficient of resistance when inserted into eqn. (20.35).

H. Schlichting [45] determined experimentally these values of equivalent sand roughness for a large number of roughnesses arranged in a regular fashion. The special experimental channel used for this purpose had a rectangular cross-section

No	item	dimensions	D [cm]	d [cm]	k [cm]	k_s [cm]	photographs
1	spheres	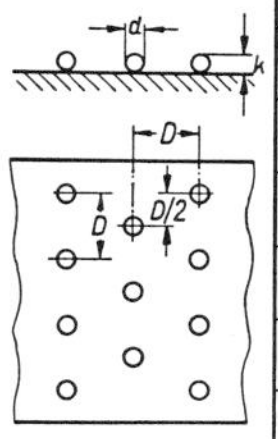	4	0.41	0.41	0.093	
2			2	0.41	0.41	0.344	
3			1	0.41	0.41	1.26	
4			0,6	0.41	0.41	1.56	
5			densest arrgt.	0.41	0.41	0.257	
6			1	0,21	0.21	0.172	
7			0.5	0.21	0.21	0.759	
8	spherical segments	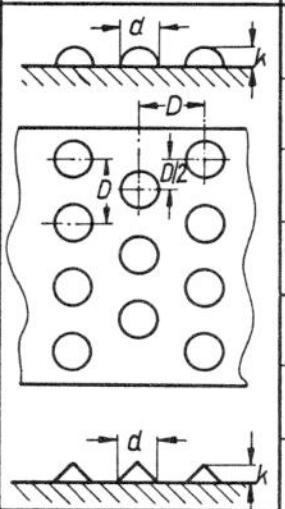	4	0.8	0.26	0.031	
9			3	0.8	0.26	0.049	
10			2	0.8	0.26	0.149	
11			densest arrgt.	0.8	0.26	0.365	
12	cones		4	0.8	0.375	0.059	
13			3	0.8	0.375	0.164	
14			2	0.8	0.375	0.374	
15	„short" angles	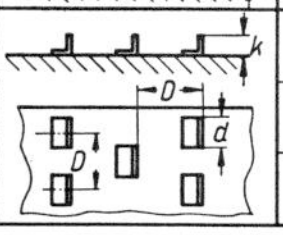	4	0.8	0.30	0.291	
16			3	0.8	0.30	0.618	
17			2	0.8	0.30	1.47	

Fig. 20.24. Results of measurements on regular roughness patterns

k — actual height of protrusion; k_S — equivalent sand roughness

with three smooth side-walls and one long, interchangeable side-wall whose roughness was varied to suit the experiment. By measuring the velocity distribution in the central cross-section it is possible to determine the shearing stress on the rough wall with the aid of the logarithmic formula and hence, also, the equivalent sand roughness. In order to do that it is only necessary to determine the constant B in the universal equation $u/v^* = 5{\cdot}75 \log (y/k) + B$ for a given value of k. On comparing with eqn. (20.32a) we obtain the equivalent sand roughness from the equation

$$5{\cdot}75 \log k_S/k = 8{\cdot}5 - B\,. \tag{20.38}$$

Some results of such measurements are seen summarized in Fig. 20.24. Similar measurements were carried out by V. L. Streeter and H. Moebius [24] on pipes which had been made artificially rough by cutting threads of different forms into them.

Generally speaking, pipes which are regarded as *smooth in* engineering *practice* cannot be taken to be *hydraulically smooth*. An example of this discrepancy is given in Fig. 20.18, where results of the measurements carried out by B. Bauer and F. Galavics [2] on a "commercially smooth" steel pipe with a flow of hot water are seen plotted together with Nikuradse's values for pipes roughened with sand.

The difficulty in applying the above calculations to practical cases lies in the fact that the value of roughness to be ascribed to a given pipe is not known. Very extensive experimental results on the resistance of commercially rough pipes are contained in a paper by L. F. Moody [25]. Fig. 20.25 shows that the graph of λ against R for different values of k_S/d is in essence identical with J. Nikuradse's diagram in Fig. 20.18. The individual values of equivalent relative sand roughness k_S/d can be obtained from the auxiliary graph in Fig. 20.26 where pipes are seen to have been arranged in the order of values on Nikuradse's equivalent sand roughness scale. This follows from the fact that the values of λ in terms of k_S/d agree with

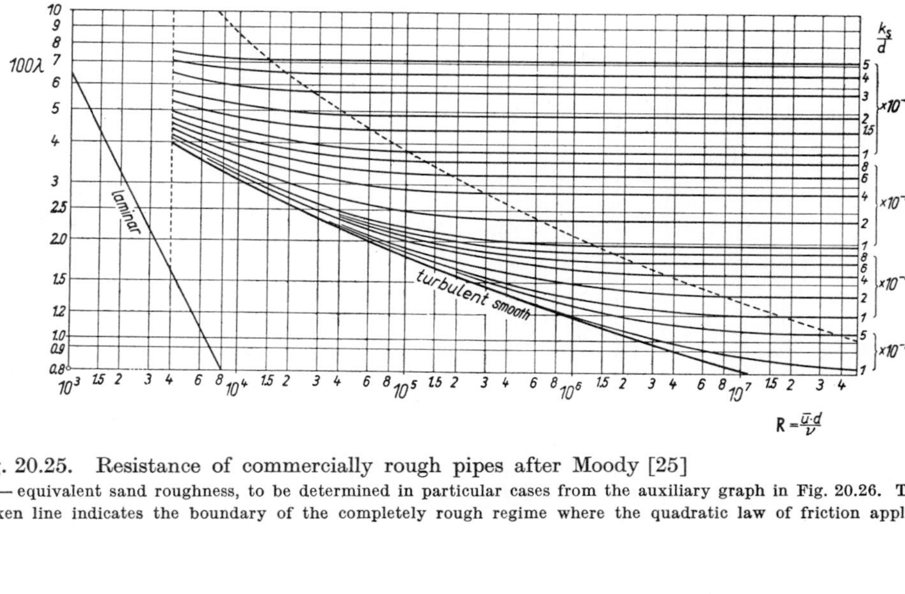

Fig. 20.25. Resistance of commercially rough pipes after Moody [25]

k_S — equivalent sand roughness, to be determined in particular cases from the auxiliary graph in Fig. 20.26. The broken line indicates the boundary of the completely rough regime where the quadratic law of friction applies

Nikuradse's values from Fig. 20.18 in the completely rough regime. The transition from hydraulically smooth conditions at small Reynolds numbers to complete roughness at large Reynolds numbers occurs much more gradually in such commercial pipes than in Nikuradse's artificially roughened ones.

It is sometimes impossible to fit commercially rough surfaces satisfactorily into the scale of sand roughness. A peculiar type of roughness giving very large values of the resistance coefficient was discovered in the water duct in the valley of the Ecker [49, 57]. This pipe had a diameter of 500 mm and after a long period of usage it was noticed that the mass flow decreased by more than 50 per cent. Upon examination it was found that the walls of the duct were covered with a rib-like deposit only 0·5 mm high, the ribs being at right angles to the flow direction. Thus the geometrical roughness had the small value of $k/R = 1/1000$, but the effective sand roughness showed values of $k_S/R = 1/40$ to $1/20$, as calculated from the resistance coefficient which was, in turn, determined with the aid of the measured values of mass flow. It appears, therefore, that rib-like corrugations lead to much higher resistances than sand roughness of the same absolute dimension. Extensive experiments on the increase in the resistance found in commercial pipes, as used in ducts for air-conditioning, can be found described in a paper by E. Huebner [19].

Further details concerning the resistance offered to flow by rough walls, particularly those due to single protrusions, will be given in Chap. XXI in connexion with the discussion on the resistance of flat plates.

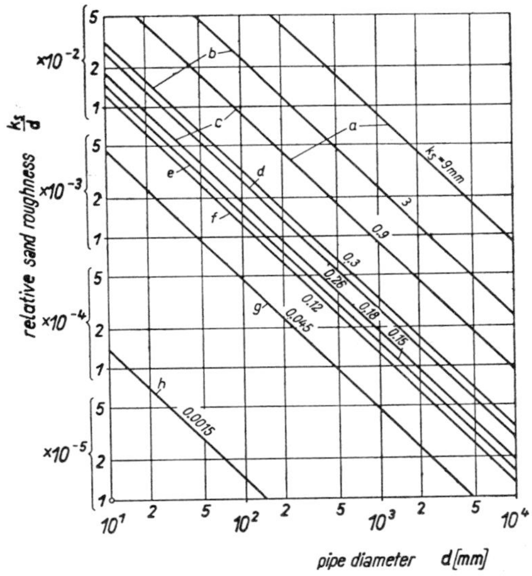

Fig. 20.26. Auxiliary diagram for the evaluation of equivalent relative sand roughness for commercial pipes after Moody [25]

a) riveted steel
b) reinforced concrete
c) wood
d) cast iron
e) galvanized steel
f) bitumen-coated steel
g) structural and forged steel
h) drawn pipes

h. Flow in curved pipes

The preceding considerations concerning pipe flow are valid only for straight pipes. In curved pipes there exists a secondary flow, because the particles near the flow axis which have a higher velocity are acted upon by a larger centrifugal force than the slower particles near the walls. This leads to the emergence of a secondary flow which is directed outwards in the centre and inwards (i. e. towards the centre of curvature) near the wall, Fig. 20.27.

The influence of curvature is stronger in laminar than in turbulent flow. C. M. White [56] and M. Adler [1] carried out experiments on laminar flow. The turbulent case was investigated experimentally by H. Nippert [31], H. Richter [39], C. M. White [56a] and H. Ito [19a]. Theoretical calculations for the laminar case were carried out by W. R. Dean [7] and M. Adler [1]. The characteristic dimensionless variable, which determines the influence of curvature *in the laminar case*, is the *Dean number*

$$\mathsf{D} = \tfrac{1}{2}\,\mathsf{R}\sqrt{R/r} = \frac{uR}{\nu}\sqrt{\frac{R}{r}}$$

where R is the radius of the cross-section and r is the radius of curvature.

The measurements carried out by M. Adler for the values: $r/R = 50$, 100, and 200, demonstrated the existence of a large increase in the resistance to flow caused by the curvature for $\mathsf{R}\sqrt{R/r} > 10^{1/2}$. According to his calculations the resistance coefficient λ for laminar flow in a curved pipe is given by

$$\frac{\lambda}{\lambda_0} = 0{\cdot}1064\left[\mathsf{R}\sqrt{\frac{R}{r}}\right]^{\frac{1}{2}},$$

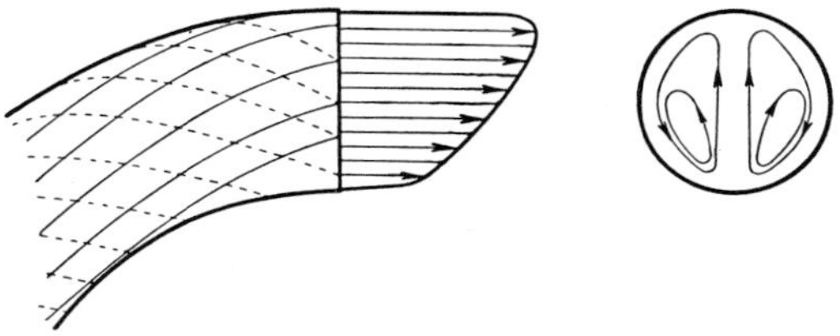

Fig. 20.27. Flow in a curved pipe, after Prandtl [35]

where λ_0 denotes the coefficient of resistance of a straight pipe, eqn. (20.30). Measurements indicate, however, that the above equation only has asymptotic validity, and may be used for values of the parameter $\sqrt{R/r}$ exceeding about $10^{2{\cdot}8}$. The results of measurements are approximated with a higher degree of precision by the following empirical equation, first given by L. Prandtl [36]:

$$\frac{\lambda}{\lambda_0} = 0{\cdot}37\ \mathsf{D}^{0{\cdot}36}.$$

This equation gives good agreement with experimental results in the range

$$10^{1{\cdot}6} < \mathsf{R}\,(R/r)^{1/2} < 10^{3{\cdot}0}\,.$$

C. M. White [56a] has found that the resistance coefficient for *turbulent flow* in a curved pipe can be represented by the equation

$$\frac{\lambda}{\lambda_0} = 1 + 0{\cdot}075\ \mathsf{R}^{1/4}\left(\frac{R}{r}\right)^{1/2}\ \dagger$$

† H. Ito [19a] gives:

$$\lambda\left(\frac{R}{r}\right)^{1/2} = 0{\cdot}029 + 0{\cdot}304\left[\mathsf{R}\left(\frac{R}{r}\right)^{2}\right]^{-0{\cdot}25} \qquad 300 > \mathsf{R}(R/r)^2 > 0{\cdot}034$$

$$\frac{\lambda}{\lambda_0} = \left[\mathsf{R}\left(\frac{R}{r}\right)^{2}\right]^{1{\cdot}20} \qquad \mathsf{R}(R/r)^2 > 6\,.$$

These differ somewhat from, but are in general agrement with C. M. White's equation above.

whose form indicates clearly that the Dean number can no longer serve as a suitable independent variable. In more recent times, H. Cumings [5a] carried out an investigation into the phenomenon of secondary flow in curved pipes. W. R. Hawthorne [16a] gave an analytical study of the subject.

Extensive measurements and theoretical calculations on frictional losses in turbulent flow have also been carried out by R. W. Detra [8] who included curved pipes of noncircular cross-section in his investigations. It is found that the resistance offered by an elliptic pipe is greater when the major axis of the ellipse lies in the plane of curvature than when it is perpendicular to it.

E. Becker [3] studied secondary flows in a rectangular channel of constant curvature in which the radial extent of the cross-section is much larger than its height. The formation of dead-water areas and separation in a 90° rectangular bend provided with a sharp entrance was investigated by D. Haase [15].

The curvature of the pipe has a marked effect upon the transition Reynolds number causing transition to be delayed to higher Reynolds numbers.

i. Non-steady flow through a pipe

The problem of pulsating flow, i. e. of a steady mean flow on which there is superimposed a periodic pulsation, was investigated by F. Schultz-Grunow [47]. The experimental arrangement consisted of a pipe which was fed with water at a constant head and whose end section was rhythmically increased and decreased in area. The velocity profiles for the periods of acceleration and deceleration respectively differ markedly from one another. They are very similar to steady flow profiles through a gradually convergent pipe or channel during the periods of acceleration, and during periods of deceleration they resemble steady-state profiles in a divergent channel (diffuser), as explained in Chap. XXII, where such profiles will be found plotted in detail. Under certain circumstances both reversal of flow and separation near the wall may occur during periods of deceleration. The time-averaged value of the coefficient of resistance does not differ considerably from its steady-state value when the pulsations are gradual and slow. In a further paper, F. Schultz-Grunow [48] described a practical method for the measurement of the rate of discharge in pulsating flow.

References

[1] M. Adler, Strömung in gekrümmten Rohren. ZAMM **14**, 257 (1934).
[2] B. Bauer and F. Galavics, Experimentelle und theoretische Untersuchungen über die Rohrreibung von Heizwasserleitungen. Mitteilg. d. Fernheizkraftwerkes d. ETH Zürich 1936; see also F. Galavics, Schweizer Archiv **5**, 12, 337 (1939).
[3] E. Becker, Beitrag zur Berechnung von Sekundärströmungen. ZAMM **36**, Sonderheft, pp. 3—8 (1956); see also Rep. of the Max-Planck-Institut für Strömungsforschung **13** (1956).
[4] H. Blasius, Das Ähnlichkeitsgesetz bei Reibungsvorgängen in Flüssigkeiten. Forschungsheft 131, Berlin (1913).
[5] C. F. Colebrook, Turbulent flow in pipes with particular reference to the transition region between the smooth and rough pipe laws. Journ. Institution Civil Engineers, 1939; see also Engineering Hydraulics, ed. by H. Rouse, Chap. VI, Steady flow in pipes and conduits by V. L. Streeter, New York 1950.
[5a] H. G. Cumings, The secondary flow in curved pipes. ARC R & M 2880 (1955).

[6] H. Darcy, Recherches experimentales relatives aux mouvements de l'eau dans tuyaux. Mém. prés a l'Academie des Sciences de l'Institute de France **15**, 141 (1858).
[7] W. R. Dean, The streamline motion of a fluid in a curved pipe. Phil. Mag. (7) **4**, 208 (1927); and **5**, 673 (1928).
[8] R. W. Detra, The secondary flow in curved pipes. Reports of the Aero. Inst. of the E.T.H. Zürich, No. 20 (1953).
[9] E. R. G. Eckert and T. F. Irvine, Flow in corners with non-circular cross-sections. Trans. ASME **78**, 709—718 (1956); see also Jour. Aero. Sci. **22**, 65/66 (1955).
[10] W. Fritsch, Einfluß der Wandrauhigkeit auf die turbulente Geschwindigkeitsverteilung in Rinnen. ZAMM **8**, 199 (1928).
[11] K. Fromm, Strömungswiderstand in rauhen Rohren. ZAMM **3**, 339 (1923).
[12] W. Frössel, Strömung in glatten, geraden Rohren mit Über- und Unterschallgeschwindigkeit. Forschg. a. d. Geb. d. Ing.-Wesens **7**, 75 (1936).
[13] S. Goldstein, A note on roughness. ARC R & M 1763 (1936).
[14] S. Goldstein, The similarity theory of turbulence, and flow between planes and through pipes. Proc. Roy. Soc. London, A **159**, 473 (1937).
[15] D. Haase, Strömung in einem 90° Knie. Ing. Arch. **22**, 282—292 (1954).
[16] For additional references see H. W. Hahnemann, Der Strömungswiderstand in Rohrleitungen und Leitungselementen. Forschung Ing.-Wes. **16**, 113 (1950).
[16a] W. R. Hawthorne, Secondary circulation in fluid flow, Proc. Roy. Soc. London, A **206**, 374 (1951).
[17] R. Hermann, Experimentelle Untersuchungen zum Widerstandsgesetz des Kreisrohres bei hohen Reynoldsschen Zahlen und großen Anlauflängen. Dissertation Leipzig, Akad. Verlagsgesellschaft Leipzig 1930.
[18] L. Hopf, Die Messung der hydraulischen Rauhigkeit. ZAMM **3**, 329 (1923).
[19] E. Hübner, Über den Druckverlust in Rohren mit Einbauten. Forschung Ing. Wes. **19**, 1—16 (1953).
[19a] H. Ito, Friction factors in turbulent flow in curved pipes, Trans. ASME D **81** (Jour. Basic Eng'g.), 123 (1959).
[20] M. Jakob and S. Erk, Der Druckabfall in glatten Rohren und die Durchflußziffer von Normaldüsen. Forschungs-Arb. Ing.-Wesen, No. 267, Berlin (1924).
[21] Th. von Kármán, Über laminare und turbulente Reibung. ZAMM **1**, 233 (1921).
[22] H. Kirsten, Experimentelle Untersuchungen der Entwicklung der Geschwindigkeitsverteilung der turbulenten Rohrströmung. Thesis Leipzig 1927.
[23] E. Meyer, Einfluß der Querschnittsverformung auf die Entwicklung der Geschwindigkeits- und Druckverteilung bei turbulenten Geschwindigkeitsverteilungen in Rohren. VDI-Forschungsheft 389 (1938).
[24] H. Möbius, Experimentelle Untersuchungen des Widerstandes und der Geschwindigkeitsverteilung in Rohren mit regelmäßig angeordneten Rauhigkeiten bei turbulenter Strömung. Phys. Z. **41**, 202—225 (1940).
[25] L. F. Moody, Friction factors for pipe flow. Trans. Amer. Soc. Mech. Eng. **66** 671 (1944).
[26] A. Naumann, Druckverlust in Rohren nichtkreisförmigen Querschnittes bei hohen Geschwindigkeiten. ZAMM **36**, Sonderheft (special issue), p. 25 (1956).
[27] J. Nikuradse, Untersuchungen über die Geschwindigkeitsverteilung in turbulenten Strömungen. Thesis Göttingen 1926. VDI-Forschungsheft 281, Berlin (1926).
[28] J. Nikuradse, Turbulente Strömung in nicht kreisförmigen Rohren. Ing.-Arch. **1**, 306 (1930).
[29] J. Nikuradse, Gesetzmäßigkeit der turbulenten Strömung in glatten Rohren. Forschungsheft 356 (1932).
[30] J. Nikuradse, Strömungsgesetze in rauhen Rohren. Forschungsheft 361 (1933).
[31] H. Nippert, Über den Strömungswiderstand in gekrümmten Kanälen. Forschungsheft 320 (1929).
[32] W. Nusselt, Wärmeübergang in Rohrleitungen. Forschungs-Arb. Ing.-Wesen 89, Berlin (1910).
[33] H. Ombeck, Druckverlust strömender Luft in geraden zylindrischen Rohrleitungen. Forschungs-Arb. Ing.-Wesen No. 158/159, Berlin (1914).
[34] L. Prandtl, Über den Reibungswiderstand strömender Luft. Ergebnisse Aerodyn. Versuchsanst. Göttingen, **III** series, München (1927); see also L. Prandtl, Rep. of the Aerodyn. Versuchsanst. Göttingen, **I** series, 136 (1921).

[35] L. Prandtl, The mechanics of viscous fluids. In W. F. Durand, Aerodynamic Theory, III, 142 (1935); see also comprehensive review by L. Prandtl, Neuere Ergebnisse der Turbulenzforschung. Z. VDI **77**, 105 (1933).
[36] L. Prandtl, Führer durch die Strömungslehre. 3rd. ed. p. 159, Braunschweig 1949. (Engl. transl. by Miss W. M. Deans, Blackie & Son, London 1952).
[37] H. Reichardt, Die Wärmeübertragung in turbulenten Reibungsschichten. ZAMM **20**, 297—328 (1940).
[38] H. Reichardt, Vollständige Darstellung der turbulenten Geschwindigkeitsverteilung in glatten Leitungen. ZAMM **31**, 208—219 (1951).
[39] H. Richter, Der Druckabfall in gekrümmten glatten Rohrleitungen. Forschungs-Arb. Ing.-Wesen, No. 338 (1930).
[40] J. Rotta, Das in Wandnähe gültige Geschwindigkeitsgesetz turbulenter Strömungen. Ing.-Arch. **18**, 277—280 (1950).
[41] V. Saph and E. H. Schoder, An experimental study of the resistance to the flow of water in pipes. Trans. Amer. Soc. Civ. Engr. **51**, 944 (1903).
[42] L. Schiller, Über den Strömungswiderstand von Rohren verschiedenen Querschnitts und Rauhigkeitsgrades. ZAMM **3**, 2—13 (1923).
[43] L. Schiller, Rohrwiderstand bei hohen Reynoldsschen Zahlen. Vorträge a. d. Gebiet d. Aerodynamik und verwandter Gebiete, 69, Berlin 1930.
[44] L. Schiller, Strömung in Rohren. Handb. d. Exper. Physik **IV**, Part 4, Leipzig (1931).
[45] H. Schlichting, Experimentelle Untersuchungen zum Rauhigkeitsproblem. Ing.-Arch. **7**, 1—34 (1936). Engl. transl. in Proc. ASME (1936); see also Werft, Reederei, Hafen, 99 (1936), and Jb. der Schiffbautechn. Ges., 418 (1936).
[46] N. Scholz, Strömungsvorgänge in Grenzschichten. VDI-Berichte **4**, 7—12 (1956).
[47] F. Schultz-Grunow, Pulsierender Durchfluß durch Rohre. Forschg. Ing.-Wesen **11**, 170 (1940).
[48] F. Schultz-Grunow, Durchflußmeßverfahren für pulsierende Strömungen. Forschg. Ing-Wesen **12**, 117 (1941).
[49] R. Seiferth and W. Krüger, Überraschend hohe Reibungsziffer einer Fernwasserleitung. Z. VDI **92**, 189 (1950).
[50] T. E. Stanton, The mechanical viscosity of fluids. Proc. Roy. Soc. London, A **85**, 366 (1911).
[51] T. E. Stanton and J. R. Pannel, Similarity of motion in relation of the surface friction of fluids. Phil. Trans. Roy. Soc. A **214**, 199 (1914); see also Proc. Roy. Soc. London, A **91**, 46 (1915).
[52] V. L. Streeter, Frictional resistance in artificially roughened pipes. Proc. Amer. Soc. Civil Engr. **61**, 163 (1935).
[53] W. Szablewski, Berechnung der turbulenten Strömung im Rohr auf der Grundlage der Mischungsweghypothese. ZAMM **31**, 131—142 (1951).
[54] W. Szablewski, Der Einlauf einer turbulenten Rohrströmung. Ing. Arch. **21**, 323—330 (1953).
[55] G. I. Taylor, Flow in pipes and between parallel planes. Proc. Roy. Soc. London, A **159**, 496 (1937).
[56] C. M. White, Streamline flow through curved pipes. Proc. Roy. Soc. London, A **123**, 645 (1929).
[56a] C. M. White, Fluid friction and its relation to heat transfer, Trans. Inst. Chem. Engineers, **10**, 66 (1932).
[57] W. Wiederhold, Über den Einfluß von Rohrablagerungen auf den hydraulischen Druckabfall. Gas- u. Wasserfach **99**, 634 (1949).
[58] K. Wieghardt, Turbulente Grenzschichten. Göttingen Monograph, Part B 5, 1946.

CHAPTER XXI

Skin friction drag of a flat plate at zero incidence; Rotating disks; Roughness

It might be surmised that it would be possible to perform calculations on the turbulent boundary layer along a flat plate or along any shape, for that matter, from the equations of motion and by the same general methods as those applied to laminar boundary layers, having first established an expression for the magnitude of the viscous forces with the aid of one of the hypotheses which have been discussed in Chap. XIX. So far, however, this scheme has met with no success owing to insurmountable difficulties, nothing being know about the zone of transition from the turbulent boundary layer to the laminar sub-layer which exists in the immediate neighbourhood of the wall, and the laws of friction in the sub-layer are also unknown. From this point of view conditions are more favourable as far as problems of so-called *free turbulent flows* are concerned. These include turbulent motions in which no solid boundaries exist, such as when a jet of fluid is mixed with the surrounding atmosphere at rest, or when the wake behind a body diffuses into the stream. Such cases can be solved with the aid of the differential equations together with the empirical laws of turbulent friction. As far as the other problems of turbulent flow are concerned no successful scheme for the integration of the equations of motion has yet been advanced. The only methods available at the present time for the mathematical treatment of turbulent boundary layers are approximate methods of the type used in laminar boundary layer theory. These are based, principally, on the momentum theorem which has been used successfully in the study of laminar boundary layers too.

The simplest case of a turbulent boundary layer occurs on a flat plate at zero incidence; it is, furthermore, of great practical importance. It occurs, for example, in the calculation of the skin friction drag on ships, on lifting surfaces and aeroplane bodies in aeronautical engineering, and on the blades of turbines and rotary compressors. The flat plate at zero incidence is simpler to consider, because the pressure gradient along the wall is zero so that the velocity outside the boundary layer is constant. In some of the above examples the pressure gradient may differ from zero but, just as was the case with laminar flow, the skin friction in such instances is not materially different from that on a flat plate, provided that there is no separation. The study of the flat plate is thus the basis for the calculation of the skin friction drag for all body shapes which do not suffer appreciably from separation. The next chapter will contain an extension of this study to the case of a turbulent boundary layer with a definite pressure gradient. In many practical cases (ships, aeroplanes) the Reynolds numbers $\mathsf{R} = U_\infty l/\nu$ (U_∞ — free steam velocity; l—length of plate) are so large that they cannot be subjected to measurement in a laboratory. Moreover, even at moderate Reynolds numbers it is much more difficult to carry out measurements in the boundary layer on a plate than in that inside a pipe. It is, therefore, very advantageous that it is possible to calculate the skin friction on a plate from the extensive data available for pipes by the use of a method due to L. Prandtl [35] and Th. von Kármán [25]. This calculation of the skin friction drag on a plate can be carried out both for smooth and for rough walls.

a. The smooth flat plate

The approximate method to be applied to this problem is based on the momentum integral equation of boundary layer theory as given in eqn. (8.35) of Chap. VIII, the velocity profile over the boundary layer thickness being approximated by a suitable empirical equation. The momentum equation then provides a relation between the *characteristic parameters* of the boundary layer, i. e. between displacement thickness, momentum thickness and shearing stress at the wall.

In the following argument we shall assume at first that the boundary layer is turbulent already at the leading edge ($x=0$) and we shall choose a system of co-ordinates as shown in Fig. 21.1, b denoting the width of the plate. The boundary layer thickness $\delta(x)$ increases with x and on translating the data for a pipe into those for a plate we notice that the maximum velocity, U, of the former corresponds to the free stream velocity, U_∞, of the latter, the radius, R, of the pipe corresponding to the boundary layer thickness, δ.

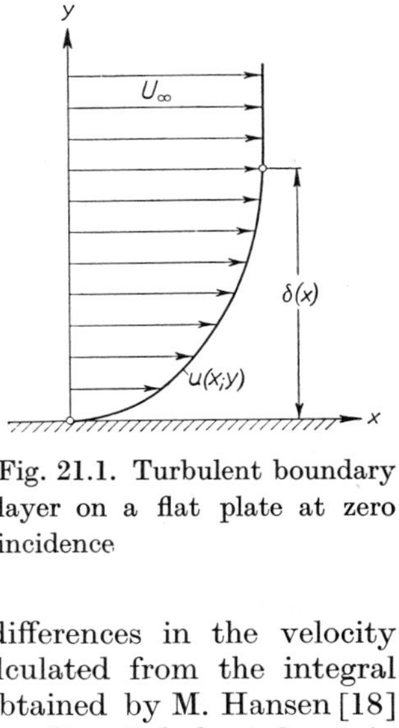

Fig. 21.1. Turbulent boundary layer on a flat plate at zero incidence

At this stage we introduce with L. Prandtl the fundamental assumption that the velocity distribution in the boundary layer on a plate is identical with that inside a circular pipe. This assumption cannot, certainly, be exact, because the velocity distribution in a pipe is formed under the influence of a pressure gradient, whereas on a plate the pressure gradient is zero. However, small differences in the velocity distribution are unimportant, because the drag is calculated from the integral of momentum. Furthermore, the experimental results obtained by M. Hansen [18] and J. M. Burgers [4] prove that this assumption is well satisfied at least in the range of moderately large Reynolds numbers ($U_\infty l/\nu < 10^6$). They both found that the velocity profile in the boundary layer on a plate can be described fairly well by a power formula of the form of eqn. (20.6), as found for a pipe. We shall revert once more to this problem (p. 541), when we shall discuss some systematic deviations between the velocity profiles in pipes and on plates at larger Reynolds numbers.

The skin friction $D(x)$ on a flat plate of lenght x on one side satisfies the following relation as seen from eqns. (12.1) and (12.2) in Chap. XII:

$$D(x) = b\int_0^x \tau_0(x')\,\mathrm{d}x' = b\,\varrho\int_0^{\delta(x)} u(U_\infty - u)\,\mathrm{d}y\,. \tag{21.1}$$

Here $\tau_0(x)$ denotes the shearing stress at a distance x from the leading edge, and the second integral is evaluated at x over the boundary layer thickness. Introducing the momentum thickness θ, defined by $\theta\, U_\infty^2 = \int_0^\delta u(U_\infty - u)\, dy$ in eqn. (8.34), we can rewrite eqn. (21.1) as follows:

$$D(x) = b\, \varrho\, U_\infty^2\, \theta(x)\,. \tag{21.2}$$

From eqns. (21.1) and (21.2) we obtain the local shearing stress:

$$\frac{1}{b}\,\frac{\mathrm{d}D}{\mathrm{d}x} = \tau_0(x) = \varrho\, U_\infty^2\, \frac{\mathrm{d}\theta}{\mathrm{d}x}\,. \tag{21.3}$$

Equation (21.3) is identical with the momentum theorem of boundary layer theory, eqn. (8.35), in the case of uniform potential flow $U(x) = U_\infty = \text{const.}$

We shall now perform the calculation of the drag on a flat plate on the assumption of a $\frac{1}{7}$-th-power law for the velocity profile which is true for moderate Reynolds numbers and we shall then confine ourselves to quoting the results for the logarithmic law which is valid for arbitrarily large Reynolds numbers, Fig. 20.4, because the complete calculation for this case is fairly tedious.

1. Resistance formula deduced from the $\frac{1}{7}$-th-power velocity distribution law. In accordance with the preceding argument and with eqn. (20.6) it is seen that the $\frac{1}{7}$-th-power law of velocity distribution in a pipe leads to the following velocity distribution in the boundary layer on a flat plate

$$\frac{u}{U_\infty} = \left(\frac{y}{\delta}\right)^{\frac{1}{7}}, \tag{21.4}$$

where $\delta = \delta(x)$ denotes the boundary layer thickness which is a function of distance, x, and is to be determined in the course of the calculation. The assumption in eqn. (21.4) implies that the velocity profiles along a flat plate are *similar*, i. e. that all velocity profiles plot as one curve of u/U_∞ versus y/δ.

The equation for shearing stress at the wall is also taken over directly from the circular pipe, eqn. (20.12a):

$$\frac{\tau_0}{\varrho U_\infty^2} = 0{\cdot}0225 \left(\frac{\nu}{U_\infty\, \delta}\right)^{\frac{1}{4}}. \tag{21.5}$$

From eqns. (8.33) and (8.34), together with eqn. (21.4) we can calculate the displacement thickness, δ^*, and the momentum thickness, θ:

$$\delta^* = \frac{\delta}{8}\,; \qquad \theta = \frac{7}{72}\,\delta\,. \tag{21.6}†$$

From eqns. (21.3) and (21.6) we have

$$\frac{\tau_0}{\varrho U_\infty^2} = \frac{7}{72}\,\frac{\mathrm{d}\delta}{\mathrm{d}x}\,, \tag{21.7}$$

† In the general case of a power law $u/U = (y/\delta)^{1/n}$ we have

$$\frac{\delta^*}{\delta} = \frac{1}{1+n} \qquad \frac{\theta}{\delta} = \frac{n}{(1+n)\,(2+n)}$$

so that on comparing eqns. (21.5) and (21.7) we obtain

$$\frac{7}{72}\frac{\mathrm{d}\delta}{\mathrm{d}x} = 0{\cdot}0225 \left(\frac{\nu}{U_\infty \delta}\right)^{\frac{1}{4}},$$

which is the differential equation for $\delta(x)$. Integration from the initial value $\delta = 0$ at $x = 0$ gives

$$\delta(x) = 0{\cdot}37\, x \left(\frac{U_\infty x}{\nu}\right)^{-\frac{1}{5}} \qquad (21.8)$$

and hence

$$\theta(x) = 0{\cdot}036\, x \left(\frac{U_\infty x}{\nu}\right)^{-\frac{1}{5}}. \qquad (21.9)$$

The boundary layer thickness is seen to increase with the power $x^{4/5}$ of the distance, whereas in laminar flow we had $\delta \sim x^{1/2}$. The total skin friction drag on a flat plate of length l and width b wetted on one side is, by eqn. (21.2), given by

$$D = 0{\cdot}036\, \varrho\, U_\infty^2\, b\, l\, (U_\infty l/\nu)^{-1/5}.$$

The drag on a plate in turbulent flow is seen to be proportional to $U_\infty^{9/5}$ and $l^{4/5}$ compared with $U_\infty^{3/2}$ and $l^{1/2}$ respectively for laminar flow, eqn. (7.36). Introducing dimensionless coefficients for the local and the total skin friction by putting

$$c_f' = \frac{\tau_0}{\frac{1}{2}\varrho U_\infty^2} \qquad \text{or} \qquad c_f = \frac{D}{\frac{1}{2}\varrho U_\infty^2 bl},$$

we obtain from eqns. (21.3) and (21.2) that

$$c_f' = 2\frac{\mathrm{d}\theta}{\mathrm{d}x}, \qquad c_f = 2\,\frac{\theta(l)}{l}. \qquad (21.10)$$

Hence from eqn. (21.9) we can write $c_f' = 0{\cdot}0576\,(U_\infty x/\nu)^{-1/5}$ and $c_f = 0{\cdot}072\,(U_\infty l/\nu)^{-1/5}$. The last equation is in very good agreement with experimental results for plates whose boundary layers are turbulent from the leading edge onwards, if the numerical constant 0·072 is changed to 0·074. Thus

$$c_f = 0{\cdot}074\,(\mathsf{R}_l)^{-1/5}; \qquad 5 \times 10^5 < \mathsf{R}_l < 10^7. \qquad (21.11)$$

The resistance formula (21.11) is seen plotted as curve (2) in Fig. 21.2. The range of validity of this formula is restricted to $U_\infty\, \delta/\nu < 10^5$ in accordance with the limitation on Blasius' pipe resistance formula. By eqn. (21.8) this corresponds to $U_\infty\, l/\nu < 6 \times 10^6$. Since for $\mathsf{R}_l < 5 \times 10^5$ the boundary layer on a plate is fully laminar, it is possible to specify the following range of validity for eqn. (21.11): $5 \times 10^5 < \mathsf{R}_l < 10^7$. Introducing the necessary corrections for the numerical coefficients we obtain the following expression for the local coefficient of skin friction

$$\frac{\tau_0}{\varrho U_\infty^2} = \frac{1}{2}\, c_f' = 0{\cdot}0296\,(\mathsf{R}_x)^{-1/5} = 0{\cdot}0128 \left(\frac{U_\infty \theta}{\nu}\right)^{-\frac{1}{4}}. \qquad (21.12)$$

Equation (21.11), as already mentioned, is valid on the assumption that the boundary layer is turbulent from the leading edge onwards. In reality the boundary layer will be laminar to begin with, and will change to a turbulent one further downstream. The position of the point of transition will depend on the intensity of turbulence in the external flow and will be defined by the value of the critical Reynolds number which ranges over $(U_\infty x/\nu)_{crit} = \mathsf{R}_{crit} = 3 \times 10^5$ to 3×10^6 (see Sec. XVIa).

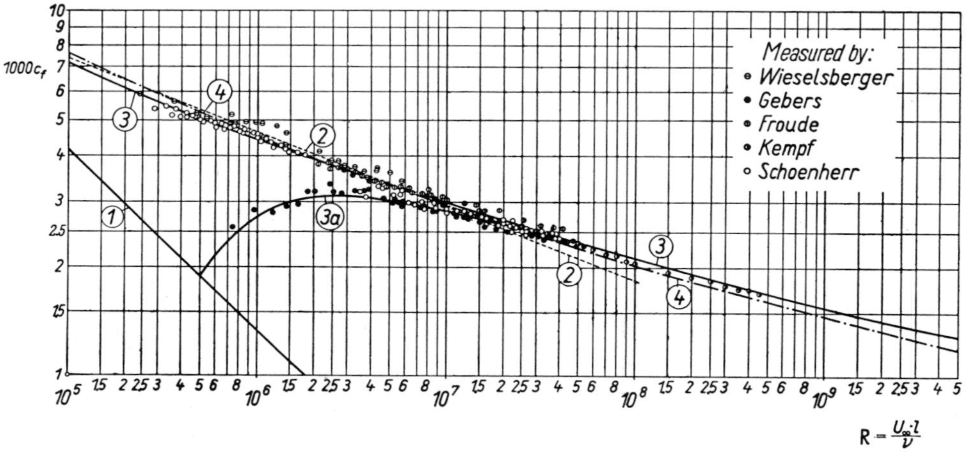

Fig. 21.2. Resistance formula for smooth flat plate at zero incidence; comparison between theory and measurement

Theoretical curves: curve (1) from eqn. (7.37), laminar, Blasius; curve (2) from eqn. (21.11), turbulent, Prandtl; curve (3) from eqn. (21.16), turbulent, Prandtl-Schlichting; curve (3a) from eqn. (21.16a), laminar-to-turbulent transition; curve (4) from eqn. (21.19), turbulent, Schultz-Grunow

The existence of the laminar section causes the drag to decrease and, following L. Prandtl, the decrease can be estimated if it is assumed that behind the point of transition the turbulent boundary layer behaves as if it were turbulent from the leading edge. Thus from the drag of a wholly turbulent boundary layer it is necessary to subtract the turbulent drag of the length up to the point of transition at x_{crit} and to add the laminar drag for the same length. Thus the decrease becomes $\Delta D = -(\varrho/2)\ U_\infty^2\ b\ x_{crit}\ (c_{f,t} - c_{f,l})$, where $c_{f,t}$ and $c_{f,l}$ denote the coefficient of turbulent and laminar skin friction, respectively, for the total drag at the section where transition occurs, i. e. at R_{crit}. Hence the correction for c_f is

$$\Delta c_f = -(x_{crit}/l)\,[c_{f,t} - c_{f,l}] = -(\mathsf{R}_{crit}/\mathsf{R}_l)\,[c_{f,t} - c_{f,l}]\,.$$

Putting $\Delta c_f = -A/\mathsf{R}_l$ we find that the value of the constant A is determined by the position of the point of transition R_{crit}, namely

$$A = \mathsf{R}_{crit}\,[c_{f,t} - c_{f,l}]\,.$$

Consequently the coefficient of total skin friction including the effect of the laminar initial length becomes

$$c_f = \frac{0{\cdot}074}{\sqrt[5]{\mathsf{R}_l}} - \frac{A}{\mathsf{R}_l}, \quad 5 \times 10^5 < \mathsf{R}_l < 10^7 . \tag{21.13}$$

Taking $c_{f,t}$ from eqn. (21.11) and $c_{f,l} = 1{\cdot}328\ \mathsf{R}_x^{-1/2}$ from the Blasius formula, eqn. (7.37), we obtain the following values for A:

R_{crit}	3×10^5	5×10^5	10^6	3×10^6
A	1050	1700	3300	8700

2. Resistance formula deduced from the logarithmic velocity distribution law. The Reynolds numbers which occur in practical applications in connexion with flat plate problems considerably exceed the range of validity of eqn. (21.13)†, and it is, therefore, necessary to find a resistance formula which would be valid for much higher Reynolds numbers. In principle such a formula can be derived in the same way as before, except that the universal logarithmic velocity profile equation should be used instead of the $\frac{1}{7}$-th-power formula, in analogy with eqns. (20.13) and (20.14) for pipe flow. Since the universal logarithmic formula, as shown earlier, may be extrapolated to arbitrarily large Reynolds numbers in the case of pipe flow, we may expect to obtain a resistance formula for the plate which would also lend itself to extrapolation to arbitrarily large Reynolds numbers. In any case, it is again implied that pipe flow and boundary layer flow on a flat plate exhibit identical velocity profiles (see also p. 541).

The derivation is not so simple for the logarithmic law as it was for the $\frac{1}{7}$-th power formula. This is mainly due to the fact that the application of the logarithmic law to the flat plate does not lead to similar profiles any longer. We shall, therefore, refrain from reproducing here the details of the calculation, referring the reader to L. Prandtl's original paper [35].

The logarithmic formula for pipe flow was derived in eqn. (20.13) in the form

$$\phi = A_1 \ln \eta + D_1 \tag{21.14}$$

where

$$\phi = \frac{\bar{u}}{v_*} \quad \text{and} \quad \eta = \frac{y\, v_*}{\nu}$$

with

$$v_* = \sqrt{\tau_0/\varrho}$$

denoting the characteristic velocity formed with the wall shearing stress τ_0. In the case of pipe flow considered in Chap. XX, the constants were indicated to have the

† In large and fast aeroplanes the Reynolds numbers of the wing are of the order of $\mathsf{R}_l = 5 \times 10^7$; airships reach values of about 5×10^8 and a large, modern fast steamer reaches about $\mathsf{R}_l = 5 \times 10^9$; see also Table 21.3, p. 560.

numerical values $A_1 = 5{\cdot}75$ and $D_1 = 5{\cdot}5$. However, extensive experimental investigations (see Fig. 21.3) have demonstrated that the velocity profiles in the two cases under consideration, in a pipe and on a flat plate, are somewhat different and it becomes necessary to modify the numerical values to

$$A_1 = 5{\cdot}85\;; \quad D_1 = 5{\cdot}56\,. \tag{21.15}$$

The calculation leads to a fairly cumbersome set of equations for the local and total coefficients of skin friction in terms of the length Reynolds number $\mathsf{R}_l = U_\infty l/\nu$. In the process, a formula for the dimensionless boundary layer thickness $v_* \, \delta/\nu = \eta_\delta$ is also obtained. The numerical results are shown in Table 21.1 and the graph of c_f *versus* R_l has been plotted in Fig. 21.2 as curve (3).

Since the exact formulae from which the resistance law represented by Table 21.1 has been evaluated is exceedingly inconvenient, H. Schlichting fitted the relation between c_f and R_l from Table 21.1 into an empirical equation of the form

$$c_f = \frac{0{\cdot}455}{(\log \mathsf{R}_l)^{2{\cdot}58}}\,. \tag{21.16}†$$

Table 21.1. Resistance formula for flat plate computed from the logarithmic velocity profile in eqns. (21.14) and (21.15); see curve (3) in Fig. 21.2

$\left(\frac{v_* \delta}{\nu}\right) \cdot 10^{-3} = \eta_\delta \cdot 10^{-3}$	$\mathsf{R}_l \cdot 10^{-6}$	$c_f' \cdot 10^3$	$c_f \cdot 10^3$
0·200	0·107	5·51	7·03
0·353	0·225	4·54	6·04
0·500	0·355	4·38	5·48
0·707	0·548	4·03	5·05
1·00	0·864	3·74	4·59
1·30	1·20	3·53	4·33
2·00	2·07	3·22	3·92
3·00	3·43	2·97	3·57
5·00	6·43	2·69	3·23
7·07	9·70	2·53	3·02
12·0	18·7	2·30	2·71
20·0	34·3	2·11	2·48
28·3	51·8	2·00	2·34
50·0	102	1·83	2·12
100	229	1·65	1·90
170	425	1·53	1·75
283	768	1·42	1·63
500	1476	1·32	1·50

† The results for the coefficient of local skin friction, c_f, in Table 21.1 can also be fitted into an empirical equation as follows

$$c_f' = (2 \log \mathsf{R}_x - 0{\cdot}65)^{-2{\cdot}3}$$

In order to make an allowance for the laminar initial length, it is required to make the same deduction as before, eqn. (21.13). Thus

$$\boxed{c_f = \frac{0{\cdot}455}{(\log \mathsf{R}_l)^{2{\cdot}58}} - \frac{A}{\mathsf{R}_l}}\,, \tag{21.16a}$$

where the value of the constant A depends on the position of the point of transition as specified in the Table on p. 539. This is the *Prandtl-Schlichting skin-friction formula for a smooth flat plate at zero incidence.* It is valid in the whole range of Reynolds numbers up to $\mathsf{R}_l = 10^9$ and it agrees with eqn. (21.13) up to $\mathsf{R}_l = 10^7$. It is seen plotted as curve (3a) in Fig. 21.2 where $A = 1700$ was chosen, corresponding to transition at $\mathsf{R}_x = 5 \times 10^5$. Blasius' curve for laminar flow corresponding to $c_f = 1{\cdot}328\ \mathsf{R}_l^{-1/2}$ is also shown for comparison, curve (1).

A very similar theoretical calculation for the skin friction of a flat plate was devised by Th. von Kármán [24]. K. E. Schoenherr [42] made use of von Kármán's scheme and derived from it the expression

$$\frac{1}{\sqrt{c_f}} = 4{\cdot}13 \log (\mathsf{R}_l\, c_f)\,. \tag{21.17}$$

Results of numerous experimental measurements are seen plotted together with these theoretical curves in Fig. 21.2. The measurements performed by C. Wieselsberger [55] on cloth-covered glazed plates lie somewhat above the turbulent curve (2) which would indicate that there was no substantial laminar length in his experiments and that the roughness was small. The measurements due to F. Gebers [16], which range from $\mathsf{R}_l = 10^6$ to 3×10^7, fall on the transition curve (3a), eqn. (21.16a), at the lower end of the range. At the higher Reynolds numbers his results lie on curve (3) from eqn. (21.16). The measurements reported by K. E. Schoenherr [42] also show good agreement with theory. The highest Reynolds numbers have been achieved by G. Kempf [26]† who attained values of up to $\mathsf{R}_l = 5 \times 10^8$. They show excellent agreement with the theoretical curve from eqn. (21.16a). Extensive measurements have been described by D. W. Smith and J. D. Walker [47a]. On summing up, it is possible to state that the preceding results have been confirmed by measurement over the whole range of Reynolds numbers.

3. Further refinements. As already stated, the preceding method of calculation is based on the assumption that the velocity profiles in the boundary layer on a plate and inside a pipe are identical, if the maximum velocity U and the radius R of the circular tube are replaced by the free stream velocity U_∞ and the boundary layer thickness δ of the plate. This assumption was checked by F. Schultz-Grunow [44] on the basis of very careful measurements on the boundary layer on a plate. The investigation showed that the velocity profile in the outer portion of the boundary layer of a plate deviates systematically upwards from the logarithmic velocity distribution law of a circular pipe. The results of his measurements on a plate are given in Fig. 21.3. They can be well represented by the law

$$\frac{U_\infty - u}{v_*} = f_1\left(\frac{y}{\delta}\right),$$

as already found in the case of a pipe, eqn. (20.23). It is seen that the loss of momentum on a plate is somewhat smaller than that given by the logarithmic pipe formula and, consequently,

† He measured only local frictional coefficients. L. Prandtl evaluated the corresponding total values by integration, see Reports AVA Goettingen, part IV.

the drag must be smaller than that obtained by the direct application of pipe formulae. The function $f_1(y/\delta)$ determined empirically by Schultz-Grunow shows no dependence on the Reynolds number†.

F. Schultz-Grunow repeated the derivation of the resistance formula from the preceding system of equations and with the aid of the function $f_1(y/\delta)$ which he found by measurement. The result can be represented by the following interpolation formulae

$$c_f' = 0{\cdot}370 (\log \mathsf{R}_x)^{-2{\cdot}584} \tag{21.18}$$

$$c_f = 0{\cdot}427 (\log \mathsf{R}_l - 0{\cdot}407)^{-2{\cdot}64} . \tag{21.19}$$

The last equation has been plotted in Fig. 21.2 as curve (4), and it will be noticed that the deviation from the Prandtl-Schlichting curve (3) is small.

The different methods for the calculation of turbulent skin friction have been critically examined by L. Landweber [28].

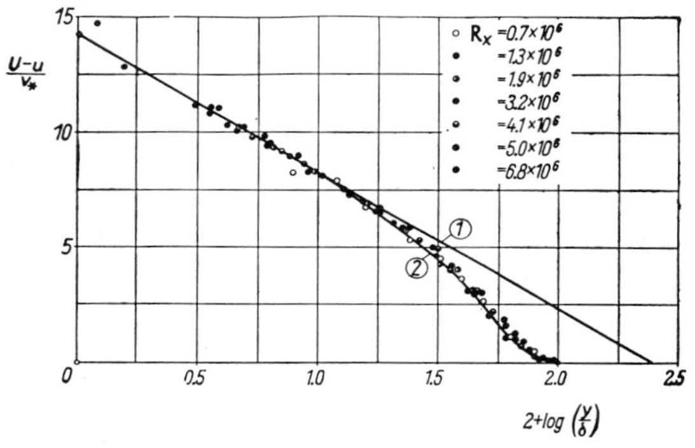

Fig. 21.3. Velocity distribution in the boundary layer on a flat plate at zero incidence after Schultz-Grunow [44]

Curve (1) logarithmic law of pipe flow. In the outer portion the velocity distribution on a plate is seen to deviate markedly from that inside a circular tube. Curve (2) was used by Schultz-Grunow as a basis for the calculation of the boundary layer of a plate and led to eqns. (21.18) and (21.19)

K. Wieghardt [53] advanced an explanation for the difference between the velocity profile in a pipe and that on a plate, pointing out that the influence of turbulence at the outer edge of the boundary layer differs in the two cases. In the case of a plate a low degree of turbulence in the external stream gives rise to velocity fluctuations which are practically zero at the outer edge of the boundary layer, whereas in the centre of the pipe they would still have an appreciable magnitude because of the influence of the other side. To the smaller intensity of turbulence on a plate there corresponds a steeper increase in velocity and hence a thinner total boundary layer. He was also able to show that the velocity profile on a plate becomes very close to that in pipe flow if the external flow is made highly turbulent.

J. Nikuradse [33] also conducted a very comprehensive series of experiments on flat plates. He found that in the range of large Reynolds numbers of $\mathsf{R}_x = 1{\cdot}7 \times 10^6$ to 18×10^6 the velocity profiles are similar, if u/U is plotted against y/δ^*, where δ^* denotes the displacement thickness. The universal velocity distribution law $u/U = f(y/\delta^*)$ turns out to be independent of the Reynolds number. The local and total coefficients of skin friction have been calculated from the measured velocity profiles with the aid of the momentum theorem.

† On applying the pipe formula we have

$$f_1(y/\delta) = A \ln (\delta/y) = 2{\cdot}5 \ln (\delta/y) ,$$

which leads to a straight line in Fig. 21.3. The points near the wall are seen to fall on this straight line; the portion of the curve which corresponds to the outer portion of the boundary layer deviates strongly downwards from the straight line.

The following interpolation formulae were obtained for the velocity distribution, displacement thickness, momentum thickness, and coefficients of skin friction respectively:

$$\frac{u}{U_\infty} = 0{\cdot}737\left(\frac{y}{\delta^*}\right)^{0{\cdot}1315}$$

$$\frac{U_\infty \delta^*}{\nu} = 0{\cdot}01738\ \mathsf{R}_x^{\ 0{\cdot}861}$$

$$H = \frac{\delta^*}{\theta} = 1{\cdot}30\,.$$

$$c_f' = 0{\cdot}02296\ \mathsf{R}_x^{\ -0{\cdot}139}$$

$$c_f = 0{\cdot}02666\ \mathsf{R}_l^{\ -0{\cdot}139}\,.$$

In connexion with the calculation of skin friction on a plate, the paper by V. M. Falkner [14] may also be consulted. In a paper by D. Coles [6a] the velocity profiles are represented by a linear combination of two universal functions, one of which is called the law of the wake, the other one being the law of the wall.

Measurements performed by H. Motzfeld [32] concerned themselves with the turbulent boundary layer on a wavy wall. H. Schlichting [39] gave some estimates concerning the turbulent boundary layer on a flat plate with suction and discharge respectively. In the case of uniform suction the asymptotic boundary layer thickness is constant, as it was in the case of laminar flow, but it is considerably more sensitive to changes in the suction volume than that in laminar flow.

4. Influence of Mach number. To date, the calculation of turbulent boundary layers in incompressible flow has not developed to a point where it could be classed as being more than a semi-empirical theory. It is, therefore, not surprising that the same remark applies to the calculation of compressible turbulent boundary layers. In the case of incompressible turbulent boundary layers a starting point is provided by the hypotheses which were discussed in the preceding chapters, namely by Prandtl's mixing length hypothesis, by von Kármán's similarity rule or by Prandtl's universal velocity distribution law. The authors of numerous contemporary papers have endeavoured to create a semi-empirical theory of compressible turbulent boundary layers by transposing these hypotheses and by adapting them to the compressible case. This necessitated the introduction of additional *ad hoc* hypotheses. In the absence of detailed investigations into the mechanics of compressible turbulent flows, the transposition of the semi-empirical theories of turbulent flows from the incompressible to the compressible case involves a good deal of arbitrariness. When, in spite of that, the calculations in isolated cases do agree with measurement to a certain extent, one might conclude that from among the large number of possible assumptions one has been selected which gives the best agreement under the circumstances.

An important first step forward was taken by E. R. van Driest [11], who adapted the argument on turbulent stresses given in Chap. XVIII to the case of compressible flow. He obtained explicit formulae for turbulent skin friction on a flat plate, both with and without heat transfer, which account for the influence of the Reynolds and the Mach numbers simultaneously. For the case of an adiabatic wall the formula for the coefficient of total skin friction has the form

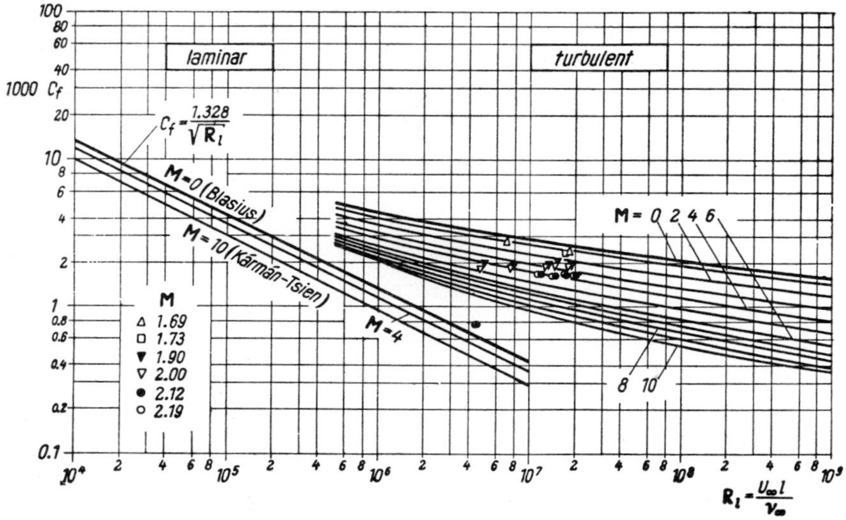

Fig. 21.4. Coefficient of total skin friction for an adiabatic flat plate at zero incidence for laminar and turbulent boundary layer. Theoretical curves for turbulent flow from eqn. (21.20a), after E. R. van Driest [11]; $\gamma = 1{\cdot}4$, $\omega = 0{\cdot}76$, $\mathsf{P} = 1$

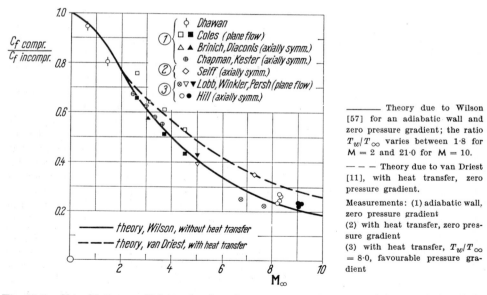

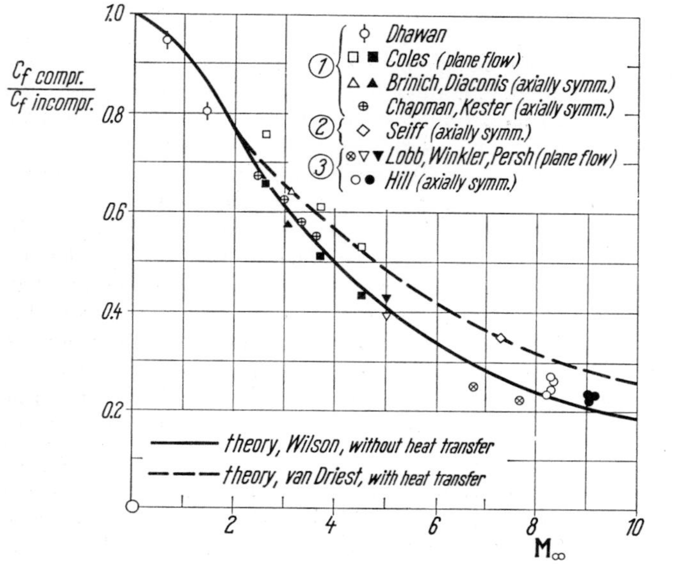

——— Theory due to Wilson [57] for an adiabatic wall and zero pressure gradient; the ratio T_w/T_∞ varies between 1·8 for $\mathsf{M} = 2$ and 21·0 for $\mathsf{M} = 10$.

— — — Theory due to van Driest [11], with heat transfer, zero pressure gradient.

Measurements: (1) adiabatic wall, zero pressure gradient
(2) with heat transfer, zero pressure gradient
(3) with heat transfer, $T_w/T_\infty = 8{\cdot}0$, favourable pressure gradient

Fig. 21.5. Skin friction coefficient of a flat plate at zero incidence as a function of the Mach number for a turbulent boundary layer; comparison between theory and measurement; $\mathsf{R}_x \approx 10^7$, from [19]

$$\frac{0{\cdot}242}{\sqrt{c_f}}\,(1-\lambda^2)^{\frac{1}{2}}\,\frac{\sin^{-1}\lambda}{\lambda} = \log\,(\mathsf{R}_l \cdot c_f) + \frac{1+2\omega}{2}\log\,(1-\lambda^2) \qquad (21.20)$$

where

$$1-\lambda^2 = \frac{1}{1+\frac{\gamma-1}{2}\,\mathsf{M}_\infty^2} \qquad (21.21)$$

and $\mathsf{M}_\infty = U_\infty/c_\infty$ denotes the free-stream Mach number. The symbol ω denotes the exponent in the viscosity law $\mu/\mu_0 = (T/T_0)^\omega$ from eqn. (15.1). For $\mathsf{M}_\infty \to 0$ eqn. (21.20) transforms into von Kármán's resistance formula, eqn. (21.17). Fig. 21.4 gives a plot of eqn. (21.20) and a comparison with experimental results. The measure of agreement between theory and experiment is not satisfactory in all cases, but in this connexion it must be pointed out that measurements at high Mach numbers are somewhat uncertain. Further experimental results are contained in Fig. 21.5 which shows a plot of the ratio of the skin friction coefficients in compressible and incompressible flow in terms of the Mach number, covering a range which includes very high Mach numbers. The graph contains two theoretical curves; the first one, due to R. E. Wilson [57] presupposes an adiabatic wall and the second one, derived by E. R. van Driest [11] includes the effect of heat transfer. The measurements were performed by several workers [3, 7, 19, 30, 47] and show good agreement with theory. Additional information concerning the influence of heat transfer on skin friction is contained in Fig. 21.6 which was also based on van Driest's calculations [11]. The diagram shows that the skin friction on an adiabatic wall is somewhat smaller than is the case when heat flows from the fluid to the wall.

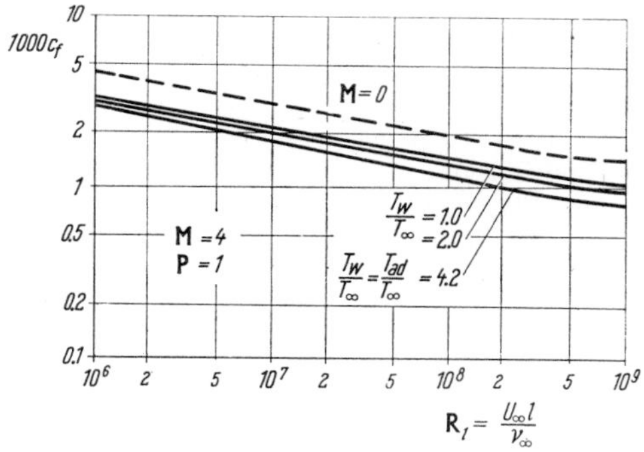

Fig. 21.6. Skin friction coefficient for a flat plate at zero incidence in turbulent flow *with* heat transfer as a function of Reynolds number for different values of the temperature ratio T_w/T_∞, after E. R. van Driest [11]

The curve for $\frac{T_w}{T_\infty} = \frac{T_{ad}}{T_\infty} = 4{\cdot}2$ corresponds to the case with heat transfer $\mathsf{M} = 4$, $\mathsf{P} = 1$

An example of the velocity profile in a compressible turbulent boundary layer is given in Fig. 21.7 which contains a plot of u/U_∞ in terms of y/θ as measured by R. M. O'Donnel [10] at $\mathsf{M}_\infty = 2{\cdot}4$ (θ — momentum thickness). In the adopted system of co-ordinates the points for different Reynolds numbers arrange themselves well on a single curve. The theoretical curve shown on the graph deviates from the corresponding curves for incompressible flow much less than was the case with laminar flow, Fig. 15.9. Recently, F. K. Hill [19] performed measurements of velocity distributions at the very high Mach number of $\mathsf{M} \approx 9$, see Fig. 21.8; they extended well into the laminar sublayer. The comparative curves which correspond to the universal law for incompressible flows allow us to conclude that the latter remains valid for extremely large Mach numbers on condition that the

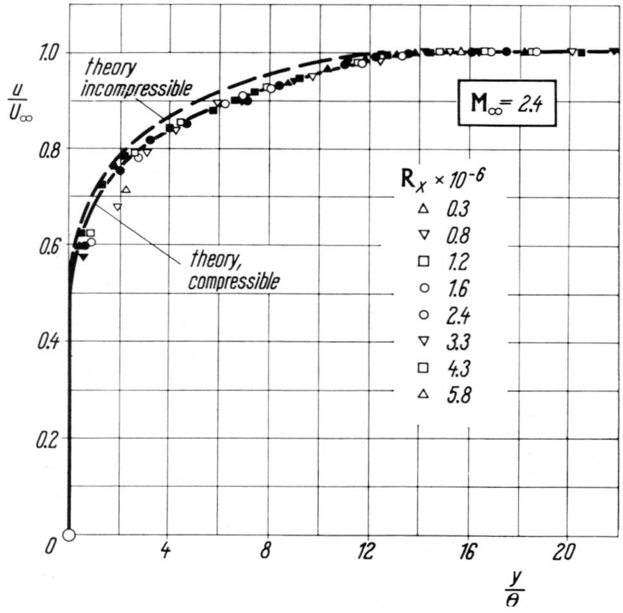

Fig. 21.7. Measurements on velocity distribution in turbulent boundary layer on flat plate at zero incidence at supersonic velocity, after R. M. O'Donnel [10]

$M_\infty = 2{\cdot}4$; θ — momentum thickness from eqn. (15.52)

Incompressible theory: $\frac{u}{U_\infty} = 0{\cdot}716 \left(\frac{u}{\theta}\right)^{1/7}$;

Compressible theory: $\frac{u}{U_\infty} = 0{\cdot}683 \left(\frac{u}{\theta}\right)^{1/7}$

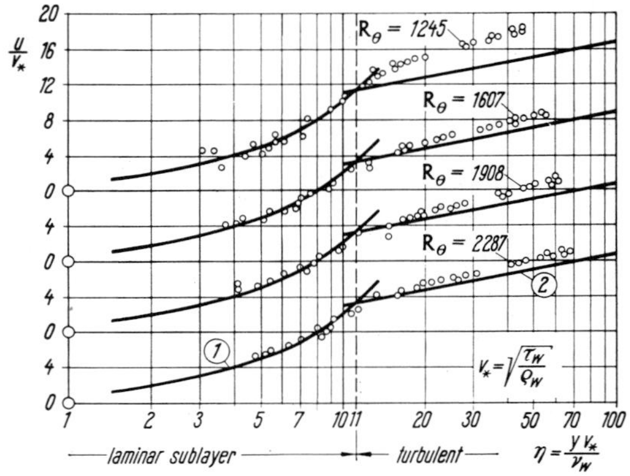

Fig. 21.8. Universal logarithmic velocity distribution law for turbulent boundary layer with favourable pressure gradient in hypersonic flow; $M_\infty = 9$, as measured by F. K. Hill [19]

Curves (1) and (2): theoretical laws for incompressible flow; (1) laminar sublayer $\phi = \eta$, (2) universal logarithmic law

$$\phi = 5{\cdot}5 + 5{\cdot}75 \log \eta$$

friction velocity v_* is calculated with reference to the density at the wall, i. e. from the formula $v_* = \sqrt{\tau_w/\varrho_w}$; the kinematic viscosity must also be evaluated at the wall.

When the wall is rough, the influence of the Mach number on skin friction is even greater. According to H. W. Liepmann and F. E. Goddard [30a], the ratio $c_{f\,compr}/c_{f\,inc}$ for the completely rough regime becomes proportional to the density ratio ϱ_w/ϱ_∞, and hence

$$\frac{c_{f\,compr}}{c_{f\,inc}} = \frac{1}{1 + r\frac{\gamma - 1}{2} M_\infty^2}$$

where r denotes the recovery factor.

b. The rotating disk

1. The "free" disk. The flow in the neighbourhood of a rotating disk is of great practical importance, particularly in connexion with rotary machines. It becomes turbulent at larger Reynolds numbers, $\mathsf{R} = UR/\nu > 3 \times 10^5$, in the same way as the flow about a plate. Here R denotes the radius and $U = \omega R$ is the tip velocity of the disk. The character of this kind of flow was described in Sec. V. 10, which contained the complete solution for the laminar case when the disk rotates in an infinitely extended body of fluid ("free" disk). Owing to friction, the fluid in the immediate neighbourhood of the disk is carried by it and then forced outwards by the centrifugal acceleration. Thus the velocity in the boundary layer has a radial and a tangential component and the mass of fluid which is driven outwards by centrifugal forces is replaced by an axial flow. Making a simple estimation of the balance of viscous and centrifugal forces in laminar flow it was possible to show (p. 85) that the boundary layer thickness δ is proportional to $\sqrt{\nu/\omega}$, and hence independent of the radius, and that the torque, M, which is proportional to $\mu R^3 U/\delta$, must be given by an expression of the form $M \sim \varrho U^2 R^3 (U R/\nu)^{-1/2}$. The exact solution for the laminar case showed, further, that the dimensionless moment coefficient, defined as

$$C_M = \frac{2M}{\frac{1}{2}\varrho \omega^2 R^5} \tag{21.22}$$

for a disk wetted on both sides, is given by eqn. (5.49), and is equal to

$$C_M = 3{\cdot}87\,\mathsf{R}^{-1/2}, \quad \text{(laminar)} \tag{21.23}$$

where $\mathsf{R} = R^2\omega/\nu$, Fig. 5.14.

It is now proposed to make the same estimation for the turbulent case basing it on the same resistance formula for turbulent flow as was used in the case of the flat plate, i. e., in the simplest case, on the $\frac{1}{7}$-th-power law for the velocity distribution. A fluid particle which rotates in the boundary layer at a distance r from the axis is acted on by a centrifugal force per unit volume of magnitude $\varrho r \omega^2$. The centrifugal force on a volume of area $dr \times ds$ and height δ becomes $\varrho r \omega^2 \delta\, dr \times ds$. The shearing stress τ_0 forms an angle θ with the tangential direction and its radial component must balance the centrifugal force. Hence we have $\tau_0 \sin\theta\, dr \times ds = \varrho r \omega^2 \delta\, dr \times ds$ or

$$\tau_0 \sin\theta = \varrho r \omega^2 \delta\,.$$

On the other hand the tangential component of shearing stress can be expressed with the aid of eqn. (21.5) which was used in the case of a flat plate, replacing U_∞ by the tangential velocity $r\omega$. Thus

$$\tau_0 \cos\theta \sim \varrho (\omega r)^{7/4} (\nu/\delta)^{1/4}\,.$$

Equating τ_0 in these two expressions, we find that

$$\delta \sim r^{3/5} (\nu/\omega)^{1/5}\,.$$

It is seen that in the turbulent case the boundary layer thickness increases outwards in proportion to $r^{3/5}$ and does not remain constant as in the laminar case. Further the torque becomes $M \sim \tau_0 R^3 \sim \varrho R \omega^2 (\nu/\omega)^{1/5} R^{3/5} R^3$ so that

$$M \sim \varrho U^2 R^3 \left(\frac{\nu}{U R}\right)^{1/5}.$$

Th. von Kármán [25] investigated the turbulent boundary layer on a rotating disk with the aid of an approximate method based on the momentum equation and similar to the one applied in the preceding section to the study of the flat plate. The variation of the tangential velocity component through the boundary layer was assumed to obey the $\frac{1}{7}$-th-power law. The viscous torque for a disk wetted on both sides was shown to be equal to

$$2 M = 0{\cdot}073 \, \varrho \, \omega^2 R^5 (\nu/\omega R^2)^{1/5} \tag{21.24}$$

and the moment coefficient defined in eqn. (21.22) becomes

$$C_M = 0{\cdot}146 \, \mathsf{R}^{-1/5} \quad \text{(turbulent)} . \tag{21.25}$$

This equation has been plotted in Fig. 5.14 as curve (2). It shows very good agreement with the experimental results due to W. Schmidt and G. Kempf† for $\mathsf{R} > 3 \times 10^5$. The numerical factor in the equation of boundary layer thickness which was left undetermined becomes

$$\delta = 0{\cdot}526 \, r \, (\nu/r^2 \omega)^{1/5}, \tag{21.26}$$

and the volume of flow in the axial direction is given by

$$Q = 0{\cdot}219 \, R^3 \omega \, \mathsf{R}^{-1/5} , \tag{21.27}$$

as compared with eqn. (5.50) for laminar flow.

An approximate calculation based on the logarithmic velocity distribution law $u/v_* = A \ln (y v_*/\nu) + D$ was performed by S. Goldstein [17], who found the following formula for the torque:

$$\frac{1}{\sqrt{C_M}} = 1{\cdot}97 \log (\mathrm{Re} \sqrt{C_M}) + 0{\cdot}03 \quad \text{(turbulent)} , \tag{21.28}$$

It is noteworthy that this equation has the same form as the universal pipe resistance formula, eqn. (20.30). The numerical factors have been adjusted to obtain the best possible agreement with experimental results. This equation is seen plotted as curve (3) in Fig. 5.14.

2. The disk in a housing. The disks in turbines or rotary compressors mostly revolve in very tight housings in which the width of the gap, s, is small compared with the radius, R, of the disk, Fig. 21.9. Consequently it was found necessary to investigate the case of a disk rotating in a housing.

† See refs. [16] and [31] in Chap. V.

Laminar flow. The relations become particularly simple when the flow is laminar, $\mathsf{R} < 10^5$, and when the gap is very small. If the gap, s, is smaller than the boundary layer thickness the variation of the tangential velocity across the gap becomes linear in the manner of Couette-flow. Hence the shearing stress at a distance r from the axis is equal to $\tau = r\,\omega\,\mu/s$ and the moment of the viscous forces on one side of a disk is given by

$$M = 2\pi \int_0^R \tau\, r^2\, \mathrm{d}r = \frac{\pi}{2} \frac{\omega\, \mu\, R^4}{s}.$$

Consequently for both sides we have

$$2\,M = \pi\,\omega\,R^4\,\mu/s$$

and the moment coefficient from eqn. (21.22) becomes

$$C_M = 2\pi \frac{R}{s} \frac{1}{\mathsf{R}} \quad \text{(laminar)}\,. \tag{21.29}$$

This equation is seen plotted as curve (1) in Fig. 21.10 for a value of $s/R = 0{\cdot}02$. It shows very good agreement with the experimental values due to O. Zumbusch [45].

C. Schmieden [41] investigated the influence of the width σ of the lateral spacing of a disk in a cylindrical housing, Fig. 21.9, on the assumption of very small Reynolds numbers (creeping motion). The Navier-Stokes equations can be simplified because of the very low Reynolds numbers (see Sec. IVd) and the solution

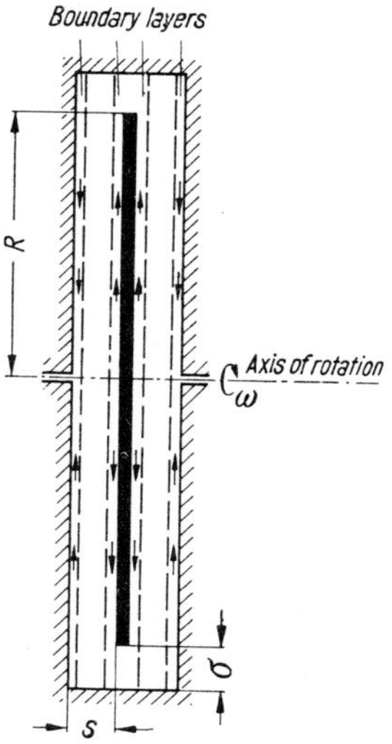

Fig. 21.9. Explanation of symbols for the problem of a disk rotating in a housing

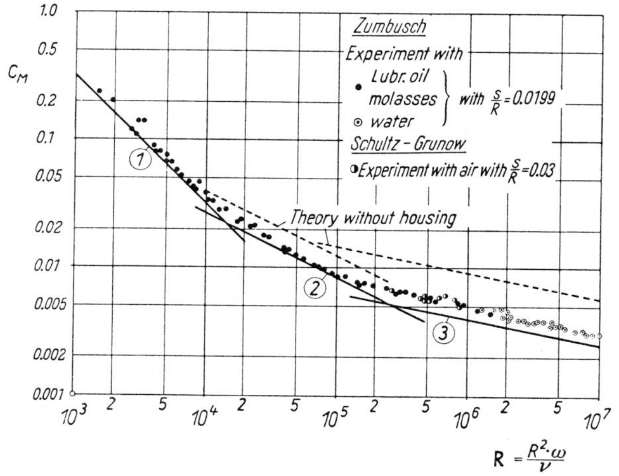

Fig. 21.10. Viscous drag of disk rotating in a housing
Curve (1), from eqn. (21.29), laminar; curve (2), from eqn. (21.30), laminar; curve (3), from eqn. (21.31), turbulent. Theory with no housing (free disk) see Fig. 5.14

for the moment coefficient appears in the form $C_M = K/\mathsf{R}$ in analogy with eqn. (21.29). The constant K depends on the two dimensionless ratios s/R and σ/R. In the case of very small values of σ/R ($< 0{\cdot}1$) the values of C_M are markedly larger than those in eqn. (21.29), whereas for large values of σ/R eqn. (21.29) retains its validity ($K = 2\pi\ R/s$).

The flow pattern in the case of larger gaps differs considerably from the above simple scheme. This latter case was investigated theoretically and experimentally by F. Schultz-Grunow [45]. If the gap is a multiple of the boundary layer thickness, then an additional boundary layer will be formed on the housing, Fig. 21.9. The fluid in the boundary layer on the rotating disk is centrifuged outwards and this is compensated by a flow inwards in the boundary layer on the housing at rest. There is no appreciable radial component in the intermediate layer of fluid which rotates with about half the angular velocity of the disk. F. Schultz-Grunow investigated this flow both for the laminar and for the turbulent case. The expression for the torque is of the same form as for the free disk in eqn. (5.49), only the numerical factor has a different value. The frictional moment of a disk in laminar flow and wetted on both sides becomes $2\ M = 1{\cdot}334\ \mu\ R^4\ \omega \sqrt{\omega/\nu}$, and hence the coefficient

$$C_M = 2{\cdot}67\ \mathsf{R}^{-1/2} \quad \text{(laminar)}\,. \tag{21.30}$$

This equation is seen plotted as curve (2) in Fig. 21.10. It agrees with measured values up to about $\mathsf{R} = 2 \times 10^5$ and connects fairly well with eqn. (21.29).

Turbulent flow. For Reynolds numbers $\mathsf{R} > 3 \times 10^5$ the flow around a disk rotating in a housing becomes turbulent as usual. This case was also solved by F. Schultz-Grunow who used an approximate method based on the scheme of Fig. 21.9. The tangential velocity was assumed to obey the $\frac{1}{7}$-th-power law and it was shown that the core revolves with about half the angular velocity in this case too. The moment coefficient was shown to be equal to

$$C_M = 0{\cdot}0622\ (\mathsf{R})^{-1/5} \quad \text{(turbulent)}\,. \tag{21.31}$$

This equation has been plotted in Fig. 21.10 as curve (3). Compared with measurement it leads to values which are too small by about 17 per cent, and this must be attributed to the crude assumptions made in the calculation.

It is particularly noteworthy that, apart from the case of very small gaps, eqn. (21.29), the moment of viscous forces is completely independent of the width of the gap as seen from eqns. (21.30) and (21.31). However, in a recent paper, J. W. Daily and R. E. Nece [7a] established equations for the moment coefficient which take into account the influence of the relative gap width. Comparing the frictional moment on a "free" disk and on one rotating in a housing, eqns. (21.30) and (21.31) as against eqn. (21.23) and (21.25), it is seen that the moment on a free disk is greater than that on a disk in a housing .This fact can be explained by the existence of the core which moves at half the angular velocity. This decreases the transverse gradient of the tangential velocity to approximately one half of what it would be on a free disk and, consequently, the drag is also smaller than on a "free" disk.

c. The rough plate

1. The resistance formula for a uniformly rough plate. In most practical applications connected with the flat plate (e. g. ships, lifting surfaces of an aircraft, turbine blades) the wall cannot be considered hydraulically smooth. Consequently, the flow past a rough plate is of as much practical interest as that through a rough pipe.

The relative roughness k/R of the pipe is now replaced by the quantity k/δ, where δ denotes the boundary layer thickness. The essential difference between the flow through a rough pipe and that over a rough plate consists in the fact that the relative roughness k/δ decreases along the plate when k remains constant because δ increases downstream, whereas in a pipe k/R remains constant. This circumstance causes the front of the plate to behave differently from its rearward portion as far as the influence of roughness on drag is concerned. Assuming, for the sake of simplicity, that the boundary layer is turbulent from the leading edge onwards, we find completely rough flow over the forward portion, followed by the transition regime and, eventually, the plate may become hydraulically smooth if it is sufficiently long. The limits between these three regions are determined by the dimensionless roughness parameter $v_* \, k_S/\nu$ as given in eqn. (20.37) for sand roughness.

The result of the calculation for pipes can be transposed to the case of rough plates in exactly the same way as for smooth plates in complete analogy with the detailed description given in Sec. XXIa. Such calculations were carried out by L. Prandtl and H. Schlichting [36] with the use of Nikuradse's results on pipes roughened with sand (Sec. XXf). The calculation was based on the logarithmic velocity distribution law for rough pipes in the form of eqn. (20.32), whence $u/v_* = 2{\cdot}5 \ln (y/k_S) + B$. The dependence of the roughness function B on the roughness parameter $v_* k_S/\nu$ is given by the plot in Fig. 20.21. The calculation, which is essentially the same as in Sec. XXIa, must be carried out separately for the transition and completely rough regimes respectively. For the details of this method reference should be made to the original paper.

The result can be represented in two graphs, Figs. 21.11 and 21.12, in which the coefficient of total skin frictional drag, c_f, and the local coefficient, c_f', have been plotted against the Reynolds number $\mathsf{R} = U_\infty \, l/\nu$ with the relative roughness l/k_S as a parameter. In the case of the local coefficient, $U_\infty \, x/\nu$ and x/k_S are used. In addition the diagrams contain curves of $U_\infty \, k_S/\nu = \text{const}$, which can be computed at once from the previous ones. The two families of curves have the following significance: if the velocity on a given plate is changed, l/k_S remains constant and the coefficient of skin friction varies along a curve $l/k_S = \text{const}$. If, on the other hand, the length of the plate is changed, $U_\infty \, k_S/\nu$ remains constant, and the coefficient of skin friction varies along a curve $U_\infty \, k_S/\nu = \text{const}$. Both graphs have been computed on the assumption that the turbulent boundary layer begins right at the leading edge. The broken curve shown in the diagrams corresponds to the limit of complete roughness and it may be noted that a given relative roughness causes the coefficient of skin friction to increase only if the Reynolds number exceeds a certain value, in complete similarity with pipe flow (see Sec. XXId).

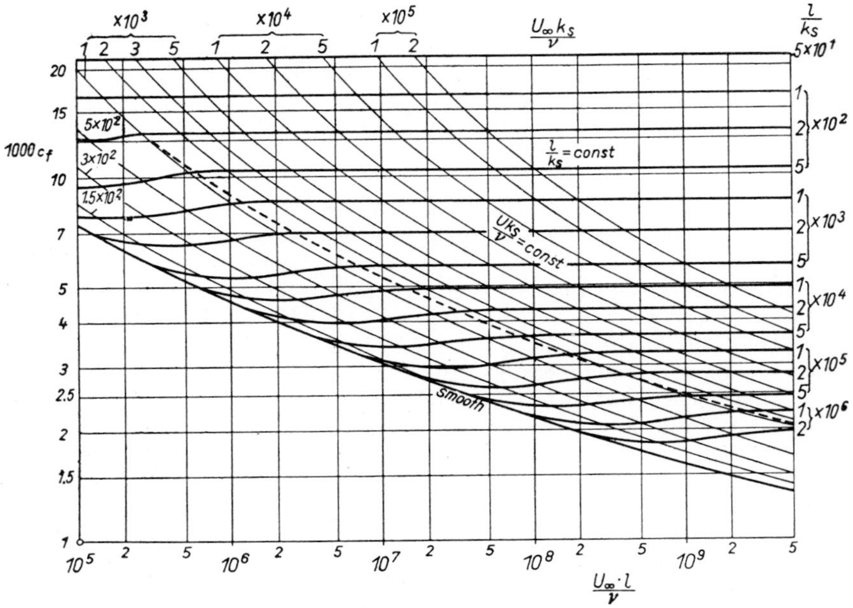

Fig. 21.11. Resistance formula of sand-roughened plate; coefficient of *total* skin friction

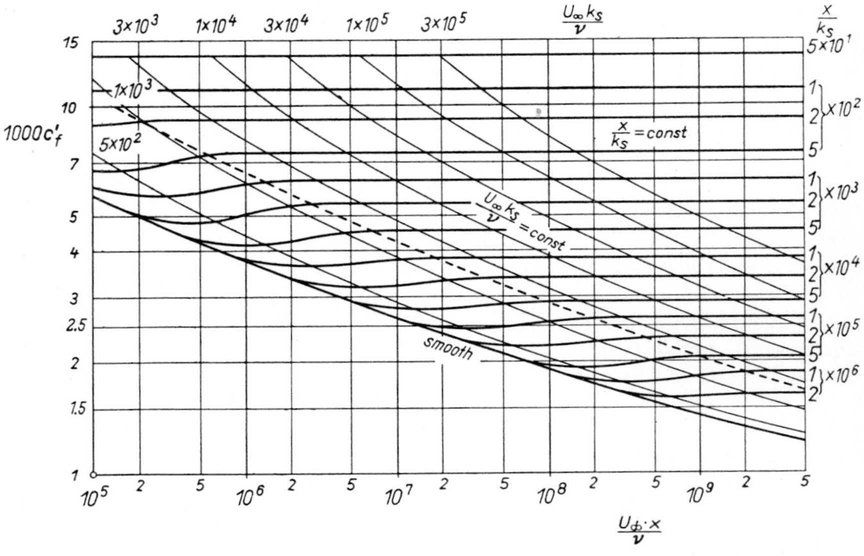

Fig. 21.12. Resistance formula of sand-roughened plate; coefficient of *local* skin friction

In the completely rough regime it is possible to make use of the following interpolation formulae for the coefficients of skin friction in terms of relative roughness:

$$c_f' = \left(2{\cdot}87 + 1{\cdot}58 \log \frac{x}{k_S}\right)^{-2\cdot5}, \tag{21.32}$$

$$c_f = \left(1{\cdot}89 + 1{\cdot}62 \log \frac{l}{k_S}\right)^{-2\cdot5}, \tag{21.33}$$

which are valid for $10^2 < l/k_S < 10^6$.

In order to use these diagrams for roughnesses other than the sand roughness assumed here, it is necessary to determine the equivalent sand roughness as explained in Sec. XXg.

In the calculation of the drag on ships it is important to consider plates with very small roughness (painted metal plates) as well as smooth plates covered with single protuberances, such as rivet heads, welded seams, joints, etc. F. Schultz-Grunow [43] carried out a large number of measurements on such surfaces in the open channel of the Institute in Goettingen, mentioned in Sec. XXg. Additional comprehensive data on roughnesses occuring in shipbuilding can also be found in several papers by G. Kempf [27]. According to these measurements it is possible to use an average value of equivalent sand roughness of $k_S = 0{\cdot}3$ mm ($= 0{\cdot}012$ in approx.) for newly launched ships. At the high Reynolds numbers which occur in ships this causes an increase in resistance of 34 to 45 per cent. due to roughness, as compared with hydraulically smooth walls. Roughness due to weeds adhering to ships' hulls has a particularly detrimental effect on resistance. Increases in resistance of 50 per cent., as compared with normal conditions may well occur under such circumstances. The roughness of surfaces is also important in turbines, turbo-compressors and similar engines. The smoothness of normally manufactured blade surfaces is not sufficient to secure hydraulically smooth conditions [48]; see also p.559.

Camouflage paints used on aeroplane surfaces can be well fitted into the scale of equivalent sand roughness as proved by the investigations carried out by A. D. Young [58], during which equivalent sand roughnesses of $k_S = 0{\cdot}003$ to $0{\cdot}2$ mm ($0{\cdot}001$ to $0{\cdot}01$ in approx.) have been measured. They are equal to about $1{\cdot}6$ times the size of the mean geometrical protrusions, i. e. $k_S = 1{\cdot}6\,k$. In this connexion it is noteworthy that the increase in resistance due to roughness in the subsonic range of flow is independent of the Mach number.

W. Paeschke [34] demonstrated that the laws of friction in flows along rough walls which have emerged from these experimental investigations can be applied to the motion of natural winds over the surface of the earth. The effective roughness of surfaces covered with different kinds of vegetation could be determined by measurements of the velocity distribution of the wind in the layer just above the surface of the earth. Equation (20.32) [$u/v_* = 2{\cdot}5 \ln (y/k) + B$], which has been deduced from pipe flow results and which represents the velocity profile over a rough surface, was confirmed and the value of $B = 5$ was found when the physical height of vegetable growth is used as the roughness parameter k. In accordance with eqn. (20.38) this is the same as taking the equivalent sand roughness to be $k_S = 4\,k$.

2. Measurements on single roughness elements. K. Wieghardt [54] and W. Tillman [52] carried out a large number of measurements on roughness in the special tunnel in Goettingen.

The tunnel, operated on air, had smooth walls and a rectangular cross-section measuring 140 × 40 cm (about 4·5 × 1·3 ft) and was 6 m (about 20 ft) long. The drag was measured with the aid of a balance which was attached to a rectangular test plate (50 × 30 cm or 1·65 × 1·00 ft approx.). The test plate was accommodated in a recess in the lower wall (1·4 × 6 m or 4·5 × 20 ft approx.) of the tunnel and it was free to move over a short distance. The difference between the drag on the test plate with and without the roughness elements gave the increase in drag, ΔD, due to roughness. Generally speaking this increase consists of two terms. The first term is the form drag due to roughness itself and the second is due to the fact that the presence of roughness elements changes the velocity profile in its neighbourhood and hence the shearing stress on the wall as, for example, in the region of back flow behind a fillet or ledge. The ratio of the height of the roughness element to the boundary layer thickness, k/δ, is an important parameter for the application of such results to actual conditions on a ship's hull or an aeroplane. Its value was varied by setting up the same roughness elements at different places along the wall of the tunnel. From the point of view of practical applications it is also important to define a suitable dimensionless coefficient with the aid of the additional drag. K. Wieghardt used one defined by

$$C_D = \frac{\Delta D}{\bar{q} A}, \tag{21.34}$$

where ΔD denotes the measured additional drag, A the largest frontal area of the roughness element perpendicular to the direction of flow, and $\bar{q}$ is the stagnation pressure averaged over the height of the roughness element, or

$$\bar{q} = \frac{1}{k} \int_0^k \frac{1}{2} \varrho\, u^2(y)\, \mathrm{d}y = \frac{1}{k}\,\frac{1}{2} \varrho\, U^2 \int_0^k \left(\frac{y}{\delta}\right)^{\frac{2}{7}} \mathrm{d}y\,.$$

Here $u(y)$ denotes the velocity distribution on the smooth wall, that is, e. g. $u/U = (y/\delta)^{1/7}$. A large variety of roughness elements was subjected to test, including rectangular ribs arranged at right angles or at an acute angle to the stream, shaped fillets of triangular and circular cross-section, sheet metal joints, single rivet heads and rows of rivets, cavities in the wall and others. Some of the results for rectangular ribs at right angles to the stream are seen plotted in Fig. 21.13.

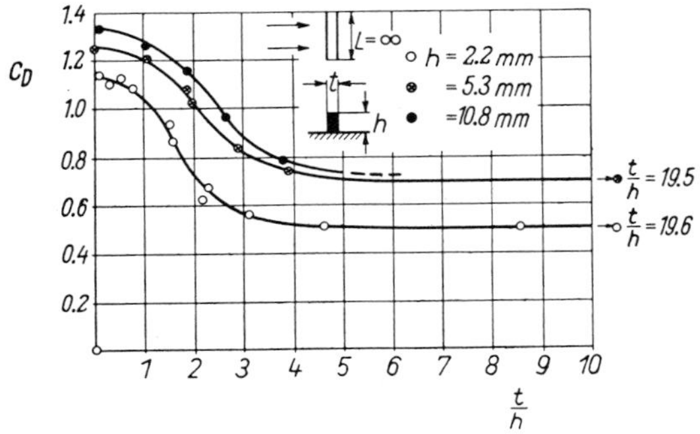

Fig. 21.13. Resistance coefficient for rectangular ribs, as measured by Wieghardt [54]

The value of the coefficient C_D decreases with increasing t/h (t — width, h — height). Holes and cavities in the surface lead to increased values of the resistance coefficient because the external flow causes the fluid in the cavity to take part in the motion.

Fig. 21.14 presents the increase in drag caused by circular cavities shown in the sketch (diameter d and depth h). Since the definition of q adopted previously loses its sense in this case, the drag was made dimensionless with reference to the stagnation pressure outside the boundary layer, $\Delta c_D = \Delta D / \frac{1}{4}\, q\, \pi\, d^2$. The increase in drag is smaller for smaller values of the ratio of the depth of cavity, h, to the boundary layer thickness, δ. It is noteworthy that all curves have a common maximum at $h/d \approx -0{\cdot}5$. Further small local maxima occur at $-h/d \approx 0{\cdot}1$ and $1{\cdot}0$. The minima between them occur at $-h/d \approx 0{\cdot}2$, $0{\cdot}8$, and $1{\cdot}35$. Depending on the depth of the cavity it may sometimes happen that regular vortex patterns are formed in it, leading to the different values of drag. As seen from the symmetry of the curves about $h/d = 0$ shallow cavities of up to $-d/h = 0{\cdot}1$ give the same increase in drag as corresponding small protuberances.

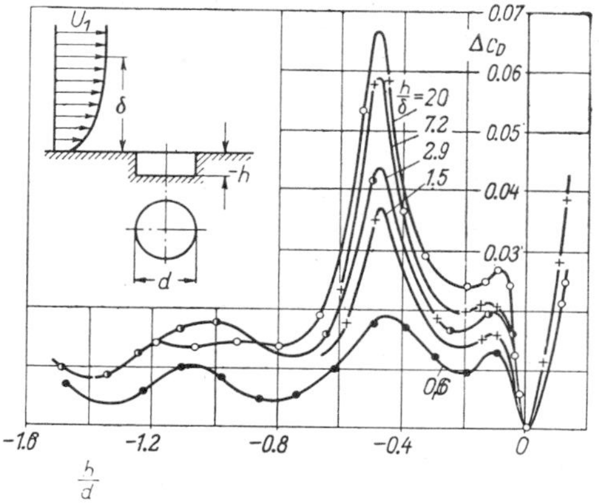

Fig. 21.14. Resistance coefficient of circular cavities of varying depth in a flat wall, as measured by Wieghardt [54]

The flow pattern which exists behind an obstacle placed in the boundary layer near a wall differs markedly from that behind an obstacle placed in the free stream. This circumstance emerges clearly from an experiment performed by H. Schlichting [38] and illustrated in Fig. 21.15. The experiment consisted in the measurement of the velocity field behind a row of spheres placed on a smooth flat surface. The pattern of curves of constant velocity clearly shows a kind of *negative wake effect*. The smallest velocities have been measured in the free gaps in which no spheres are present over the whole length of the plate; on the other hand, the largest velocities have been measured behind the rows of spheres where precisely the smaller velocities

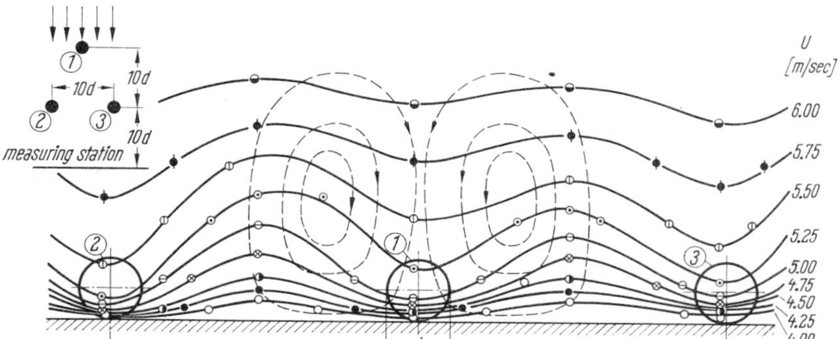

Fig. 21.15. Curves of constant velocity in the flow field behind a row of spheres (full lines) as measured by H. Schlichting [38], and accompanying it the secondary flow (broken lines) in the boundary layer behind sphere (1), as calculated by F. Schultz-Grunow [46]. In the neighbourhood of the wall, the velocity behind the spheres is larger than that in the gaps. The spheres produce a "negative wake effect" which is explained by the existence of secondary flow
Diameter of spheres $d = 4$ mm

would be expected to exist. W. Jacobs [22] carried out a more detailed investigation of this peculiar effect. According to a remark made by F. Schultz-Grunow [46], the reason for such behaviour seems to be connected with the existence of secondary flow of a kind which is similar to that on a lift-generating body. The streamlines of this secondary flow have been shown sketched in Fig. 21.15. The existence of this effect was confirmed by D. H. Williams and A. F. Brown [56] who performed measurements on an aerofoil provided with rows of rivets.

There is in existence a very extensive literature concerning the roughness of aerofoils [9, 20, 21].

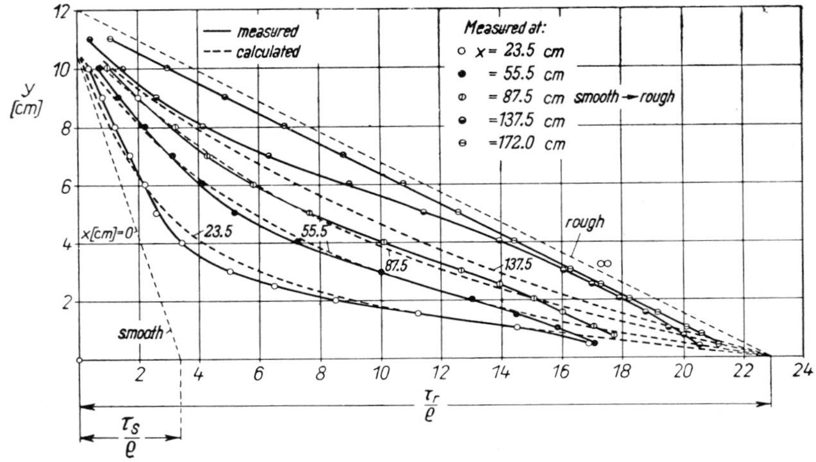

Fig. 21.16. Variation of shearing stress in the boundary layer on passing from a *smooth* to a *rough* portion of wall, as measured by W. Jacobs [23]

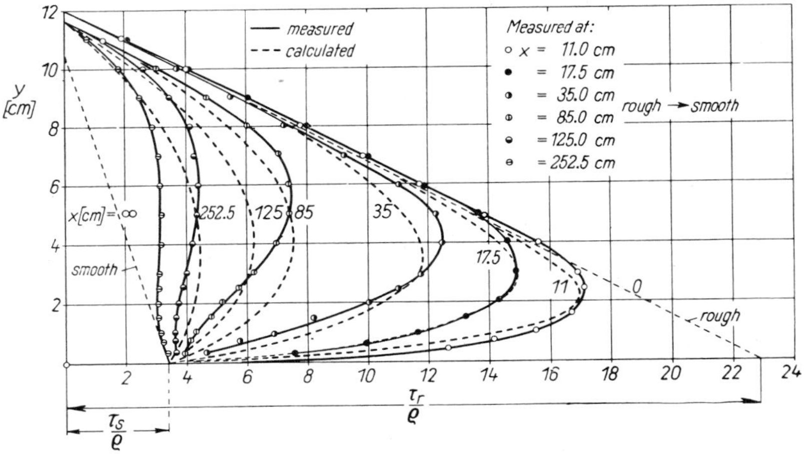

Fig. 21.17. Variation of shearing stress in the boundary layer on passing from a *rough* to a *smooth* portion of wall, as measured by W. Jacobs [23]

3. Transition from a smooth to a rough surface. W. Jacobs [23] investigated the flow pattern near a wall which consisted of a smooth section followed by a rough one, or vice versa. The problem is of some interest in meteorology and occurs when a wind passes from sea to land, or from land to sea, flowing past surfaces whose roughnesses differ considerably from each other. It is noticed that the velocity profile which corresponds to the downstream section of the wall forms only at a certain distance behind the boundary between the two sections. The variation of shearing stress calculated from the measured velocity profile with the aid of Prandtl's hypothesis, i. e. $\tau = \varrho\, l^2\, (\mathrm{d}u/\mathrm{d}y)^2$, is seen plotted in Figs. 21.16 and 21.17. The diagrams show one remarkable feature, namely that the shearing stress at the wall assumes its new value which corresponds to fully developed flow immediately behind the boundary between the two sections. This result is important, e. g. when it is desired to calculate the drag on a plate which consists of a smooth and a rough section. In the zone of transition the variation of shearing stress at right angles to the wall, $\tau(y)$, has a form which is intermediate between the linear functions characteristic of fully developed flow over a rough and a smooth wall respectively. The shearing stress function $\tau(y)$ obtained from measurement can be interpolated with the aid of the empirical relation

$$\tau\,(x, y) = \left\{ \tau_s - (\tau_s - \tau_r)\, \mathrm{e}^{-11{\cdot}6\,\frac{y}{x}} \right\} \frac{h-y}{h}, \qquad \text{(smooth} \rightarrow \text{rough)} \qquad (21.35)$$

which is shown dotted in Figs. 21.16 and 21.17. Here τ_r and τ_s denote the shearing stresses on the rough and smooth wall, respectively, both for fully developed flow, x is the distance along the wall measured from the border line between the two portions of the plate, y is the distance from the wall and h denotes the height of the channel. For the reverse order of transition (rough $\rightarrow$ smooth) the same formula may be used, except that τ_s and τ_r must be interchanged.

d. Admissible roughness

The amount of roughness which is considered "admissible" in engineering applications is that maximum height of individual roughness elements which causes no increase in drag compared with a smooth wall. The practical importance of determining the amount of admissible roughness for a given set of circumstances is very great, because it determines the amount of labour which it is worth spending in manufacturing a given surface. The answer to this question is essentially different depending on whether the flow under consideration is laminar or turbulent.

In the case of *turbulent boundary layers* roughness has no effect and the wall is hydraulically smooth, if all protuberances are contained within the laminar sublayer. As mentioned before, the thickness of the latter is only a small fraction of the boundary layer thickness. In connexion with pipe flow it was found that the condition for a wall to be hydraulically smooth is given by eqn. (20.37) which stated that the dimensionless roughness Reynolds number

$$\frac{v_* k}{\nu} < 5 \quad \text{(hydraulically smooth)}\,. \qquad (21.36)$$

where $v_* = \sqrt{\tau_0/\varrho}$ denotes the friction velocity.

This result can be considered valid also for the flat plate at zero incidence. However, from the practical point of view it seems more convenient to specify a value of relative roughness k/l. Referring to the diagram in Fig. 21.11, which represents the resistance formula for a plate, we can obtain the admissible value of k/l from the point at which a given curve $l/k =$ const. deviates from the curve for a smooth wall. It is seen that the admissible value of k/l decreases as the Reynolds number $U_\infty l/\nu$

is increased. Rounded-off values from Fig. 21.11 are listed in Table 21.2. They can be summarized by the following simple formula:

$$\frac{U_\infty k_{adm}}{\nu} = 100\,, \tag{21.37}$$

whose approximate validity can also be deduced directly from Fig. 21.11.

Table 21.2. Admissible height of protuberances in terms of the Reynolds number

$\mathsf{R}_l = \frac{U_\infty l}{\nu}$	10^5	10^6	10^7	10^8	10^9
$\left(\frac{k}{l}\right)_{adm}$	10^{-3}	10^{-4}	10^{-5}	10^{-6}	10^{-7}

This formula gives only one value of k_{adm} for the whole length of the plate. Since, however, the boundary layer thickness is smaller near the leading edge, the admissible value of k is smaller upstream than further downstream. A formula which takes this circumstance into account is obtained when $v_*^2/U_\infty^2 = \tau_0/\varrho\, U_\infty^2 = \frac{1}{2}\, c_f'$ is introduced, c_f' denoting the local coefficient of skin friction, as given in Table 21.1. Thus we obtain

$$\frac{U_\infty k_{adm}}{\nu} < \frac{7}{\sqrt{c_f'}}\,. \tag{21.38}$$

For small Reynolds numbers $\mathsf{R}_x < 10^6$ eqns. (21.37) and (21.38) give practically the same results, whereas at larger Reynolds numbers eqn. (21.38) gives somewhat greater values. We are, thus, justified in retaining the simpler equation (21.37) because there is no danger of finding values of k_{adm} which are too high. Equation (21.37) states that the *admissible height of roughness elements is independent of the length of the plate*; it is determined solely by the velocity and by the kinematic viscosity in accordance with the condition

$$\boxed{k_{adm} \leq 100\, \frac{\nu}{U_\infty}}\,. \tag{21.39}$$

It follows that the absolute values of admissible roughness for a model and its original are equal, if the velocity and kinematic viscosity are the same in both cases. For long bodies this may lead to extremely small admissible roughnesses as compared with their linear dimensions, see Table 21.3.

For practical applications it is still more convenient to relate the admissible value of roughness directly to the length of the plate, l, or more generally, to the length, l, of the body under consideration, (e. g. length of ship's hull, wing chord, blade chord in turbines or rotary compressors), because this leads to a more graphic measure for the required surface smoothness. To achieve this, equation (21.39) may be rewritten as

$$k_{adm} \leq l \cdot \frac{100}{\mathsf{R}_l}, \tag{21.40}$$

where $\mathsf{R}_l = U_\infty l/\nu$. The diagram in Fig. 21.18 may be used to facilitate calculations with the aid of eqn. (21.40). The diagram contains a plot of admissible sizes of protuberances against Reynolds number with the characteristic lenght as a parameter. The ranges of Reynolds numbers encountered in various engineering applications (ship, airship, aircraft, compressor blades, steam turbine blades) have been

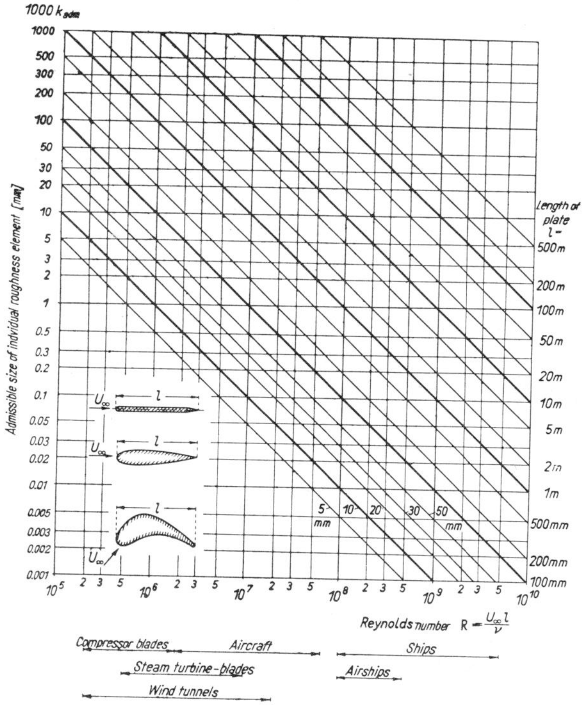

Fig. 21.18. Admissible roughness k_{adm} for rough plates at zero incidence and aircraft wings from eqn. (21.39)

shown at the bottom of the diagram for convenience of reference. In addition Table 21.3 gives a summary of several examples which have been computed with the aid of Fig. 21.18. In the case of *ship's hulls* admissible roughnesses are of the order of several hundredths of one millimetre (several tenths of one thousandth to several thousandths of an inch); such values cannot be attained in practice and it is always necessary to allow for a considerable increase in drag due to roughness. The same is true of *airships*. As far as *aircraft surfaces* are concerned it is seen that admissible roughness dimensions lie between 0·01 and 0·1 mm (0·0004 and 0·004 in). With very careful preparation of the surface it is possible to meet these demands. In the case of *model aircraft* and *compressor blades* which require the same order of smoothness, i. e. 0·01 to 0·1 mm (0·0004 to 0·004 in), hydraulically smooth surfaces can be obtained without undue difficulty. The Reynolds numbers encountered in *steam turbines* are comparatively large because in spite of the small linear dimensions,

Table 21.3. Examples on the calculation of admissible roughness from Fig. 21.18

Item	Description	Length l	Velocity w			Kinematic viscosity $10^6 \times \nu$		$R = \frac{w\,l}{\nu}$	Admissible roughness k_{adm}	
		m (ft)	km/h	m/sec	ft/sec	m²/sec	ft²/sec		mm	in
Ship's hull	large fast	250 (820)	56 30 knots	15	49	1·0	10	4×10^9	0·007	0·00028
	small slow	50 (165)	18 10 knots	5	165	1·0	10	3×10^8	0·02	0·0008
Airship	—	250 (820)	120	33	1100	15	150	5×10^8	0·05	0·002
Aeroplane (wing)	large fast	4† (13)	600	166	545	15	150	5×10^7	0·01	0·0004
	small slow	2 (6·5)	200	55	180	15	150	8×10^6	0·025	0·001
Compressor blades	slow	0·1 (0·33)	—	150	490	15	150	1×10^6	0·01	0·0004
Model wings	small	0·2 (0·65)	144	40	130	15	150	5×10^5	0·05	0·002
Steam turbine blades	high pressure $t = 300$ C (∼550 F)	10 mm (0·4 in)	—	200	650	0·4	4	5×10^6	0·0002	0·000008
	high pressure $t = 500$ C (∼950 F)	10 mm (0·4 in)	—	200	650	0·8	8	$2{\cdot}5 \times 10^6$	0·0005	0·00002
	low pressure	100 mm	—	400	1300	8	80	5×10^6	0·002	0·00008

† Chord.

the pressures are comparatively high† and admissible roughness values are, consequently, very small. The required values of between 0·0002 to 0·002 mm (10^{-5} to 10^{-4} in) can hardly be attained on newly manufactured blades. They are certainly exceeded after a period of operation due to corrosion and scaling. It may now be remarked that the preceding considerations apply to tightly spaced protuberances which correspond to sand roughness. In the case of widely spaced obstacles and in the case of wall waviness the admissible values are somewhat larger.

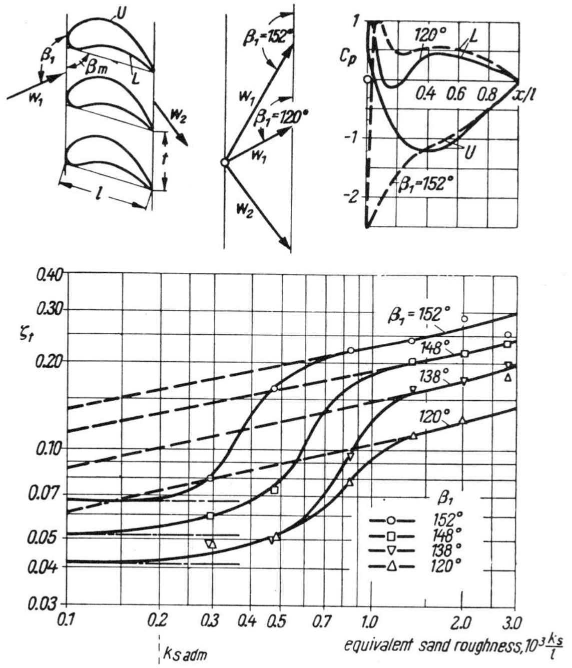

Fig. 21.19. Loss coefficients for turbine blades provided with sand roughness, as measured by L. Speidel [49]

$\zeta_t = \Delta g/\frac{1}{2}\varrho\, w_2^2$;
Δg — loss in total head. Solidity $t/l = 0{\cdot}67$;
mean blade angle $\beta_m = 72°$;
Reynolds number $\mathsf{R} = w_2\, l/\nu = 5 \times 10^5$;
$C_p = (p - p_2)/\frac{1}{2}\varrho\, w_2^2$

The influence of roughness on the losses in a steam turbine stage depends to a great extent on the pressure drop across it, i. e. on the degree of reaction of the stage. This point emerges clearly from Fig. 21.19 which represents the results of measurements performed by L. Speidel [49] on turbine cascades with varying sand roughness. The diagram contains a plot of the loss coefficient $\zeta_t = \Delta g/\frac{1}{2}\varrho\, w_2^2$, where Δg denotes the mean value of the loss in total head averaged over one pitch; the loss has been made dimensionless with reference to the total head at exit (w_2-denotes the leaving velocity). The increase in the value of the loss coefficient ζ_t as β_1 is increased is caused by an increase in w_1 with β_1, as may be verified with reference to the velocity triangle. The broken straight lines in Fig. 21.19 represent the rate at which ζ_t increases on the assumption that the boundary layer is turbulent all along the blade. For lower roughness values the measured points fall considerably below these straight lines.

† For values of the kinematic viscosity of superheated steam consult Escher Wyss Reports, vol. X, No. 1, p. 3 (1937), or NBS-NACA Tables of Thermodynamic Properties of Gases, Washington, 1954.

It has been ascertained during the investigation that this behaviour results from the existence of long stretches of laminar boundary layers; as the roughness is increased the length of the laminar portion of the boundary layer decreases. The estimate of the amount of permissible roughness from eqn. (21.40) leads here to a value of $k_S/l = 0{\cdot}2 \times 10^{-3}$ at $\mathsf{R} = w_2\, l/\nu = 5 \times 10^5$. This limit has been marked in Fig. 21.19 and it is seen that it agrees well with the experimental results.

The height of a protuberance which causes transition in a laminar boundary layer will be called *critical height* or *critical roughness.* Roughness affects the resistance offered by the wall by moving the point of transition in an upstream direction and, depending on the shape of the body, the drag may be either increased or decreased. The drag is *increased* by such a shift in the point of transition when the drag of the body is predominantly due to skin fricton (for example an aerofoil). It may be *decreased* under certain circumstances if the drag of the body is mainly due to form drag (e. g. circular cylinder). In accordance with some Japanese measurements [51], this critical value of the roughness is given by

$$\frac{v_* \, k_{crit}}{\nu} = 15 \,. \tag{21.41}$$ †

We shall now calculate the value of k_{crit} for a wing of length $l = 2$ m (abt. 6·5 ft) in air ($\nu = 14 \times 10^{-6}$ m²/sec) at a velocity $U_\infty = 83$ m/sec $= 300$ km/hr (about 185 mph). We have $\mathsf{R}_l = U_\infty\, l/\nu \approx 10^7$. Consider a point on the wing at $x = 0{\cdot}1\; l$, i. e. at $\mathsf{R}_x = U_\infty\, x/\nu \approx 10^6$. The boundary layer can remain laminar as far as this point owing to the existence of a negative pressure gradient. The shearing stress at the wall for a laminar boundary layer is given by eqn. (7.35) and is $\tau_0/\varrho = 0{\cdot}332\; U_\infty^2 \sqrt{\nu/U_\infty x} = 0{\cdot}332 \times 6900 \times 10^{-3} = 2{\cdot}29$ m²/sec². Hence $v_* = \sqrt{\tau_0/\varrho} = 1{\cdot}52$ m/sec. Inserting into eqn. (21.41) we have

$$k_{crit} = 15\,\frac{\nu}{v_*} = \frac{15}{1{\cdot}52} \times 0{\cdot}14 \times 10^{-4}\,\mathrm{m} = 0{\cdot}14\ \mathrm{mm}\ \text{(about 0·0056 in)}\,.$$

This shows that the critical size of a protuberance which causes transition is about ten times larger than the value of about 0·02 mm (0·0008 in) in the turbulent boundary layer, as calculated in Table 21.3, for the case in hand (small aeroplane). The laminar boundary layer "can stand" much larger roughnesses than the turbulent boundary layer. K. Scherbarth [40] carried out experiments on the behaviour of laminar boundary layers on walls provided with single obstacles (rivet heads). It was ascertained that behind the obstacle there forms a wedge-like turbulent disturbed region whose angle of spread is about 14° to 18°.

The more recent and very extensive measurements carried out by E. G. Feindt [14a] have led to a refinement of the criterion for the critical height given in eqn. (21.41) as mentioned in Sec. XVIIg.

† Newer investigations carried out by K. Kraemer show that the critical roughness element size which causes transition in the laminar boundary layer can also be found from the condition

$$\frac{U\, k_{crit}}{\nu} \le 900\,.$$

The above formula is of the same form as eqn. (21.39) for the admissible size of a roughness element, the numerical constant having now a different value (*cf.* also ref. [48a] of Chap. XVI).

The influence of roughness on form drag can be summarized as follows: bodies with sharp edges, such as e. g. a flat plate at right angles to the stream, are quite insensitive to surface roughness, because the point of transition is determined by

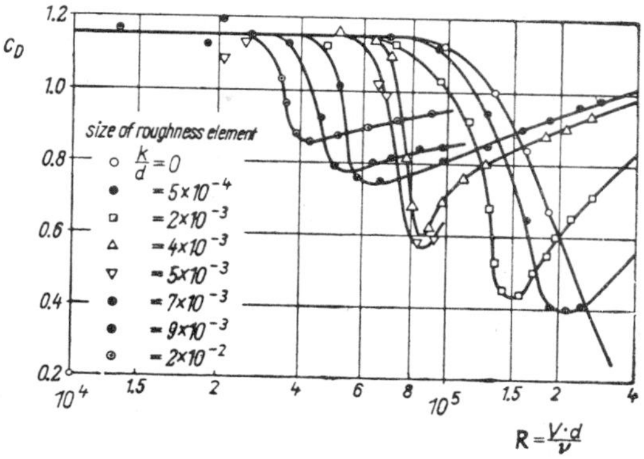

Fig. 21.20. Drag on circular cylinders at varying roughness, after Fage and Warsap [13]

the edges. On the other hand, the drag of bluff bodies, such as circular cylinders, is very sensitive to roughness. The value of the critical Reynolds number for which the drag shows a sudden drop (Fig. 1.4) depends to a marked degree on the roughness of the surface. According to measurements, [1, 13], as shown in Fig. 21.20, the critical Reynolds number decreases with increasing relative roughness k/R ($d = 2\ R =$ diameter of cylinder). The boundary layer appears to be disturbed by roughness to such a degreee that transition occurs at considerably lower Reynolds numbers than is the case with smooth cylinders. Roughness has, therefore, the same effect as Prandtl's tripping wire (Fig. 2.21); namely, it does reduce drag in a certain range of Reynolds numbers. In any case the drag in the supercritical range of Reynolds numbers is always larger for the rough than for the smooth cylinders.

References

[1] J. Ackeret, Schweizerische Bauzeitung, **108**, 25 (1936).

[2] H. Blenk and H. Trienes, Strömungstechnische Beiträge zum Windschutz. Grundlagen der Landtechnik. VDI-Verlag No. 8, 1956.

[3] P. F. Brinich and N. S. Diaconis, Boundary layer development and skin friction at Mach number 3·05. NACA TN 2742 (1952).

[4] J. M. Burgers, The motion of a fluid in the boundary layer along a plane smooth surface. Proc. First Intern. Congress for Applied Mechanics 121, Delft (1924).

[5] D. R. Chapmann and R. H. Kester, Measurements of turbulent skin friction in cylinders in axial flow at subsonic and supersonic velocities. Jour. Aero. Sci. **20**, 441—448 (1953).

[6] D. Coles, The problem of the turbulent boundary layer. ZAMP **5**, 3, 181—202 (1954).

[6a] D. Coles, The law of the wake in the turbulent boundary layer. J. Fluid Mech. **1**, 191—226 (1956).

[7] D. Coles, Measurements of turbulent friction on a smooth flat plate in supersonic flow. Jour. Aero. Sci. **21**, 433—448 (1954).

[7a] J. W. Daily and R. E. Nece, Chamber dimension effects on induced flow and frictional resistance of enclosed rotating disks. Trans. ASME D **82** (Tour. Basic Eng.), 217 (1960).

[8] S. Dhawan, Direct measurement of skin friction. NACA Rep. No. 1121 (1953).

[9] H. DOETSCH, Einige Versuche über den Einfluß von Oberflächenstörungen auf die Profileigenschaften, insbesondere auf den Profilwiderstand im Schnellflug. Jb. d. dt. Luftfahrtforschung **I**, 88 (1939).
[10] R. M. O'DONNEL, Experimental investigation at Mach number of 2·41 of average skin friction coefficients and velocity profiles for laminar and turbulent boundary layers and assessment of probe effects. NACA TN 3122 (1954).
[11] E. R. VAN DRIEST, Turbulent boundary layer in compressible fluids. Jour. Aero. Sci. **18**, 145—160 (1951).
[12] E. R. VAN DRIEST, The turbulent boundary layer with variable Prandtl Number. "Fifty years of boundary layer research", Braunschweig, pp. 257—271, 1955.
[13] A. FAGE and J. H. WARSAP, The effects of turbulence and surface roughness on the drag of circular cylinders. ARC R & M 1283 (1930).
[14] V. M. FALKNER, The resistance of a smooth flat plate with turbulent boundary layer. Aircraft Engineering **15**, March 1943.
[14a] E. G. FEINDT, Untersuchungen über die Abhängigkeit des Umschlages laminar-turbulent von der Oberflächenrauhigkeit und der Druckverteilung. Thesis Braunschweig 1956. Jahrbuch d. Schiffbautechn. Ges., **50**, 180—203 (1957).
[15] C. FERRARI, Comparison of theoretical and experimental results for the turbulent boundary layer in supersonic flow along a flat plate. Jour. Aero. Sci. **18**, 555—564 (1951).
[16] F. GEBERS, Schiffbau **9**, 435 and 475 (1908), also Schiffbau **22** (1919).
[17] S. GOLDSTEIN, On the resistance to the rotation of a disk immersed in a fluid. Proc. Cambr. Phil. Soc. **31**, Part 2, 232 (1935).
[18] M. HANSEN, Die Geschwindigkeitsverteilung in der Grenzschicht an einer eingetauchten Platte. ZAMM **8**, 185 (1928); NACA TM 585 (1930).
[19] F. K. HILL, Boundary layer measurements in hypersonic flow. Jour. Aero. Sci. **23**, 35—42 (1956).
[20] M. J. HOOD, The effects of some common surface irregularities on wing drag. NACA TN 695 (1939).
[21] E. N. JACOBS, Airfoil section characteristic as affected by protuberances. NACA Report No. 446 (1932).
[22] W. JACOBS, Strömung hinter einem einzelnen Rauhigkeitselement. Ing.-Arch. **9**, 343 (1938).
[23] W. JACOBS, Umformung eines turbulenten Geschwindigkeits-Profils. ZAMM **19**, 87 (1939).
[24] TH. VON KÁRMÁN, Mechanische Ähnlichkeit und Turbulenz. Proc. 3rd. Intern. Congr. Appl. Mech., Stockholm 1931, p. 85; and Hydromechanische Probleme des Schiffsantriebes, Hamburg 1932; see also J. Aero. Sci. **1**, 1 (1934); NACA TM 611 (1931).
[25] TH. VON KÁRMÁN, Über laminare und turbulente Reibung. ZAMM **1**, 233 (1921); NACA TM 1092 (1946).
[26] G. KEMPF, Neue Ergebnisse der Widerstandsforschung. Werft, Reederei, Hafen **10**, 234 und 247 (1929).
[27] G. KEMPF, Über den Einfluß der Rauhigkeit auf den Widerstand von Schiffen. Jahrb. d. Schiffbautechn. Gesellschaft **38**, 159 and 233 (1937); also: The effect of roughness on the resistance of ships. Engineering, London **143**, 417 (1937); see also Trans. Inst. Nav. Architects **79**, 109 and 137 (1937).
[28] L. LANDWEBER, Der Reibungswiderstand der längsangeströmten ebenen Platte. Jahrb. Schiffb. Ges. **46**, 137—150 (1952).
[29] H. W. LIEPMANN and G. H. FILA, Investigations of effects of surface temperature and single roughness elements on boundary layer transition. NACA Rep. No. 890 (1947).
[30] R. K. LOBB, E. M. WINKLER and J. PERSH, Experimental investigation of turbulent boundary layers in hypersonic flow. Naval Ord. Lab. NAVORD-Report No. 3880 (1955).
[30a] H. W. LIEPMANN and F. E. GODDARD, Note on the Mach number effect upon the skin friction of rough surfaces. Jour. Aero. Sci. **24**, 784 (1957).
[31] E. J. MOTTARD and J. D. LOPOSER, Average skin friction drag coefficient from tank tests of a parabolic body of revolution (NACA RM-10). NACA Rep. No. 1161 (1954).
[32] H. MOTZFELD, Die turbulente Strömung an welligen Wänden. ZAMM **17**, 193 (1937).
[33] J. NIKURADSE, Turbulente Reibungsschichten an der Platte. Ed. by Zentr. wiss. Ber.-Wesen. Obtainable from R. Oldenbourg, Munich and Berlin 1942.
[34] W. PAESCHKE, Experimentelle Untersuchungen zum Rauhigkeits- und Stabilitätsproblem in der bodennahen Luftschicht. Thesis Göttingen 1937, Summary in Beiträge zur Physik der freien Atmosphäre **24**, 163 (1937); see also Z. Geophysik **13**, 14 (1937).

[35] L. Prandtl, Über den Reibungswiderstand strömender Luft. Reports of the Aerod. Versuchsanst. Göttingen, 3rd. series (1927) see also: Zur turbulenten Strömung in Rohren und längs Platten. Reports of the Aerod. Versuchsanst. Göttingen, 4th. series (1932); First mention in 1st. series 136 (1921).

[36] L. Prandtl and H. Schlichting, Das Widerstandsgesetz rauher Platten. Werft, Reederei, Hafen 1—4 (1934).

[37] L. Prandtl, The mechanics of viscous fluids, in W. F. Durand, Aerodynamic theory, **III** (1935).

[38] H. Schlichting, Experimentelle Untersuchungen zum Rauhigkeitsproblem. Ing.-Arch. **7**, 1—34 (1936); NACA TM 823 (1937).

[39] H. Schlichting, Die Grenzschicht an der ebenen Platte mit Absaugung und Ausblasen. Luftfahrtforschung **19**, 293 (1942).

[40] K. Scherbarth, Grenzschichtmessungen hinter einer punktförmigen Störung in laminarer Strömung. Jb. d. dt. Luftfahrtforschung **I**, 51 (1942).

[41] C. Schmieden, Über den Widerstand einer in einer Flüssigkeit rotierenden Scheibe. ZAMM **8**, 460—479 (1928).

[42] K. E. Schoenherr, Resistance of flat surfaces moving through a fluid. Trans. Soc. Nav. Arch. and Mar. Engrs. **40**, 279 (1932).

[43] F. Schultz-Grunow, Der hydraulische Reibungswiderstand von Platten mit mäßig rauher Oberfläche, insbesondere von Schiffsoberflächen. Jb. d. Schiffbautechn. Ges. **39**, 176—199 (1938).

[44] F. Schultz-Grunow, Neues Widerstandsgesetz für glatte Platten. Luftfahrtforschung **17**, 239 (1940), also NACA Tech. Mem. No. 986 (1941).

[45] F. Schultz-Grunow, Der Reibungswiderstand rotierender Scheiben in Gehäusen. ZAMM **15**, 191 (1935); see also H. Föttinger, ZAMM **17**, 356 (1937) and K. Pantell, Forschg. Ing.-Wes. **16**, 97 (1950).

[46] F. Schultz-Grunow, Der Mechanismus des Widerstandes von Einzelrauhigkeiten. ZAMM **36**, 309 (1956).

[47] A. Seiff, Examination of the existing data on the heat transfer of turbulent boundary layers at supersonic speeds from the point of view of Reynolds analogy. NACA TN 3254 (1954).

[47a] D. W. Smith and J. D. Walker, Skin friction measurements in incompressible flow, NASA TR R—26 (1959).

[48] E. Sörensen, Wandrauhigkeitseinfluß bei Strömungsmaschinen. Forsch. Ing.-Wes. **8**, 25 (1937).

[49] L. Speidel, Einfluß der Oberflächenrauhigkeit auf die Strömungsverluste in ebenen Schaufelgittern. Forschung Ing. Wes. **20**, 129—140 (1954).

[50] W. Szablewski, Berechnung der turbulenten Strömung längs der ebenen Platte. ZAMM **31**, 309—324 (1951).

[51] J. Tani, R. Hama and S. Mituisi, On the permissible roughness in the laminar boundary layer. Aero. Res. Inst. Tokyo, 199 (1940).

[52] W. Tillmann, Neue Widerstandsmessungen an Oberflächenstörungen in der turbulenten Grenzschicht. Forschungshefte für Schiffstechnik, No. 2 (1953).

[53] K. Wieghardt, Über die turbulente Strömung im Rohr und längs der Platte. ZAMM **24**, 294 (1944).

[54] K. Wieghardt, Erhöhung des turbulenten Reibungswiderstandes durch Oberflächenstörungen. Techn. Berichte 10, No. 9 (1943); see also Forschungshefte für Schiffstechnik **1**, 65—81 (1953).

[55] C. Wieselsberger, Reports of the Aerod. Versuchsanst. Göttingen, 1st. series, 121.

[56] D. H. Williams and A. F. Brown, Experiments on a riveted wing in the compressed air tunnel. ARC R & M 1855 (1938).

[57] R. E. Wilson, Turbulent boundary layer characteristics at supersonic speeds. Jour. Aero. Sci. **17**, 585—594 (1950).

[58] A. D. Young, The drag effects of roughness at high subcritical speeds. Jour. Roy. Aero. Soc. **18**, 534 (1950).

[59] A. Walz, Näherungstheorie für kompressible turbulente Grenzschichten. ZAMM **36**, Sonderheft (special issue) pp. 50—56 (1956)

CHAPTER XXII

The turbulent boundary layer with positive and negative pressure gradient

In the present chapter we shall discuss the behaviour of a turbulent boundary layer in the presence of a positive or negative pressure gradient along the wall, thus providing an extension of the subject matter of the preceding chapter in which the boundary layer on a flat plate with no pressure gradient was considered. The present case is particularly important for the calculation of the drag of an aeroplane wing or a turbine blade as well as for the understanding of the processes which take place in a diffuser. Apart from skin friction we are interested in knowing whether the boundary layer will separate under given circumstances and if so, we shall wish to determine the point of separation. The existence of a negative and, in particular, of a positive pressure gradient exerts a strong influence on the formation of the layer just as was the case with laminar layers. At the present time these very complicated phenomena are far from being understood completely but there are in existence several semi-empirical methods of calculation which lead to comparatively satisfactory results. The empirical relations which have been used for the study of flows in pipes and along plates do not suffice for the development of such semi-empirical methods, and additional hypotheses become necessary. For this reason we shall begin by giving a short account of some experimental results.

a. Some experimental results

Systematic experiments on two-dimensional flows with pressure drop and pressure rise in convergent and divergent channels with flat walls have been carried out by F. Doench [5], J. Nikuradse [27], H. Hochschild [15], R. Kroener [18] and J. Polzin [29]. Measurements on circular diffusers, and particularly on the efficiency of the process of energy transformation, are described in papers by F. A. L. Winternitz and W. J. Ramsay [51] as well as by J. M. Robertson and D. Ross [31]. These experiments demonstrate that the shape of the velocity profile depends very strongly on the pressure gradient. Fig. 22.1 shows the velocity profiles which were measured by J. Nikuradse during his experiments with slightly convergent or divergent channels. The half included angle of the channels ranged over the values $\alpha = -8°, -4°, -2°, 0°, 1°, 2°, 3°, 4°$. The boundary layer thickness in a convergent channel is much smaller than that at zero pressure gradient, whereas in a divergent channel it becomes very thick and extends as far as the centre-line of the channel. For semi-angles up to 4° in a divergent channel the velocity profile is fully symmetrical over the width of the channel and shows no features associated with separation. On increasing the semi-angle beyond 4° the shape of the velocity profile undergoes a fundamental change. The velocity profiles for channels with 5°, 6° and 8° of divergence respectively, shown in Figs. 22.2, 22.3 and 22.4 cease to be symmetrical. With a 5° angle of divergence, Fig. 22.2, no back-flow can yet be discerned, but separation is about to begin on one of the channel walls. In addition the flow becomes unstable so that, depending on fortuitous disturbances, the stream adheres alternately to the one or the other wall of the channel. Such an instability is characteristic of incipient separation. J. Nikuradse observed the first occurrence of separation at an angle between $\alpha = 4{\cdot}8°$ and $5{\cdot}1°$. At an angle of $\alpha = 6°$ the lack of symmetry in the velocity profile is even more pronounced and the flow has completely separated from one of the walls. At $\alpha = 8°$, Fig. 22.4, the width of the region of reversed flow is considerably larger than for $\alpha = 6°$, and frequent oscillation of the stream from one side to the other is observed, the phenomenon being absent at $\alpha = 5°$ and $6°$. However, the duration of one particular flow configuration is sufficiently long for a full set of readings to be obtained. As the angle of divergence is increased, the region of reverse flow becomes wider and the beats are more frequent.

Very thorough experimental investigations into the behaviour of turbulent boundary layers with pressure gradients have been recently performed by G. B. Schubauer and P. S. Klebanoff [41], by J. Laufer [19], and by F. H. Clauser [3]. The first of the above papers contains, in particular, results of measurements on turbulent fluctuations and on the correlation coefficients which were defined in Chap. XVIII. The last paper contains extensive results of measurements on shearing stresses.

The calculations described in the following sections can evidently apply only to flows which adhere completely to the walls, that is, to cases which are similar to the one shown in Fig. 22.1.

b. The calculation of two-dimensional turbulent boundary layers

1. General remarks. All methods for the calculation of turbulent boundary layers are approximate ones and of the type which was described in Chap. XII in relation to laminar boundary layers. They are based on the integral forms of the momentum and energy equations as deduced in Chap. VIII, eqns. (8.35) and (8.38). Since, however, no general expressions for shear and dissipation in turbulent flow can be deduced by purely theoretical considerations, it is necessary to make additional suitable assumptions; these can only be obtained from the results of systematic measurements and, consequently, the calculation of turbulent boundary layers is semi-empirical.

Since the experimental techniques are being continuously improved with the course of time, it has proved possible concurrently to improve the methods of calculation. Moreover, the improvements relate to the methods of computation as well, and not only to their physical basis. Some of the older methods of calculation have now gone out of use, but the fundamental ideas contained in them are indispensable to a good understanding of more modern methods. We shall now, therefore, attempt to give a comprehensive account of the most important methods

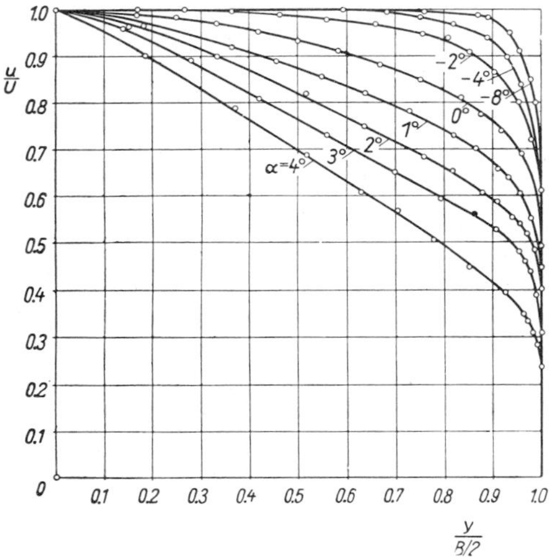

Fig. 22.1. Velocity distribution in *convergent and divergent* channels with flat walls as measured by Nikuradse [27]
α — half included angle; B — width of channel

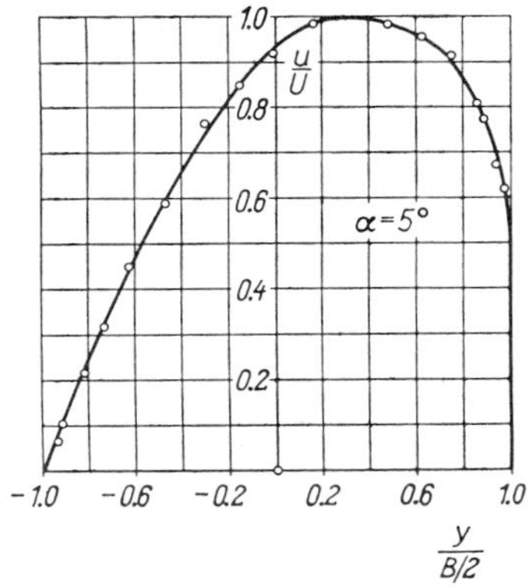

Fig. 22.2. Velocity distribution in a *divergent* channel of half included angle $\alpha = 5°$. The lack of symmetry in the velocity distribution signifies incipient separation

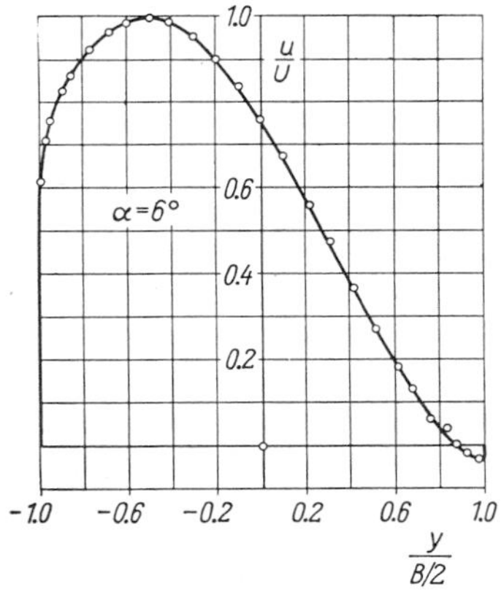

Fig. 22.3. Velocity distribution in a *divergent* channel of half included angle $\alpha = 6°$. Reverse flow and separation are seen to be setting in on the right-hand wall; B — width of channel

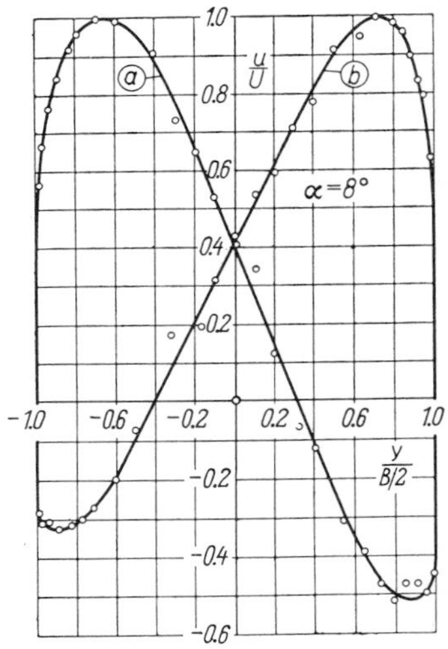

Fig. 22.4. Velocity distribution in a *divergent* channel of half included angle $\alpha = 8°$. Reverse flow is completely developed. The flow oscillates at longer intervals between patterns (a) and (b)

of calculation which have so far been advanced. This account will be followed by a more detailed presentation of one of the more recent methods in order to pave the way for a practical, numerical example.

2. The characteristic parameters of a boundary layer. The first method of calculating turbulent boundary layers with pressure gradient is due to E. Gruschwitz [11]. The empirical values used in this theory were later checked and improved by A. Kehl [17]. At about the same time A. Buri [2] indicated a method which was based on a similar fundamental assumption, and a method due to E. A. von Doenhoff and N. Tetervin [4] has been tested in the United States. H. C. Garner [10] developed a method which starts from the same premises as that due to von Doenhoff and Tetervin but is superior to it in its arrangement of numerical calculations. In this connexion the paper by W. Coleman [3a] is also worth mentioning. E. Truckenbrodt [46] established a simple method of integration which is applicable both to two-dimensional and axially symmetrical flows; it is based on the results of the most recent investigations into turbulent boundary layers due to K. Wieghardt [48], H. Ludwieg and W. Tillmann [22], and J. Rotta [33, 34].

All these methods have the following in common:

1. *The momentum thickness*, defined by eqn. (8.34) as

$$\theta = \int_0^\delta \frac{u}{U}\left(1 - \frac{u}{U}\right) \mathrm{d}y \tag{22.1}$$

is used as the characteristic boundary layer dimension.

2. In order to specify the velocity profile which, as mentioned, depends strongly on the pressure gradient, a velocity profile *shape factor* is introduced. Buri chose for this purpose the dimensionless quantity

$$\Gamma = \frac{\theta}{U}\frac{\mathrm{d}U}{\mathrm{d}x}\left(\frac{U\theta}{\nu}\right)^{\frac{1}{4}}, \tag{22.2}$$

which is analogous to the factor used in laminar flow. Here $\Gamma > 0$ corresponds to accelerated and $\Gamma < 0$ to decelerated flow†. In accordance with measurements performed by J. Nikuradse separation occurs when $\Gamma \approx -0{\cdot}06$.

E. Gruschwitz introduced the shape factor

$$\eta = 1 - \left(\frac{u(\theta)}{U}\right)^2, \tag{22.3}$$

where $u(\theta)$ denotes the velocity in the boundary layer at a distance $y = \theta$ from the wall. The usefulness of this shape factor for the analysis of turbulent boundary layer flow is demonstrated by the plot in Fig. 22.5 which represents the results of

† The turbulent shape factor Γ corresponds to the laminar shape factor K from eqn. (12.27)

$$K = \frac{\theta^2}{\nu}\frac{\mathrm{d}U}{\mathrm{d}x} = \frac{\theta}{U}\frac{\mathrm{d}U}{\mathrm{d}x}\frac{U\theta}{\nu}$$

Nikuradse's measurements. Velocity profiles with decreasing pressure correspond to $\eta < 0{\cdot}46$ and those with pressure rise correspond to $\eta > 0{\cdot}46$, separation occurring for $\eta \approx 0{\cdot}8$.

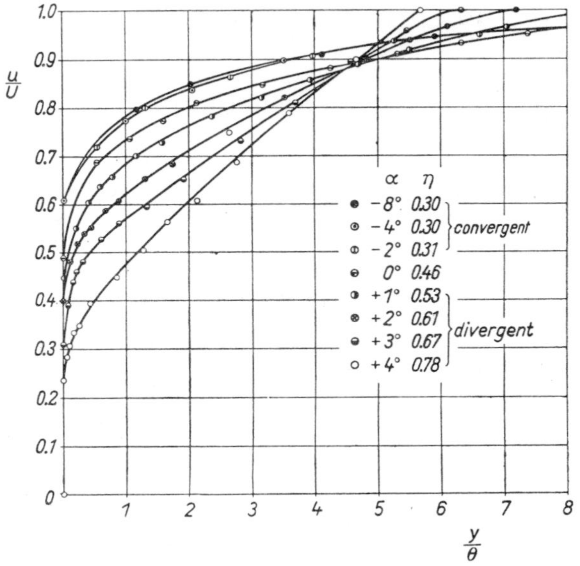

Fig. 22.5. Velocity profiles in convergent and divergent channels replotted from Fig. 21.1 in terms of u/U *versus* y/θ

θ — momentum thickness;
η — shape factor introduced by Gruschwitz, eqn. (22.3)
y — distance from wall

The methods due to A. E. von Doenhoff and N. Tetervin [4] as well as to H. C. Garner [10] employ the ratio of the displacement thickness, δ^*, to the momentum thickness, θ, thus

$$H = \frac{\delta^*}{\theta} \tag{22.4}$$

where

$$\delta^* = \int_0^\delta \left(1 - \frac{u}{U}\right) dy$$

is the displacement thickness from eqn. (8.33). Seperation occurs at $H \approx 1{\cdot}8$ to $2{\cdot}4$. The plot in Fig. 22.6 shows that there exists a unique relationship between the shape factors η and H, and the same fact follows from the assumption that turbulent velocity profiles can be represented by a one-parameter family of curves. This assumption is well substantiated by the results of measurements. According to J. Pretsch [30] this relation is given by

$$\eta = 1 - \left[\frac{H-1}{H\,(H+1)}\right]^{(H-1)} \qquad (22.5)\,\dagger$$

† This can be proved as follows: According to the footnote on p. 536 $H = \delta^*/\theta = (2+n)/n$, or $n = 2/(H-1)$. Hence $\theta/\delta = (H-1)/H(H+1)$, and the shape factor becomes

$$\eta = 1 - \left(\frac{\theta}{\delta}\right)^{2/n} = 1 - \left[\frac{H-1}{H\,(H+1)}\right]^{(H-1)}.$$

if the velocity profile is assumed to have the form of a power law

$$\frac{u}{U} = \left(\frac{y}{\delta}\right)^{1/n}.$$

This relation is shown as curve (1) in Fig. 22.6; it is seen to fit the experimental points well.

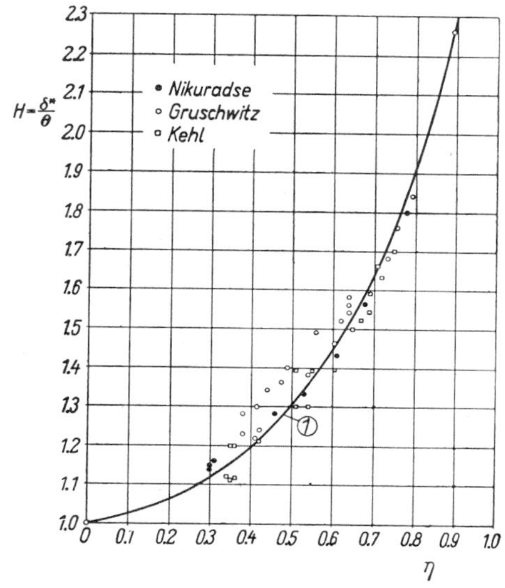

Fig. 22.6. Universal relation between the shape factors $H = \delta^*/\theta$ and η

Curve (1) is a plot of eqn. (22.5)

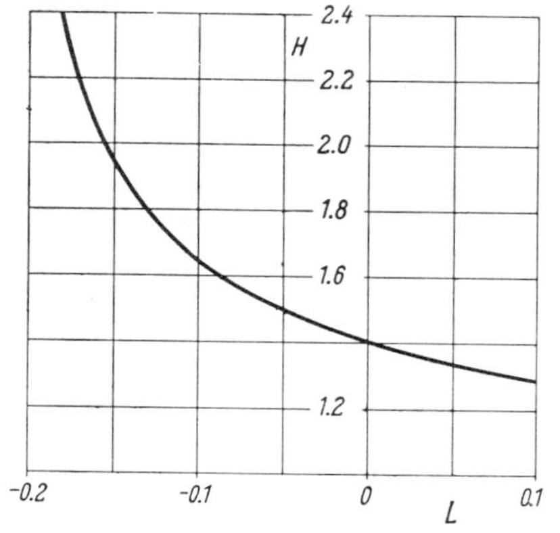

Fig. 22.7. Relation between the ratio of boundary layer thicknesses, H, and the shape factor, L, for a turbulent boundary layer; after Truckenbrodt [46]

E. Truckenbrodt also makes use of the fact that turbulent velocity profiles form a one-parameter family of curves and introduces a shape factor L which is related to $H = \delta^*/\theta$ in a simple manner. The relation between L and H is seen plotted in Fig. 22.7. More details about the function $L(H)$ will be given later in eqn. (22.29). Separation occurs at $L \approx -0{\cdot}13$ to $-0{\cdot}18$.

3. Calculation of the momentum thickness. With the exception of the method due to E. Truckenbrodt, all methods calculate the momentum thickness, θ, from the momentum integral equation of boundary layer theory. In accordance with eqn. (8.35) we can write the momentum integral equation in the form

$$\frac{d\theta}{dx} + (H+2)\frac{\theta}{U}\frac{dU}{dx} = \frac{\tau_0}{\varrho U^2}. \tag{22.6}$$

In order to be in a position to determine the variation of momentum thickness along the contour of the body it is necessary to possess data on the ratio of thicknesses,

H, and the shearing stress at the wall, $\tau_0/\varrho U^2$. This information was obtained by each author in a different way.

Laws for flat plate at zero incidence: The shearing stress at the wall is assumed to be of the same form as that for the flat plate at zero incidence, eqn. (21.12), except that instead of the constant external velocity U_∞ the variable velocity $U(x)$ is substituted. Hence

$$\frac{\tau_0}{\varrho U^2} = \frac{\alpha}{(U\theta/\nu)^{1/n}} . \tag{22.7}$$

The quantities α and n still depend to a certain extent on the Reynolds number and the following correlation may be used:

$$n = 4: \quad \alpha = 0{\cdot}0128 \text{ (Prandtl, eqn. (21.12))}$$
$$n = 6: \quad \alpha = 0{\cdot}0065 \text{ (Falkner [7]).}$$

Since the quantity H always occurs in the group $2 + H$, it is sufficient to work with a mean value for H, say, with the flat plate value $H = 1{\cdot}4$. Taking account of this simplification and introducing the assumption for shearing stress, eqn. (22.7), into the momentum equation (22.6), we obtain a differential equation which can be integrated in closed terms. In accordance with the Appendix to [46], we have

$$\theta \left(\frac{U\theta}{\nu}\right)^{1/n} = U^{-b}\left(C_1 + a \int_{x=x_t}^{x} U^b \, \mathrm{d}x\right), \tag{22.8}$$

where $a = [(n+1)/n]\,\alpha$ and $b = [(n+1)/n](H+2) - 1/n$. The turbulent boundary layer begins at x_t, and C_1 is a constant to be determined from the laminar boundary layer at the point of transition $x = x_t$. The numerical values for a and b are given in Table 22.1

Table 22.1. Constants in the integrated equations for momentum thickness

	Eqn.	n	4	6
Factor in front of integral	(22·8)	a	0·016	0·0076
	(22·14)	c	0·016	—
	(22·19)	A	0·016	0·0076
Exponent of the velocity profile function	(22·8)	b	4·0	3·67
	(22·14)	d	4·0	—
	(22·19)	$3 + \frac{2}{n}$	3·5	3·33

The assumption for the shearing stress at the wall given in eqn. (22.7) was used by E. Gruschwitz with $n = 4$, and by H. C. Garner, who stipulated $n = 6$. A. E. von Doenhoff and N. Tetervin based their calculations on the logarithmic law for the shearing stress given by H. B. Squire and A. D. Young [39]. This has the form

$$\frac{\tau_0}{\varrho U^2} = \frac{0{\cdot}0288}{\left[\log\left(4{\cdot}075\,\frac{U\theta}{\nu}\right)\right]^2}, \tag{22.9}$$

and it can be shown that the differences between it and the assumption made by Falkner are small and inessential.

Analogy with laminar boundary layer: In a manner analogous with K. Pohlhausen's approximate method for laminar boundary layers, A. Buri [2] assumes that the shearing stress at the wall, τ_0, and the ratio of thicknesses, H, for a turbulent boundary layer are also functions of the shape factor Γ alone. Thus

$$\frac{\tau_0}{\varrho U^2} = f_1(\Gamma) \Big/ \left(\frac{U\theta}{\nu}\right)^{1/n} \tag{22.10}$$

and

$$H = \frac{\delta^*}{\theta} = f_2(\Gamma)\,. \tag{22.11}$$

Introducing the assumptions in eqns. (22.10) and (22.11), we obtain†

$$\frac{\mathrm{d}}{\mathrm{d}x}\left[\theta\left(\frac{U\theta}{\nu}\right)^{1/n}\right] = F(\Gamma) \tag{22.12}$$

with

$$F(\Gamma) = \frac{n+1}{n}\,f_1(\Gamma) - \left[2 + \frac{1}{n} + \frac{n+1}{n}\,f_2(\Gamma)\right]\Gamma\,.$$

The plot of the function $F(\Gamma)$ is very nearly linear, as seen from Fig. 22.8, and can be represented by the relation

$$F(\Gamma) = c - d\Gamma = c - d\,\frac{\theta}{U}\,\frac{\mathrm{d}U}{\mathrm{d}x}\left(\frac{U\theta}{\nu}\right)^{1/n} \tag{22.13}$$

Introducing eqn. (22.13) into (22.12), we can now perform the integration in closed terms and obtain

$$\theta\left(\frac{U\theta}{\nu}\right)^{1/n} = U^{-d}\left(C_1 + c\int\limits_{x=x_t}^{x} U^d\,\mathrm{d}x\right)\,. \tag{22.14}$$

A. Buri determined the numerical values of the parameters c and d from Nikuradse's measurements [27] and with the assumption that $n = 4$. In decelerated flow he obtained $c = 0{\cdot}017$ and $d = 4{\cdot}15$. His own measurements, which were carried out in accelerated streams only, led to the values of $c = 0{\cdot}01475$ and $d = 3{\cdot}94$. In order to include both cases, we may put

$$c = 0{\cdot}016 \text{ and } d = 4{\cdot}0,$$

see Table 22.1.

† See, again, the Appendix to [46].

It is very remarkable that in spite of the essentially different assumptions for the shearing stress, τ_0, and thickness ratio, H, used in the solutions (22.8) and (22.14), the variations in the momentum thickness given by these two solutions completely agree with each other, see Table 22.1.

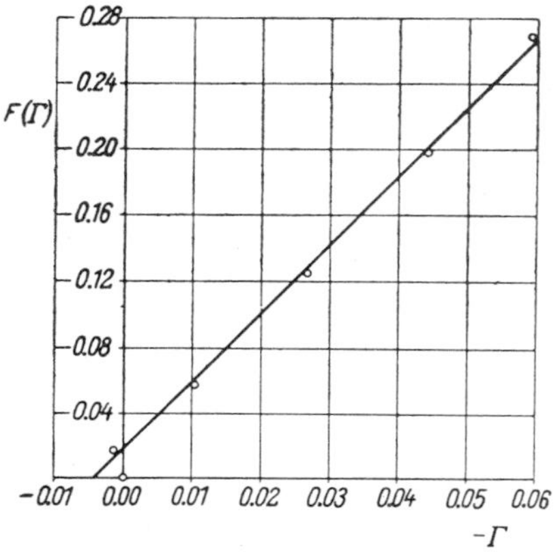

Fig. 22.8. The universal function $F(\Gamma)$ after Buri, eqn. (22.12), from the measurements due to Nikuradse [27]
$F(\Gamma) = 0{\cdot}017 - 4{\cdot}15\ \Gamma$

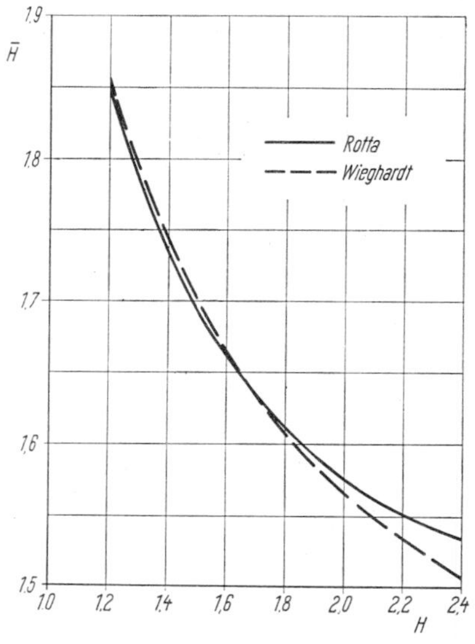

Fig. 22.9. The ratio of boundary layer thicknesses $\overline{H} = \delta^{**}/\theta$ plotted against $H = \delta^*/\theta$, after Rotta [34] and Wieghardt [48]

The method due to E. Truckenbrodt: In calculating the momentum thickness, E. Truckenbrodt [46] followed a somewhat different path in that he made use of the energy integral equation and not of the momentum integral equation. As seen from eqn. (8.38), the energy integral equation may be written as

$$\frac{1}{U^3}\frac{\mathrm{d}}{\mathrm{d}x}(U^3\,\delta^{**}) = 2\,\frac{d_1 + t_1}{\varrho\, U^3}\,, \tag{22.15}$$

where δ^{**} denotes the energy thickness as defined in eqn. (8.37). Assuming that all velocity profiles constitute a one-parameter family, it is found that there exists a unique relationship between the quotient $\delta^{**}/\theta = \overline{H}$ and the already familiar thickness ratio $H = \delta^*/\theta$. This relation is shown plotted in Fig. 22.9. It has been deduced from experimental results by J. Rotta [34]. An analytic evaluation of this relation from the velocity law $u/U = (y/\delta)^{1/n}$ performed by K. Wieghardt gives $\overline{H} = 1{\cdot}269\ H/(H - 0{\cdot}379)$, where the numerical constants have been adjusted to give agreement with experiment. The deviation between these two forms is very small.

The quantity
$$\frac{d_1 + t_1}{\varrho\, U^3} = \int_0^\delta \frac{\tau}{\varrho\, U^2} \frac{\partial}{\partial y}\left(\frac{u}{U}\right) \mathrm{d}y \tag{22.16}$$

represents the dimensionless friction work performed in the boundary layer by the shearing stresses τ. The quantity d_1 is the portion which is transformed into heat (dissipation) and t_1 is the energy of the turbulent motion. In general t_1 may be neglected with respect to d_1. Fig. 22.10 shows a plot of $d_1/\varrho\, U^3$ in terms of the Reynolds number $U\,\theta/\nu$ for various values of the thickness ratio H. It has been deduced by E. Truckenbrodt [46] from the results given by J. Rotta [34]. It turns out that the curves are almost independent of H, and we may assume with a good degree of approximation that
$$\frac{d_1}{\varrho\, U^3} = \frac{0{\cdot}56 \times 10^{-2}}{(U\theta/\nu)^{1/6}}. \tag{22.17}$$

For the purpose of comparison, Fig. 22.11 shows how strongly the shearing stress at the wall depends on the shape factor H. The experimental values for the shearing stress at the wall can be approximated quite well by the empirical formula
$$\frac{\tau_0}{\varrho\, U^2} = 0{\cdot}123 \times 10^{-0{\cdot}678\,H}\left(\frac{U\theta}{\nu}\right)^{-0{\cdot}268} \tag{22.18}$$

which has also been plotted in Fig. 22.11.

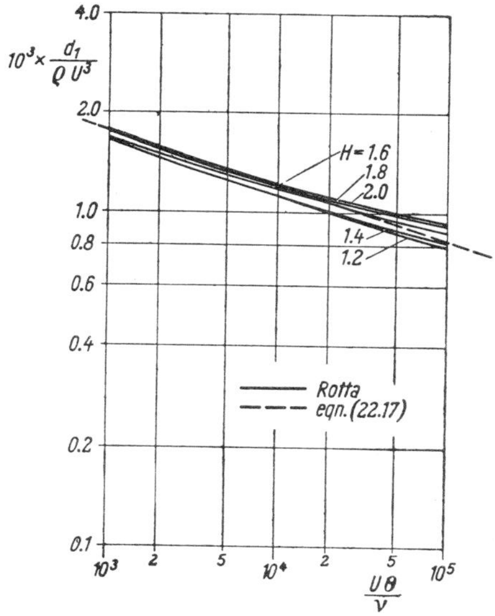

Fig. 22.10. Turbulent dissipation, after Rotta [34]

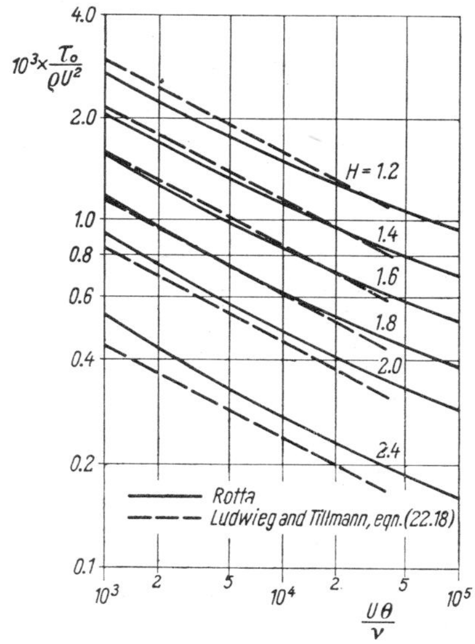

Fig. 22.11. Turbulent shearing stress at the wall after H. Ludwieg and W. Tillman [22], eqn. (22.18), and J. Rotta [34]

Introducing the expression for frictional work, eqn. (22.17), into the energy integral equation (22.15), and assuming a mean value for $\bar{H}$ we can once more integrate in closed terms. We obtain

$$\theta\left(\frac{U\theta}{\nu}\right)^{1/n} = \frac{C_1 + A\int\limits_{x=x_t}^{x} U^{3+2/n}\,dx}{U^{3+2/n}}\,, \qquad (22.19)\dagger$$

with the numerical values $n = 6$ and $A = 0{\cdot}0076$; see Table 22.1.

A comparison of the numerical values in Table 22.1 shows that the three different formulae for the momentum thickness, eqns. (22.8), (22.14), and (22.19), are entirely equivalent.

The constant in eqn. (22.19) can be expressed with the aid of the coefficient of skin friction, c_f, for a flat plate at zero incidence. It will be recalled that c_f depends on the Reynolds number $U_\infty l/\nu$. According to eqn. (21.10) we have $c_f = 2\,\theta/l$, so that with $C_1 = 0$, $x_t = 0$, $x = l$ and $U = U_\infty$, eqn. (22.19) yields

$$\left(\frac{c_f}{2}\right)^{(n+1)/n}\left(\frac{U_\infty l}{\nu}\right)^{1/n} = A\,.$$

Thus the momentum thickness from eqn. (22.19) becomes

$$\frac{\theta(x)}{l} = \left(\frac{U}{U_\infty}\right)^{-3}\left\{C_1{}^* + \left(\frac{c_f}{2}\right)^{(n+1)/n}\int\limits_{x_t/l}^{x/l}\left(\frac{U}{U_\infty}\right)^{3+2/n} d\left(\frac{x}{l}\right)\right\}^{n/(1+n)}. \qquad (22.20)$$

In turbulent flow we have $4 < n < 6$, where $n = 4$ is valid for small Reynolds numbers and $n = 6$ is valid for large Reynolds numbers. The constant $C_1{}^*$ takes into accout the laminar portion of the boundary layer and x_t denotes the position of the point of transition. Its value is found to be

$$C_1{}^* = \left[\frac{1}{2}\,c_{fl}\left(\int\limits_0^{x_t/l}\left(\frac{U}{U_\infty}\right)^5 d\left(\frac{x}{l}\right)\right)^{1/2}\right]^{(n+1)/n}. \qquad (22.21)$$

where c_{fl} denotes the laminar coefficient of skin friction for a flat plate at zero incidence at a Reynolds number $\mathsf{R} = U_\infty l/\nu$.

4. Calculation of the shape factor. In cases when the boundary layer does not separate the calculation of the momentum thickness $\theta(x)$ along the contour of the body essentially completes the calculation of the turbulent boundary layer. The local coefficient of skin friction can be obtained from eqn. (22.7) or (22.9), as a first approximation. A more accurate value would be obtained from eqn. (22.18), but this would require the knowledge of the shape factor H. The method of calculating the shape factor will be described later in this section.

† This equation is also valid for laminar boundary layers if the values $n = 1$ and $A = 0{\cdot}470$ are used. *Cf.* eqn. (12.37).

The total coefficient of skin friction is obtained by integration. The calculation of pressure drag which will be discussed in Chap. XXIV requires only the knowledge of the momentum thickness at the trailing edge, provided that no separation occurs. However, in many cases it is impossible to know in advance whether separation will or will not occur and, furthermore, it may be desirable to assess the susceptibility of the boundary layer to separate. In such cases it becomes necessary to determine the variation of one of the shape factors around the contour of the body in addition, because only in this way is it possible to draw conclusions concerning separation. As already reported in Sec. XXIIb, 2, various authors made use of different shape factors for the turbulent velocity profiles and established differential equations for them as well as for the momentum thickness. Unfortunately, the various differential equations involving shape factors cannot be compared with each other in such a simple way as those involving momentum thickness. As already mentioned, E. Gruschwitz [11] made use of the shape factor η, defined in eqn. (22.3). He obtained the differential equation for η from the consideration that the change in the energy of a fluid particle which moves along a path parallel to the wall and at a distance $y = \theta$ from it must depend on $u(\theta)$, U, θ, and ν. From a dimensional analysis of the problem he obtained the empirical relation

$$\frac{\theta}{q} \frac{\mathrm{d}g(\theta)}{\mathrm{d}x} = F\left(\eta, \frac{U\theta}{\nu}\right) \tag{22.22}$$

where $g(\theta) = p + \frac{1}{2}\varrho\, u^2(\theta) = p + q(1-\eta)$ denotes the total head (energy) in the boundary layer at a distance $y = \theta$; $q = \frac{1}{2}\varrho\, U^2$ denotes the dynamic pressure in the external stream and p is the static pressure which remains constant over the boundary layer thickness and which satisfies the relation $p + \frac{1}{2}\varrho\, U^2 = \text{const.}$ Thus eqn. (22.22) may also be written as

$$\theta \frac{\mathrm{d}\eta}{\mathrm{d}x} = -2\eta \frac{\theta}{U}\frac{\mathrm{d}U}{\mathrm{d}x} - F\left(\eta, \frac{U\theta}{\nu}\right). \tag{22.23}$$

Gruschwitz found from his own measurements that the function F can be represented by the expression

$$F = A\,\eta - B \tag{22.24}$$

with

$$A = 0{\cdot}00894 \text{ and } B = 0{\cdot}00461\,.$$

In a range of measurements extending over Reynolds numbers

$$6 \times 10^2 < U\theta/\nu < 5 \times 10^3,$$

Gruschwitz could not detect any dependence of the parameters A or B on the Reynolds number. A. Kehl [17] extended these measurements to higher Reynolds numbers and was able to confirm the value of A, but he found that B depended on the Reynolds number. The two equations (22.23) and (22.24) constitute a differential equation for the shape factor η. In order to determine it, it is necessary to calculate the variation of $\theta\,(x)$ by the method described earlier. Separation occurs when η exceeds the value of 0·8.

A. E. von Doenhoff and N. Tetervin [4] used the ratio of thicknesses $H = \delta^*/\theta$ as their shape factor. They found that the shape factor H satisfies the empirical equation:

$$\theta \frac{\mathrm{d}H}{\mathrm{d}x} = \mathrm{e}^{4{\cdot}680\,(H-2{\cdot}975)} \left[-\frac{\theta}{q}\frac{\mathrm{d}q}{\mathrm{d}x}\frac{2q}{\tau_0} - 2{\cdot}035\,(H - 1{\cdot}286) \right], \qquad (22.25)$$

which was deduced on the basis of comprehensive American measurements. In deducing this equation the shearing stress near the wall was assumed to obey H. B. Squire's and A. D. Young's [39] formula for the flat plate at zero incidence, given earlier as eqn. (22.9). In an endeavour to simplify the above procedure, H. C. Garner [10] modified eqn. (22.25) and re-evaluated the empirical constants. He obtained

$$\left(\frac{U\theta}{\nu}\right)^{\frac{1}{6}} \theta \frac{\mathrm{d}H}{\mathrm{d}x} = \mathrm{e}^{5\,(H-1{\cdot}4)} \left[-\left(\frac{U\theta}{\nu}\right)^{\frac{1}{6}} \frac{\theta}{U}\frac{\mathrm{d}U}{\mathrm{d}x} - 0{\cdot}0135\,(H - 1{\cdot}4) \right]. \qquad (22.26)$$

Equation (22.25), or eqn. (22.26) allow us to determine the variation of the shape factor $H(x)$ from the previously determined variation of the momentum thickness, $\theta(x)$. Separation occurs when the shape factor exceeds the value of about 1·8.

E. Truckenbrodt [46] indicated a reasonably well-founded method of calculating the shape factor. Subtracting the momentum equation (22.6) from the energy equation (22.15) and re-arranging, we obtain

$$\theta \frac{\mathrm{d}\bar{H}}{\mathrm{d}x} = (H - 1)\,\bar{H}\,\frac{\theta}{U}\frac{\mathrm{d}U}{\mathrm{d}x} + 2\,\frac{d_1 + t_1}{\varrho\,U^3} - \bar{H}\,\frac{\tau_0}{\varrho\,U^2}\,. \qquad (22.27)$$

The above equation contains the already familar shape factor $\bar{H} = \delta^{**}/\theta$ in addition to the shape factor $H = \delta^*/\theta$. The two shape factors satisfy the relation which was shown plotted in Fig. 22.9. As already shown in Fig. 22.10 and 22.11 and in eqns. (22.17) and (22.18) the work of the shearing stresses and the shearing stresses themselves can be represented in the form of simple functions of the Reynolds number $U\,\theta/\nu$ and of the shape factor H. When these facts are taken into account, eqn. (22.27) is seen to represent a differential equation for the shape factor H, provided that the variation of the momentum thickness is known, just as was the case with eqn. (22.25). In contrast with the other authors, E. Truckenbrodt succeeded in transforming this equation in such a way that integration becomes possible. On re-arranging eqn. (22.27), he obtains

$$\left(\frac{U\theta}{\nu}\right)^{1/n} \theta \frac{\mathrm{d}L}{\mathrm{d}x} = \left(\frac{U\theta}{\nu}\right)^{1/n} \frac{\theta}{U}\frac{\mathrm{d}U}{\mathrm{d}x} - K(L)\,, \qquad (22.28)$$

where

$$L = \int\limits_{\bar{H}=\bar{H}_0}^{\bar{H}} \frac{\mathrm{d}\bar{H}}{(H-1)\,\bar{H}} \qquad (22.29)$$

is a new shape factor. Its relation to the shape factor H has already been represented in Fig. 22.7. The lower limit of integration in eqn. (22.29) has been so chosen as to make $L = 0$ correspond to the case of zero pressure gradient (flat plate), i. e.

$\bar{H} = \bar{H}_0 \approx 1{\cdot}73$ and $H_0 \approx 1{\cdot}4$; see Fig. 22.9. The function $K(L)$ is seen plotted in Fig. 22.12. It can be represented by the linear relation

$$K(L) = a(L - b) \tag{22.30}$$

with a satisfactory degree of accuracy. The numerical values are

$$a = 0{\cdot}0304 \quad \text{and} \quad b = 0{\cdot}07 \log \frac{U\theta}{\nu} - 0{\cdot}23\,. \tag{22.30a}$$

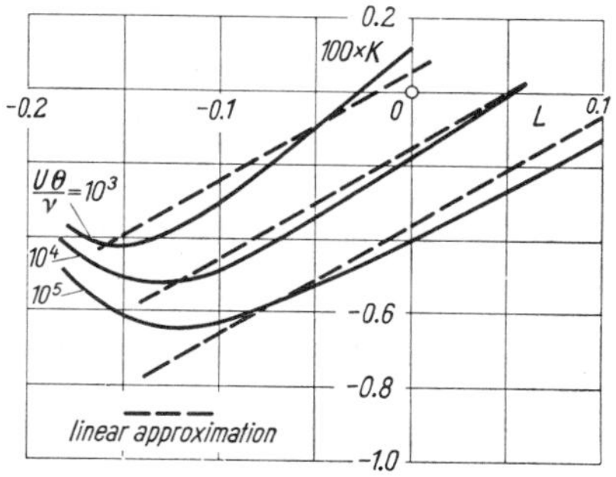

Fig. 22.12. The function $K(L)$ for the calculation of the shape factor for a turbulent boundary layer; after E. Truckenbrodt [46]

Inserting this expression for $K(L)$ into eqn. (22.28) we obtain a linear differential equation for L which can be integrated in closed terms. Introducing the contraction

$$\xi = \left[C_1{}^* + \left(\frac{1}{2}\,c_f\right)^{(n+1)/n} \int\limits_{x_t/l}^{x/l} \left(\frac{U}{U_\infty}\right)^{3+2/n} \mathrm{d}\frac{x}{l}\right]^m \tag{22.31}$$

and assuming $m = 4$ and $n = 6$, we obtain the final result in the form:

$$L = \frac{\xi_1}{\xi}\,L_1 + \ln \frac{U(\xi)}{U_1} + \frac{1}{\xi} \int\limits_{\xi_1}^{\xi} \left[b(\xi) - \ln \frac{U(\xi)}{U_1(\xi_1)}\right] \mathrm{d}\xi\,. \tag{22.32}†$$

The values with the subscript 1 refer to the point of transition $x = x_t$. The work of numerical calculation is considerably simplified by the fact that the expression for the new variable, ξ, has occurred in the calculation of the momentum thickness, eqn. (22.20), already. Separation occurs for $L = -0{\cdot}13$ to $-0{\cdot}18$, which corresponds to $H = 1{\cdot}8$ to $2{\cdot}4$.

5. Procedure and numerical example. The procedure in calculating a turbulent boundary layer by E. Truckenbrodt's method is as follows: The *given* quantities include the ideal, potential velocity distribution, $U(x)$, and the Reynolds number $\mathsf{R}_l = U_\infty l/\nu$. These allow us to calculate the coefficient of turbulent skin friction for a flat plate, c_f, which corresponds to R_l, as well as the constant $C_1{}^*$ from eqn. (22.21)

† This equation is also valid for laminar boundary layers if we put $n = 1$, $m = 8$ and $b = 0$.

with the fixed constant $n = 6$. It is *required* to determine the variation of the momentum thickness $\theta(x)$ and of the shape factor $L(x)$ or $H(x)$.

We begin by determining the variation of momentum thickness $\theta(x)$ from eqn. (22.20) with the aid of a simple quadrature. Next we form the Reynolds number $U\,\theta/\nu$ and hence the quantity $b(x)$ from eqn. (22.30a). We now proceed to determine the new variable ξ from eqn. (22.31) and integrate the function $[b(\xi) - \ln(U/U_1)]$. Equation (22.32) finally permits us to determine the variation of the shape factor $L(x)$ and hence that of $H(x)$ with the aid of Fig. 22.7†.

The advantage in using E. Truckenbrodt's method, as compared with the other methods, lies in the fact that only simple quadratures are required in the process and that no derivatives of the ideal, potential velocity function $U(x)$ with respect to x are needed.

Initial values: If the turbulent boundary layer does not begin at the leading edge (upstream stagnation point) but appears at the point of transition at x_t, it is necessary to satisfy the condition that the laminar and turbulent momentum thicknesses are equal at x_t, i. e. that

$$\theta_t(x_t) = \theta_l(x_t)\,. \tag{22.33}$$

This condition is satisfied in eqn. (22.20) by the value of $C_1{}^*$ from eqn. (22.21). Following Truckenbrodt we shall assume that the value of the shape factor at the point of transition changes by $-\Delta H$, so that

$$H_t(x_t) = H_l(x_t) - \Delta H\,. \tag{22.34}$$

The variation of ΔH with the value of the Reynolds number at the point of transition, $(U\,\theta/\nu)_t$, is shown plotted in Fig. 22.13. If the initial value $H_t(x_t) = H_1$ is

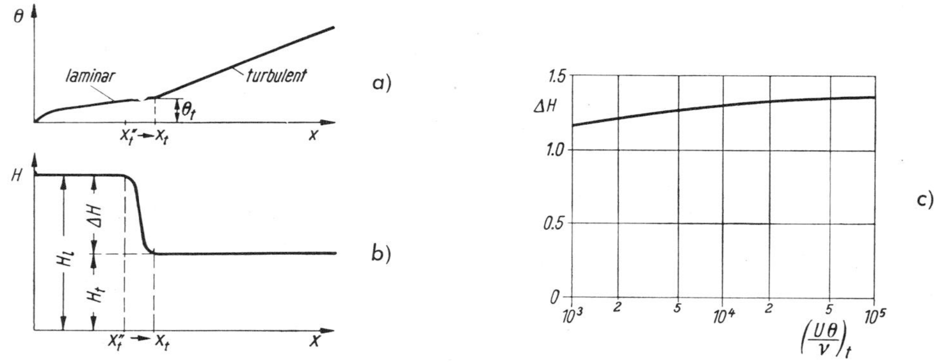

Fig. 22.13. Variation of the shape factor H in the range of transition from laminar to turbulent flow. a) Variation of momentum thickness, θ, along wall; b) Variation of shape factor, H, along wall; c) Change ΔH in value of shape factor, H, in the neighbourhood of point of transition in terms of the Reynolds number $\mathsf{R} = U\,\theta_{tr}/\nu$

† K. Kraemer [17a] prepared suitable nomograms in order to simplify the calculations implied by eqns. (22.20) and (22.32); these, in particular, provide a convenient way of calculating the momentum thickness with the aid of a special slide rule.

known, the initial value of the shape factor L, denoted by L_1, can be determined at once from Fig. 22.7.

By way of *example*, Fig. 22.14 contains the results of a complete calculation for the suction side of an NACA 65 (216)-222 aerofoil. The calculation was based on a velocity distribution of external flow, $U(x)$, which had been evaluated from the measured pressure distribution. Such an arrangement has the advantage of making certain that the differences between the measured and calculated boundary layer parameters are not due to any disagreement between the theoretical and actual pressure distribution. On comparing the measured values of the boundary layer parameters with those calculated by different methods, the following conclusions can be drawn: In relation to the momentum thickness, Fig. 22.14b, there is good agreement between all methods of calculation and measurement. On the other hand, the values of the shape factor, Fig. 22.14c, show considerable divergence. In particular, it is noted that Gruschwitz's method of calculations is less satisfactory than the others.

The method of calculation, described in this section and conceived by E. Truckenbrodt is based on the assumption that the velocity profile in the boundary layer obeys a power-law. W. Szablewski [42, 43, 44] derived more exact laws for the velocity distribution in a boundary layer with the velocity gradient from a generalised mixing law. An alternative method for the calculation of turbulent, incompressible boundary layers along smooth as well as rough walls

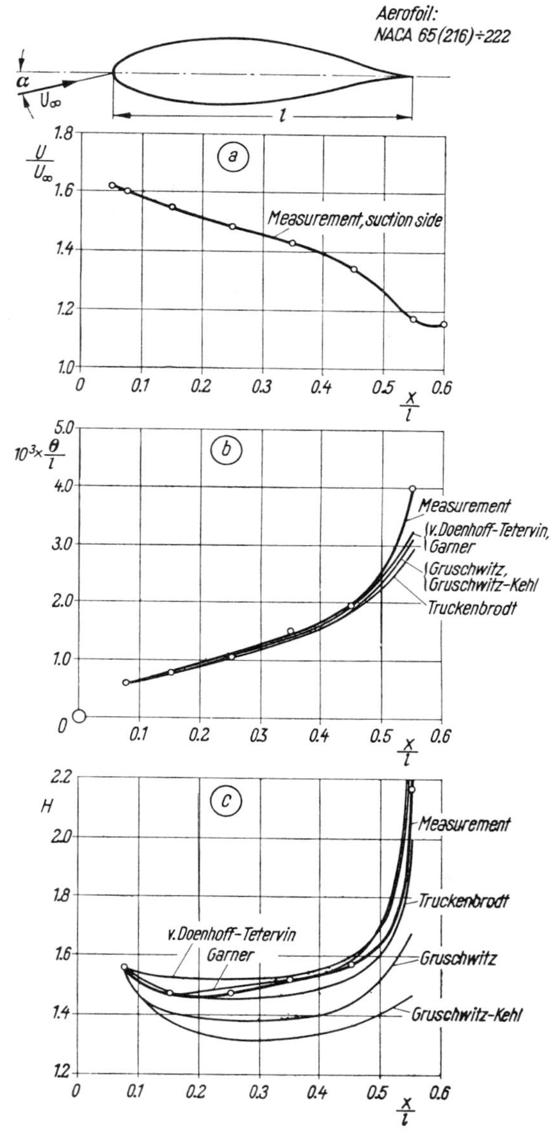

Fig. 22.14. The turbulent boundary layer on a wing (NACA—65 (216)—222). Angle of incidence $\alpha = 10{\cdot}1°$ a) Measured external velocity b) Momentum thickness θ: comparison between measurement and calculation by different procedures c) Shape factor H: comparison between measurement and calculation by different procedures. Separation at $H = 1{\cdot}8$ to $2{\cdot}2$

Reynolds number $U_\infty l/\nu = 2{\cdot}64 \times 10^6$; measurements from [4]

was recently indicated by J. Rotta; it is also based on the application of the momentum and energy integral equations. The essential refinement of Rotta's method, as compared with Truckenbrodt's, consists in the fact that the velocity profile in the boundary layer is now pieced together from a portion close to the wall and one external to it. Consequently, its description involves the local value of the skin friction coefficient c_f' and not exclusively the shape factor H, as before. J. Rotta's method of calculation has been described in ref. [35] in a form suitable for direct application; the reference also contains numerous working tables.

When applied to actual problems involving the flow of air past solid bodies, the preceding methods allow us first to calculate the *skin friction* only, it being the integral of the shearing stress at the wall around the contour. Even in cases when there is no separation the skin friction must be augmented by *pressure* or *form drag*. The reason for the existence of form drag lies in the fact that the boundary layer displaces the external, potential flow. The potential stream-lines around the body become displaced by a distance which is equal to the displacement thickness and the pressure distribution around the contour is thereby changed even in the absence of separation. The resultant of these modified pressure forces taken in the direction of flow is no longer equal to zero but gives a pressure drag which must be added to the value of skin friction. The sum of these two terms gives what is known as *profile or total drag*. We shall revert to the problem of calculating profile drag in Chap. XXIV.

Measurements: Fig. 22.15 shows the results of measurements performed by J. Stueper [40] on a turbulent boundary layer around an aerofoil in actual flight. In the case under consideration the boundary layer on the pressure side is turbulent from the nose onwards because on this side there is pressure increase all along the surface. On the suction side the point of transition lies a short distance downstream

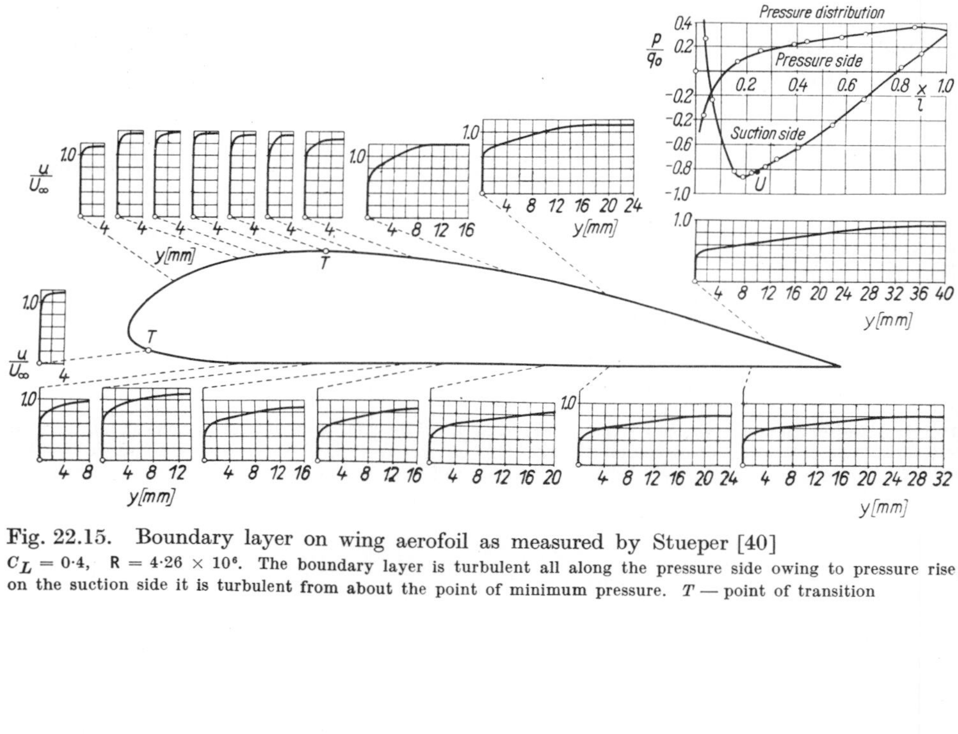

Fig. 22.15. Boundary layer on wing aerofoil as measured by Stueper [40]
$C_L = 0{\cdot}4$, $R = 4{\cdot}26 \times 10^6$. The boundary layer is turbulent all along the pressure side owing to pressure rise; on the suction side it is turbulent from about the point of minimum pressure. T — point of transition

of the point of minimum pressure. The fact that the boundary layer becomes turbulent can be recognized with reference to the considerable thickening of the boundary layer in the direction of the length co-ordinate.

6. Turbulent boundary layers with suction. The possibility of influencing the flow in a boundary layer by blowing or suction is of some practical importance, particularly with a view to increasing the maximum lift of aerofoils. The procedure for calculating laminar boundary layers with suction was given in Sec. XIIIb and we now propose to give some indication as to how the same can be done for turbulent boundary layers. We shall restrict ourselves to the case when the distribution of suction velocity is continuous, and given, say, by the function $-v_0(x)$ along the surface of the body. Evidently, in the present case one must expect that the procedure will be subject to even greater uncertainties than that which related to turbulent boundary layers without suction. This is so, because very little is known about the mechanics of this type of flow.

An approximate method for the calculation of turbulent boundary layer on a flat plate with suction was given by H. Schlichting [36a]; it was based on the application of the momentum integral equation which was augmented by an additional suction term and generally, made use of the same assumptions as those in the preceding section. Recently the method was extended to include the energy integral equation (see Sec. XIII b. 1 on p. 277) and to take into account an arbitrary external velocity distribution $U(x)$ by W. Pechau [28]. The method assumes that the law for the shearing stress given in eqn. (22.7) retains its validity in the presence of suction. By introducing the contraction

$$\Theta = \theta \left(\frac{U\theta}{\nu}\right)^{1/n} U^b \tag{22.35}$$

in analogy with eqn. (22.8), it is possible to obtain from the momentum integral equation the following differential equation for the momentum thickness $\theta(x)$:

$$\frac{d\Theta}{dx} = a\,U^b - \left(\frac{n+1}{n}\right) U^{H+1} \left(\frac{\Theta}{\nu}\right)^{\frac{1}{1+n}} [-v_0(x)]\,. \tag{22.36}$$

The constants a and b retain the values quoted in conjunction with eqn. (22.8). In the case without suction, $v_0(x) \equiv 0$, the preceding equation transforms into eqn. (22.8), as it should. When applied to the case of a flat plate with uniform suction, the preceding equation reduces to a form which was found earlier by H. Schlichting [36a].

In order to estimate the onset of separation it is possible to make use of the shape factor $\bar{H} = \delta^{**}/\theta$, first defined on p. 574; it is equal to the ratio of the energy thickness to the momentum thickness. It will be recalled that this shape factor was related to the shape factor $H = \delta^*/\theta$, which represents the ratio of displacement to momentum thickness, and that the relation was a universal one in the case without suction; it was given in the graph of Fig. 22.9. It turns out that the validity of the same relationship is confirmed by measurements for the case with suction. The value for separation $H_{sep} \approx 2{\cdot}0$ corresponds to $\bar{H}_{sep} = 1{\cdot}58$.

The variation of the shape factor along the flow, i. e. the function $\bar{H}(x)$, can be determined from the energy integral equation by making the assumption that turbulent dissipation is described by putting

$$\frac{d_1}{\varrho\,U^3} = \frac{\beta}{(U\,\theta/\nu)^{1/n}} \tag{22.37}$$

in a manner similar to the case without suction, eqn. (22.17). Here the exponent n is the same as the one in the shearing-stress (22.7). The resulting solution appears in the form of an explicit integral

$$\bar{H} = \frac{U^{H-1}}{\Theta^{\,n/(n+1)}} \int_0^x \left(\frac{2\,\beta\,U^{[(3-1/n)+(H+2)/n]}}{\Theta^{1/(n+1)}} - \frac{[-v_0(x)]\,U^2}{\nu^{\,1/(n+1)}}\right) dx \tag{22.38}$$

which can be evaluated easily if $\Theta(x)$ is known from eqn. (22.36). For $n = 4$ we have $\alpha = 0{\cdot}0128$ in eqn. (22.7) as indicated on p. 572, and in eqn. (22.37) we have $\beta = 1{\cdot}125 \times 10^{-2}$; furthermore, then $H = 1{\cdot}4$. In the absence of suction the preceding equation yields

$$\overline{H} = \frac{2\,\beta}{U^3\,\theta} \int_0^x \frac{U^3\,dx}{\left(\frac{U\,\theta}{\nu}\right)^{1/n}}, \tag{22.38a}$$

as can be verified after a short computation.

References [36b] and [36c] contain calculations performed with the aid of this procedure; they illustrate the effect of the magnitude and position of the suction zone on the minimum suction flow required to eliminate separation on aerofoils. It turns out that the optimum arrangement is to concentrate the suction zone in a narrow region on the suction side of the aerofoil and to place it at a short distance behind the nose. This is understandable, because the largest local adverse pressure gradients occur in that region when the angles of incidence are large. The required minimum suction rates, as described by the suction coefficients (see eqn. (13.2) on p. 270) $c_{Q\,min}$, are of the order of 0·002 to 0·004.

7. Boundary layers on cambered walls. Two-dimensional boundary layers on curved walls have been investigated by H. Wilcken [50], (see also A. Betz [1a]). If the wall is *concave* the faster particles are pressed against it by centrifugal forces and slower particles are deflected away from it. Thus the process of turbulent mixing which takes place between faster and slower fluid particles is accentuated and the intensity of turbulence is increased. The reverse is true of *convex* walls in the neighbourhood of which the faster particles are forced away from the wall, the slower particles being pressed towards it, and turbulent mixing is impeded. Consequently. with equal pressure gradients, the thickness of a turbulent boundary layer on a concave wall is greater than, and that on a convex wall is smaller than, the thickness on a flat plate. H. Schmidbauer [37] extended Gruschwitz's method to include the case of convex walls.

c. Three-dimensional boundary layers

1. Boundary layers on bodies of revolution. C. B. Millikan [26] was the first to calculate a turbulent boundary layer on a body of revolution, the method having been based on the momentum integral equation. The relevant momentum equation was given in eqn. (12.38). In the same way as was the case with two-dimensional boundary layers, E. Truckenbrodt [46] was able to show that the use of the energy integral equation leads to a solution in closed terms as far as the momentum thickness is concerned. If the length of arc along a meridian is denoted by x, and if $R(x)$ denotes the radius of a cross-section taken at right angles to the axis, then the solution has the form

$$\frac{\theta\,(x)}{l} = \frac{\left[C_1{}^* + \left(\frac{1}{2}\,c_f\right)^{(n+1)/n} \int_{x_t/l}^{x/l} \left(\frac{U}{U_\infty}\right)^{3+2/n} \left(\frac{R}{l}\right)^{(n+1)/n} d\left(\frac{x}{l}\right)\right]^{n/(n+1)}}{\left(\frac{U}{U_\infty}\right)^3 \frac{R}{l}}, \tag{22.39}$$

where

$$C_1{}^* = \left\{\frac{1}{2}\,c_{fl}\left[\int_0^{x_t/l} \left(\frac{U}{U_\infty}\right)^5 \left(\frac{R}{l}\right)^2 d\left(\frac{x}{l}\right)\right]^{1/2}\right\}^{(n+1)/n}. \tag{22.40}$$

The symbol c_f in eqn. (23.39) denotes the coefficient of skin friction of a flat plate at zero incidence in turbulent flow at a Reynolds number $U_\infty l/\nu$, and the symbol c_{fl} in eqn. (22.40) denotes the coefficient of skin friction of a flat plate in laminar flow. The equation for the shape factor is the same as for the two-dimensional case, eqn. (22.32). The method for the calculation of two-dimensional turbulent boundary layers proposed by H. B. Squire and A. D. Young, and mentioned previoulsy, was also extended to include the axially symmetrical case [52]. As far as experimental results are concerned, there exists a large number of reports [8, 9, 23, 28. 38], most of which concern themselves with boundary layers on models of aircraft components and, in particular, with transition from laminar to turbulent flow.

2. Boundary layers on rotating bodies. The calculation of laminar boundary layers on rotating bodies placed in an axial stream was discussed in Sec. X c and Chap. XII. The method of calculation which makes use of momentum integral equations, formulated for the meridional and circumferential directions respectively, has recently been extended by E. Truckenbrodt [47] to include the turbulent case. He was, moreover, fortunate to succeed in giving convenient integrals for the calculation of the parameters of the boundary layer.

A method for the calculation of three-dimensional boundary layers on stationary bodies as well as on rotating ones, such as propellers or blades of rotary compressors and turbines, was indicated by A. Mager [24]; comparative measurements are contained in ref. [25]. H. Himmelskamp [14] carried out measurements in the boundary layer on a rotating airscrew. The principal results of his measurements was the discovery that all profiles show markedly increased lift coefficients near the hub, and the effect can be traced to delayed separation. For example, in this manner a maximum lift coefficient of 3·2 was observed as against its value of 1·4 in the absence of rotation. The Coriolis forces in the boundary layer give rise to an additional acceleration in the direction of flow, and that has the same effect as a favourable pressure gradient. In addition, but to a lesser extent, the centrifugal forces acting in the boundary layer carried with the body exert a beneficial influence by delaying separation. Fluid particles in the boundary layer are acted upon by a centrifugal force which is proportional to the radius. Consequently, less fluid is transported to each blade from the centre than away from it and outwards, and the boundary layer is thinner than would be the case in two-dimensional flow about the same shape. F. Gutsche [13] made the flow in the boundary layer on a propeller visible by painting the former with a dye.

3. Convergent and divergent boundary layers. The methods for the calculation of turbulent boundary layers which were described in Sec. XXIIb have been extended by A. Kehl [17] to include cases when the stream-lines either converge or diverge sideways, Fig. 22.16. Boundary layers of this type occur in a diffuser or in a nozzle and also near the bow or the stern of a body of revolution. In this connexion the measurements due to Gruschwitz have been extended to $\mathsf{R}_\theta = U\,\theta/\nu = 3\times10^4$ and his method of calculation has been generalized to include this case as well. Assuming a system of co-ordinates as shown in Fig. 22.16, x and z being chosen in the plane of the wall, y being measured at right angles to it, we notice that along the stream-line which coincides with the axis, i. e. along that for which $w = 0$, the same equation of motion is satisfied as that for the two-dimensional case, eqn. (8.32). On the other hand the equation of continuity changes to

$$\frac{\partial u}{\partial x} + \frac{\partial v}{\partial y} + \frac{\partial w}{\partial z} = 0 .$$

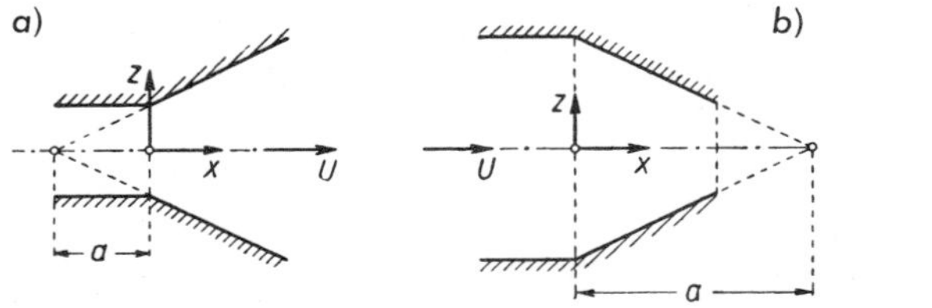

Fig. 22.16. Convergent and divergent boundary layers; system of co-ordinates;
a) divergent, $a + x > 0$;
b) convergent, $a + x < 0$

The momentum integral equaticn (22.6) obtains an additional term which stems from the convergence or divergence of the stream-lines, as the case may be. Retracing the steps in the derivation of the momentum equation, which was given in Sec. VIIIe in connexion with eqn. (8.32), we see that the integral of the second term in the first equation of motion becomes

$$\int_0^h v \frac{\partial u}{\partial y} \mathrm{d}y = - U \frac{\partial}{\partial x} \int_0^h u \, \mathrm{d}y + u \int_0^h \frac{\partial u}{\partial x} \mathrm{d}y - U \int_0^h \frac{\partial w}{\partial z} \mathrm{d}y + \int_0^h u \frac{\partial w}{\partial z} \mathrm{d}y .$$

The two last terms on the right-hand side are due to the divergence of the flow in the z-direction.

Taking into account the divergence of the stream-lines, we have

$$\frac{w}{u} = \frac{z}{x+a} \quad \text{and} \quad \left(\frac{\partial w}{\partial z}\right)_{z=0} = \frac{u}{x+a} .$$

Hence the two additional terms become

$$- \frac{1}{x+a} \int_0^h u \, (U - u) \, \mathrm{d}y = - \frac{\theta}{x+a} U^2 ,$$

and the momentum integral equation must be supplemented with the additional term $\theta U^2/(x + a)$. Consequently, the momentum integral equation for the plane of symmetry which replaces eqn. (22.6) is now

$$\frac{\mathrm{d}\theta}{\mathrm{d}x} + \theta \left(\frac{1}{a+x} + \frac{H+2}{U} \frac{\mathrm{d}U}{\mathrm{d}x} \right) = \frac{\tau_0}{\varrho U^2} . \tag{22.41}$$

For divergent stream-lines we have $a + x > 0$, and $a + x < 0$ corresponds to a convergent stream, Fig. 22.16. It follows at once from eqn. (22.41) that the increase in the momentum thickness proceeds at a smaller rate in the case of divergent, and at a larger rate in the case of convergent stream-lines, both compared with the two-dimensional case. This result is also to be expected from physical considerations.

References

[1] J. Ackeret, Zum Entwurf dicht stehender Schaufelgitter. Schweizerische Bauzeitung **120**, 103 (1942).

[1a] A. Betz, Über turbulente Reibungsschichten an gekrümmten Wänden. Vorträge auf dem Gebiet der Aerodynamik und verwandter Gebiete, Aachen 1929. Published by Springer, pp. 10—18, Berlin 1930.

[2] A. Buri, Eine Berechnungsgrundlage für die turbulente Grenzschicht bei beschleunigter und verzögerter Strömung. Thesis Zürich 1931.

[3] F. H. Clauser, Turbulent boundary layers in adverse pressure gradients. Jour. Aero. Sci. **21**, 91—108 (1954).

[3a] W. S. Coleman, Analysis of the turbulent boundary layer for adverse pressure gradients involving separation. Q-ly. Appl. Mech. **5**, 1947, 182—216.

[4] A. E. von Doenhoff and N. Tetervin, Determination of general relations for the behavior of turbulent boundary layers. NACA Rep. 772 (1943).

[5] F. Dönch, Divergente und konvergente Strömungen mit kleinen Öffnungswinkeln. Thesis Göttingen 1925. VDI Forschungsarbeiten No. 292 (1926).

[6] A. Fage and W. G. Raymer, Note on empirical relations for a turbulent boundary layer. ARC R & M 2255 (1948).

[7] V. M. Falkner, Aircraft Engineering **15**, 65 (1943).

[8] H. B. Freeman, Measurements of flow in the boundary layer of a 1/40-scale model of the US airship "Akron". NACA Rep. 430 (1931).

[9] H. B. Freeman, Force measurements on a 1/40-scale model of the US airship "Akron". NACA Rep. 432 (1932).

[10] H. C. Garner, The development of turbulent boundary layers. ARC R & M 2133 (1944).

[11] E. Gruschwitz, Die turbulente Reibungsschicht in ebener Strömung bei Druckabfall und Druckanstieg. Ing.-Arch., **2**, 321—346 (1931); abstract in ZFM **23**, 308 (1932).

[12] E. Gruschwitz, Turbulente Reibungsschichten mit Sekundärströmungen. Ing. Arch. **6**, 355—365 (1935).

[13] F. Gutsche, Versuche an umlaufenden Flügelschnitten mit abgerissener Strömung. Jb. d. Schiffbautechn. Ges. **41**, 188 (1940).

[14] H. Himmelskamp, Profiluntersuchungen an einem umlaufenden Propeller. Thesis Göttingen 1945. Rep. of the Max-Planck-Institut für Strömungsforschung, Göttingen, No. 2, (1950).

[15] H. Hochschild, Versuche über Strömungsvorgänge in erweiterten und verengten Kanälen. VDI Forschungsarbeiten No. 114 (1910).

[16] L. Howarth, The theoretical determination of the lift coefficient for a thin elliptic cylinder. Proc. Roy. Soc. London, A **149**, 558 (1935).

[17] A. Kehl, Untersuchungen über konvergente und divergente turbulente Reibungsschichten. Ing.-Arch. **13**, 293—329 (1943).

[17a] K. Kraemer, Zur praktischen Berechnung von Grenzschichten. Rep. 56/A/02 of the AVA (1956); abstract in Luftfahrttechnik **2**, 8—13, (1956).

[18] R. Kröner, Versuche über Strömungen in stark erweiterten Kanälen. VDI Forschungsarbeiten No. 222 (1920).

[19] J. Laufer, Investigation of turbulent flow in a two-dimensional channel. NACA Rep. No. 1053 (1951).

[20] N. van Le and Th. von Kármán, Integral method as applied to a turbulent boundary layer. Jour. Aero. Sci. **19**, 647—468 (1952); Jour. Aero. Sci. **20**, 439—440 (1953).

[21] H. Ludwieg, Ein Gerät zur Messung der Wandschubspannung turbulenter Reibungsschichten. Ing.-Arch. **17**, 207—218 (1949).

[22] H. Ludwieg and W. Tillmann, Untersuchungen über die Wandschubspannung in turbulenten Reibungsschichten. Ing.-Arch. **17**, 288—299 (1949). Summary of both papers in ZAMM **29**, 15 (1949). Engl. transl. in NACA TM 1285 (1950).

[23] H. M. Lyon, Flow in the boundary layer of streamline bodies. ARC R & M 1622 (1934).

[24] A. Mager, Generalization of boundary-layer momentum-integral equations to three-dimensional flows including those of rotating system. NACA Rep. 1067 (1952).

[25] A. Mager, I. I. Mahoney and R. E. Budinger, Discussion of boundary layer characteristics near the wall of an axial-flow compressor. NACA Rep. No. 1085 (1952).

[26] C. B. Millikan, The boundary layer and skin friction for a figure of revolution. Trans. ASME (J. Appl. Mech.), **54**, 2, 29 (1932).

[27] J. NIKURADSE, Untersuchungen über die Strömungen des Wassers in konvergenten und divergenten Kanälen. VDI Forschungsarb. No. 289 (1929).
[28] E. OWER and C. T. HUTTON, Investigation of the boundary layers and the drag of two streamline bodies. ARC R & M 1271 (1929).
[28a] W. PECHAU, Ein Näherungsverfahren zur Berechnung der ebenen und rotationssymmetrischen turbulenten Grenzschicht mit beliebiger Absaugung oder Ausblasung. Jahrb. der WGL 1958, pp. 82—92.
[29] J. POLZIN, Strömungsuntersuchungen an einem ebenen Diffusor. Ing.-Arch. **11**, 361 (1940).
[30] J. PRETSCH, Zur theoretischen Berechnung des Profilwiderstandes. Jb. d. dt. Luftfahrtforschung **I**, 61 (1938).
[31] I. M. ROBERTSON and D. ROSS, Water tunnel diffuser flow studies, Part II: Experimental research. Pennsylvania State College, Ordnance Research Laboratory Report No. 7958—143 (1949).
[32] D. ROSS, Evaluation of the momentum integral equation for turbulent boundary layers. Jour. Aero. Sci. **20**, 502 (1953).
[33] J. ROTTA, Beitrag zur Berechnung der turbulenten Grenzschichten. Ing.-Arch. **19**, 31—41 (1951) and Rep. of the Max-Planck-Institut für Strömungsforschung No. 1, Göttingen 1950; NACA TM 1344.
[34] J. ROTTA, Schubspannungsverteilung und Energiedissipation bei turbulenten Grenzschichten. Ing. Arch. **20**, 195—207 (1952).
[35] J. ROTTA, Näherungsverfahren zur Berechnung turbulenter Grenzschichten unter Benutzung des Energiesatzes. Rep of the Max-Planck-Inst. f. Strömungsforschung, No. 8, Göttingen (1953).
[36] V. A. SANDBORN and R. J. SLOGAR, Study of the momentum distribution of turbulent boundary layers in adverse pressure gradients. NACA TN 3264 (1955).
[36a] H. SCHLICHTING, Die Grenzschicht an der ebenen Platte mit Absaugung und Ausblasen. Luftfahrtforschung **19**, 293—301 (1942).
[36b] H. SCHLICHTING, Einige neuere Ergebnisse über Grenzschichtbeeinflussung. Proc. 1st. Intern. Congress Aero. Sci., Madrid; Adv. in Aero. Sci. Pergamon Press, London, vol. II, pp. 563—586, 1959.
[36c] H. SCHLICHTING and W. PECHAU, Auftriebserhöhung von Tragflügeln durch kontinuierlich verteilte Absaugung (Prof. C. DORNIER's anniversary volume) Zeitschr. für Flugwiss. **7**, 113—119 (1959).
[37] H. SCHMIDBAUER, Verhalten turbulenter Reibungsschichten an erhaben gekrümmten Wänden. Diss. Munich 1934; see also Luftfahrtforschung **XIII**, 161 (1936). Engl. transl. in NACA TM 791 (1936).
[38] L. F. G. SIMMONS, Experiments relating to the flow in the boundary layer of an airship model. ARC R & M 1268 (1929).
[39] H. B. SQUIRE and A. D. YOUNG, The calculation of profile drag of airflow. ARC R & M 1838 (1938).
[40] J. STÜPER, Untersuchung von Reibungsschichten am fliegenden Flugzeug. Luftfahrtforschung **XI**, 26 (1934); see also NACA TM 751 (1934).
[41] G. B. SCHUBAUER and P. S. KLEBANOFF, Investigation of separation of the turbulent boundary layer. NACA Rep. No. 1030 (1951).
[42] W. SZABLEWSKI, Turbulente Strömung in konvergenten Kanälen. Ing.-Arch. **20**, 37 (1952).
[43] W. SZABLEWSKI, Turbulente Strömungen in divergenten Kanälen (mittlerer und starker Druckanstieg). Ing.-Arch. **22**, 268 (1954).
[44] W. SZABLEWSKI, Wandnahe Geschwindigkeitsverteilung turbulenter Grenzschichtströmungen mit Druckanstieg. Ing.-Arch. **23**, 295 (1955).
[45] N. TETERVIN and C. C. LIN, A general integral form of the boundary layer equation for incompressible flow with an application to the calculation of the separation point of turbulent boundary layers. NACA Rep. No. 1046 (1951).
[46] E. TRUCKENBRODT, Ein Quadraturverfahren zur Berechnung der laminaren und turbulenten Reibungsschicht bei ebener und rotationssymmetrischer Strömung. Ing. Arch. **20**, 211—228 (1952).
[47] E. TRUCKENBRODT, Ein Quadraturverfahren zur Berechnung der Reibungsschicht an axial angeströmten rotierenden Drehkörpern. Ing.-Arch. **22**, 21—35 (1954).
[48] K. WIEGHARDT and W. TILLMANN, Zur turbulenten Reibungsschicht bei Druckanstieg. UM 6617 (1941).
[49] K. WIEGHARDT, Turbulente Grenzschichten. Göttingen Monograph, Part B 5, 1945/46.

[50] H. Wilcken, Turbulente Grenzschichten an gewölbten Wänden. Ing.-Arch. **1**, 357—376 (1930).
[51] F. A. L. Winternitz and W. J. Ramsay, Effects of inlet boundary layer on the pressure recovery in conical diffusers. Mechan. Eng. Res. Lab., Fluid Mechanics Division. East Kilbride, Glasgow. Rep. No. 41, 1956.
[52] A. D. Young, The calculation of the total and skin friction drags of bodies of revolution at 0° incidence. ARC R & M 1874 (1939).

CHAPTER XXIII

Free turbulent flows; jets and wakes

a. General remarks

In the preceding chapters we have considered turbulent flows along solid walls and we propose to continue the study of turbulent streams with the discussion of several examples of so-called *free turbulent flow*. Turbulent flows will be termed free if they are not confined by solid walls. We shall discern three kinds of turbulent flows, Fig. 21.1: free jet boundaries, free jets, and wakes.

A jet boundary occurs between two streams which move at different speeds in the same general direction. Such a surface of discontinuity in the velocity of flow is unstable and gives rise to a zone of turbulent mixing downstream of the point, where the two streams first meet. The width of this mixing region increases in a downstream direction, Fig. 23.1 a.

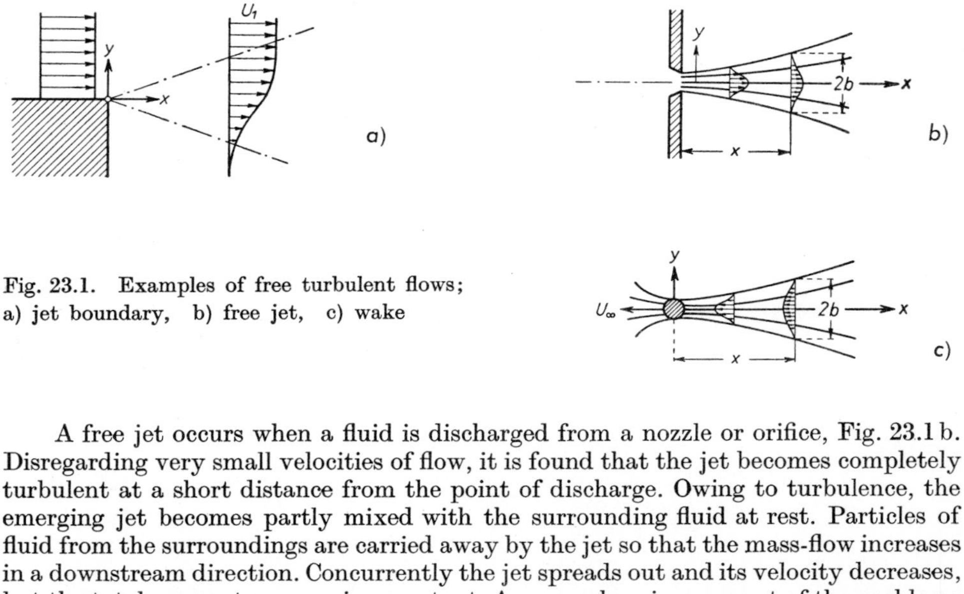

Fig. 23.1. Examples of free turbulent flows; a) jet boundary, b) free jet, c) wake

A free jet occurs when a fluid is discharged from a nozzle or orifice, Fig. 23.1 b. Disregarding very small velocities of flow, it is found that the jet becomes completely turbulent at a short distance from the point of discharge. Owing to turbulence, the emerging jet becomes partly mixed with the surrounding fluid at rest. Particles of fluid from the surroundings are carried away by the jet so that the mass-flow increases in a downstream direction. Concurrently the jet spreads out and its velocity decreases, but the total momentum remains constant. A comprehensive account of the problems encountered in the study of free jets was recently given by S. I. Pai [15].

A wake is formed behind a solid body which is being dragged through fluid at rest, Fig. 23.1 c, or behind a solid body which has been placed in a stream of fluid. The velocities in a wake are smaller than those in the main stream and the losses in the velocity in the wake amount to a loss of momentum which is due to the drag on the body. The spread of the wake increases as the distance from the body is increased and the differences between the velocity in the wake and that outside become smaller.

Qualitatively such flows resemble similar flows in the laminar region (Chaps. IX and X), but there are large quantitative differences which are due to the very much larger turbulent friction. Free turbulent flows are much more amenable to mathematical analysis than turbulent flows along walls because turbulent friction is much larger than laminar friction in the whole region under consideration. Consequently laminar friction may be wholly neglected in problems involving free turbulent flows, which is not the case in flows along solid walls. It will be recalled that in the latter case, by contrast, laminar friction must always be taken into account in the immediate neighbourhood of the wall (i. e. in the laminar sub-layer), and that causes great mathematical difficulties.

Furthermore, it will be noted that problems in free turbulent flow are of a *boundary layer* nature, meaning that the region of space in which a solution is being sought does not extend far in a transverse direction, as compared with the main direction of flow, and that the transverse gradients are large. Consequently it is permissible to study such problems with the aid of the boundary layer equations. In the two-dimensional case these are

$$\frac{\partial u}{\partial t} + u \frac{\partial u}{\partial x} + v \frac{\partial u}{\partial y} = \frac{1}{\varrho} \frac{\partial \tau}{\partial y} \tag{23.1}$$

$$\frac{\partial u}{\partial x} + \frac{\partial v}{\partial y} = 0 . \tag{23.2}$$

Here τ denotes the turbulent shearing stress and the pressure term has been dropped in the equation of motion because in all problems to be considered it is permissible to assume, at least to a first approximation, that the pressure remains constant. In the case of wakes this assumption is satisfied only from a certain distance from the body onwards.

In order to be in a position to integrate the system of equations (23.1) and (23.2), it is necessary to express the turbulent shearing stress in terms of the parameters of the main flow. At present such an elimination can only be achieved with the aid of semi-empirical assumptions. These have already been discussed in Chap. XIX. In this connexion it is possible to make use of Prandtl's mixing length theory, eqn. (19.6):

$$\tau = \varrho\, l^2 \left| \frac{\partial u}{\partial y} \right| \frac{\partial u}{\partial y} \tag{23.3}$$

or of its extension in eqn. (19.8)

$$\tau = \varrho\, l^2 \frac{\partial u}{\partial y} \sqrt{\left(\frac{\partial u}{\partial y}\right)^2 + l_1^{\,2} \left(\frac{\partial^2 u}{\partial y^2}\right)^2} , \tag{23.4}$$

where the mixing lengths l and l_1 are to be regarded as purely local functions. They must be suitably dealt with in each particular case. Further, it is possible to use Prandtl's hypothesis in eqn. (19.10), namely

$$\tau = \varrho\, \varepsilon \frac{\partial u}{\partial y} = \varrho\, \varkappa_1\, b\, (u_{max} - u_{min}) \frac{\partial u}{\partial y}, \tag{23.5}$$

where b denotes the width of the mixing zone and $\varkappa_1$ is an empirical constant. Moreover

$$\varepsilon = \varkappa_1\, b\, (u_{max} - u_{min}) \tag{23.5a}$$

is the virtual kinematic viscosity, assumed constant over the whole width and, hence, independent of x†. In addition it is possible to use von Kármán's hypothesis, eqn. (19.23) and that due to G. I. Taylor, eqn. (19.15).

When either of the assumptions (23.3), (23.4) or (23.5) is used it is found that the results differ from each other only comparatively little. The best measure of agreement with experimental results is furnished by the assumption in eqn. (23.5) and, in addition, the resulting equations are more convenient to solve. For these reasons we shall express a preference for this hypothesis. Nevertheless, some examples will be studied with the aid of the hypothesis in eqns. (23.3) and (23.4) in order to exhibit the differences in the results when different hypotheses are used. Moreover, the mixing length formula, eqn. (23.3), has rendered such valuable service in the theory of pipe flow that it is useful to test its applicability to the type of flow under consideration. It will be recalled that, among others, the universal logarithmic velocity distribution law has been deduced from it.

b. Estimation of the increase in width and of the decrease in velocity

Before proceeding to integrate eqns. (23.1) and (23.2) for several particular cases we first propose to make estimations of orders of magnitude. In this way we shall be able to form an idea of the type of law which governs the increase in the width of the mixing zone and of the decrease in the 'height' of the velocity profile with increasing distance x. The following account will be based on one first given by L. Prandtl [17].

When dealing with problems of turbulent jets and wakes it is usually assumed that the mixing length l is proportional to the width of jet, b, because in this way we are led to useful results. Hence we put

$$\frac{l}{b} = \beta = \text{const}. \tag{23.6}$$

† The assumption that the virtual kinematic viscosity is approximately constant in the z-direction was first discussed by H. Reichardt. In his critical review of the phenomenological theory of turbulent flows, Reichardt [19] provided a comparison of the results which follow from the alternative assumptions $A(y) = \text{const}$, $l(y) = \text{const}$, and $\Lambda(y) = \text{const}$. See also Sec. XXIIId.

In addition, the following rule has withstood the test of time: The rate of increase of the width, b, of the mixing zone with time is proportional to the transverse velocity v':

$$\frac{\mathrm{D}b}{\mathrm{D}t} \sim v' .$$

Here $\mathrm{D}/\mathrm{D}t$ denotes, as usual, the substantive derivative, so that $\mathrm{D}/\mathrm{D}t = u\,\partial/\partial x + v\,\partial/\partial y$. According to a previous estimate, eqn. (19.4), we have $v' \sim l\,\partial u/\partial y$, and thus

$$\frac{\mathrm{D}b}{\mathrm{D}t} \sim l\,\frac{\partial u}{\partial y} .$$

Further, the mean value of $\partial u/\partial y$ taken over half the width of the jet may be assumed to be approximately proportional to u_{max}/b. Consequently

$$\frac{\mathrm{D}b}{\mathrm{D}t} = \text{const} \times \frac{l}{b}\,u_{max} = \text{const} \times \beta\,u_{max} . \tag{23.7}$$

Jet boundary: With the use of the preceding relations we shall now estimate the rate at which the width of the mixing zone which accompanies a free jet boundary increases with the distance, x. For the jet boundary we have

$$\frac{\mathrm{D}b}{\mathrm{D}t} \sim u_{max}\,\frac{\mathrm{d}b}{\mathrm{d}x} . \tag{23.8}$$

On comparing eqns. (23.8) and (23.7) we obtain

$$\frac{\mathrm{d}b}{\mathrm{d}x} = \text{const} \times \frac{l}{b} = \text{const} ,$$

or

$$b = \text{const} \times x ,$$

which means that the width of the mixing zone associated with a free jet boundary is proportional to the distance from the point where the two jets meet. The constant of integration which must, strictly speaking, appear in the above equation can be made to vanish by a suitable choice of the origin of the co-ordinate system.

Two-dimensional and circular jet: Equation (23.8) remains valid in the case of a two-dimensional and of a circular jet, u_{max} denoting now the velocity at the centre-line. Thus in such cases we also have

$$b = \text{const} \times x . \tag{23.9}$$

The relation between u_{max} and x can be obtained from the momentum equation. Since the pressure remains constant the integral of the x-component of momentum taken over the whole cross-sectional area must remain constant and independent of x, i. e.

$$J = \varrho \int u^2\,\mathrm{d}A = \text{const} .$$

In the case of a *two-dimensional jet* we have $J' = \text{const} \times \varrho\, u^2_{max}\, b$, where J' denotes momentum per unit length, and hence $u_{max} = \text{const} \times b^{-1/2} \sqrt{J'/\varrho}$. In view of eqn. (23.9) we have, further,

$$u_{max} = \text{const} \times \frac{1}{\sqrt{x}} \sqrt{\frac{J'}{\varrho}} \quad \text{(two-dimensional jet).} \tag{23.10}$$

In the case of a *circular jet* the momentum is

$$J = \text{const} \times \varrho\, u^2_{max}\, b^2$$

and hence

$$u_{max} = \text{const} \times \frac{1}{b} \sqrt{\frac{J}{\varrho}}\,.$$

In view of eqn. (23.9) we now have

$$u_{max} = \text{const} \times \frac{1}{x} \sqrt{\frac{J}{\varrho}} \quad \text{(circular jet)}\,. \tag{23.11}$$

Two-dimensional and circular wake: Instead of eqn. (23.8) we now have

$$\frac{\mathrm{D}b}{\mathrm{D}t} = U_\infty \frac{\mathrm{d}b}{\mathrm{d}x}\,,$$

and eqn. (23.7) is replaced by

$$\frac{\mathrm{D}b}{\mathrm{D}t} = \text{const} \times \frac{l}{b}\, u_1 = \text{const} \times \beta\, u_1\,,$$

where $u_1 = U_\infty - u$. On equating the two expressions, we obtain

$$U_\infty \frac{\mathrm{d}b}{\mathrm{d}x} \sim \frac{l}{b}\, u_1 = \beta\, u_1$$

or

$$\frac{\mathrm{d}b}{\mathrm{d}x} \sim \beta\, \frac{u_1}{U_\infty} \quad \text{(two-dimensional and circular wake)}\,. \tag{23.12}$$

The calculation of momentum in problems involving wakes differs from that for the case of jets, because now there is a direct relationship between momentum and the drag on the body. As already mentioned, eqn. (9.40), the momentum integral is

$$D = J = \varrho \int u\, (U_\infty - u)\, \mathrm{d}A\,,$$

provided that the control surface has been placed so far behind the body that the static pressure has become equal to that in the undisturbed stream. At a large distance behind the body $u_1 = U_\infty - u$ is small compared with U_∞ so that we may put $u\,(U_\infty - u) = (U_\infty - u_1)\, u_1 \approx U_\infty\, u_1$. Thus for two-dimensional and circular wakes

$$J = D \approx \varrho\, U_\infty \int u_1\, \mathrm{d}A\,. \tag{23.13}$$

Two-dimensional wake: Let h denote the height of the cylindrical body and d its diameter; its drag will then be $D = \frac{1}{2} c_D \varrho U_\infty^2 h d$ and the momentum, eqn. (23.13), is $J \sim \varrho U_\infty u_1 h b$. Equating, according to eqn. (23.13), we have

$$\frac{u_1}{U_\infty} \sim \frac{c_D d}{2b} . \qquad (23.14)$$

Inserting eqn. (23.12) for the rate of increase in width, we obtain

$$2b \frac{db}{dx} \sim \beta c_D d$$

or

$$b \sim (\beta x c_D d)^{1/2} \quad \text{(two-dimensional wake)} . \qquad (23.15)$$

Inserting this value into eqn. (23.14) we find that the rate at which the 'depression' in the velocity curve decreases downstream is represented by

$$\frac{u_1}{U_\infty} \sim \left(\frac{c_D d}{\beta x}\right)^{\frac{1}{2}} \quad \text{(two-dimensional wake)} . \qquad (23.16)$$

In other words, the width of a two-dimensional wake increases as $\sqrt{x}$ and the velocity decreases as $1/\sqrt{x}$.

Circular wake: Denoting the frontal area of the body by A we can write its drag as $D = \frac{1}{2} c_D A \varrho U_\infty^2$ and the momentum, eqn. (23.13), becomes $J \sim \varrho U_\infty u_1 b^2$. Equating D and J, we obtain

$$\frac{u_1}{U_\infty} \sim \frac{c_D A}{b^2} . \qquad (23.17)$$

Inserting this value into eqn. (23.12), we find that the increase in width is given by

$$b^2 \frac{db}{dx} \sim \beta c_D A$$

or

$$b \sim (\beta c_D A x)^{1/3} \quad \text{(circular wake)} . \qquad (23.18)$$

Inserting eqn. (23.18) into (23.17) we find for the decrease in the depression in the velocity profile the expression

$$\frac{u_1}{U_\infty} \sim \left(\frac{c_D A}{\beta^2 x^2}\right)^{1/3} \quad \text{(circular wake)} . \qquad (23.19)$$

Thus for a circular wake we find that the width of the wake increases in proportion to $x^{1/3}$ and that the velocity decreases in proportion to $x^{-2/3}$.

The power-laws for the width and for the velocity in the centre have been summarized in Table 23.1. The corresponding laminar cases, which were partly considered in Chaps. IX and X, have been added for completeness.

Table 23.1. Power-laws for the increase in width and for the decrease in the centre-line velocity in terms of distance x for problems of free turbulent flow

	Laminar		Turbulent	
	width b	Centre-line velocity u_{max} or u_1	width b	Centre-line velocity u_{max} or u_1
Free jet boundary	$x^{1/2}$	x^0	x	x^0
Two-dimensional jet	$x^{2/3}$	$x^{-1/3}$	x	$x^{-1/2}$
Circular jet	x	x^{-1}	x	x^{-1}
Two-dimensional wake	$x^{1/2}$	$x^{-1/2}$	$x^{+1/2}$	$x^{-1/2}$
Circular wake	$x^{1/2}$	x^{-1}	$x^{+1/3}$	$x^{-2/3}$

c. Examples

The preceding estimates give in themselves a very good idea of the essential features encountered in problems involving free turbulent flows. We shall, however, now go one step further and shall examine several particular cases in much greater detail deducing the complete velocity distribution function from the equations of motion. In order to achieve this result it is necessary to draw on one of the hypotheses in eqns. (23.3) to (23.5). The examples which have been selected here for consideration all have the common feature that the *velocity profiles* which occur in them are *similar* to each other. This means that the velocity profiles at different distances x can be made congruent by a suitable choice of a velocity and a width scale factor.

1. The smoothing out of a velocity discontinuity. As our first example we shall consider the problem of the smoothing out of a velocity discontinuity which was first treated by L. Prandtl [17]. At time $t = 0$ there are two streams moving at two different velocities U_1 and U_2 respectively, their boundary being at $y = 0$ (Fig. 23.2). As already mentioned, the boundary across which the velocity varies discontinuously is unstable and the process of turbulent mixing smoothes out the transition so that it becomes continuous. The width of the zone over which this continuous transition from velocity U_1 to velocity U_2 takes place increases with increasing time. We are here concerned with a problem in non-steady parallel flow for which

$$u = u\,(y, t)\ ; \qquad v = 0\,. \tag{23.20}$$

The convective terms in eqn. (23.1) vanish identically. Making use of Prandtl's mixing theory, eqn. (23.3), we can transform eqn. (23.1) to give

$$\frac{\partial u}{\partial t} = l^2 \left|\frac{\partial u}{\partial y}\right| \frac{\partial^2 u}{\partial y^2}\,. \tag{23.21}$$

The width of the mixing zone, b, increases with time and $b = b(t)$; the mixing length is assumed to be proportional to b in the same way as before so that $l = \beta b$. Assuming that the velocity profiles are similar, we may put

$$u \sim f(\eta)$$

with $\eta = y/b$ and $b \sim t^p$. The exponent p in the expression for the width can be determined from the condition that in eqn. (23.21) the acceleration and frictional terms must be proportional to equal powers of time, t. Thus $\partial u/\partial t$ is proportional to t^{-1}, whereas the right-hand side is proportional to $t^{2p-3p} = t^{-p}$, so that $p = 1$.

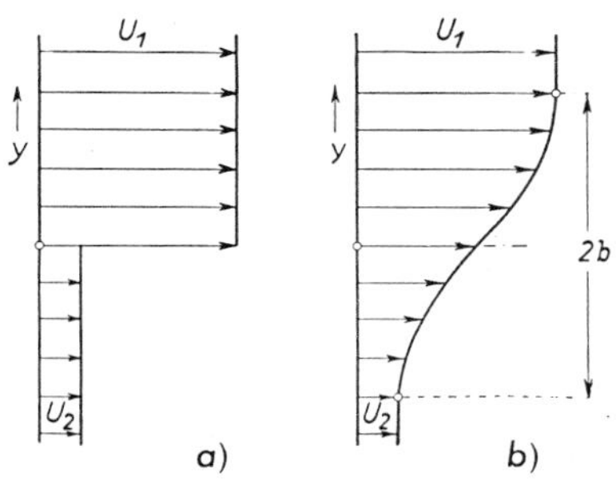

Fig. 23.2. The smoothing out of a velocity discontinuity, after Prandtl [17]; a) Initial pattern ($t = 0$), b) Pattern at later instant

In this manner we obtain the following assumptions for the problem in hand:

$$b = B\,t\;; \qquad \eta = \frac{y}{b} = \frac{y}{B\,t}\,.$$

The velocity u is best assumed to be of the form

$$u = \tfrac{1}{2}(U_1 + U_2) + \tfrac{1}{2}(U_1 - U_2)\,f(\eta) \tag{23.22}$$

or

$$u = U_m + A\,f(\eta)$$

with $U_m = \frac{1}{2}(U_1 + U_2)$ and $A = \frac{1}{2}(U_1 - U_2)$. In order to make sure that at the edges of the mixing zone, i. e. at $y = \pm b$, the velocity becomes equal to U_1 and U_2 respectively, we must put $f = \pm 1$ at $\eta = \pm 1$. Inserting the value from eqn. (23.22) into eqn. (23.21) we obtain the following differential equation for $f(\eta)$:

$$\eta\,f' + \frac{\beta^2 A}{B}\,f'\,f'' = 0\,.$$

The equation has one solution $f' = 0$, i. e. $f =$ const, which represents the trivial case of a constant velocity. If, however, f' differs from zero, we may divide through, whence we find

$$\eta + \frac{\beta^2 A}{B}\,f'' = 0\,.$$

Upon integration, we have

$$f(\eta) = c_0\,\eta^3 + c_1\,\eta\,,$$

with $c_0 = - B/6\,\beta^2 A$. The above solution satisfies the condition $f(0) = 0$ so that the constants c_0 and c_1 can be determined from the condition $f(\eta) = 1$ and $f'(\eta) = 0$ at $y = b$, i. e. at $\eta = 1$. Hence

$$c_0 = -\tfrac{1}{2}\,, \qquad c_1 = \tfrac{3}{2}\,.$$

Introducing these values into eqn. (23.22) we obtain the solution in its final form

$$u(y, t) = \frac{1}{2}\,(U_1 + U_2) + \frac{1}{2}\,(U_1 - U_2)\left[\frac{3}{2}\left(\frac{y}{b}\right) - \frac{1}{2}\left(\frac{y}{b}\right)^3\right] \tag{23.23}$$

with

$$b = \tfrac{3}{2}\,\beta^2\,(U_1 - U_2)\,t\,. \tag{23.24}$$

The velocity distribution from eqn. (23.23) is seen plotted in Fig. 23.2. It has the remarkable property that the velocity in the mixing region does not go over into the two free-stream velocities asymptotically. Transition occurs at a finite distance $y = b$ with a discontinuity in $\partial^2 u/\partial y^2$. This is a general property of all solutions obtained on the basis of Prandtl's hypothesis (23.3) for the shearing stress in turbulent flow. It constitutes what may be called an esthetical deficiency of this hypothesis. The improved hypotheses (23.4) or (23.5) are free of this blemish.

The quantity $\beta = l/b$ is the only empirical constant which appears in the solution; it can be determined solely from experimental data.

2. Free jet boundary. The conditions at a free jet boundary are closely related to those in the preceding example. With reference to Fig. 23.1 a we shall consider the more general case when at $x = 0$ there is a meeting of two streams whose constant velocities are U_1 and U_2 respectively, it being assumed that $U_1 > U_2$. Downstream of the point of encounter the streams will form a mixing zone whose width b increases proportionately to x, Fig. 23.1 a. The first solution to the problem under consideration was given by W. Tollmien [32], who made use of Prandtl's mixing length hypothesis for turbulent shear, eqn. (23.3). We shall review here the mathematically simpler solution due to H. Goertler [9] who based it on Prandtl's hypothesis in eqn. (23.5). Since the virtual kinematic viscosity ε is independent of x, eqns. (23.1) and (23.5) give

$$u\,\frac{\partial u}{\partial x} + v\,\frac{\partial u}{\partial y} = \varepsilon\,\frac{\partial^2 u}{\partial y^2}\,. \tag{23.25}$$

Putting $b = c\,x$ we obtain the following expression for the virtual kinematic viscosity, eqn. (23.5a), which is applicable to our case:

$$\varepsilon = \varkappa_1\,c\,x\,(U_1 - U_2)\,. \tag{23.26}$$

In view of the similarity of the velocity profiles u and v are functions of y/x. Putting $\xi = \sigma\,y/x$ we can integrate the equation of continuity by the adoption of a stream function $\psi = x\,U\,F(\xi)$ where $U = \tfrac{1}{2}\,(U_1 + U_2)$. Then $u = U\,\sigma\,F'(\xi)$ and eqn. (23.25) leads to the following differential equation for $F(\xi)$:

$$F''' + 2\,\sigma^2\,F\,F'' = 0\,, \tag{23.27}$$

where $\sigma = \frac{1}{2}(\varkappa_1 c \lambda)^{-1/2}$ and $\lambda = (U_1 - U_2)/(U_1 + U_2)$. The boundary conditions are $\xi = \pm\infty : F'(\xi) = 1 \pm \lambda$. The differential equation (23.27) is identical with Blasius' equation for the flat plate at zero incidence, eqn. (7.29), but the present boundary conditions are different. H. Goertler solved eqn. (23.27) by assuming a power-series expansion of the form

$$\sigma F(\xi) = F_0(\xi) + \lambda F_1(\xi) + \lambda^2 F_2(\xi) + \ldots \tag{23.28}$$

with $F_0 = \xi$. Substituting (23.28) into (23.27) and arranging in ascending powers of λ, we obtain a system of differential equations which is solved by recursion. The first of the differential equations is of the form

$$F_1''' + 2\,\xi\,F_1'' = 0 \tag{23.29}$$

with the boundary conditions $F'_1(\xi) = \pm 1$ at $\xi = \pm\infty$. The solution of (23.29) is given by the error function

$$F_1'(\xi) = \operatorname{erf}\xi = \frac{2}{\sqrt{\pi}}\int_0^{\xi} e^{-z^2}\,dz\,.$$

The contributions of the succeeding terms of the series in eqn. (23.28) are not significant. Hence the solution becomes

$$u = \frac{U_1 + U_2}{2}\left\{1 + \frac{U_1 - U_2}{U_1 + U_2}\operatorname{erf}\xi\right\} \tag{23.30}$$

with

$$\xi = \sigma\frac{y}{x}\,.$$

Figure 23.3 compares the theoretical solution with H. Reichardt's [19] measurements for the case when $U_2 = 0$ and agreement is seen to be very good. The quantity σ is the only empirical constant left free to be adjusted from experiment. According to the measurements performed by H. Reichardt the width $b_{0 \cdot 1}$ of the mixing zone, measured between stations where $(u/U_1)^2 = 0{\cdot}1$ (corresponding to $\xi = -0{\cdot}345$) and $(u/U_1)^2 = 0{\cdot}9$ (corresponding to $\xi = 0{\cdot}975$) has the value $b_{0\cdot 1} = 0{\cdot}098\,x$, which yields $\sigma = 13{\cdot}5$. The virtual kinematic viscosity becomes $\varepsilon = 0{\cdot}014\, b_{0\cdot1} \times U_1$.

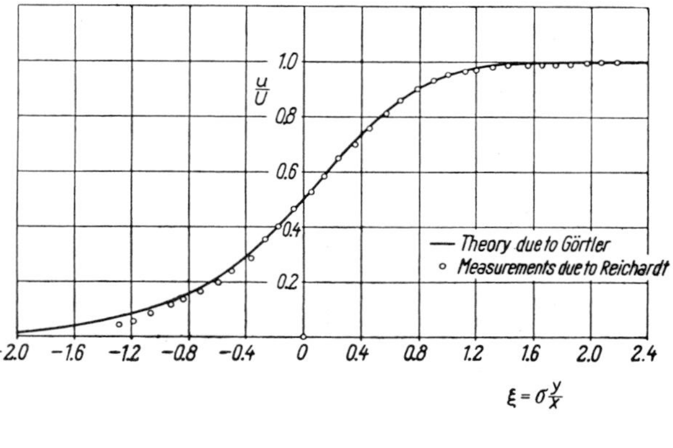

Fig. 23.3. Velocity distribution in the mixing zone of a jet; $\sigma = 13{\cdot}5$

W. Szablewski [28, 29, 30] extended these calculations, as well as those given in Sec. XXIIIc. 1, to cases when there is a large difference in the densities of the two streams, but a small difference in their velocities. It turns out that the widths of the mixing zones are affected only very slightly by this difference in density. Nevertheless, as the difference in the densities is increased, the zone of mixing becomes displaced in the direction of the less dense jet. The preceding results can also be applied when the two jets differ in their chemical concentrations. P. B. Gooderum, G. P. Wood and H. J. Brevoort [8] carried out an experimental investigation into the conditions at the free boundary of a supersonic jet. The results showed that the mixing zone is somewhat narrower and the level of turbulence is somewhat smaller than in incompressible flow.

3. Two-dimensional wake behind a single body. Two-dimensional wakes were first investigated by H. Schlichting [22] in his thesis presented to Goettingen University. The investigation was based on Prandtl's mixing length hypothesis, eqn. (23.3). A solution for the same problem which was based on Prandtl's hypothesis in eqn. (23.5) was later given by H. Reichardt [19] and H. Goertler [9]. We shall now give a short account of both solutions in order to illustrate the fact that the two results do not differ much one from the other.

In the case of a wake, the velocity profiles become similar only at large distances downstream from the body, there being no similarity at smaller distances. We shall restrict ourselves to the consideration of large distances x so that the velocity difference

$$u_1 = U_\infty - u \tag{23.31}$$

is small compared with the free stream velocity U_∞. At large distances the static pressure in the wake is equal to the static pressure in the free stream. Consequently the application of the momentum theorem to a control surface which encloses the body, assumed to be a cylinder of height h, gives

$$D = h\,\varrho \int\limits_{y=-\infty}^{+\infty} u\,(U_\infty - u)\,\mathrm{d}y = h\,\varrho \int\limits_{y=-\infty}^{+\infty} u_1\,(U_\infty - u_1)\,\mathrm{d}y\,.$$

Neglecting u_1^2, we obtain

$$D = h\,\varrho\,U_\infty \int\limits_{y=-\infty}^{+\infty} u_1\,\mathrm{d}y\,.$$

Substituting $D = \frac{1}{2}\,c_D\,d\,h\,\varrho\,U_\infty^2$, where d denotes the thickness of the cylinder, we obtain

$$\int\limits_{y=-\infty}^{+\infty} u_1\,\mathrm{d}y = \tfrac{1}{2}\,c_D\,d\,U_\infty\,. \tag{23.32}$$

As deduced in Sec. XXIIIb, the width and the velocity difference varies in a manner to give $b \sim x^{1/2}$ and $u_1 \sim x^{-1/2}$.

Shearing stress hypothesis from eqn. (23.3): Since the term $v\,\partial u/\partial y$ in eqn. (23.1) is small, we obtain

$$-\,U_\infty \frac{\partial u_1}{\partial x} = 2\,l^2\,\frac{\partial u_1}{\partial y}\,\frac{\partial^2 u_1}{\partial y^2}\,. \tag{23.33}$$

It is assumed that the mixing length l is constant over the width b and proportional to it, i. e. that $l = \beta\, b(x)$. In view of the similarity of the velocity profiles the ratio $\eta = y/b$ is introduced as the independent variable. In agreement with the power laws for the width and for the depth of depression in the velocity profile we make the assumptions:

$$b = B\,(c_D\, d\, x)^{1/2} \tag{23.34}$$

$$u_1 = U_\infty \left(\frac{x}{c_D d}\right)^{-\frac{1}{2}} f(\eta)\,. \tag{23.35}$$

Inserting into eqn. (23.33), we are led to the following differential equation for the function $f(\eta)$:

$$\frac{1}{2}\,(f + \eta\, f') = \frac{2\beta^2}{B}\, f'\, f''$$

with the boundary conditions $u_1 = 0$ and $\partial u_1/\partial y = 0$ at $y = b$, i. e. $f = f' = 0$ at $\eta = 1$. Integrating once, we obtain

$$\frac{1}{2}\,\eta\, f = \frac{\beta^2}{B}\, f'^2\,,$$

where the constant of integration has been made equal to zero in view of the boundary condition. Repeated integration yields

$$f = \frac{1}{9}\,\frac{B}{2\beta^2}\,(1 - \eta^{3/2})^2\,.$$

Now it only remains to determine the constant of integration B from the momentum integral (23.32); we thus obtain $B = \sqrt{10}\,\beta$†, and the final solution becomes

$$b = \sqrt{10}\,\beta\,(x\, c_D\, d)^{1/2} \tag{23.36}$$

$$\frac{u_1}{U_\infty} = \frac{\sqrt{10}}{18\,\beta}\left(\frac{x}{c_D d}\right)^{-\frac{1}{2}} \left\{1 - \left(\frac{y}{b}\right)^{\frac{3}{2}}\right\}^2. \tag{23.37}$$

It is noticed that the resulting width has a finite magnitude, the same feature having been observed in connexion with the solution for the smoothing out of a velocity discontinuity, for which the same assumption for shearing stress had been used. At the edge, $y = b$, there is again a discontinuity in the curvature of the velocity profile. Moreover, in the centre at $y = 0$ the second derivative $\partial^2 u/\partial y^2$ even becomes infinitely large and the velocity profile exhibits here a sharp kink. The results of this theoretical calculation, eqn. (23.37) have been compared with Schlichting's measurements [22] in Fig. 23.4. The measurements were performed in the wake behind a circular cylinder, and the theoretical curve is shown as curve (1). It is seen that there is an excellent measure of agreement. The single free constant, the constant β in eqns. (23.36) and (23.37), must, again, be determined on the basis of measured values. The value of β can be deduced from Fig. 23.5, in which the width of the wake has been plotted against the distance, x, from the body. The measured points have

† It will be noted that $\int\limits_{-1}^{+1} (1 - \eta^{3/2})^2\, \mathrm{d}\eta = \frac{9}{10}$.

been obtained by H. Reichardt [19] and H. Schlichting [22] in the wakes behind circular cylinders of different diameters d. According to these $b_{1/2} = \frac{1}{4}\,(x\,c_D\,d)^{1/2}$, where $b_{1/2}$ denotes half the width at half depth. Since $b_{1/2} = 0{\cdot}441\,b$, we have $0{\cdot}441\,\sqrt{10}\,\beta = \frac{1}{4}$ and thus

$$\beta = \frac{l}{b} = 0{\cdot}18\,.$$

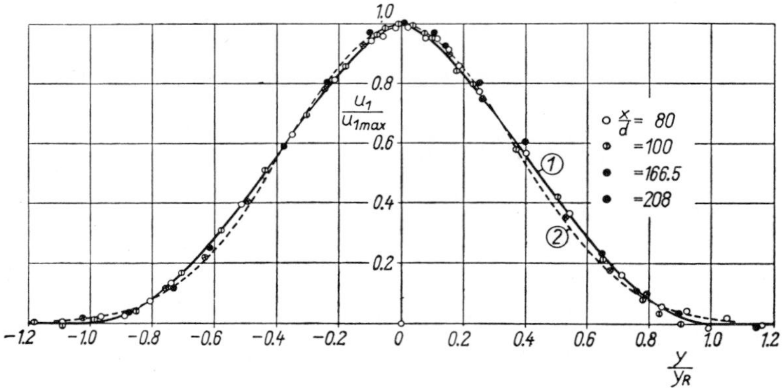

Fig. 24.4. Velocity distribution in a two-dimensional wake behind circular cylinders. Comparison between theory and measurement after Schlichting [22]

Theory: curve (1) corresponds to eqn. (23.37); curve (2) corresponds to eqn. (23.39)

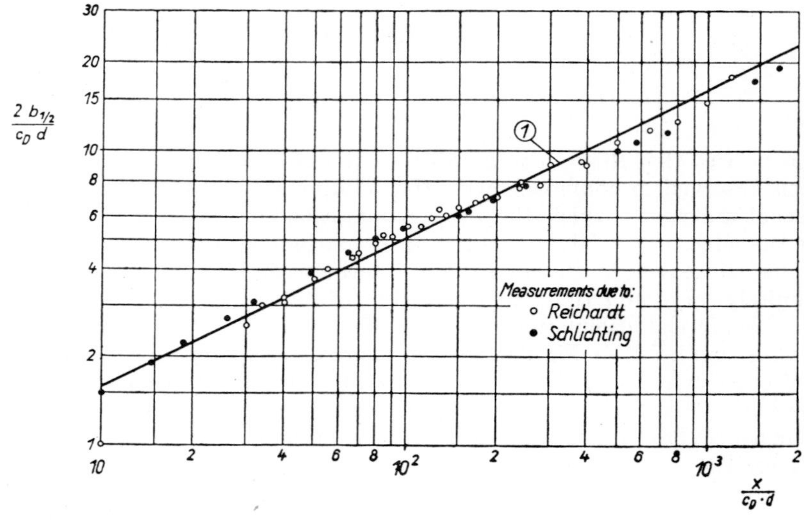

Fig. 23.5. Two-dimensional wake. Increase in width of wake behind circular cylinder

Curve (1): $b_{1/2} = \frac{1}{4}\,(x\,c_D\,d)^{1/2}$

The preceding solution constitutes an approximation for large distances x; measurements show that it is valid for $x/c_D\, d > 50$. In the case of smaller distances it is possible to calculate additional terms for the velocity, the terms being proportional to x^{-1} and $x^{-3/2}$ respectively.

Shearing stress hypothesis from eqn. (23.5): From eqns. (23.1) and (23.5) we now obtain

$$U_\infty \frac{\partial u_1}{\partial x} = \varepsilon \frac{\partial^2 u_1}{\partial y^2} . \tag{23.38}$$

The virtual kinematic viscosity is here $\varepsilon = \varkappa_1 u_{1max} b$ and, hence, constant and equal to ε_0, say. Consequently, the differential equation for u_1 is identical with that for a laminar wake, eqn. (9.44), except that the laminar kinematic viscosity ν must be replaced by ε_0. Thus we can simply copy the solution which was found in Chap. IX. Denoting $\eta = y \sqrt{U_\infty/\varepsilon_0\, x}$ we obtain from eqns. (9.44) and (9.48) that

$$u_1 = U_\infty C \left(\frac{x}{d}\right)^{-\frac{1}{2}} \exp\left(-\frac{1}{4}\eta^2\right) .$$

The constant C follows from the momentum integral, and is

$$C = \frac{c_D}{4\sqrt{\pi}} \sqrt{\frac{U_\infty d}{\varepsilon_0}} ,$$

so that finally

$$\frac{u_1}{U_\infty} = \frac{1}{4\sqrt{\pi}} \sqrt{\frac{U_\infty c_D d}{\varepsilon_0}} \left(\frac{x}{c_D d}\right)^{-\frac{1}{2}} \exp\left(-\frac{1}{4}\eta^2\right) . \tag{23.39}$$

The value of half the width at half the depth is $b_{1/2} = 1{\cdot}675 \sqrt{\varepsilon_0/U_\infty c_D d}\, (x\, c_D\, d)^{1/2}$. Comparing with the preceding measured value of $b_1/_2$ it is found that the empirical quantity ε_0 has the value

$$\frac{\varepsilon_0}{U_\infty c_D d} = 0{\cdot}0222 .$$

Taking into account that $U_\infty c_D d = 2{\cdot}11 \times 2\, b_{1/2}\, u_{1m}$ we have

$$\varepsilon_0 = 0{\cdot}047 \cdot 2\, b_{1/2}\, u_{1m} .$$

The preceding solution shows that the velocity distribution in the wake can be represented by Gauss' function. The alternative solution from eqn. (23.39) is seen plotted in Fig. 23.4 as curve (2). The difference between this solution and that in eqn. (23.37) is very small.

W. Tollmien [33] solved the same problem on the basis of von Kármán's hypothesis from eqn. (19.23). In the neighbourhood of the points of inflexion in the velocity profile, where $\partial^2 u/\partial y^2 = 0$, it has proved necessary to make additional assumptions.

Extensive experiments, which were carried out by A. A. Townsend [34] in the wake of a cylinder and which were concerned with turbulent fluctuations at Reynolds numbers near 8000, showed that at a distance equal to about 80 to 150 diameters the turbulent microstructure is not yet fully developed. Furthermore, oscillograms taken in the stream demonstrate that the flow is fully turbulent only around the centre, and fluctuates between laminar and turbulent in the neighbourhood of the outer boundaries of the wake. H. Muttray [14] performed measurements in the wake behind a symmetrical aerofoil.

Circular wakes have been investigated by Miss L. M. Swain [27] who based the calculation on the hypothesis in eqn. (23.3). She obtained the same expression for velocity as in the two-dimensional case, eqn. (23.37), but the power-laws for the width and for the centre-line velocity were found to be different, namely $b \sim x^{1/3}$ and $u_{1max} \sim x^{-2/3}$, as already shown in Table 23.1.

4. The wake behind a row of bars. The wake behind a row, or cascade, of bodies, such as that behind a row which is composed of a very large number of cylindrical bars (whose pitch is equal to λ), Fig. 23.6, is closely related to the wake behind a single body. The present case was investigated both theoretically and experimentally by R. Gran Olsson [10]. At a certain distance from the row, the width of the wake cast by a single element of the row is equal to the pitch, i. e. $b = \lambda$. The velocity difference $u_1 = U_\infty - u$ is here also small compared with U_∞, and eqn. (23.1) can be simplified to

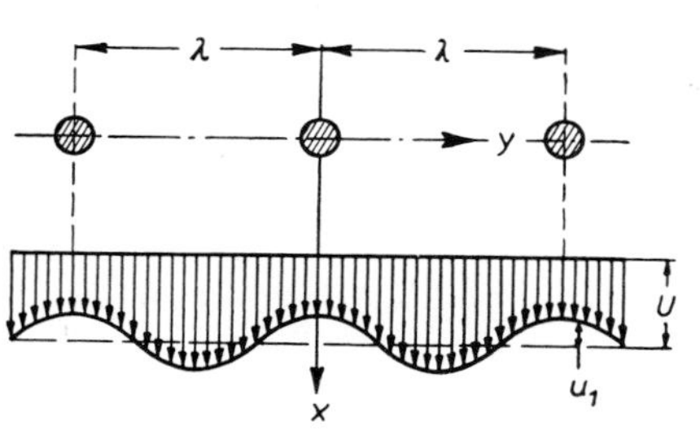

Fig. 23.6. Flow pattern behind a row of bars. Explanatory sketch

$$-U_\infty \frac{\partial u_1}{\partial x} = \frac{1}{\varrho} \frac{\partial \tau}{\partial y}. \tag{23.40}$$

The calculation for the case in hand becomes very simple when the more general mixing length hypothesis from eqn. (23.4) is used. The first step consists in the determination of the exponent in the power function for the decrease of u_1 with x. On putting $u_1 \sim x^p f(y)$, we have $\partial u_1/\partial x \sim x^{p-1}$. The right-hand side of eqn. (23.40) becomes proportional to $\partial\tau/\partial y \sim (\partial u/\partial y) \cdot (\partial^2 u/\partial y^2) \sim x^{2p}$, because the mixing length, being proportional to the width, is constant. Thus $p - 1 = 2p$ and it follows that $p = -1$, or, that the velocity difference u_1 decreases in proportion to x^{-1}.

In the case of fully developed flow the velocity distribution must be expected to be a periodic function in y whose period is equal to λ. Thus we assume

$$u_1 = U_\infty A \left(\frac{x}{\lambda}\right)^{-1} \cos\left(2\pi \frac{y}{\lambda}\right).$$

The point $y = 0$ has here been made to coincide with the centre of one depression in the velocity distribution, and A is a free constant whose value is still to be determined. We now form the expression for the shearing stress τ from eqn. (23.4) with $l = \text{const}$ and assume that $l_1 = \lambda/2\pi$, which seems permissible. The result is a very simple expression of the form

$$\frac{1}{\varrho} \frac{\partial \tau}{\partial y} = l^2 \left(\frac{x}{\lambda}\right)^{-2} U_\infty{}^2 A^2 \left(\frac{2\pi}{\lambda}\right)^3 \cos\left(2\pi \frac{y}{\lambda}\right).$$

Inserting this expression into eqn. (23.40), we obtain $A = (\lambda/l)^2/8\,\pi^3$ and hence the final solution

$$u_1 = \frac{U_\infty}{8\pi^3}\left(\frac{\lambda}{l}\right)^2 \frac{\lambda}{x} \cos\left(2\pi\,\frac{y}{\lambda}\right). \tag{23.41}$$

According to the measurements performed by Gran Olsson this equation is valid for $x/\lambda > 4$.

Behind a row of circular bars for which $\lambda/d = 8$ the magnitude of the mixing length is given by

$$\frac{l}{\lambda} = 0{\cdot}103\,.$$

R. Gran Olsson also studied the case with τ from eqn. (23.3) which implies $l_1 = 0$; with this assumption the calculation becomes much more cumbersome. H. Goertler [9] solved the same problem with the aid of assumption (23.5) for τ and found that the solution was identical with eqn. (23.41)†. A second approximation for smaller distances from the cascade was deduced by G. Cordes [3].

Cascades with a very narrow spacing between the bars are often used in wind tunnels to obtain a locally uniform velocity distribution. In this way several jets close in on each other and this process prevents the velocity from becoming uniform. J. G. von Bohl [2] made a more detailed study of such phenomena and performed experiments on several rows of parallel, polygonal bars varying the solidity m, i.e. the ratio of that portion of the cross-section which is filled by bars to the total channel cross-section over the values $m = 0{\cdot}308$, $0{\cdot}462$ and $0{\cdot}615$. When the value of m is small the single jets remain parallel; the closing-in of jets occurs at about $m = 0{\cdot}37$ to $0{\cdot}46$.

5. The two-dimensional jet. The turbulent two-dimensional jet was first calculated by W. Tollmien [32] who used Prandtl's mixing length hypothesis, eqn. (23.3). In the present section we shall, however, give a short account of the simpler solution based on Prandtl's second hypothesis, eqn. (23.5), which was given by H. Goertler [9]. Measurements of the velocity distribution were performed by E. Foerthmann [6] and H. Reichardt [19].

The rate of increase in the width of the jet, $b \sim x$, and that of the decrease in the centre-line velocity, $U \sim x^{-1/2}$ have already been given in Table 23.1. Equations (23.1) and (23.5) lead to the differential equation

$$u\,\frac{\partial u}{\partial x} + v\,\frac{\partial u}{\partial y} = \varepsilon\,\frac{\partial^2 u}{\partial y^2}\,, \tag{23.42}$$

which must be combined with the equation of continuity. The virtual kinematic viscosity is given by

$$\varepsilon = \varkappa_1\, b\, U\,,$$

† With $\varepsilon = K\,\lambda(u_{max} - u_{min})$ we have $u = \dfrac{U_\infty}{8\,\pi^2 K}\,\dfrac{\lambda}{x}\,\cos\left(2\pi\,\dfrac{y}{\lambda}\right)$ or, on comparing with eqn. (23.41), $K = \pi(l/\lambda)^2 = 0{\cdot}103^2 = 0{\cdot}0333$. Thus the virtual kinematic viscosity becomes $\varepsilon = 0{\cdot}0333\,\lambda\,(u_{max} - u_{min})$.

where U denotes the centre-line velocity. Denoting the centre-line velocity and the width of the jet at a fixed characteristic distance s from the orifice by U_s and b_s respectively, we may write

$$U = U_s \left(\frac{x}{s}\right)^{-\frac{1}{2}}; \qquad b = b_s \frac{x}{s}.$$

Consequently

$$\varepsilon = \varepsilon_s \left(\frac{x}{s}\right)^{\frac{1}{2}} \quad \text{with} \quad \varepsilon_s = \varkappa_1 \, b_s \, U_s.$$

Further, we put

$$\eta = \sigma \frac{y}{x},$$

where σ denotes a free constant. The equation of continuity is integrated by the use of a stream function ψ, which is assumed to be of the form

$$\psi = \sigma^{-1} \, U_s \, s^{1/3} \, x^{1/2} \, F(\eta).$$

Thus

$$u = U_s \left(\frac{x}{s}\right)^{-\frac{1}{2}} F'; \qquad v = \sigma^{-1} \, U_s \, s^{1/2} \, x^{-1/2} \left(\eta F' - \frac{1}{2} F\right).$$

On substituting into eqn. (23.42) we obtain the following differential equation for $F(\eta)$:

$$\frac{1}{2} F' + \frac{1}{2} F F'' + \frac{\varepsilon_s}{U_s s} \sigma^2 F''' = 0$$

with the boundary conditions $F = 0$ and $F' = 1$ at $\eta = 0$, and $F' = 0$ at $\eta = \infty$. Since ε_s contains the free constant $\varkappa_1$, we may put

$$\sigma = \frac{1}{2} \sqrt{\frac{U_s s}{\varepsilon_s}}. \tag{23.43}$$

This substitution simplifies the preceding differential equation which can now be integrated twice, whence we obtain

$$F^2 + F' = 1. \tag{23.44}$$

This is exactly the same equation as that for the two-dimensional laminar jet, eqn. (9.56). Its solution is $F = \tanh \eta$ so that the velocity is $u = U_s (x/s)^{-1/2} (1 - \tanh^2 \eta)$. The characteristic velocity can be expressed in terms of the constant momentum per unit length: $J = \varrho \int_{-\infty}^{+\infty} u^2 \, dy$. Hence $J = \frac{4}{3} \varrho U_s^2 \, s/\sigma$. With $J/\varrho = K$ (kinematic momentum) we obtain the final form of the solution:

$$\left.\begin{aligned} u &= \frac{\sqrt{3}}{2} \sqrt{\frac{K\sigma}{x}} \, (1 - \tanh^2 \eta), \\ v &= \frac{\sqrt{3}}{4} \sqrt{\frac{K}{x\sigma}} \left\{ 2\eta \, (1 - \tanh^2 \eta) - \tanh \eta \right\}, \\ \eta &= \sigma \frac{y}{x}. \end{aligned}\right\} \tag{23.45}$$

The value of the single empirical constant σ was determined experimentally by H. Reichardt [19] who found that $\sigma = 7{\cdot}67$. Fig. 23.7 contains a comparison between the theoretical curve from eqn. (23.45) with the measurements due to E. Foerthmann, curve (2). The theoretical curve obtained by W. Tollmien [32] on the basis of Prandtl's mixing length hypothesis, curve (1), has also been shown for comparison. The first theoretical curve shows a slightly superior agreement with measurement as it is fuller near its maximum.

From the given numerical value of σ we obtain $\varepsilon = \frac{1{\cdot}125}{4\,\sigma}\, b_{1/2}\, U$, or

$$\varepsilon = 0{\cdot}037\, b_{1/2}\, U \; ,$$

where $b_1/_2$ again denotes half the width at half depth.

6. The circular jet. Experimental results on circular jets were given by W. Zimm [38] and P. Ruden [21] as well as by H. Reichardt [19] and W. Wuest [37]. Some results of measurements on circular jets are also contained in the series of reports published by the Aerodynamic Institute in Goettingen [39].

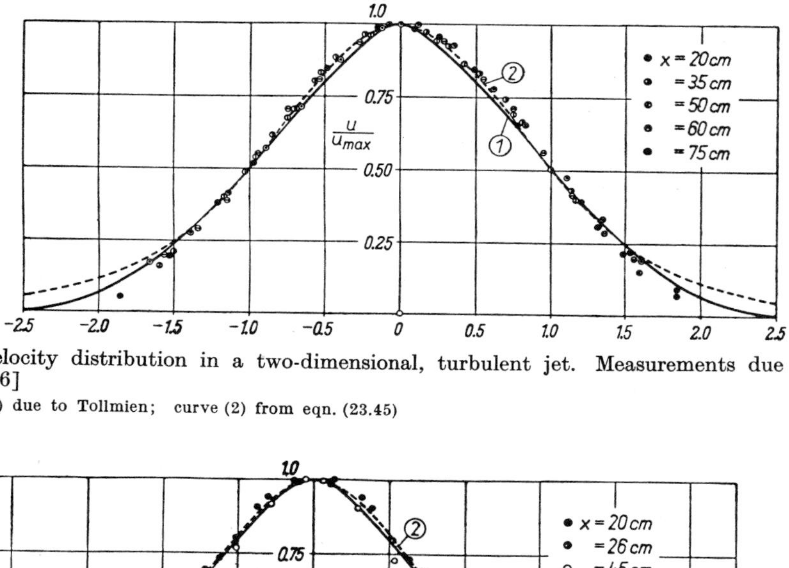

Fig. 23.7. Velocity distribution in a two-dimensional, turbulent jet. Measurements due to Foerthmann [6]
Theory: curve (1) due to Tollmien; curve (2) from eqn. (23.45)

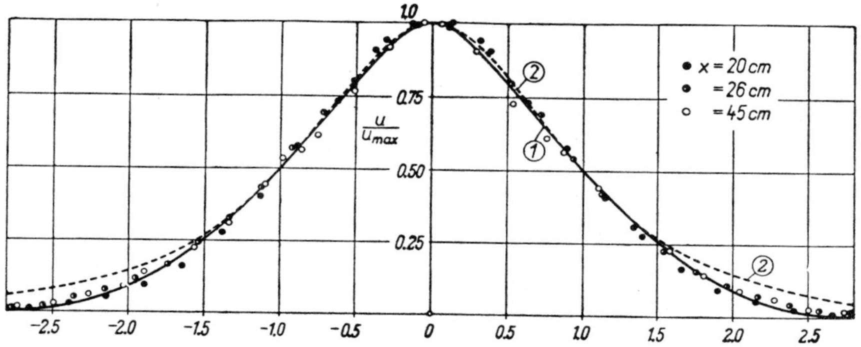

Fig. 23.8. Velocity distribution in a circular, turbulent jet. Measurements due to Reichardt [19]
Theory: curve (1) due to Tollmien; curve (2) from eqns. (23.46)

The first theoretical treatment of a circular jet was given by W. Tollmien [32] who based his study on Prandtl's mixing length theory. In this case, as well as in the preceding one, the assumption for shearing stress given in eqn. (23.5) leads to a considerably simpler calculation. According to Table 23.1 the width of the jet is proportional to x and the centre-line velocity $U \sim x^{-1}$. Thus the virtual kinematic viscosity becomes

$$\varepsilon = \varkappa_1\, b\, U \sim x^0 = \text{const} = \varepsilon_0\,.$$

which means that it remains constant over the whole of the jet, as it was in the two-dimensional wake. Consequently, the differential equation for the velocity distribution becomes formally identical with that for the laminar jet, it being only necessary to replace the kinematic viscosity, ν, of laminar flow by the virtual kinematic viscosity, ε_0, of turbulent flow. It is, theorefore, possible to carry over the solution for the laminar, circular jet, eqns. (10.19) to (10.21). Introducing, once more, the constant kinematic momentum, K, as a measure of the strength of the jet†, we obtain

$$\left.\begin{aligned} u &= \frac{3}{8\pi}\,\frac{K}{\varepsilon_0\,\pi}\,\frac{1}{\left(1+\frac{1}{4}\eta^2\right)^2}\,, \\ v &= \frac{1}{4}\sqrt{\frac{3}{\pi}}\,\frac{\sqrt{K}}{x}\,\frac{\eta-\frac{1}{4}\eta^2}{\left(1+\frac{1}{4}\eta^2\right)^2}\,, \\ \eta &= \frac{1}{4}\sqrt{\frac{3}{\pi}}\,\frac{\sqrt{K}}{\varepsilon_0}\,\frac{y}{x}\,. \end{aligned}\right\} \qquad (23.46)$$

The empirical constant is now equal to $\sqrt{K}/\varepsilon_0$. According to the measurement performed by H. Reichardt the width of the jet is given by $b_{1/2} = 0{\cdot}0848\, x$. With $\eta = 1{\cdot}286$ at $u = \frac{1}{2}\, u_m$ we have $b_{1/2} = 5{\cdot}27\, x\, \varepsilon_0/\sqrt{K}$, and hence

$$\frac{\varepsilon_0}{\sqrt{K}} = 0{\cdot}0161\,.$$

On the other hand we have

$$\sqrt{K} = 1{\cdot}59\, b_{1/2}\, U$$

so that

$$\varepsilon_0 = 0{\cdot}0256\, b_{1/2}\, U$$

where, as before, $b_{1/2}$ denotes half the width at half depth.

The diagram in Fig. 23.8 contains a comparison between measured velocity distribution points and the theoretical results from eqns. (23.46) shown as curve (2). Curve (1) provides a further comparison with the theory due to W. Tollmien [32]. The mixing length theory leads here also to a velocity distribution curve which is somewhat too pointed near the maximum, whereas eqns. (23.46) give excellent agreement over the whole width. The pattern of stream-lines is shown plotted in

† We have $K = 2\pi \int\limits_0^\infty u^2\, y\, \mathrm{d}y\,.$

Fig. 23.9. It is seen that the jet draws in at its boundary fluid from the surrounding mass at rest so that the mass of fluid carried by the jet increases in a downstream direction. The mass of fluid carried at a distance x from the orifice can be calculated from eqn. (10.22). Inserting the above value for ε_0, we obtain

$$Q = 0{\cdot}404 \sqrt{K}\, x. \tag{23.47}$$

Calculations on the velocity and temperature distributions in two-dimensional and circular jets have also been carried out by L. Howarth [12], both on the basis of L. Prandtl's and of G. I. Taylor's assumption concerning turbulent mixing. The mechanism which governs the mixing of a jet issuing from a circular nozzle with the fluid in a large pipe was studied experimentally by K. Viktorin [35]. The experiments covered a range of values of the velocity ratio in the pipe to that in the jet of from 0 to 4. Compared with the mixing of a free jet with the surrounding fluid it is noticed that the pressure increases in the direction of flow in a manner which resembles the phenomena near a sudden increase in cross-sectional area and sometimes described as Carnot's loss. A theoretical calculation based on Prandtl's mixing length hypothesis showed that the velocity distribution behaves in the same way as in a circular wake (width $\sim x^{-1/3}$, centre-line velocity $\sim x^{-2/3}$).

When a jet of finite width emerges into a uniform stream, the uniform velocity distribution becomes transformed near the mouth of the nozzle into the preceding profile. The case in hand was studied by A. M. Kuethe [13] and H. B. Squire J. Trouncer [24].

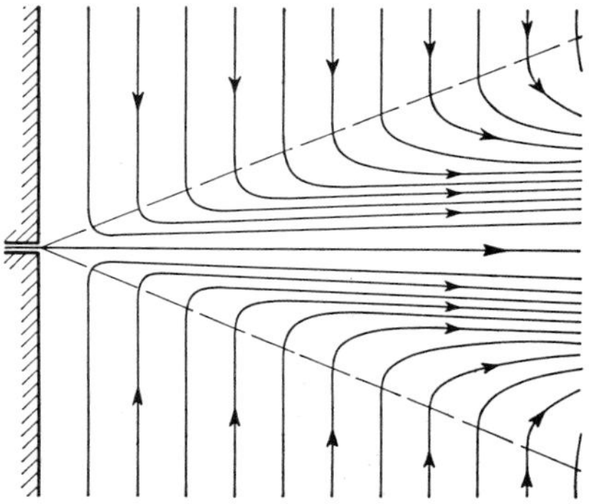

Fig. 23.9. Pattern of stream-lines in a circular, turbulent free jet

d. Inductive theory of turbulence due to H. Reichardt

The preceding numerous examples on free turbulent flows have shown that the real phenomena can be described in an excellent way by the use of different semi-empirical hypotheses for turbulent stresses. Furthermore, the velocity distribution curves which are obtained from the alternative assumptions differ but little from each other. The theories of turbulence discussed so far had the common feature that a suitable assumption was made for the unknown relation between the turbulent shearing stresses and the mean motion. More or less complicated examples have then been calculated with the aid of this assumption and a final comparison with experiment was made. Such a *deductive theory of turbulence* suffers from the deficiency that it is impossible to determine which of the alternative *a priori* assumptions comes closest to physical reality. The main reason for the deficiency lies in the fact that the results of these alternative theories of turbulence do not differ much from each other, as already stated.

H. Reichardt [18, 19] made an attempt to proceed in the reverse direction and to formulate an *inductive theory of turbulence*. Instead of beginning with a hypothesis, such as the mixing length hypothesis, which can be confronted with experiment only after a protracted mathematical deduction, H. Reichardt tried to dispense with hypotheses altogether. After a critical examination of the voluminous experimental data on free turbulent flows, which he supplemented with his own very careful measurements, he discovered that the velocity profiles under consideration could be approximated very successfully by Gauss' function, or by its integral — the error function †. Starting with this premiss, H. Reichardt attempted to cover all cases of free turbulent flow with the aid of a simple set of formulae instead of endeavouring to solve the differential equations of fluid dynamics, the latter being a tedious and often abstruse process. He tried, furthermore, to derive expressions for the quantities which are difficult to measure in terms of those which are readily measurable (total pressure distribution) without the use of any hypotheses on turbulence. Reichardt's theory is based on the momentum equation for the time-averages of velocity. In the case of two-dimensional frictionless flow this can be written as

$$\frac{\partial}{\partial x}\left(\frac{\overline{p}}{\varrho} + \overline{u^2}\right) + \frac{\partial}{\partial y}(\overline{u\,v}) = 0\,. \tag{23.48}$$

The preceding equation is a time-average of the equation of motion in the x-direction. It was already used by O. Reynolds when he formulated the equation for virtual turbulent stresses. In this connexion reference may be made to eqn. (18.6a) and (18.8), Chap. XVIII. In the case of free turbulent flows the pressure term in the above equation vanishes. The second basic equation is of an empirical nature and has the form

$$\overline{u\,v} = -\Lambda\,\frac{\partial \overline{u^2}}{\partial y}\,. \tag{23.49}$$

Here $\Lambda = \Lambda\,(x)$ has the dimension of a length and must be determined empirically. It constitutes what might be termed a *momentum transfer length*. The left-hand side of eqn. (23.49) represents the shearing stress, except for the factor ϱ, and can be regarded as the quantity of the x-component of momentum which is being transferred in the y-direction (flux of momentum). This empirical *law of momentum transfer* states that the flux of the x-component of momentum which is transferred in a transverse direction is proportional to the transverse gradient of momentum. This law of momentum transfer is thus seen to be analogous to Fourier's law of heat conduction, according to which the heat flux is proportional to the temperature gradient. The momentum transfer length, Λ, is analogous to the conductivity, k. On eliminating $\overline{u\,v}$ from eqns. (23.48) and (23.49) and on putting $\overline{p} = 0$ for free turbulent flows, we obtain Reichardt's fundamental equation

$$\frac{\partial \overline{u^2}}{\partial x} = \Lambda\,(x)\,\frac{\partial^2 \overline{u^2}}{\partial y^2}\,, \tag{23.50}$$

which describes the distribution of velocity (x-component of momentum) in free turbulent flows. If we had $\Lambda =$ const the equation would be identical with the one-

† The theoretical reasoning of the preceding section gave the same result for the two-dimensional wake and for the free jet.

dimensional heat conduction equation with x denoting time and y denoting the single space co-ordinate. Thus, according to Reichardt, the distribution of momentum in free turbulent flow is governed by a generalized heat conduction equation in which the conductivity is a function of time. As is well known from the theory of heat conduction, the solutions of eqn. (23.50) involve the Gauss or the error function. Thus eqn. (23.50) constitutes a simple mathematical expression for the statement that velocity profiles in free turbulent flow can be expressed with the aid of these functions, as determined empirically by H. Reichardt.

An example may serve to provide an illustration of Reichardt's approach to the problem. According to existing experimental results, the distribution of momentum in a jet and in a two-dimensional wake can be represented with a good degree of precision by the expression

$$\overline{u^2} = c_1 + \frac{c_2}{b} \exp\{-(y/b)^2\}\,,$$

where c_1 and c_2 are constants, and b denotes a length which varies with x, and which describes the width of the mixing zone. It is easy to verify that this function constitutes a solution of the differential equation (23.50) if the momentum transfer length is assumed to be of the form

$$\Lambda(x) = \frac{b}{2}\frac{\mathrm{d}b}{\mathrm{d}x}\,.$$

The power laws for the width and the centre-line velocity can also be deduced from Reichardt's system of equations without the use of any of the hypotheses mentioned in Sec. XXIII a.

e. Heat transfer in free turbulent flow

The process of turbulent mixing causes a transfer of the properties of the fluid in a direction at right angles to the main stream. On the one hand the mixing motion causes *momentum* to flow away from the main stream, on the other hand, particles suspended in the fluid (floating particles of dust, chemical additives) are directed into the stream, and in addition there is a transfer of heat. The intensity of the transfer of a given property in turbulent motion is usually described by a suitable coefficient. Denoting the coefficient for momentum transfer by A_τ and that for heat by A_q, we can define them by writing

$$\tau = A_\tau \frac{\mathrm{d}u}{\mathrm{d}y}\,; \quad q = c_p\, g\, A_q \frac{\mathrm{d}T}{\mathrm{d}y}\,.$$

Here u and $c_p\, g\, T$ denote momentum and heat per unit mass, respectively, and τ and q denote the flux of momentum and heat (= quantity of heat per unit area and time) respectively. In this connexion u and T denote temporal means. Since the mechanisms for the transfer of momentum and heat are not identical the values of A_τ and A_q are, generally speaking, different. However, according to Prandtl's mixing length theory the mechanisms of the transfer of momentum and heat in free turbulent flows are identical which means that A_τ and A_q are assumed equal to each other. The measurement performed by A. Fage and V. M. Falkner [31] in the wake behind a row of heated bars have shown that the temperature profile is wider than the velocity profile and that, by way of approximation, we may assume $A_q = 2A_\tau$. This result agrees with G. I. Taylor's theory which was discussed in Chap. XVIII, and according to which turbulent mixing motion causes an exchange of vorticity rather than momentum. The problem of the transfer of heat in free turbulent flows was also considered by H. Reichardt [20], who made both theoretical and experimental contributions. The theoretical work is closely related to that described in the preceding section. First, empirical relations have been deduced for the temperature profile from experimental results in the same way as was done previously for the velocity (momentum) distribution, hypotheses on turbulent flow having been avoided. On the basis of an argument which we shall omit here, Reichardt succeeded in deriving a remarkable relation between the temperature and the velocity distribution. This is given by

$$\frac{T}{T_{max}} = \left(\frac{u}{u_{max}}\right)^{A_\tau/A_q} .$$

Here the subscript *max* refers to the maximum values and the scales for u and T must be so arranged as to render the points for which $u = 0$ and $T = 0$ coincident. Reichardt's experimental results for the two-dimensional jet (Fig. 23.10) and for the two-dimensional wake show good agreement with the law $T/T_{max} = (u/u_{max})^{1/2}$ which implies $A_q/A_\tau = 2$. Measurements on the temperature distribution in a heated circular turbulent jet have been performed by S. Corrsin and M. S. Uberoi [4], as well as by J. O. Hinze and B. G. van der Hegge Zijnen [11]. The temperature distribution behind a plane row of bars was also measured by R. Gran Olsson as was reported in a paper already quoted [10].

H. Reichardt [20a, b] made an extensive investigation into the transfer of heat across turbulent *boundary layers*; he obtained values of A_q/A_τ close to 1·3. In recent times, H. Ludwieg [13a] developed a very accurate method for the experi-

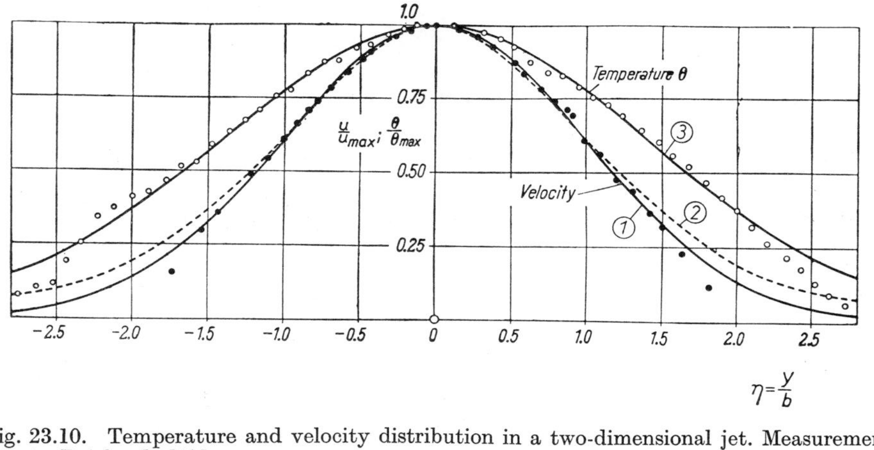

Fig. 23.10. Temperature and velocity distribution in a two-dimensional jet. Measurements are due to Reichardt [19]

Curve (1): $u/u_{max} = \exp(-\frac{1}{2}\eta^2)$; curve (2): $u/u_{max} = 1 - \tanh^2(\eta)$, eqn. (23.45); curve (3): $\theta/\theta_{max} = \exp(-\frac{1}{4}\eta^2) = (u/u_{max})^{1/2}$

mental determination of A_q/A_τ. The variation of this ratio across a turbulent stream in a pipe determined by this method yielded values from 1·5 (near the axis) to 1·1 (near the wall).

Natural convection, i. e. the transfer of heat in a stream created by thermal buoyancy, was investigated by W. Schmidt [23] who considered the following two cases: 1. two-dimensional flow above a linear source of heat placed on a horizontal floor and 2. axi-symmetrical flow above a point-source. In both cases the width of the velocity and temperature profile increases in direct proportion to the height above the floor, x. In the two-dimensional case the velocity remains constant at all heights, whereas the temperature decreases as x^{-1}. In the axially symmetrical case the velocity is proportional to $x^{-1/3}$, the temperature being proportional to $x^{-5/2}$. The two-dimensional case was treated theoretically on the basis of Prandtl's mixing length theory (transport of momentum) as well as on the basis of G. I. Taylor's vorticity transport theory. The axially symmetrical case could be investigated only with the aid of Prandtl's theory because G. I. Taylor's theory breaks down in this case. Measurements performed for the axi-symmetrical case confirm the theoretical calculations. The transfer of heat behind a point-source and behind a linear source placed in the boundary layer on a flat plate were investigated experimentally by K. Wieghardt [36]. In the case of the point-source it is found that the transfer of heat is much larger sideways than at right angles to the wall. The paper contains equations which allow us to transpose the experimental results to similar cases. In this connexion the paper by B. Frost [7] may also be consulted.

References

[1] E. Anderlik, Math. termeszett. Ertes **52**, 54 (1935).

[2] J. G. von Bohl, Das Verhalten paralleler Luftstrahlen. Ing.-Arch. **11**, 295—314 (1940).

[3] G. Cordes, Statische Druckmessung in turbulenter Strömung. Ing.-Arch. **8**, 245 (1937).

[4] S. Corrsin and M. S. Uberoi, Further experiments on the flow and heat transfer in a heated turbulent air jet. NACA TN 998 (1950).

[5] D. R. Davies, The problem of diffusion into a turbulent boundary layer from a plane area source, bounded by two straight perpendicular edges. Quart. Jour. Mech. Appl. Math. **VII**, 468—471 (1954).

[6] E. Förthmann, Über turbulente Strahlausbreitung. Ing.-Arch. **5**, 42 (1934); NACA TM 789 (1936).

[7] B. Frost, Turbulence and diffusion in the lower atmosphere. Proc. Roy. Soc. London, A **186**, 20 (1946).

[8] P. B. Gooderum, G. P. Wood and M. J. Brevoort, Investigation with an interferometer of the turbulent mixing of a free supersonic jet. NACA Rep. 963 (1950).

[9] H. Görtler, Berechnung von Aufgaben der freien Turbulenz auf Grund eines neuen Näherungsansatzes. ZAMM **22**, 244—254 (1942).

[10] R. Gran Olsson, Geschwindigkeits- und Temperaturverteilung hinter einem Gitter bei turbulenter Strömung. ZAMM **16**, 257—267 (1936).

[11] J. O. Hinze and B. G. van der Hegge Zijnen, Transfer of heat and matter in the turbulent mixing zone of an axially symmetric jet. Proc. 7th Intern. Congr. Appl. Mech. **2**, Part I, 286—299 (1948).

[12] L. Howarth, Concerning the velocity and temperature distributions in plane and axially symmetrical jets. Proc. Cambr. Phil. Soc. **34**, 185 (1938).

[13] A. M. Kuethe, Investigations of the turbulent mixing regions formed by jets. Jour. Appl. Mech. **2**, A 87—95 (1935).

[13a] H. Ludwieg, Bestimmung des Verhältnisses der Austauschkoeffizienten für Wärme und Impuls bei turbulenten Strömungen. Zeitschr. Flugwiss. **4**, 73—81 (1956).

[14] H. Muttray, Die experimentellen Tatsachen des Widerstandes ohne Auftrieb. Handb. d. Exper.-Physik **IV**, Part 2, 233 (1931).
[15] S. I. Pai, Fluid Dynamics of Jets. New York 1954.
[16] S. I. Pai, On turbulent jet mixing of two gases at constant temperature. Jour. Appl. Mech. **22**, 41—47 (1955).
[17] L. Prandtl, The mechanics of viscous fluids. In W. F. Durand, Aerodynamic Theory, **III**, 166 (1935); see also Proc. 2nd. Intern. Congr. of Appl. Mech. Zürich 1926.
[18] H. Reichardt, Über eine neue Theorie der freien Turbulenz. ZAMM **21**, 257 (1941).
[19] H. Reichardt, Gesetzmäßigkeiten der freien Turbulenz. VDI-Forschungsheft, 414 (1942), 2. ed. 1951.
[20] H. Reichardt, Impuls- und Wärmeaustausch in freier Turbulenz. ZAMM **24**, 268 (1944).
[20a] H. Reichardt, Der Wärmeübergang in turbulenten Grenzschichten. ZAMM **20**, 297—328 (1940).
[20b] H. Reichardt, Die Grundlagen des turbulenten Wärmeüberganges. Arch. f. Wärmetechn. 6/7, 129—142 (1951).
[21] P. Ruden, Turbulente Ausbreitung im Freistrahl. Naturwissenschaften **21**, 375—378 (1933).
[22] H. Schlichting, Über das ebene Windschattenproblem. Thesis Göttingen 1930. Ing. Arch. **1**, 533—571 (1930).
[23] W. Schmidt, Turbulente Ausbreitung eines Stromes erhitzter Luft. ZAMM **21**, 265 and 271 (1941).
[24] H. B. Squire and J. Trouncer, Round jets in a general stream. ARC R & M 1974 (1944).
[25] H. B. Squire, Reconsideration of the theory of free turbulence. Phil. Mag. **39**, 1—20 (1948).
[26] H. B. Squire, Jet flow and its effect on aircraft. Aircraft Engineering **22**, 62—67 (1950).
[27] L. M. Swain, On the turbulent wake behind a body of revolution. Proc. Roy. Soc. London, A **125**, 647 (1929).
[28] W. Szablewski, Zur Theorie der turbulenten Strömung von Gasen stark veränderlicher Dichte. Ing.-Arch. **20**, 67 (1952).
[29] W. Szablewski, Zeitliche Auflösung einer ebenen Trennungsfläche der Geschwindigkeit und Dichte. ZAMM **35**, 464—468 (1955).
[30] W. Szablewski, Turbulente Vermischung zweier ebener Luftstrahlen von fast gleicher Geschwindigkeit und stark unterschiedlicher Temperatur. Ing.-Arch. **20**, 73 (1952).
[31] G. I. Taylor, The transport of vorticity and heat through fluids in turbulent motion. Appendix by A. Fage and V. M. Falkner, Proc. Roy. Soc. London, A **135**, 685 (1932).
[32] W. Tollmien, Berechnung turbulenter Ausbreitungsvorgänge. ZAMM **6**, 468—478 (1926). NACA TM 1085 (1945).
[33] W. Tollmien, Die von Kármánsche Ähnlichkeitshypothese in der Turbulenz-Theorie und das ebene Windschattenproblem. Ing.-Arch. **4**, 1 (1933).
[34] A. A. Townsend, Momentum and energy diffusion in the turbulent wake of a cylinder. Proc. Roy. Soc. London, A **197**, 124—140 (1949).
[35] K. Viktorin, Untersuchungen turbulenter Mischvorgänge. Forschg. Ing.-Wes. **12**, 16 (1941); NACA TM 1096 (1946).
[36] K. Wieghardt, Über Ausbreitungsvorgänge in turbulenten Reibungsschichten. ZAMM **28**, 346 (1948).
[37] W. Wuest, Turbulente Mischvorgänge in zylindrischen und kegeligen Fangdüsen. Z. VDI. **92**, 1000 (1950).
[38] W. Zimm, Über die Strömungsvorgänge im freien Luftstrahl. VDI-Forschungsheft 234 (1921).
[39] Reports of the Aerodynamische Versuchsanstalt, Göttingen, 2nd. series 69 (1923).

CHAPTER XXIV

Determination of profile drag

a. General remarks

The total drag on a body placed in a stream of fluid consists of *skin friction* (equal to the integral of all shearing stresses taken over the surface of the body) and of *form* or *pressure drag* (integral of normal forces). The sum of the two is called *total* or *profile drag*. The skin friction can be calculated with some accuracy by the use of the methods of the preceding chapters. The form drag, which does not exist in frictionless flow, is due to the fact that the presence of the boundary layer modifies the pressure distribution on the body as compared with ideal flow, but its computation is very difficult. Consequently, reliable data on total drag must, in general, be obtained by measurement. In more modern times methods of estimating the amount of profile drag have, nevertheless, been established. We shall discuss them briefly at the end of the present chapter.

In many cases the determination of total drag by weighing lacks in accuracy because, when measurements are performed for example in a wind tunnel, the drag on the suspension wires is too large compared with the force to be measured. In some cases even, such as in free flight experiments, its direct determination becomes impossible. In such cases the method of determining profile drag from the velocity distribution in the wake (Pitot traverse method), which has already been described in Chap. IX, becomes very useful. Moreover, it is often the only practicable way of performing this kind of measurement. In principle it can only be used in two-dimensional and axially symmetrical cases, but we shall restrict ourselves to the consideration of the two-dimensional case.

The formula in eqn. (9.41) which was deduced in Chap. IX and which serves to determine the magnitude of drag from the velocity distribution in the wake is valid only for comparatively large distances from the body. According to it the total drag on a body† is given by the expression:

$$D = b\,\varrho \int\limits_{y=-\infty}^{+\infty} u\,(U_\infty - u)\,\mathrm{d}y\,. \tag{24.1}$$

Here b denotes the length of the cylindrical body in the direction of the axis of the cylinder, U_∞ is the free stream velocity and $u(y)$ denotes the velocity distribution in the wake. The integral must be taken at such a large distance from the body that

† In Chap. IX the total drag on a body was denoted by $2\,D$ (for the two sides of the plate); in this chapter the symbol D is used for it.

the static pressure at the measuring section becomes equal to that in the undisturbed stream. In practical cases, whether in a wind tunnel or in free flight measurements, it is necessary to come much closer to the body. Consequently it becomes necessary to take into account the contribution from the pressure term and eqn. (24.1) must be modified. This correction term has an appreciable value when measurements are performed close to the body (e. g. at distances less than one chord in the case of aerofoils) and it is, therefore, important to have a comparatively accurate expression for it. The correction term was first calculated by A. Betz [2] and later by B. M. Jones [16]. At present most measurements are being evaluated with the aid of the formula due to Jones because of its comparative simplicity. Nevertheless, we propose to discuss Betz's formula as well because its derivation exhibits several very interesting features.

b. The experimental method due to Betz

With reference to Fig. 24.1 we select a control surface around the body as shown. In the entry cross-section I in front of the body the flow is lossless, its total pressure being g_∞. The total pressure in cross-section II behind the body is $g_2 < g_\infty$. The remaining cross-sections of the control surface are imagined placed far enough from the body for the flow in them to be undisturbed. In order to satisfy the condition of continuity, the velocity u_2 in cross-section II must in some places exceed the undisturbed velocity U_∞. Applying the momentum theorem to the control surface gives the following expression for the drag on a cylinder of length b:

$$D = b\{\int_{y=-\infty}^{+\infty} (p_1 + \varrho u_1^2)\,\mathrm{d}y - \int_{-\infty}^{+\infty} (p_2 + \varrho u_2^2)\,\mathrm{d}y\}. \tag{24.2}$$

In order to adapt this equation to the evaluation of experimental results it is necessary to transform the above integrals so that they need only be evaluated over that section of the velocity curve which includes the depression in the profile. The total pressures satisfy the conditions:

$$\left.\begin{aligned} &\text{at infinity:} && g_\infty = p_\infty + \frac{1}{2}\varrho U_\infty^2 \\ &\text{at cross-section I:} && g_\infty = p_1 + \frac{1}{2}\varrho u_1^2 \\ &\text{at cross-section II:} && g_2 = p_2 + \frac{1}{2}\varrho u_2^2 . \end{aligned}\right\} \tag{24.3}$$

Thus eqn. (24.2) becomes

$$D = b\left\{\int_{-\infty}^{+\infty} (g_\infty - g_2)\,\mathrm{d}y + \frac{1}{2}\varrho\int_{-\infty}^{+\infty} (u_1^2 - u_2^2)\,\mathrm{d}y\right\}. \tag{24.4}$$

The first integral already has the desired form, because the total pressure is equal to g_∞ everywhere outside the depression. In order to transform the second integral in the same way we introduce a hypothetical flow $u_2'(y)$ in cross-section II which is identical with u_2 everywhere outside the depression but which differs from u_2 in the region of the depression in that the total pressure for u_2' is equal to g_∞. Thus

$$g_\infty = p_2 + \frac{1}{2}\varrho u_2'^2 . \tag{24.5}$$

Since the actual flow u_1, u_2 satisfies the equations of continuity, the mass flow of the hypothetical flow u_1, u_2' is too large across section II. This is equivalent to the existence of a source which is located, essentially, at the body and whose strength is

$$Q = b \int (u_2' - u_2)\, dy . \tag{24.6}$$

A source which exists in a frictionless parallel stream of velocity U_∞ suffers a thrust equal to

$$R = -\varrho U_\infty Q . \tag{24.7}$$

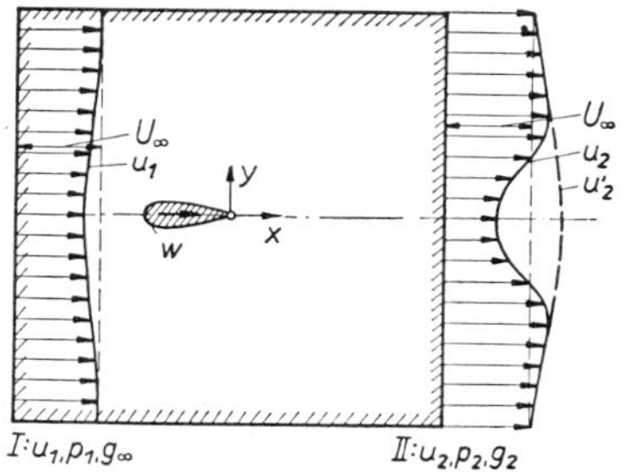

Fig. 24.1. Determination of profile drag by the method due to Betz [2]

We now apply the momentum theorem from eqn. (24.4) to the hypothetical flow, i. e. we assume a velocity u_1 in section I, and a velocity u_2' in section II. Since $g_2' = g_\infty$ and since the resultant force is equal to R from eqn. (24.7), we obtain

$$-\varrho U_\infty Q = b \frac{1}{2} \varrho \int (u_1^2 - u_2'^2)\, dy .$$

Subtracting this value from eqn. (24.4) we have

$$D + \varrho U_\infty Q = b \left\{ \int (g_\infty - g_2)\, dy + \frac{1}{2} \varrho \int (u_2'^2 - u_2^2)\, dy \right\} . \tag{24.8}$$

In view of eqn. (24.6) we have now

$$D = b \left\{ \int (g_\infty - g_2)\, dy + \frac{1}{2} \varrho \int (u_2'^2 - u_2^2)\, dy - \varrho U_\infty \int (u_2' - u_2)\, dy \right\} .$$

Each of the above integrals need only be evaluated over the wake since outside it $u_2' = u_2$. Since $u_2'^2 - u_2^2 = (u_2' - u_2)(u_2' + u_2)$, the above can be transformed to

$$D = b \left\{ \int (g_\infty - g_2)\, dy + \frac{1}{2} \varrho \int (u_2' - u_2)(u_2' + u_2 - 2 U_\infty)\, dy \right\} . \tag{24.9}$$

In order to determine the drag, D, it is necessary to measure the total pressure, g_2, and the static pressure, p_2, over the cross-section II behind the body. Thus we also obtain g_∞ as it is equal to g_2 outside the depression. The hypothetical velocity u_2' is defined in eqn. (24.5) from which it can be calculated.

In cases when the static pressure over the measuring station equals that in the undisturbed stream, i. e. when $p_2 = p_\infty$, we also have $u_2' = U_\infty$ and eqn. (24.9) transforms back into eqn. (24.1).

Defining a dimensionless coefficient of drag by writing

$$D = c_w \, b \, l \, q_\infty, \tag{24.9a}$$

where $q_\infty = \frac{1}{2} \varrho \, U^2{}_\infty$ denotes the dynamic pressure and $b \times l$ is the reference area, we can rewrite eqn. (24.9) to read:

$$c_D = \int \frac{g_\infty - g_2}{q_\infty} \, \mathrm{d}\left(\frac{y}{l}\right) + \\ + \int \left(\sqrt{\frac{g_\infty - p_2}{q_\infty}} - \sqrt{\frac{g_2 - p_2}{q_\infty}} \right) \left(\sqrt{\frac{g_\infty - p_2}{q_\infty}} + \sqrt{\frac{g_2 - p_2}{q_\infty}} - 2 \right) \mathrm{d}\left(\frac{y}{l}\right). \tag{24.10}$$

This is the most convenient form for the evaluation of experimental results.

c. The experimental method due to Jones

Some time later, B. M. Jones [16] indicated a similar method for the determination of profile drag. The final formula due to Jones is somewhat simpler than that due to A. Betz.

The cross-section II (Fig. 24.2) in which measurements are performed is located behind the body at a short distance from it; the static pressure p_2 at the measuring station is still markedly different from the static pressure in the undisturbed stream. Cross-section I is placed so far behind the body that $p_1 = p_\infty$. Applying eqn. (24.1) to cross-section I, we obtain

$$D = b \, \varrho \int u_1 \, (U_\infty - u_1) \, \mathrm{d}y_1 \, . \tag{24.11}$$

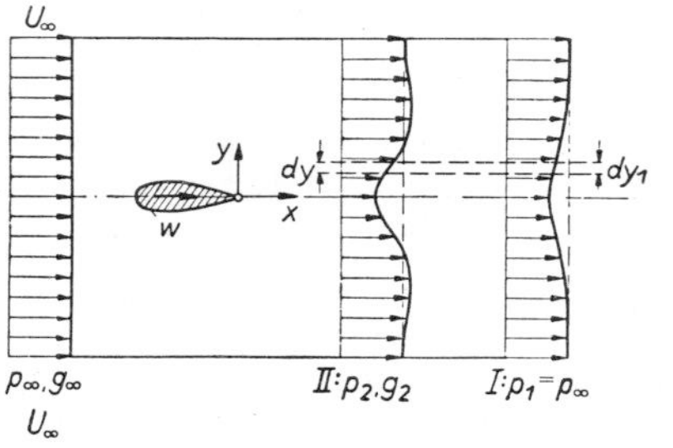

Fig. 24.2. Determination of profile drag by the method due to B. M. Jones [16]

In order to confine the determination of u_1 to the use of results obtained from measurements in cross-section II, we first apply the equation of continuity along a stream-tube

$$\varrho \, u_1 \, \mathrm{d}y_1 = \varrho \, u_2 \, \mathrm{d}y \, . \tag{24.12}$$

Hence

$$D = b \, \varrho \int u_2 \, (U_\infty - u_1) \, \mathrm{d}y \, . \tag{24.13}$$

Secondly, according to Jones, we make the assumption that the flow proceeds from section II to section I without losses, i. e. that the total pressure remains constant along every stream-line between the stations I and II:

$$g_2 = g_1 \, . \tag{24.14}$$

Introducing the total pressures

$$p_\infty + \frac{1}{2} \varrho \, U_\infty{}^2 = g_\infty \, ; \quad p_\infty + \frac{1}{2} \varrho \, u_1{}^2 = g_1 = g_2 ; \quad p_2 + \frac{1}{2} \varrho \, u_2{}^2 = g_2 \, ,$$

we see from eqn. (24.13) that

$$D = 2b \int \sqrt{g_2 - p_2} \left(\sqrt{g_\infty - p_\infty} - \sqrt{g_2 - p_\infty} \right) \mathrm{d}y \,, \tag{24.15}$$

where the integral extends over cross-section II. In this case, as in the previous one, the integrand differs from zero only across the disturbed portion of the velocity profile. Introducing a dimensionless coefficient, in the same way as in eqn. (24.9a), and taking into account that $g_\infty - p_\infty = q_\infty$, we have

$$\boxed{c_D = 2 \int \sqrt{\frac{g_2 - p_2}{q_\infty}} \left(1 - \sqrt{\frac{g_2 - p_\infty}{q_\infty}} \right) \mathrm{d}\left(\frac{y}{l}\right)} \,. \tag{24.16}$$

Jones' preceding equation also transforms into the simple equation (24.1) in cases when the static pressure at the measuring station is equal to the undisturbed static pressure, $p_2 = p_\infty$.

A. D. Young [44] indicated a transformation of Jones' formula which simplifies the evaluation of the integral in eqn. (24.16). The resulting equation contains an additive correction term apart from the integral of the total pressure loss taken over the depression in the velocity profile. The correction term depends on the shape of the velocity profile in the measuring station, but it can be computed once and for all.

The preceding two experimental methods have been used very frequently for the determination of profile drag both in flight and in wind tunnel measurements, [3, 8, 11, 18, 21, 22, 32, 33, 38, 39], and have led to very satisfactory results. H. Doetsch [3] demonstrated that both the Betz and the Jones formulae can be used when the distance between the measuring station behind the aerofoil and the aerofoil itself is as short as 5 per cent. chord. In this case the correction term in Betz's formula amounts to about 30 per cent. of the first term. Both methods are particularly suitable when the influence of surface roughnesses on profile drag is being determined as well as to the determination of the very small drag of laminar aerofoils. Some critical remarks on this method are contained in a note written by G. I. Taylor [36].

A. D. Young [40] extended the applicability of Jones' method to compressible flows. Retracing the steps in that derivation, we apply the continuity equation for compressible flow,

$$\varrho_1 u_1 \, \mathrm{d}y_1 = \varrho_2 u_2 \, \mathrm{d}y_2 \,, \tag{24.17}$$

and deduce the following formula for drag:

$$D = b \int_{-\infty}^{+\infty} \varrho_2 u_2 (U_\infty - u_1) \, \mathrm{d}y_2 \,. \tag{24.18}$$

Here, again, it is necessary to express u_1 in terms of the quantities measured in plane II. In the realm of compressible flow it is necessary to replace Jones' assumption that $g_1 = g_2$ by the assumption that the entropy remains constant along a streamline from plane II to plane I. This leads to the isentropic relation

$$\frac{p_2}{\varrho_2^{\gamma}} = \frac{p_1}{\varrho_1^{\gamma}} \,. \tag{24.19}$$

If, now, the stagnation pressure measured by the Pitot tube in compressible flow is denoted by g, we have

$$g = p_0 = \frac{\varrho_0}{\varrho}\left(\frac{\gamma-1}{2}\frac{\varrho}{2}w^2 + p\right), \tag{24.20}$$

and it can be verified that eqn. (24.19) also leads to the assumption $g_1 = g_2$. The velocity u_1 can be determined from the Bernoulli equation for compressible flow, namely

$$u_1{}^2 = \frac{2\gamma}{\gamma-1}\frac{p_1}{\varrho_1}\left[\left(\frac{g_2}{p_1}\right)^{\frac{\gamma-1}{\gamma}} - 1\right]. \tag{24.21}$$

In order to solve the problem in principle, it is only necessary to express the velocity u_2 in terms of the measured pressures g_2 and p_2 in plane II. A measurement of the total and static pressures in plane II is again sufficient for the determination of the drag of the body. However, the complicated relation between velocities and pressures in the compressible Bernoulli equation leads to a very cumbersome equation. For this reason, A. D. Young expanded the velocities u_1 and u_2 into series of the form

$$u^2 = \frac{2\gamma}{\gamma-1}\frac{p}{\varrho}\left[\frac{\gamma-1}{\gamma}\frac{g-p}{p} - \frac{\gamma-1}{2\gamma^2}\left(\frac{g-p}{p}\right)^2 + \cdots\right]. \tag{24.22}$$

In this manner, the terms in eqn. (24.15) derived by Jones for the incompressible case can now be separated, and the remaining terms can be arranged in a power series in terms of the Mach number. Thus

$$c_D = c_{D,i} + A_1 \mathsf{M}_\infty^2 + A_2 \mathsf{M}_\infty^4 + \cdots, \tag{24.23}$$

where $c_{D,i}$ denotes the drag coefficient for the incompressible case, as given by eqn. (24.16), and the coefficients $A_1, A_2, \ldots$ represent certain integrals which can be calculated from the measured data in plane II. Restricting oneself to low Mach numbers, and hence to two terms in the expansion (24.23), one obtains

$$c_D = 2\int\limits_{y=-\infty}^{+\infty}\sqrt{\frac{g_2-p_2}{q_\infty}}\left(1-\frac{g_2-p_\infty}{q_\infty}\right)\left\{1+\frac{\mathsf{M}_\infty^2}{8}\left[3\frac{p_2-p_\infty}{q_\infty}+3-\right.\right.$$
$$\left.\left.-2\gamma-2\frac{g_2-p_\infty}{q_\infty}-(2\gamma-1)\sqrt{\frac{g_2-p_\infty}{q_\infty}}\right]\right\}\mathrm{d}\left(\frac{y}{l}\right). \tag{24.24}$$

where

$$q_\infty = g_\infty - p_\infty.$$

The additional term which depends on the Mach number provides a negative contribution to the drag coefficient. It is possible to evaluate this additional term once and for all if a suitable assumption is made for the shape of the depression in the velocity profile in the wake; this was also done by A. D. Young.

d. Calculation of profile drag

Methods which can be used for the calculation of profile drag, and which are based on the same principles as the above experimental methods, have been devised by J. Pretsch [23] and H. B. Squire and A. D. Young [35]. These are tied in with the calculation of boundary layers, as described in Chap. XXII. However, in order to be in a position to calculate pressure drag it is necessary in each case to make use of certain additional empirical relations.

We now propose to give a short description of H. B. Squire's and A. D. Young's method of calculation taking into account some more recent results. We shall begin by transforming eqn. (24.1), which relates the drag on a body with the velocity profile in the wake behind the body. Introducing the momentum thickness θ_∞ from eqn. (8.34) and the drag coefficient from eqn. (24.9a), we can rewrite it as

$$c_D = 2\,\frac{\theta_\infty}{l}\,. \tag{24.25}$$

Here

$$\theta_\infty = \int\limits_{y=-\infty}^{\infty} \frac{u}{U_\infty}\left(1 - \frac{u}{U_\infty}\right) \mathrm{d}y$$

denotes the momentum thickness of the wake at a large distance from the body. On the other hand, the calculation described in Chap. XXII permits us to evaluate the momentum thickness at the trailing edge, for which the symbol θ_1 will be used. The essence of Squire's method consists in relating these two quantities, θ_∞ and θ_1, in such a way as to permit the calculation of drag from eqn. (24.25).

The momentum integral equation of boundary layer theory, eqn. (22.6), is valid also for the wake behind a body with the only difference that the shearing stress τ_0 must be equated to zero. Thus we have

$$\frac{\mathrm{d}\theta}{\mathrm{d}x} + (H+2)\,\theta\,\frac{U'}{U} = 0, \tag{24.26}$$

where $H = \delta^*/\theta$ and $U' = dU/dx$. The symbol x denotes now the distance from the trailing edge of the body measured along the centre-line of the wake. The last equation can also be written in the form

$$\frac{1}{\theta}\,\frac{\mathrm{d}\theta}{\mathrm{d}x} = -(H+2)\,\frac{\mathrm{d}}{\mathrm{d}x}\left(\ln\frac{U}{U_\infty}\right).$$

Integrating over x from the trailing edge of the body (subscript 1) to a station sufficiently far downstream, so as to have $U = U_\infty$ and $p = p_\infty$, we obtain

$$\Big[\ln\theta\Big]_\infty^1 = -\left[(H+2)\ln\frac{U}{U_\infty}\right]_\infty^1 + \int\limits_\infty^1 \ln\frac{U}{U_\infty}\,\frac{\mathrm{d}H}{\mathrm{d}x}\,\mathrm{d}x\,.$$

At a large distance behind the body we have $H = 1$, and consequently

$$\ln\frac{\theta_1}{\theta_\infty} + (H_1+2)\ln\frac{U_1}{U_\infty} = \int\limits_{H=1}^{H=H_1} \ln\frac{U}{U_\infty}\,\mathrm{d}H\,.$$

Here $H_1 = \delta^*{}_1/\theta_1$ denotes the value of the shape factor $H = \delta^*/\theta$ at the trailing edge which is known from the calculation of the boundary layer. This equation gives the required relation between θ_∞ and θ_1, provided that U_1/U_∞ and the value of the integral on the right-hand side are known. First we find that

$$\theta_\infty = \theta_1 \left(\frac{U_1}{U_\infty}\right)^{H_1+2} \exp\left(\int_1^{H_1} \ln \frac{U_\infty}{U}\, \mathrm{d}H\right) . \tag{24.27}$$

In order to be in a position to evaluate the integral, it is necessary to know the relation between the static pressure in the wake, which determines the value of U, and the velocity distribution in the wake which, in turn, determines the value of the shape factor H. The magnitude of $\ln (U_\infty/U)$ decreases monotonically along the wake, starting with the value $\ln (U_\infty/U_1)$ at the trailing edge until it reaches zero at a large distance. Simultaneously H decreases from the value H_1 at the trailing edge, until it reaches unity at a large distance. H. B. Squire established an empirical relation between $\ln (U_\infty/U)$ and H. According to experiment:

$$\frac{\ln (U_\infty/U)}{H-1} = \frac{\ln (U_\infty/U_1)}{H_1-1} = \text{const} ,$$

so that

$$\int_1^{H_1} \ln \frac{U_\infty}{U}\, \mathrm{d}H = \frac{H_1-1}{2} \ln \frac{U_\infty}{U_1} .$$

On substituting into eqn. (24.27), we obtain

$$\theta_\infty = \theta_1 \left(\frac{U_1}{U_\infty}\right)^{(H_1+5)/2} ,$$

or, with the rounded-off value of $H_1 = 1{\cdot}4$:

$$\theta_\infty = \theta_1 \left(\frac{U_1}{U_\infty}\right)^{3\cdot 2} .$$

On substituting this value into eqn. (24.25) we obtain an expression for the coefficient of total drag in the form

$$\boxed{c_D = 2\, \frac{\theta_1}{l} \left(\frac{U_1}{U_\infty}\right)^{3\cdot 2}} . \tag{24.28}$$

The coefficient of profile drag can be evaluated from the above equation, if the momentum thickness at the trailing edge is known from the boundary layer calculation and if, in addition, the ideal, potential velocity at the trailing edge, U_1, is known. The latter can be found, for example, from a reading of the static pressure at the trailing edge. According to a method proposed by H. B. Helmbold [14] the determination of U_1/U_∞ can also proceed as follows: We begin by evaluating the momentum thickness at the trailing edge, θ_1/l, from eqn. (22.20) using the value $n = 4$. This value is then substituted into eqn. (24.28), and in the resulting formula U_1/U_∞ is raised to the power $+\ 0{\cdot}2$. Thus this factor can be approximated by the value of unity, because U_1/U_∞ itself does not differ much from unity, and the value of the coefficient of profile drag for one side ($\mathsf{R} = U_\infty l/\nu$) can be found from eqn. (24.28) to be

$$c_D = \frac{0{\cdot}074}{\mathsf{R}^{1/5}} \left\{ \int\limits_{x_u/l}^{1} \left(\frac{U}{U_\infty}\right)^{3\cdot5} \mathrm{d}\left(\frac{x}{l}\right) + C \right\}^{0\cdot8} \qquad (24.29)\dagger$$

with

$$C = 62{\cdot}5\ \mathsf{R}^{1/4} \left(\frac{\theta_t}{l}\right)^{5/4} \left(\frac{U_t}{U_\infty}\right)^{3\cdot75}. \qquad (24.30)$$

The subscript t refers to the point of transition and the value of the constant C can be determined from the condition that the laminar and turbulent momentum thicknesses must be equal to each other at the point of transition, $\theta_t = \theta_{t\,turb} = \theta_{t\,lam}$ (*cf.* eqn. (22.33) on p. 580). The value of $\theta_{t\,lam}$ can be found from eqn. (12.37). For uniform potential flow with $U = U_\infty$, eqn. (24.29) transforms to the corresponding expression for the flat plate at zero incidence, eqn. (21.11), if, in addition, we put $C = 0$ for fully developed turbulent flow.

E. Truckenbrodt [37] transformed eqn. (24.29) replacing the potential velocity distribution by the co-ordinates of the aerofoil section thus, evidently, effecting a considerable simplification.

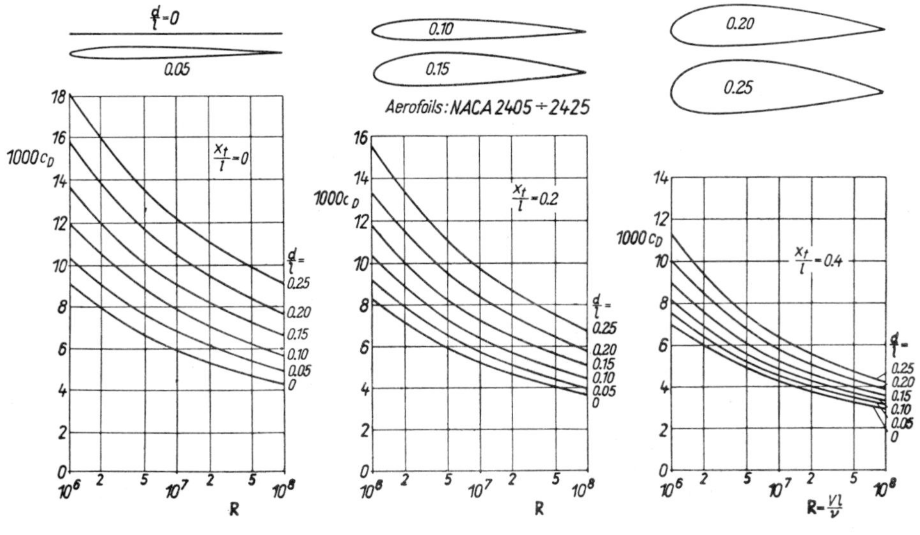

Fig. 24.3. Profile drag in terms of Reynolds number as evaluated by Squire and Young [35] x_t denotes the position of the point of transition

† L. Speidel [34] tested the validity of this simple equation against a very large number of actual examples.

H. B. Squire and A. D. Young [35] evaluated a number of examples by the use of a different method. We shall now describe some of them, referring to Fig. 24.3, which contains a *resumé* of these results. The thickness of the aerofoils was varied from $d/l = 0$ (flat plate) to $d/l = 0{\cdot}25$ and the Reynolds numbers $\mathsf{R} = U_\infty l/\nu$ ranged from 10^6 to 10^8. It is found that the profile drag is very sensitive to the position of the point of transition from laminar to turbulent flow. This latter parameter was varied from $x_t/l = 0$ to $0{\cdot}4$. The increase in profile drag with thickness is, essentially, due to an increase in form drag. Fig. 24.4 shows the relation between

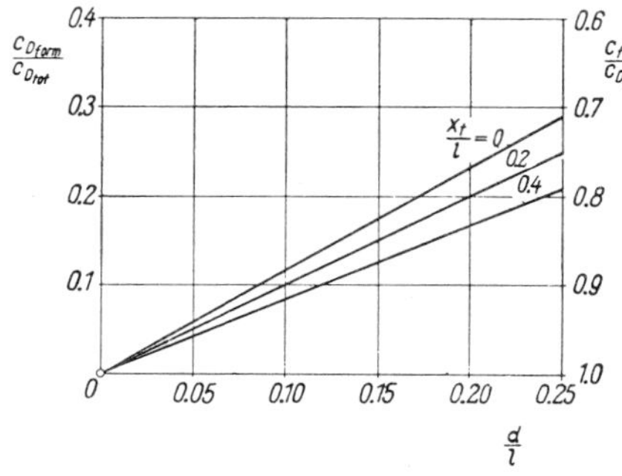

Fig. 24.4. Relation between pressure drag $c_{D\,form}$, and skin friction, c_f, at varying thickness ratios

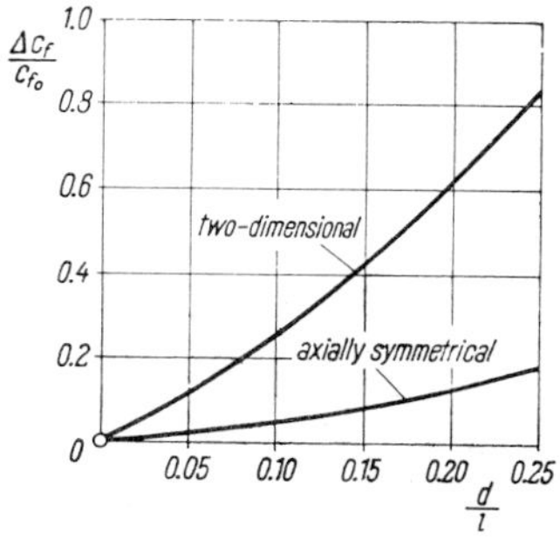

Fig. 24.5. Increase in the coefficient of profile drag plotted in terms of relative thickness, as calculated by Scholz [29]

Total or profile drag $c_{D\,tot} = c_{D\,form} + c_f$

form and profile drag. Analogous calculations were performed by J. Pretsch [23] in relation to von Kármán-Trefftz aerofoils. The measure of agreement between calculation and experiment depends decisively on the assumed position of the point of transition. It will be recalled from Chap. XVII that the position of the point of transition is largely dependent on the pressure gradient of the respective potential flow. It was pointed out there, Fig. 17.6, that as a first approximation it is possible to assume that the point of transition coincides with the point of minimum pressure provided that the Reynolds number is large, say $\mathsf{R} \approx 10^7$. Numerical values obtained on the basis of this assumption show satisfactory agreement with measured values.

The preceding method was first generalized to include axially symmetrical cases by A. D. Young [41]. The method proposed by N. Scholz [29] has been considerably developed and can be, both for two-dimensional and for axially symmetrical cases, applied to rough walls (equivalent sand roughness) as well. From a very large number of calculated examples on aerofoils (two-dimensional case) and bodies of revolution, it proved possible to deduce relations to describe the influence of thickness on profile drag. These are shown plotted in Fig. 24.5. The difference $\Delta c_f = c_f - c_{f0}$ denotes the increase in the coefficient of profile drag, related to the wetted surface, as against its value for a flat plate at zero incidence,

c_{f0}. The curve for the two-dimensional case agrees fairly well with the results shown plotted in Fig. 24.3 for the case of a fully turbulent boundary layer ($x_t/l = 0$). In this connexion the paper by P. S. Granville [13] may also be consulted.

These calculations give an indication about the effect of friction on lift. The displacement of the external stream-lines caused by the boundary layer modifies the pressure distribution on an aerofoil and causes the experimental value to become lower than that given by potential theory. This loss of lift was calculated by K. Kraemer [19] for the range of angles of incidence below the stalling angle.

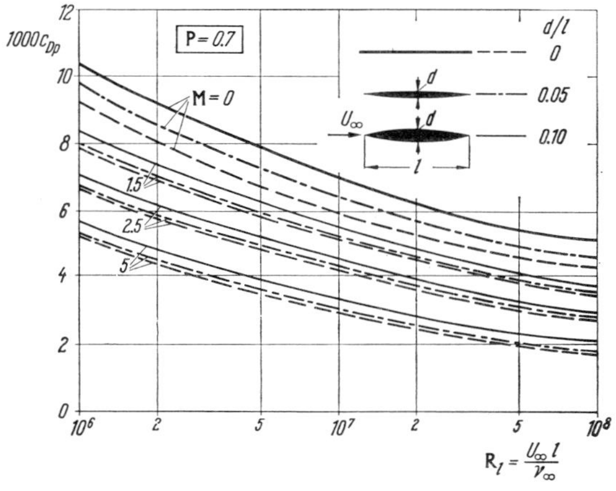

Fig. 24.6. Drag coefficients for biconvex profiles in supersonic flow and with fully developed turbulent boundary layer, after A. D. Young and S. Kirkby [45]; no heat transfer
Prandtl number $P = 0{\cdot}7$. The drag coefficient must be augmented by the contribution from wave drag, eqn. (24.31)

The preceding method of evaluating total drag by the application of the momentum equation was extended by A. D. Young and S. Kirkby [45] to the case of supersonic flow. Some results of their calculations for biconvex profiles of varying thickness ratio and at zero incidence are shown plotted in Fig. 24.6. The drag coefficient c_{Dp} includes pressure drag and skin friction and must be augmented by the contribution of the wave drag which exists in supersonic, ideal flow. For biconvex profiles, according to the linearized theory, the latter is given by

$$C_{D\,wave} = \frac{16}{3}\left(\frac{d}{l}\right)^2 \frac{1}{(\mathsf{M}^2 - 1)^{1/2}} \,. \qquad (24.31)$$

According to the results shown in Fig. 24.6, the influence of the thickness of the aerofoil on drag is very small, particularly in the supersonic range. The influence of the Mach number is approximately of the same order as in the case of a flat plate at zero incidence.

e. Losses in the flow through cascades

The method for the numerical calculations of the total drag of a single aerofoil which was explained in the preceding section has been extended by H. Schlichting and N. Scholz [25] to include the case of a row or cascade of aerofoils and can, therefore, be applied to the flow through blades. When discussing axial turbine or turbo-compressor stages, it is customary to simplify the problem by taking a co-axial cylindrical section through the stationary and moving row of blades and to develop the resulting pattern on to a plane. The pattern of aerofoils thus obtained is known as a *two-dimensional cascade*. The arrangement of blades in a cascade is usually described by specifying the *solidity ratio* t/l and the *mean blade angle* or *angle of stagger*, β_m, Fig. 24.7. In contrast to the case of flow past a single aerofoil, the application of potential theory to the case of flow past a cascade leads to the conclusion that, generally speaking, there exists a difference in the pressure in front of and behind the cascade. The pressure decreases downstream, when the cascade transforms pressure into velocity (turbine blading). When the cascade performs the reverse (compressor blading), the pressure increases in the direction of flow. The existence of a positive or negative pressure gradient across the cascade has a large effect on the formation of the boundary layer. The pressure distribution and the boundary layer are seen sketched in Fig. 24.7 for the two cases of turbine and compressor blading respectively. The shape of the blade (infinitely thin aerofoil), the pitch of the cascade, and the ratio of the velocities in front of and behind the cascade (for frictionless flow) have been made equal in both cases so that the compressor cascade is obtained from the turbine cascade by simply reversing the direction of flow. The angle of inflow, β_1, is in both cases the *ideal angle of incidence* so

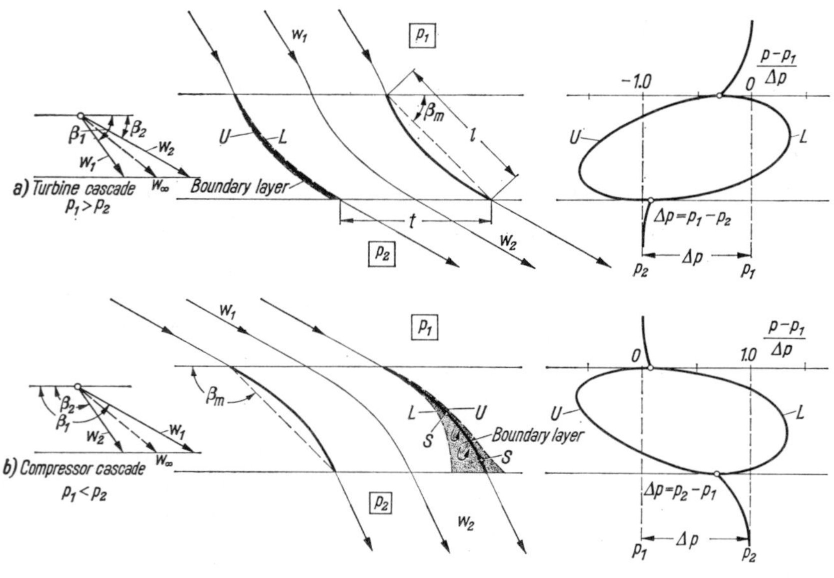

Fig. 24.7. Pressure distribution and shape of boundary layer on a blade (a) in a turbine cascade (accelerated flow), and (b) in a compressor cascade (decelerated flow) after Schlichting and Scholz [25]

Solidity ratio $t/l = 1{\cdot}0$. For turbine cascade: $\beta_m = 45°$, $\beta_1 = 60°$, $\beta_2 = 35°$, $w_2/w_1 = 1{\cdot}51$. For compressor cascade: $\beta_m = 135°$, $\beta_1 = 145°$, $\beta_2 = 120°$, $w_2/w_1 = 0{\cdot}66$. U = upper side L = lower side. Reynolds number $\mathsf{R} = w_\infty l/\nu = 10^6$. Owing to large acceleration, the boundary layer on the *turbine cascade* is very thin; there is no separation. The large deceleration along the *compressor cascade* gives rise to thick boundary layers with separation on both sides (S = point of separation); consequently losses are much larger

that there is no flow around the leading edge of the blade. The loading on the blade is described by specifying the lift coefficient $c_L = L/\frac{1}{2}\,\varrho\, w_\infty^2\, l = 0{\cdot}86$. The symbol w_∞ denotes here the vectorial mean between the velocity of inflow, w_1, and the outflow velocity, w_2. It is seen from the pressure plot that in the case of turbine blading, Fig. 24.7a, the pressure generally decreases on both sides of the blade, whereas in the case of compressor blading, Fig. 24.7b, there is a general increase in pressure. When calculating the boundary layer it has been assumed that the point of transition coincides with the point of minimum pressure, and that the Reynolds number $\mathsf{R} = w_\infty\, l/\nu = 10^6$.

a)

b)

Fig. 24.8. Photographs of flow patterns about cascades made with the aid of interferometer, after Eckert; a) Turbine cascade; b) Compressor cascade

a) Turbine cascade (decreasing pressure): $\beta_1 = 48°$; $t/l = 0{\cdot}524$; $\mathsf{R} = 1{\cdot}59 \times 10^5$. b) Compressor cascade (increasing pressure): $\beta_1 = 20°$; $t/l = 0{\cdot}614$; $\mathsf{R} = 1{\cdot}97 \times 10^5$. The edge of the boundary layer corresponds to kinks in fringes. a) At the turbine blade there is no separation on lower side near trailing edge. b) At the compressor blade there is very strong separation on upper side right at leading edge. Arrows denote direction of approaching wind

The boundary layer thickness at the turbine blading remains very small over the whole length owing to the fact that a decrease in pressure predominates; there is also no separation. However, along the compressor blades the strong pressure rise causes a rapid increase in the boundary layer thickness in the direction of flow. Separation occurs on both sides of the blade and the separated boundary layers cause considerable blockage of the passage near the trailing edge. Consequently, the drag on a compressor blade (loss of momentum) is considerably larger than on a turbine blade. This fundamental difference in the behaviour of turbine and compressor stages has long been known to designers of turbomachinery. Reference [25] contains the description of a method of calculating losses in a two-dimensional cascade in terms of its geometrical parameters (shape of blade, pitch) and varying angles of approach. The method is based on that discussed in Sec. XXIVd. The paper by N. Scholz and L. Speidel [31] contains a systematic scheme for the performance of such calculations as well as comparisons with experimental results. The reader may wish to consult two review papers by H. Schlichting [28a] on this subject.

The difference in the behaviour of the boundary layer in turbine as against compressor cascades is confirmed by the photographs of flow patterns shown in

Fig. 24.8. The patterns were obtained with the aid of an interferometer, so that shifts in the fringes are a measure of the change in density with respect to that in the undisturbed stream. The outer edge of the boundary layer corresponds to the kinks which are visible in the photographs. The internal friction in the boundary layer generates temperature differences which give rise to differences in density. Separation can be recognized because it manifests itself as a large thickening of the boundary layer. In the case of the turbine blade shown in Fig. 24.8a it is seen that there is no separation at all on the lower side (concave in the figure), whereas on the upper (convex) side there is some separation near the trailing edge as indicated by the broken line in the photograph. On the other hand, the flow past the compressor blading in Fig. 24.8b shows strong separation on the lower (concave) side already near the leading edge. Separation gives rise to a stagnant region which fills about half the passage.

The velocity distribution immediately behind the exit plane of the cascade shows strong depressions which stem from the boundary layers of the individual blades. Turbulent mixing causes these velocity differences to smooth out further downstream, thus giving rise to an additional loss of energy. The amount of *loss due to mixing* can be evaluated with the aid of the momentum theorem. When determining the total loss in the flow through cascades, it is necessary to take this mixing loss into account in addition to the loss of energy in the boundary layers of the individual blades. Thus a calculation of losses in a cascade consists of the following three partial calculations: 1. Determination of the ideal, potential pressure distribution around the contour of the blades. 2. Calculations of the (laminar or turbulent) boundary layer at a blade. 3. Determination of the losses due to mixing in the wake behind the cascade.

The total amount of losses associated with a cascade is best specified by indicating the difference Δg in the total pressures between the undisturbed flow in front of the cascade and the "smoothed out" actual flow far behind it. Thus

$$\Delta g = g_1 - g_2' = p_1 + \tfrac{1}{2}\,\varrho\, w_1^2 - (p_2' + \tfrac{1}{2}\,\varrho\, w_2'^2)\,, \tag{24.32}$$

where p_2' and w_2' denote the pressure and velocity in the real (i. e. affected by losses) flow far behind the cascade, respectively. These should be distinguished from the values p_2 and w_2, respectively, which refer to ideal (lossless) flow. It is convenient to render the total loss Δg dimensionless with reference to the dynamic head formed with the axial velocity component $w_{ax} = w_1 \sin\beta_1 = w_2 \sin\beta_2$, as it determines the mass of fluid which passes through the cascade. For reasons of continuity its value must be the same in front of as behind the cascade. We then introduce the following coefficient:

$$\zeta_t = \frac{\Delta g}{\tfrac{1}{2}\,\varrho\, w_{ax}^2}\,. \tag{24.33}$$ †

Some results of the systematic investigations on cascades, carried out at the Brunswick Engineering University [26, 27, 30, 31, 34], are shown in Fig. 24.9.

† In the design of steam turbines it is usual to employ a *velocity coefficient*, ψ, which is defined as the ratio of the real exit velocity to its value in ideal flow, so that $\psi = w'_2/w_2$. Consequently the two coefficients satisfy the relation $\zeta_t = (1 - \psi^2)/\sin^2\beta_2$.

These represent a comparison between measured and calculated values of the loss coefficient. All blades were derived from the symmetrical NACA 0010 aerofoil. The variable parameters included the solidity ratio t/l ($= 0{\cdot}5$, $0{\cdot}75$ and $1{\cdot}0$) and the mean blade angle β_m ($= 90°$, corresponding to unstaggered blades, $120°$ and $150°$). The loss coefficient defined in eqn. (24.33) is seen plotted in terms of the deflexion coefficient or deflexion ratio

$$\delta_d = \Delta w_d / w_{ax} ,$$

where Δw_d denotes the transverse component of velocity (i. e. velocity in circumferential direction) created by the cascade. For straight, unstaggered cascades ($\beta_m = 90°$) both positive and negative values of δ_d correspond to compressor cascades, whereas for staggered blades positive values of δ_d correspond to compressor cascades, and negative values correspond to turbine cascades. In the range of small deflexions the loss coefficient increases rapidly with decreasing solidity ratio. The reason for it lies in the fact that the number of blades increases as the pitch is decreased and that the loss coefficient is, to a first approximation, proportional to the number of blades, if the deflexion is small. At larger values of the deflexion ratio there is a sudden increase in the value of the loss coefficient. The reason for it lies in the flow separating on the suction side of the blade owing to heavy loading. Generally speaking, turbine cascades show lower values of the loss coefficient and permissible deflexions are larger than for compressor cascades. These results are in agreement with what is known about the differences in the behaviour of turbine and compressor blades, as explained earlier.

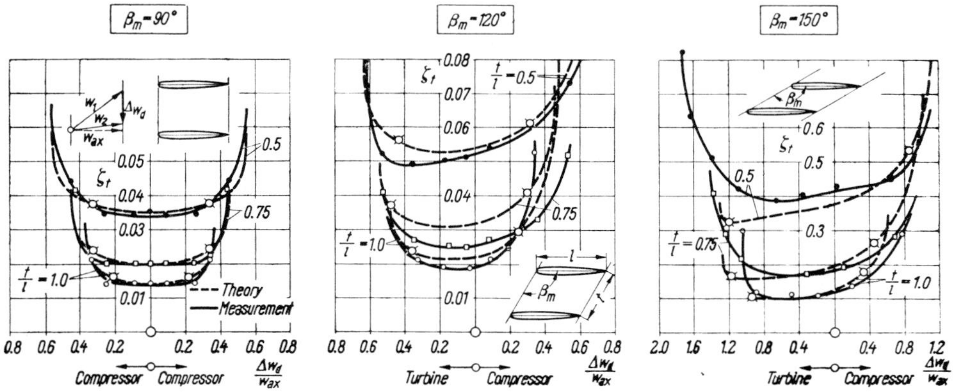

Fig. 24.9. Loss coefficient ζ_t from eqn. (24.33) in terms of the deflexion ratio $\delta_d = \Delta w_d/w_{ax}$ for cascades of different solidity ratio, t/l, and mean blade angle (angle of stagger) β_m, after [26] and [27]. Blade section NACA 0010. Reynolds number $\mathsf{R} = w_2\, l/\nu = 5 \times 10^5$. Measurements performed by N. Scholz [31], theory due to L. Speidel [34]

The measurements and the calculations were carried out for a Reynolds number $\mathsf{R} = w_2\, l/\nu = 5 \times 10^5$. The calculations were performed on the assumption that the boundary layer was turbulent all along the blades. In the experimental arrangement the boundary layers were made turbulent by the provision of tripping wires near the leading edges. The calculated and measured values of the loss coefficient show very good agreement with each other. Further, the theory succeeds in predicting the variation of the loss coefficient with Reynolds number, as shown by K. Gersten [9a]. The steep increase in the value of the loss coefficient at large deflexions which is due to separation is also seen to be reproduced satisfactorily by the theoretical calculation.

References

[1] J. H. Abbott, A. E. von Doenhoff and L. S. Stivers, Summary of airfoil data. NACA-Report 824 (1945).
[2] A. Betz, Ein Verfahren zur direkten Ermittlung des Profilwiderstandes. ZFM **16**, 42 (1925).
[3] H. Doetsch, Profilwiderstandsmessungen im großen Windkanal der DVL. Luftfahrtforschung **14**, 173 and 370 (1937).
[4] E. M. Dowlen, A shortened method for the calculation of aerofoil profile drag. Jour. Roy. Aero. Soc. **LVI**, 109—116 (1952).
[5] G. Drougge, Comparison between different methods of calculating the profile drag as determined by the pitot traverse method at high speeds. The Aeronautical Research Institute Flygtekniska Försöksanstalten Stockholm. Report No. 21 (1950). (Swedish).
[6] N. Eastman, E. N. Jacobs and A. Sherman, Aerofoil section characteristics as affected by variation of the Reynolds number. NACA Rep. 586 (1937).
[7] A. Fage, V. M. Falkner and W. S. Walker, Experiments on a series of symmetrical Joukowsky sections. ARC R & M 1241 (1929).
[8] A. Fage, Profile and skin-friction airfoil drags. ARC R & M 1852 (1938).
[9] K. Gersten, Experimenteller Beitrag zum Reibungseinfluß auf die Strömung durch ebene Schaufelgitter. Proc. Braunschweig. Wiss. Ges. Vol. **VII**, pp. 93—99 (1955).
[9a] K. Gersten, Der Einfluß der Reynoldszahl auf die Strömungsverluste in ebenen Schaufelgittern, Proc. Braunschw. Wissen. Gesellschaft **II**, 5—19 (1959).
[10] H. J. Goett and W. K. Bullivant, Tests of NACA 0009, 0012, 0018 aerofoils in the full scale tunnel. NACA Rep. 647 (1938).
[11] H. J. Goett, Experimental investigation of the momentum method for determining profile drag. NACA Rep. 660 (1939).
[12] B. Göthert, Widerstandsbestimmung bei hohen Unterschallgeschwindigkeiten aus Impulsverlustmessungen. Jahrbuch der deutschen Luftfahrtforschung I, 148 (1941).
[13] P. S. Granville, The calculation of the viscous drag of bodies of revolution. David W. Taylor Basin Rep. 849 (1953).
[14] H. B. Helmbold, Zur Berechnung des Profilwiderstandes. Ing.-Arch. **17**, 273 (1949).
[15] E. N. Jacobs, K. E. Ward and R. M. Pinkerton, The characteristics of 78 related airfoil sections from tests in the variable density wind tunnel. NACA Rep. 460 (1935).
[16] B. M. Jones, The measurement of profile drag by the pitot traverse method. ARC R & M 1688, (1936).
[17] R. Jones and D. H. Williams, The profile drag of aerofoils at high Reynolds number in the CAT. ARC R & M 1804 (1937).
[18] B. M. Jones, Flight experiments on boundary layers. Jour. Aero. Sci. **5**, 81 (1938); also Engineering **145**, 397 (1938) and Aircraft Eng'g. **10**, 135 (1938).
[19] K. Kraemer, Grenzschichtrechnungen an zwölf Profilen. Report 55/A/01 of the Aerodyn. Versuchsanstalt, Göttingen (1955).
[20] C. N. H. Lock, W. F. Hilton and S. Goldstein, Determination of profile drag at high speeds by a Pitot traverse method. ARC R & M 1971 (1946).
[21] N. A. V. Piercy, J. H. Preston and L. G. Whitehead, Approximate prediction of skin friction and lift. Phil. Mag. **26**, 791 (1938).
[22] W. Pfenninger, Vergleich der Impulsmethode mit der Wägung bei Profilwiderstandsmessungen. Reports of the Aero. Inst., ETH. Zürich, No. 8 (1943).
[23] J. Pretsch, Zur theoretischen Berechnung des Profilwiderstandes. Jahrb. d. dt. Luftfahrtforschung **I**, 61 (1938). Engl. transl. NACA TM 1009 (1942).
[24] H. Schäfer, Untersuchungen über die dreidimensionale Strömung durch axiale Schaufelgitter mit zylindrischen Schaufeln. Thesis Braunschweig 1954. Forschung Ing.-Wesen **21**, 9—19 and 41—49 (1955).

[25] H. Schlichting and N. Scholz, Über die theoretische Berechnung der Strömungsverluste eines ebenen Schaufelgitters. Ing.-Archiv **19**, 42 (1951).
[26] H. Schlichting, Ergebnisse und Probleme von Gitteruntersuchungen. Zeitschr. Flugwiss. **I**, 109—122 (1953).
[27] H. Schlichting, Problems and results of investigations on cascade flow. Jour. Aero. Sci. **21**, 163—178 (1954).
[28] H. Schlichting, Berechnung der reibungslosen inkompressiblen Strömung für ein vorgegebenes ebenes Schaufelgitter. VDI-Forschungsheft 447 (1955).
[28a] H. Schlichting, Application of boundary layer theory in turbo-machinery, Trans. ASME Ser. D **81** (Jour. Basic Eng'g), pp. 543—551 (1959), see also: Anwendung der Grenzschichttheorie auf Strömungsprobleme der Turbomaschinen, Siemens Zeitschr. **33**, 429—438 (1959).
[29] N. Scholz, Über eine rationelle Berechnung des Strömungswiderstandes schlanker Körper mit beliebig rauher Oberfläche. Jahrb. Schiffbautechn. Ges. **45**, 244—259 (1951).
[30] N. Scholz, Strömungsuntersuchungen an Schaufelgittern. VDI-Forschungsheft 442 (1954).
[31] N. Scholz and L. Speidel, Systematische Untersuchungen über die Strömungsverluste von ebenen Schaufelgittern. VDI-Forschungsheft 464 (1957).
[32] M. Schrenk, Über die Profilwiderstandsmessung im Fluge nach dem Impulsverfahren. Luftfahrtforschung **2**, 1 (1928); NACA TM 557 and 558 (1930).
[33] J. E. Serby, M. B. Morgan and E. R. Cooper, Flight tests on the profile drag of 14% and 25% thick wings. ARC R & M 1826 (1937).
[34] L. Speidel, Berechnung der Strömungsverluste von ungestaffelten ebenen Schaufelgittern. Thesis Braunschweig 1953. Ing.-Arch. **22**, 295—322 (1954).
[35] H. B. Squire and A. D. Young, The calculation of the profile drag of aerofoils. ARC R & M 1838 (1938).
[36] G. I. Taylor, The determination of drag by the Pitot traverse method. ARC R & M 1808 (1937).
[37] E. Truckenbrodt, Die Berechnung des Profilwiderstandes aus der vorgegebenen Profilform. Ing.-Arch. **21**, 176—186 (1953).
[38] A. Wanner and P. Kretz, Druckverteilungs- und Profilwiderstandsmessungen im Flug an den Profilen NACA 23012 und Göttingen 549. Jb. d. dt. Luftfahrtforschg. **I**, 111 (1941).
[39] H. Weidinger, Profilwiderstandsmessungen an einem Junkers-Tragflügel. Jb. d. Wiss. Ges. f. Luftfahrt 112 (1926); NACA TM 428 (1927).
[40] A. D. Young, Note of the effect of compressibility on Jones' momentum method of measuring profile drag. ARC R & M 1881 (1939).
[41] A. D. Young, The calculation of the total and skin friction drags of bodies of revolution at 0° incidence. ARC R & M 1947 (1939).
[42] A. D. Young, B. A. Winterbottom and N. E. Winterbottom, Note on the effect of compressibility on the profile drag of aerofoils at subsonic Mach numbers in the absence of shock waves. ARC R & M 2400 (1950).
[43] A. D. Young, Note on momentum methods of measuring profile drags at high speeds. ARC R & M 1963 (1946).
[44] A. D. Young, Note on a method of measuring profile drag by means of an integrating comb. ARC R & M 2257 (1948).
[45] A. D. Young and S. Kirkby, The profile drag of biconvex wing sections at supersonic speeds. "Fifty years of boundary layer research", Braunschweig 1955, pp. 419—431.

Bibliography

Text-books, general treatises, and surveys

[1] ADVANCES IN APPLIED MECHANICS, published from time to time by the Academic Press, New York.

Vol. I, ed. by R. von Mises and Th. von Kármán, 1948

H. L. DRYDEN, Recent advances in the mechanics of boundary layer flow, pp. 2—40.

J. M. BURGERS, A mathematical model illustrating the theory of turbulence, pp. 171—199.

Vol. II, ed. by R. von Mises and Th. von Kármán, 1951

TH. VON KÁRMÁN and C. C. LIN, On the statistical theory of isotropic turbulence, pp. 2—19.

G. KUERTI, The laminar boundary layer in compressible flow, pp. 23—92.

Vol. III, ed. by R. von Mises and Th. von Kármán, 1953

F. N. FRENKIEL, Turbulent diffusion: Mean concentration distribution in a flow field of a homogeneous turbulence, pp. 61—107.

L. ROSENHEAD, Vortex systems in wakes, pp. 185—195.

Vol. IV, ed. by H. L. Dryden and Th. von Kármán, 1956

F. H. CLAUSER, The turbulent boundary layer, pp. 2—51.

F. K. MOORE, Three-dimensional boundary layer theory, pp. 160—228.

Vol. VI, ed. by H. L. Dryden, Th. von Kármán and G. Kuerti, 1960

K. STEWARTSON, The theory of unsteady laminar boundary layers

G. LUDWIG and M. HEIL, Boundary-layer theory with dissociation and ionization

W. CHESTER, The propagation of shock waves along ducts of varying cross section

K. OSWATITSCH, Similarity and equivalence in compressible flow

R. WILLE, Kármán vortex streets

[2] G. K. BATCHELOR and R. M. DAVIES, ed., Surveys in mechanics. The G. I. Taylor 70th anniversary volume. Cambridge University Press, 1956.

[3] G. K. BATCHELOR, The theory of homogeneous turbulence. Cambridge University Press, 1953.

[4] A. BETZ, Ziele, Wege und konstruktive Auswertung der Strömungsforschung. Z. VDI **91**, 253—258 (1949).

[5] E. A. BRUN ed., Seminaire d'Aérothermique de la Faculté des Sciences de Paris, Année 1957—1958. Publications Scientifiques et Techniques du Ministère de l'Air, No. N. T. 85 (1959).

[6] W. H. CORCORAN, J. B. OPFELL and B. H. SAGE, Momentum transfer in fluids, Academic Press, New York, 1956.

[7] H. L. DRYDEN, Fifty years of boundary layer theory and experiment. Science **121**, 375—380 (1955).

[8] H. L. DRYDEN, F. P. MURNAGHAN and H. BATEMAN, Hydrodynamics. Repr. Dover Publications, New York 1956.

[9] E. R. G. ECKERT, Einführung in den Wärme- und Stoffaustausch, Springer, Berlin, 1959.

[10] E. R. G. ECKERT and R. M. DRAKE JR., Heat and mass transfer. McGraw-Hill, New York, 1959.

[11] FIAT-Review of German Science 1939—1946. (FIAT = Field Information Agency, Technical,) Wiesbaden 1948—1949.

a) Vol. 5, Pt. II, Mathematische Grundlagen der Strömungslehre, ed. by A. Walther. In particular contributions by H. Görtler entitled "Zähe Flüssigkeiten" and "Turbulenz".

b) Vol. 11, Hydro- und Aerodynamik. Ed. by A. Betz, in particular the following articles:

A. Betz, Inkompressible Strömungen.

W. Tollmien, Laminare Grenzschichten.

L. Prandtl, Turbulenz.

A. Betz, Kompressible Strömungen.

G. Vogelpohl, Die Hydrodynamik des Schmierfilms.

[12] D. A. Frank-Kamenetzki, Stoff- und Wärmeübertragung in der chemischen Kinetik. Springer, Berlin 1959.
[13] H. Goertler and W. Tollmien, ed., Fünfzig Jahre Grenzschichtforschung — Fifty years of boundary layer research. Braunschweig 1955.
[14] S. Goldstein, ed., Modern developments in fluid dynamics, vols. 1 and 2, Oxford University Press, 1938.
[15] H. Goertler, ed., Grenzschichtforschung — Boundary Layer Research. IUTAM Symposium, Freiburg (Germany) 1957, Publ. by Springer, Berlin 1958.
[16] U. Grigull, ed., Gröber/Erk/Grigull, Die Grundgesetze der Wärmeübertragung, 3rd. rev. ed., Springer, Berlin, 1955.
[17] D. Hayes and F. Probstein, Hypersonic flow theory. Academic Press, New York, 1959.
[18] S.F.Hoerner, Fluid dynamic drag. Published by the Author, Midland Park, New Jersey, 1958.
[19] D. W. Holder, The interaction between shock waves and boundary layers. Fifth International Aeronautical Conference, Los Angeles, New York, 1955.
[20] L. Howarth, ed., Modern developments in fluid dynamics. High speed flow, vols. 1 and 2, Oxford University Press, 1953.
[21] L. Howarth, ed., Boundary layer effects in aerodynamics. Proc. of a Symposium held at the National Physical Laboratory (NPL), London, 1955.
[22] L. Howarth, Laminar boundary layers, article in "Handbuch der Physik", (Encyclopedia of Physics), ed. by S. Flügge, Vol. VIII/1, pp. 264—350, Berlin, 1959.
[23] M. Jakob, Heat transfer, vols. I, II. John Wiley & Sons, New York, 1950 and 1957.
[24] Th. von Kármán, Collected works of Theodore von Kármán, 4 vols., Butterworth, 1956.
[25] W. Kaufmann, Technische Hydro- und Aerodynamik. Springer, 1954.
[26] J. G. Knudsen and D. L. Katz, Fluid dynamics and heat transfer. McGraw-Hill, New York, 1958.
[27] N. J. Kotschin, I. A. Kibel and N. W. Rose, Theoretische Hydromechanik, Vols. I, II, Akademie-Verlag, Berlin 1954.
[28] H. Lamb, Hydrodynamics, 6th ed. reprinted Dover Publ., New York, 1945. German transl. with supplements by R. von Mises, Lehrbuch der Hydrodynamik, 2nd. ed. Leipzig, 1931.
[29] H. W. Liepmann and A. Roshko, Elements of gasdynamics. John Wiley, New York, 1957.
[30] C. C. Lin, The theory of hydrodynamic stability. Cambridge University Press, 1955.
[31] W. Müller, Einführung in die Theorie der zähen Flüssigkeiten. Leipzig, 1932.
[32] S. I. Pai, Viscous flow theory. Vol. I, Laminar flow, New York, 1956; Vol. II, Turbulent flow, Van Nostrand, New York, 1957.
[33] S. I. Pai, Fluid dynamics of jets. D. van Nostrand, New York, 1954.
[34] L. Prandtl, Ueber Flüssigkeitsbewegung bei sehr kleiner Reibung. Proc. III. Intern. Math. Congr. Heidelberg, 1904. Reprinted in "Vier Abhandlungen zur Hydrodynamik und Aerodynamik", Göttingen, 1927.
[35] L. Prandtl and O. Tietjens, Hydro- und Aerodynamik, 2 Vols., Berlin 1929 and 1931. Engl. transl. see [35a] and [35b].
[35a] Fundamentals of Hydro- and Aeromechanics, based on lectures of L. Prandtl by O. G. Tietjens, transl. by L. Rosenhead, McGraw-Hill, transl. of vol. I of [35], New York/London, 1934.
[35b] Applied Hydro- and Aeromechanics, based on lectures of L. Prandtl by O. G. Tietjens, transl. by J. P. den Hartog, McGraw-Hill, New York/London, 1934. Transl. of vol. II of [35].
[36] L. Prandtl, The mechanics of viscous fluids. In W. F. Durand, "Aerodynamic Theory", Vol. III, pp. 34—208, Springer, Berlin, 1935.
[37] L. Prandtl, Führer durch die Strömungslehre. 4th ed., Braunschweig, 1956. Essentials of fluid dynamics, Engl. transl. by Miss W. M. Deans, Blackie and Son, London, 1952.
[38] L. Prandtl, Gesammelte Abhandlungen zur angewandten Mechanik, Hydro- und Aerodynamik. Ed. by W. Tollmien, H. Schlichting and H. Görtler, 3 vols., Springer, 1960.
[39] Princeton Series, High Speed Aerodynamics and jet propulsion.
Vol. V, ed. by C. C. Lin, Turbulent flows and heat transfer, 1959
Sec. A H. L. Dryden, Transition from laminar to turbulent flow
Sec. B G. B. Schubauer and C. M. Tchen, Turbulent flow
Sec. C C. C. Lin, Statistical theories of turbulence
Sec. E R. G. Deissler and R. H. Sabersky, Convective heat transfer and friction in flow of liquids
Sec. F E. R. van Driest, Convective heat transfer in gases
Sec. G S. W. Yuan, Cooling by protective fluid films

Vol. VI, General theory of high speed aerodynamics, ed. by W. R. Sears, 1954
Vol. IX, Physical measurements in gas dynamics and combustion, ed. by R. W. Ladenburg, B. Lewis, R. M. Pease and H. S. Taylor, 1954
Sec. F L. S. G. Kovasznay, Turbulence measurements.

[40] H. Schlichting and E. Truckenbrodt, Aerodynamik des Flugzeuges. Springer, Berlin, Vol. I, 1959, Vol. II, 1960.

[41] H. Schlichting, Entstehung der Turbulenz. Article in "Handbuch der Physik — Encyclopedia of Physics" ed. by S. Flügge, Vol. VIII/1. pp. 351—450, Springer, 1959.

[42] H. Schlichting, Some developments in boundary layer research in the past thirty years (The Third Lanchester Memorial Lecture) J. Roy. Aero. Soc., Vol. 64, p. 63—80 (1960). See also: H. Schlichting, Entwicklung der Grenzschichttheorie in den letzten drei Jahrzehnten (Dritte Lanchester Gedächtnis-Vorlesung). Zeitschr. Flugwiss. **8** (1960), 93—111.

[43] H. Schlichting, Application of boundary layer theory in turbo-machinery. Trans. ASME D **81** (Jour. of Basic Engin.), pp. 543—551 (1959); see also: Siemens-Zeitschrift, Vol. 33, pp. 429—438 (1959).

[44] H. Schlichting, Einige neuere Ergebnisse über Grenzschichtbeeinflussung. Advances in Aero. Sci. Vol. II, Proc. First. Intern. Congress in the Aero. Sci., Madrid 1958, Pergamon Press, pp. 563—586 (1959).

[45] E. Schmidt, Einführung in die technische Thermodynamik und in die Grundlagen der Chemischen Thermodynamik. 7th ed., Berlin, 1958.

[46] E. Schmidt, Thermodynamics, transl. by J. Kestin, Clarendon Press, Oxford, 1949.

[47] A. H. Shapiro, The dynamics and thermodynamics of compressible flow, vols. I and II, Ronald Press, New York, 1953.

[48] A. Sommerfeld, Vorlesungen über theoretische Physik, vol. II, Mechanik der deformierbaren Körper, 2nd. ed., Wiesbaden, 1947. Engl. transl. see [48a].

[48a] A. Sommerfeld, Lectures in theoretical physics, vol. II, Mechanics of deformable bodies, transl. by G. Kuerti, Academic Press, New York, 1950.

[49] W. Tollmien, Fortschritte der Turbulenzforschung, ZAMM **33**, 200—211 (1953).

[50] W. Tollmien, Articles "Grenzschichttheorie" and "Turbulente Strömungen" in "Handbuch der Experimentalphysik", ed. by. W. Wien and F. Harms, vol. 4, part I, Leipzig, 1931.

[51] A. A. Townsend, The structure of turbulent shear flow. Cambridge University Press, 1956.

[52] R. W. Truitt, Hypersonic aerodynamics, Ronald Press, 1959.

[53] G. Vogelpohl, Betriebssichere Gleitlager. Berechnungsverfahren für Konstruktion und Betrieb. Springer, Berlin, 1958.

[54] A. D. Young, Boundary layers (in compressible flow). Article in [20], vol. I, Chap. X.

Index of Authors

Subject Index